LINEAR ANALYSIS

MEASURE AND INTEGRAL, BANACH AND HILBERT SPACE, LINEAR INTEGRAL EQUATIONS

BY

ADRIAAN CORNELIS ZAANEN

PROFESSOR OF MATHEMATICS
AT THE TECHNOLOGICAL UNIVERSITY
DELFT, NETHERLANDS

NORTH-HOLLAND PUBLISHING CO. — AMSTERDAM
P. NOORDHOFF N.V. — GRONINGEN
1953

Sole-agency U.S.A.:

Interscience Publishers Inc. New York

PREFACE

The present work is devoted to some mathematical theories which all of them may claim to belong to the domain of "linear analysis". It will, however, be clear that it is impossible to comprise everything that might deserve to be so designated into a book of moderate size. The central and larger part of the book (Ch. 6—12) is formed by an introduction to Banach space and Hilbert space, and to some aspects of the theory of bounded and compact linear transformations in these spaces. In order to have at hand non-trivial examples by which to illustrate this theory, the necessity arises to make an appeal to such notions as Lebesgue measure and integral, and Lebesgue function spaces L_p. It is to a concise discussion of these subjects, complete in itself but leaving aside everything which is unessential for the applications in question, that Part I (Ch. 1—5) is devoted. The emphasis is on the algebraic aspects of measure and integral, and topological notions are only introduced when discussing special examples such as Lebesgue or Stieltjes integrals. I wish to express my gratitude to Prof. N. G. de Bruijn for the free use I could make of his lecture notes on measure and integral. The study of these notes led to the dominant part played by semirings in Chapter 2, and to the definition of the integral as a product measure in the product space of the underlying measure space and the straight line. Furthermore it will appear on comparison with the standard treatises of Halmos (Measure Theory, New York, 1950) and Saks (Theory of the Integral, Warsaw, 1937) that they have not failed to leave their marks in the present discussion. In Chapter 5 we introduce besides the Lebesgue spaces $L_p(1 \leqslant p \leqslant \infty)$, their generalizations: the Orlicz spaces L_Φ. Most of the properties of spaces L_p may be carried over to spaces L_Φ, although several proofs need some modification. As a rule the proofs in question gain thereby in transparency, since a certain amount of juggling with conjugated exponents p and q is replaced by more straightforward arguments.

After defining Banach and Hilbert space in Chapter 6, and deriving their most obvious properties, Chapter 7 is devoted to a first study of bounded linear transformations in Banach space, although closed, possibly unbounded, linear transformations are not altogether forgotten. Bounded linear functionals, their extension, the first and second adjoint transformations, weak convergence and projections are among the subjects which receive attention. Chapter 8 deals with linear transformations in a space of finite dimension (rank and nullity, characteristic values, canonical form of a matrix, elementary divisors), and Chapter 9 with bounded linear transformations in Hilbert space (unitary, self-adjoint, normal and symmetrisable transformations, projections, Fredholm theory for transformations of finite double-norm). The spectral theory of bounded normal transformations has not been included, since there exist several treatises containing an excellent discussion of this subject (cf. the references in Ch. 6, § 1). In Chapter 10 the mutual relations between the ranges and null spaces of a bounded linear transformation and its adjoint are discussed, and we introduce resolvent and spectrum, while Chapter 11 gives a rather thorough account of compact linear transformations in Banach space (Riesz-Schauder theory, resolvent, algebraic multiplicity of characteristic values, mean ergodic theorems). Finally, in Chapter 12, the last chapter of Part II, we consider compact transformations in Hilbert space which are either self-adjoint, normal or symmetrisable (expansion theorems, minimax theorems, perturbation theorems). The reader who is not interested in symmetrisable transformations, will find some advice on how to read this chapter in § 1.

Examples illustrating the abstract theory, are scattered through the text, and more of them may be found at the end of each chapter.

Part III (Ch. 13—17) deals with non-singular linear integral equations, that is, with the Fredholm theory and spectral theory of linear integral transformations one of whose iterates is compact. In Chapter 13, which may be read, if one wishes, immediately after Chapter 11, the Fredholm theory is lifted out of the L_2-sphere, wherein it was imprisoned until rather recently, and placed in more natural surroundings: the Lebesgue spaces L_p and the Orlicz spaces L_Φ. In Chapter 14 equations with normal, Hermitian or positive definite kernels are discussed, and the remaining chapters, finally, deal with equations having a symmetrisable kernel. Anyone who has ever taken note of what Hellinger and Toeplitz in their "Encyklopädie" paper of 1927 say about equations with symmetrisable kernels, will know that the state of affairs at that time was rather unsatisfactory. We cite: "Der wesentliche Mangel dieses ganzen allgemeinen Ansatzes ist aber das Fehlen der eigentlichen Entwicklungssätze", and "... der Ansatz der symmetrisierbaren Kerne in seiner formalen Allgemeinheit ins Unbestimmte greift". Fortunately, it has been proved since 1927 that the situation is not so bad as one might infer from these quotations. There exist expansion theorems in the case of a general symmetrisable kernel (Marty kernel), although of a slightly different nature than in the case where we have to do with a Hermitian kernel.

The knowledge required for a proper understanding of the contents of the present work, does nowhere, with one exception, go beyond the elements of ordinary analysis (determinants and linear equations, continuity, Riemann integral, ordinary and uniform convergence of series, complex numbers, simple properties of power series). The exception is in Ch. 13, § 14, where we use a theorem on entire functions which lies somewhat deeper.

The conventions on cross references are as follows: by § 4, Th. 2 is meant § 4, Theorem 2 of the chapter in which the reference occurs, and by Theorem 3 is meant Theorem 3 of the paragraph in which the reference occurs. Numerals in square brackets refer to the list of bibliographical references at the end of each chapter. No claim to completeness is made with regard to these lists. The idea is merely to illustrate some striking points in the text by a name and a date. Part I, being of an introductory nature, contains no bibliographical references.

All suggestions from readers which might lead to future improvements in the text will be very welcome.

My sincere thanks are due to the editors of the "Bibliotheca Mathematica" for their invitation to publish this book in their series. Furthermore, I wish to express my gratitude to Prof. H. D. Kloosterman who critically examined part of the manuscript, and to W. A. J. Luxemburg who assisted in the proof reading.

Delft, May 1953 A. C. ZAANEN

PART I

MEASURE AND INTEGRAL, THE LEBESGUE FUNCTIONSPACES L_p AND THE ORLICZ FUNCTIONSPACES L_Φ

CHAPTER 1

POINT SETS. EUCLIDEAN SPACE

§ 1. Definitions and Some Simple Properties

We consider a set X, the elements $x, y, \ldots$ of which will be called points. If A is a subset of X, we write $x \in A$ in case the point x is an element of A. Hence $x \in X$ for every point x. Given two subsets A and B of X, we write $A \subset B$ or, equivalently, $B \supset A$ when A is a subset of B, in other words, when every point of A is also a point of B. In particular $A \subset A$ for every set A. The *empty set*, that is, the set containing no points at all, is denoted by 0, and this set is considered to be a subset of every subset. Hence $0 \subset A$ for every $A \subset X$.

Given a sequence (finite or infinite) $A_n (n = 1, 2, \ldots)$ of sets (we shall not repeat every time that all point sets considered are subsets of X), we call *sum*, or *union*, of these sets and denote by ΣA_n, or $A_1 + A_2 + \ldots$, the set of all points belonging to at least one of the A_n. We call *product*, or *intersection*, and denote by ΠA_n, or $A_1 A_2 \ldots$, the set of all points belonging at the same time to all the A_n. Given two sets A and B, the set of all points belonging to A, but not to B, is called the *difference* of A and B, and denoted by $A - B$. By $A - B - C$ we mean $(A - B) - C$.

If the sequence A_n is infinite, the set of all points x such that $x \in A_n$ holds for an infinity of values of n is called the *upper limit* of A_n, and denoted by lim sup A_n. The set of all points x belonging to all the sets A_n from some n_0 onwards (n_0 may vary with x) is called the *lower limit* of the sequence and denoted by lim inf A_n. Obviously lim inf $A_n \subset$ lim sup A_n. Whenever lim inf $A_n =$ lim sup A_n ($A = B$ for two sets A and B means that $A \subset B$ and $B \subset A$ hold simultaneously), the sequence A_n is said to be convergent; lower and upper limit are called *limit*, and denoted by lim A_n.

Theorem 1. *lim sup* $A_n = \Pi_{k=1}^{\infty} \Sigma_{n=k}^{\infty} A_n$.

Proof. Let $x \in \limsup A_n$. Then $x \in \Sigma_{n=k}^{\infty} A_n$ for every k, hence $x \in \Pi_{k=1}^{\infty} \Sigma_{n=k}^{\infty} A_n$.

Let conversely $x \in \Pi_{k=1}^{\infty} \Sigma_{n=k}^{\infty} A_n$. Then $x \in \Sigma_{n=k}^{\infty} A_n$ for every k, which shows that $x \in A_n$ holds for an infinity of values of n. Hence $x \in \limsup A_n$.

Theorem 2. *$\liminf A_n = \Sigma_{k=1}^{\infty} \Pi_{n=k}^{\infty} A_n$.*
Proof. Let $x \in \liminf A_n$. Then there exists a positive integer k_0 such that $x \in A_n$ for $n \geqslant k_0$. Hence $x \in \Pi_{n=k_0}^{\infty} A_n$, which implies $x \in \Sigma_{k=1}^{\infty} \Pi_{n=k}^{\infty} A_n$.

Let conversely $x \in \Sigma_{k=1}^{\infty} \Pi_{n=k}^{\infty} A_n$. Then $x \in \Pi_{n=k}^{\infty} A_n$ for at least one index k, hence $x \in A_n$ for $n \geqslant k$ or $x \in \liminf A_n$.

If, for a sequence A_n of sets, $A_n \subset A_{n+1}$ for all n, the sequence is called *ascending* or *non-decreasing*; if $A_{n+1} \subset A_n$ for all n, the sequence is called *descending* or *non-increasing*. Ascending and descending sequences are said to be *monotone*.

Theorem 3. 1°. *A monotone (infinite) sequence is convergent.*
2°. *$\lim A_n = \Sigma A_n$ for an ascending sequence.*
3°. *$\lim A_n = \Pi A_n$ for a descending sequence.*
Proof. 1°. We have to prove that $\limsup A_n \subset \liminf A_n$. Let us assume, for this purpose, that $x \in \limsup A_n$, so that $x \in A_n$ holds for an infinity of values of n. If now the sequence A_n is ascending and n_0 is the smallest index n for which $x \in A_n$ holds, then $x \in A_n$ for $n \geqslant n_0$, and hence $x \in \liminf A_n$. If, on the other hand, the sequence A_n is descending and $x \in A_k$ for a certain k, then $x \in A_n$ for $n \leqslant k$. Hence, since $x \in A_k$ holds for infinitely many k, we have $x \in A_n$ for all n, so that certainly $x \in \liminf A_n$.

2°. If the sequence A_n is ascending, we have

$$\lim A_n = \liminf A_n = \Sigma_{k=1}^{\infty} \Pi_{n=k}^{\infty} A_n = \Sigma_{k=1}^{\infty} A_k.$$

3°. If the sequence A_n is descending, we have

$$\lim A_n = \limsup A_n = \Pi_{k=1}^{\infty} \Sigma_{n=k}^{\infty} A_n = \Pi_{k=1}^{\infty} A_k.$$

If A is a subset of X, the set $X - A$ is called the *complementary set* or, shortly, the *complement* of A, and is sometimes denoted by A'. Evidently $X' = 0$, $0' = X$, $(A')' = A$, and $A \subset B$ implies $A' \supset B'$.

Theorem 4. *We have $A - B = AB'$.*
Proof. We have $x \in A - B$ if and only if $x \in A$ and $x \in B'$ hold simultaneously.

Theorem 5. *We have* $\Pi\, A_n = (\Sigma\, A_n')'$ *and* $\Sigma\, A_n = (\Pi\, A_n')'$.

Proof. We have $x \in \Pi\, A_n$ if and only if $x \in A_n'$ holds for no value of n, hence, if and only if $x \in (\Sigma\, A_n')'$.

We have $x \in \Sigma\, A_n$ if and only if $x \in A_n'$ does not hold for all values of n, hence, if and only if $x \in (\Pi\, A_n')'$.

Theorem 6. *We have* $\limsup A_n = (\liminf A_n')'$ *and* $\liminf A_n = (\limsup A_n')'$.

Proof. Similar to that of the preceding theorem.

Remark. The set $A - B$ is called the complement of B relative to A. It is easily seen that, if all sets A_n are contained in A, the Theorems 5 and 6 remain true also if all complements are taken relative to A (A takes over the part of X).

The function of a point, equal to one at all points of a set A, and to zero at all points of $A' = X - A$, is called the *characteristic function* $c_A(x)$ of A. Evidently, if $A = \Sigma\, A_n$ and $A_i A_j = 0$ $(i \neq j)$, that is, if no two of the sets A_n have common points, then $c_A(x) = \Sigma\, c_{A_n}(x)$. If the sequence A_n is monotone, the sequence of the characteristic functions is (for every point x) also monotone, non-decreasing if A_n is ascending and non-increasing if A_n is descending.

Theorem 7. *If* $\limsup A_n = P$ *and* $\liminf A_n = Q$, *then*

$$c_P(x) = \limsup c_{A_n}(x),$$

$$c_Q(x) = \liminf c_{A_n}(x).$$

Proof. We have $c_P(x) = 1$ if and only if $x \in A_n$ holds for infinitely many values of n, that is, if and only if $c_{A_n}(x) = 1$ for infinitely many values of n. Hence $c_P(x) = 1$ if and only if $\limsup c_{A_n}(x) = 1$. Since both $c_P(x)$ and $\limsup c_{A_n}(x)$ can only assume the values zero and one, the relation $c_P(x) = \limsup c_{A_n}(x)$ holds for all x.

We have $c_Q(x) = 1$ if and only if there exists an index n_0 such that $x \in A_n$ for $n \geqslant n_0$, that is, if and only if $c_{A_n}(x) = 1$ for $n \geqslant n_0$. Hence $c_Q(x) = 1$ if and only if $\liminf c_{A_n}(x) = 1$. Since both $c_Q(x)$ and $\liminf c_{A_n}(x)$ can only assume the values zero and one, there is equality for all x.

Theorem 8. *The sequence A_n converges to the set A if and only if*

$$\lim c_{A_n}(x) = c_A(x).$$

Proof. Let $A = \lim A_n$, so that, with the notations of the preceding theorem, $P = A = Q$. Then

$$\limsup c_{A_n}(x) = c_P(x) = c_A(x) = c_Q(x) = \liminf c_{A_n}(x),$$

hence $c_A(x) = \lim c_{A_n}(x)$.

Let now conversely $c_A(x) = \lim c_{A_n}(x) = \limsup c_{A_n}(x) = \liminf c_{A_n}(x)$, so that $c_A(x) = c_P(x) = c_Q(x)$. Then $A = P = Q$, hence $A = \lim A_n$.

A function $f(x)$, assuming only a finite number of different (real or complex) values on X is called a *simple function*. If these values are $\alpha_1, \ldots, \alpha_p$, and the set on which the value α_i is taken is denoted by $A_i (i = 1, \ldots, p)$, then $X = \Sigma_{i=1}^p A_i$, where no two of the sets A_i have common points, and $f(x) = \Sigma_{i=1}^p \alpha_i c_{A_i}(x)$.

§ 2. Euclidean Space

By *Euclidean space* of m dimensions R_m we mean the set of all systems of m real numbers $(x_1, x_2, \ldots, x_m)$. The number x_k is called the k-th *coordinate* of the point $x = (x_1, x_2, \ldots, x_m)$. Obviously all notions introduced in the preceding paragraph, may be applied to point sets in R_m. We shall introduce here some further conceptions in which the distance $\rho(x, y)$ between two points x and y of R_m plays a part.

The *distance* $\rho(x, y)$ between $x = (x_1, x_2, \ldots, x_m)$ and $y = (y_1, y_2, \ldots, y_m)$ is defined as the non-negative number

$$[(x_1 - y_1)^2 + (x_2 - y_2)^2 + \ldots + (x_m - y_m)^2]^{1/2}.$$

The space R_1 is also termed *straight line* and the space R_2 *plane*. In R_1 the distance $\rho(x, y)$ is simply $| x - y |$.

If E is a subset of R_m, the upper bound (also called lowest upper bound; abbreviation l.u.b.) of the numbers $\rho(x, y)$ subject to $x \in E$ and $y \in E$ is the *diameter* of E, and is denoted by $\delta(E)$. If $\delta(E)$ is finite, the set E is called *bounded*. For a collection M of sets, the upper bound of $\delta(E)$ for all sets E belonging to M is called the *characteristic number* of M. By the distance $\rho(x, E)$ of a point x and a set E we mean the lower bound (often called greatest lower bound; abbreviation g.l.b.) of $\rho(x, y)$ for all $y \in E$, and by the distance $\rho(E_1, E_2)$ of two sets E_1 and E_2 the lower bound of $\rho(x, y)$ for x running through E_1 and y through E_2.

If $r > 0$ is given, the set of all points y such that $\rho(x, y) < r$ is called the (*spherical*) *neighbourhood* of x with radius r. A point x is called a *point of accumulation* of a set E when every neighbourhood of x contains infinitely many points of E. It is not necessary, therefore, that x itself belongs to E. This definition is equivalent to the definition that x is a point of accumulation of E when every neighbourhood of x contains at least one point of E different from x. All points of E that are no points of accumulation of E are said to be *isolated points* of E. The set E^+ of all points of accumulation of E is the *derived set* of E. If E^+ is contained in E, the set E is termed *closed*. For every set E, the set E^+ is closed. Indeed, let x be a point of accumulation of E^+. We have to prove that $x \in E^+$. If $r > 0$ is arbitrarily given, there exists a point $y \in E^+$ in the neighbourhood of x with radius $r/2$. Consider now a neighbourhood of y with radius smaller than $r/2$. This neighbourhood contains, on account of $y \in E^+$, an infinity of points of E. Since moreover it is wholly contained in the neighbourhood of x with radius r, we have proved that infinitely many points of E are lying in the latter neighbourhood, and this shows that $x \in E^+$.

A point x is called *limit* of a sequence of points x_n when $\lim \rho(x, x_n) = 0$. We write $x = \lim x_n$, and the sequence x_n is said to be converging to x. Obviously, by the definition of distance and by Cauchy's Theorem, the sequence x_n is convergent if and only if $\lim \rho(x_p, x_q) = 0$ as $p, q \to \infty$. Furthermore, it is evident that the limit of a convergent sequence with an infinity of different points belonging to a set E is a point of accumulation of E.

If two points $a = (a_1, a_2, \ldots, a_m)$ and $b = (b_1, b_2, \ldots, b_m)$ in R_m are given, and if $a_k < b_k$ for $k = 1, 2, \ldots, m$, we call *closed interval* $[a_1, b_1; \ldots; a_m, b_m]$ the set of all points $(x_1, x_2, \ldots, x_m)$ such that $a_k \leqslant x_k \leqslant b_k$ for $k = 1, 2, \ldots, m$. If we replace $a_k \leqslant x_k \leqslant b_k$ by $a_k < x_k < b_k$ or $a_k \leqslant x_k < b_k$ or $a_k < x_k \leqslant b_k$, we obtain the definition of *open interval* $(a_1, b_1; \ldots; a_m, b_m)$ or *interval right open* $[a_1, b_1; \ldots; a_m, b_m)$ or *interval left open* $(a_1, b_1; \ldots; a_m, b_m]$ respectively. In what follows we shall mean by interval a closed interval, whereas an interval left open will be called a *cell*.

Theorem 1 (*Theorem of Bolzano-Weierstrass*). *Every bounded set in R_m containing an infinity of points has at least one point of accumulation.*

Proof. If E is the set in question, it is contained in an interval V_1. Dividing V_1 into 2^m congruent non-overlapping intervals, such that the diameter of each of these intervals is $\delta(V_1)/2$, one at least of these intervals, say V_2, contains an infinity of points of E. Repeating this process, we obtain a descending sequence of intervals $V_n (n = 1, 2, \ldots)$ such that each V_n contains infinitely many points of E and $\lim \delta(V_n) = 0$. This implies that, if $V_n = [a_1^{(n)}, b_1^{(n)}; \ldots; a_m^{(n)}, b_m^{(n)}]$, the sequence of numbers $a_k^{(1)}, a_k^{(2)}, \ldots$ is non-decreasing, the sequence $b_k^{(1)}, b_k^{(2)}, \ldots$ is non-increasing and $\lim (b_k^{(n)} - a_k^{(n)}) = 0$ for $k = 1, \ldots, m$. We may conclude therefore that $x_k = \lim a_k^{(n)} = \lim b_k^{(n)}$ exists for $k = 1, \ldots, m$. The point $x = (x_1, x_2, \ldots, x_m)$ is now a point of accumulation of E. Indeed, since evidently $x \in V_n$ for all n and $\lim \delta(V_n) = 0$, the intervals V_n are contained in an arbitrary neighbourhood of x for n sufficiently large, so that an infinity of points of E is lying in this neighbourhood.

§ 3. Open and Closed Sets

We consider a subset A of the Euclidean space R_m and a set E contained in A. Let $E'_A = A - E$ be the complement of E relative to A, and x a point of A. Then x is called an *internal point* of E (relative to A) whenever $\rho(x, E'_A) > 0$, x is called an *external point* of E (relative to A) whenever it is an internal point of E'_A (that is, whenever $\rho(x, E) > 0$), and x is said to be on the *boundary* (relative to A) of E and also on the boundary of E'_A whenever it is neither an internal nor an external point of E, that is, whenever $\rho(x, E) = \rho(x, E'_A) = 0$. Evidently every set can only contain internal points and points on its boundary.

The set E is called *closed* (relative to A) when it contains its boundary (relative to A). The set E is called *open* (relative to A) when it contains no point of its boundary (relative to A), that is, whenever it contains only internal points (relative to A). The boundary of A itself is considered to be empty, and A is therefore closed as well as open relative to itself.

We may replace the set A in these definitions by the whole space R_m, and it is easily seen that a set E is closed in the sense described earlier (E is closed whenever $E^+ \subset E$) if and only if E is closed relative to R_m. Indeed, let us assume first that $E^+ \subset E$, and let x be on the boundary of E. Then $\rho(x, E) = 0$, which shows that either $x \in E$ or $x \in E^+$, so that on account of $E^+ \subset E$ we find $x \in E$ in any case. The set E contains therefore its boundary. Conversely, if E contains its boundary and

$x \in E^+$, then $\rho(x, E) = 0$, so that x is an internal point of E or on its boundary; hence $x \in E$ in any case. This implies $E^+ \subset E$.

Theorem 1. *The set $E \subset A$ is closed relative to A if and only if its complement $E'_A = A - E$ is open relative to A.*
Proof. Follows immediately from the definitions.

Theorem 2. *Sum and product of a finite number of open sets are open. Sum and product of a finite number of closed sets are closed.*
Proof. 1°. Let $x \in \Sigma O_n$, where all O_n are open. Then $x \in O_n$ for at least one n, and with the point x a whole neighbourhood of x (as far as this neighbourhood is contained in the set A, relative to which O_n is open) is contained in the set O_n. This neighbourhood is therefore also contained in ΣO_n, in other words, x is an internal point of ΣO_n. It follows that ΣO_n is open.

2°. Consider two open sets O_1 and O_2 with complements O_1' and O_2' (relative to a set A or to the whole space R_m). If x is a point of O_1O_2, then $\rho(x, O_1') > 0$ and $\rho(x, O_2') > 0$, hence $\rho(x, O_1' + O_2') > 0$ or, since $O_1' + O_2' = (O_1O_2)'$ by § 1, Th. 5, $\rho\{x, (O_1O_2)'\} > 0$. This shows that x is an internal point of O_1O_2, so that O_1O_2 is open. The extension to the product of more than two open sets is evident.

3°. If $F_1, \ldots, F_n$ are closed sets, the complements $F_1', \ldots, F_n'$ are open, so that, by what we have already proved, $\Pi_{i=1}^n F_i'$ is also open. This implies that $\Sigma_{i=1}^n F_i = (\Pi_{i=1}^n F_i')'$ is closed.

4°. If once more $F_1, \ldots, F_n$ are closed, then $\Sigma_{i=1}^n F_i'$ is open, so that $\Pi_{i=1}^n F_i = (\Sigma_{i=1}^n F_i')'$ is closed.

Theorem 3. *The sum of an enumerable infinity of open sets is open, and the product of an enumerable infinity of closed sets is closed.*
Proof. In order to prove the first statement, we have only to repeat the proof of the first part of the preceding theorem.

Let now $F_1, F_2, \ldots$ be closed. Then their complements $F_1', F_2', \ldots$ are open, so that $\Sigma_{i=1}^\infty F_i'$ is also open. Hence its complement $\Pi_{i=1}^\infty F_i$ is closed.

Remark. The sum of an enumerable infinity of closed sets is not necessarily closed. Considering for example the sum of all points with rational coordinates in the linear interval [0, 1], we have a sum of closed sets which is not closed itself. It follows that the product of an enumerable infinity of open sets is not necessarily open.

Theorem 4. *If the sets F_1 and F_2 are closed relative to the whole space R_m and have no common points, while one at least of them, say F_1, is bounded, then* $\rho(F_1, F_2) > 0$.

Proof. Let us suppose that $\rho(F_1, F_2) = 0$. Then there exist two sequences of points $x_n \in F_1$ and $y_n \in F_2$ such that $\lim \rho(x_n, y_n) = 0$. The set F_1 being bounded, the sequence x_n contains, by the Bolzano-Weierstrass Theorem, a subsequence z_n ($z_1 = x_{n_1}$, $z_2 = x_{n_2}$, ...) converging to a point z. Hence, if t_n is the corresponding subsequence of y_n, we have $\lim \rho(z, z_n) = 0$ and $\lim \rho(z_n, t_n) = 0$. Since $\rho(z, t_n) \leqslant \rho(z, z_n) + \rho(z_n, t_n)$, this implies $\lim \rho(z, t_n) = 0$. From $\lim \rho(z, z_n) = 0$, $z_n \in F_1$ it follows now that $z \in F_1$, whereas $\lim \rho(z, t_n) = 0$, $t_n \in F_2$ shows that $z \in F_2$. This is impossible, F_1 and F_2 having no common points. Hence $\rho(F_1, F_2) > 0$.

Remark. If neither F_1 nor F_2 is bounded, the theorem is not necessarily true, e.g. in the two-dimensional case that F_1 is the set of all points (x, y) such that $x < 0$, $y \geqslant -x^{-1}$ and F_2 is the set of all points (x, y) such that $x > 0$, $y \geqslant x^{-1}$.

§ 4. Nets. Decomposition of an Open Set

If Δ is a closed interval in R_m, we call *net of closed intervals* on Δ any sequence of closed non-overlapping intervals whose sum is identical with Δ. By *net of cells* on R_m we mean a sequence of cells no two of which have common points and whose sum covers R_m. A sequence N_k ($k = 1, 2, \ldots$) of nets is called *regular* if each interval of N_{k+1} is contained in an interval of N_k and if the characteristic number of N_k (cf. § 2) tends to zero as $k \to \infty$.

Theorem 1. *A set E, which is open relative to a closed interval Δ, is the sum of a sequence of closed non-overlapping intervals. A set E, which is open relative to R_m, is the sum of a sequence of cells without common points.*

Proof. Let E be open relative to Δ, and let N_k be a regular sequence of nets of closed intervals on Δ, such that every net N_k contains only a finite number of intervals. Let, furthermore, M_1 be the sum of those intervals of N_1 that lie in E, and let M_k, for $k \geqslant 2$, be the sum of those intervals of N_k that lie in E, but not in any of the preceding $M_l (l < k)$. Since the characteristic number of N_k tends to zero and E is open, the enumerable collection of intervals ΣM_k covers E.

Given a set E, open relative to R_m, we may repeat the proof for cells without common points, using now a regular sequence of nets of cells on R_m.

§ 5. The Heine-Borel-Lebesgue Covering Theorem

It is sometimes convenient to know under what conditions a point set which is covered by an infinity of other point sets, may already be covered by a finite number of these sets. The theorem which follows now gives sufficient conditions for this situation to arise.

Theorem 1 (*Heine-Borel-Lebesgue Covering Theorem*). *Let F be a set, bounded, and closed relative to R_m, and let S be a collection of sets, open relative to R_m and such that every point of F belongs to one at least of them. Then F is covered by a finite number of the open sets of S.*

Proof. Since F is bounded, there exists a closed interval Δ containing F. The set $\Delta - F$ is open relative to Δ, which implies that every point of $\Delta - F$ is an internal point of a set O, open relative to R_m and having no points in common with F (we may take for example $O = O_1 - F$, where O_1 is an open interval containing Δ). Adding this open set O to the collection S, we obtain a collection T of open sets. Evidently every $x \in \Delta$ is a point of at least one of the sets (T). In order to show now that F is covered by a finite number of the sets (S), it is clearly sufficient to prove that Δ is covered by a finite number of the sets (T). For this purpose we consider a regular sequence N_k of nets of closed intervals on Δ, each net N_k containing only a finite number of intervals. The theorem will be proved once we have shown the existence of an index k such that each of the finite number of intervals of N_k is contained in a set (T). If such an index k did not exist, we could take for every value of k an interval Δ_k of N_k, not contained in a set (T). The centres x_k of the intervals Δ_k (whose diameters tend to zero) would have, in virtue of the Bolzano-Weierstrass Theorem, at least one point of accumulation x belonging to Δ, and in every neighbourhood of x there would be consequently an interval Δ_k not covered by a set (T). This however is impossible since x is an internal point of one of the sets (T).

EXAMPLES

1) In § 2 we have used that if x, y and z are three arbitrary points in Euclidean space R_m, then $\rho(x, y) \leqslant \rho(x, z) + \rho(y, z)$. Prove this inequality.

(It is no restriction of the generality to suppose that z has all its coordinates equal to zero. From $ab \leqslant (a^2 + b^2)/2$, holding for $a, b \geqslant 0$, we derive, taking $a = |x_i|/(\Sigma x_i^2)^{1/2}$, $b = |y_i|/(\Sigma y_i^2)^{1/2}$ and summing over i, that $\Sigma |x_i y_i| \leqslant (\Sigma x_i^2 . \Sigma y_i^2)^{1/2}$. Hence, replacing y_i by $x_i - y_i$,

$$\rho^2(x, y) = \Sigma (x_i - y_i)^2 \leqslant \Sigma |x_i| . |x_i - y_i| + \Sigma |y_i| . |x_i - y_i| \leqslant \{(\Sigma x_i^2)^{1/2} + (\Sigma y_i^2)^{1/2}\} \{\Sigma (x_i - y_i)^2\}^{1/2},$$

from which the result follows).

2) In connection with the Heine-Borel-Lebesgue Covering Theorem, it may be proved that in each of the following cases the set T is not covered by a finite number of sets of the collection S:

(*a*) T is the open interval $(0, 1)$, S is the collection of all open intervals $(x, 1)$ such that $0 < x < 1$.

(*b*) $T = R_1$ (the whole straight line), S is the collection of all open linear intervals.

(*c*) T is the set consisting of the points $x_0, x_1, x_2, \ldots$, where $x_0 = 0$, $x_n = 1/n$ $(n = 1, 2, \ldots)$, S is the collection of all sets X_n, where X_n consists of the point x_n only.

Chapter 2

MEASURE. MEASURABLE FUNCTIONS

§ 1. Semirings and σ-Rings of Point Sets

As in § 1 of the preceding chapter, X is a general point set, and all point sets considered are subsets of X.

Definition. *A collection Γ of point sets is called a semiring whenever:*

(*a*) *The empty set belongs to Γ, hence $0 \in \Gamma$.*

(*b*) *If $A \in \Gamma$ and $B \in \Gamma$, then $AB \in \Gamma$.*

(*c*) *If $A \in \Gamma$, $B \in \Gamma$ and $B \subset A$, then $A - B = \Sigma C_n$, where ΣC_n is a finite sum, all $C_n \in \Gamma$ and $C_i C_j = 0$ $(i \neq j)$.*

Theorem 1. *If Γ is a semiring and $A_1, \ldots, A_n \in \Gamma$, there exist sets $B_1, \ldots, B_p \in \Gamma$ such that $B_i B_j = 0$ $(i \neq j)$ and each A_i is the sum of several B_j.*

Proof. Suppose first that $n = 2$. Then $A_1 = A_1A_2 + (A_1 - A_1A_2)$, $A_2 = A_1A_2 + (A_2 - A_1A_2)$, and no two of the sets A_1A_2, $A_1 - A_1A_2$ and $A_2 - A_1A_2$ have common points. The desired result follows therefore from the properties of the semiring Γ.

Let now $n = 3$. There exist sets $C_1, \ldots, C_k \in \Gamma$ such that $C_iC_j = 0$ $(i \neq j)$ and both A_1, A_2 are sums of several C_i. For the purposes of our decomposition proof we may therefore replace A_1, A_2, A_3 by $C_1, \ldots, C_k$, A_3. This collection is now split up into $C_1A_3, \ldots, C_kA_3, C_1 - C_1A_3, \ldots, C_k - C_kA_3$ and $A_3 - C_1A_3 - \ldots - C_kA_3$, no two of which have common points. Hence, the desired result follows once again from the properties of the semiring Γ.

The extension to the case $n > 3$ is now evident.

Theorem 2. *In Euclidean space R_m the collection of all cells (left open intervals), together with the empty set, is a semiring Γ.*

Proof. It is evident that the properties (*a*) and (*b*) of a semiring are satisfied. Considering now first on the straight line R_1 two sets $A \in \Gamma$

and $B \in \Gamma$ for which $B \subset A$, we have either $A - B = 0$ or $A - B = C_1$ or $A - B = C_1 + C_2$, where $C_1, C_2 \in \Gamma$ and $C_1C_2 = 0$. Hence property (*c*) is satisfied. The extension to the space R_m $(m > 1)$ is now immediate.

Definition. *A non-empty collection Λ of point sets is called a σ-ring whenever*:

(*a*) *If $A_n \in \Lambda$ $(n = 1, 2, \dots)$, then $\Sigma_1^\infty A_n \in \Lambda$.*

(*b*) *If $A \in \Lambda$ and $B \in \Lambda$, then $A - B \in \Lambda$.*

Theorem 3. *If Λ is a σ-ring, then*:

1°. $0 \in \Lambda$.

2°. *If $A_n \in \Lambda$ $(n = 1, 2, \dots)$, then $\Pi_1^\infty A_n \in \Lambda$, $\limsup A_n \in \Lambda$ and $\liminf A_n \in \Lambda$.*

3°. *Λ is a semiring.*

Proof. 1°. Since Λ contains at least one set A, we have $0 = A - A \in \Lambda$ by (*b*).

2°. If $A_n \in \Lambda$ $(n = 1, 2, \dots)$, then $A = \Sigma A_n \in \Lambda$, hence the complements $A_n' = A - A_n$ belong to Λ for every n. It follows that

$$\Pi A_n = (\Sigma A_n')' = A - \Sigma A_n' \in \Lambda.$$

Observing now that $\limsup A_n = \Pi_{k=1}^\infty \Sigma_{n=k}^\infty A_n$ and $\liminf A_n = \Sigma_{k=1}^\infty \Pi_{n=k}^\infty A_n$, we see that both these sets belong to Λ.

3°. Follows immediately from what we have already proved.

Remark. Once we know that $0 \in \Lambda$, it hardly needs observing that $A_n \in \Lambda$ $(n = 1, \dots, p)$ implies $\Sigma_1^p A_n \in \Lambda$, and therefore also $\Pi_1^p A_n \in \Lambda$.

§ 2. Measure on a Semiring

In what follows we shall frequently have to do with functions assuming real values, the values $+\infty$ and $-\infty$ not excluded. To avoid any misunderstandings, we make once for all the following conventions:

$$a + (\pm\infty) = (\pm\infty) + a = \pm\infty \text{ for } a \neq \mp\infty,$$
$$(+\infty) + (-\infty) = (-\infty) + (+\infty) = (\pm\infty) - (\pm\infty) = 0,$$
$$a(\pm\infty) = (\pm\infty)a = \pm\infty \text{ for } a > 0,$$
$$a(\pm\infty) = (\pm\infty)a = \mp\infty \text{ for } a < 0,$$
$$0(\pm\infty) = (\pm\infty)0 = 0,$$
$$a/(\pm\infty) = 0,$$
$$a/0 = +\infty,$$
$$-\infty < a < +\infty \text{ for every finite } a.$$

Definition. *Let there be associated to every point set A of a semiring Γ a real number $\mu(A)$. This function $\mu(A)$ of a set is called a measure on Γ whenever:*

(*a*) $\mu(0) = 0$ *and* $0 \leqslant \mu(A) \leqslant \infty$ *for every* $A \in \Gamma$.

(*b*) *If* $A \in \Gamma$, $A_n \in \Gamma$ $(n = 1, 2, \ldots)$ *and* $A \subset \Sigma_1^\infty A_n$, *then* $\mu(A) \leqslant \Sigma_1^\infty \mu(A_n)$.

(*c*) *If* $A \in \Gamma$, $A_n \in \Gamma$ $(n = 1, \ldots, p)$, $A_i A_j = 0$ $(i \neq j)$ *and* $A \supset \Sigma_1^p A_n$, *then* $\mu(A) \geqslant \Sigma_1^p \mu(A_n)$.

Theorem 1. *If $\mu(A)$ is a measure on the semiring Γ, then:*

1°. *If* $A \in \Gamma$, $A_n \in \Gamma$ $(n = 1, \ldots, p)$ *and* $A \subset \Sigma_1^p A_n$, *then* $\mu(A) \leqslant \Sigma_1^p \mu(A_n)$.

2°. *The measure is monotone, that is, if* $A \in \Gamma$, $B \in \Gamma$ *and* $A \subset B$, *then* $\mu(A) \leqslant \mu(B)$.

3°. *If* $A \in \Gamma$, $A_n \in \Gamma$ $(n = 1, 2, \ldots)$, $A_i A_j = 0$ $(i \neq j)$ *and* $A = \Sigma_1^\infty A_n$, *then* $\mu(A) = \Sigma_1^\infty \mu(A_n)$.

Proof. 1°. Follows immediately from property (*b*) of a measure by taking $A_n = 0$ for $n > p$.

2°. Follows also from (*b*) by taking $A_1 = B$ and $A_n = 0$ for $n \geqslant 2$.

3°. We have $\mu(A) \leqslant \Sigma_1^\infty \mu(A_n)$ by (*b*), and $\mu(A) \geqslant \Sigma_1^p \mu(A_n)$ for each p by (*c*).

On account of property 3° the measure $\mu(A)$ is said to be *completely additive*, and not merely finitely additive, on Γ.

§ 3. Exterior Measure

From now on we shall suppose that $\mu(A)$ is a measure on the semiring Γ, and that the point set X, which contains all considered point sets as subsets, has the property that $X = \Sigma P_n$, where $P_n \in \Gamma$ and $\mu(P_n) < \infty$ for all n. It is sometimes said, in order to express this property of the measure $\mu(A)$, that $\mu(A)$ is *σ-finite*.

Definition. *Let $S \subset X$ be an arbitrary point set. Then the exterior measure $\mu^*(S)$ of S is defined by*

$$\mu^*(S) = \textit{lower bound } \Sigma_1^\infty \mu(A_n)$$

over all possible sets $\Sigma_1^\infty A_n \supset S$ with $A_n \in \Gamma$ for every n.

Obviously, since X is a sum ΣP_n with $P_n \in \Gamma$ $(n = 1, 2, \ldots)$, every set

S may be covered by at least one set ΣA_n with $A_n \in \Gamma$ ($n = 1, 2, \ldots$), so that the definition makes sense.

Theorem 1. 1°. *The exterior measure is subadditive, that is, if* S_n ($n = 1, 2, \ldots$) *are arbitrary, then*

$$\mu^*(\Sigma S_n) \leqslant \Sigma \mu^*(S_n).$$

2°. $\mu^*(0) = 0$ *and* $0 \leqslant \mu^*(S) \leqslant \infty$ *for every* S.

3°. *The exterior measure is monotone, that is, if* $S \subset T$, *then* $\mu^*(S) \leqslant \mu^*(T)$.

Proof. 1°. There is nothing to prove unless $\Sigma \mu^*(S_n) < \infty$. Suppose therefore that this is the case. If now $\varepsilon > 0$ is arbitrary, there exist sets $A_{nj} \in \Gamma$ ($n, j = 1, 2, \ldots$) such that $S_n \subset \Sigma_j A_{nj}$ and $\Sigma_j \mu(A_{nj}) < \mu^*(S_n) + \varepsilon/2^n$ for every n. Then $\Sigma S_n \subset \Sigma_n \Sigma_j A_{nj}$ and $\Sigma_n \Sigma_j \mu(A_{nj}) < \Sigma \mu^*(S_n) + \varepsilon$. Hence $\mu^*(\Sigma S_n) < \Sigma \mu^*(S_n) + \varepsilon$, from which, since $\varepsilon > 0$ is arbitrary, the desired result follows.

2°. Since $\mu^*(S)$ is the lower bound of a set of non-negative numbers, we have $0 \leqslant \mu^*(S) \leqslant \infty$ for every S. If $S = 0$, we may cover S by a set ΣA_n, where $A_n = 0$ for all n. Then $\mu^*(S) \leqslant \Sigma \mu(A_n) = 0$, hence $\mu^*(0) = 0$.

3°. If $S \subset T$ and $T \subset \Sigma A_n$ with $A_n \in \Gamma$ for every n, then also $S \subset \Sigma A_n$. Hence $\mu^*(S) \leqslant \mu^*(T)$.

One may ask what is the exterior measure of a set A belonging to the semiring Γ. It is reasonable to conjecture that $\mu^*(A) = \mu(A)$ in this case, and our next theorem shows this conjecture to be true.

Theorem 2. *If* $A \in \Gamma$, *then* $\mu^*(A) = \mu(A)$.

Proof. If $A \subset \Sigma A_n$ with $A_n \in \Gamma$ ($n = 1, 2, \ldots$), then $\mu(A) \leqslant \Sigma \mu(A_n)$ by property (*b*) of a measure. This holds for all admitted coverings ΣA_n of A, hence $\mu(A) \leqslant \mu^*(A)$. On the other hand, since A itself is also an admitted covering of A, we have $\mu^*(A) \leqslant \mu(A)$. Hence $\mu^*(A) = \mu(A)$.

§ 4. The Collection of Measurable Sets

As before, we shall denote, for any point set E, by E' its complement relative to X. Then, if S and E are arbitrary sets, we have $S = SE + SE'$, hence, by the subadditivity of the exterior measure μ^*,

$$\mu^*(S) \leqslant \mu^*(SE) + \mu^*(SE').$$

Definition. *The set E is called μ-measurable (or shortly measurable, if no confusion is possible) whenever*

$$\mu^*(S) = \mu^*(SE) + \mu^*(SE')$$

holds for every set S. We shall denote the collection of all measurable sets by Λ.

Theorem 1. *If $E \in \Lambda$, then $E' \in \Lambda$. The sets X and 0 belong to Λ.*

Proof. The first statement is an immediate consequence of the definition of measurability, this definition being symmetric in E and E'. If $E = X$ and S is arbitrary, we have $SE = S$ and $SE' = 0$, so that, since $\mu^*(S) = \mu^*(S) + \mu^*(0)$, the set $E = X$ is measurable.

Theorem 2. *If $E_1 \in \Lambda$ and $E_2 \in \Lambda$, then $E_1 + E_2 \in \Lambda$. Furthermore, if $E_1E_2 = 0$ and S is arbitrary, then*

$$\mu^*\{S(E_1 + E_2)\} = \mu^*(SE_1) + \mu^*(SE_2).$$

In particular, in this case,

$$\mu^*(E_1 + E_2) = \mu^*(E_1) + \mu^*(E_2).$$

Proof. We have (not yet assuming that $E_1E_2 = 0$)

$$E_1 + E_2 = E_1 + E_1'E_2, \qquad (E_1 + E_2)' = E_1'E_2'.$$

Hence, using first that E_2 and next that E_1 is measurable,

$$\mu^*(S) \leqslant \mu^*\{S(E_1 + E_2)\} + \mu^*\{S(E_1 + E_2)'\} \leqslant$$

$$\mu^*(SE_1) + \mu^*(SE_1'E_2) + \mu^*(SE_1'E_2') =$$

$$\mu^*(SE_1) + \mu^*(SE_1') = \mu^*(S)$$

for any set S. It follows that there is equality everywhere in the above chain of inequalities, and this shows that $E_1 + E_2$ is measurable.

The equality everywhere, applied to $S_1 = S(E_1 + E_2)$ instead of S, implies in particular $\mu^*\{S(E_1 + E_2)\} = \mu^*(SE_1) + \mu^*(SE_1'E_2)$; hence, if $E_1E_2 = 0$ or, equivalently, $E_1'E_2 = E_2$, then

$$\mu^*\{S(E_1 + E_2)\} = \mu^*(SE_1) + \mu^*(SE_2).$$

Corollary. *If $E_n \in \Lambda$ $(n = 1, \ldots, p)$, then $\Sigma_1^p E_n \in \Lambda$ and $\Pi_1^p E_n \in \Lambda$. Furthermore, if $E_iE_j = 0$ $(i \neq j)$, then*

$$\mu^*(\Sigma_1^p E_n) = \Sigma_1^p \mu^*(E_n).$$

The exterior measure μ^* is therefore finitely additive on Λ.

Proof. The only statement not immediately evident is $\Pi_1^p E_n \in \Lambda$. However, since $\Pi E_n = (\Sigma E_n')'$ and all E_n' are measurable, ΠE_n is also measurable.

Theorem 3. *If $E_1 \in \Lambda$ and $E_2 \in \Lambda$, then $E_1 - E_2 \in \Lambda$.*
Proof. Follows from $E_1 - E_2 = E_1 E_2'$ (cf. Ch. 1, § 1, Th. 4).

Theorem 4. *If $E_n \in \Lambda$ $(n = 1, 2, \ldots)$, then $\Sigma_1^\infty E_n \in \Lambda$. Furthermore, if $E_i E_j = 0$ $(i \neq j)$ and S is arbitrary, then*

$$\mu^*(S\, \Sigma_1^\infty E_n) = \Sigma_1^\infty \mu^*(S E_n).$$

In particular, in this case,

$$\mu^*(\Sigma_1^\infty E_n) = \Sigma_1^\infty \mu^*(E_n).$$

The exterior measure μ^* is therefore completely additive on Λ.
Proof. We have

$$\Sigma_1^\infty E_n = E_1 + (E_2 - E_1) + (E_3 - E_1 - E_2) + \ldots,$$

where no two of the measurable sets on the right have common points. It is therefore no restriction of the generality to assume immediately that $E_i E_j = 0$ $(i \neq j)$. Then, if S is an arbitrary set,

$$\mu^*(S) = \mu^*(S\, \Sigma_1^p E_n) + \mu^*\{S(\Sigma_1^p E_n)'\} =$$

$$\Sigma_1^p \mu^*(SE_n) + \mu^*(S\, \Pi_1^p E_n') \geqslant \Sigma_1^p \mu^*(SE_n) + \mu^*(S\, \Pi_1^\infty E_n')$$

$$= \Sigma_1^p \mu^*(SE_n) + \mu^*\{S(\Sigma_1^\infty E_n)'\}$$

for every p, hence, using the subadditivity of μ^*,

$$\mu^*(S) \geqslant \Sigma_1^\infty \mu^*(SE_n) + \mu^*\{S(\Sigma_1^\infty E_n)'\} \geqslant$$

$$\mu^*(S\Sigma_1^\infty E_n) + \mu^*\{S(\Sigma_1^\infty E_n)'\} \geqslant \mu^*(S).$$

It follows that in this last chain of inequalities there is equality everywhere, so that $\Sigma_1^\infty E_n$ is measurable. Furthermore, replacing S by $S_1 = S\, \Sigma_1^\infty E_n$, we obtain

$$\mu^*(S\, \Sigma_1^\infty E_n) = \Sigma_1^\infty \mu^*(SE_n).$$

We may conclude from the results obtained so far that the collection Λ of measurable sets is a σ-ring on which the exterior measure μ^* is completely additive. It will be proved now that the semiring Γ, from which we started, is a subcollection of Λ.

Theorem 5. *If $A \in \Gamma$, then $A \in \Lambda$.*

Proof. We have only to show that $\mu^*(S) \geqslant \mu^*(SA) + \mu^*(SA')$ for every set S satisfying $\mu^*(S) < \infty$. Let $S \subset \Sigma_1^\infty B_n$ with $B_n \in \Gamma$ and $\Sigma\, \mu(B_n) < \infty$. Then $SA \subset \Sigma\, B_n A$, hence

$$\mu^*(SA) \leqslant \Sigma\, \mu(B_n A) < \infty. \tag{1}$$

Furthermore $SA' \subset \Sigma B_n A' = \Sigma\,(B_n - B_n A)$, where each of the sets $B_n - B_n A$ may be written as a finite sum $\Sigma_j\, C_{nj}$ with all $C_{nj} \in \Gamma$ and $C_{ni} C_{nj} = 0$ $(i \neq j)$. Hence

$$\mu^*(SA') \leqslant \Sigma_n \Sigma_j\, \mu(C_{nj}). \tag{2}$$

Now, since $\mu(B_n) < \infty$ and $B_n = B_n A + \Sigma_j\, C_{nj}$, where no two sets on the right have common points, we have

$$\mu(B_n) - \mu(B_n A) = \Sigma_j\, \mu(C_{nj})$$

for every n, so that, in view of (2),

$$\mu^*(SA') \leqslant \Sigma\{\mu(B_n) - \mu(B_n A)\}. \tag{3}$$

Addition of (1) and (3) yields therefore

$$\mu^*(SA) + \mu^*(SA') \leqslant \Sigma\, \mu(B_n).$$

Taking the lower bound over all admitted coverings ΣB_n of S, we obtain finally

$$\mu^*(SA) + \mu^*(SA') \leqslant \mu^*(S).$$

Observing that the σ-ring Λ may be considered as a semiring and that $\mu^*(A) = \mu(A)$ for any $A \in \Gamma$ (cf. § 3, Th. 2), our final conclusion is therefore that μ^* is a measure on Λ, and that μ^* on Λ is an extension of μ on Γ. Hence we may, without fear of confusion, write $\mu(E)$ instead of $\mu^*(E)$, and simply speak about the measure of E, for any measurable set E.

§ 5. Properties of Measurable Sets

We collect some properties of measurable sets.

Theorem 1. *If the exterior measure $\mu^*(E)$ of a set E is zero, then E is measurable. Hence, every subset of a set of measure zero is measurable and of measure zero.*

Proof. If $\mu^*(E) = 0$, then $\mu^*(SE) = 0$ for any set S, hence $\mu^*(S) \leqslant \mu^*(SE) + \mu^*(SE') = \mu^*(SE')$. On the other hand, since $S \supset SE'$, we have $\mu^*(S) \geqslant \mu^*(SE')$. Hence

$$\mu^*(S) = \mu^*(SE') = \mu^*(SE) + \mu^*(SE'),$$

and this shows that E is measurable.

The definition which follows is based upon the theorem which has just been proved.

Definition. *If every point of a set S, except at most the points belonging to a subset of S of measure zero, possesses a certain property (P), it is said that the condition (P) is satisfied almost everywhere on S, or that almost every point of S has the property (P). In particular, we shall say that the sets E and F are almost equal, and write $E \sim F$, whenever their characteristic functions are equal almost everywhere on X.*

Theorem 2. *We have $E \sim F$ if and only if $\mu(E - F) = \mu(F - E) = 0$. The relation $E \sim F$ implies $\mu^*(E) = \mu^*(F) = \mu^*(EF)$. If $E \sim F$ and $F \sim H$, then $E \sim H$.*

Proof. The first statement is an immediate consequence of the definition of $E \sim F$. Next, if $E \sim F$, then $\mu^*(E) \leqslant \mu^*(EF) + \mu^*(E - F) = \mu^*(EF) \leqslant \mu^*(E)$, hence $\mu^*(E) = \mu^*(EF)$. In the same way $\mu^*(F) = \mu^*(EF)$.

Finally, if $E \sim F$ and $F \sim H$, we have, introducing complementary sets, $\mu(EF') = \mu(E'F) = \mu(FH') = \mu(F'H) = 0$, hence, since $E - H = EH' = EFH' + EF'H' \subset FH' + EF'$, also $\mu(E - H) = 0$. In the same way $\mu(H - E) = 0$. Hence $E \sim H$.

We now discuss some special collections of measurable sets. Any set $O = \Sigma_1^\infty A_n$ such that $A_n \in \Gamma$ $(n = 1, 2, \ldots)$ will be called a *σ-set*. Evidently, if the sets $O_i (i = 1, 2, \ldots)$ are σ-sets, then $\Sigma_1^\infty O_i$ is also a σ-set, and so is any finite product $\Pi_1^p O_i$. The complementary set $F = O' = \Pi_1^\infty A_n'$ of any σ-set O will be called a *δ-set*. It follows that if F_i $(i = 1, 2, \ldots)$ are δ-sets, then $\Pi_1^\infty F_i$ and any finite sum $\Sigma_1^p F_i$ are also δ-sets.

Theorem 3. *If $O = \Sigma A_n$, where all $A_n \in \Gamma$, is a given σ-set, then it may be written in the form $O = \Sigma B_n$ with all $B_n \in \Gamma$ and $B_i B_j = 0$ $(i \neq j)$.*

Furthermore

$$\mu(O) = \Sigma\, \mu(B_n) \leqslant \Sigma\, \mu(A_n).$$

Hence, if S is an arbitrary set,

$$\mu^*(S) = \textit{lower bound}\ \mu(O)$$

over all σ-sets O covering S.

Proof. The existence of the sets B_n follows upon observing that $\Sigma A_n = A_1 + (A_2 - A_1) + (A_3 - A_1 - A_2) + \ldots$, and that each of the sets on the right, no two of which have common points, is a sum of a finite number of sets belonging to Γ, no two of which have common points. Then

$$\Sigma\, \mu(A_n) \geqslant \mu(A_1) + \mu(A_2 - A_1) + \mu\,(A_3 - A_1 - A_2) + \ldots =$$
$$\Sigma\, \mu(B_n) = \mu(\Sigma\, B_n) = \mu(O).$$

Theorem 4. *If S is an arbitrary set, then*

$$\mu^*(S) = \textit{lower bound}\ \mu(E)$$

over all measurable sets E covering S.

Proof. In virtue of the preceding theorem we have only to show that $\mu^*(S) \leqslant \mu(E)$ for any measurable $E \supset S$. This however is evident on account of $\mu^*(S) \leqslant \mu^*(E) = \mu(E)$.

We shall call a set $O_\delta = \Pi_1^\infty O_n$, where all O_n are σ-sets, a *σ_δ-set*. Similarly, a set $F_\sigma = \Sigma_1^\infty F_n$, where all F_n are δ-sets, will be called a *δ_σ-set*. Evidently all σ_δ-sets and all δ_σ-sets are measurable.

Theorem 5. *If the set S is of finite exterior measure, there exists a σ_δ-set O_δ covering S such that $\mu(O_\delta) = \mu^*(S)$. Hence, if moreover S is measurable, the sets S and O_δ are almost equal.*

Proof. There exists a sequence O_n $(n = 1, 2, \ldots)$ of σ-sets such that $S \subset O_n$ and $\mu^*(S) \leqslant \mu(O_n) < \mu^*(S) + n^{-1}$, Writing $O_\delta = \Pi_1^\infty O_n$, we have $S \subset O_\delta \subset O_n$ for all n, hence

$$\mu^*(S) \leqslant \mu(O_\delta) \leqslant \mu(O_n) < \mu^*(S) + n^{-1}$$

for all n, which implies $\mu^*(S) = \mu(O_\delta)$.

Theorem 6. *If E is measurable ($\mu(E) = \infty$ is admitted), there exists a σ_δ-set O_δ covering E such that E and O_δ are almost equal.*

Proof. Since the measure μ is σ-finite, E may be written in the form $E = \Sigma E_n$, where all E_n are measurable and all $\mu(E_n) < \infty$. To each E_n we now assign a sequence of σ-sets O_{nj} such that $E_n \subset O_{nj}$ and $\mu(O_{nj} - E_n) < (j.2^n)^{-1}$. Then, writing $O_j = \Sigma_n O_{nj}$, the set O_j is a σ-set such that $E \subset O_j$ and $\mu(O_j - E) < j^{-1}$. The set $O_\delta = \Pi_1^\infty O_j$ has now the desired properties.

Theorem 7. *If E is measurable and $\varepsilon > 0$, there exists a σ-set O and a δ-set F such that $F \subset E \subset O$ and $\mu(O - E) < \varepsilon$, $\mu(E - F) < \varepsilon$. Consequently, if E is measurable, there exists a σ_δ-set O_δ and a δ_σ-set F_σ such that $F_\sigma \subset E \subset O_\delta$ and the sets F_σ, E and O_δ are almost equal.*

Proof. Only the statement concerning F needs a proof. There exists a σ-set O^*, covering the complementary set E' of E, and such that $\mu(O^* - E') < \varepsilon$. Then the complementary δ-set $F = (O^*)'$ of O^* satisfies $F \subset E$ and $E - F = EF' = EO^* = O^* - E'$. Hence $\mu(E - F) < \varepsilon$.

Theorem 8. *The set E is measurable if and only if to every $\varepsilon > 0$ there exist two measurable sets E_1 and E_2 such that $E_1 \subset E \subset E_2$ and $\mu(E_2 - E_1) < \varepsilon$.*

Proof. If E is measurable, the existence of the sets E_1 and E_2 with the desired properties has been proved in the preceding theorem (we may even take for E_1 a δ-set F and for E_2 a σ-set O). Let us suppose now, conversely, that E has the property that to every $\varepsilon > 0$ there exist two measurable sets E_1 and E_2 such that $E_1 \subset E \subset E_2$ and $\mu(E_2 - E_1) < \varepsilon$. Consequently, there exist two sequences E_{1n} and $E_{2n} (n = 1, 2, \ldots)$ of measurable sets such that $E_{1n} \subset E \subset E_{2n}$ and $\mu(E_{2n} - E_{1n}) < n^{-1}$ for every n. Writing now $E_\sigma = \Sigma E_{1n}$, $E_\delta = \Pi E_{2n}$, we have $E_{1n} \subset E_\sigma \subset E \subset E_\delta \subset E_{2n}$ for every n, hence $\mu(E_\delta - E_\sigma) = 0$. Since $E - E_\sigma$ is a subset of $E_\delta - E_\sigma$, the set $E - E_\sigma$ is measurable (and of measure zero). Finally, in virtue of $E = E_\sigma + (E - E_\sigma)$, we see that the set E is measurable.

Considering the σ-ring Λ of all μ-measurable sets as a semiring, and $\mu(E)$ as a measure $\bar{\mu}(E)$ on this semiring, one might start the whole procedure anew, and define, for an arbitrary set S, the exterior measure $\bar{\mu}^*(S)$ by

$$\bar{\mu}^*(S) = \text{lower bound } \Sigma \mu(E_n)$$

over all sets $\Sigma E_n \supset S$, where $E_n \in \Lambda$ for each n. Observing however that $\Sigma E_n = \Sigma E_n^*$ with $E_n^* \in \Lambda$ and $E_i^* E_j^* = 0 \;\; (i \neq j)$, so that

$$\bar{\mu}^*(S) = \text{lower bound } \mu(E)$$

over all $E \in \Lambda$ covering S, we see that, by Theorem 4,

$$\bar{\mu}^*(S) = \mu^*(S)$$

for every set S. No new extension is obtained therefore; the collection of all $\bar{\mu}$-measurable sets is identical with the collection Λ of all μ-measurable sets.

§ 6. Sequences of Measurable Sets

We shall consider a sequence $E_n (n = 1, 2, \ldots)$ of measurable sets, and we recall that if the sequence is monotone, then $E = \lim E_n$ exists ($E = \Sigma E_n$ if E_n is ascending and $E = \Pi E_n$ if E_n is descending).

Theorem 1. *If the sequence E_n is ascending and $E = \lim E_n$, then $\mu(E) = \lim \mu(E_n)$.*

Proof. We have

$$\mu(E) = \mu(\Sigma E_n) = \mu\{E_1 + (E_2 - E_1) + (E_3 - E_2) + \ldots\} =$$
$$\mu(E_1) + \mu(E_2 - E_1) + \mu(E_3 - E_2) + \ldots =$$
$$\lim \{\mu(E_1) + \mu(E_2 - E_1) + \ldots + \mu(E_n - E_{n-1})\} =$$
$$\lim \mu\{E_1 + (E_2 - E_1) + \ldots + (E_n - E_{n-1})\} = \lim \mu(E_n).$$

Theorem 2. *If the sequence E_n is descending with limit E, and one at least of the sets E_n has finite measure, then $\mu(E) = \lim \mu(E_n)$.*

Proof. If $\mu(E_m) < \infty$, then $\mu(E_n) \leqslant \mu(E_m) < \infty$ for $n \geqslant m$. Hence, since $E \subset E_n$ for all n, also $\mu(E) < \infty$. Observing that $E_m - E_n$ (m fixed, n variable) is an ascending sequence, we find now

$$\mu(E_m) - \mu(E) = \mu(E_m - E) = \mu\{\lim (E_m - E_n)\} =$$
$$\lim \mu(E_m - E_n) = \mu(E_m) - \lim \mu(E_n),$$

so that $\mu(E) = \lim \mu(E_n)$.

Theorem 3. *If the sequence E_n of measurable sets is arbitrary, then*

$$\mu(\liminf E_n) \leqslant \liminf \mu(E_n).$$

Furthermore, if $\mu(E_n + E_{n+1} + \ldots) < \infty$ for at least one value of n, then

$$\mu(\limsup E_n) \geqslant \limsup \mu(E_n).$$

In particular, if E_n is a convergent sequence, and $\mu(E_n + E_{n+1} + \ldots) < \infty$

for at least one value of n, we have

$$\mu(\lim E_n) = \lim \mu(E_n).$$

Proof. Since $\liminf E_n = \Sigma_{n=1}^{\infty} \Pi_{k=n}^{\infty} E_k$, the set $\liminf E_n$ is the limit of the ascending sequence $P_n = \Pi_{k=n}^{\infty} E_k$. Hence, by Theorem 1,

$$\mu(\liminf E_n) = \lim \mu(P_n) \leqslant \liminf \mu(E_n).$$

In a similar way, since $\limsup E_n = \Pi_{n=1}^{\infty} \Sigma_{k=n}^{\infty} E_k$, the set $\limsup E_n$ is the limit of the descending sequence $S_n = \Sigma_{k=n}^{\infty} E_k$. If therefore $\mu(S_n) = \mu(E_n + E_{n+1} + \ldots) < \infty$ for at least one value of n, we have, by Theorem 2,

$$\mu(\limsup E_n) = \lim \mu(S_n) \geqslant \limsup \mu(E_n).$$

§ 7. Lebesgue Measure and Stieltjes Measure

As examples we shall discuss Lebesgue measure in m-dimensional Euclidean space R_m and Stieltjes measure on the straight line R_1.

In § 1, Th. 2 we have seen that in R_m the collection of all cells (left open intervals), together with the empty set, is a semiring Γ.

Theorem 1. *If we define $m(A) = 0$ in case A is the empty set, and $m(A) = \Pi_{i=1}^{m} (b_i - a_i)$ in case A is the cell $(a_1, b_1; \ldots; a_m, b_m]$, then $m(A)$ is a σ-finite measure on Γ.*

Proof. The conditions that $m(0) = 0$ and $0 \leqslant m(A) \leqslant \infty$ for any $A \in \Gamma$ are satisfied. We have to prove first that if $A \in \Gamma$, $A_n \in \Gamma$ for $n = 1, \ldots, p$, $A_iA_j = 0$ $(i \neq j)$ and A covers $\Sigma_1^p A_n$, then $m(A) \geqslant \Sigma_1^p m(A_n)$. By § 1, Th. 1 there exist sets $B_1, \ldots, B_q \in \Gamma$ such that $B_iB_j = 0$ $(i \neq j)$ and each of the sets $A, A_1, \ldots, A_p$ is the sum of several B_i. Evidently, in the case which we consider here, $A = \Sigma_1^q B_i$, $m(A) = \Sigma_1^q m(B_i)$, and every B_k which is used in adding up a certain A_i is no more used in adding up any other A_j. Hence $m(A) = \Sigma_1^q m(B_i) \geqslant \Sigma_1^p m(A_i)$.

Next, we have to show that if $A \in \Gamma$, $A_n \in \Gamma (n = 1, 2, \ldots)$ and $A \subset \Sigma_1^{\infty} A_n$, then $m(A) \leqslant \Sigma_1^{\infty} m(A_n)$. We may clearly assume that $\Sigma_1^{\infty} m(A_n) < \infty$. Suppose now that, contrary to what we wish to prove, $m(A) > \Sigma_1^{\infty} m(A_n)$, so that there exists a positive number α satisfying

(1) $$m(A) > \Sigma_1^{\infty} m(A_n) + 2\alpha.$$

Taking now a closed interval F contained in A such that $m(A) < m(F_0)$

$+ \alpha$, where F_c is the cell having the same endpoints as F, and assigning to every A_n an open interval O_n and a set $B_n \in \Gamma$ such that $A_n \subset O_n \subset B_n$ and $m(B_n) < m(A_n) + \alpha/2^n$, the bounded closed set F is covered by $\Sigma\, O_n$. Hence, by the Heine-Borel-Lebesgue Covering Theorem, F is already covered by the sum of a finite number of these O_n. The cell F_c is therefore covered by a finite sum of the cells B_n, so that, by a similar argument as above, $m(F_c)$ does not exceed the sum of the measures of these B_n. Then certainly $m(F_c) \leqslant \Sigma\, m(B_n) < \Sigma\, m(A_n) + \alpha$, which implies $m(A) < m(F_c) + \alpha < \Sigma\, m(A_n) + 2\alpha$, in contradiction with our hypothesis (1). We may, therefore, draw the conclusion that $m(A) \leqslant \Sigma_1^\infty\, m(A_n)$.

Finally, since the whole space R_m is a sum of an enumerable infinity of non-overlapping cells of finite measure, the measure $m(A)$ is σ-finite.

The above measure $m(A)$ on the semiring Γ may be extended as a completely additive measure on to the σ-ring Λ of all measurable sets. The sets belonging to this σ-ring are called *Lebesgue measurable,* and the measure $m(E)$ of a set $E \in \Lambda$ is said to be the *Lebesgue measure* of E. By considering a closed interval as the limit of a descending sequence of cells, it is seen immediately that it has the same measure as the cell with the same endpoints. A similar argument shows the same for an open interval or a right open interval. Furthermore, a set which one might call a *degenerate interval,* that is, a set $[a_1, b_1; \ldots; a_m, b_m]$ with $a_k = b_k$ for at least one value of k, has measure zero. In particular, a set consisting of one single point has measure zero, and the same is therefore true of any set consisting of an enumerable infinity of points, such as e.g. the set of all points in R_m with only rational coordinates. We next observe that on the straight line R_1 the measure of an interval is exactly the length of this interval, and in the plane R_2 the measure of an interval is the area of the rectangle corresponding with the interval. Lebesgue measure in these cases is therefore identical with the classical concept.

Every open set in R_m is a sum of cells by Ch. 1, § 4, Th. 1, and is therefore what we have called in § 5 a σ-set. The converse is not true (a sum of cells, consisting of one single term, is not open). The statement (which we shall presently prove) that the exterior measure $m^*(S)$ of an arbitrary set S is the lower bound of $m(O)$ over all open sets $O \supset S$, is therefore a slight extension of § 5, Th. 3 where we took the lower bound over all σ-sets covering S.

Theorem 2. *If S is arbitrary, then*

$$m^*(S) = \text{lower bound } m(O)$$

over all open sets $O \supset S$.

If E is measurable and $\varepsilon > 0$, there exists an open set O and a closed set F such that $F \subset E \subset O$ and $m(O - E) < \varepsilon$, $m(E - F) < \varepsilon$. Consequently, if E is measurable, there exists a set O_δ, which is a product of open sets, and a set F_σ, which is a sum of closed sets, such that $F_\sigma \subset E \subset O_\delta$ and F_σ, E and O_δ are almost equal.

Proof. If ΣA_n is an arbitrary σ-set (all $A_n \in \Gamma$) and $\varepsilon > 0$, there exist open intervals B_n such that $A_n \subset B_n$ and $m(B_n) < m(A_n) + \varepsilon/2^n$ for each n. Hence $O = \Sigma B_n$ is open and $m(O) \leqslant \Sigma m(B_n) < \Sigma m(A_n) + \varepsilon$. It follows that the lower bound of $m(O)$ over all open sets $O \supset S$ is the same as over all σ-sets covering S.

The proofs of the remaining statements are similar to those of the corresponding statements in § 5.

In order to introduce a Stieltjes measure on the straight line R_1, we assume that $g(x)$ is a real function of the real variable x, monotonely non-decreasing ($g(x_1) \leqslant g(x_2)$ for $x_1 < x_2$) and right continuous ($g(x+) = \lim g(x+h) = g(x)$ as h tends to zero through positive values). Γ is once more the semiring consisting of all cells (left open intervals) and the empty set.

Theorem 3. *If we define $\mu(A) = 0$ in case A is the empty set, and $\mu(A) = g(b) - g(a)$ in case A is the cell $(a, b]$, then $\mu(A)$ is a σ-finite measure on Γ.*

Proof. Identical with the proof of Theorem 1.

The measure $\mu(A)$, defined in this way on the semiring Γ, may be extended as a completely additive measure on to the σ-ring Λ of all μ-measurable sets. The sets of this σ-ring are now termed *Stieltjes measurable* (relative to $g(x)$), and the measure $\mu(E)$ of a set $E \in \Lambda$ is called the *Stieltjes measure* of E (relative to $g(x)$). Obviously, for $g(x) = x$, the Stieltjes measure is identical with the Lebesgue measure.

We remark that although the left limit $g(x-) = \lim g(x+h)$ for $h \to 0$, $h < 0$, exists for every x, this limit may differ from $g(x)$. Hence, the measure $g(b) - g(a-)$ of the closed interval $[a, b]$ may be different from the measure $g(b) - g(a)$ of the cell $(a, b]$. Similarly, the measure $g(x) - g(x-)$ of the set, consisting of the single point x, may be different from zero.

§ 8. Measurable Functions

In the present paragraph we assume that Λ is a σ-ring consisting of subsets of the point set X. It is not necessary, therefore, that X itself belongs to Λ. The sets of Λ will be called measurable sets, although this terminology is not meant to indicate that Λ is the σ-ring of all μ-measurable sets with respect to some measure μ.

If $f(x)$ is a real function of a point, finite or infinite (the values $+\infty$ and $-\infty$ are therefore admitted), defined at all points x of the measurable set E, we shall mean by $E(f \geqslant a)$, $E(f < a)$, ... the subset of E on which $f(x) \geqslant a$, $f(x) < a$, ...

Definition. *The function $f(x)$ is called measurable on E whenever the set $E(f > a)$ is measurable for each finite a.*

Theorem 1. *If $f(x)$ is measurable on E, and E_1 is a measurable subset of E, then $f(x)$ is measurable on E_1. Conversely, if $f(x)$ is measurable on E_1 and the measurable set E covers E_1, then, defining $f(x) = 0$ on $E - E_1$, $f(x)$ is measurable on E.*

Proof. For each finite a we have $E_1(f > a) = E_1 . E(f > a)$.

Theorem 2. *If $f(x)$ is measurable on E, the sets $E(f \geqslant a)$, $E(f < a)$, $E(f \leqslant a)$ and $E(f = a)$ are measurable for each finite a. The same holds for the sets $E(f = +\infty)$, $E(f = -\infty)$, $E(f < +\infty)$ and $E(f > -\infty)$. If $a < b$ (a and b finite or infinite), and $f(x)$ is measurable on E, then the sets $E(a < f(x) \leqslant b)$, $E(a < f(x) < b)$ and $E(a \leqslant f(x) < b)$ are measurable.*

Proof. We have $E(f \geqslant a) = \Pi_{n=1}^{\infty} E(f > a - n^{-1})$; hence $E(f \geqslant a)$, as a product of measurable sets, is measurable. Furthermore $E(f < a) = E - E(f \geqslant a)$, $E(f \leqslant a) = E - E(f > a)$ and $E(f = a) = E(f \geqslant a) . E(f \leqslant a)$ are measurable.

Next $E(f = +\infty) = \Pi_{n=1}^{\infty} E(f > n)$, $E(f = -\infty) = \Pi_{n=1}^{\infty} E(f < -n)$, $E(f < +\infty) = E - E(f = +\infty)$ and $E(f > -\infty) = E - E(f = -\infty)$ are measurable.

Finally $E(a < f(x) \leqslant b) = E(f > a) . E(f \leqslant b)$ is measurable, and the remaining cases are dealt with by a similar argument.

Theorem 3. *In order that $f(x)$ be measurable on E, it is sufficient that one of the sets $E(f > a)$, $E(f \geqslant a)$, $E(f < a)$, $E(f \leqslant a)$ should be so for all values of a belonging to an arbitrary everywhere dense set S of real numbers.*

Proof. We give the proof for $E(f > a)$. For every real a, the set S contains a decreasing sequence of numbers r_n converging to a. We have therefore $E(f > a) = \Sigma\, E(f > r_n)$, and every term of the sum being measurable by hypothesis, the same holds for the sum itself.

Theorem 4. *If $f(x)$ is measurable, the same is true of $f(x) + a$ and $af(x)$ for every finite a.*

Proof. Follows from the definition of measurability and (in case $a < 0$ in $af(x)$) from Theorem 2.

Theorem 5. *If $f(x)$ and $g(x)$ are measurable, the sets $E(f > g)$, $E(f \geqslant g)$ and $E(f = g)$ are measurable.*

Proof. We have $E(f > g) = \Sigma_{n=1}^{\infty} E(f > r_n).E(g < r_n)$, where r_n is the sequence of all rational numbers. Hence $E(f > g)$ is measurable. The same is then true of $E(f \geqslant g) = E - E(f < g)$ and of $E(f = g) = E(f \geqslant g).E(f \leqslant g)$.

Theorem 6. *If $f(x)$ and $g(x)$ are measurable on E, and a, b are real constants, then $af(x) + bg(x)$ is measurable on E.*

Proof. In view of Theorem 4 it is sufficient to prove that $f(x) + g(x)$ is measurable. Writing $E_0 = E(f = +\infty,\ g = -\infty) + E(f = -\infty,\ g = +\infty)$, the sets E_0 and $E_1 = E - E_0$ are measurable, and we have $f(x) + g(x) = 0$ on E_0. Since $E_1(f + g > a) = E_1(f > a - g)$, and $a - g(x)$ is measurable for each finite a by Theorem 4, the set $E_1(f + g > a)$ is measurable for each finite a. Observing that

$$E(f + g > a) = E_1(f + g > a) + E_0 \quad \text{for } a < 0,$$

$$E(f + g > a) = E_1(f + g > a) \qquad \text{for } a \geqslant 0,$$

we obtain the desired result.

Theorem 7. *If $f(x)$ is measurable and α is a real number, then $|f(x)|^\alpha$ is also measurable.*

Proof. If $\alpha \geqslant 0$, we have $E(|f|^\alpha < a) = E(-a^{1/\alpha} < f(x) < a^{1/\alpha})$ for $a > 0$, whereas $E(|f|^\alpha < a)$ is empty for $a \leqslant 0$. Hence $E(|f|^\alpha < a)$ is measurable.

If $\alpha < 0$, we have $E(|f|^\alpha < a) = E(|f|^{-\alpha} > a^{-1})$ for $a > 0$, and $E(|f|^\alpha < a)$ is once again empty for $a \leqslant 0$.

Theorem 8. *If $f(x)$ and $g(x)$ are measurable on E, the same holds for $f(x)g(x)$.*

Proof. We observe first that the eight sets

$$
\begin{aligned}
U_1 &= E\ (f = +\infty,\ 0 < g < \infty),\\
U_2 &= E\ (f = +\infty,\ -\infty < g < 0),\\
U_3 &= E\ (f = -\infty,\ 0 < g < \infty),\\
U_4 &= E\ (f = -\infty,\ -\infty < g < 0),\\
U_5 &= E\ (0 < f < \infty,\ g = +\infty),\\
U_6 &= E\ (-\infty < f < 0,\ g = +\infty),\\
U_7 &= E\ (0 < f < \infty,\ g = -\infty),\\
U_8 &= E\ (-\infty < f < 0,\ g = -\infty)
\end{aligned}
$$

are measurable, so that $E_0 = \Sigma_{i=1}^{8} U_i$ and $E_1 = E - E_0$ are also measurable. On E_1 we have $fg = [(f + g)^2 - (f - g)^2]/4$, which implies, $(f + g)^2$ and $(f - g)^2$ being measurable on E_1 by the preceding theorems, that $E_1(fg > a)$ is a measurable set for each finite a. Observing finally that

$$E\ (fg > a) = E_1\ (fg > a) + U_1 + U_4 + U_5 + U_8,$$

we obtain the desired result.

Lemma α. *Given the sequence of (real) finite or infinite numbers a_n, the sequence h_n = upper bound $[a_{n+1}, a_{n+2}, \ldots]$ is non-increasing and*

$$\lim h_n = \text{lower bound } h_n = \limsup a_n.$$

Proof. If $\limsup a_n = +\infty$, then $h_n = +\infty$ for each n, hence $\lim h_n = \limsup a_n$. If $\limsup a_n = -\infty$, then $\lim a_n = -\infty$, so that $\lim h_n = -\infty$ as well; hence $\lim h_n = \limsup a_n$ also in this case. Let us assume now that $-\infty < p = \limsup a_n < +\infty$. Then, if $\varepsilon > 0$ is arbitrary, $a_n > p - \varepsilon$ for an infinity of values of n, so that $h_n > p - \varepsilon$ for all n. Hence $\lim h_n \geqslant p$. On the other hand we have $a_n \leqslant p + \varepsilon$ for all but a finite number of values of n, so that $h_n \leqslant p + \varepsilon$ for n sufficiently large. Hence $\lim h_n \leqslant p$. The final result is therefore that $\lim h_n = p = \limsup a_n$.

Theorem 9. *Given a sequence of measurable functions $f_n(x)$, finite or infinite, the functions $h(x) =$ upper bound $f_n(x)$, $k(x) =$ lower bound $f_n(x)$, $p(x) = \limsup f_n(x)$ and $q(x) = \liminf f_n(x)$ are also measurable. In particular, given a sequence of measurable functions, having a limit $f(x)$, the function $f(x)$ is measurable.*

Proof. The measurability of $h(x)$ follows from $E(h > a) = \Sigma E(f_n > a)$, holding for each finite a. For the lower bound the proof is derived by change of sign, observing that lower bound $f_n(x) = -$ upper bound $[-f_n(x)]$. By what we have already proved, the functions $h_n(x) =$ upper bound $[f_{n+1}(x), f_{n+2}(x), \ldots]$ are measurable, and, using Lemma α, we see that the same is therefore true of the function $\lim h_n(x) =$ lower bound $h_n(x) = \limsup f_n(x)$. For $q(x) = \liminf f_n(x)$ the proof is once more derived by change of sign, observing that $\liminf f_n(x) = -\limsup [-f_n(x)]$.

Theorem 10. *Every function $f(x)$ that is measurable and non-negative on the measurable set E is the limit of a non-decreasing sequence of simple functions, finite, measurable and non-negative on E.*

Proof. If we write for each positive integer n, and for $x \in E$,

$$f_n(x) = (i-1)/2^n \text{ if } (i-1)/2^n \leqslant f(x) < i/2^n \ (i = 1, \ldots, 2^n n),$$

$$f_n(x) = n \qquad \text{if } f(x) \geqslant n,$$

the functions $f_n(x)$ thus defined are evidently simple, non-negative and measurable. Furthermore, as we see easily, the sequence $f_n(x)$ is non-decreasing for every $x \in E$. Finally $\lim f_n(x) = f(x)$ for every $x \in E$, since for $f(x) < \infty$ we have $0 \leqslant f(x) - f_n(x) \leqslant 1/2^n$ as soon as $n > f(x)$, and for $f(x) = \infty$ we have $f_n(x) = n$ for every value of n.

§ 9. Egoroff's Theorem

We now assume the σ-ring Λ to be the collection of all μ-measurable sets with respect to some measure $\mu(E)$.

Lemma α. *If E is a measurable set of finite measure, and if $f_n(x)$ is a sequence of finite measurable functions converging on E to a finite measurable function $f(x)$, there exists, for every pair of positive numbers ε, η, a positive integer $N(\varepsilon, \eta)$ and a measurable subset H (also depending on ε and η) of E such that $\mu(H) < \eta$ and $|f(x) - f_n(x)| < \varepsilon$ for every $n > N$ and every $x \in E - H$.*

Proof. Let E_m be the subset of E consisting of all points x for which $|f(x) - f_n(x)| < \varepsilon$ whenever $n > m$. These sets E_m are measurable and form an ascending sequence since $E_m = \Pi_{n=m+1}^{\infty} E(|f - f_n| < \varepsilon)$. The relation $f = \lim f_n$, holding on the whole set E, implies that every $x \in E$ belongs to at least one E_m, so that $E = \Sigma E_m = \lim E_m$, and therefore, by § 6, Th. 1, $\mu(E) = \lim \mu(E_m)$ or $\lim \mu(E - E_m) = 0$ (it is here that we use $\mu(E) < \infty$). Hence, from a sufficiently large m_0 onwards, $\mu(E - E_m) < \eta$. Choosing $N(\varepsilon, \eta) = m_0$ and $H = E - E_{m_0}$, we obtain the desired result.

Theorem 1 (*Egoroff's Theorem*). *If E is a measurable set of finite measure, and if $f_n(x)$ is a sequence of measurable functions, finite almost everywhere on E and converging almost everywhere on E to a finite measurable function $f(x)$, then there exists, for every $\eta > 0$, a measurable subset Q of E such that $\mu(Q) < \eta$ and $f_n(x)$ converges uniformly to $f(x)$ on $E - Q$ (that is, given the positive numbers ε, η, there exists a positive integer $N(\varepsilon, \eta)$ and a measurable subset Q of E, this set Q depending only on η, such that $\mu(Q) < \eta$ and $|f(x) - f_n(x)| < \varepsilon$ for $n > N$ and $x \in E - Q$).*

Proof. Let $E_0 \subset E$ be the set of all points x at which one at least of the functions $f_n(x)$ is not finite or $f(x) = \lim f_n(x)$ does not hold. Then $\mu(E_0) = 0$, hence, writing $E^* = E - E_0$, we have $\mu(E^*) = \mu(E)$. In virtue of Lemma α we may assign now to each integer $m > 0$ a measurable set $H_m(\eta) \subset E^*$ and a positive integer $N_m(\eta)$ such that $\mu(H_m) < \eta/2^m$ and

$$|f(x) - f_n(x)| < 1/2^m \text{ for } n > N_m \text{ and } x \in E^* - H_m.$$

Defining Q by $Q = E_0 + \Sigma_{m=1}^{\infty} H_m$, we see that the set Q depends only on η, and that $\mu(Q) \leqslant \Sigma\mu(H_m) < \Sigma\, \eta/2^m = \eta$. Furthermore, $x \in E - Q$ implies $x \in E^* - H_m$ for all values of m, hence $|f(x) - f_n(x)| < 1/2^m$ for $n > N_m(\eta)$. Let now m_0 be the smallest index m satisfying $1/2^m < \varepsilon$. Then, for $x \in E - Q$ and $n > N_{m_0}(\eta) = N(\varepsilon, \eta)$, we have $|f(x) - f_n(x)| < 1/2^{m_0} < \varepsilon$, which is what we set out to prove.

§ 10. Extension to Functions with Complex Values

The theory of measurable functions may be extended to the case that the functions which we consider, defined at all points of the measurable set E, assume complex values. The function $f(x) = g(x) + ih(x)$, where $g(x)$ and $h(x)$ are real functions (and $i^2 = -1$), is called *measurable* on E whenever both $g(x)$ and $h(x)$ are measurable on E. It is evident that the following statements remain true for complex functions:

1°. Every linear combination of measurable functions with constant (complex) coefficients represents a measurable function.

2°. The product of two measurable functions is measurable.

3°. If $f(x)$ is measurable, the same holds for $|f(x)|$.

4°. Given a sequence of measurable functions having a limit $f(x)$, the function $f(x)$ is measurable.

5°. Egoroff's Theorem.

The proof of the third statement is derived by observing that $f = g+ih$ (g and h real) implies $|f| = (g^2 + h^2)^{1/2}$.

EXAMPLES

1) Divide the interval [0, 1] in R_1 into three equal parts, and remove the interior of the middle part. Next divide each of the two remaining parts into three equal parts and remove the interior of the middle parts of each of them; and repeat this process indefinitely. Let C be the set of points that remain (Cantor's ternary set). Then the Lebesgue measure $m(C)$ of C is zero.

(If E_n is the set which remains after n steps, then $C = \Pi E_n$).

2) Let T be the transformation of the straight line R_1 into itself, defined by $T(x) = \alpha x + \beta$, where α and β are real numbers and $\alpha \neq 0$. Let $T^{-1}(x)$ be the inverse transformation, $T^{-1}(x) = (x - \beta)/\alpha$. If, for an arbitrary subset S of R_1, S_T denotes the image of S (that is, S_T is the set of all points $\alpha x + \beta$ with $x \in S$) then the exterior Lebesgue measure $m^*(S_T)$ of S_T satisfies

$$m^*(S_T) = |\alpha| m^*(S).$$

The set E_T is Lebesgue measurable if and only if E is so.

(If $\alpha < 0$, the transformation T is the result of the transformations T_1 and T_2 applied successively, where $T_1(x) = |\alpha| x + \beta$ and $T_2(x) = -x$. The proof that T_2 leaves exterior measure invariant and preserves measurability, is easy. Let therefore $\alpha > 0$. Then T and T^{-1} transform cells into cells, and $m(A_T) = \alpha m(A)$ for any cell A. Hence, since T and T^{-1} transform open sets into open sets, we have $m(O_T) = \alpha m(O)$ for any open set O. Furthermore, $O \supset S$ for any open set O implies $O_T \supset S_T$, and conversely. Hence, by taking lower bounds, $m^*(S_T) = \alpha m^*(S.)$

If E is measurable and S is arbitrary, then

$$m^*(SE_T) + m^*(SE'_T) = m^*\{(S_{T^{-1}}E)_T\} + m^*\{(S_{T^{-1}}E')_T\} =$$
$$\alpha m^*(S_{T^{-1}}E) + \alpha m^*(S_{T^{-1}}E') = \alpha m^*(S_{T^{-1}}) = m^*(S),$$

so that E_T is measurable. The same argument with T replaced by T^{-1} shows that E is measurable if E_T is measurable).

3) Let in the plane R_2 the sets E_n ($n = 1, 2, \ldots$) be the closed intervals $[0, n^{-1}; 0, n]$, so that the Lebesgue measures $m(E_n)$ satisfy $m(E_n) = 1$. The set

$E = \lim E_n$ exists, and consists of all points $(0, y)$ with $y \geqslant 0$, so that $m(E) = 0$. It follows that $m(\lim E_n) = \lim m(E_n)$ is not satisfied.

(We have $m(E_n + E_{n+1} + \ldots) = 1 + (n+1)^{-1} + (n+2)^{-1} + \ldots = \infty$).

4) If $f(x)$ is continuous on the interval Δ in Euclidean space R_m, then $f(x)$ is measurable on Δ.

(We may assume that $f(x)$ is real. Then $\Delta(f > a)$ is open for each finite a).

Chapter 3

INTEGRATION

§ 1. Product Measure

If X_1 and X_2 are point sets, and $A \subset X_1$, $B \subset X_2$, we shall denote by $A \times B$ the set of all pairs of points (x, y) subject to $x \in A$ and $y \in B$. The set $A \times B$ is called the *combinatory product* or *Cartesian product* of A and B. If one at least of the sets A and B is empty, we define $A \times B$ to be empty as well, hence $A \times 0 = 0 \times B = 0$. Evidently, if A, A_1, $A_2 \subset X_1$ and B, B_1, $B_2 \subset X_2$, then

$$A \times B \subset X_1 \times X_2,$$

$$(A_1 \times B_1).(A_2 \times B_2) = A_1A_2 \times B_1B_2, \tag{1}$$

$$A_2 \times B_2 - A_1 \times B_1 = (A_2 - A_1) \times B_2 + A_1A_2 \times (B_2 - B_1). \tag{2}$$

Theorem 1. *If the collection Γ_1 of subsets of X_1 is a semiring, and the same holds for the collection Γ_2 of subsets of X_2, then the collection of all subsets $C = A \times B$ of $X = X_1 \times X_2$ for which $A \in \Gamma_1$, $B \in \Gamma_2$ is a semiring $\Gamma = \Gamma_1 \times \Gamma_2$.*

Proof. Since $0 = 0 \times 0$, the empty set belongs to Γ. Furthermore, if $A_1 \times B_1$ and $A_2 \times B_2$ belong to Γ, their product belongs to Γ by (1). Finally, by (2) and the properties of the semirings Γ_1 and Γ_2, the difference $A_2 \times B_2 - A_1 \times B_1$ is a finite sum of sets belonging to Γ, no two of which have common points.

Theorem 2. *If $\mu_1(A)$ and $\mu_2(B)$ are σ-finite measures on the semirings Γ_1 (in X_1) and Γ_2 (in X_2) respectively, and we define $\mu(C) = \mu_1(A)\mu_2(B)$ for each set $C = A \times B$ belonging to the semiring $\Gamma = \Gamma_1 \times \Gamma_2$ (we recall here that $\infty.0 = 0.\infty = 0$ by our conventions), then $\mu(C)$ is a σ-finite measure on Γ.*

The proof of this theorem is rather long, and will be divided into several lemmas.

Lemma α. *We have* $\mu(0) = 0$ *and* $0 \leqslant \mu(C) \leqslant \infty$ *for any* $C \in \Gamma$. *Furthermore, if* $C_1, C_2 \in \Gamma$ *and* $C_1 \subset C_2$, *then* $\mu(C_1) \leqslant \mu(C_2)$.

Proof. Only the last statement needs any proof. If $C_1 = A_1 \times B_1$, $C_2 = A_2 \times B_2$ and $C_1 \subset C_2$, then $A_1 \subset A_2$ and $B_1 \subset B_2$, hence

$$\mu(C_1) = \mu_1(A_1)\mu_2(B_1) \leqslant \mu_1(A_2)\mu_2(B_2) = \mu(C_2).$$

Lemma β. *If* $C \in \Gamma$, $C_n \in \Gamma (n = 1, \ldots, p)$, $C_iC_j = 0$ $(i \neq j)$ *and* $C \supset \Sigma_1^p C_n$, *then* $\mu(C) \geqslant \Sigma_1^p \mu(C_n)$.

Proof. Let $C = A \times B$ and $C_n = A_n \times B_n$ $(n = 1, \ldots, p)$. Then there exist sets $D_1, \ldots, D_q \in \Gamma_1$ such that $D_iD_j = 0$ $(i \neq j)$ and each A_n is the sum of several D_i. In the same way there exist sets $E_1, \ldots, E_r \in \Gamma_2$ such that $E_iE_j = 0$ $(i \neq j)$ and each B_n is the sum of several E_i. If $A_n = {}'\Sigma\, D_i$ (the dash in front of the Σ-sign indicates that the summation is over a subsequence) and $B_n = {}'\Sigma\, E_j$, then $A_n \times B_n = {}'\Sigma\,{}'\Sigma\, D_i \times E_j$ and $\mu(A_n \times B_n) = \mu_1(A_n)\mu_2(B_n) = \{'\Sigma\, \mu_1(D_i)\}\{'\Sigma\, \mu_2(E_j)\} = {}'\Sigma\,{}'\Sigma \mu_1(D_i)\mu_2(E_j) = {}'\Sigma'\Sigma\mu(D_i \times E_j)$. Hence, observing that any $D_i \times E_j$ is contained in at most one of the $A_n \times B_n$, we find

$$\Sigma_1^p \mu(C_n) = \Sigma_1^p \mu(A_n \times B_n) \leqslant \Sigma_{i=1}^q \Sigma_{j=1}^r \mu(D_i \times E_j) =$$

$$\{\Sigma_1^q \mu_1(D_i)\}\{\Sigma_1^r \mu_2(E_j)\} \leqslant \mu_1(A)\mu_2(B) = \mu(C).$$

We remark that if $C = \Sigma_1^p C_n$, then our proof shows that $\mu(C) = \Sigma_1^p \mu(C_n)$, so that $\mu(C)$ is finitely additive on Γ.

Lemma γ. *Let* $A \times B = C \in \Gamma$ *with* $\mu_1(A) < \infty$, $A_n \times B_n = C_n \in \Gamma$ $(n = 1, 2, \ldots)$ *with* $C_iC_j = 0\ (i \neq j)$, *and* $S = \Sigma_1^\infty C_n \subset C$. *For all* $x \in A$ *let* S_x *be the set of all points* y *such that* $(x, y) \in S$. *Then* S_x *is* μ_2-*measurable and, if* $0 \leqslant \alpha < \infty$ *and* U *is the subset of* A *of all* x *such that* $\mu_2(S_x) \leqslant \alpha$, *the set* U *is* μ_1-*measurable and*

$$\alpha\mu_1(A) \leqslant \alpha\mu_1(U) + \Sigma_1^\infty \mu(A_n \times B_n).$$

Proof. For every $x \in A$ the set S_x is a sum of sets B_n, so that S_x is measurable. Writing $S_p = \Sigma_{n=1}^p A_n \times B_n$ and defining S_{px} for S_p in the same way as S_x was defined for S, the sequence $S_{px} (p = 1, 2, \ldots)$ is ascending with limit S_x. Hence $\mu_2(S_x) = \lim \mu_2(S_{px})$.

If now U_p is the subset of A of all x such that $\mu_2(S_{px}) \leqslant \alpha$, the set U_p is μ_1-measurable since $\mu_2(S_{px})$ is a simple function on A which assumes its values on measurable sets. Furthermore the sequence U_p is descending, $U \subset U_p$ for all p and, if $x \in U_p$ for all p, then $x \in U$. Hence $U = \lim U_p$, so that U is μ_1-measurable and, observing that all U_p have finite measure as subsets of A, $\mu_1(U) = \lim \mu_1(U_p)$. This shows that in the proof of the inequality we may, without loss of generality, assume that S is a finite sum $S = \Sigma_1^p A_n \times B_n$. Then, introducing the sets $D_1, \ldots, D_q$ and $E_1, \ldots, E_r$ in the same way as in the preceding lemma, we have symbolically $S = \Sigma_1^p A_n \times B_n = \Sigma_{i=1}^q \Sigma_{j=1}^r \varepsilon_{ij} D_i \times E_j$, where $\varepsilon_{ij} = 1$ or 0 according as $D_i \times E_j$ is contained or not contained in S. Hence

$$S = \Sigma' (\Sigma_{j=1}^r) + \Sigma'' (\Sigma_{j=1}^r),$$

the sum Σ' containing those indices i for which $\Sigma_{j=1}^r \varepsilon_{ij} \mu_2(E_j) \leqslant \alpha$. It follows that

$$\Sigma_1^p \mu(A_n \times B_n) = \Sigma_1^q \Sigma_1^r \varepsilon_{ij} \mu(D_i \times E_j) \geqslant$$

$$\Sigma'' \{\Sigma_{j=1}^r \varepsilon_{ij}\mu_1(D_i)\mu_2(E_j)\} \geqslant \alpha \Sigma'' \mu_1(D_i) =$$

$$\alpha \{\mu_1(A) - \mu_1(U)\}$$

or

$$\alpha\mu_1(A) \leqslant \alpha\mu_1(U) + \Sigma \mu(A_n \times B_n).$$

Lemma δ. *If* $C \in \Gamma$, $C_n \in \Gamma$ $(n = 1, 2, \ldots)$ *and* $C \subset \Sigma C_n$, *then* $\mu(C) \leqslant \Sigma \mu(C_n)$.

Proof. The set $\Sigma C_n = C_1 + (C_2 - C_1) + (C_3 - C_1 - C_2) + \ldots$ may be written as ΣD_n, where all $D_n \in \Gamma$ and $D_iD_j = 0$ $(i \neq j)$. Hence, by Lemma β, $\Sigma \mu(D_n) \leqslant \Sigma \mu(C_n)$. It is no restriction of the generality, therefore, to assume immediately that $C_iC_j = 0$ $(i \neq j)$. Next, if $C = A \times B$ and $C_n = A_n \times B_n$, we have $C = A \times B = \Sigma A_nA \times B_nB$. Hence, it will be sufficient to show that if $C = S = \Sigma C_n$, $C_iC_j = 0$ $(i \neq j)$, then $\mu(C) \leqslant \Sigma \mu(C_n)$. If $\mu(C) = \mu_1(A)\mu_2(B) = 0$, there is nothing to prove. Let therefore $\mu_1(A)\mu_2(B) > 0$, and let first $\mu_1(A) < \infty$. Then, choosing a number α such that $0 \leqslant \alpha < \mu_2(B)$ and applying Lemma γ, we have $S_x = B$ for all $x \in A$, hence $\mu_2(S_x) = \mu_2(B)$, so that $U = 0$. It follows that

$$\alpha\mu_1(A) \leqslant \Sigma \mu(A_n \times B_n) = \Sigma \mu(C_n)$$

or, since this holds for all $\alpha < \mu_2(B)$,

$$\mu(C) = \mu_1(A)\mu_2(B) \leqslant \Sigma \mu(C_n).$$

Let now $\mu_1(A) = \infty$. The measure μ_1 is σ-finite; we may write therefore $X_1 = \Sigma P_i$, where all $P_i \in \Gamma_1$, $P_iP_j = 0$ $(i \neq j)$ and $\mu_1(P_i) < \infty$ for all i. Hence $A = \Sigma AP_i$ and

$$\mu(C) = \mu_1(A)\mu_2(B) = \Sigma \mu_1(AP_i)\mu_2(B) = \Sigma \mu(AP_i \times B).$$

Furthermore, since $A \times B = \Sigma A_n \times B_n$, we have $AP_i \times B = \Sigma_n A_n P_i \times B_n$ with $\mu_1(AP_i) < \infty$, so that, by what we have already proved,

$$\mu(AP_i \times B) \leqslant \Sigma_n \mu(A_n P_i \times B_n).$$

Summing over i, we obtain finally

$$\mu(C) \leqslant \Sigma_i \Sigma_n \mu(A_n P_i \times B_n) = \Sigma_n \Sigma_i \mu_1(A_n P_i)\mu_2(B_n) =$$

$$\Sigma_n \mu_1(A_n)\mu_2(B_n) = \Sigma \mu(C_n).$$

Proof of Theorem 2. From the Lemmas α, β and δ we derive that $\mu(C)$ is a measure on Γ. Since $X_1 = \Sigma P_i$ where all $P_i \in \Gamma_1$ and $\mu_1(P_i) < \infty$ $(i = 1, 2, \ldots.)$, and $X_2 = \Sigma Q_j$ where all $Q_j \in \Gamma_2$ and $\mu_2(Q_j) < \infty$ $(j = 1, 2, \ldots.)$, we have $X_1 \times X_2 = \Sigma_i \Sigma_j P_i \times Q_j$ where all $P_i \times Q_j \in \Gamma$ and $\mu(P_i \times Q_j) < \infty$. This shows that the measure μ is σ-finite.

The measure $\mu(C)$ thus obtained on $\Gamma = \Gamma_1 \times \Gamma_2$ may now be extended as a completely additive measure on to the σ-ring Λ of all μ-measurable sets in $X_1 \times X_2$. We shall prove presently that if E_1 and E_2 are subsets of X_1 and X_2, μ_1-measurable and μ_2-measurable respectively, then $E_1 \times E_2$ is μ-measurable and $\mu(E_1 \times E_2) = \mu_1(E_1)\mu_2(E_2)$. Furthermore, if we should have taken as our point of departure the σ-rings Λ_1 and Λ_2 of all μ_1-measurable and all μ_2-measurable sets respectively, we should have obtained a measure $\bar{\mu}$ on the semiring $\Lambda_1 \times \Lambda_2$ in $X_1 \times X_2$, and one may ask what is the connection between the measures μ and $\bar{\mu}$. We shall prove that for any set $S \subset X_1 \times X_2$ the exterior measure $\bar{\mu}^*(S)$ is the same as the exterior measure $\mu^*(S)$, so that, consequently, the measures μ and $\bar{\mu}$ generate the same σ-ring of measurable sets with the same measure.

Theorem 3. *If $E_1 \in \Lambda_1$, $E_2 \in \Lambda_2$, then $E_1 \times E_2$ is measurable (hence $\Lambda_1 \times \Lambda_2 \subset \Lambda$) and $\mu(E_1 \times E_2) = \mu_1(E_1)\mu_2(E_2)$.*

Proof. Since μ_1 and μ_2 are σ-finite, we may restrict ourselves to the case that $E_1 \times E_2$ is contained in a set $A \times B \in \Gamma$, where both $\mu_1(A)$ and $\mu_2(B)$ are finite. The theorem is true whenever $E_1 \in \Gamma_1$ and $E_2 \in \Gamma_2$, and it follows immediately that the same holds whenever E_1 and E_2 are σ-sets (cf. Ch. 2, § 5), hence also whenever E_1 and E_2 are limits of descending sequences of σ-sets (cf. Ch. 2, § 6, Th. 2). Furthermore, the theorem is true whenever one at least of the sets E_1 and E_2 is of measure zero (if for example $\mu_1(E_1) = 0$, then $E_1 \times E_2 \subset O \times B$, where O is a σ-set of arbitrarily small measure, hence $\mu^*(E_1 \times E_2) \leqslant \mu_1(O)\mu_2(B)$, which shows that $E_1 \times E_2$ is measurable and of measure zero). Finally, in the case that E_1 and E_2 are arbitrary measurable sets, the proof of the theorem is derived by observing that each of them is contained in, and almost equal to, a set which is limit of a descending sequence of σ-sets (cf. Ch. 2, § 5, Th. 6).

Theorem 4. *If $\bar{\mu}$ is the measure on $\Lambda_1 \times \Lambda_2$ obtained by starting from the semirings Λ_1 and Λ_2, and S is an arbitrary set in $X_1 \times X_2$, then* $\bar{\mu}^*(S) = \mu^*(S)$.

Proof. We have

$$\bar{\mu}^*(S) = \text{lower bound } \Sigma\, \mu(E_{1n} \times E_{2n})$$

over all sets $\Sigma\, E_{1n} \times E_{2n} \supset S$ with $E_{1n} \in \Lambda_1$, $E_{2n} \in \Lambda_2$. Furthermore, by Ch. 2, § 5, Th. 4,

$$\mu^*(S) = \text{lower bound } \mu(E)$$

over all μ-measurable sets $E \supset S$. Hence, since every set $\Sigma\, E_{1n} \times E_{2n}$ is μ-measurable by the preceding theorem,

$$\mu^*(S) \leqslant \bar{\mu}^*(S).$$

On the other hand

$$\mu^*(S) = \text{lower bound } \Sigma\, \mu(A_n \times B_n)$$

over all sets $\Sigma\, A_n \times B_n \supset S$ with $A_n \in \Gamma_1$, $B_n \in \Gamma_2$. Furthermore

$$\bar{\mu}^*(S) = \text{lower bound } \bar{\mu}(\bar{E})$$

over all $\bar{\mu}$-measurable sets $\bar{E} \supset S$. Hence, since every set $\Sigma\, A_n \times B_n$ is $\bar{\mu}$-measurable and $\mu(A_n \times B_n) = \bar{\mu}(A_n \times B_n)$, we have

$$\bar{\mu}^*(S) \leqslant \mu^*(S).$$

It follows that $\bar{\mu}^*(S) = \mu^*(S)$.

The measure $\mu = \mu_1 \times \mu_2$ on the σ-ring Λ is called the *product measure* of the measures μ_1 and μ_2. If X_1 is p-dimensional Euclidean space R_p, X_2 is q-dimensional Euclidean space R_q, and m_1, m_2 are the Lebesgue measures in these spaces, it is immediately seen that the combinatory product $X_1 \times X_2$ is $(p + q)$-dimensional Euclidean space R_{p+q}, and $m = m_1 \times m_2$ is the Lebesgue measure in this space. Indeed, we have only to take as our point of departure the semirings of all cells in R_p and R_q respectively. This example also shows that, Λ_1, Λ_2 and Λ being the σ-rings of all measurable sets in these spaces, $\Lambda_1 \times \Lambda_2$ is a proper subcollection of Λ.

We now state a theorem which to some extent is a converse of earlier statements. For this purpose we first make a notational convention. If $E \subset X_1 \times X_2$ and $x \in X_1$, we shall denote by E_x the set of all $y \in X_2$ subject to $(x, y) \in E$ (cf. Lemma γ, where this notation was already used).

Theorem 5. *If $E \subset X_1 \times X_2$ is a μ-measurable set, then E_x is a μ_2-measurable set for almost every $x \in X_1$, that is, if P is the set of all x for which E_x is not μ_2-measurable, then* $\mu_1(P) = 0$.

Proof. We first assume that $\mu(E) = 0$ and that $E \subset A \times B$ with $A \in \Gamma_1$, $B \in \Gamma_2$ and $\mu_1(A) < \infty$. Then, if $\varepsilon > 0$ is given, there exists a σ-set $S = \Sigma A_n \times B_n$ such that $E \subset S \subset A \times B$ and $\Sigma \mu(A_n \times B_n) < \varepsilon$. Applying now Lemma γ with $0 < \alpha < \infty$, we find

$$\alpha\mu_1(A) \leqslant \alpha\mu_1(U) + \varepsilon,$$

where U is the set of all $x \in A$ subject to $\mu_2(S_x) \leqslant \alpha$. Hence $\alpha\mu_1(A - U) \leqslant \varepsilon$. Denoting now by V the set of all $x \in A$ for which $\mu_2^*(E_x) \leqslant \alpha$, we have $U \subset V \subset A$, so that $A - V \subset A - U$. This implies $\alpha\mu_1^*(A - V) \leqslant \varepsilon$ or, $\varepsilon > 0$ being arbitrary, $\mu_1^*(A - V) = 0$. It follows that $A - V$ and V are μ_1-measurable and that $\mu_1(A - V) = 0$.

Let now V_n be the set of all $x \in A$ for which $\mu_2^*(E_x) \leqslant n^{-1}$ ($n = 1, 2, \ldots$). Then all V_n are μ_1-measurable by what we have already proved and, if $x \in Q = \Pi V_n$, we have $\mu_2^*(E_x) = 0$. Furthermore, if $P = A - Q = A - \Pi V_n = \Sigma (A - V_n)$, then $\mu_1(P) = 0$. We may, therefore, draw the conclusion that $\mu_2^*(E_x) = 0$ for almost every x, and this shows that E_x is μ_2-measurable for almost every x.

The thus obtained result remains true for any set E satisfying $\mu(E) = 0$, since E may be written in the form ΣE_n, where $E_n \subset A_n \times B_n$ with $\mu_1(A_n) < \infty$.

Let now $E = O$ be an arbitrary σ-set $\Sigma A_n \times B_n$. Then, for every x, the set O_x is a sum of sets B_n, so that O_x is μ_2-measurable.

Finally, if E is an arbitrary μ-measurable set, there exists a descending sequence $O_n (n = 1, 2, \ldots)$ of σ-sets covering E and a set S of measure zero such that $E + S = \Pi O_n$ and $ES = 0$. Hence, for every x,

$$E_x + S_x = (\Pi O_n)_x = \Pi (O_n)_x, \; E_x S_x = 0.$$

Since all $(O_n)_x$ are μ_2-measurable for every x and S_x is μ_2-measurable for almost every x, the set E_x is μ_2-measurable for almost every x.

In the course of the proof of the last theorem we derived that $\mu(E) = 0$ implies $\mu_2(E_x) = 0$ for almost every x. We shall also prove the converse statement.

Theorem 6. *If $E \subset X_1 \times X_2$ is a μ-measurable set such that $\mu_2(E_x) = 0$ for almost every $x \in X_1$, then $\mu(E) = 0$.*

Proof. Since the measure μ is σ-finite, we may restrict ourselves to the case that $E \subset A \times B \in \Gamma$ with $\mu_1(A) < \infty$, $\mu_2(B) < \infty$. If, under this hypothesis, $\mu_2(B) = 0$, we have $\mu(E) \leqslant \mu(A \times B) = 0$. Hence, we may assume that $\mu_2(B) > 0$. Let $D = (A \times B) - E$. Then $\mu_2(D_x) = \mu_2(B)$ for almost every $x \in A$. Furthermore, there exists a σ-set S such that $D \subset S \subset A \times B$. Hence $\mu_2(S_x) = \mu_2(B)$ for almost every $x \in A$, so that, applying Lemma γ with $0 < \alpha < \mu_2(B)$, we find

$$\alpha\mu_1(A) \leqslant \mu(S) \leqslant \mu(A \times B) = \mu_1(A)\mu_2(B).$$

Making α tend to $\mu_2(B)$, we obtain $\mu(S) = \mu(A \times B)$. This holds for all σ-sets S between D and $A \times B$, hence $\mu(D) = \mu(A \times B)$, or $\mu(E) = 0$.

§ 2. The Ordinate Set of a Measurable Function

Let μ be a σ-finite measure in X, and m the Lebesgue measure on the straight line R_1. The product measure $\mu \times m$ in $X \times R_1$ will be denoted by $\bar{\mu}$.

Definition. *If $f(x)$ is a real-valued function defined on the set $S \subset X$, then the ordinate set F of $f(x)$ is the set of all points $(x, y) \in X \times R_1$ such that $x \in S$ and $-\infty < y < f(x)$.*

Theorem 1. *If $E \subset X$ is μ-measurable, and $f(x)$ is defined on E, then $f(x)$ is a μ-measurable function on E if and only if its ordinate set F is $\bar{\mu}$-measurable.*

Proof. Let first F be $\bar{\mu}$-measurable. For any $y \in R_1$ the set F_y is the set of all $x \in E$ subject to $(x, y) \in F$, that is, the set of all $x \in E$ such that $f(x) > y$. Hence $F_y = E(f(x) > y)$. By § 1, Th. 5 this set is μ-measurable for almost every $y \in R_1$, hence certainly for all points $y = r_n$ belonging to a suitably chosen sequence $r_1, r_2, \ldots$, dense in R_1. This however is sufficient to ensure the measurability of $f(x)$ (cf. Ch. 2, § 8, Th. 3).

Conversely, if $f(x)$ is μ-measurable on E, and $r_n (n = 1, 2, \ldots)$ is a sequence of real numbers dense in R_1, we define the set E_n $(n = 1, 2, \ldots)$ as the set of all $x \in E$ subject to $f(x) > r_n$ and the set B_n as the set of all $y \in R_1$ such that $-\infty < y \leqslant r_n$. Then $S = \Sigma E_n \times B_n$ is $\bar{\mu}$-measurable, and it will be sufficient therefore to prove that $F = S$. If $(x, y) \in S$, there exists an index k such that $(x, y) \in E_k \times B_k$, hence $-\infty < y \leqslant r_k < f(x)$, and this shows that $(x, y) \in F$. Conversely, if $(x, y) \in F$, then $-\infty < y < f(x)$, so that there exists a number r_k satisfying $-\infty < y < r_k < f(x)$. But then $(x, y) \in E_k \times B_k$, hence $(x, y) \in S$.

Remark. The set of all points (x, y) subject to $y = f(x)$ is sometimes called the *graph* of $f(x)$. It is important for our next theorem to observe that the $\bar{\mu}$-measure of the graph G of a measurable function $f(x)$ is zero. The measurability of G is derived from the relation $G = (\Pi F_n) - F$, where F_n $(n = 1, 2, \ldots)$ is the ordinate set of $f_n(x) = f(x) + n^{-1}$, and $\bar{\mu}(G) = 0$ is a consequence of $m(G_x) = 0$ by § 1, Th. 6.

Theorem 2. *If the real-valued functions $f_n(x)$ $(n = 1, 2, \ldots)$, measurable on the μ-measurable set E, have the ordinate sets F_n, and $h(x) =$ upper bound $f_n(x)$, $k(x) =$ lower bound $f_n(x)$, $p(x) = \limsup f_n(x)$, $q(x) = \liminf f_n(x)$ have the ordinate sets H, K, P and Q respectively, then $H = \Sigma_1^\infty F_n$, K is contained in and almost equal to $\Pi_1^\infty F_n$, P is contained in and almost equal to $\limsup F_n$, and Q is contained in and almost equal to $\liminf F_n$.*

Proof. The proofs are similar, and we shall give it for P. If $(x, y) \in P$, then $y < p(x)$, hence $y < f_n(x)$ for infinitely many values of n. It follows that $(x, y) \in \limsup F_n$. Conversely, if $(x, y) \in \limsup F_n$, then $y < f_n(x)$ for infinitely many values of n, hence $y \leqslant p(x)$. It follows that either $(x, y) \in P$ or (x, y) is a point on the graph of $p(x)$. Combining the results, we see that $P \subset \limsup F_n$ and $P \sim \limsup F_n$.

§ 3. The Integral of a Non-Negative Function

As before, we assume that μ is a σ-finite measure in X, m is the Lebesgue measure on the straight line R_1, and $\bar{\mu} = \mu \times m$. If $f(x)$ is a non-negative function defined on the set $S \subset X$, we shall mean by the *positive ordinate set* F_0 of $f(x)$ the set of all points $(x, y) \in X \times R_1$ such that $x \in S$ and $0 \leqslant y < f(x)$. Evidently, if $E \subset X$ is μ-measurable and $f(x) \geqslant 0$ is defined on E, then $f(x)$ is measurable if and only if F_0 is $\bar{\mu}$-measurable.

Definition. *If $E \subset X$ is μ-measurable, and $f(x) \geqslant 0$ is defined and measurable on E, the integral of $f(x)$ over E is defined to be the $\bar{\mu}$-measure of the positive ordinate set F_0. We write*

$$\int_E f(x)d\mu = \bar{\mu}(F_0).$$

Whenever $\bar{\mu}(F_0) < \infty$, the function $f(x)$ is called μ-summable or μ-integrable over E.

In the case that X is the m-dimensional Euclidean space R_m and μ is the Lebesgue measure in this space, we write $\int_E f(x)dx$ or, when we wish to indicate the number of dimensions,

$$\int\int \dots \int_E f(x_1, x_2, \dots, x_m)dx_1\, dx_2 \dots dx_m,$$

and this integral is called the Lebesgue integral of $f(x)$ over E. If E is the interval $[a_1, b_1; \dots; a_m, b_m]$, the Lebesgue integral is also written

$$\int_{a_1}^{b_1} \dots \int_{a_m}^{b_m} f(x_1, \dots, x_m)dx_1 \dots dx_m.$$

In the case that X is the straight line R_1 and μ is a Stieltjes measure on R_1 (relative to a non-decreasing function $g(x)$), we write $\int_E f(x)dg(x)$, and this integral is called a Lebesgue-Stieltjes integral of $f(x)$ over E.

We collect in one theorem some properties of the integral which need no proof, since they are immediate consequences of the properties of a product measure.

Theorem 1. 1°. *If $0 \leqslant \alpha \leqslant f(x) \leqslant \beta \leqslant \infty$ on E, then*

$$\alpha\mu(E) \leqslant \int_E f(x)d\mu \leqslant \beta\mu(E).$$

In particular the integral of $f(x)$ over E vanishes if either $f(x) = 0$ for all $x \in E$ or $\mu(E) = 0$. Furthermore

$$\int_E d\mu = \int_E 1.d\mu = \mu(E),$$

$$\int_E \alpha\, d\mu = \alpha\mu(E) \quad \text{for} \quad \alpha \geqslant 0.$$

2°. *If $f(x) \geqslant g(x) \geqslant 0$ on E, then*

$$\int_E f\, d\mu \geqslant \int_E g\, d\mu.$$

3°. *If D is a measurable subset of E with characteristic function $c_D(x)$, then*

$$\int_D f(x)d\mu = \int_E f(x)c_D(x)d\mu.$$

In particular, defining if necessary $f(x) = 0$ outside E, we have

$$\int_E f(x)d\mu = \int_X f(x)c_E(x)d\mu.$$

4°. *If the sets $E_n (n = 1, 2, \ldots)$ are measurable subsets of E, no two of which have common points, and if $E = \Sigma E_n$, then*

$$\int_E f \, d\mu = \Sigma \int_{E_n} f \, d\mu.$$

The integral of a non-negative measurable function is therefore completely additive on E.

Theorem 2 (*Lebesgue's Theorem on the integration of monotone sequences*). *If $f_n(x)$ is a sequence of non-negative measurable functions on E, non-decreasing for every $x \in E$, so that consequently $f(x) = \lim f_n(x)$ exists, then*

$$\int_E f \, d\mu = \lim \int_E f_n \, d\mu.$$

Proof. Follows from Ch. 2, § 6, Th. 1 by observing what has been said about the ordinate sets of $f(x)$ and $f_n(x)$ in § 2, Th. 2.

Theorem 3. *If the non-negative functions $f(x)$ and $g(x)$ are measurable on E, then*

$$\int_E (f + g) d\mu = \int_E f \, d\mu + \int_E g \, d\mu.$$

Proof. We first observe that, for any finite real number α, the positive ordinate set F_0 of $f(x)$ has the same measure as the set $F_0^{(\alpha)}$ of all points (x, y) such that $x \in E$ and $\alpha \leqslant y < f(x) + \alpha$ (translation on the straight line R_1; it is immediately seen that this translation leaves the measure of a σ-set in $X \times R_1$ invariant, and therefore the measure of an arbitrary measurable set). Hence, for $0 \leqslant \alpha < \infty$,

$$\int_E \{f(x) + \alpha\} d\mu = \bar{\mu}(F_0^{(\alpha)}) + \alpha\mu(E) =$$

$$\bar{\mu}(F_0) + \alpha\mu(E) = \int_E f(x) d\mu + \int_E \alpha d\mu.$$

This implies the truth of our theorem in case $g(x)$ is a simple function, finite, measurable and non-negative on E.

Let now $g(x)$ be measurable and non-negative on E. Then, by Ch. 2, § 8, Th. 10, $g(x)$ is the limit of a non-decreasing sequence of simple functions $g_n(x)$, finite, measurable and non-negative on E, so that by the preceding theorem

$$\int_E (f + g) d\mu = \lim \int_E (f + g_n) d\mu = \lim \{\int_E f \, d\mu + \int_E g_n \, d\mu\} =$$

$$\int_E f \, d\mu + \lim \int_E g_n \, d\mu = \int_E f \, d\mu + \int_E g \, d\mu.$$

We remark that the extension to the sum of a finite number of non-negative functions is immediate.

The theorem which has just been proved enables us to state Theorem 2 in a somewhat different form, which is of frequent use in the applications.

Theorem 4. *If $f_n(x)$ is a sequence of non-negative measurable functions on E, and $f(x) = \Sigma_1^\infty f_n(x)$, then*

$$\int_E f\,d\mu = \Sigma_1^\infty \int_E f_n\,d\mu.$$

Proof. The part of $f_n(x)$ in Theorem 2 is now played by $s_n(x) = \Sigma_{i=1}^n f_i(x)$. Observing that $\int_E s_n\,d\mu = \Sigma_{i=1}^n \int_E f_i\,d\mu$ by the preceding theorem, the proof is complete.

Theorem 5. *If $f(x)$ is measurable and non-negative on E, and $\alpha \geqslant 0$, then*

$$\int_E \alpha f(x)\,d\mu = \alpha \int_E f(x)\,d\mu.$$

Proof. The statement is true for $\alpha = 0$, and also for $\alpha = 1, 2, \ldots$ by Theorem 3. But then it is true as well for $\alpha = 1/q$ $(q = 2, 3, \ldots)$, hence for every non-negative rational number α. If α is arbitrary, it is the limit of a non-decreasing sequence of rational numbers, so that Theorem 2 yields the desired result.

Theorem 6 *(Fatou's Theorem). If $f_n(x)$ is a sequence of non-negative measurable functions on E, then*

$$\int_E \liminf f_n(x)\,d\mu \leqslant \liminf \int_E f_n(x)\,d\mu.$$

Proof. Follows from Ch. 2, § 6, Th. 3 by observing what has been said in § 2, Th. 2 about the ordinate set of lim inf $f_n(x)$ in connection with the ordinate sets of the functions $f_n(x)$.

Corollary. *If $f_n(x)$ is a sequence of non-negative measurable functions on E, having a limit $f(x)$, then*

$$\int_E f\,d\mu \leqslant \liminf \int_E f_n\,d\mu.$$

Theorem 7. *If $f_n(x)$ is a sequence of non-negative measurable functions on E, and $f_n(x) \leqslant g(x)$ for all n, where $g(x)$ is summable over E, then the function lim sup $f_n(x)$ is summable over E and*

$$\int_E \limsup f_n(x)\,d\mu \geqslant \limsup \int_E f_n(x)\,d\mu.$$

In particular, if $f(x) = \lim f_n(x)$ exists,

$$\int_E f\,d\mu = \lim \int_E f_n\,d\mu.$$

Proof. Denoting the positive ordinate sets of $f_n(x)$ and $g(x)$ by F_n and G respectively, we have $F_n \subset G$ for all n, hence $\Sigma F_n \subset G$, which shows that $\bar{\mu}(\Sigma F_n) \leqslant \bar{\mu}(G) < \infty$. Our first statement follows therefore from Ch. 2, § 6, Th. 3. The second statement is obtained by combining the first statement with Fatou's Theorem.

Theorem 8. *If $f(x)$ is non-negative and measurable on E, and*

$$\int_E f \, d\mu = 0,$$

then $f(x) = 0$ almost everywhere on E.
Proof. Writing $E_0 = E(f > 0)$ and $E_n = E(f > n^{-1})$ for $n = 1, 2, \ldots$, we have $E_0 = \Sigma E_n$. Furthermore $0 = \int_E f \, d\mu \geqslant \int_{E_n} f \, d\mu \geqslant n^{-1}\mu(E_n)$ for each n, hence $\mu(E_n) = 0$ for $n = 1, 2, \ldots$. This shows that $\mu(E_0) = 0$.

To conclude this paragraph we state a theorem that, in a certain sense, may be considered as a converse of Theorem 2.

Theorem 9. *If $f_n(x)$ is a sequence of non-negative measurable functions on E, non-decreasing for every $x \in E$, and if there exists a finite constant M such that $\int_E f_n \, d\mu \leqslant M$ for all n, then $f(x) = \lim f_n(x)$ is finite almost everywhere on E.*
Proof. If $f(x)$ should be $+\infty$ on a subset E_1 of positive measure, we should have $\int_E f \, d\mu \geqslant \int_{E_1} f \, d\mu = +\infty$. But, in virtue of Theorem 2 and our hypothesis, $\int_E f \, d\mu = \lim \int_E f_n \, d\mu \leqslant M$. This would lead to a contradiction.

Corollary. *If $f_n(x)$ is a sequence of summable non-negative functions on E, and if $\Sigma_1^\infty \int_E f_n \, d\mu < \infty$, then $f(x) = \Sigma_1^\infty f_n(x)$ is finite almost everywhere on E.*

§ 4. The Integral of a Summable Real Function

We shall now discuss the case that $f(x)$, defined and measurable on the measurable set E, assumes arbitrary real values.

For a non-positive $f(x)$ we define the integral of $f(x)$ over E by

$$\int_E f \, d\mu = -\int_E -f \, d\mu,$$

and $f(x)$ is called μ-summable or μ-integrable if and only if $-f(x)$ has that property.

In the general case we introduce the functions $f^+(x)$ and $f^-(x)$, defined by

$$f^+(x) = f(x) \text{ and } f^-(x) = 0 \text{ on } E(f \geqslant 0),$$
$$f^-(x) = f(x) \text{ and } f^+(x) = 0 \text{ on } E(f < 0).$$

These functions are evidently measurable and of constant sign, and $f(x) = f^+(x) + f^-(x)$, $|f(x)| = f^+(x) - f^-(x)$ for all $x \in E$.

Definition. *If $E \subset X$ is μ-measurable, and the real function $f(x)$ is defined and measurable on E, then $f(x)$ is said to be μ-summable or μ-integrable over E whenever both $f^+(x)$ and $f^-(x)$ have this property. In that case the integral $\int_E f\,d\mu$ of $f(x)$ over E is defined to be $\int_E f^+\,d\mu + \int_E f^-\,d\mu$. If one at least of the functions $f^+(x)$ and $f^-(x)$ is not summable, no meaning will be attributed to the integral of $f(x)$.*

Those properties of the integral, which are immediate consequences of this definition, are collected in the first theorem.

Theorem 1. 1°. *If $f(x)$ is summable over E, then $f(x)$ is finite almost everywhere on E.*

2° (*Mean Value Theorem*). *If $f(x)$ is measurable, $\mu(E) < \infty$ and $-\infty < \alpha \leqslant f(x) \leqslant \beta < \infty$ for all $x \in E$, then*

$$\alpha\mu(E) \leqslant \int_E f\,d\mu \leqslant \beta\mu(E).$$

In particular $\int_E f\,d\mu = 0$ if either $f(x) = 0$ for all $x \in E$ or $\mu(E) = 0$. Furthermore $\int_E \alpha\,d\mu = \alpha\mu(E)$ if both α and $\mu(E)$ are finite.

3°. *If $f(x)$ and $g(x)$ are summable over E, and $f(x) \geqslant g(x)$ on E, then*

$$\int_E f\,d\mu \geqslant \int_E g\,d\mu.$$

4°. *The measurable function $f(x)$ on E is summable over E if and only if $|f(x)|$ is summable over E, and in this case*

$$\left|\int_E f\,d\mu\right| \leqslant \int_E |f|\,d\mu.$$

If $f(x)$ is measurable on E, $g(x)$ is summable over E, and $|f(x)| \leqslant g(x)$ on E, then $f(x)$ is summable over E.

5°. *If D is a measurable subset of E with characteristic function $c_D(x)$, and $f(x)$ is summable over E, then $f(x)$ is summable over D, and*

$$\int_D f(x)d\mu = \int_E f(x)c_D(x)d\mu.$$

In particular, defining if necessary $f(x) = 0$ outside E, we have

$$\int_E f(x)d\mu = \int_X f(x)c_E(x)d\mu.$$

6°. *If the sets* E_n $(n = 1, 2, \ldots)$ *are measurable subsets of* E, *no two of which have common points, and if* $E = \Sigma E_n$, *then*

$$\int_E f\,d\mu = \Sigma \int_{E_n} f\,d\mu$$

for any $f(x)$ *which is summable over* E. *The integral of a summable function is therefore a completely additive function on* E.

7°. *If* $f(x)$ *is summable over* E *and* $-\infty < \alpha < \infty$, *then*

$$\int_E \alpha f(x) d\mu = \alpha \int_E f(x) d\mu.$$

Theorem 2. *If* $f(x)$ *and* $g(x)$ *are summable over* E, *then* $f(x) + g(x)$ *is summable over* E *and*

$$\int_E (f + g) d\mu = \int_E f\,d\mu + \int_E g\,d\mu.$$

Proof. Since $|f + g| \leqslant |f| + |g|$, we see that $|f + g|$, and therefore also $f + g$, is summable over E. Next, the set E can be decomposed into four sets on each of which $f(x)$ and $g(x)$ are of constant sign. In virtue of Theorem 1, 6° we may assume therefore that $f(x)$ and $g(x)$ are of constant sign on the whole set E. By § 3, Th. 3 our theorem is true whenever $f(x)$ and $g(x)$ are both non-negative or non-positive, and it only remains, therefore, to show that the same holds when $f(x)$ and $g(x)$ have on E opposite signs, the one, $f(x)$ say, being non-negative, and the other, $g(x)$, non-positive. This being so, let $E_1 = E(f + g \geqslant 0)$ and $E_2 = E(f + g < 0)$. The functions f, $f + g$ and $-g$ are non-negative on E_1, and we have therefore, by § 3, Th. 3,

$$\int_{E_1} f\,d\mu = \int_{E_1} (f + g) d\mu + \int_{E_1} (-g) d\mu = \int_{E_1} (f + g) d\mu - \int_{E_1} g\,d\mu.$$

Similarly

$$-\int_{E_2} g\,d\mu = \int_{E_2} (-g) d\mu = \int_{E_2} (-f - g) d\mu + \int_{E_2} f\,d\mu = -\int_{E_2} (f + g) d\mu + \int_{E_2} f\,d\mu.$$

Hence, for $i = 1, 2$, we have

$$\int_{E_i} (f + g) d\mu = \int_{E_i} f\,d\mu + \int_{E_i} g\,d\mu,$$

and by Theorem 1, 6° we obtain the same relation for the integrals over E.

Theorem 3. *If* $f(x)$ *is defined on* X *and* $\int_A f\,d\mu = 0$ *for all sets* A *belonging to the semiring* Γ *on which the measure* $\mu(A)$ *was originally given, then* $f(x) = 0$ *almost everywhere on* X.

Proof. We wish to prove first that $\int_E f\,d\mu = 0$ for any measurable set E contained in a set $B \in \Gamma$. Since by hypothesis $f(x)$ is summable over B, it is also summable over E, so that $\int_E f\,d\mu$ has sense. If E is a σ-set, the relation $\int_E f\,d\mu = 0$ is evident. If E is a δ-set, so that $E' = X - E$

is a σ-set, the set $B - E = E'B$ is a σ-set as well; hence $\int_{B-E} f\, d\mu = 0$, which implies $\int_E f\, d\mu = 0$. Next, if E is the limit of an ascending sequence D_n of δ-sets, we have $E = D_1 + (D_2 - D_1) + (D_3 - D_2) + \ldots$, and, the integral over each term being clearly zero, the same holds for the integral over E. Furthermore, if E is of measure zero, the integral of $f(x)$ over E is also zero. Observing finally that any measurable set E is the sum of a set E_1, which is the limit of an ascending sequence of δ-sets, and of a set E_2 of measure zero (cf. Ch. 2, § 5, Th. 7), we obtain the desired result.

Taking now for E the subsets of B on which $f(x) \geqslant 0$ and $f(x) < 0$ respectively, we find in virtue of § 3, Th. 8 that $f(x) = 0$ almost everywhere on B. Hence, since the measure μ is σ-finite, $f(x) = 0$ almost everywhere on X.

Theorem 4 (*Lebesgue's Theorem on term by term integration*). *If $f_n(x)$ is a sequence of measurable functions on E, and $| f_n(x) | \leqslant g(x)$ for all n, where $g(x)$ is summable over E, then the functions $\liminf f_n(x)$ and $\limsup f_n(x)$ are summable over E, and*

$$\int_E \liminf f_n(x) d\mu \leqslant \liminf \int_E f_n(x) d\mu \leqslant \limsup \int_E f_n(x) d\mu \leqslant \int_E \limsup f_n(x) d\mu.$$

In particular, if $f(x) = \lim f_n(x)$ exists,

$$\int_E f\, d\mu = \lim \int_E f_n\, d\mu.$$

Proof. The functions $f_n(x)$ are all summable over E, and so are the functions $g_n(x) = f_n(x) + g(x)$. Furthermore $0 \leqslant g_n(x) \leqslant 2g(x)$ for all n. Consequently, by Fatou's Theorem and § 2, Th. 7, the inequalities to be proved are true with $f_n(x)$ replaced by $g_n(x)$. But then, by subtraction of $\int_E g\, d\mu$, they are seen to be equally true for the functions $f_n(x)$.

Corollary. *Let $f_i(x)$ be a sequence of functions, measurable on E, satisfying for a summable function $g(x)$ and for all n the inequality $| s_n(x) | \leqslant g(x)$, where $s_n(x) = \Sigma_{i=1}^n f_i(x)$, and let $f(x) = \Sigma_{i=1}^\infty f_i(x)$ exist. Then $f(x)$ is summable and*

$$\int_E f\, d\mu = \Sigma_{i=1}^\infty \int_E f_i\, d\mu.$$

Theorem 5. *If $f(x)$ is summable over E, and if H is a measurable subset of E, the integral of $f(x)$ over H tends to zero with the measure of H. In other words, if $\varepsilon > 0$ is arbitrarily given, there exists a number $\delta > 0$ such that $\mu(H) < \delta$ implies $| \int_H f\, d\mu | < \varepsilon$.*

Proof. Since $|\int_H f\,d\mu| \leqslant \int_H |f|\,d\mu$, it is sufficient to consider the case that $f(x)$ is non-negative. Assuming this to be the case, and defining the functions $f_n(x)$ $(n = 1, 2, \ldots)$ by

$$f_n(x) = f(x) \text{ if } f(x) \leqslant n,$$
$$f_n(x) = n \quad \text{if } f(x) > n,$$

the function $f(x)$ is the limit of the non-decreasing sequence $f_n(x)$, so that $\int_E f\,d\mu = \lim \int_E f_n\,d\mu$. Consequently, we may take for a given $\varepsilon > 0$ the index n so large that $\int_E (f - f_n)d\mu < \varepsilon/2$. Then, since $f - f_n \geqslant 0$, we have certainly $\int_H (f - f_n)d\mu < \varepsilon/2$ for every measurable $H \subset E$, or $\int_H f\,d\mu < \int_H f_n\,d\mu + \varepsilon/2$. Choosing now the set H such that $\mu(H) < \varepsilon/2n$, we see that $\int_H f_n\,d\mu \leqslant n\mu(H) < \varepsilon/2$, and therefore $\int_H f\,d\mu < \varepsilon$.

Remark. A second proof runs as follows: Assuming once more that $f(x) \geqslant 0$, and that the mentioned condition were not satisfied, there would exist a fixed number $\varepsilon > 0$ and a sequence H_n of measurable subsets of E such that $\mu(H_n) < 1/2^n$ and $\int_{H_n} f\,d\mu > \varepsilon$. Writing $H_0 = \lim\sup H_n$, we should have $H_0 \subset \Sigma_{k=n}^{\infty} H_k$ for every n, hence $\mu(H_0) \leqslant \Sigma_{k=n}^{\infty} \mu(H_k) < 1/2^{n-1}$, so that $\mu(H_0) = 0$, and therefore also $\int_{H_0} f\,d\mu = 0$. On the other hand, observing that the set function $\nu(H) = \int_H f\,d\mu$ is a measure on the σ-ring of all μ-measurable subsets H of E, we have $\int_{H_0} f\,d\mu = \nu(H_0) \geqslant \lim\sup \nu(H_n) \geqslant \varepsilon$. This is a contradiction.

§ 5. Extension to Functions with Complex Values

The results stated in the preceding paragraph may be extended to functions with complex values. The function $f(x) = g(x) + ih(x)$, where $g(x)$ and $h(x)$ are real functions, defined on the measurable set E, will be called *summable* over E whenever $g(x)$ and $h(x)$ are summable over E, and in this case the *integral* $\int_E f\,d\mu$ is defined to be equal to

$$\int_E g\,d\mu + i \int_E h\,d\mu.$$

Theorem 1. 1°. *If $f(x) = g(x) + ih(x)$ is summable over E, then both $g(x)$ and $h(x)$ are finite almost everywhere on E.*

2°. *If $\mu(E) < \infty$ and α is arbitrarily complex, then*

$$\int_E \alpha d\mu = \alpha\mu(E).$$

3°. *If D is a measurable subset of E, and $f(x)$ is summable over E, then $f(x)$ is summable over D, and*

$$\int_D f(x)d\mu = \int_E f(x)c_D(x)d\mu.$$

In particular, defining if necessary $f(x) = 0$ outside E, we have

$$\int_E f(x)d\mu = \int_X f(x)c_E(x)d\mu.$$

4°. *The integral of a function, which is summable over E, is completely additive on E.*

5°. *If $f(x)$ and $g(x)$ are summable over E, and α, β are arbitrary complex numbers, then*

$$\int_E (\alpha f + \beta g)d\mu = \alpha \int_E f\, d\mu + \beta \int_E g\, d\mu.$$

6°. *If $f(x)$ is defined on X and $\int_A f\, d\mu = 0$ for all sets A belonging to the semiring Γ on which the measure $\mu(A)$ was originally defined, then $f(x)=0$ almost everywhere on X.*

7°. *Let $f_n(x)$ be a sequence of measurable functions on E satisfying $|f_n(x)| \leqslant g(x)$ for all n, where $g(x)$ is summable over E. Then, if $f(x) = \lim f_n(x)$ exists,*

$$\int_E f\, d\mu = \lim \int_E f_n\, d\mu.$$

8°. *If $f(x)$ is summable over E, and if $\varepsilon > 0$ is arbitrarily given, there exists a number $\delta > 0$ such that $\mu(H) < \delta$, $H \subset E$ implies $|\int_H f\, d\mu| < \varepsilon$.*

Proof. All statements are immediate consequences of the corresponding statements for real summable functions.

Theorem 2. *A measurable function $f(x)$ is summable over E if and only if $|f(x)|$ is summable over E, and in this case*

$$\left|\int_E f\, d\mu\right| \leqslant \int_E |f|\, d\mu.$$

Proof. Let us assume first that $f = g + ih$ is summable, where g and h are real. Then g and h are summable, so that the same holds for $|g|$ and $|h|$. Since $|f| \leqslant |g| + |h|$, it follows that $|f|$ is summable. If, conversely, $|f|$ is summable, then $|g|$ and $|h|$ are summable on account of $|g| \leqslant |f|$ and $|h| \leqslant |f|$. Hence, g and h are summable, and this shows that the same holds for $f = g + ih$.

Assuming now that $f(x)$ is summable over E, let us write $\int_E f\, d\mu = re^{i\varphi}$, where $r = |\int_E f\, d\mu|$ and φ is real. Then the function $f_1(x) = f(x)e^{-i\varphi}$ satisfies $\int_E f_1\, d\mu = e^{-i\varphi} \int_E f\, d\mu = r$. Hence, writing $f_1 = g_1 + ih_1$, where g_1 and h_1 are real, we have $r = \int_E g_1\, d\mu + i \int_E h_1\, d\mu$, which shows that $r = \int_E g_1\, d\mu$ and $\int_E h_1\, d\mu = 0$. This implies

$$\left|\int_E f\, d\mu\right| = r = \int_E g_1\, d\mu \leqslant \int_E |g_1|\, d\mu \leqslant \int_E |f_1|\, d\mu = \int_E |f|\, d\mu.$$

§ 6. Lebesgue Integral and Riemann Integral

We assume the reader to be acquainted with the condition of Riemann integrability of a bounded function over a bounded set in m-dimensional Euclidean space R_m.

Theorem 1. *If the bounded function $f(x)$ is Riemann integrable over the interval Δ in m-dimensional Euclidean space R_m, then $f(x)$ is Lebesgue integrable over Δ, and the values of its Lebesgue integral and its Riemann integral are equal.*

Proof. We shall suppose first that $f(x)$ has only real values. Let N_0 be a net of a finite number of cells on the interval Δ which, without loss of generality, may be supposed to be a cell itself. If $\Delta_1, \ldots, \Delta_k$ are the cells of N_0, the numbers m_i and $M_i (i = 1, \ldots, k)$ are defined to be the lower bound and the upper bound of $f(x)$ in Δ_i. Furthermore we define the functions $g_0(x)$ and $h_0(x)$ by $g_0(x) = m_i$ and $h_0(x) = M_i$ in $\Delta_i (i = 1, \ldots, k)$. Then we have

$$\Sigma\, m_i . m(\Delta_i) = \int_\Delta g_0(x) dx,\ \Sigma\, M_i . m(\Delta_i) = \int_\Delta h_0(x) dx,$$

the integrals being taken in the sense of Lebesgue.

Consider now a regular sequence $N_n (n = 0, 1, 2, \ldots)$ of nets of cells on Δ, of which the net N_0 is the first. With each net N_n correspond two functions $g_n(x)$ and $h_n(x)$ in the same way as $g_0(x)$ and $h_0(x)$ correspond with N_0. For any point $x \in \Delta$ the functions $g_n(x)$ form a non-decreasing and the functions $h_n(x)$ a non-increasing sequence, tending therefore to measurable limits $m(x)$ and $M(x)$ respectively. Consequently, we have by Lebesgue's Theorem on term by term integration,

$$\lim \int_\Delta g_n(x) dx = \int_\Delta m(x) dx, \quad \lim \int_\Delta h_n(x) dx = \int_\Delta M(x) dx$$

or

$$\lim_{n\to\infty} \Sigma\, m_i . m(\Delta_i) = \int_\Delta m(x) dx,\ \lim_{n\to\infty} \Sigma\, M_i . m(\Delta_i) = \int_\Delta M(x) dx.$$

Now, the condition of integrability of $f(x)$ in the sense of Riemann is that $\lim_{n\to\infty} \Sigma\, m_i . m(\Delta_i)$ and $\lim_{n\to\infty} \Sigma\, M_i . m(\Delta_i)$ have a common value for all possible regular sequences N_n of nets of cells on Δ, and in this case the Riemann integral of $f(x)$ is defined to be this common value. Hence, $f(x)$ being Riemann integrable by hypothesis, $\int_\Delta [M(x) - m(x)]\, dx = 0$, and, since $M(x) \geqslant f(x) \geqslant m(x)$, we derive from this relation that $M(x) = f(x) = m(x)$ almost everywhere on Δ. This shows that $f(x)$ is Lebesgue integrable over Δ, and that

$$\int_\Delta f(x) dx = \int_\Delta M(x) dx = \lim_{n\to\infty} \Sigma\, M_i . m(\Delta_i).$$

The Lebesgue integral and the Riemann integral have therefore the same value.

In the case that $f(x)$ is complex, the above proof holds for its real and imaginary parts separately, and the same result is obtained.

§ 7. Fubini's Theorem on Successive Integrations

Given two Euclidean spaces R_p and R_q, it is known since Cauchy that, if Δ_1 and Δ_2 are two intervals in R_p and R_q respectively, integration of any continuous function over the interval $\Delta_1 \times \Delta_2$ in $R_{p+q} = R_p \times R_q$ may be reduced to two successive integrations over Δ_1 and Δ_2. By repeating the process, any integral of a continuous function over an m-dimensional interval may be reduced to m successive integrations over linear intervals. This theorem was extended by Lebesgue (1902) to measurable bounded functions, and then by Fubini (1907) to Lebesgue integrable functions.

Theorem 1 (*Fubini's Theorem for non-negative functions*). *Let μ_1 and μ_2 be σ-finite measures in X_1 and X_2 respectively, and let $\mu = \mu_1 \times \mu_2$ be the product measure in $X = X_1 \times X_2$. Then, if $f(x, y)$ is a non-negative μ-measurable function on X, the following statements hold:*

(*a*) *$f(x, y)$ is on X_1 a μ_1-measurable function of x for almost every $y \in X_2$, and $\int_{X_1} f(x, y)d\mu_1$ is on X_2 a μ_2-measurable function.*

(*b*) *$f(x, y)$ is on X_2 a μ_2-measurable function of y for almost every $x \in X_1$, and $\int_{X_2} f(x, y)d\mu_2$ is on X_1 a μ_1-measurable function.*

(*c*) $\int_X f(x, y)d\mu = \int_{X_2} [\int_{X_1} f(x, y)d\mu_1]d\mu_2 = \int_{X_1}[\int_{X_2} f(x, y)d\mu_2]d\mu_1$.

Proof. By symmetry, it is sufficient to show that (*a*) and the first part of (*c*) hold. For brevity we shall say that a function $f(x, y)$ has the property (P) if it is μ-measurable and non-negative on X, and satisfies (*a*) and the first part of (*c*). The argument that follows is divided into several parts:

1°. It is evident that the sum of two functions with the property (P) has the property (P). The same holds for the difference, provided that it is non-negative and that one at least of the given functions is finite and summable over X (this last condition is added to avoid expressions of the form $\infty - \infty$).

2°. The limit $h(x, y)$ of any non-decreasing sequence of functions $h_n(x, y)$ with the property (P) has the property (P). Indeed, it is trivial that $h(x, y)$ is μ-measurable and non-negative on X, since all the functions $h_n(x, y)$ have these properties. For the same reason $h(x, y)$ is on X_1 a

μ_1-measurable function of x for almost every $y \in X_2$. Furthermore, for almost every $y \in X_2$, all integrals $\int_{X_1} h_n(x, y)\, d\mu_1$ exist (not necessarily as finite numbers), and these integrals are μ_2-measurable functions of y on X_2. By Lebesgue's Theorem on the integration of monotone sequences we have now, for almost every $y \in X_2$, the relation $\int_{X_1} h(x, y) d\mu_1 = \lim \int_{X_1} h_n(x, y) d\mu_1$, which shows that $\int_{X_1} h(x, y) d\mu_1$ is on X_2 a μ_2-measurable function. Finally, by the same theorem,

$$\int_X h(x, y) d\mu = \lim \int_X h_n(x, y) d\mu = \lim \int_{X_2} [\int_{X_1} h_n(x, y) d\mu_1] d\mu_2$$
$$= \int_{X_2} \lim [\int_{X_1} h_n(x, y) d\mu_1] d\mu_2 = \int_{X_2} [\int_{X_1} h(x, y) d\mu_1] d\mu_2.$$

3°. Denoting by Γ_1 and Γ_2 the semirings of subsets of X_1 and X_2 respectively on which the measures μ_1 and μ_2 were originally given, we shall prove now that the characteristic function $c_E(x, y)$ of any set $E = A \times B \in \Gamma = \Gamma_1 \times \Gamma_2$ has the property (P). For an arbitrary $y \in X_2$ the function $c_E(x, y)$ is on X_1 either the characteristic function of A or it vanishes identically, so that it is μ_1-measurable. Furthermore $\int_{X_1} c_E(x, y) d\mu_1$, being equal to $\mu_1(A)$ for $y \in B$ and to zero for $y \in X_2 - B$, is on X_2 a μ_2-measurable function, and

$$\int_X c_E(x, y) d\mu = \mu(E) = \mu_1(A)\mu_2(B) = \int_{X_2} [\int_{X_1} c_E(x, y) d\mu_1] d\mu_2.$$

4°. Our next step is to prove that the characteristic function $c_E(x, y)$ of any σ-set $E \subset X$ has the property (P). Since E may be written in the form $E = \Sigma E_n$, where no two of the sets E_n have common points and each of them is of the kind considered in 3°, we have $c_E(x, y) = \Sigma c_{E_n}(x, y)$, where each $c_{E_n}(x, y)$ has the property (P). Each partial sum has therefore the property (P) by 1°, and the same is true of $c_E(x, y)$ by 2°.

5°. It is an immediate consequence of what we have proved in 4° that if E is a δ-set, contained in a set $D \in \Gamma$ of finite measure, the characteristic function $c_E(x, y)$ has the property (P). Indeed, $E' = X - E$ is a σ-set, so that $D - E = DE'$ is also a σ-set. Since $c_E(x, y) = c_D(x, y) - c_{D-E}(x, y)$, where both $c_D(x, y)$ and $c_{D-E}(x, y)$ have the property (P) and are summable over X, the result follows by 1°. Hence, if E is the limit of an ascending sequence E_n of δ-sets, all contained in the set $D \in \Gamma$ of finite measure, the characteristic function $c_E(x, y)$ has the property (P) by 2°.

6°. If $E \subset X$ is of measure zero, its characteristic function $c_E(x, y)$ has the property (P). This is derived from the first part of the proof of § 1, Th. 5, where we have shown that $\mu(E) = 0$ implies $\mu_1(E_y) = 0$ for almost every $y \in X_2$; in other words, since $c_E(x, y)$ is on X_1 the characteristic function of E_y, the function $c_E(x, y)$ is μ_1-measurable on X_1 for almost every $y \in X_2$, and $\int_{X_1} c_E(x, y) d\mu_1 = \mu_1(E_y) = 0$ for these values of y. Hence also

$$\int_X c_E(x, y)d\mu = \mu(E) = 0 = \int_{X_2} [\int_{X_1} c_E(x, y)d\mu_1]d\mu_2.$$

7°. We next prove that the characteristic function $c_E(x, y)$ of any measurable set $E \subset X$ has the property (P). The measure μ being σ-finite, it will be sufficient to restrict ourselves to the case that E is contained in a set $D \in \Gamma$ of finite measure. Assuming this to be the case, the set E is the sum of a set E_1, the limit of an ascending sequence of δ-sets, and a set E_2 of measure zero, where $E_1E_2 = 0$ and $E_1 \subset D$. Observing that $c_E(x, y) = c_{E_1}(x, y) + c_{E_2}(x, y)$, the desired result is therefore derived from 5° and 6°.

8°. The final step is the proof for an arbitrary non-negative function $f(x, y)$, μ-measurable on X. By Ch. 2, § 8, Th. 10 the function $f(x, y)$ is the limit of a non-decreasing sequence of simple functions, finite, non-negative and μ-measurable on X. Each of these simple functions is a linear combination with positive coefficients of a finite number of characteristic functions of measurable sets, and has therefore the property (P). Then, in virtue of 2°, the limit $f(x, y)$ has likewise the property (P).

Theorem 2 *(Fubini's Theorem for summable functions). If $f(x, y)$ is a real or complex function, summable over X, the following statements hold:*

(a) $f(x, y)$ is summable over X_1 for almost every $y \in X_2$, and $\int_{X_1} f(x, y)d\mu_1$ is summable over X_2.

(b) $f(x, y)$ is summable over X_2 for almost every $x \in X_1$, and $\int_{X_2} f(x, y)d\mu_2$ is summable over X_1.

(c) $\int_X f(x, y)d\mu = \int_{X_2} [\int_{X_1} f(x, y)d\mu_1]d\mu_2 = \int_{X_1} [\int_{X_2} f(x, y)d\mu_2]d\mu_1$.

Proof. Let us assume first that $f(x, y)$ is real. Then $f(x, y) = f_1(x, y) - f_2(x, y)$, where f_1 and f_2 are non-negative and summable over X. For f_1 and f_2 we have by the preceding theorem

$$\int_{X_2} [\int_{X_1} f_i(x, y)\, d\mu_1]d\mu_2 = \int_X f_i(x, y)d\mu < \infty \quad (i = 1, 2),$$

and this shows that the functions $\int_{X_1} f_i(x, y)d\mu_1$ $(i = 1, 2)$ are summable over X_2. It follows by subtraction that $\int_{X_1} f(x, y)d\mu_1$ is summable over X_2. Moreover, as a summable function, $\int_{X_1} f(x, y)d\mu_1$ is finite for almost every $y \in X_2$, which implies that $f(x, y)$ is summable over X_1 for almost every $y \in X_2$. Finally, the equalities in (c) result from the corresponding equalities for f_1 and f_2 by subtraction.

In the case that $f = g + ih$, where g and h are real functions, summable over X, the theorem is true for g and h, and therefore for f.

We add some remarks. It is to be observed that in Fubini's Theorem for non-negative functions all integrals in (*c*) may be equal to $+\infty$. Next, the case that $f(x, y)$ is only defined on the measurable subset E of X may be subsumed under the present case by defining $f(x, y) = 0$ outside E. One may write then

$$\int_E f(x, y)d\mu = \int_{X_2} [\int_{E_y} f(x, y)d\mu_1]d\mu_2 = \int_{X_1} [\int_{E_x} f(x, y)d\mu_2]d\mu_1,$$

hence, in the particular case that $f(x, y)$ is the characteristic function of E,

$$\mu(E) = \int_{X_2} \mu_1(E_y)d\mu_2 = \int_{X_1} \mu_2(E_x)d\mu_1.$$

Finally, even if $f(x, y)$, not of constant sign on X, is not summable over X, both repeated integrals in (*c*) may exist as finite numbers. Thus, if we have to do with Lebesgue measure and $f(x, y) = (x^2 - y^2)/(x^2 + y^2)^2$ on the two dimensional interval $[0, 1; 0, 1]$, we have $\int_0^1 [\int_0^1 f(x, y)dy]dx = \int_0^1 (1 + x^2)^{-1}dx = \pi/4$ and $\int_0^1 [\int_0^1 f(x, y)dx]dy = \int_0^1 -(1 + y^2)^{-1}dy = -\pi/4$.

§ 8. Integration by Parts

If, in Euclidean space R_m, $[a_1, b_1; \ldots; a_m, b_m]$ is an interval, we shall admit the possibility that one or more of the numbers a_k are $-\infty$ and that one or more of the numbers b_k are $+\infty$, and we shall speak about an *infinite interval* in this case. A similar agreement will be made for cells and open intervals. Furthermore, if μ is a σ-finite measure on the straight line R_1, admitting all cells as μ-measurable sets (so that, consequently, all intervals, closed, open or half open, are μ-measurable), and $f(x)$ is μ-summable over $[a, b]$, we shall mean by $\int_a^b f(x)d\mu$ the integral over $[a, b]$. Writing $F(x) = \int_a^x f(t)d\mu$ for any x satisfying $a \leqslant x \leqslant b$, the integral over the right open interval $[a, x)$ will be denoted by $F(x -)$, where $F(a -) = 0$ by definition. The values of $F(x)$ and $F(x -)$ may be different, since, as we have seen before in the case of a Stieltjes measure, the measure of the set consisting of the single point x may be different from zero.

Theorem 1 (*Theorem on the integration by parts over a linear interval*). *If $\Delta = [a, b]$ is an interval, finite or infinite, in the space R_1, if $f(x)$ and $g(x)$, real or complex, are μ-summable over Δ, where μ is a σ-finite measure in R_1, admitting all cells as μ-measurable sets, and if finally*

$$F(x) = \int_a^x f(t)d\mu, \quad G(x) = \int_a^x g(t)d\mu$$

for $a \leqslant x \leqslant b$, then

$$\int_\Delta F(x)g(x)d\mu = F(b)G(b) - \int_\Delta f(x)G(x -)d\mu.$$

Proof. Evidently the functions $g(x)$ and $f(y)$, considered as functions of (x, y), are $\mu \times \mu$-measurable on $\Delta \times \Delta$, so that the same is true of $g(x)f(y)$. Defining now the function $P(x, y)$ on $\Delta \times \Delta$ by

$$P(x, y) = g(x)f(y) \text{ for } y \leqslant x,$$
$$P(x, y) = 0 \qquad \text{ for } y > x,$$

$P(x, y)$ is also $\mu \times \mu$-measurable, since $P(x, y) = g(x)f(y)h(x, y)$, where $h(x, y) = 1$ for $y \leqslant x$ and $h(x, y) = 0$ for $y > x$ (the function $h(x, y)$ is therefore the characteristic function of a set which is easily seen to be $\mu \times \mu$-measurable). Moreover, $P(x, y)$ is $\mu \times \mu$-summable over $\Delta \times \Delta$ in virtue of

$$\int_{\Delta \times \Delta} | P(x, y) | \, d(\mu \times \mu) \leqslant \int_{\Delta \times \Delta} | g(x)f(y) | \, d(\mu \times \mu) =$$
$$\int_\Delta | g(x) | \, d\mu . \int_\Delta | f(y) | \, d\mu < \infty.$$

Consequently, by Fubini's Theorem,

$$\int_\Delta F(x)g(x)d\mu = \int_\Delta g(x) \left(\int_a^x f(y)d\mu\right)d\mu =$$
$$\int_{\Delta \times \Delta} P(x, y)d(\mu \times \mu) = \int_\Delta f(y) \left(\int_y^b g(x)d\mu\right)d\mu =$$
$$\int_\Delta f(y) \{G(b) - G(y -)\} \, d\mu = F(b)G(b) - \int_\Delta f(x)G(x -)d\mu.$$

Remark. If the measure μ is such that any set consisting of a single point has measure zero, the distinction between $G(x)$ and $G(x -)$ becomes redundant, and in this case it is also indifferent whether Δ is closed, open or half open. Hence, for Lebesgue measure,

$$\int_a^b F(x)g(x)dx = F(b)G(b) - \int_a^b f(x)G(x)dx.$$

§ 9. The Gamma Function and Fractional Integration

In the present paragraph we shall write shortly "measurable" and "summable" for "Lebesgue measurable" and "Lebesgue summable".

Theorem 1. *The function $e^{-x}x^{p-1}$ is summable over $[0, \infty)$ for $p > 0$, but not for $p \leqslant 0$.*

Proof. Since

$$\int_0^1 e^{-1} x^{p-1} \, dx \leqslant \int_0^1 e^{-x} x^{p-1} \, dx \leqslant \int_0^1 x^{p-1} \, dx,$$

the integral in the middle is finite for $p > 0$ and infinite for $p \leqslant 0$. Furthermore, if the real number p is given, there exists a positive constant k such that $x^{p-1}e^{-x/2} < k$ for $x \geqslant 1$, hence $e^{-x}x^{p-1} < ke^{-x/2}$ in $[1, \infty)$, which shows that $e^{-x}x^{p-1}$ is summable over $[1, \infty)$.

Definition. *For $p > 0$, the Gamma function $\Gamma(p)$ of p is defined by*

$$\Gamma(p) = \int_0^\infty e^{-x} x^{p-1}\, dx.$$

Theorem 2. *For $p > 0$ we have*

$$\Gamma(p + 1) = p\Gamma(p).$$

Furthermore, if $\lambda > 0$ and p is a positive integer, then

$$\int_0^\infty e^{-\lambda x} x^p\, dx = p!/\lambda^{p+1}.$$

In particular

$$\Gamma(p + 1) = p!$$

Proof. It is easily seen by a similar argument as in Theorem 1 that $e^{-\lambda x} x^{p-1}$ is summable over $[0, \infty)$ for $\lambda > 0$, $p > 0$. For $x \geqslant 0$ and $p > 0$, we define $f(x) = px^{p-1}$ and $g(x) = e^{-\lambda x}$, hence

$$F(x) = \int_0^x f(t)dt = x^p, \quad G(x) = \int_0^x g(t)dt = (1 - e^{-\lambda x})/\lambda.$$

Integration by parts over $[0, y]$ gives

$$\int_0^y e^{-\lambda x} x^p dx = \int_0^y F(x)g(x)dx = F(y)G(y) - \int_0^y f(x)G(x)dx =$$

$$y^p\lambda^{-1}(1 - e^{-\lambda y}) - p\lambda^{-1} \int_0^y (1 - e^{-\lambda x})x^{p-1}dx =$$

$$- \lambda^{-1}y^p e^{-\lambda y} + p\lambda^{-1} \int_0^y e^{-\lambda x}x^{p-1}dx,$$

and, making $y \to \infty$, we find

$$\int_0^\infty e^{-\lambda x} x^p dx = p\lambda^{-1} \int_0^\infty e^{-\lambda x} x^{p-1}dx.$$

Taking $\lambda = 1$ in this relation, we derive

$$\Gamma(p + 1) = p\Gamma(p).$$

Also, assuming now that p is a positive integer, we obtain by induction

$$\int_0^\infty e^{-\lambda x} x^p dx = p!\lambda^{-p} \int_0^\infty e^{-\lambda x}\, dx = p!/\lambda^{p+1}.$$

Theorem 3. *If p and q are positive, then*

$$\Gamma(p)\Gamma(q) = \Gamma(p + q) \int_0^1 u^{q-1}(1 - u)^{p-1}dx.$$

Furthermore

$$\Gamma(1/2) = \pi^{1/2}.$$

Proof. Using that $\int_a^b f(x)dx = \int_{a+c}^{b+c} f(x - c)dx$ for any finite real c, we have

$$e^{-y}\Gamma(p) = \int_0^\infty e^{-x-y} x^{p-1}dx =$$

$$\int_y^\infty e^{-x}(x - y)^{p-1}\, dx = \int_0^\infty f(x, y)dx,$$

where $y \geqslant 0$ and

$$f(x, y) = e^{-x}(x - y)^{p-1} \text{ for } 0 \leqslant y < x,$$
$$f(x, y) = 0 \qquad \text{for } 0 \leqslant x \leqslant y.$$

Furthermore

$$\int_0^\infty dy \int_0^\infty y^{q-1} f(x, y) dx =$$
$$\int_0^\infty \Gamma(p) e^{-y} y^{q-1} dy = \Gamma(p)\Gamma(q) < \infty.$$

Consequently, observing that $y^{q-1}f(x, y)$ is measurable on $0 \leqslant x, y < \infty$, we may apply Fubini's Theorem, and we find

$$\Gamma(p)\Gamma(q) = \int_0^\infty dx \int_0^\infty f(x, y) y^{q-1} dy.$$

Now, by the ordinary rules for Riemann integration,

$$\int_0^\infty f(x, y) y^{q-1} dy = e^{-x} \int_0^x y^{q-1}(x - y)^{p-1} dy =$$
$$e^{-x} x^{p+q-1} \int_0^1 u^{q-1}(1 - u)^{p-1} du,$$

where, if necessary, the integral $\int_0^x$ is to be considered as $\lim \int_\delta^{x-\delta}$ for δ tending to zero through positive values.

Hence

$$\Gamma(p)\Gamma(q) = \int_0^\infty e^{-x} x^{p+q-1} dx \,.\, \int_0^1 u^{q-1}(1 - u)^{p-1} du =$$
$$\Gamma(p + q) \int_0^1 u^{q-1}(1 - u)^{p-1} du.$$

Finally, choosing $p = q = 1/2$ in this result, we easily obtain $\{\Gamma(1/2)\}^2 = \pi$.

Theorem 4. *If $\alpha > 0$, and $f(x)$ is summable over $[0, b]$ where $0 < b < \infty$, the integral*

$$\int_0^x (x - t)^{\alpha-1} f(t) dt$$

exists for almost every x in $[0, b]$, and represents a function $h(x)$ of x, summable over $[0, b]$.

Proof. Writing $g(u) = u^{\alpha-1}$ for $0 \leqslant u \leqslant b$ and $g(u) = 0$ elsewhere, we have to investigate the existence on $[0, b]$ and the summability over $[0, b]$ of $h(x) = \int_0^b g(x - t) f(t) dt$. It is not difficult to see that $F(x, t) = g(x - t) \mid f(t) \mid$ is a measurable function of (x, t) on $[-\infty, +\infty; 0, b]$, hence

$$\int_{-\infty}^\infty \int_0^b F(x, t) dx\, dt = \int_0^b dt \mid f(t) \mid \int_{-\infty}^\infty g(x - t) dx =$$
$$\int_0^b \mid f(t) \mid dt \int_{-\infty}^\infty g(x) dx < \infty.$$

This shows that $g(x - t)f(t)$ is summable over $[0, b;\ 0, b]$, and an application of Fubini's Theorem yields the desired result.

Definition. *If $\alpha > 0$, and $f(x)$ is summable over $[0, b]$, where $0 < b < \infty$, the fractional integral of $f(x)$ of order α is defined on $[0, b]$ by*

$$I_\alpha f(x) = \frac{1}{\Gamma(\alpha)} \int_0^x (x-t)^{\alpha-1} f(t)dt.$$

The justification for this name is found in the case $\alpha = 1$ and in the theorem which follows next.

Theorem 5. *If α and β are positive, the fractional integral of order β of the fractional integral of order α of $f(x)$ is the fractional integral of order $\alpha + \beta$ of $f(x)$. Shortly*

$$I_\beta I_\alpha f(x) = I_{\alpha+\beta} f(x).$$

Proof. We have

$$\Gamma(\alpha)\,\Gamma(\beta)\, I_\beta I_\alpha f(x) = \int_0^x (x-t)^{\beta-1} dt \int_0^t (t-u)^{\alpha-1} f(u)du.$$

From

$$\int_u^x (x-t)^{\beta-1} (t-u)^{\alpha-1} dt = \int_0^{x-u} (x-u-t)^{\beta-1} t^{\alpha-1} dt =$$

$$(x-u)^{\alpha+\beta-1} \int_0^1 (1-t)^{\beta-1} t^{\alpha-1} dt = (x-u)^{\alpha+\beta-1}\, \Gamma(\alpha)\,\Gamma(\beta)/\Gamma(\alpha+\beta)$$

we derive

$$\int_0^x (x-t)^{\beta-1} dt \int_0^t (t-u)^{\alpha-1} \mid f(u) \mid du =$$

$$\frac{\Gamma(\alpha)\Gamma(\beta)}{\Gamma(\alpha+\beta)} \int_0^x (x-u)^{\alpha+\beta-1} \mid f(u) \mid du = \Gamma(\alpha)\,\Gamma(\beta) I_{\alpha+\beta} \mid f(x) \mid,$$

and this is finite for almost every x in $[0, b]$. We may invert therefore, for these values of x, the order of integration in $\Gamma(\alpha)\Gamma(\beta)I_\beta I_\alpha f(x)$, and we find

$$\Gamma(\alpha)\,\Gamma(\beta)\, I_\beta I_\alpha f(x) = \frac{\Gamma(\alpha)\Gamma(\beta)}{\Gamma(\alpha+\beta)} \int_0^x (x-u)^{\alpha+\beta-1} f(u)du = \Gamma(\alpha)\Gamma(\beta) I_{\alpha+\beta} f(x).$$

This is the desired result.

EXAMPLES

1) If the real function $f(x)$ is measurable on the set E of finite measure $\mu(E)$, and if $E_n = E(n-1 \leqslant f < n)$ for $n = 0, \pm 1, \pm 2, \ldots$, then $f(x)$ is summable over E if and only if $\Sigma_{n=-\infty}^{\infty} \mid n \mid \mu(E_n) < \infty$.

2) If $f(x)$ is non-negative and summable over the set E, and if $f_n(x) = f(x)$ on $E(f \leqslant n)$ and $f_n(x) = 0$ elsewhere, then $\int_E f d\mu = \lim \int_E f_n d\mu$.

3) If $f(x)$, real or complex, is summable over the set E, and $E_n = E(|f| \geqslant n)$ for $n = 1, 2, \ldots$, then $\lim n\mu(E_n) = 0$.

4) The function

$$f(x) = \frac{d}{dx}\left(x^2 \sin \frac{1}{x^2}\right) = 2x \sin \frac{1}{x^2} - \frac{2}{x} \cos \frac{1}{x^2}$$

is not Lebesgue integrable over $[0, 1]$, although it is continuous in $[\varepsilon, 1]$ for every ε satisfying $0 < \varepsilon < 1$, and $\lim_{\varepsilon \to 0} \int_\varepsilon^1 f(x)dx$ exists.

(We have $\int_0^1 |f| \, dx = +\infty$ on account of $|f(x)| \geqslant 2x^{-1} |\cos x^{-2}| - 2x \geqslant x^{-1} - 2x$ in each of the intervals $\{(2n + 1/3)\pi\}^{-1/2} \leqslant x \leqslant \{(2n - 1/3)\pi\}^{-1/2}$).

5) If $f(x) = 0$ on every point of Cantor's ternary set, and $f(x) = p$ on each of the complementary intervals of length 3^{-p}, then $\int_0^1 f(x)dx = 3$.

(The integral is equal to $S = \Sigma_1^\infty \frac{1}{2}n(\frac{2}{3})^n$. Hence $\frac{2}{3}S = \Sigma_1^\infty \frac{1}{2}n(\frac{2}{3})^{n+1} = \Sigma_2^\infty \frac{1}{2}(n-1)(\frac{2}{3})^n$. Subtraction yields $\frac{1}{3}S = \frac{1}{3} + \frac{1}{2}\Sigma_2^\infty (\frac{2}{3})^n = 1$).

6) If p and q are positive, then

$$\int_0^1 \frac{x^{p-1}}{1 + x^q} dx = \frac{1}{p} - \frac{1}{p+q} + \frac{1}{p+2q} - \frac{1}{p+3q} + \ldots;$$

in particular, for $p = 1, q = 1$,

$$\log 2 = \int_0^1 \frac{dx}{1+x} = 1 - \tfrac{1}{2} + \tfrac{1}{3} - \tfrac{1}{4} + \ldots,$$

and for $p = 1, q = 2$,

$$\pi/4 = \int_0^1 \frac{dx}{1+x^2} = 1 - \tfrac{1}{3} + \tfrac{1}{5} - \tfrac{1}{7} + \ldots.$$

(For $0 < x < 1$ we have

$$x^{p-1}(1 + x^q)^{-1} = x^{p-1}(1 - x^q + x^{2q} - x^{3q} + \ldots) = \Sigma_{n=0}^\infty f_n(x),$$

where $f_n(x) = (1 - x^q)x^{p-1+2nq} \geqslant 0$; hence $\int_0^1 x^{p-1}(1 + x^q)^{-1} dx = \Sigma_{n=0}^\infty \int_0^1 f_n(x)dx$, from which the result follows).

7) If the functions $f_n(x)$ $(n = 1, 2, \ldots)$, real or complex, are μ-summable over the set E of finite measure $\mu(E)$, and if the sequence $f_n(x)$ converges uniformly to $f(x)$ on E, then $f(x)$ is μ-summable over E and $\int_E f d\mu = \lim \int_E f_n d\mu$.

8) If the functions $f_n(x)$ $(n = 2, 3, \ldots)$ are defined on $[1, \infty)$ by $f_n(x) = x^{-1}$ on $1 \leqslant x \leqslant n$ and $f_n(x) = 0$ for $x > n$, then all $f_n(x)$ are Lebesgue integrable over $[1, \infty)$ and the sequence $f_n(x)$ converges uniformly to $f(x) = x^{-1}$, but $f(x)$ is not Lebesgue integrable over $[1, \infty)$.

9) If, with the notations of § 8, we write $2F_m(x) = F(x) + F(x-)$ and $2G_m(x) = G(x) + G(x-)$, then

$$\int_\Delta F_m(x)g(x)d\mu = F(b)G(b) - \int_\Delta f(x)G_m(x)d\mu.$$

Chapter 4

ADDITIVE SET FUNCTIONS

§ 1. Additive Set Functions

Let Λ be a σ-ring consisting of subsets of the point set X. The sets of Λ will be called measurable sets. If E is one of these measurable sets, and if with every measurable set $D \subset E$ (the empty set included therefore) corresponds a finite real number $\nu(D)$, then $\nu(D)$ is called a real finite *set function,* defined on E.

Definition. *The finite real set function $\nu(D)$, defined on the measurable set E, is said to be additive (or completely additive) whenever $\nu(\Sigma D_n) = \Sigma \nu(D_n)$ for every sequence of measurable sets D_n contained in E, no two of which have common points.*

In the case that Λ is the σ-ring of all μ-measurable sets with respect to a measure μ, and $f(x)$ is μ-summable over E, the integral $\int_D f \, d\mu$ is an additive set function on E. In particular, if $\mu(E) < \infty$, the measure $\mu(D)$ is an additive set function on E. More generally, if μ_1 and μ_2 are measures on Λ, and both $\mu_1(E)$ and $\mu_2(E)$ are finite, then $\nu(D) = \alpha\mu_1(D) + \beta\mu_2(D)$, where α and β are real constants, is an additive set function on E. Conversely, if $\nu(D)$ is an additive set function on E, and $\nu(D) \geqslant 0$ for every measurable set $D \subset E$, then ν is a finite measure on the σ-ring of all measurable subsets of E. It will be one of our objectives to prove that every additive set function on E is the difference of two finite measures of this kind, and this property makes it clear why additive set functions are sometimes called signed measures.

Theorem 1. *If $\nu(D)$ is additive on E, then*

$$\nu(\lim D_n) = \lim \nu(D_n)$$

for every monotone sequence D_n of measurable sets contained in E. If *moreover* $\nu(D) \geqslant 0$ *for every measurable set* $D \subset E$, *then*

$$\nu(\text{lim inf } D_n) \leqslant \text{lim inf } \nu(D_n) \leqslant \text{lim sup } \nu(D_n) \leqslant \nu(\text{lim sup } D_n)$$

for every sequence D_n *of measurable sets contained in* E.

Proof. The proof of the first statement may be taken over from the corresponding proof for a measure in Ch. 2, § 6, Th. 1 and Th. 2, replacing $\mu(E_n)$ by $\nu(D_n)$. The truth of the second statement is an immediate consequence of the fact that on account of $\nu(D) \geqslant 0$ the set function $\nu(D)$ is a finite measure on the σ-ring of all measurable subsets D of E.

§ 2. The Variations of an Additive Function

If $\nu(D)$ is additive on E, the upper and lower bounds that $\nu(D)$ assumes on the measurable subsets D of E, are called the *upper variation* and *lower variation* of ν on E, and denoted by $\nu^+(E)$, $\nu^-(E)$ respectively. Since $\nu(D) = 0$ if D is the empty set, we evidently have $\nu^-(E) \leqslant 0 \leqslant \nu^+(E)$. The number $|\nu|(E) = \nu^+(E) + |\nu^-(E)| = \nu^+(E) - \nu^-(E)$ is called the *total variation* of ν on E.

Theorem 1. *If* $\nu(D)$ *is additive on* E, *its variations on* E *are finite.*

Proof. Let us suppose that $|\nu|(E) = +\infty$. Then there exists a sequence D_n of measurable subsets of E such that

$$D_n \subset D_{n-1} (n > 1), \; |\nu|(D_n) = +\infty, \; |\nu(D_n)| \geqslant n - 1.$$

Indeed, let us take $D_1 = E$, and suppose that the sets $D_1, \ldots, D_k$ are already defined in such a way that the above conditions are satisfied for $n = 1, \ldots, k$. By the second condition there exists a measurable set $A \subset D_k$ such that $|\nu(A)| \geqslant |\nu(D_k)| + k$. If now $|\nu|(A) = +\infty$, we choose $D_{k+1} = A$, and then all conditions are satisfied for $n = k + 1$. If $|\nu|(A)$ is finite, then $|\nu|(D_k - A) = +\infty$, and since $|\nu(D_k - A)| \geqslant |\nu(A)| - |\nu(D_k)| \geqslant k$, we have only to choose $D_{k+1} = D_k - A$ in order to satisfy all conditions for $n = k + 1$.

The descending sequence D_n being thus defined, we should have $|\nu(\lim D_n)| = |\lim \nu(D_n)| = \infty$, which is impossible, since $\nu(\lim D_n)$ is finite by definition.

Corollary. *If* $\nu(D)$ *is additive on* E, $\nu(D)$ *is not only finite for every measurable set* $D \subset E$, *but even bounded on* E.

Proof. We have

$$|\nu(D)| \leqslant \max \{\nu^+(E), |\nu^-(E)|\} \leqslant |\nu|(E)$$

or any measurable set $D \subset E$.

Theorem 2 (*Jordan decomposition of an additive function*). *If $\nu(D)$ is additive on E, then $\nu^+(D)$, $\nu^-(D)$ and $|\nu|(D)$ are also additive on E, and*

$$\nu(D) = \nu^+(D) + \nu^-(D)$$

for every measurable set $D \subset E$. Every additive set function on E is therefore the difference of two non-negative additive set functions on E, that is, it is the difference of two finite measures.

Proof. Let us consider for example $\nu^+(D)$. Since $\nu^+(D)$ is finite for every measurable set $D \subset E$, we have only to show that $\nu^+(\Sigma D_n) = \Sigma \nu^+(D_n)$ for any sequence D_n of measurable subsets of E, no two of which have common points. We observe first that for any measurable set $D \subset \Sigma D_n$ we have $\nu(D) = \Sigma_n \nu(D.D_n) \leqslant \Sigma \nu^+(D_n)$, hence $\nu^+(\Sigma D_n) \leqslant \Sigma \nu^+(D_n)$. On the other hand, if A_n is a measurable set variable in D_n, we have $\nu^+(\Sigma D_n) \geqslant \nu(\Sigma A_n) = \Sigma \nu(A_n)$, so that also $\nu^+(\Sigma D_n) \geqslant \Sigma \nu^+(D_n)$. Combining the two inequalities, we obtain the desired result. The proof for $\nu^-(D)$ is similar.

Finally, we observe that if $A \subset D$ is measurable, then $\nu(A) = \nu(D) - \nu(D - A) \leqslant \nu(D) - \nu^-(D)$, hence $\nu^+(D) \leqslant \nu(D) - \nu^-(D)$. Similarly $\nu^-(D) \geqslant \nu(D) - \nu^+(D)$. Combining these inequalities, we find

$$\nu(D) = \nu^+(D) + \nu^-(D).$$

Theorem 3. *If $\nu(D)$ is additive on E, then*

$$\nu(\lim D_n) = \lim \nu(D_n)$$

for any convergent sequence of measurable sets D_n contained in E.

Proof. By the second part of § 1, Th. 1, the theorem is true if $\nu(D)$ assumes only non-negative values. Observing now that by the preceding theorem any additive $\nu(D)$ is the difference of two non-negative additive functions, the general result is seen to be true.

Theorem 4 (*Hahn decomposition of a set with respect to an additive function*). *If $\nu(D)$ is additive on E, there exists a measurable set $A \subset E$ such that $\nu^-(A) = \nu^+(E - A) = 0$, in other words, $\nu(D) \geqslant 0$ for every measurable set $D \subset A$ and $\nu(D) \leqslant 0$ for every measurable set $D \subset E - A$.*

Proof. For every positive integer n, there exists a set $D_n \subset E$ such that $\nu(D_n) \geqslant \nu^+(E) - 1/2^n$. This implies

$$\nu^+(E - D_n) \leqslant 1/2^n, \; \nu^-(D_n) = \nu(D_n) - \nu^+(D_n) \geqslant \nu(D_n) - \nu^+(E) \geqslant -1/2^n.$$

Writing $A = \liminf D_n$, we have $E - A = \limsup (E - D_n) \subset \Sigma_{n=k}^{\infty}$

$(E - D_n)$ for $k = 1, 2, \ldots$, hence

$$\nu^+(E - A) \leqslant \Sigma_{n=k}^{\infty} \nu^+(E - D_n) \leqslant 1/2^{k-1},$$

which shows that $\nu^+(E - A) = 0$. To prove that $\nu^-(A) = 0$, we observe that $|\nu^-(D)|$ is a non-negative additive function on E, hence, by § 1, Th. 1, $|\nu^-(A)| \leqslant \liminf |\nu^-(D_n)| = 0$.

Remark. The set A is not necessarily uniquely determined since, if P is a measurable subset of E with the property that $|\nu|(P) = 0$, an arbitrary measurable part of P may be contained in A.

§ 3. Absolutely Continuous Additive Set Functions

We now suppose that the σ-ring Λ is the collection of all measurable sets with respect to some σ-finite measure μ.

Definition. *An additive function $\nu(D)$ on a measurable set E is said to be absolutely continuous on E with respect to μ whenever $\nu(D) = 0$ for every measurable subset D of E satisfying $\mu(D) = 0$.*

Evidently, if $f(x)$ is μ-summable over E, the additive function $\nu(D) = \int_D f\, d\mu$ is absolutely continuous on E (cf. Ch. 3, § 4, Th. 5). It will be shown presently that, conversely, every absolutely continuous additive set function $\nu(D)$ on E is of the form $\nu(D) = \int_D f\, d\mu$, where $f(x)$ is μ-summable over E.

Theorem 1. 1°. *The additive function $\nu(D)$ on E is absolutely continuous if and only if its two variations are so.*

2°. *Every linear combination with constant (real) coefficients of two absolutely continuous additive functions on E is absolutely continuous on E.*

3°. *If a sequence $\nu_n(D)$ of absolutely continuous additive functions on E converges to an additive function $\nu(D)$ for every measurable set $D \subset E$, then $\nu(D)$ is absolutely continuous on E.*

4°. *If the additive function $\nu(D)$ is absolutely continuous on E, it is so on every measurable subset of E.*

5°. *If $E = \Sigma E_n$, where E_n is a sequence of measurable sets, and if the additive function $\nu(D)$ on E is absolutely continuous on each of the sets E_n, then $\nu(D)$ is absolutely continuous on E.*

Proof. The truth of all statements follows immediately from the definition of absolute continuity.

Theorem 2. *The additive function $\nu(D)$ on E is absolutely continuous on E if and only if with each number $\varepsilon > 0$ corresponds a number $\delta > 0$ such that $\mu(D) < \delta$ for any measurable set $D \subset E$ implies $|\nu(D)| < \varepsilon$.*
Proof. Evidently the condition is sufficient. To prove that it is also necessary, let us assume that $\nu(D)$ is absolutely continuous on E. We may, without loss of generality, suppose $\nu(D)$ to be non-negative on E, replacing if necessary $\nu(D)$ by its total variation. If, under these assumptions, the mentioned condition were not satisfied, there would exist a fixed number $\varepsilon > 0$ and a sequence D_n of measurable subsets of E such that $\mu(D_n) < 1/2^n$ and $\nu(D_n) > \varepsilon$ for all n. Writing $D_0 = \lim\sup D_n$, we should have $D_0 \subset \Sigma_{k=n}^{\infty} D_k$ for every n, hence $\mu(D_0) \leqslant \Sigma_{k=n}^{\infty} \mu(D_k) < 1/2^{n-1}$, so that $\mu(D_0) = 0$ and therefore also $\nu(D_0) = 0$. But, by § 1, Th. 1, $\nu(D_0) \geqslant \lim\sup \nu(D_n) \geqslant \varepsilon$. This is a contradiction.

The reader should compare the present proof with the second proof of Ch. 2, § 4, Th. 5.

The lemma, which follows now, prepares the way for the proof of our main theorem.

Lemma α. *If $\nu(D)$ is a non-negative additive function on the set E of finite measure, and if p is a positive number, there exists a decomposition of E into a sequence of measurable sets $H, E_1, E_2, \ldots$ such that $\mu(H) = 0$ and*

$$p(n-1)\mu(D) \leqslant \nu(D) \leqslant pn\mu(D)$$

for every measurable set $D \subset E_n$ $(n = 1, 2, \ldots)$.
Proof. Since $\mu(E)$ is finite, the set function $\mu(D)$ is additive on E. Hence, by § 2, Th. 4, there exists for every positive integer n a measurable set $A_n \subset E$ such that $\nu(D) - pn\mu(D) \geqslant 0$ for every measurable set $D \subset A_n$ and $\nu(D) - pn\mu(D) \leqslant 0$ for every measurable set $D \subset E - A_n$. At first, one might expect that as a consequence of this property the sequence A_n is descending. This would be true if the sets A_n were uniquely determined. However, uniqueness being absent in general, one cannot assert anything on the monotony of the sequence A_n. Instead, writing $B_n = \Sigma_{k=n}^{\infty} A_k$ for $n = 1, 2, \ldots$, we shall prove that the sequence B_n, which is evidently descending, has the same properties as the sequence A_n. Since any measurable set $D \subset B_n$ may be written in the form $D = \Sigma_{k=n}^{\infty} D_k$, where no two of the measurable sets $D_k \subset A_k$ $(k = n, n+1, \ldots)$ have common points, we have $\nu(D) = \Sigma_{k=n}^{\infty} \nu(D_k) \geqslant \Sigma_{k=n}^{\infty} pk\mu(D_k) \geqslant pn\mu(D)$. Hence

$$\nu(D) \geqslant pn\mu(D) \text{ for } D \subset B_n,$$
$$\nu(D) \leqslant pn\mu(D) \text{ for } D \subset E - B_n \subset E - A_n.$$

Writing now $E_1 = E - B_1$, $E_n = B_{n-1} - B_n$ for $n = 2, 3, \ldots$, and $H = \lim B_n$, the sets $H, E_1, E_2, \ldots$ are measurable, and no two of them have common points. Moreover, $E = H + \Sigma_{n=1}^{\infty} E_n$, and, on account of $H \subset B_n$ for every n, we have $\nu(H) \geqslant pn\mu(H)$, hence $\mu(H) = 0$. Finally, it is evident that $p(n-1)\mu(D) \leqslant \nu(D) \leqslant pn\mu(D)$ for every measurable set $D \subset E_n$.

Theorem 3 (*Theorem of Radon-Nikodym*). *If $\nu(D)$ is additive on E, then $\nu(D)$ is absolutely continuous on E if and only if $\nu(D)$ is the integral over D of a μ-summable function $f(x)$ for every measurable set $D \subset E$. In this case $f(x)$ is uniquely determined in the sense that if $\nu(D) = \int_D f_1\, d\mu = \int_D f_2\, d\mu$ for all $D \subset E$, then $f_1(x) = f_2(x)$ almost everywhere on E.*

Proof. The condition is evidently sufficient. Let us suppose therefore that $\nu(D)$ is absolutely continuous on E. Since every absolutely continuous additive function on E is the difference of two non-negative functions of the same kind, we may assume $\nu(D)$ to be non-negative. Furthermore, we shall suppose first that E is of finite measure. In other words, we restrict ourselves, to begin with, to the case that both μ and ν are finite measures on E.

This being so, there exists, in virtue of the preceding lemma, for every positive integer p a decomposition of E into a sequence of measurable sets $H^{(p)}, E_1^{(p)}, E_2^{(p)}, \ldots$, no two of which have common points, such that

$$(1) \qquad \begin{cases} E = H^{(p)} + \Sigma_{n=1}^{\infty} E_n^{(p)}, & \mu(H^{(p)}) = 0, \\ 2^{-p}(n-1)\mu(D) \leqslant \nu(D) \leqslant 2^{-p}n\mu(D) & \text{for } D \subset E_n^{(p)}. \end{cases}$$

Hence, for all positive integers p, n and k,

$$2^{-p}n\mu(E_n^{(p)}.E_k^{(p+1)}) \geqslant \nu(E_n^{(p)}.E_k^{(p+1)}) \geqslant 2^{-p-1}(k-1)\mu(E_n^{(p)}.E_k^{(p+1)})$$

and

$$2^{-p-1}k\mu(E_n^{(p)}.E_k^{(p+1)}) \geqslant \nu(E_n^{(p)}.E_k^{(p+1)}) \geqslant 2^{-p}(n-1)\mu(E_n^{(p)}.E_k^{(p+1)}),$$

which implies $(2n - k + 1)\mu(E_n^{(p)}.E_k^{(p+1)}) \geqslant 0$ and $(k - 2n + 2)$ $\mu(E_n^{(p)}.E_k^{(p+1)}) \geqslant 0$. It follows that $\mu(E_n^{(p)}.E_k^{(p+1)}) = 0$ for $k > 2n + 1$ and $k < 2n - 2$, so that

$$(2) \qquad E_n^{(p)} \subset E_{2n-2}^{(p+1)} + E_{2n-1}^{(p+1)} + E_{2n}^{(p+1)} + E_{2n+1}^{(p+1)} + Q_n^{(p)},$$

where $\mu(Q_n^{(p)}) = 0$. Writing $H = \Sigma_{p=1}^{\infty} H^{(p)} + \Sigma_{p,\,n=1}^{\infty} Q_n^{(p)}$, we find therefore $\mu(H) = 0$. Defining now $f_p(x) = 2^{-p}(n-1)$ on $E_n^{(p)} - H$ $(n = 1, 2, \ldots)$ and $f_p(x) = 0$ on H, we obtain a sequence $f_p(x)$ of non-negative measurable functions on E. From (2) we derive $|f_{p+1}(x) - f_p(x)| \leqslant 2^{-p}$ for every $x \in E$, so that $f_p(x)$ converges uniformly on E to a non-negative measurable function $f(x)$.

For every measurable set $D \subset E$ and for every positive integer p we have now, by (1) and the absolute continuity of ν (which is used here for the first time),

$$\nu(D) \geqslant \nu(D.H) + \Sigma_n 2^{-p}(n-1)\mu(D.E_n^{(p)}) = \int_D f_p \, d\mu$$

and

$$\nu(D) \leqslant \nu(D.H) + \Sigma_n 2^{-p}n\mu(D.E_n^{(p)}) = \int_D f_p \, d\mu + 2^{-p}\mu(D).$$

Hence, making $p \to \infty$ and observing that $\mu(D) < \infty$, we find

$$\nu(D) = \int_D f(x) \, d\mu.$$

If E is not of finite measure, we have $E = \Sigma A_n$, where no two of the sets A_n of finite measure have common points, so that, by what we have already proved, there exists on A_n a non-negative μ-summable function $f^{(n)}(x)$ such that $\nu(D.A_n) = \int_{D.A_n} f^{(n)}(x) d\mu$ $(n = 1, 2, \ldots)$ for any measurable set $D \subset E$. Hence, writing $f(x) = f^{(n)}(x)$ on A_n, we have

$$\nu(D) = \Sigma_n \int_{D.A_n} f^{(n)} d\mu = \int_D f \, d\mu.$$

The uniqueness of $f(x)$ results from the fact that $\int_D (f_1 - f_2) d\mu = 0$ for every $D \subset E$ implies $\int_{D_1} = \int_{D_2} = 0$, where $D_1 = E(f_1 - f_2 \geqslant 0)$ and $D_2 = E(f_1 - f_2 < 0)$, hence $f_1 = f_2$ almost everywhere by Ch. 2, § 3, Th. 8.

Remark. Our proof shows that if $\nu(D)$ is an additive set function on the μ-measurable set E, then

$$\nu(D) = \int_D f \, d\mu + \nu(D.H),$$

where $f(x)$ is μ-summable over E and $H \subset E$ is a fixed set of μ-measure zero. Every additive function $\nu(D)$ on E may therefore be expressed in the form $\nu = \nu_1 + \nu_2$, where ν_1 is absolutely continuous and ν_2 is singular, that is, there exists a set H of μ-measure zero such that ν_2 vanishes identically on $E - H$. This Lebesgue decomposition of an additive function is unique since $\nu = \nu_1 + \nu_2 = \bar{\nu}_1 + \bar{\nu}_2$ implies $\nu_1 - \bar{\nu}_1 = \bar{\nu}_2 - \nu_2$, so that, the function $\nu_1 - \bar{\nu}_1 = \bar{\nu}_2 - \nu_2$ being absolutely continuous and singular at the same time, it vanishes identically on E.

§ 4. Extension to Complex Additive Set Functions

The main theorems for real additive set functions may be extended to additive set functions assuming complex values.

Definition. *The finite complex set function* $\nu(D)$ *on the measurable set* E *will be called additive whenever* $\nu(\Sigma D_n) = \Sigma \nu(D_n)$ *for every sequence of measurable sets* D_n *contained in* E, *no two of which have common points.*

Evidently, if $\nu(D)$ is a complex additive function on E, then $\nu(D) = \nu_1(D) + i\nu_2(D)$, where $\nu_1(D)$ and $\nu_2(D)$ are real additive functions on E. Hence $\nu(\lim D_n) = \lim \nu(D_n)$ for every convergent sequence of measurable sets D_n contained in E.

Definition. *The additive function* $\nu(D)$ *on the* μ*-measurable set* E *is said to be absolutely continuous with respect to* μ *whenever* $\nu(D) = 0$ *for every* μ*-measurable subset* D *of* E *satisfying* $\mu(D) = 0$.

Evidently, if $\nu = \nu_1 + i\nu_2$, ν_1 and ν_2 real, ν is absolutely continuous on E if and only if ν_1 and ν_2 are so. Hence, $\nu(D)$ is absolutely continuous on E if and only if with each number $\varepsilon > 0$ corresponds a number $\delta > 0$ such that $\mu(D) < \delta$ for any measurable set $D \subset E$ implies $|\nu(D)| < \varepsilon$. Also, $\nu(D)$ is absolutely continuous on E if and only if $\nu(D)$ is the integral over D of a μ-summable function $f(x)$ for every measurable set $D \subset E$.

EXAMPLES

1) Let $f(x)$ be Lebesgue summable over the straight line R_1, and H the set consisting of the points $x_1, x_2, \ldots$ on R_1. Denoting the set consisting of the single point x_n also by x_n, and defining $\nu(x_n) = \alpha_n$, where $\Sigma \alpha_n$ is convergent and $\neq 0$, the set function

$$\nu(D) = \int_D f\,dx + \nu(D.H)$$

is additive, but not absolutely continuous.

2) Let $\nu(D)$ be a non-negative absolutely continuous additive function on the μ-measurable set E, hence $\nu(D) = \int_D g\,d\mu$, where $g(x) \geqslant 0$. Let, furthermore, $\lambda(D)$ be additive on E and absolutely continuous with respect to ν, hence $\lambda(D) = \int_D f\,d\nu$. Then $\lambda(D) = \int_D fg\,d\mu$ on E.

(We may assume that $f(x) \geqslant 0$. Let $f_n(x)$ be a non-decreasing sequence of simple functions, non-negative and measurable on E, such that $f(x) = \lim f_n(x)$ on E. Then

$$\lim \int_D f_n\,d\nu = \int_D f\,d\nu, \quad \lim \int_D f_n g\,d\mu = \int_D fg\,d\mu.$$

Furthermore, if F is measurable with characteristic function c_F,

$$\int_D c_F\,d\nu = \nu(D.F) = \int_{D.F} g\,d\mu = \int_D c_F\,g\,d\mu,$$

hence, by linear combination, $\int_D f_n\,d\nu = \int_D f_n g\,d\mu$ for all $f_n(x)$. This implies $\lambda(D) = \int_D f\,d\nu = \int_D fg\,d\mu$).

3) If $\nu(D) = \int_D f\, d\mu$ on E, where $f(x)$ is real and μ-summable over E, and $f^+(x) = \max\{f(x), 0\}$, $f^-(x) = \min\{f(x), 0\}$, then $\nu^+(D) = \int_D f^+ d\mu$, $\nu^-(D) = \int_D f^- d\mu$ and $|\nu|(D) = \int_D |f|\, d\mu$.

4) If Γ is the semiring of all cells with integer endpoints on the straight line R_1, and μ is Lebesgue measure on Γ, then any μ-measurable set E is of the form $E = \Sigma A_n$, where $A_n \in \Gamma$.

5) If μ and $\bar{\mu}$ are σ-finite measures on the semirings Γ and $\bar{\Gamma}$ of subsets of X, then μ and $\bar{\mu}$ generate the same σ-ring of measurable sets with the same measure if and only if $\mu^* = \bar{\mu}$ on $\bar{\Gamma}$ and $\bar{\mu}^* = \mu$ on Γ. The preceding example shows that $\bar{\mu}^* = \mu$ on Γ alone is not sufficient.

(We show that the condition is sufficient. If S is an arbitrary set and if $\varepsilon > 0$, there exist sets $B_n \in \bar{\Gamma}$ such that $S \subset \Sigma B_n$ and $\bar{\mu}^*(S) > \Sigma \bar{\mu}(B_n) - \varepsilon/2 = \Sigma \mu^*(B_n) - \varepsilon/2$. Hence, there exist sets $A_{nj} \in \Gamma$ such that $S \subset \Sigma\Sigma A_{nj}$ and $\bar{\mu}^*(S) > \Sigma\Sigma \mu(A_{nj}) - \varepsilon$. This implies $\bar{\mu}^*(S) \geqslant \mu^*(S)$. Similarly $\mu^*(S) \geqslant \bar{\mu}^*(S)$).

6) If (r, φ) are polar coordinates in Euclidean space R_2, and $\bar{\mu}$ is Lebesgue measure on the semiring $\bar{\Gamma}$ of all ringsectors A, defined by $0 \leqslant r_1 \leqslant r < r_2 < \infty$, $\varphi_1 \leqslant \varphi < \varphi_2$ $(\varphi_2 - \varphi_1 \leqslant 2\pi)$, then $\bar{\mu}$ generates the σ-ring of all Lebesgue measurable sets in R_2 with Lebesgue measure.

7) If $\bar{\Gamma}$ is the semiring of the preceding example, and the measure $\pi(A)$ on $\bar{\Gamma}$ is defined by $\pi(A) = (r_2 - r_1)(\varphi_2 - \varphi_1)$, then every π-measurable set is Lebesgue measurable, and conversely. Moreover, $m(E) = \int_E r\, d\pi = \int_E r\, dr\, d\varphi$ for any measurable set E.

(We may restrict ourselves to sets E contained in a ring $0 < a \leqslant r < b < \infty$, since the whole space R_2 is the sum of the origin and a sequence of such rings. The relation $m(E) = \int_E r\, d\pi$ holds if $E \in \bar{\Gamma}$, hence also if E is a σ-set, and also if E is the limit of a descending sequence of σ-sets. It remains only to prove that $\pi(E) = 0$ implies $m(E) = 0$, and conversely. This is readily derived from $a \leqslant m(E)/\pi(E) \leqslant b$, holding for any σ-set E).

8) If $f(x, y)$ is Lebesgue integrable over the set $E \subset R_2$, then $rf(x, y)$ is π-summable over E, and $\int_E f\, dx\, dy = \int_E fr\, d\pi = \int_E fr\, dr\, d\varphi$.

(Follows by combining the result of the preceding example with that of Example 2).

CHAPTER 5

THE LEBESGUE SPACES L_p AND THE ORLICZ SPACES L_Φ

§ 1. Definition of the Lebesgue Space L_p. Hölder's, Schwarz's and Minkowski's Inequalities

If μ is a σ-finite measure on the set X, and if $f(x)$ is a μ-measurable function on the μ-measurable set Δ, assuming real or complex values, then $f(x)$ is said to belong to the *Lebesgue functionspace* $L_p(\Delta, \mu)$, where $1 \leqslant p < \infty$, whenever $|f(x)|^p$ is μ-summable over Δ. We shall write $f \in L_p(\Delta, \mu)$, or shortly $f \in L_p$ if it is not necessary to specify the set Δ and the measure μ. The space L_1 is denoted simply by L. If $f(x) \in L_p$ $(1 \leqslant p < \infty)$, we shall write $\| f \|_p = (\int_\Delta |f|^p d\mu)^{1/p}$. The μ-measurable function $f(x)$, defined on Δ, is said to belong to the *Lebesgue functionspace* $L_\infty(\Delta, \mu)$ whenever there exists a finite non-negative number M such that $|f(x)| \leqslant M$ for almost every $x \in \Delta$. The lower bound A of all numbers M having this property is at the same time the smallest number having this property, as may be seen by observing that $\Delta(|f| > A) = \sum_{n=1}^\infty \Delta(|f| > A + n^{-1})$ is of measure zero. If $f(x) \in L_\infty$, we shall write $\| f \|_\infty = A$.

The spaces $L_p(1 \leqslant p \leqslant \infty)$ are linear, by which we mean that they are closed under addition and multiplication by complex numbers. Indeed, it is evident that if $f \in L_p$ and α is complex, then $\alpha f \in L_p$. Furthermore, if $f \in L_\infty$ and $g \in L_\infty$, then $f + g \in L_\infty$. Finally, if $f \in L_p$, $g \in L_p$, $1 \leqslant p < \infty$, we consider the sets $\Delta_1 = \Delta(|f| \geqslant |g|)$ and $\Delta_2 = \Delta(|f| < |g|)$. For $x \in \Delta_1$ we have $|f + g|^p \leqslant (|f| + |g|)^p \leqslant (2|f|)^p = 2^p |f|^p$, and for $x \in \Delta_2$ in the same way $|f + g|^p < 2^p |g|^p$; hence $|f + g|^p \leqslant 2^p(|f|^p + |g|^p)$ on Δ, which implies $f + g \in L_p$.

The spaces $L_p(1 \leqslant p \leqslant \infty)$ and $L_q(1 \leqslant q \leqslant \infty)$ are called complementary whenever $1/p + 1/q = 1$. The spaces L and L_∞ are therefore complementary, and L_2 is complementary to itself.

Theorem 1 (*Hölder's inequality*). *If* $1 \leqslant p \leqslant \infty$, $1/p+1/q=1$, $f(x) \in L_p$

and $g(x) \in L_q$, *then* $f(x)g(x) \in L$, *and*

$$|\int_\Delta fg\, d\mu| \leqslant \int_\Delta |fg|\, d\mu \leqslant \| f \|_p . \| g \|_q.$$

Proof. For $p = 1$ and $p = \infty$ the proof is trivial. Let therefore $1 < p < \infty$, hence $q = p/(p-1)$. On $\Delta' = \Delta(|g| \leqslant |f|^{p-1})$ we have $|fg| \leqslant |f|^p$, so that fg is summable over Δ'. On the complementary set $\Delta - \Delta'$ we have $|f| < |g|^{1/(p-1)}$, hence $|fg| < |g|^{p/(p-1)} = |g|^q$, so that fg is summable over $\Delta - \Delta'$ as well. Consequently $fg \in L$.

If one at least of the numbers $\| f \|_p$ and $\| g \|_q$ vanishes, then $f(x) = 0$ or $g(x) = 0$ almost everywhere on Δ, so that in this case $0 = \int_\Delta |fg|\, d\mu = \| f \|_p . \| g \|_q$. It remains to consider the case that $\| f \|_p$ and $\| g \|_q$ do not vanish. Integrating the inequality $t^{m-1} < 1 (t > 1,\ 0 < m < 1)$ over $[1, y]$, we find

$$y^m - 1 < m(y-1) \quad (y > 1,\ 0 < m < 1),$$

so that, writing $y = a/b$ $(a > b > 0)$, $m = 1/p$, and multiplying by b, we obtain $a^{1/p}b^{1-1/p} - b < (a-b)/p$ or $a^{1/p}b^{1/q} < b + (a-b)/p = a/p + b/q$. Since this relation is symmetrical in a and b, it holds for any pair of unequal non-negative numbers a and b. For $a = b \geqslant 0$ it becomes an equality. Taking now $a = |f(x)|^p/\| f \|_p^p$ and $b = |g(x)|^q/\| g \|_q^q$, we derive from it

$$\frac{|fg|}{\| f \|_p . \| g \|_q} \leqslant \frac{|f|^p}{p \| f \|_p^p} + \frac{|g|^q}{q \| g \|_q^q},$$

hence, integrating over Δ,

$$\frac{1}{\| f \|_p . \| g \|_q} \int_\Delta |fg|\, d\mu \leqslant \frac{1}{p} . \frac{\| f \|_p^p}{\| f \|_p^p} + \frac{1}{q} . \frac{\| g \|_q^q}{\| g \|_q^q} = \frac{1}{p} + \frac{1}{q} = 1.$$

This shows that

$$|\int_\Delta fg\, d\mu| \leqslant \int_\Delta |fg|\, d\mu \leqslant \| f \|_p . \| g \|_q.$$

Corollary (*Schwarz's inequality*). *If* $f(x) \in L_2$ *and* $g(x) \in L_2$, *then* $f(x)g(x) \in L$, *and*

$$|\int_\Delta fg\, d\mu| \leqslant \int_\Delta |fg|\, d\mu \leqslant \| f \|_2 . \| g \|_2.$$

Theorem 2. *If* $f(x) \in L_p (1 \leqslant p < \infty)$, *and* L_q *is the complementary space, then*

$$\| f \|_p = \max |\int_\Delta fg\, d\mu| = \max \int_\Delta |fg|\, d\mu$$

for all $g \in L_q$ *satisfying* $\| g \|_q \leqslant 1$.

If $f(x) \in L_\infty$, *then*

$$\| f \|_\infty = \textit{upper bound } |\int_\Delta fg\, d\mu| = \textit{upper bound } \int_\Delta |fg|\, d\mu$$

for all $g \in L$ *satisfying* $\| g \|_1 \leqslant 1$.

Proof. By Hölder's inequality we see that $|\int_\Delta fg\, d\mu| \leqslant \int_\Delta |fg|\, d\mu \leqslant \| f \|_p$ for $\| g \|_q \leqslant 1$, and this holds for $1 \leqslant p < \infty$ as well as for $p = \infty$. Hence, the maximum or upper bound in question does not surpass $\| f \|_p$. In order to prove that it equals $\| f \|_p$ we first define, for any complex number α, the number sgn α by $\operatorname{sgn} \alpha = \alpha/|\alpha|$ for $0 < |\alpha| < \infty$ and $\operatorname{sgn} \alpha = 1$ for $\alpha = 0$ or $|\alpha| = \infty$, so that $\alpha/\operatorname{sgn} \alpha = |\alpha|$ for finite α. It follows that $h(x) = 1/\operatorname{sgn} f(x)$ belongs to L_∞, and $\| h \|_\infty = 1$. Hence, for $p = 1$, taking $g(x) = h(x)$, we have $|\int_\Delta fg\, d\mu| = \int_\Delta |f|\, d\mu = \| f \|_1$ (and therefore also $\int_\Delta |fg|\, d\mu = \| f \|_1$), so that $\| f \|_1$ is the desired maximum. For $1 < p < \infty$, the function $k(x) = |f(x)|^{p-1}/\operatorname{sgn} f(x)$ belongs to L_q since $|k|^q = |k|^{p/(p-1)} = |f|^p$, and $\| k \|_q^q = \| f \|_p^p$ or $\| k \|_q = \| f \|_p^{p/q}$. Hence $g(x) = k(x)/\| f \|_p^{p/q}$ also belongs to L_q, and $\| g \|_q = 1$. Furthermore $|\int_\Delta fg\, d\mu| = \int_\Delta |f|^p\, d\mu/\| f \|_p^{p/q} = \| f \|_p^{p-p/q} = \| f \|_p$, which shows that $\| f \|_p$ is the desired maximum.

Finally, if $f(x) \in L_\infty$ and $\varepsilon > 0$ is arbitrary, the set $\Delta(|f| > \| f \|_\infty - \varepsilon)$ contains a subset E of finite positive measure, so that, if we define $g(x) = [\mu(E) \operatorname{sgn} f(x)]^{-1}$ on E and $g(x) = 0$ elsewhere on Δ, the function $g(x)$ belongs to L and $\| g \|_1 = 1$. Furthermore $|\int_\Delta fg\, d\mu| = \int_\Delta |f|\, d\mu/\mu(E) \geqslant \| f \|_\infty - \varepsilon$, which is equivalent to the announced result.

Theorem 3 (*Minkowski's inequality*). *If* $1 \leqslant p \leqslant \infty$, $f(x) \in L_p$ *and* $g(x) \in L_p$, *then*

$$\| f + g \|_p \leqslant \| f \|_p + \| g \|_p.$$

Proof. For $p = 1$ and $p = \infty$ the proof is trivial. The same is true if $\| f + g \|_p = 0$. We may assume therefore that $\| f + g \|_p \neq 0$ and $1 < p < \infty$, hence $1/p + 1/q = 1$ for $q = p/(p-1)$.

Then

$$\int_\Delta |f + g|^p\, d\mu \leqslant \int_\Delta |f| . |f + g|^{p-1}\, d\mu + \int_\Delta |g| . |f + g|^{p-1}\, d\mu \leqslant$$

$$\| f \|_p \{\int_\Delta |f + g|^p\, d\mu\}^{1/q} + \| g \|_p \{\int_\Delta |f + g|^p\, d\mu\}^{1/q}$$

by Hölder's inequality. Dividing by $\{\int_\Delta |f + g|^p\, d\mu\}^{1/q}$, the result follows.

§ 2. The Completeness of the Spaces L_p

In the present paragraph we shall prove for spaces L_p the analogue of Cauchy's Theorem for real numbers, asserting that any sequence

a_n of real numbers, satisfying $\lim | a_n - a_m | = 0$ as $m, n \to \infty$, converges to a real number a.

Theorem 1. *The spaces $L_p (1 \leqslant p \leqslant \infty)$ are complete, that is, if $f_n(x) \in L_p$ $(n = 1, 2, \ldots)$ and $\lim \| f_n - f_m \|_p = 0$ as $m, n \to \infty$, there exists a function $f(x) \in L_p$ such that $\lim \| f_n - f \|_p = 0$. This function $f(x)$ is uniquely determined apart from sets of measure zero.*

Proof. We consider first the case that $p = \infty$. There exists a fixed set $E \subset \Delta$ of measure zero such that $| f_n(x) - f_m(x) | \leqslant \| f_n - f_m \|_\infty$ for all $x \in \Delta - E$ and for all m, n simultaneously. Hence, if $\varepsilon > 0$ is arbitrary, we have by hypothesis $| f_n(x) - f_m(x) | < \varepsilon$ for $m, n \geqslant N(\varepsilon)$ and all $x \in \Delta - E$. It follows that on $\Delta - E$ the function $f(x) = \lim f_n(x)$ exists and that $| f(x) | \leqslant | f_N(x) | + \varepsilon$ on this set. Defining $f(x) = 0$ on E, we have therefore $f \in L_\infty$. Moreover, $| f_n(x) - f(x) | \leqslant \varepsilon$ on $\Delta - E$ for $n \geqslant N(\varepsilon)$, so that $\lim \| f_n - f \|_\infty = 0$.

Let now $1 \leqslant p < \infty$. Since by hypothesis $\lim \| f_n - f_m \|_p = 0$, there exists a sequence of indices n_k such that $\Sigma_{k=1}^\infty \| f_{n_{k+1}} - f_{n_k} \|_p < \infty$ (one may take n_1 to be the smallest integer n such that $\| f_n - f_m \|_p < 1$ for $m > n$, n_2 the smallest integer $n > n_1$ such that $\| f_n - f_m \| < 1/2$ for $m > n$, n_3 the smallest integer $n > n_2$ such that $\| f_n - f_m \| < 1/2^2$ for $m > n$, and so on). Then, since for every set $E \subset \Delta$ of finite measure $\int_E | f_{n_{k+1}} - f_{n_k} | \, d\mu \leqslant \| f_{n_{k+1}} - f_{n_k} \|_p \, (\int_E d\mu)^{1/q}$, we see that $\Sigma_{k=1}^\infty \int_E | f_{n_{k+1}} - f_{n_k} | \, d\mu < \infty$ as well, and this implies, in virtue of Ch. 3, § 3, Th. 9, Corollary, that the partial sums $f_{n_k}(x)$ of the series $f_{n_1}(x) + \Sigma_{k=1}^\infty [f_{n_{k+1}}(x) - f_{n_k}(x)]$ are tending almost everywhere on E to a measurable limit $f(x)$. Since Δ may be expressed in the form ΣE_n, where each E_n is of finite measure, we have therefore $f(x) = \lim f_{n_k}(x)$ almost everywhere on Δ. It is easily seen by Minkowski's inequality that $\lim \| f_n - f_m \|_p = 0$ implies the boundedness of the sequence $\| f_n \|_p$; Fatou's Theorem shows then that $f \in L_p$ since $\| f \|_p \leqslant \lim\inf \| f_{n_k} \|_p$. Furthermore, once again by Fatou's Theorem, $\| f_{n_k} - f \|_p \leqslant \lim\inf_{l \to \infty} \| f_{n_k} - f_{n_l} \|_p$ becomes arbitrarily small for k sufficiently large; hence $\lim \| f_{n_k} - f \|_p = 0$. Finally, from $\| f_n - f \|_p \leqslant \| f_n - f_{n_k} \|_p + \| f_{n_k} - f \|_p$, we derive $\lim \| f_n - f \|_p = 0$.

In order to prove that $f(x)$ is uniquely determined apart from sets of measure zero, let us suppose that $\lim \| f_n - f \|_p = \lim \| f_n - g \|_p = 0$, where $1 \leqslant p \leqslant \infty$. Then $\| f - g \|_p = 0$, since $\| f - g \|_p \leqslant \| f - f_n \|_p + \| f_n - g \|_p$ for every value of n. This shows that $f(x) = g(x)$ almost everywhere on Δ.

Definition. *If the sequence of functions $f_n(x) \in L_p$ $(1 \leqslant p \leqslant \infty)$ has the property that there exists a function $f(x) \in L_p$ such that $\lim \| f_n - f \|_p = 0$, it is said that the sequence $f_n(x)$ converges on Δ in mean with index p to $f(x)$.*

The theorem which has just been proved asserts therefore that if $\lim \| f_n - f_m \|_p = 0$ as $m, n \to \infty$, then $f_n(x)$ converges on Δ in mean with index p to a function $f(x) \in L_p$. Furthermore, the proof shows the existence of a subsequence $f_{n_k}(x)$, converging almost everywhere on Δ in the ordinary sense to $f(x)$.

§ 3. The Separability of the Spaces L_p

The measure μ will be called *separable* whenever there exists a finite or enumerable subcollection Z of μ-measurable sets of finite measure having the property that if E is an arbitrary μ-measurable set of finite measure, there exists to each $\varepsilon > 0$ a set $F \in Z$ such that $\mu(E - F) + \mu(F - E) < \varepsilon$.

It is sufficient for the separability of μ that the semiring Γ, on which μ was originally defined, contains a finite or enumerable number of sets. In this case we may take for Z the collection of all finite sums of sets of finite measure from Γ. This collection Z, which is evidently finite or enumerable, has the required property. Indeed, if E is an arbitrary set of finite measure, and if $\varepsilon > 0$, there exists a σ-set $S = \Sigma A_n$ such that $E \subset S$ and $\mu(S - E) < \varepsilon/2$. Furthermore, if $F = \Sigma_1^k A_n$, then $F \in Z$ and $\mu(S - F) < \varepsilon/2$ for k sufficiently large. Hence $\mu(F - E) \leqslant \mu(S - E) < \varepsilon/2$ and $\mu(E - F) \leqslant \mu(S - F) < \varepsilon/2$.

It follows that Lebesgue measure in Euclidean space R_m is separable since, instead of starting from the semiring of all cells in R_m, we may just as well take the enumerable semiring of all rational cells (cells with rational endpoints) as our point of departure.

If μ is a Stieltjes measure on the straight line R_1 relative to the function $g(x)$ (cf. Ch. 2, § 7), then μ is separable. We first prove that the number of points where $g(x)$ is not continuous is at most enumerable (we recall that $g(x)$ is assumed to be right continuous). Evidently the set E_0 of points in the finite interval $a < x \leqslant b$, at which $g(x) - g(x-) > 1$, is finite. The same holds for the set E_n $(n = 1, 2, \ldots)$ of points at which $1/(n+1) < g(x) - g(x-) \leqslant 1/n$, so that the set $E = \Sigma_0^\infty E_n$ in $a < x \leqslant b$, at which $g(x)$ is not continuous, is at most enumerable. The same is then true in $-\infty < x < \infty$. Choosing now the sequence S of real numbers in such a way that S is dense in R_1 and contains all points of discontinuity of $g(x)$, the semiring Γ of all cells with endpoints in S is enumerable, and this semiring may be used to generate the σ-ring of all μ-measurable sets.

If Z is the finite or enumerable collection, introduced above, we shall call any finite linear combination of characteristic functions c_F of sets $F \in Z$ with finite rational complex coefficients (the real and imaginary parts of the coefficients are rational therefore) a *rational simple function* on Z. The collection of all rational simple functions on Z is evidently enumerable, and every rational simple function on Z belongs to $L_p(X, \mu)$ for $1 \leqslant p \leqslant \infty$, and therefore also to $L_p(\Delta, \mu)$ for any measurable set Δ.

Theorem 1. *If the measure μ is separable, the spaces $L_p(\Delta, \mu)$ $(1 \leqslant p < \infty)$ are separable, by which we mean that L_p contains an enumerable subcollection having the property that, if $f(x) \in L_p$ is arbitrary, there exists to each $\varepsilon > 0$ a function $g(x)$ belonging to this subcollection such that $\| f - g \|_p < \varepsilon$.*

Proof. We shall prove that the collection of all rational simple functions on Z has the required property. Let, for this purpose, $f(x) \in L_p$ and $\varepsilon > 0$ be given. Since $\Delta = \Sigma\, \Delta_i$, where each Δ_i is of finite measure, the integral of $| f |^p$ over Δ is the limit of the integral over $S_n = \Sigma_1^n\, \Delta_i$, that is, the integral over $\Delta - S_n$ tends to zero. Hence, there exists a set $\Delta_1 \subset \Delta$ of finite measure ($\Delta_1 = S_n$ for a suitable n) such that if we define $f_1 = f$ on Δ_1 and $f_1 = 0$ elsewhere, then $\| f - f_1 \|_p < \varepsilon/3$.

We next observe that $f_1 = (g_1 - g_2) + i(h_1 - h_2)$, where g_1, g_2, h_1 and h_2 are non-negative, belonging to L_p, and vanishing outside Δ_1. Considering for example g_1, there exists a non-decreasing sequence of simple functions $g^{(n)}(x)$, non-negative and vanishing outside Δ_1, assuming only finite rational values and such that $g_1(x) = \lim g^{(n)}(x)$. Consequently, since $| g_1 - g^{(n)} |^p \leqslant | g_1 |^p$ and $\lim | g_1 - g^{(n)} |^p = 0$ almost everywhere on Δ_1, we have $\lim \int_\Delta | g_1 - g^{(n)} |^p \, d\mu = 0$. It follows that $\| g_1 - g^{(n)} \|_p < \varepsilon/12$ for sufficiently large n. Subjecting g_2, h_1 and h_2 to the same process, we obtain by linear combination a simple function $f_2(x)$, vanishing outside Δ_1 and assuming only finite rational complex values, such that $\| f_1 - f_2 \|_p < \varepsilon/3$. This function $f_2(x)$ may be written in the form $f_2(x) = \Sigma_1^k\, \alpha_i c_{E_i}(x)$, where all α_i are rational, $E_i E_j = 0$ $(i \neq j)$ and $\Sigma\, E_i = \Delta_1$.

To each E_i there exists a set $F_i \in Z$ such that $\mu(E_i - F_i) + \mu(F_i - E_i) < (\varepsilon/3k \mid \alpha_i \mid)^p$, hence $\| c_{E_i} - c_{F_i} \|_p \leqslant \{\mu(E_i - F_i) + \mu(F_i - E_i)\}^{1/p} < \varepsilon/3k \mid \alpha_i \mid$. Consequently, writing $f_3(x) = \Sigma_1^k\, \alpha_i c_{F_i}(x)$, we have $\| f_2 - f_3 \|_p$

$\leqslant \Sigma_1^k | \alpha_i | . \| c_{E_i} - c_{F_i} \|_p < \varepsilon/3$. Observing that $f_3(x)$ is a rational simple function on Z, and that

$$\| f - f_3 \|_p \leqslant \| f - f_1 \|_p + \| f_1 - f_2 \|_p + \| f_2 - f_3 \|_p < \varepsilon,$$

our proof is complete.

§ 4. Young's Inequality

Let $v = \varphi(u)$, for $u \geqslant 0$, be a non-decreasing function of u such that $\varphi(0) = 0$. Then, for every $u > 0$, the number $\varphi(u -) = \lim_{h\to 0,\, h>0} \varphi(u - h)$ exists; the same is true, for every $u \geqslant 0$, of $\varphi(u +) = \lim_{h\to 0,\, h>0} \varphi(u + h)$, and $\varphi(u -) \leqslant \varphi(u) \leqslant \varphi(u +)$, if we define $\varphi(0 -) = \varphi(0) = 0$. At those values of u where $\varphi(u -) = \varphi(u +)$ the function $\varphi(u)$ is continuous; at those values of u where $\varphi(u -) < \varphi(u +)$ we say that $\varphi(u)$ has a jump $j = \varphi(u +) - \varphi(u -)$. If $0 < u_0 < \infty$, the set E_0 of values $u \leqslant u_0$ at which $\varphi(u)$ has a jump j for which $j > 1$ is finite. The same holds for the set E_n $(n = 1, 2, \ldots)$ of values $u \leqslant u_0$ at which $\varphi(u)$ has a jump the value j of which satisfies $1/(n + 1) < j \leqslant 1/n$. Hence, the set $E = \Sigma_0^\infty E_n$ of values $u \leqslant u_0$ at which $\varphi(u)$ has a jump is at most enumerable. This result may be extended immediately to the case that $u_0 = \infty$.

We shall assume now that $\varphi(u) = \varphi(u -)$ for every $u \geqslant 0$, which is equivalent to assuming that $\varphi(u)$ is left continuous. Then $\varphi(u)$ is Lebesgue measurable on $[0, \infty)$, since the set on which $\varphi(u) \leqslant a$ is empty for $a < 0$, and a closed interval $[0, b]$ or the whole set $[0, \infty)$ for $a \geqslant 0$. By $u = \psi(v)$ the inverse function of $\varphi(u)$ is defined, on the understanding that if $\varphi(u)$ makes a jump at $u = a$, then $\psi(v) = a$ for $\varphi(a -) < v \leqslant \varphi(a +)$, while, if $\varphi(u) = c$ for $a < u \leqslant b$, but $\varphi(u) < c$ for $u < a$, then $\psi(c) = a$. Furthermore $\psi(0) = 0$, and, if $\lim_{u\to\infty} \varphi(u) = l$ is finite, then $\psi(v) = +\infty$ for $v > l$. With these conventions $u = \psi(v)$ is evidently non-decreasing for $v \geqslant 0$, and left continuous for those values of v at which $\psi(v)$ is finite. It follows that $\psi(v)$ is also Lebesgue measurable on $[0, \infty)$.

It is clear from the definitions above that $v = \varphi(u)$ implies $u \geqslant \psi(v) = \psi(v -)$, and that, similarly, $u = \psi(v)$ implies $v \geqslant \varphi(u) = \varphi(u -)$ for finite u.

Lemma α. *If $v < \varphi(u)$ for a point (u, v) in the quadrant $u \geqslant 0$, $v \geqslant 0$, then $u > \psi(v)$; if $v > \varphi(u)$, then $u \leqslant \psi(v)$.*

Proof. The relation $v < \varphi(u)$ implies the existence of a positive number p such that $v + p = \varphi(u)$, hence $u \geqslant \psi(v + p) \geqslant \psi(v)$. But $u = \psi(v)$ is impossible, for this would imply $v \geqslant \varphi(u)$.

Let now $v > \varphi(u)$, so that there exists a positive number p such that $v - p = \varphi(u)$. This implies $u \leqslant \psi(t)$ for all $t > v - p$, hence in particular $u \leqslant \psi(v)$.

Lemma β. *If E_1 is the positive ordinate set of $\varphi(u)$, E_2 is the positive ordinate set of $\psi(v)$, and E_3 is the set of all points (u, v) at which one at least of the relations $v = \varphi(u)$, $u = \psi(v)$ holds, then these sets are Lebesgue measurable, no two of them have common points, their sum is the quadrant $u \geqslant 0$, $v \geqslant 0$, and the (twodimensional) Lebesgue measure of E_3 is zero.*

Proof. It follows from Lemma α that the quadrant $u \geqslant 0$, $v \geqslant 0$ may be divided into the set E_1 on which $v < \varphi(u)$, $u > \psi(v)$, the set E_3' on which $v = \varphi(u)$, the set E_3'' on which $v > \varphi(u)$, $u = \psi(v)$, and the set E_2 on which $v > \varphi(u)$, $u < \psi(v)$. Writing $E_3 = E_3' + E_3''$, we have the desired decomposition. The sets E_1 and E_2, being ordinate sets of measurable functions, are measurable, and E_3, being the sum of the graphs of $\varphi(u)$ and $\psi(v)$, is of measure zero.

Definition. *If the non-decreasing functions $v = \varphi(u)$ and $u = \psi(v)$, inverse to each other, satisfy the above conditions, then the functions $\Phi(u)$ and $\Psi(v)$, defined for $u \geqslant 0$, $v \geqslant 0$ by the Lebesgue integrals*

$$\Phi(u) = \int_0^u \varphi(\bar{u})d\bar{u}, \quad \Psi(v) = \int_0^v \psi(\bar{v})d\bar{v},$$

are termed complementary in the sense of Young.

Theorem 1 *(Young's inequality). If the functions $\Phi(u)$ and $\Psi(v)$ are complementary in the sense of Young, then*

$$uv \leqslant \Phi(u) + \Psi(v)$$

for arbitrary $u \geqslant 0$, $v \geqslant 0$, with equality if and only if one at least of the relations $v = \varphi(u)$, $u = \psi(v)$ is satisfied.

Proof. Let $u_0 \geqslant 0$, $v_0 \geqslant 0$ be given, denote the interval $[0, u_0; 0, v_0]$ by Δ, and the twodimensional measure of a measurable set E by $m(E)$. Then, using the same notations as above, we have

$$u_0 v_0 = m(\Delta) = m(\Delta . E_1) + m(\Delta . E_2) =$$
$$\int_\Delta d(u, v) du\, dv + \int_\Delta e(u, v) du\, dv,$$

where $d(u, v)$ and $e(u, v)$ are the characteristic functions of $\Delta . E_1$ and $\Delta . E_2$ respectively. Now, by Fubini's Theorem,

$$\int_\Delta d(u, v) du\, dv = \int_0^{u_0} du \int_0^{m(u)} dv,$$

where $m(u) = \min [v_0, \varphi(u)]$, hence

$$\int_\Delta d(u, v)du\, dv \leqslant \int_0^{u_0} du \int_0^{\varphi(u)} dv = \int_0^{u_0} \varphi(u)du = \Phi(u_0),$$

with equality if and only if $v_0 \geqslant \varphi(u_0)$. In the same way

$$\int_\Delta e(u, v)du\, dv \leqslant \Psi(v_0),$$

with equality if and only if $u_0 \geqslant \psi(v_0)$. Hence

$$u_0 v_0 \leqslant \Phi(u_0) + \Psi(v_0),$$

with equality if and only if $v_0 \geqslant \varphi(u_0)$ and $u_0 \geqslant \psi(v_0)$. This is equivalent to the condition that (u_0, v_0) is a point of the set E_3 ($v_0 > \varphi(u_0)$ and $u_0 > \psi(v_0)$ being incompatible by Lemma α). Hence, we have equality if and only if one at least of the relations $v = \varphi(u)$, $u = \psi(v)$ is satisfied.

§ 5. Definition and Some Properties of the Orlicz Space L_Φ

We shall assume that $\Phi(u)$ and $\Psi(v)$ are complementary in the sense of Young, and that $\Phi(u)$ does not vanish identically (that is, $\varphi(u)$ does not vanish identically). Furthermore, we assume μ to be a σ-finite measure on the set X. Then, if $f(x)$ is a μ-measurable function, assuming real or complex values on the μ-measurable set Δ, the function $\varphi \mid f(x) \mid$ is also μ-measurable on Δ, since $\Delta(\varphi \mid f \mid \leqslant a)$ is empty for $a < 0$, and equal to a set $\Delta(\mid f \mid \leqslant b)$ or to $\Delta(\mid f \mid < \infty)$ for any $a \geqslant 0$. In the same way it is seen that $\psi \mid f(x) \mid$, $\Phi \mid f(x) \mid$ and $\Psi \mid f(x) \mid$ are measurable on Δ.

Definition. *By the class $L_\Phi^* = L_\Phi^*(\Delta, \mu)$ we shall mean the collection of all complex functions $f(x)$, μ-measurable on Δ, for which $\Phi \mid f(x) \mid$ is μ-summable over Δ. The class L_Ψ^* is defined similarly.*

If $\Phi(u) = cu^p$ (c a positive constant, $1 \leqslant p < \infty$), the class L_Φ^* consists of the same functions as the Lebesgue space L_p. For $p > 1$ we have $\Psi(v) = c_1 v^q$, where $1/p + 1/q = 1$, so that the complementary class L_Ψ^* consists of the same functions as L_q. For $p = 1$ it is readily seen that $\Psi(v) = 0$ for $0 \leqslant v \leqslant c$, and $\Psi(v) = +\infty$ for $v > c$, so that L_Ψ^* consists of all functions $f(x)$, μ-measurable on Δ, and satisfying $\mid f(x) \mid \leqslant c$ almost everywhere on Δ.

The classes L_Φ^* and L_Ψ^* are, as a rule, not linear, that is, the summability of $\Phi \mid f_1(x) \mid$ and $\Phi \mid f_2(x) \mid$ does not necessarily imply the summability of $\Phi \mid \alpha f_1(x) + \beta f_2(x) \mid$. If, to mention an example, $\Phi(u) = e^u - 1$ and $\Delta = [0, 1]$, the function $\Phi \mid f(x) \mid$, where $f(x) = \log x^{-1/2}$, is Lebesgue integrable over Δ, but $\Phi \mid 2f(x) \mid$ is not. Also, if $\Phi(u) = u$, the class L^*_Ψ is evidently not linear. In order to remedy this defect, we shall define linear classes, called Orlicz spaces L_Φ and L_Ψ, containing L^*_Φ and L^*_Ψ as subclasses. For this purpose we introduce, if $f(x)$ is an arbitrary measurable function on Δ, the numbers $\| f \|_\Phi$ and $\| f \|_\Psi$ by

$$\| f \|_\Phi = \text{upper bound} \int_\Delta | fg | \, d\mu \text{ for } \int_\Delta \Psi | g | \, d\mu \leqslant 1,$$

$$\| f \|_\Psi = \text{upper bound} \int_\Delta | fg | \, d\mu \text{ for } \int_\Delta \Phi | g | \, d\mu \leqslant 1.$$

Definition. *The Orlicz space $L_\Phi = L_\Phi(\Delta, \mu)$ is the collection of all complex functions $f(x)$, μ-measurable on Δ, for which $\| f \|_\Phi < \infty$. Similarly, the Orlicz space L_Ψ is the collection of all μ-measurable functions $f(x)$ satisfying $\| f \|_\Psi < \infty$.*

Theorem 1. *The space L_Φ is linear and contains L^*_Φ as a subclass. For any $f \in L^*_\Phi$ we have $\| f \|_\Phi \leqslant \int_\Delta \Phi | f | \, d\mu + 1$. Furthermore, $\| f \|_\Phi = 0$ if and only if $f(x) = 0$ almost everywhere on Δ. Finally, if $f \in L_\Phi$, then $\| f \|_\Phi =$ upper bound $| \int_\Delta fg \, d\mu |$ for $\int_\Delta \Psi | g | \, d\mu \leqslant 1$. A similar theorem holds for L_Ψ.*

Proof. The linearity of L_Φ is evident. If f and g are measurable, we have $\int_\Delta | fg | \, d\mu \leqslant \int_\Delta \Phi | f | \, d\mu + \int_\Delta \Psi | g | \, d\mu$ by Young's inequality, hence $\int_\Delta | fg | \, d\mu \leqslant \int_\Delta \Phi | f | \, d\mu + 1$, provided $\int_\Delta \Psi | g | \, d\mu \leqslant 1$. This shows that $f \in L^*_\Phi$ implies $f \in L_\Phi$ and $\| f \|_\Phi \leqslant \int_\Delta \Phi | f | \, d\mu + 1$.

To prove that $\| f \|_\Phi = 0$ implies $f(x) = 0$ at almost every $x \in \Delta$ (the converse is trivial), we first recall that $\varphi(u)$ does not vanish identically, so that there exist positive numbers u_0, v_0 such that $v_0 = \varphi(u_0)$. This implies $u_0 \geqslant \psi(v_0)$, hence $\psi(v) \leqslant u_0$ for $v \leqslant v_0$. It follows that $\Psi(v) \leqslant u_0 v$ for $v \leqslant v_0$, and consequently $\lim_{v \to 0} \Psi(v) = 0$. If therefore $\Delta_1 \subset \Delta$ is of finite positive measure, there exists a positive number p such that $\Psi(p) \leqslant 1/\mu(\Delta_1)$. Taking now $g(x) = p$ on Δ_1 and $g(x) = 0$ elsewhere, we have $\int_\Delta \Psi | g | \, d\mu = \int_{\Delta_1} \Psi(p) \, d\mu \leqslant 1$, so that by hypothesis $f(x)g(x) = 0$ almost everywhere on Δ, and therefore $f(x) = 0$ almost everywhere on Δ_1. In virtue of the measure μ being σ-finite this implies $f(x) = 0$ almost everywhere on Δ.

The truth of our last statement follows from $\int_\Delta | fg | \, d\mu = | \int_\Delta fg_1 \, d\mu |$, where $g_1 = | g | / \operatorname{sgn} f$.

The proof for L_Ψ is similar.

Remark. Our proof also shows that if $f \in L_\Phi$ or $f \in L_\Psi$, then $| f(x) | < \infty$ almost everywhere on Δ.

Theorem 2. *If $f(x) \in L_\Phi$, there exists a constant $p > 0$ such that $pf(x) \in L_\Phi^*$. More precisely, if $f(x) \in L_\Phi$ and $f(x) \neq 0$ on a set of positive measure, then*

$$\int_\Delta \Phi[|f|/\|f\|_\Phi]d\mu \leqslant 1.$$

A similar theorem holds for any $g(x) \in L_\Psi$.

Proof. We shall prove first that $\Psi(qv) \geqslant q\Psi(v)$ for $q \geqslant 1$, $v \geqslant 0$. We may assume that $q > 1$, $v > 0$, and then

$$\Psi(qv) - \Psi(v) = \int_v^{qv} \psi(\bar{v})d\bar{v} \geqslant (q-1)v\,\psi(v) =$$

$$(q-1)\int_0^v \psi(v)d\bar{v} \geqslant (q-1)\int_0^v \psi(\bar{v})d\bar{v} = (q-1)\Psi(v),$$

hence $\Psi(qv) \geqslant q\Psi(v)$ or $\Psi(v) \leqslant \Psi(qv)/q$.

Let us assume now that $f \in L_\Phi$ and $g \in L_\Psi^*$. Then

$$\int_\Delta |fg|\,d\mu \leqslant \|f\|_\Phi \text{ provided } \rho(g) = \int_\Delta \Psi|g|\,d\mu \leqslant 1.$$

If $1 < \rho(g) < \infty$, we observe that $\Psi|g/\rho(g)| \leqslant \Psi|g|/\rho(g)$ by what we have just proved, so that $\int_\Delta \Psi|g/\rho(g)|\,d\mu \leqslant 1$, hence

$$\int_\Delta |fg/\rho(g)|\,d\mu \leqslant \|f\|_\Phi \text{ or } \int_\Delta |fg|\,d\mu \leqslant \|f\|_\Phi \cdot \rho(g).$$

We may draw, therefore, the inference that in any case

$$\int_\Delta |fg|\,d\mu \leqslant \|f\|_\Phi \cdot \rho'(g), \text{ where } \rho'(g) = \max\,[\rho(g),1].$$

In the case that $f(x)$ is bounded and vanishing outside a set $\Delta_1 \subset \Delta$ of finite measure, the bounded functions $\Phi[|f|/\|f\|_\Phi]$ and $\Psi[\varphi\{|f|/\|f\|_\Phi\}]$ are summable over Δ, hence, Young's inequality becoming an equality for $g = \varphi\{|f|/\|f\|_\Phi\}$,

$$\rho'(g) \geqslant \int_\Delta \left| \frac{f}{\|f\|_\Phi} g \right| d\mu = \int_\Delta \Phi\left[\frac{|f|}{\|f\|_\Phi}\right] d\mu + \rho(g).$$

If $\rho(g) = \rho'(g)$, we have $\int_\Delta \Phi[|f|/\|f\|_\Phi]d\mu = 0$; if $\rho(g) < \rho'(g)$, we have $\rho'(g) = 1$, so that $\int_\Delta \Phi[|f|/\|f\|_\Phi]d\mu \leqslant 1$. This is the desired result for this particular case.

In the general case we consider Δ as the limit of an ascending sequence of sets Δ_n of finite measure, and we write $f_n(x) = 0$ outside Δ_n, $f_n(x) = f(x)$ on $\Delta_n(|f| \leqslant n)$ and $f_n(x) = n$ on $\Delta_n(|f| > n)$. Then the non-decreasing sequence of functions $|f_n(x)|$ converges to $|f(x)|$ on Δ, and $\int_\Delta \Phi[|f_n|/\|f_n\|_\Phi]d\mu \leqslant 1$ by what has already been proved. Furthermore, since $\int_\Delta |f_n g|\,d\mu \leqslant \int_\Delta |fg|\,d\mu$, we have $\|f_n\|_\Phi \leqslant \|f\|_\Phi$ for every n. It follows that $|f_n|/\|f\|_\Phi \leqslant |f_n|/\|f_n\|_\Phi$, so that $\int_\Delta \Phi[|f_n|/\|f\|_\Phi]\,d\mu \leqslant 1$ for every n. Observing that $\Phi(u)$ is continuous, we see finally by Lebesgue's Theorem on the integration of monotone sequences that

$$\int_\Delta \Phi[|f|/\|f\|_\Phi]d\mu = \lim \int_\Delta \Phi[|f_n|/\|f\|_\Phi]d\mu \leqslant 1.$$

Let us suppose now that $g \in L_\Psi$. If $\Psi(v) < \infty$ for all $v < \infty$, which is equivalent to $\lim_{u\to\infty} \varphi(u) = \infty$, the proof of $\int_\Delta \Psi[| g |/\| g \|_\Psi] d\mu \leqslant 1$ offers no new aspects. If however $\lim_{u\to\infty} \varphi(u) = l < \infty$, we observe first that $| g |/\| g \|_\Psi \leqslant l$ almost everywhere on Δ. Indeed, assuming that $| g(x) | > l \| g \|_\Psi$ on a set E of finite positive measure, we might put $f(x) = [l\mu(E)]^{-1}$ on E and $f(x) = 0$ elsewhere, and then, in virtue of $\Phi(u) \leqslant lu$, we should have

$$\int_\Delta \Phi | f | \, d\mu = \mu(E)\Phi[l\mu(E)]^{-1} \leqslant 1$$

and

$$\int_\Delta | fg | \, d\mu = \int_E | g | \, d\mu/[l\mu(E)] > \| g \|_\Psi$$

at the same time, which is impossible. Hence, supposing first that $g(x)$ vanishes outside a set $\Delta_1 \subset \Delta$ of finite measure, and choosing the arbitrary but fixed number δ such that $0 < \delta < 1$, we see that both $\Psi[\delta | g |/\| g \|_\Psi]$ and $\Phi | f |$, where $f = \psi\{\delta | g |/\| g \|_\Psi\}$, are bounded almost everywhere on Δ_1, and therefore summable over Δ. Writing $\pi(f) = \int_\Delta \Phi | f | \, d\mu$ and $\pi'(f) = \max [\pi(f), 1]$, we have now

$$\delta\pi'(f) \geqslant \int_\Delta \left| \frac{\delta g}{\| g \|_\Psi} f \right| d\mu = \int_\Delta \Psi[\delta | g |/\| g \|_\Psi] \, d\mu + \pi(f),$$

from which we derive, since $\pi'(f) = 1$ on account of $\pi(f) \leqslant \delta\pi'(f) < \pi'(f)$, that $\int_\Delta \Psi[\delta | g |/\| g \|_\Psi] d\mu \leqslant \delta < 1$. Making $\delta \to 1$ and observing that $\Psi(v) = \Psi(v -)$ (also at $v = l$), we obtain the desired result. The extension to the case that $g(x) \neq 0$ on a subset of infinite measure is now evident.

Corollary. *If there exists a constant $M > 0$ such that $\Phi(2u) \leqslant M\Phi(u)$ for $u \geqslant 0$, the class L_Φ^* contains the same functions as L_Φ. The same holds if $\Phi(2u) \leqslant M\Phi(u)$ is only satisfied for $u \geqslant u_0 > 0$, provided Δ is of finite measure.*

Proof. We know already that $L_\Phi^* \subset L_\Phi$. Let now $f(x) \in L_\Phi$, where we may suppose that $\| f \|_\Phi \neq 0$. Then $f/\| f \|_\Phi \in L_\Phi^*$; hence, since $\| f \|_\Phi \leqslant 2^p$ for a suitable non-negative integer p, we have $\Phi | f | \leqslant M^p \Phi[| f |/\| f \|_\Phi]$, which shows that $f \in L_\Phi^*$.

If $\Phi(2u) \leqslant M\Phi(u)$ only for $u \geqslant u_0 > 0$, and Δ is of finite measure, we write $f = f_1 + f_2$, where $f_1 = f$ on $\Delta(| f |/\| f \|_\Phi < u_0)$ and $f_1 = 0$ elsewhere on Δ. The function $\Phi | f_1 |$ is bounded and therefore summable over Δ, and the summability of $\Phi | f_2 |$ is proved in the same way as above. Since $\Phi | f | = \Phi | f_1 | + \Phi | f_2 |$, we have again $f \in L_\Phi^*$.

Theorem 3. *If L_Φ and L_Ψ are complementary spaces, $f \in L_\Phi$ and $g \in L_\Psi$, then fg is summable over Δ, and*

$$\left| \int_\Delta fg \, d\mu \right| \leqslant \int_\Delta |fg| \, d\mu \leqslant \| f \|_\Phi \cdot \| g \|_\Psi.$$

Proof. If $\| g \|_\Psi = 0$, the proof is trivial. If $\| g \|_\Psi \neq 0$, we have

$$\int_\Delta |fg| \, d\mu = \int_\Delta \left| f \frac{g}{\| g \|_\Psi} \right| d\mu . \| g \|_\Psi \leqslant \| f \|_\Phi \cdot \| g \|_\Psi$$

by the definition of $\| f \|_\Phi$, since $\int_\Delta \Psi[| g |/\| g \|_\Psi] d\mu \leqslant 1$.

Theorem 4. *If $f \in L_\Phi$ and $g \in L_\Phi$, then*

$$\| f + g \|_\Phi \leqslant \| f \|_\Phi + \| g \|_\Phi.$$

Proof. Follows immediately from $\int_\Delta |(f+g)h| \, d\mu \leqslant \int_\Delta |fh| \, d\mu + \int_\Delta |gh| \, d\mu$.

If $\Phi(u) = cu^p$ $(c > 0,\ 1 \leqslant p < \infty)$, we have $\Phi(2u) = 2^p \Phi(u)$ for $u \geqslant 0$; the Orlicz space L_Φ contains therefore the same functions as the class L_Φ^*, which in its turn, as we have already seen, contains the same functions as the Lebesgue space L_p. For $1 < p < \infty$ the complementary Orlicz space L_Ψ contains the same functions as the complementary Lebesgue space L_q, where $q = p/(p-1)$, and for $p = 1$ the complementary Orlicz space L_Ψ is easily seen to contain the same functions as the complementary Lebesgue space L_∞. More generally in a certain sense, if $\lim_{u \to \infty} \varphi(u) = l < \infty$ and Δ is of finite measure, the spaces L_Φ and L_Ψ contain the same functions as L and L_∞ respectively. Indeed, if $g \in L_\Psi$, we have seen in the proof of Theorem 2 that $| g |/\| g \|_\Psi \leqslant l$ almost everywhere on Δ, hence $g \in L_\infty$. Conversely, if $g \in L_\infty$, we have $pg(x) < l/2$ almost everywhere on Δ for a suitable positive constant p, hence $pg(x) \in L_\Psi^*$ since Δ is of finite measure, so that $g \in L_\Psi$. Let now $f \in L_\Phi$. Then fg is summable over Δ for every $g \in L_\Psi$, in particular for $g(x) = 1$, and this shows that $f \in L$. Conversely, if $f \in L$, we have $\int_\Delta \Phi | f | \, d\mu \leqslant l \int_\Delta | f | \, d\mu < \infty$, hence $f \in L_\Phi$. Note that $\mu(\Delta) < \infty$ is not used in the proofs of $L_\Psi \subset L_\infty$ and $L \subset L_\Phi$.

Considering the particular case that $\Phi(u) = u^p/p$ $(1 < p < \infty)$, so that $\Psi(v) = v^q/q$, where $q = p/(p-1)$, it is not true that $\| f \|_\Phi = \| f \|_p$. The quotient $\| f \|_\Phi/\| f \|_p$ however is independent of $f(x)$, as may be seen by observing that

$$\| f \|_\Phi = \text{upper bound} \int_\Delta |fg| \, d\mu \text{ for } \int_\Delta | g |^q \, d\mu \leqslant q,$$

$$\| f \|_p = \text{upper bound} \int_\Delta |fg| \, d\mu \text{ for } \int_\Delta | g |^q \, d\mu \leqslant 1.$$

This shows that $\| f \|_\Phi = q^{1/q} \| f \|_p$. For $p = 1$, hence $\Phi(u) = u$, we find similarly $\| f \|_\Phi = \| f \|_1$ and $\| f \|_\Psi = \| f \|_\infty$.

§ 6. The Completeness of the Spaces L_Φ

The Lebesgue spaces L_p being particular cases of Orlicz spaces, it is natural to conjecture that Orlicz spaces, as well as Lebesgue spaces, are complete.

Theorem 1. *The Orlicz spaces L_Φ and L_Ψ are complete, by which we mean that if $f_n(x) \in L_\Phi$ $(n = 1, 2, \ldots)$ and $\lim \| f_n - f_m \|_\Phi = 0$ as $m, n \to \infty$, there exists a function $f(x) \in L_\Phi$ such that $\lim \| f_n - f \|_\Phi = 0$. This function $f(x)$ is uniquely determined apart from sets of measure zero.*

Proof. If $\varepsilon > 0$ is given, and $g(x)$ satisfies $\int_\Delta \Psi \mid g \mid d\mu \leqslant 1$, we have by hypothesis

(1) $$\int_\Delta \mid f_n - f_m \mid . \mid g \mid d\mu \leqslant \varepsilon \text{ for } m, n \geqslant N(\varepsilon).$$

We now write Δ in the form $\Delta = \Sigma\, \Delta_i$, where each Δ_i is of finite positive measure and $\Delta_i \Delta_j = 0$ $(i \neq j)$. Choosing the positive number p such that $\mu(\Delta_1)\Psi(p) \leqslant 1$, and writing $g(x) = p$ on Δ_1 and $g(x) = 0$ elsewhere, we have $\int_\Delta \Psi \mid g \mid d\mu \leqslant 1$, hence $\int_{\Delta_1} \mid f_n - f_m \mid d\mu \leqslant \varepsilon/p$ for $m, n \geqslant N(\varepsilon)$. This shows that $\lim \int_{\Delta_1} \mid f_n - f_m \mid d\mu = 0$ as $m, n \to \infty$. By the completeness of the Lebesgue space $L(\Delta_1, \mu)$ there exists a subsequence $f_n^{(1)}(x)$ of $f_n(x)$, converging almost everywhere on Δ_1 in the ordinary pointwise sense to a function $f(x)$. In the same way we find that $f_n^{(1)}(x)$ contains a subsequence $f_n^{(2)}(x)$, converging almost everywhere on Δ_2 to a function which we may call $f(x)$ as well. Proceeding in this way, the sequence $f_n^{(n)}(x)$ converges almost everywhere on Δ to $f(x)$. Applying now Fatou's Theorem, we derive from (1), letting $f_m(x)$ run through the sequence $f_n^{(n)}(x)$, that $\int_\Delta \mid f_n - f \mid . \mid g \mid d\mu \leqslant \varepsilon$ for $n \geqslant N(\varepsilon)$ and $\int_\Delta \Psi \mid g \mid d\mu \leqslant 1$. Hence $f_n - f \in L_\Phi$, $f \in L_\Phi$, and $\| f_n - f \|_\Phi \leqslant \varepsilon$ for $n \geqslant N(\varepsilon)$. The uniqueness of $f(x)$ is proved in the same way as in the case of the spaces L_p.

§ 7. The Separability of the Spaces L_Φ

As in the case of Lebesgue spaces L_p, we shall prove that under certain conditions the Orlicz spaces L_Φ are separable.

Lemma α. *Let there exist a constant $M > 0$ such that $\Phi(2u) \leqslant M\Phi(u)$ for $u \geqslant 0$, so that $L_\Phi = L_\Phi^*$, let $f(x) \in L_\Phi$ and $\int_\Delta \Phi \mid f \mid d\mu = \rho(f)$. Then,* *if $\rho(f)$ is small, $\| f \|_\Phi$ is small. More precisely, if there exists a non-negative integer p such that $\rho(f) \leqslant 1/M^p$, then $\| f \|_\Phi \leqslant 2/2^p$. In particular, if $f_n(x) \in L_\Phi$ and $\lim \rho(f_n) = 0$, then $\lim \| f_n \|_\Phi = 0$.*

Proof. For $\rho(f) \leqslant 1/M^p$ we have

$$\int_\Delta \Phi[2^p \mid f \mid] d\mu \leqslant M^p \int_\Delta \Phi \mid f \mid d\mu = M^p \rho(f) \leqslant 1,$$

hence, if $\int_\Delta \Psi \mid g \mid d\mu \leqslant 1$,

$$\int_\Delta 2^p \mid fg \mid d\mu \leqslant \int_\Delta \Phi[2^p \mid f \mid] d\mu + \int_\Delta \Psi \mid g \mid d\mu \leqslant 2,$$

so that $\| f \|_\Phi \leqslant 2/2^p$.

Theorem 1. *If the measure μ is separable, and there exists a constant $M > 0$ such that $\Phi(2u) \leqslant M\Phi(u)$ for $u \geqslant 0$, the space $L_\Phi(\Delta, \mu)$ is separable, that is, L_Φ contains an enumerable subcollection having the property that if $f(x) \in L_\Phi$ is arbitrary, there exists to each $\varepsilon > 0$ a function $g(x)$ belonging to this subcollection such that $\| f - g \|_\Phi < \varepsilon$.*

Proof. If Z is the finite or enumerable collection of μ-measurable subsets of X, introduced in § 3 for any separable measure μ, we shall prove that the collection of all rational simple functions on Z has the desired property. Let, for this purpose, $f(x) \in L_\Phi$ and $\varepsilon > 0$ be given. We choose the positive integer p so large that $2/2^p < \varepsilon/3$, and after that the number $\eta > 0$ such that $\eta \leqslant 1/M^p$. Since $f \in L_\Phi = L_\Phi^*$, there exists a function $f_1(x)$, vanishing outside a set $\Delta_1 \subset \Delta$ of finite measure, identical with $f(x)$ on Δ_1, and satisfying $\rho(f - f_1) < \eta$. Then $\rho(f - f_1) \leqslant 1/M^p$, hence $\| f - f_1 \|_\Phi \leqslant 2/2^p < \varepsilon/3$ by Lemma α.

We next observe that $f_1 = (g_1 - g_2) + i(h_1 - h_2)$, where g_1, g_2, h_1 and h_2 are non-negative, belonging to $L_\Phi = L_\Phi^*$, and vanishing outside Δ_1. Considering for example g_1, there exists a non-decreasing sequence of simple functions $g^{(n)}(x)$, non-negative and vanishing outside Δ_1, assuming only finite rational values, and such that $g_1(x) = \lim g^{(n)}(x)$. Consequently, since $\Phi \mid g_1 - g^{(n)} \mid \leqslant \Phi \mid g_1 \mid$ and $\lim \Phi \mid g_1 - g^{(n)} \mid = 0$ almost everywhere on Δ_1, we have $\lim \int_\Delta \Phi \mid g_1 - g^{(n)} \mid d\mu = 0$. It follows from Lemma α that $\| g_1 - g^{(n)} \|_\Phi < \varepsilon/12$ for sufficiently large n. Subjecting g_2, h_1 and h_2 to the same process, we obtain by linear combination a simple function $f_2(x)$, vanishing outside Δ_1, and assuming only finite rational complex values, such that $\| f_1 - f_2 \|_\Phi < \varepsilon/3$. This function $f_2(x)$ may be written in the form $f_2(x) = \sum_1^k \alpha_i c_{E_i}(x)$, where all α_i are rational, $E_i E_j = 0$ $(i \neq j)$ and $\sum E_i = \Delta_1$.

If $c_E(x)$ is the characteristic function of the μ-measurable set E, we have $\rho(c_E) = \int_\Delta \Phi \mid c_E \mid d\mu = \int_{E.\Delta} \Phi(1) d\mu \leqslant \Phi(1)\mu(E)$, hence $\lim \rho(c_E) = 0$, and therefore also $\lim \| c_E \|_\Phi = 0$, as $\lim \mu(E) = 0$. This implies that to each E_i there exists a set $F_i \in Z$ such that $\| c_{E_i} - c_{F_i} \|_\Phi < \varepsilon/3k \mid \alpha_i \mid$. Consequently, writing $f_3(x) = \Sigma_1^k \alpha_i c_{F_i}(x)$, we have $\| f_2 - f_3 \|_\Phi \leqslant \Sigma_1^k \mid \alpha_i \mid . \| c_{E_i} - c_{F_i} \|_\Phi < \varepsilon/3$. Observing that $f_3(x)$ is a rational simple function on Z, and that

$$\| f - f_3 \|_\Phi \leqslant \| f - f_1 \|_\Phi + \| f_1 - f_2 \|_\Phi + \| f_2 - f_3 \|_\Phi < \varepsilon,$$

our proof is complete.

EXAMPLES

1) If $f(x) \in L_\infty(\Delta, \mu)$, then $\| f \|_\infty = \max \mid \int_\Delta fg \, d\mu \mid = \max \int_\Delta \mid fg \mid d\mu$ for $\| g \|_1 \leqslant 1$ if and only if $\mid f(x) \mid = \| f \|_\infty$ on a set of positive measure.

(If $f \in L_\infty$ and $\mid f(x) \mid = \| f \|_\infty$ on the set E of finite positive measure, we may take $g(x) = [\mu(E) . \operatorname{sgn} f]^{-1}$ on E and $g(x) = 0$ elsewhere. Then $\| g \|_1 = 1$ and $\mid \int_\Delta fg \, d\mu \mid = \| f \|_\infty$. If however $f \in L_\infty$ and $h(x) = \| f \|_\infty - \mid f(x) \mid > 0$ almost everywhere on Δ, then $A = \int_\Delta \mid hg \mid d\mu > 0$ for every $g(x)$ satisfying $\| g \|_1 = 1$, for $A = 0$ would imply $h(x) = 0$ on the set of positive measure on which $\mid g(x) \mid > 0$. From $A > 0$ we derive easily $\int_\Delta \mid fg \mid d\mu < \| f \|_\infty$).

2) If $\Phi(u)$ and $\Psi(v)$ are complementary in the sense of Young, one may raise the question whether there always exists a constant $M > 0$ such that either $\Phi(2u) \leqslant M\Phi(u)$ for sufficiently large u or $\Psi(2v) \leqslant M\Psi(v)$ for sufficiently large v. The answer is negative.

(Take a sequence $1 < M_1 < M_2 < \ldots$, such that $\lim M_n = \infty$. The graph of $\varphi(u)$ consists of straight linesegments connecting the points $(0, 0)$, (u_1, v_1), (u_2, v_2), $\ldots$, where u_1, v_1 are arbitrarily positive; $u_2 = 2u_1$, $v_2 = M_1 v_1$; $u_3 = M_2 u_2$, $v_3 = 2u_3$; $u_4 = 2u_3$, $v_4 = M_3 v_3$, and so on. Then $\Phi(u_2) > \frac{1}{2} M_1 \Phi(u_1)$, $\Psi(v_3) > \frac{1}{2} M_2 \Psi(v_2)$, and so on).

3) If Δ is of finite measure, $f(x) \in L_\Phi^*(\Delta, \mu)$ and $\Phi_1(u) < \Phi(u)$ for $u \geqslant u_0 \geqslant 0$, then $f(x) \in L_{\Phi_1}^*(\Delta, \mu)$. In particular, if $f(x) \in L_p(\Delta, \mu)$, then $f(x) \in L_q(\Delta, \mu)$ for $1 \leqslant q \leqslant p$.

4) If $f \in L_p$ and $f \in L_q$, where $p < q$, then $f \in L_r$ for all r satisfying $p \leqslant r \leqslant q$, without any restriction on the measure of Δ.

(Consider separately the sets on which $\mid f \mid \leqslant 1$ and $\mid f \mid > 1$).

5) If $\Delta = [0, 1/2]$ and μ is Lebesgue measure, then $(x \log^2 x^{-1})^{-1}$ belongs to $L(\Delta, \mu)$, but not to any $L_p(\Delta, \mu)$ for $p > 1$.

6) If $\Delta = [0, \infty)$ and μ is Lebesgue measure, then $\{x^{1/2}(1 + \log \mid x \mid)\}^{-1}$ belongs to $L_2(\Delta, \mu)$, but not to $L_p(\Delta, \mu)$ for any other value of p.

7) If the sequence of μ-measurable functions $f_n(x)$ satisfies $\mid f_n(x) \mid \leqslant C$ on the set Δ of finite measure, and $f(x) = \lim f_n(x)$ exists, then $\lim \int_\Delta \Phi \mid f - f_n \mid d\mu = 0$. The same holds with Φ replaced by Ψ, provided $\Psi(2C) < \infty$. In particular, $f_n(x)$ converges on Δ in mean to $f(x)$, with any finite index.

8) A sequence may converge in mean without converging pointwise. Consider the sequence of closed intervals $[0, 1/2]$, $[1/2, 1]$, $[0, 1/3]$, $[1/3, 2/3]$, $[2/3, 1]$, $[0, 1/4]$, $\ldots$, and write $f_n(x) = 1$ on the n-th interval and $f_n(x) = 0$ elsewhere on $[0, 1]$. Then $\lim \int_0^1 \Phi \mid f_n \mid dx = 0$ (in particular, $f_n(x)$ converges on $[0, 1]$ in mean to zero, with any finite index), but $f_n(x)$ does not tend to zero for any x.

9) If a sequence converges both pointwise and in mean, then the limits are identical. More precisely, if $f_n(x)$ and $f(x)$ belong to L_Φ, $\lim \| f - f_n \|_\Phi = 0$ and $\lim f_n(x) = g(x)$ almost everywhere on Δ, then $f(x) = g(x)$ almost everywhere on Δ.

(Observe that $\lim \| f - f_n \|_\Phi = 0$ implies the existence of a subsequence, tending almost everywhere on Δ to $f(x)$).

10) If Φ and Ψ are complementary, $\lim \| f - f_n \|_\Phi = 0$ and $\lim \| g - g_n \|_\Psi = 0$, then $\int_\Delta fg\, d\mu = \lim \int_\Delta f_n g_n\, d\mu$.

(Observe that $fg - f_n g_n = (f - f_n)g + f(g - g_n) + (f_n - f)(g - g_n)$).

11) For $u > 0$, $v > 0$, we have $uv \leqslant e^{u-1} + v \log v$.

(For $\Phi(u) = e^{u-1} - e^{-1}$ we have $\Psi(v) = 0$ for $0 \leqslant v \leqslant e^{-1}$ and $\Psi(v) = v \log v + e^{-1}$ for $v \geqslant e^{-1}$, hence $uv \leqslant e^{u-1} - e^{-1}$ for $v \leqslant e^{-1}$ and $uv \leqslant e^{u-1} + v \log v$ for $v \geqslant e^{-1}$. But, since $-e^{-1} \leqslant v \log v$, the desired result holds for all $v > 0$).

12) If $\log' x = \log x$ for $x \geqslant e$ and $\log' x = 1$ for $0 \leqslant x \leqslant e$, and $e^{|f(x)|}$ and $|g(x)| \log' |g(x)|$ are summable over Δ, then fg is summable over Δ.

(Observe that $|f|$ is summable over Δ, and consider separately the sets on which $|g| < e$ and $|g| \geqslant e$).

13) If $1 \leqslant p, q, r \leqslant \infty$, $1/p + 1/q + 1/r = 1$, $f \in L_p$, $g \in L_q$ and $h \in L_r$, then $\int_\Delta |fgh|\, d\mu \leqslant \| f \|_p \cdot \| g \|_q \cdot \| h \|_r$.

14) If $f(x)$ is uniformly continuous on $\Delta = [0, \infty)$, μ is Lebesgue measure, and $f(x) \in L_p(\Delta, \mu)$ for an index p satisfying $1 \leqslant p < \infty$, then $\lim f(x) = 0$ as $x \to \infty$. A similar statement holds for a function of more variables.

(Assuming that $\lim x_n = \infty$, $|f(x_n)| > \varepsilon > 0$, there exists a number $\delta > 0$ such that $|f(x)| > \varepsilon/2$ on all intervals $[x_n - \delta, x_n + \delta]$. This implies $\int_0^\infty |f|^p\, dx = +\infty$, in contradiction with the hypothesis).

15) If $\Phi(2u) \leqslant M\Phi(u)$ for $u \geqslant 0$, μ is Lebesgue measure in Euclidean space R_m, $\Delta \subset R_m$ and $f(x) \in L_\Phi(\Delta, \mu)$, there exists to each $\varepsilon > 0$ a continuous function $g(x)$, vanishing outside a finite interval, such that $\| f - g \|_\Phi < \varepsilon$.

(There exists a rational simple function $h(x)$, vanishing in the distance, such that $\| f - h \|_\Phi < \varepsilon/2$, and it is obvious that there exists a continuous $g(x)$, vanishing in the distance, such that $\| h - g \|_\Phi < \varepsilon/2$).

16) If $\Phi(2u) \leqslant M\Phi(u)$ for $u \geqslant 0$, μ is Lebesgue measure in R_m and $f(x) \in L_\Phi(R_m, \mu)$, then $\lim \| f(x + h) - f(x) \|_\Phi = 0$ as $h \to 0$.

(To each $\varepsilon > 0$ there exists a continuous function $g(x)$, vanishing in the distance, such that $\| f(x) - g(x) \|_\Phi < \varepsilon/3$. Then $\| f(x + h) - g(x + h) \|_\Phi < \varepsilon/3$ for every h, and $\| g(x + h) - g(x) \|_\Phi < \varepsilon/3$ for h sufficiently near the origin).

17) If Φ and Ψ are complementary, $\Phi(2u) \leqslant M\Phi(u)$ for $u \geqslant 0$, μ is Lebesgue measure in R_m, $f(x) \in L_\Phi(R_m, \mu)$ and $g(x) \in L_\Psi(R_m, \mu)$, then $F(t) = \int_{R_m} f(x + t) g(x)\, dx$ is a continuous function of t.

(Observe that $|F(t + h) - F(t)| \leqslant \| f(x + t + h) - f(x + t) \|_\Phi \cdot \| g \|_\Psi$).

18) If, under the hypotheses of the preceding example, also $\Psi(2v) \leqslant M\Psi(v)$ for $v \geqslant 0$, the function $F(t)$ satisfies $\lim F(t) = 0$ as $t \to \infty$.

(On the straight line R_1 we may write, for $t > 0$, $|F(t)| \leqslant \int_{-\infty}^{-t/2} |f(x+t)g(x)|\, dx + \int_{t/2}^\infty |f(x)g(x - t)|\, dx \leqslant A \| f \|_\Phi + B \| g \|_\Psi$, where $\lim A = \lim B = 0$ as $t \to \infty$. For $t \to -\infty$ the proof is similar. In a space of more dimensions we observe that $\lim t = \infty$ if and only if one at least of the coordinates of t tends to $\pm \infty$. If e.g. the first coordinate t_1 tends to $+\infty$, we split $\int_{-\infty}^\infty dx_1$ up into $\int_{-\infty}^{-t/2} + \int_{-t/2}^\infty$).

19) If μ is Lebesgue measure on the straight line, $\Delta = [0, b]$ where $0 < b < \infty$, and $f(x) \in L_p(\Delta, \mu)$ for an index p satisfying $1 < p < \infty$, then its fractional integral $I_\alpha f(x)$ is continuous for $\alpha > 1/p$. If $f(x) \in L(\Delta, \mu)$, then $I_\alpha f(x)$ is continuous for $\alpha \geqslant 1$.

(Writing $I_\alpha f(x) = f_\alpha(x)$, we have

$$\Gamma(\alpha)[f_\alpha(x+h) - f_\alpha(x)] = \int_{-h}^{0} (x-t)^{\alpha-1} f(t+h)dt + \int_0^x (x-t)^{\alpha-1}[f(t+h) - f(t)]dt.$$

Hence, for $1 < p < \infty$, $q = p/(p-1)$, $\alpha > 1/p$, we have $(\alpha - 1)q > -1$, so that

$$\Gamma(\alpha) \mid f_\alpha(x+h) - f_\alpha(x) \mid \leqslant \left(\int_{-h}^{0} (x-t)^{(\alpha-1)q} dt\right)^{1/q} \left(\int_0^h \mid f(t) \mid^p dt\right)^{1/p}$$
$$+ \left(\int_0^x (x-t)^{(\alpha-1)q} dt\right)^{1/q} \left(\int_0^x \mid f(t+h) - f(t) \mid^p dt\right)^{1/p},$$

which tends to zero with h. For $p = 1$, $\alpha \geqslant 1$, we observe that $(x-t)^{\alpha-1}$ is bounded for $-h \leqslant t \leqslant x$).

PART II

BOUNDED TRANSFORMATIONS AND COMPACT TRANSFORMATIONS IN BANACH SPACE AND HILBERT SPACE

CHAPTER 6

BANACH SPACE AND HILBERT SPACE

§ 1. Introduction

The theory of Hilbert space has its origin in D. Hilbert's theory of quadratic forms $\Sigma\, a_{ij}x_i x_j$ of an enumerable infinity of variables $x_1, x_2, \ldots$. Only such sequences $x_1, x_2, \ldots$ (we restrict ourselves to real numbers x_j in this introduction) are considered for which $\Sigma x_i^2 < \infty$, and it is sometimes customary to say that the numbers $x_1, x_2, \ldots$ are the components of the vector $x = (x_1, x_2, \ldots)$ with norm or length $\| x \| = (\Sigma\, x_i^2)^{1/2}$. The inner product (x, y) of the vectors $x = (x_1, x_2, \ldots)$ and $y = (y_1, y_2, \ldots)$ is then defined to be $(x, y) = \Sigma\, x_i y_i$. The set of all these vectors was the first non-trivial example of a set whose elements satisfy the conditions, characteristic for what at present is called a Hilbert space. It is when we apply a linear transformation $y_i = \Sigma_j\, a_{ij}x_j$ $(i = 1, 2, \ldots)$ to a vector x of this space (where the numbers a_{ij} satisfy certain conditions to ensure the convergence of $\Sigma\, y_i^2$), and then form the inner product (x, y) of the old vector x and the new vector y, that we obtain the quadratic form $\Sigma\, a_{ij}x_i x_j$. In developing the theory of these quadratic forms, D. HILBERT [1] found as an important result new proofs for the main theorems in the theory of linear integral equations (1906).

It was however not before 1929 that J. VON NEUMANN [2] gave the first axiomatical treatment of the theory of Hilbert space. Later important contributions are due to F. RIESZ [3] and M. H. STONE [4], and the publications of these and other authors on this subject cover now an extensive field.

At about the same time (around 1930) that the theory of Hilbert space was brought into a more abstract form, a second theory, at present called the theory of Banach space, and which had its roots in earlier investigations of M. Fréchet, F. Hausdorff, F. Riesz and some others, took a more definite shape in the hands of the Polish mathematician S. Banach and his school, and came to the attention of a larger group of people by the publication of Banach's well-known book (1932) [5] on linear transformations. The effect was a rapid expansion which goes on until the present time, mainly by the work of Polish, American and Russian mathematicians.

There is a close relation between the theories of Hilbert and Banach spaces. To every Banach space E we may assign a second Banach space E^*, the adjoint space of E, and under rather general conditions this correspondence between E and E^* is dual, that is to say, the adjoint space of E^* is again the original space E. A Hilbert space may now be described as a Banach space with the special property that it may be considered in many respects as self-dual. It will be evident that, due to this special position in the class of all Banach spaces, many theorems in Hilbert space may be pronounced in a more rounded-off form than the corresponding theorems in Banach space.

We shall, in what follows, restrict ourselves to a rather simple part of the theory because we shall deal mainly with compact linear transformations and applications to systems of one or more non-singular linear integral equations. Readers wishing to familiarize themselves with other aspects of the theory, in particular with the spectral resolution of general self-adjoint or normal transformations in Hilbert space, are referred to the treatises of S. Banach [5] and E. Hille [6] (for Banach space), M. H. Stone [4], B. von Sz. Nagy [7] and P. R. Halmos [14] (for Hilbert space).

§ 2. Definition of Banach Space

A set E with elements $f, g, \ldots$ will be called a *Banach space* whenever it satisfies the following Axioms A, B and C:

Axiom A. *For the elements of E there exist two uniquely defined operations: an addition and a multiplication by complex numbers such that, if f and g are arbitrary elements of E and α is an arbitrary complex number, $f + g$ and αf are elements of E. For these operations the following rules hold:*

1°. $f + g = g + f$.
2°. $(f + g) + h = f + (g + h)$.
3°. *If* $f + g = f + h$, *then* $g = h$.
4°. $\alpha(f + g) = \alpha f + \alpha g$.
5°. $(\alpha\beta)f = \alpha(\beta f)$, α *and* β *complex.*
6°. $(\alpha + \beta)f = \alpha f + \beta f$.
7°. $1.f = f$.

It follows from these rules that there exists a uniquely determined *null element*, denoted by 0 (there will be no confusion with the complex number 0, for it will always be clear whether 0 is to represent a number or an element of Banach space), with the property that $f + 0 = f$ for every $f \in E$. Indeed, if we substitute $\alpha = 1$, $\beta = 0$ in 6°, it results from 7° that $f = f + 0f$; the equation $f = f + x$ admits therefore the solution $x = 0f$, and this solution is on account of 3° uniquely determined. To show the existence of the null element, we have therefore still to prove that $0f = 0g$ for two arbitrary elements, $f, g \in E$. Now

$$f + g = (f + 0f) + g = f + (0f + g) = f + (g + 0f) = (f + g) + 0f,$$

$$f + g = \qquad\qquad f + (g + 0g) = (f + g) + 0g,$$

so that, again by 3°, $0f = 0g$.

Substituting $g = 0$ in 4°, we see that the null element satisfies $\alpha 0 = 0$ for arbitrary complex α.

It is convenient to introduce a subtraction by the definitions $-f = (-1)f$, $f - g = f + (-1)g$. Evidently the element $x = f - g$ is the uniquely determined solution of the equation $g + x = f$. The elements of E form therefore, relative to the addition, a commutative group.

Finally, the elements $f_1, \ldots, f_n$ are said to be linearly independent if $\Sigma_{i=1}^{n} \alpha_i f_i = 0$ implies $\alpha_1 = \ldots = \alpha_n = 0$.

Axiom B. *With every element $f \in E$ corresponds a non-negative number $\| f \|$, called the norm of f, with the properties*

1°. $\| \alpha f \| = | \alpha | . \| f \|$, *$\alpha$ complex,*
2°. $\| f + g \| \leqslant \| f \| + \| g \|$,
3°. $\| f \| > 0$ *for* $f \neq 0$.

We observe that 1° implies $\| -f \| = \| f \|$; hence, from 2°, $\| f + g \| \geqslant \big| \| f \| - \| g \| \big|$. Furthermore, taking $f = 0$ in 1°, we see that $\| 0 \| = \| \alpha . 0 \| = | \alpha | . \| 0 \|$ for any α, hence $\| 0 \| = 0$, so that, by 3°, $\| f \| = 0$ if and only if $f = 0$.

Axiom C (*Axiom of completeness*). *If a sequence f_n of elements satisfies the condition lim $\| f_m - f_n \| = 0$ as $m, n \to \infty$, then there exists an element $f \in E$ such that lim $\| f - f_n \| = 0$ as $n \to \infty$.*

There is still another axiom, Axiom D, which runs as follows:

Axiom D. *There exists an enumerable sequence of elements $f_n \in E$ such* *that, if $\varepsilon > 0$ and $f \in E$ are arbitrarily given, one at least of the elements f_n satisfies $\| f - f_n \| < \varepsilon$,*

and any Banach space E, satisfying this axiom, is called *separable.* We shall however, in what follows, not suppose the Axiom D to be necessarily valid, and expressly state it every time we assume its validity. Sometimes also we shall consider sets satisfying the Axioms A and B, but not C. In these cases, expressly stated, we shall speak of a non-complete Banach space.

Definition. *If E is a Banach space, the norm $\| f - g \|$ is said to be the distance between the elements f and g.*

We see that $\| f - g \|$ has the properties, characteristic for a distance function:

$\| f - g \| \geqslant 0$,
$\| f - g \| = 0$ if and only if $f = g$,
$\| f - g \| = \| g - f \|$,
$\| f - g \| \leqslant \| f - h \| + \| h - g \|$ (triangle inequality).

The definitions, given in Ch. 1, § 2 for the case of point sets in Euclidean space R_m, of diameter of a set, boundedness of a set, distance of a point and a set, distance of two sets, neighbourhood of a point, point of accumulation and isolated point, derived set, closed set, limit of a sequence, remain the same for sets of elements in a Banach space E. Thus, e.g., a sequence of elements $f_n \in E$ converges to $f \in E$ if $\lim \| f - f_n \| = 0$. We shall write $\lim f_n = f$ or $f_n \to f$. We add the following definition: A set S is called *dense* in E if the sum of S and its derived set S^+ is identical with the whole space E. Hence, if E is separable, we may say that there exists an enumerable set S dense in E.

Theorem 1. *The norm $\| f \|$ is a continuous function of f; that is, if $\lim f_n = f$, then $\lim \| f_n \| = \| f \|$.*
Proof. Follows immediately from

$$\| f \| - \| f_n - f \| \leqslant \| f_n \| \leqslant \| f \| + \| f_n - f \|.$$

Theorem 2. *If E is a non-complete Banach space, there exists a complete Banach space $\bar{E}$, containing E as a subset, and such that E is dense in $\bar{E}$.*
Proof. The space $\bar{E}$ is obtained from E by a process of adjunction of

"ideal" elements, similar to that whereby the irrational numbers may be introduced. For this purpose we let correspond with every fundamental sequence $f_n \in E$ (that is, a sequence for which $\lim \| f_m - f_n \| = 0$), if it has not already a limit belonging to E, an "ideal" limitelement f. Limit-elements, corresponding with equivalent sequences f_n and g_n (that is, sequences for which $\lim (f_n - g_n) = 0$), are considered to be identical. If the sequences f_n and g_n have limits f and g, one at least of which, say f, is an ideal element, we define $f + g = \lim (f_n + g_n)$ and $\alpha f = \lim \alpha f_n$ for complex α. Furthermore, in this case, we define $\| f \| = \lim \| f_n \|$, which is permitted because $\lim \| f_n \|$ exists on account of $| \| f_m \| - \| f_n \| | \leqslant \| f_m - f_n \|$. Adding the ideal elements to the space E, we obtain the space $\bar{E}$, termed the closure of E, and it is readily seen that E satisfies the Axioms A, B and C. Finally E is evidently dense in $\bar{E}$.

§ 3. Linear Subspace. Complete Sets. The Dimension of *E*

By a *linear subspace* $[L]$ of a Banach space E (complete or non-complete) we mean a subset $[L]$ of E, satisfying:

1°. If $f, g \in [L]$, then also $\alpha f + \beta g \in [L]$ for arbitrary complex α, β.

2°. $[L]$ is closed, that is, $f_n \in [L]$ and $\lim \| f_n - f \| = 0$ imply $f \in [L]$.

We see that a linear subspace of a Banach space is itself a Banach space.

Given a set S of elements from a Banach space E, the set of all finite linear combinations $\Sigma\, \alpha_i f_i$ (α_i complex, $f_i \in S$) is called the *linear manifold* determined by S, and denoted by $L(S)$. The set obtained by adding to $L(S)$ all its points of accumulation is evidently a linear subspace of E. For this reason it is called the linear subspace determined by S, and denoted by $[L(S)]$.

The set S is called *complete* whenever $[L(S)]$ is identical with the whole space E. If there exists a complete set consisting of n elements, but no complete set consisting of less than n elements, the space E is said to be *n-dimensional*. If there exists an enumerable complete set, but no finite complete set, E is said to be of *enumerably infinite dimension*. In both cases E is evidently separable since, if the finite or enumerable set f_i is complete and the complex numbers α_i are rational complex (that is, their real and imaginary parts are rational), the set of all finite sums $\Sigma\, \alpha_i f_i$ is enumerable and dense in E. If there exists no finite or enumerable complete set, the space E is said to have a *more than enumerably infinite dimension*. It is clear that in this case E is not separable.

§ 4. Banach Spaces of Finite Dimension. Direct Sum

If E is an n-dimensional Banach space, there are by definition n elements $f_1, \ldots, f_n$ such that the set of all linear combinations $\Sigma_{i=1}^n \alpha_i f_i$ (α_i complex) is dense in E. Evidently $f_1, \ldots, f_n$ are linearly independent since, in the opposite case, E would have a dimension less than n. We shall show now that the set of all elements $\Sigma \alpha_i f_i$ is not only dense in E, but identical with E.

Theorem 1. *If the set $f_1, \ldots, f_n$ is complete in the n-dimensional Banach space E, every element $f \in E$ may be written uniquely in the form $f = \Sigma_{i=1}^n \alpha_i f_i$.*

Proof. Let L be the set of all elements $\Sigma_{i=1}^n \alpha_i f_i$. We have to prove the existence of a limitelement, belonging to L, for every sequence g_k for which $g_k \in L$ and $\lim \| g_k - g_l \| = 0$ as $k, l \to \infty$. For this purpose it is sufficient to show that $\lim_{k\to\infty} \| \Sigma_{i=1}^n \alpha_i^{(k)} f_i \| = 0$ implies $\lim_{k\to\infty} \alpha_i^{(k)} = 0$ $(i = 1, \ldots, n)$, for, once this is established, Cauchy's Theorem allows us to infer the existence of the desired limitelement. Let us suppose therefore that we have a sequence of elements $h_k = \Sigma_{i=1}^n \alpha_i^{(k)} f_i$ satisfying $\lim \| h_k \| = 0$ although $\Sigma_{i=1}^n | \alpha_i^{(k)} | = 1$. Then there exists a subsequence $h_l (l = k_1, k_2, \ldots)$ for which $\lim \alpha_i^{(l)} = \alpha_i$ $(i = 1, \ldots, n)$, so that $\Sigma_{i=1}^n | \alpha_i | = 1$. Since this subsequence converges to $\Sigma_{i=1}^n \alpha_i f_i$ and $\lim \| h_k \| = 0$, we have $\Sigma_{i=1}^n \alpha_i f_i = 0$, hence $\alpha_1 = \ldots = \alpha_n = 0$ on account of the linear independence of $f_1, \ldots, f_n$. This however is in contradiction with $\Sigma_{i=1}^n | \alpha_i | = 1$. It follows that L and E are identical.

The uniqueness of the numbers α_i in $f = \Sigma_{i=1}^n \alpha_i f_i$ follows from the linear independence of $f_1, \ldots, f_n$.

Theorem 2. *Every set $g_1, \ldots, g_n$ of linearly independent elements in an n-dimensional Banach space E is complete, so that it is impossible that E contains more than n linearly independent elements.*

Proof. We have already proved that there exist n elements $f_1, \ldots, f_n$, linearly independent and such that every $f \in E$ is expressible in the form $f = \Sigma_{i=1}^n \alpha_i f_i$. Let us suppose now that $g_1, \ldots, g_n$ are linearly independent. If $g_1 = \Sigma_{i=1}^n \alpha_i f_i$, one at least of the numbers α_i does not vanish, and we may suppose without loss of generality that $\alpha_1 \neq 0$. But then f_1 depends linearly on $g_1, f_2, \ldots, f_n$; hence, since every $f \in E$ depends linearly on $f_1, f_2, \ldots, f_n$, every $f \in E$ also depends linearly on $g_1, f_2, \ldots, f_n$. In particular $g_2 = \beta_1 g_1 + \gamma_2 f_2 + \ldots + \gamma_n f_n$, and, the elements g_1, g_2 being linearly independent, one at least of the numbers $\gamma_i (i = 2, \ldots, n)$ does not vanish. We may suppose that $\gamma_2 \neq 0$, which shows that f_2 depends linearly on $g_1, g_2, f_3, \ldots, f_n$. It follows that every $f \in E$ depends linearly on $g_1, g_2, f_3, \ldots, f_n$. Proceeding in this way, we finally conclude that every $f \in E$ is a linear combination of $g_1, \ldots, g_n$.

Corollary. *If the elements $f_1, \ldots, f_n$ of a Banach space E are linearly independent, the set L of all $f = \Sigma_{i=1}^n \alpha_i f_i$ is an n-dimensional linear subspace of E.*

Proof. It follows from Theorem 1 that L is a linear subspace, and from Theorem 2 that the dimension of L is not less than n.

Definition. *A set $Z \subset E$ is called compact if every infinite subset contains a converging subsequence. It is not necessary that the limitelement belongs to Z.*

Theorem 3. *If Z is a bounded subset of the n-dimensional Banach space E, then Z is compact.*

Proof. Every $f \in E$ is expressible in the form $f = \Sigma_{i=1}^n \alpha_i f_i$, where $f_1, \ldots, f_n$ are linearly independent. We have to prove that the boundedness of $\| f \|$ implies the boundedness of all numbers α_i since, once this is established, the Theorem of Bolzano-Weierstrass guarantees the existence of the desired converging subsequence. Let us suppose therefore that we have a sequence for which $\| f \|$ is bounded, although $\Sigma_{i=1}^n | \alpha_i |$ diverges to $+\infty$. Multiplying every element by $(\Sigma_{i=1}^n | \alpha_i |)^{-1}$, we obtain a sequence converging to 0, and for which $\Sigma_{i=1}^n | \alpha_i | = 1$. As we have seen in the proof of Theorem 1, this however leads to a contradiction.

Theorem 4. *Let $[L_1]$ and $[L_2]$ be linear subspaces of a Banach space E (complete or non-complete), having only the null element in common, while moreover $[L_1]$ is of finite dimension. If $[L]$ is the set of all elements $f = g + h$, where g runs through $[L_1]$ and h through $[L_2]$, then $[L]$ is a linear subspace.*

Proof. Evidently we have only to prove that $[L]$ is closed. Let us suppose therefore that $\lim (g_n + h_n) = f$ $(g_n \in [L_1],\ h_n \in [L_2])$. If $\| g_n \|$ is not bounded, there is a subsequence $g_i (i = n_1, n_2, \ldots)$ for which $\lim \| g_i \| = \infty$; hence, writing $g_i / \| g_i \| = \bar{g}_i$ and $h_i / \| g_i \| = \bar{h}_i$, we have $\lim (\bar{g}_i + \bar{h}_i) = 0$ with $\| \bar{g}_i \| = 1$. Since $\bar{g}_i \in [L_1]$ and the sequence $\bar{g}_i$ is bounded, it contains on account of Theorem 3 a subsequence $\bar{g}_j$, converging to an element $\bar{g}_0 \in [L_1]$, where $\| \bar{g}_0 \| = 1$. Furthermore, since $\lim (\bar{g}_j + \bar{h}_j) = 0$, we have $\lim \bar{h}_j = \bar{h}_0 \in [L_2]$, hence $\bar{g}_0 + \bar{h}_0 = 0$ or $\bar{g}_0 = -\bar{h}_0$. Since however $[L_1]$ and $[L_2]$ have only the null element in common, we find $\bar{g}_0 = \bar{h}_0 = 0$, in contradiction with $\| \bar{g}_0 \| = 1$. We may suppose therefore that $\| g_n \|$ in the relation $\lim (g_n + h_n) = f$ is bounded. Then, by Theorem 3, the sequence g_n contains a subsequence g_k for which $\lim g_k = g_0 \in [L_1]$, so that $\lim h_k = h_0 \in [L_2]$. Hence $f = \lim (g_k + h_k) = g_0 + h_0$ $(g_0 \in [L_1],\ h_0 \in [L_2])$, so that $f \in [L]$. This shows that $[L]$ is closed.

Definition. *Let $[L_1]$ and $[L_2]$ be linear subspaces of a Banach space E (complete or non-complete), having only the null element in common. If L is the set of all elements $f = g + h$, where g runs through $[L_1]$ and h through $[L_2]$, then L is called the direct sum of $[L_1]$ and $[L_2]$.*

The theorem which we have just proved may now be announced in the following form:

Theorem 4a. *The direct sum of $[L_1]$ and $[L_2]$, where one at least of these subspaces is of finite dimension, is a linear subspace.*

Theorem 5. *If L is the direct sum of $[L_1]$ and $[L_2]$, so that $f = g + h$ $(g \in [L_1], h \in [L_2])$ for every $f \in L$, then g and h are uniquely determined by f.*

Proof. Let $f = g + h = g_1 + h_1$ $(g, g_1 \in [L_1],\ h, h_1 \in [L_2])$. Then $g - g_1 = h_1 - h$. Since $g - g_1 \in [L_1]$ and $h_1 - h \in [L_2]$, it follows that $g - g_1 = h_1 - h = 0$ because $[L_1]$ and $[L_2]$ have only the null element in common.

Theorem 6. *Let $[L_1]$ and $[L_2]$ be linear subspaces of a Banach space E (complete or non-complete), such that $[L_1]$ is a proper subspace of $[L_2]$. Then, for every ε such that $0 < \varepsilon < 1$, there exists an element $g \in [L_2]$ such that $\| g \| = 1$ and $\| g - f \| \geqslant 1 - \varepsilon$ for every $f \in [L_1]$.*

Proof. Let $h \in [L_2]$, but not $h \in [L_1]$, and let d be the distance of h and $[L_1]$. Evidently $d > 0$, since $[L_1]$ is a subspace. Given ε such that $0 < \varepsilon < 1$, we put $\eta = d\varepsilon/(1 - \varepsilon)$, and we denote by f_0 an element of $[L_1]$ satisfying $d \leqslant \| h - f_0 \| \leqslant d + \eta$. Then, writing $g = (h - f_0)/\| h - f_0 \|$, we have $\| g \| = 1$, and, for every $f \in [L_1]$ (observing that $f_0 + \| h - f_0 \| . f \in [L_1]$),

$$\| g - f \| = \| h - f_0 - \| h - f_0 \| . f \| / \| h - f_0 \| \geqslant d / \| h - f_0 \|$$
$$\geqslant d/(d + \eta) = 1 - \varepsilon.$$

This completes the proof.

Theorem 7. *Let the elements of the sequence $f_1, f_2, \ldots$ be linearly independent (that is, $f_1, \ldots, f_k$ are linearly independent for every integer*

$k \geqslant 1$), and let $[L_n]$ be the subspace of all linear combinations $\Sigma_{i=1}^n \alpha_i f_i$ (α_i complex). Then there exists a sequence of elements $g_1, g_2, \ldots$ such that, for $n = 1, 2, \ldots$, we have

$$g_n \in [L_n],\ \| g_n \| = 1 \text{ and } \| g_{n+1} - f \| \geqslant 1/2 \text{ for every } f \in [L_n].$$

Proof. We put $g_1 = f_1/\| f_1 \|$, hence $g_1 \in [L_1]$ and $\| g_1 \| = 1$. The rest of the statement follows immediately from the preceding theorem.

§ 5. Factorspace

Let $[L]$ be a linear subspace of the complete Banach space E. Then, writing for a moment $f_1 \equiv f_2$ if and only if $f_1 - f_2 \in [L]$, it is readily seen that $f_1 \equiv f_2$ and $g_1 \equiv g_2$ imply $f_1 + g_1 \equiv f_2 + g_2$ and $\alpha f_1 \equiv \alpha f_2$ for every complex α. Dividing now the space E into classes of elements $[f]$, where $[f]$ contains all elements g such that $g \equiv f$, it is evident that every element is contained in one and only one of these classes. Furthermore, defining in the set $E/[L]$ of all classes $[f]$ sum and product by $[f] + [g] = [f + g]$ and $\alpha[f] = [\alpha f]$ for every complex α, we see that these definitions are not contradictory and that the set $E/[L]$ satisfies Axiom A of Banach space. The element $[0]$ is identical with the class $[L]$. Defining now $\| [f] \| =$ lower bound $\| f \|$ for all $f \in [f]$, the relation $\| [\alpha f] \| = | \alpha | . \| [f] \|$ is trivial, and $\| f + g \| \leqslant \| f \| + \| g \|$ implies lower bound $\| f + g \| \leqslant$ lower bound $\| f \| +$ lower bound $\| g \|$, where f runs through $[f]$ and g through $[g]$; hence $\| [f + g] \| \leqslant \| [f] \| + \| [g] \|$. Finally, if $\| [f] \| = 0$, there is a sequence $f_n \in [f]$ such that $\lim \| f_n \| = 0$, hence $\lim f_n = 0$. But then $\lim (f - f_n) = f$, so that, since $f - f_n \in [L]$ and $[L]$ is closed, $f = \lim (f - f_n) \in [L]$, from which we conclude that $[f] = [L] = [0]$. The set $E/[L]$ satisfies therefore Axiom B of Banach space.

We want to show now that $E/[L]$ is complete. For this purpose we add to $E/[L]$, supposing that it is not complete, ideal elements $\overline{[f]}$ (cf. § 2, Th. 2) such that $E/[L]$ together with these elements $\overline{[f]}$ forms the comple[illegible] Banach space $\overline{E/[L]}$. Furthermore we shall make repeatedly use o[illegible] fact that for every $[f] \in E/[L]$ there is an element $f \in [f]$ suc[illegible] $\| f \| \leqslant 2 \| [f] \|$. Let now $\overline{[f]}$ be an arbitrary element of $\overline{E/[L]}$; le[illegible] be such that $\| \overline{[f]} \| < M/2$; let $\varepsilon_i = 2M/2^i$ and $\eta_i = \varepsilon_i/2 =$ [illegible] $2, \ldots$). Hence $\| \overline{[f]} \| < \eta_1$. Then there exists a sequence [illegible] elements belonging to E, such that

1°. $\| \overline{[f]} - [f_1] \| < \eta_2$ and $\| f_1 \| < \varepsilon_1$,

2°. $\| \overline{[f]} - \Sigma_{i=1}^n [f_i] \| < \eta_{n+1}$ and $\| f_n \| < \varepsilon_n$ ($n = 2, 3, \ldots$).

It follows that $\overline{[f]} = \lim \Sigma_{i=1}^{n} [f_i]$, and since $\Sigma_{i=1}^{\infty} \| f_i \| < \Sigma_{i=1}^{\infty} 2M/2^i < \infty$, also that $\lim \| \Sigma_1^n f_i - \Sigma_1^m f_i \| = 0$ as $m, n \to \infty$, so that $\lim \Sigma_1^n f_i = f_0$ exists. Hence $\overline{[f]} = \lim \Sigma_1^n [f_i] = \lim [\Sigma_1^n f_i] = [f_0] \in E/[L]$, which shows that $E/[L]$ and $\overline{E/[L]}$ are identical, so that $E/[L]$ is complete.

The set $E/[L]$ is therefore a complete Banach space; it is called the *factorspace of E modulo* $[L]$.

We observe that if the Banach space E is not complete, we may nevertheless construct the factorspace $E/[L]$, but of course this factorspace, considered as a Banach space, will as a rule be non-complete as well.

Finally, if E is separable, the same holds for $E/[L]$ because, if the sequence $f_n (n = 1, 2, \ldots)$ is dense in E, then the sequence $[f_n]$ is dense in $E/[L]$. Indeed, $\| f - f_n \| < \varepsilon$ implies

$$\| [f] - [f_n] \| = \| [f - f_n] \| \leqslant \| f - f_n \| < \varepsilon.$$

§ 6. Examples of Banach Spaces

In the present paragraph we shall give some examples of Banach spaces.

Example A. *The Lebesgue spaces* $L_p (1 \leqslant p \leqslant \infty)$

In the functionspaces $L_p(\Delta, \mu)$ $(1 \leqslant p \leqslant \infty)$, introduced in Ch. 5, § 1, we may divide the functions $f(x) \in L_p$ (for a fixed p) into classes such that $f_1(x)$ and $f_2(x)$ are in the same class if and only if $\| f_1 - f_2 \|_p = 0$. We may say as well that $f_1(x)$ and $f_2(x)$ are in the same class if and only if $f_1(x)$ and $f_2(x)$ are equal almost everywhere on Δ. Evidently, if $\| f_1 - f_2 \|_p = 0$ and $\| g_1 - g_2 \|_p = 0$, then $\|(f_1 + g_1) - (f_2 + g_2) \|_p = 0$ (by Minkowski's inequality, Ch. 5, § 1, Th. 3), and also $\| \alpha(f_1 - f_2) \|_p = 0$ for any complex α. Denoting by f the class which contains $f(x)$, the classes may therefore be considered as the elements of a set in which addition multiplication by a complex number α are defined by

g = the class which contains $f(x) + g(x)$,

the class which contains $\alpha f(x)$.

A of Banach space is evidently satisfied. The null element ontaining all functions which vanish almost everywhere on ore, if we define the norm $\| f \|$ of the element f by $\| f \| =$ ollows readily from this definition and Minkowski's inequality om B of Banach space is satisfied as well. Finally, by Ch. 5,

§ 2, Th. 1, which says that the space L_p is complete, we see that Axiom C, the axiom of completeness, holds. With these definitions our set of elements f is therefore a Banach space. No confusion will arise if we denote it by L_p, and the norm of its element f by $\| f \|_p$, while moreover we shall often speak about the function $f(x) \in L_p$ as an element of the Banach space L_p when, strictly speaking, we mean the class f to which $f(x)$ belongs. Theorem 1 in Ch. 5, § 3 shows that, for $1 \leqslant p < \infty$ and any separable measure μ, the Banach space L_p is separable (compare Ch. 5, § 3 and Axiom D, the axiom of separability). If the measure μ is non-atomic, that is, if it has the property that every set E of positive measure $\mu(E)$ contains a subset of measure α for any α satisfying $0 \leqslant \alpha \leqslant \mu(E)$, the spaces $L_p (1 \leqslant p \leqslant \infty)$ are not of finite dimension since for any arbitrary positive integer n, if $E_1, \ldots, E_n$ are n measurable sets of finite, positive measure, contained in Δ, no two of which have common points, the characteristic functions of these sets are evidently linearly independent.

Example B. *The Orlicz spaces* L_Φ

In the functionspaces $L_\Phi(\Delta, \mu)$, introduced in Ch. 5, § 5, we may divide the functions $f(x) \in L_\Phi$ (for a fixed function $\Phi(u)$) into classes such that $f_1(x)$ and $f_2(x)$ are in the same class if and only if $\| f_1 - f_2 \|_\Phi = 0$, or, which is equivalent, if and only if $f_1(x)$ and $f_2(x)$ are equal almost everywhere on Δ (cf. Ch. 5, § 5, Th. 1). Denoting again by f the class which contains $f(x)$, addition and multiplication by a complex number α of the elements f are defined as in the preceding example, while the norm $\| f \|$ of f is given by $\| f \| = \| f \|_\Phi$. Then the Axioms A and B of Banach space are satisfied (cf. Ch. 5, § 5, Th. 4). From Ch. 5, § 6, where it is proved that the space L_Φ is complete, we see that Axiom C is satisfied as well. With these definitions the set of elements f is therefore a Banach space, which we shall denote by L_Φ (cf. the remarks about notation in the preceding example). From Ch. 5, § 7 we see that the Banach space L_Φ is separable if there exists a constant $M > 0$ such that $\Phi(2u) \leqslant M\Phi(u)$ for every $u \geqslant 0$, and the measure μ is separable. Finally, the same argument as in the preceding example shows that the spaces L_Φ are not of finite dimension, provided μ is non-atomic.

The spaces L_p may be considered as particular examples of spaces L_Φ; the only difference is that, for $1 < p < \infty$, the norm $\| f \|_\Phi$ (where $\Phi(u) = u^p/p$) is not identical with $\| f \|_p$, but $\| f \|_\Phi = q^{1/q} \| f \|_p$ where $1/p + 1/q = 1$ (cf. the Remark in Ch. 5, § 5). Since the numerical factor $q^{1/q}$ is of no importance in most of the applications, the difference is not essential.

We observe finally that what we have said about the functionspaces L_Φ applies equally well to their complementary spaces L_Ψ, even in the case that $\lim_{u\to\infty} \varphi(u)$ is finite.

Example C. *The spaces* $l_p (1 \leqslant p \leqslant \infty)$

Let Δ be the linear interval $0 \leqslant x < \infty$, μ Lebesgue measure on Δ, and, given any sequence $f_1, f_2, \ldots$ of real or complex numbers, let the function $f(x)$ on Δ be defined by $f(0) = 0$, $f(x) = f(i) = f_i$ for $i - 1 < x \leqslant i$ $(i = 1, 2, \ldots)$. Then the element $f = \{f_1, f_2, \ldots\}$ is said to belong to the set $l_p (1 \leqslant p \leqslant \infty)$ if the thus defined function $f(x)$ belongs to $L_p(\Delta, \mu)$. For $1 \leqslant p < \infty$ this means that $f \in l_p$ if and only if $\Sigma_{i=1}^{\infty} | f_i |^p < \infty$; for $p = \infty$ we have $f \in l_\infty$ if and only if the sequence $f_i (i = 1, 2, \ldots)$ is bounded. Defining, for $f = \{f_1, f_2, \ldots\}$ and $g = \{g_1, g_2, \ldots\}$,

$$f + g = \{f_1 + g_1, f_2 + g_2, \ldots\},$$

$$\alpha f = \{\alpha f_1, \alpha f_2, \ldots\} \text{ for any complex } \alpha,$$

$$\| f \| = \| f(x) \|_p$$

(hence $\| f \| = (\Sigma_{i=1}^{\infty} | f_i |^p)^{1/p}$ for $1 \leqslant p < \infty$, and $\| f \| =$ upper bound $| f_i |$ for $p = \infty$), we see that the set l_p satisfies the Axioms A and B of Banach space. Hölder's inequality takes the form: If $1 \leqslant p \leqslant \infty$, $1/p + 1/q = 1$, $f \in l_p$, $g \in l_q$, then $\{f_1 g_1, f_2 g_2, \ldots\} \in l$, and

$$| \Sigma f_i g_i | \leqslant \Sigma | f_i g_i | \leqslant \| f \|_p . \| g \|_q .$$

To show that l_p satisfies Axiom C as well, we observe that in the proof of the completeness of the functionspace L_p (cf. Ch. 5, § 2, Th. 1), where $\lim \| f_n(x) - f_m(x) \|_p = 0$ $(m, n \to \infty)$ is given, the limit function $f(x)$, for which $\lim \| f_n(x) - f(x) \|_p = 0$ holds, is almost everywhere on Δ the ordinary pointwise limit of a subsequence $f_{n_k}(x)$. If therefore all functions $f_n(x)$ have the property to be constant on all intervals $i - 1 < x \leqslant i$ $(i = 1, 2, \ldots)$, the same holds for $f(x)$. The set l_p is therefore a Banach space. Evidently, for $1 \leqslant p < \infty$, the set of all elements $f = \{f_1, f_2, \ldots, f_k, 0, 0, \ldots\}$, where all f_i except a finite (but not fixed) number vanish and where the non-vanishing f_i are all rational complex, is dense in l_p, so that the space l_p is separable for these values of p.

Considering the subset $E_{p,n}$ of all elements $f = \{f_1, \ldots, f_n, 0, 0, \ldots\}$ for a fixed n, we see readily that this subset is an n-dimensional subspace of l_p, since (omitting all numbers 0 after f_n) the elements $\{1, 0, \ldots, 0\}$, $\{0, 1, 0, \ldots, 0\}$, $\ldots$, $\{0, 0, \ldots, 1\}$ are linearly independent and form a complete set in $E_{p,n}$. The subspace $E_{2,n}$ is usually called complex n-

dimensional Euclidean space, because in $E_{2,n}$ we have $\| f \| = (\Sigma_{i=1}^n | f_i |^2)^{1/2}$.

Example D. *The Besicovitch spaces B_p - a.p.* [8]

For the classes of functions $f(x)$ and $g(x)$, where μ is Lebesgue measure on the straight line, $f(x) \in L_p\{[-T, T], \mu\}$ $(1 \leqslant p \leqslant \infty$, T real) and $g(x) \in L_q\{[-T, T], \mu\}$ $(1/p + 1/q = 1)$ for every finite linear interval $[-T, T]$, we introduce the following notations:

$$(f, g; T) = \frac{1}{2T} \int_{-T}^{T} f(x) \overline{g(x)} \, dx$$

(where $\overline{g(x)}$ is the conjugate complex number of $g(x)$ for every x),

$$\| f; T \|_p = \begin{cases} \left(\dfrac{1}{2T} \displaystyle\int_{-T}^{T} | f |^p \, dx \right)^{1/p} & \text{for} \quad 1 \leqslant p < \infty, \\ \| f \|_\infty \text{ in } -T \leqslant x \leqslant T & \text{for} \quad p = \infty, \end{cases}$$

$$(f, g) = \lim_{T\to\infty} (f, g;\ T),$$

$$\| f \|_p = \limsup_{T\to\infty} \| f;\ T \|_p,$$

where the last two expressions are only defined for those functions for which these limits exist as finite numbers.

Let us consider in particular the trigonometric functions $\varphi\lambda(x) = e^{i\lambda x}$ (λ real). Here

$$\| \varphi_\lambda;\ T \|_p^p = \begin{cases} \dfrac{1}{2T} \displaystyle\int_{-T}^{T} dx = 1 & \text{for} \quad 1 \leqslant p < \infty, \\ 1 & \text{for} \quad p = \infty, \end{cases}$$

hence

$$\| \varphi_\lambda \|_p = 1,$$

and for $\lambda \neq \mu$

$$(\varphi_\lambda, \varphi_\mu; T) = \frac{1}{2T} \int_{-T}^{T} e^{i(\lambda-\mu)x} \, dx = \frac{1}{T} \int_0^T \cos{(\lambda - \mu)x} \, dx,$$

hence

$$(\varphi_\lambda, \varphi_\mu) = 0.$$

Consequently, if $f(x) = \Sigma_1^n \alpha_i \varphi_{\lambda_i}(x)$ and $g(x) = \Sigma_1^n \beta_i \varphi_{\lambda_i}(x)$ are trigonometric polynomials, we see readily that (f, g) exists and $(f, g) = \Sigma_1^n \alpha_i \overline{\beta}_i$. Furthermore, for any trigonometric polynomial $f(x)$, the expression $\| f \|_p$ is finite because $f(x)$ is bounded.

Let now the function $f(x)$ be such that there exists a sequence $s_n(x)$ of trigonometric polynomials for which $\| f - s_n \|_p$ exists and tends to 0 as $n \to \infty$. We shall prove that in this case $\| f \|_p$ exists and that $\| f \|_p = \lim \| s_n \|_p$. Indeed, by Minkowski's inequality, we have $\| f; T \|_p \leqslant \| s_n; T \|_p + \| f - s_n; T \|_p$. Hence, if $T \to \infty$, we obtain $\limsup \| f; T \|_p \leqslant \| s_n \|_p + \| f - s_n \|_p$ for every value of n, so that, $\varepsilon > 0$ being arbitrarily given and taking N so large that $\| f - s_n \|_p < \varepsilon$ for $n \geqslant N$, we see that $\limsup \| f; T \|_p \leqslant \| s_N \|_p + \varepsilon$. This shows that $\| f \|_p$ exists. Evidently $\| f \|_p \leqslant \| s_n \|_p + \varepsilon$ for $n \geqslant N$. Since on the other hand $\| s_n; T \|_p \leqslant \| f; T \|_p + \| f - s_n; T \|_p$, we have also $\| s_n \|_p \leqslant \| f \|_p + \varepsilon$ for $n \geqslant N$, so that

$$\| f \|_p - \varepsilon \leqslant \| s_n \|_p \leqslant \| f \|_p + \varepsilon \quad \text{for} \quad n \geqslant N.$$

Hence $\| f \|_p = \lim \| s_n \|_p$.

Finally, let the functions $f(x)$ and $g(x)$ be such that there exist sequences $s_n(x)$ and $t_n(x)$ of trigonometric polynomials for which $\lim \| f - s_n \|_p = 0$, $\lim \| g - t_n \|_q = 0$, $1/p + 1/q = 1$. We shall show that in this case (f, g) exists and that $(f, g) = \lim (s_n, t_n)$. By what we have already proved, $\| f \|_p$ and $\| g \|_q$ exist. If now $M = \max (\| f \|_p, \| g \|_q) + 1$, there exists an index N such that, if $\varepsilon > 0$ is given, we have $\| t_n \|_q < 2M$, $\| f - s_n \|_p < \varepsilon/8M$ and $\| g - t_n \|_q < \varepsilon/8M$ simultaneously for $n \geqslant N$. Then, since by Hölder's inequality

$$| (f, g; T) - (s_N, t_N; T) | = | (f, g - t_N; T) + (f - s_N, t_N; T) |$$
$$\leqslant \| f; T \|_p . \| g - t_N; T \|_q + \| f - s_N; T \|_p . \| t_N; T \|_q,$$

we find

$$\limsup_{T\to\infty} | (f, g; T) - (s_N, t_N; T) |$$
$$\leqslant \| f \|_p . \| g - t_N \|_q + \| f - s_N \|_p . \| t_N \|_q < \varepsilon/2,$$

hence, for $T > T_0$,

$$| (f, g; T) - (s_N, t_N; T) | < \varepsilon/2.$$

But, for $T > T_1$, we have

$$| (s_N, t_N) - (s_N, t_N; T) | < \varepsilon/2;$$

hence, for $T > \max (T_0, T_1)$,

$$| (f, g; T) - (s_N, t_N) | < \varepsilon.$$

Denoting the real part of the complex number $(f, g; T)$ by $R(f, g; T)$ and the imaginary part by $I(f, g; T)$, we infer from this

$$\limsup_{T\to\infty} R(f, g; T) - \liminf_{T\to\infty} R(f, g; T) < 2\varepsilon,$$

$$\limsup_{T\to\infty} I(f, g; T) - \liminf_{T\to\infty} I(f, g; T) < 2\varepsilon,$$

so that, since ε is arbitrarily positive, $(f, g) = \lim (f, g; T)$ exists. The relation $| (f, g) - (s_n, t_n) | \leqslant \varepsilon$, holding for every $n \geqslant N$, shows finally that $(f, g) = \lim (s_n, t_n)$.

Moreover, since by Hölder's inequality $| (f, g; T) | \leqslant \| f; T \|_p . \| g; T \|_q$, we find

$$| (f, g) | \leqslant \| f \|_p . \| g \|_q .$$

For a fixed $p(1 \leqslant p \leqslant \infty)$, we consider now the set $B_p\text{-}a.p.$, consisting of all trigonometric polynomials and all functions $f(x)$ for which there exists a sequence $s_n(x)$ of trigonometric polynomials such that $\lim \| f - s_n \|_p = 0$. Evidently, if $f(x)$ and $g(x)$ are in this set, so is $\alpha f(x) + \beta g(x)$ for α and β arbitrarily complex. We may divide this set into classes such that $f_1(x)$ and $f_2(x)$ are in the same class if and only if $\| f_1 - f_2 \|_p = 0$. It is clear that, for $1 \leqslant p < \infty$, if $\| f_1 - f_2 \|_p = 0$, the functions $f_1(x)$ and $f_2(x)$ may still be different on a set of positive and even infinite measure. Denoting by f the class which contains $f(x)$, addition and multiplication by a complex number α are defined by

$$f + g = \text{the class which contains } f(x) + g(x),$$

$$\alpha f = \text{the class which contains } \alpha f(x).$$

The Axiom A of Banach space is then evidently satisfied. The null element is the class of all $f(x)$ for which $\| f \|_p = 0$. Defining now the norm $\| f \|$ of the element f by $\| f \| = \| f \|_p$, Axiom B of Banach space is satisfied as well.

We shall prove now that the set of classes f is complete. First we observe that if there exists a function $f(x)$ and a sequence of functions $f_n(x) \in B_p\text{-}a.p.$, satisfying $\lim \| f - f_n \|_p = 0$, then also $f(x) \in B_p\text{-}a.p.$. Indeed, if ε_n is a sequence of positive numbers tending to 0, we may assign to every $f_n(x)$ a trigonometric polynomial $s_n(x)$ such that $\| f_n - s_n \|_p < \varepsilon_n$, and on account of $\| f - s_n \|_p \leqslant \| f - f_n \|_p + \| f_n - s_n \|_p$ it follows that $\lim \| f - s_n \|_p = 0$, hence $f(x) \in B_p\text{-}a.p.$. To show completeness it is sufficient therefore, if $\lim \| f_m - f_n \|_p = 0$ ($m, n \to \infty$, $f_i \in B_p\text{-}a.p.$ for all i) is given, to prove the existence of a function $f(x)$ for which $\lim \| f - f_n \|_p = 0$ holds.

We shall dispose first of the case $p = \infty$. If $\lim \| f_n - f_m \|_\infty = 0$, there exists a sequence ε_n of positive numbers tending to 0 for which $\| f_n - f_{n+q} \|_\infty < \varepsilon_n$ holds for all n and $q > 0$; hence $| f_n(x) - f_{n+q}(x) | < \varepsilon_n$ for almost every x on $-\infty < x < \infty$. It follows that $f(x) = \lim f_n(x)$ exists for these values of x, and that $\| f_n - f \|_\infty \leqslant \varepsilon_n$.

Let us suppose now that $1 \leqslant p < \infty$, $f_n(x) \in B_p\text{-}a.p.$ $(n = 1, 2, \ldots)$ and $\lim \| f_n - f_m \|_p = 0$ as $m, n \to \infty$ [9]. Then also $\lim \| f_n - f_m \|_p^* = 0$, where

$$\| f \|_p^* = \limsup_{T\to\infty} \left(\frac{1}{T} \int_0^T | f |^p \, dx \right)^{1/p},$$

so that there exists a sequence ε_n of positive numbers tending to 0 such that

$$\limsup_{T\to\infty} \frac{1}{T} \int_0^T | f_n - f_{n+q} |^p \, dx < \varepsilon_n \text{ for all } n \text{ and } q > 0.$$

We shall construct a function $f(x)$ defined for $x > 0$, and a sequence $0 = T_0 < T_1 < T_2 < \ldots \to \infty$ satisfying

$$\text{(1)} \qquad \frac{1}{T} \int_0^T | f - f_n |^p \, dx < 2\varepsilon_n \text{ for } T > T_n \text{ and all } n,$$

which involves $(\| f - f_n \|_p^*)^p \leqslant 2\varepsilon_n$, hence $\lim \| f - f_n \|_p^* = 0$. An analogous procedure is followed for $x < 0$, and the resulting function on the whole x-axis is the desired function $f(x)$. Restricting ourselves therefore to $x > 0$, we first define

$$f(x) = f_i(x) \text{ for } T_{i-1} < x \leqslant T_i \ (i = 1, 2, \ldots),$$

and we shall show that the numbers T_i may be chosen in such a way that (1) is satisfied. We first set up a number of conditions for $T_1, T_2, \ldots$, arranged in certain groups, which involve (1); afterwards we shall see that these conditions can be satisfied simultaneously.

Group 1. The inequality (1) is satisfied for $n = 1$, if

$$\frac{1}{T} \int_0^T | f_2 - f_1 |^p \, dx < \varepsilon_1 \quad \text{for} \quad T > T_1 \qquad \boxed{T_1}$$

$$\frac{1}{T} \int_0^T | f_3 - f_1 |^p \, dx < \varepsilon_1 \quad \text{for} \quad T > T_2 \qquad \boxed{T_2}$$

$$\frac{1}{T} \int_0^T | f_4 - f_1 |^p \, dx < \varepsilon_1 \quad \text{for} \quad T > T_3 \qquad \boxed{T_3}$$

$$\ldots\ldots\ldots\ldots\ldots\ldots\ldots$$

and

$$\frac{1}{T_2 - T_1} \int_{T_1}^{T_2} | f_2 - f_1 |^p \, dx < \varepsilon_1 \qquad \boxed{T_2(T_1)}$$

$$\frac{1}{T_3 - T_2} \int_{T_2}^{T_3} | f_3 - f_1 |^p \, dx < \varepsilon_1 \qquad \boxed{T_3(T_2)}$$

$$\ldots\ldots\ldots\ldots\ldots\ldots,$$

because, if $T > T_1$ lies between T_m and T_{m+1}, we have

$$\int_0^T |f - f_1|^p\, dx = \int_0^{T_1} + \int_{T_1}^{T_2} + \dots + \int_{T_{m-1}}^{T_m} + \int_{T_m}^{T} |f - f_1|^p\, dx$$
$$< 0 + \varepsilon_1(T_2 - T_1) + \dots + \varepsilon_1(T_m - T_{m-1}) + \varepsilon_1 T < 2\varepsilon_1 T.$$

Group 2. The inequality (1) is satisfied for $n = 2$, if

$$\frac{1}{T}\int_0^T |f_3 - f_2|^p\, dx < \varepsilon_2 \quad \text{for} \quad T > T_2 \qquad \boxed{T_2}$$

$$\frac{1}{T}\int_0^T |f_4 - f_2|^p\, dx < \varepsilon_2 \quad \text{for} \quad T > T_3 \qquad \boxed{T_3}$$

$$\dots\dots\dots\dots$$

and

$$\frac{1}{T_2}\int_0^{T_1} |f_1 - f_2|^p\, dx < \varepsilon_2 \qquad \boxed{T_2(T_1)}$$

$$\frac{1}{T_3 - T_2}\int_{T_2}^{T_3} |f_3 - f_2|^p\, dx < \varepsilon_2 \qquad \boxed{T_3(T_2)}$$

$$\frac{1}{T_4 - T_3}\int_{T_3}^{T_4} |f_4 - f_2|^p\, dx < \varepsilon_2 \qquad \boxed{T_4(T_3)}$$

$$\dots\dots\dots\dots,$$

because, if $T > T_2$ lies between T_m and T_{m+1}, we have

$$\int_0^T |f - f_2|^p\, dx = \int_0^{T_2} + \int_{T_2}^{T_3} + \dots + \int_{T_{m-1}}^{T_m} + \int_{T_m}^{T} |f - f_2|^p\, dx$$
$$< \varepsilon_2 T_2 + \varepsilon_2(T_3 - T_2) + \dots + \varepsilon_2(T_m - T_{m-1}) + \varepsilon_2 T < 2\varepsilon_2 T.$$

Group 3. The inequality (1) is satisfied for $n = 3$, if

$$\frac{1}{T}\int_0^T |f_4 - f_3|^p\, dx < \varepsilon_3 \quad \text{for} \quad T > T_3 \qquad \boxed{T_3}$$

$$\frac{1}{T}\int_0^T |f_5 - f_3|^p\, dx < \varepsilon_3 \quad \text{for} \quad T > T_4 \qquad \boxed{T_4}$$

$$\dots\dots\dots\dots$$

and

$$\frac{1}{T_3}\left[\int_0^{T_1} |f_1 - f_3|^p\, dx + \int_{T_1}^{T_2} |f_2 - f_3|^p\, dx\right] < \varepsilon_3 \qquad \boxed{T_3(T_1, T_2)}$$

$$\frac{1}{T_4 - T_3}\int_{T_3}^{T_4} |f_4 - f_3|^p\, dx < \varepsilon_3 \qquad \boxed{T_4(T_3)}$$

$$\dots\dots\dots\dots,$$

and so on.

After each condition the T_n concerned are indicated in a rectangle. An indication like $T_2(T_1)$ means that we have to do with a condition on T_2 after T_1 has been chosen. By hypothesis, every condition on T_n is satisfied for all sufficiently large values of T_n. Since there are only a finite number of conditions for every T_n, and since the composed conditions are of the form $T_n(\ldots)$, where the T_i in the bracket have lower indices than n, the numbers $T_1, T_2, \ldots$ can be chosen successively in such a way as to satisfy all mentioned conditions.

The result is that our set of classes f is a complete Banach space. Following the same convention as in the preceding examples, we shall denote it by B_p-$a.p.$, and the norm of its element f by $\| f \|_p$, while we shall speak of the function $f(x) \in B_p$-$a.p.$ as an element of this space, when, strictly speaking, we mean the class f to which $f(x)$ belongs.

The Besicovitch space B_p-$a.p.$ is not separable. Indeed, let us assume on the contrary that the enumerable set $f_1, f_2, \ldots$ is dense in B_p-$a.p.$. Since there exists for every f_i a sequence $s_1^{(i)}(x), s_2^{(i)}(x), \ldots$ of trigonometric polynomials such that $\| f_i - s_n^{(i)} \|_p < 1/n$, so that the number of $\varphi_\lambda(x) = e^{i\lambda x}$ occurring in all polynomials $s_n^{(i)}(x)$ $(i, n = 1, 2, \ldots)$ together is enumerable, the set of these $\varphi_\lambda(x)$, say $\varphi_{\lambda_1}(x), \varphi_{\lambda_2}(x), \ldots$, is complete in the sense of § 3. Let now $\lambda \neq \lambda_i$ $(i = 1, 2, \ldots)$ and $0 < \varepsilon < 1$. Then $\| \varphi_\lambda - s \|_p < \varepsilon$ for a certain polynomial $s(x) = \Sigma_{i=1}^n \alpha_i \varphi_{\lambda_i}(x)$, hence $| (\varphi_\lambda, \varphi_\lambda - s) | \leqslant \| \varphi_\lambda \|_q \cdot \| \varphi_\lambda - s \|_p = \| \varphi_\lambda - s \|_p < \varepsilon < 1$, where $1/p + 1/q = 1$. But $(\varphi_\lambda, \varphi_\lambda - s) = (\varphi_\lambda, \varphi_\lambda) - (\varphi_\lambda, s) = 1 - 0 = 1$, which leads to a contradiction.

§ 7. Definition of Hilbert Space

A set R with elements $f, g, \ldots$ will be called a *Hilbert space* if it satisfies the following Axioms A, BH and C:

Axiom A. *Identical with Axiom A of Banach space.*

Axiom BH. *With every pair of elements of R corresponds a complex number (f, g), called the inner product of f and g, with the properties:*

1°. $(\alpha f, g) = \alpha(f, g)$, *$\alpha$ complex,*

2°. $(f_1 + f_2, g) = (f_1, g) + (f_2, g)$,

3°. $(f, g) = \overline{(g, f)}$, *where $\overline{(g, f)}$ is the complex conjugate of (g, f),*

4°. $(f, f) > 0$ *for* $f \neq 0$.

Immediate consequences are

$$(f, g_1 + g_2) = (f, g_1) + (f, g_2),$$
$$(f, \alpha g) = \bar{\alpha}(f, g),$$
$$(f, 0) = 0 \text{ (since } (f, 0) = (f, 0) + (f, 0)).$$

In particular, $(0, 0) = 0$, so that, by 4°, $(f, f) = 0$ if and only if $f = 0$.

The non-negative number $(f, f)^{1/2}$ is called the *norm* of f and denoted by $\| f \|$.

Axiom C (*Axiom of completeness*). *Identical with Axiom C of Banach space (with the above* $\| f \|$ *as norm).*

Any Hilbert space satisfying the Axiom D (Axiom of separability), identical with Axiom D of Banach space, will be called separable [10]. Any set satisfying Axioms A and BH, but not Axiom C, will be called a non-complete Hilbert space.

§ 8. Schwarz's and Minkowski's Inequalities. Hilbert Space as a Special Case of Banach Space

Theorem 1 (*Schwarz's inequality*). *For any two elements f, g of Hilbert space we have*

$$| (f, g) | \leqslant \| f \| \cdot \| g \|.$$

Proof. For $g = 0$ the theorem is trivial, since in this case $(f, g) = 0$. Let us suppose therefore that $g \neq 0$. Substituting in $(f + \alpha g, f + \alpha g) = (f, f) + \alpha(g, f) + \bar{\alpha}(f, g) + \alpha\bar{\alpha}(g, g) \geqslant 0$, holding for every complex α, the value $\alpha = -(f, g)/(g, g)$, we obtain

$$(f, f) - \frac{(f, g)\,(g, f)}{(g, g)} - \frac{(g, f)\,(f, g)}{(g, g)} + \frac{(f, g)\,(g, f)}{(g, g)^2}\,(g, g) \geqslant 0$$

or

$$(f, f) - \frac{(f, g)\,(g, f)}{(g, g)} \geqslant 0;$$

hence $(f, g)\,(g, f) \leqslant (f, f)\,(g, g)$ or $| (f, g) | \leqslant \| f \| \cdot \| g \|$.

Theorem 2 (*Minkowski's inequality*). *For any two elements f, g of Hilbert space we have*

$$\| f + g \| \leqslant \| f \| + \| g \|.$$

Proof. For $\| f+g \| = 0$ the theorem is trivial. For $\| f+g \| \neq 0$ we have

$$\| f+g \|^2 = (f+g, f+g) = (f+g, f) + (f+g, g)$$
$$\leqslant \| f+g \| . \| f \| + \| f+g \| . \| g \|,$$

or

$$\| f+g \| \leqslant \| f \| + \| g \|.$$

Theorem 3. *Any Hilbert space may be considered as a Banach space in such a way that the notions of norm of an element are identical in both spaces.*

Proof. Let R be a Hilbert space. We have to prove only that the norm $\| f \|$ in R satisfies Axiom B of Banach space, since the Axioms A and C are identical for Hilbert space and Banach space. We have

$$\| \alpha f \|^2 = (\alpha f, \alpha f) = \alpha\bar{\alpha}(f, f) = | \alpha |^2 . \| f \|^2,$$

hence

(B.1) $$\| \alpha f \| = | \alpha | . \| f \| \text{ for any complex } \alpha.$$

Furthermore

(B.2) $$\| f+g \| \leqslant \| f \| + \| g \|$$

by Minkowski's inequality, and

(B.3) $$\| f \| > 0 \text{ for } f \neq 0$$

by (BH.4°).

It follows that all notions introduced for Banach spaces in the preceding paragraphs may be carried over to Hilbert space without any change.

Theorem 4. *The inner product (f, g) is a continuous function of f and g; in other words, if $\lim f_n = f$ and $\lim g_n = g$, then $\lim (f_n, g_n) = (f, g)$.*

Proof. We have $| (f, g) - (f_n, g_n) | = | (f - f_n, g) + (f_n, g - g_n) | = | (f - f_n, g) + (f, g - g_n) + (f_n - f, g - g_n) | \leqslant \| f - f_n \| . \| g \| + \| f \| . \| g - g_n \| + \| f_n - f \| . \| g - g_n \|$, which tends to 0 as $n \to \infty$.

Theorem 5. *If R is a non-complete Hilbert space, there exists a complete Hilbert space $\bar{R}$, containing R as a subset, and such that R is dense in $\bar{R}$.*

Proof. We proceed as in the case of Banach space (cf. § 2, Th. 2). To every fundamental sequence $f_n \in R$ ($\lim \| f_m - f_n \| = 0$), if it has not already a limit belonging to R, is therefore assigned an "ideal" limitelement f. Limitelements corresponding with equivalent sequences f_n and g_n ($\lim (f_n - g_n) = 0$) are considered to be identical. If the sequences f_n and g_n have limits f and g, these limits belonging to R or being ideal elements, we see readily that $\lim (f_n, g_n)$ exists. Indeed, $\lim \| f_m - f_n \| = \lim \| g_m - g_n \| = 0$ implies the boundedness of $\| f_n \|$ and $\| g_n \|$; hence, if $\varepsilon > 0$ is given,

$$| (f_m, g_m) - (f_n, g_n) | \leqslant | (f_m, g_m - g_n) | + | (f_m - f_n, g_n) | < \varepsilon$$

for m and n sufficiently large. We define now $(f, g) = \lim (f_n, g_n)$, and on account of the preceding theorem this is not in contradiction with what we have proved in the case that f and g belong to R. Adding the ideal elements to R, we obtain the closure $\bar{R}$, and it follows easily that $\bar{R}$ satisfies the Axioms A, BH and C. Finally R is evidently dense in $\bar{R}$.

Theorem 6. *If the set S of elements is complete in R and $(f, h) = (g, h)$ for every $h \in S$, then $f = g$.*

Proof. We recall that S is called complete in R whenever the set $L(S)$ of all finite linear combinations $\Sigma\, \alpha_i h_i$ (α_i complex, $h_i \in S$) is dense in R. If therefore $(f - g, h) = 0$ for every $h \in S$, then $(f - g, l) = 0$ for every $l \in L(S)$; hence, since there exists by hypothesis a sequence $l_n \in L(S)$ converging to $f - g$, we have $(f - g, f - g) = \lim (f - g, l_n) = 0$ or $f = g$.

§ 9. Orthonormal Systems. Schmidt's Orthogonalization Process

The elements f and g of Hilbert space R (complete or non-complete) are called *orthogonal* when $(f, g) = 0$. The system Q of elements is called *orthonormal* when, for $\varphi \in Q$, $\psi \in Q$, we have

$$(\varphi, \psi) = \begin{cases} 1 \text{ for } \varphi = \psi, \\ 0 \text{ for } \varphi \neq \psi. \end{cases}$$

Evidently every subset of an orthonormal system is also orthonormal.

Theorem 1. *If the elements $\varphi_1, \varphi_2, \ldots, \varphi_n$ form an orthonormal system, they are linearly independent.*

Proof. $\Sigma_1^n\, \alpha_i \varphi_i = 0$ implies $\Sigma_{i=1}^n\, \alpha_i(\varphi_i, \varphi_k) = 0$ for $k = 1, \ldots, n$; hence $\alpha_1 = \ldots = \alpha_n = 0$.

Theorem 2. *If the dimension of R is more than enumerably infinite, the number of elements in a complete orthonormal system is more than enumerably* *infinite. If the dimension of R is enumerably infinite, the number of elements in a complete orthonormal system is enumerably infinite.*

Proof. The first part of the theorem is an immediate consequence of the definition of dimension. As regards the second part, let the space R be of enumerably infinite dimension, and let Q be a complete orthonormal system. Then there exists an enumerable complete set S; the set S', consisting of all finite linear combinations of elements of S with rational complex coefficients, is therefore enumerable and dense in R. Consequently we can assign to every $\varphi \in Q$ an element $f_\varphi \in S'$ such that $\| \varphi - f_\varphi \| < \sqrt{2}/2$. Elements f_φ and f_ψ, for which $\varphi \neq \psi$, are different since $f_\varphi = f_\psi$ would imply $\| \varphi - \psi \| = \| (\varphi - f_\varphi) - (\psi - f_\psi) \| \leqslant \| \varphi - f_\varphi \| + \| \psi - f_\psi \| < \sqrt{2}$, in contradiction with $\| \varphi - \psi \|^2 = \| \varphi \|^2 - (\varphi, \psi) - (\psi, \varphi) + \| \psi \|^2 = 1 - 0 - 0 + 1 = 2$. The set Q corresponds therefore with a subset of the enumerable set S', from which we conclude that Q is at most enumerable. Finally, it is impossible that Q is finite since R is not of finite dimension.

Theorem 3 (*Schmidt's orthogonalization process* [11]). *Given a finite or enumerable set S, there exists an orthonormal system Q such that*

$$L(S) = L(Q).$$

Proof. Let $f_1, f_2, \ldots$ be the elements of S. We consider the sequence S^* of elements $f_1^*, f_2^*, \ldots$, obtained from S by leaving out all elements f_n depending linearly on $f_1, \ldots, f_{n-1}$. Then the elements $f_1^*, \ldots, f_n^*$ are linearly independent for every value of n, and $L(S) = L(S^*)$. The orthonormal system Q with elements $\varphi_1, \varphi_2, \ldots$ is now defined by Schmidt's orthogonalization process in the following way:

$$\varphi_1 = f_1^*/\| f_1^* \|, \; g_2 = f_2^* - (f_2^*, \varphi_1)\varphi_1, \; \varphi_2 = g_2/\| g_2 \|, \; \ldots .$$

Generally, if $\varphi_1, \ldots, \varphi_{n-1}$ are already defined,

$$g_n = f_n^* - \Sigma_{k=1}^{n-1} (f_n^*, \varphi_k)\varphi_k, \; \varphi_n = g_n/\| g_n \|.$$

To justify this definition of φ_n it is necessary to show that $\| g_n \| \neq 0$ on the assumption that the existence of $\varphi_1, \ldots, \varphi_{n-1}$ has already been established. Every φ_k is however a linear combination of $f_1^*, \ldots, f_k^*$, so that g_n may be written in the form $g_n = f_n^* - \Sigma_{k=1}^{n-1} \alpha_k f_k^*$; the linear independence of $f_1^*, \ldots, f_n^*$ guarantees therefore that $g_n \neq 0$. The existence of the system Q being thus established, we see easily that it is orthonormal. Moreover, every φ_n is a linear combination of $f_1^*, \ldots, f_n^*$, and every f_n^* is a linear combination of $\varphi_1, \ldots, \varphi_n$; hence $L(Q) = L(S^*) = L(S)$.

Theorem 4. *If the dimension of R is finite or enumerably infinite, there exists in R a complete orthonormal system.*

Proof. Since, by hypothesis, there exists in R a finite or enumerable complete set S, and since we may, by Schmidt's orthogonalization process, obtain a finite or enumerable system Q such that $L(Q) = L(S)$, the set $L(Q)$ is dense in R. The system Q is therefore complete.

§ 10. Unitary Space

Any Hilbert space of finite dimension is called a *unitary space.* If R is an n-dimensional unitary space, there exist by definition n linearly independent elements $f_1, \ldots, f_n$, forming a complete set in R, and by § 4, Th. 1 every $f \in R$ may be expressed in the form $f = \Sigma_{i=1}^n \alpha_i f_i$. We may, by Schmidt's orthogonalization process, replace $f_1, \ldots, f_n$ by the complete orthonormal system $\varphi_1, \ldots, \varphi_n$, and we see therefore that every $f \in R$ may be expressed in the form $f = \Sigma_{i=1}^n \beta_i \varphi_i$. Furthermore, if $\psi_1, \ldots, \psi_m$ is any other complete orthonormal system, then $m = n$. Indeed, by § 4, Th. 2, the space R does not contain more than n linearly independent elements; hence, the elements of an orthonormal system being linearly independent, their number is at most n. If the system is complete, their number is exactly n since the space R is n-dimensional. Finally, any orthonormal system containing n elements is complete, once again by § 4, Th. 2.

§ 11. Series of Orthogonal Elements. Bessel's Inequality. Parseval's Relation

Let the Hilbert space R be complete or non-complete. If the partial sums $\Sigma_1^n f_i$ of the series of elements $\Sigma_1^\infty f_i$ converge to an element f, we shall say that the series converges to the limit f, and we shall write $\Sigma_1^\infty f_i = f$.

Theorem 1. *Let $\varphi_n (n = 1, 2, \ldots)$ be a sequence of orthonormal elements. Then, if $f = \Sigma_1^\infty \alpha_n \varphi_n$, the series $\Sigma_1^\infty |\alpha_n|^2$ converges and $\alpha_n = (f, \varphi_n)$ $(n = 1, 2, \ldots)$. If the space R is complete, the convergence of $\Sigma_1^\infty |\alpha_n|^2$ implies conversely that of $\Sigma_1^\infty \alpha_n \varphi_n$.*

Proof. Let $f = \Sigma_1^\infty \alpha_n \varphi_n$. Writing $s_n = \Sigma_1^n \alpha_i \varphi_i$, we have for $n > m$ the relation $\| s_n - s_m \|^2 = \| \Sigma_{m+1}^n \alpha_i \varphi_i \|^2 = (\Sigma_{m+1}^n \alpha_i \varphi_i, \Sigma_{m+1}^n \alpha_i \varphi_i) = \Sigma_{m+1}^n |\alpha_i|^2$, so that, since by hypothesis $\lim \| s_n - s_m \|^2 = 0$, we see that

$\Sigma_1^\infty \mid \alpha_i \mid^2 < \infty$. Furthermore $f = \Sigma_1^\infty \alpha_i \varphi_i$ implies

$$(f, \varphi_n) = \lim_{k\to\infty} (\Sigma_1^k \alpha_i\varphi_i, \varphi_n) = \alpha_n (n = 1, 2, \ldots).$$

Let now the space R be complete and $\Sigma_1^\infty \mid \alpha_i \mid^2 < \infty$. Then $\lim \| s_n - s_m \|^2 = \lim \Sigma_{m+1}^n \mid \alpha_i \mid^2 = 0$ as $m, n \to \infty$; the sequence s_n, being a fundamental sequence, has therefore a limit in R.

Theorem 2 (*Bessel's inequality*). *Let φ_n $(n = 1, 2, \ldots)$ be a sequence of orthonormal elements. Then, for any element f, we have*

$$\Sigma_1^\infty \mid (f, \varphi_n) \mid^2 \leqslant \| f \|^2.$$

Proof. We write $(f, \varphi_n) = \alpha_n$, $s_n = \Sigma_1^n \alpha_i\varphi_i$, $f - s_n = r_n$. Then, for $k = 1, \ldots, n$, we have $\alpha_k = (f, \varphi_k) = (s_n, \varphi_k) + (r_n, \varphi_k) = \alpha_k + (r_n, \varphi_k)$, and therefore $(r_n, s_n) = (r_n, \Sigma_{k=1}^n \alpha_k\varphi_k) = 0$. Consequently $\| f \|^2 = (f, f) = (s_n + r_n, s_n + r_n) = (s_n, s_n) + (r_n, r_n) = \Sigma_1^n \mid \alpha_i \mid^2 + \| r_n \|^2$ or, since n is arbitrary, $\Sigma_1^\infty \mid \alpha_i \mid^2 \leqslant \| f \|^2$.

Theorem 3. *Let Q be an orthonormal system of elements. Then, for any $f \in R$, the number of elements $\varphi \in Q$ for which $(f, \varphi) \neq 0$ is at most enumerable.*

Proof. For any enumerable subset $\varphi_1, \varphi_2, \ldots$ of Q Bessel's inequality $\Sigma_1^\infty \mid (f, \varphi_n) \mid^2 \leqslant \| f \|^2$ holds; we see therefore that for every $\varepsilon > 0$ the number of elements $\varphi \in Q$ for which $\mid (f, \varphi) \mid > \varepsilon$ is finite. Hence, since every $\varphi \in Q$ for which $(f, \varphi) \neq 0$ satisfies one of the conditions $\mid (f, \varphi) \mid > 1$ or $1/n \geqslant \mid (f, \varphi) \mid > 1/(n + 1)$ $(n = 1, 2, \ldots)$, and since the number of $\varphi \in Q$ satisfying each condition is finite, the number of $\varphi \in Q$ for which $(f, \varphi) \neq 0$ is at most enumerable.

Theorem 4. *Let Q be an orthonormal system of elements. Then the following conditions on Q are equivalent:*

1°. *Q is complete.*

2°. *If $f \in R$ is arbitrary, and $\varphi_1, \varphi_2, \ldots$ is the sequence of $\varphi \in Q$ satisfying $(f, \varphi) \neq 0$, then $f = \Sigma (f, \varphi_n)\varphi_n$.*

3° (*Parseval's relation*). *If $f \in R$ and $g \in R$ are arbitrary, and $\varphi_1, \varphi_2, \ldots$ is the sequence of $\varphi \in Q$ satisfying one at least of the inequalities $(f, \varphi) \neq 0$ and $(g, \varphi) \neq 0$, then*

$$(f, g) = \Sigma(f, \varphi_n) \overline{(g, \varphi_n)}.$$

4°. *If $f \in R$ is arbitrary, and $\varphi_1, \varphi_2, \ldots$ is the sequence of $\varphi \in Q$ satisfying $(f, \varphi) \neq 0$, then $\| f \|^2 = \Sigma \mid (f, \varphi_n) \mid^2$.*

Proof. We shall prove the implications $1° \to 2° \to 3° \to 4° \to 1°$.

$1° \to 2°$. We consider the closure $\bar{R}$ of R. Since, by Bessel's inequality,

$\Sigma \mid (f, \varphi_n) \mid^2 \leqslant \| f \|^2$, and the space $\bar{R}$ is complete, it follows from Theorem 1 that $\Sigma(f, \varphi_n)\varphi_n$ converges to an element $g \in \bar{R}$. But, $L(Q)$ being dense in R and R being dense in $\bar{R}$, $L(Q)$ is dense in $\bar{R}$; the system Q is therefore complete in $\bar{R}$ as well. Hence, $g = \Sigma (f, \varphi_n)\varphi_n$ implying $(f, \varphi) = (g, \varphi)$ for every $\varphi \in Q$, we find on account of § 8, Th. 6 the equality $f = g = \Sigma (f, \varphi_n)\varphi_n$.

$2° \to 3°$. Writing $\alpha_n = (f, \varphi_n)$ and $\beta_n = (g, \varphi_n)$, we find

$(f, g) = \lim_{N\to\infty} (\Sigma_1^N \alpha_n \varphi_n, \Sigma_1^N \beta_n \varphi_n) = \lim_{N\to\infty} \Sigma_1^N \alpha_n \bar{\beta}_n = \Sigma_1^\infty \alpha_n \bar{\beta}_n.$

$3° \to 4°$. We take $g = f$ in 3°.

$4° \to 1°$. Assuming the system Q to be not complete, there exists an element $f \in R$ and a number $\varepsilon > 0$ such that $\| f - s_n \| > \varepsilon$ for every polynomial $s_n = \Sigma_1^n \alpha_i \varphi_i$. Taking in particular $\alpha_i = (f, \varphi_i)$, we find as in the proof of Bessel's inequality $\| f \|^2 = \| s_n \|^2 + \| f - s_n \|^2$, hence $\| f \|^2 > \Sigma_1^n \mid (f, \varphi_i) \mid^2 + \varepsilon^2$ for every n, so that $\| f \|^2 \geqslant \Sigma \mid (f, \varphi_i) \mid^2 + \varepsilon^2$, in contradiction with 4°.

§ 12. Orthogonal Subspaces. Factorspace

A set S of elements in Banach space or Hilbert space is called *convex* whenever $f_1 \in S$, $f_2 \in S$ implies $(f_1 + f_2)/2 \in S$.

Theorem 1. *Let the set S in Hilbert space be convex, and let d = lower bound $\| f \|$ for all $f \in S$. Then, if the sequence f_n of elements of S has the property that $\lim \| f_n \| = d$, it is a fundamental sequence.*

Proof. From the identity $\| f + g \|^2 + \| f - g \|^2 = 2 \| f \|^2 + 2 \| g \|^2$ follows

$$\left\| \frac{f_n - f_m}{2} \right\|^2 = \tfrac{1}{2} \| f_n \|^2 + \tfrac{1}{2} \| f_m \|^2 - \left\| \frac{f_n + f_m}{2} \right\|^2.$$

Since $(f_n + f_m)/2 \in S$, we have $\| (f_n + f_m)/2 \| \geqslant d$, hence

$$\| (f_n - f_m)/2 \|^2 \leqslant \| f_n \|^2/2 + \| f_m \|^2/2 - d^2.$$

The right side of this inequality tends to 0, so that also $\lim \| f_n - f_m \| = 0$.

Theorem 2. *Let $[L]$ be a linear subspace of the Hilbert space R (complete or non-complete). Then the set $[M]$ of all elements orthogonal to all elements of the subspace $[L]$ is a linear subspace.*

Proof. Since $(f, l) = (g, l) = 0$ for $l \in [L]$ implies $(\alpha f + \beta g, l) = 0$ for α and β arbitrarily complex, $[M]$ is linear. Since $(f_n, l) = 0$ and $\lim f_n = f$ imply $(f, l) = 0$, $[M]$ is closed.

Definition. *The linear subspace of all elements orthogonal to all elements of the linear subspace* $[L]$ *is called the orthogonal complement of* $[L]$, *and denoted by* $R \ominus [L]$.

Theorem 3. *Let the linear subspace* $[L]$, *considered as a Hilbert space, be complete (the space* R *itself may be complete or not). Then* R *is the direct sum of* $[L]$ *and* $R \ominus [L]$ [12].

Proof. Let $f \in R$ be arbitrary but fixed, and let $d =$ lower bound $\| f - g \|$ for all $g \in [L]$. Then there exists a sequence $g_n \in [L]$ such that $\lim \| f - g_n \| = d$. Since the set of all elements $f - g$ with $g \in [L]$ is convex, the sequence $f - g_n$ is, by Theorem 1, a fundamental sequence. The same is therefore true of the sequence g_n. Hence, $[L]$ being a complete Hilbert space, $\lim g_n = g$ exists, and $g \in [L]$. Evidently $\| f - g \| = d$.

Let now l be an arbitrary element of $[L]$. Then, since $g + \alpha l \in [L]$ for every complex α, we have $\| f - (g + \alpha l) \| \geqslant d$, hence $0 \leqslant \| f - (g + \alpha l) \|^2 - \| f - g \|^2 = - \bar{\alpha}(f - g, l) - \alpha(l, f - g) + \alpha\bar{\alpha} \| l \|^2$. Taking $\alpha = \lambda(f - g, l)$, where λ is real, we obtain $- 2\lambda \mid (f - g, l) \mid^2 + \lambda^2 \mid (f - g, l) \mid^2 . \| l \|^2 \geqslant 0$. This inequality holds for every real value of λ, which is only possible if $(f - g, l) = 0$; in other words, if $f - g \in R \ominus [L]$. Hence, writing $f - g = h$, we find $f = g + h$ with $g \in [L]$ and $h \in R \ominus [L]$.

It remains to show that $[L]$ and $R \ominus [L]$ have only the null element in common. This however is evident, for supposing that $f \in [L]$ and $f \in R \ominus [L]$ hold simultaneously, we have $(f, f) = 0$, hence $f = 0$.

We recall that by § 4, Th. 5 the decomposition $f = g + h$ ($g \in [L]$, $h \in R \ominus [L]$) is unique.

Theorem 4. *Let the linear subspace* $[L]$, *considered as a Hilbert space, be complete. Then the orthogonal complement of* $R \ominus [L]$ *is* $[L]$.

Proof. Let L_1 be the set of all elements orthogonal to $R \ominus [L]$. Evidently $[L] \subset L_1$. It is sufficient, therefore, to prove that $L_1 \subset [L]$. For any $f \in R$ we have on account of the preceding theorem $f = g + h$ ($g \in [L]$, $h \in R \ominus [L]$), so that $(g, h) = 0$. If now in particular $f \in L_1$, we have moreover $(f, h) = 0$; hence $(f - g, h) = 0$ or $(h, h) = 0$, so that $h = 0$. But then $f = g \in [L]$, and this shows that $L_1 \subset [L]$.

Remark. If $[L]$ is non-complete, the Theorems 3 and 4 need not be true, as shown by the following example. Let φ_n ($n = 1, 2, \ldots$) be a complete orthonormal system in the separable complete Hilbert space $\bar{R}$, and let $p = \Sigma_2^\infty \gamma_i\varphi_i$, where $\Sigma_2^\infty \mid \gamma_i \mid^2 < \infty$, be a fixed element of $\bar{R}$

with the property that $\gamma_i \neq 0$ for an infinity of values of i. Furthermore, let $q = \varphi_1 + p$, and let $[L]$ be the set of all finite linear combinations $\Sigma_2\, \alpha_i\varphi_i$. The space R is now defined to be the set of all elements $\alpha q + g$, where α is arbitrarily complex and $g \in [L]$. Then the element p does not belong to R, since in the opposite case we should have $p = \alpha q + g$ or $\Sigma_2^\infty\, \gamma_i\varphi_i = \alpha\varphi_1 + \alpha p + g$, hence $\alpha = 0$ because the representation in terms of the elements φ_n is uniquely determined. But then $\Sigma_2^\infty\, \gamma_i\varphi_i = g \in [L]$, in contradiction with $\gamma_i \neq 0$ for an infinite number of values of i. It follows that φ_1 does not belong to R either, since $\varphi_1 \in R$ would imply $p = q - \varphi_1 \in R$. Furthermore R is dense in $\bar{R}$ since, if $f = \Sigma_1^\infty\, \beta_i\varphi_i \in \bar{R}$ is given and the elements $h_n \in R$ are defined by $h_n = \beta_1 q + \Sigma_2^n\, (\beta_i - \beta_1\gamma_i)\varphi_i$, we have

$$f - h_n = \Sigma_1^\infty\, \beta_i\varphi_i - \beta_1\varphi_1 - \Sigma_2^\infty\, \beta_1\gamma_i\varphi_i - \Sigma_2^n\, (\beta_i - \beta_1\gamma_i)\varphi_i$$
$$= \Sigma_{n+1}^\infty\, (\beta_i - \beta_1\gamma_i)\varphi_i,$$

hence

$$\| f - h_n \| \leqslant \| \Sigma_{n+1}^\infty\, \beta_i\varphi_i \| + \| \Sigma_{n+1}^\infty\, \beta_1\gamma_i\varphi_i \|$$
$$= (\Sigma_{n+1}^\infty \mid \beta_i \mid^2)^{1/2} + (\Sigma_{n+1}^\infty \mid \beta_1\gamma_i \mid^2)^{1/2},$$

which tends to 0 as $n \to \infty$. Finally we observe that $[L]$ is a linear subspace of R. To prove this statement, we have to show that $g_n \in [L]$, $\lim g_n = g_0$ implies $g_0 \in [L]$. Observing that $(\varphi_1, g_n) = 0$ $(n = 1, 2, \ldots)$, we see that $(\varphi_1, g_0) = 0$, hence, since g_0 is of the form $g_0 = \alpha q + g = \alpha\varphi_1 + \alpha p + g$, we must have $\alpha = 0$, so that $g_0 = g \in [L]$.

Since now, in $\bar{R}$, the only elements orthogonal to $[L]$ are the elements $\beta\varphi_1$(β complex), and these elements do not belong to R, the orthogonal complement $R \ominus [L]$ contains only the null element. As a consequence, Theorem 3 on the orthogonal decomposition does not hold for the element $q \in R$, and Theorem 4 does not hold either, since the orthogonal complement of $R \ominus [L]$ is the whole space R.

Theorem 5. *Let either the linear subspace $[L]$ or its orthogonal complement $R \ominus [L]$, considered as a Hilbert space, be complete. Then the factorspace $R/[L]$ and the orthogonal complement $R \ominus [L]$ may be identified in this sense that there is a one-to-one correspondence between the elements of these spaces which preserves addition and multiplication by complex numbers, and such that corresponding elements have the same norm.*

Proof. By Theorem 3, every $f \in R$ has a uniquely determined decomposition $f = g + h$ $(g \in [L],\ h \in R \ominus [L])$. Then, since $\| f \|^2 = \| g \|^2 + \| h \|^2$, we have

$$\| [f] \|^2 = \text{lower bound}_{\,g \in [L]} \| g + h \|^2 = \| h \|^2.$$

If therefore we define $[f] \in R/[L]$ and $h \in R \ominus [L]$ to be corresponding elements, the conditions stated in the theorem are evidently satisfied.

Remark. In a similar way the subspace $[L]$ itself may be identified with the factorspace $R/(R \ominus [L])$.

Corollary. *If R is separable, then $[L]$ and $R \ominus [L]$ are separable as well.*
Proof. The separability of R implies by § 5 the separability of both factorspaces $R/[L]$ and $R/(R \ominus [L])$, and therefore also the separability of $R \ominus [L]$ and $[L]$.

Remark. The present statement is only a particular case of the general theorem that every subset of a separable set is separable itself.

§ 13. Examples of Hilbert Spaces

In the present paragraph we shall give some examples of Hilbert spaces.

Example A. *The Lebesgue space L_2*

In § 6, Example A we have seen that the functionspaces $L_p(\Delta, \mu)$ $(1 \leqslant p < \infty)$ are complete separable Banach spaces of enumerably infinite dimension, provided μ is separable and non-atomic. Considering in particular $L_2(\Delta, \mu)$, we may define the inner product of two elements f and g of this space by

$$(f, g) = \int_\Delta f(x)\, \overline{g(x)}\, d\mu.$$

By Schwarz's inequality (cf. Ch. 5, § 1, Th. 1, Corollary) this integral is finite. It is easily seen that Axiom BH of Hilbert space is satisfied, so that the functionspace $L_2(\Delta, \mu)$ is a complete separable Hilbert space of enumerably infinite dimension.

According to our definition (cf. § 9), the system Q of functions belonging to L_2 is orthonormal when, for $\varphi(x) \in Q$, $\psi(x) \in Q$, the relations

$$\int_\Delta \varphi(x)\, \overline{\psi(x)}\, d\mu = \begin{cases} 1 \text{ for } \varphi(x) = \psi(x), \\ 0 \text{ for } \varphi(x) \neq \psi(x), \end{cases}$$

hold. By § 9, Th. 2 the system Q is at most enumerable; furthermore the functions of Q are linearly independent. Given a finite or enumerable set S of functions belonging to $L_2(\Delta, \mu)$, we may find by Schmidt's orthogonalization process an orthonormal system Q such that $L(S) = L(Q)$; in other words, such that the set of all finite linear combinations of functions of S is identical with the set of all finite linear combinations of functions of Q. Finally, since L_2 is separable, there exists a complete orthonormal system Q_c, having therefore the property that $L(Q_c)$ is dense in L_2.

We recall that, according to Ch. 5, § 2, the series $\Sigma_1^\infty f_i(x)$ of functions $f_i(x) \in L_2$ converges on Δ in mean (with index 2) to $f(x) \in L_2$ when $\lim_{n\to\infty} \| f - \Sigma_1^n f_i \|^2 = \lim_{n\to\infty} \int_\Delta | f(x) - \Sigma_1^n f_i(x) |^2 \, d\mu = 0$. To avoid confusion with ordinary pointwise convergence, we shall denote this by $f(x) \sim \Sigma_1^\infty f_i(x)$. If the sequence $\varphi_n(x)$ is orthonormal, the results of § 11 show that the convergence in mean of $\Sigma \alpha_n\varphi_n(x)$ is equivalent with the convergence of $\Sigma | \alpha_n |^2$. Furthermore $f(x) \sim \Sigma \alpha_n\varphi_n(x)$ implies $\alpha_n = \int_\Delta f(x) \overline{\varphi_n(x)} \, d\mu$ for every value of n, and Bessel's inequality takes the form $\Sigma | \alpha_n |^2 \leqslant \int_\Delta | f |^2 \, d\mu$. Moreover, the following statements are equivalent:

1°. The orthonormal sequence $\varphi_n(x)$ is complete.

2°. For every $f(x) \in L_2$ we have $f(x) \sim \Sigma (f, \varphi_n)\varphi_n(x)$.

3° (Parseval's relation). For every $f(x) \in L_2$ and $g(x) \in L_2$ we have

$$\int_\Delta f(x) \overline{g(x)} \, d\mu = \Sigma (f, \varphi_n) \overline{(g, \varphi_n)}.$$

4°. For every $f(x) \in L_2$ we have $\int_\Delta | f |^2 \, d\mu = \Sigma | (f, \varphi_n) |^2$.

For reasons of historical interest we still mention separately the following theorem, which was one of the startingpoints of the theory of orthogonal series.

Theorem 1 (*Riesz-Fischer's Theorem*, 1907, [13]). *When the orthonormal system of functions* $\varphi_n(x)$ *and the sequence* α_n *of complex numbers satisfying* $\Sigma | \alpha_n |^2 < \infty$ *are given, there exists a function* $f(x) \in L_2$ *such that* $\alpha_n = \int_\Delta f(x) \overline{\varphi_n(x)} \, d\mu$ *for every value of* n.

Proof. Since $\Sigma | \alpha_n |^2 < \infty$ and the space L_2 is complete, the series $\Sigma \alpha_n\varphi_n(x)$ converges in mean to a function $f(x) \in L_2$. But $f(x) \sim \Sigma \alpha_n\varphi_n(x)$ implies $\alpha_n = (f, \varphi_n) = \int_\Delta f(x) \overline{\varphi_n(x)} \, d\mu$ for every value of n.

Let us suppose now that $[L]$ is a linear subspace of L_2. This means that, if $f(x)$ and $g(x)$ belong to $[L]$ and α, β are arbitrarily complex, then $\alpha f(x) + \beta g(x) \in [L]$, while moreover, if the sequence of functions $f_n(x)$ belonging to $[L]$ converges in mean to $f(x)$, then $f(x) \in [L]$. The orthogonal subspace $L_2 \ominus [L]$ is then the set of all $g(x) \in L_2$ satisfying $\int_\Delta f(x) \overline{g(x)} \, d\mu = 0$ for all $f(x) \in [L]$. Both subspaces, considered separately, are complete Hilbert spaces, and by § 12, Th. 3 there exists for every $f(x) \in L_2$ a uniquely determined decomposition $f(x) = g(x) + h(x)$ with $g(x) \in [L]$ and $h(x) \in L_2 \ominus [L]$. The subspaces $[L]$ and $L_2 \ominus [L]$ are separable, the existence of orthonormal sequences $\psi_n(x)$ and $\chi_n(x)$, complete in $[L]$ and $L_2 \ominus [L]$ respectively, is therefore guaranteed. Then, for every $f(x) \in L_2$, we have

$$f(x) \sim \Sigma\, \alpha_n \psi_n(x) + \Sigma\, \beta_n \chi_n(x), \quad \alpha_n = \textstyle\int_\Delta f(x)\, \overline{\psi_n(x)}\, d\mu, \quad \beta_n = \textstyle\int_\Delta f(x)\, \overline{\chi_n(x)}\, d\mu.$$

Example B. *The space l_2*

In § 6, Example C we have seen that the sequence-spaces l_p $(1 \leqslant p < \infty)$ are complete separable Banach spaces of enumerably infinite dimension. Considering in particular l_2, we may define the inner product of two elements $f = \{f_1, f_2, \ldots\}$ and $g = \{g_1, g_2, \ldots\}$ of this space by

$$(f, g) = \Sigma_1^\infty f_i \bar{g}_i.$$

It is easily seen that Axiom BH of Hilbert space is satisfied, so that the sequence-space l_2 is a complete separable Hilbert space of enumerably infinite dimension. The elements $\varphi_1 = \{1, 0, 0, \ldots\}$, $\varphi_2 = \{0, 1, 0, \ldots\}$, $\varphi_3 = \{0, 0, 1, \ldots\}, \ldots$ form an orthonormal system in l_2. This system is complete since, if $f = \{f_1, f_2, \ldots\}$ is arbitrarily given, we have $f = \Sigma\, f_i \varphi_i$.

Theorem 2. *If μ is separable and non-atomic, there exists a one-to-one correspondence $f(x) \leftrightarrow f$ between the elements $f(x)$ of $L_2(\Delta, \mu)$ and the elements $f = \{f_1, f_2, \ldots\}$ of l_2, having the properties that $\alpha f(x) + \beta g(x) \leftrightarrow \alpha f + \beta g$, $(f(x), g(x)) = \int_\Delta f(x)\, \overline{g(x)}\, d\mu = \Sigma\, f_i \bar{g}_i = (f, g)$.*

Proof. Let $\varphi_n(x)$ be a complete orthonormal system in $L_2(\Delta, \mu)$. Then the correspondence is defined by $f(x) \leftrightarrow f = \{f_1, f_2, \ldots\}$, where $f_i = \int_\Delta f(x)\, \overline{\varphi_i(x)}\, d\mu$ $(i = 1, 2, \ldots)$. If $f(x) \in L_2$, we have by Parseval's relation $\Sigma\, | f_i |^2 = \int_\Delta | f |^2\, d\mu$, hence $f \in l_2$. Conversely every $f \in l_2$ corresponds by Riesz-Fischer's Theorem with at least one $f(x) \in L_2$. This $f(x)$ however is uniquely determined since $\int_\Delta f \bar{\varphi}_n\, d\mu = \int_\Delta g \bar{\varphi}_n\, d\mu$ for every n implies $(f - g, \varphi_n) = \int_\Delta (f - g) \bar{\varphi}_n\, dx = 0$ for every n, hence $f(x) = g(x)$ almost everywhere on Δ by the completeness of the system $\varphi_n(x)$. The thus defined correspondence is therefore one-to-one. The correspondence $\alpha f(x) + \beta g(x) \leftrightarrow \alpha f + \beta g$ is evident, and $\int_\Delta f(x)\, \overline{g(x)}\, d\mu = \Sigma\, f_i \bar{g}_i$ is Parseval's relation.

Considering the subset $E_{2,n}$ of all elements $f = \{f_1, \ldots, f_n, 0, 0, \ldots\}$ for a fixed n, we see readily that this subset is an n-dimensional unitary space which, in § 6, Example C, we have already called complex n-dimensional Euclidean space. No confusion will arise if we write $f = \{f_1, \ldots, f_n\}$ instead of $f = \{f_1, \ldots, f_n, 0, 0, \ldots\}$. With this notation the system $\varphi_1 = \{1, 0, 0, \ldots, 0\}$, $\varphi_2 = \{0, 1, 0, \ldots, 0\}, \ldots$, $\varphi_n = \{0, 0, \ldots, 0, 1\}$ is orthonormal and complete in $E_{2,n}$.

As already observed in § 1, the space l_2 was the first example of a Hilbert space of (enumerably) infinite dimension that was considered, and this is not astonishing since it is the most natural generalization of a complex Euclidean space of finite dimension.

Example C. *The Besicovitch space B_2 - a.p.*

In § 6, Example D we have seen that the functionspaces B_p - *a.p.* $(1 \leqslant p \leqslant \infty)$ are complete non-separable Banach spaces whose dimension is therefore more than enumerably infinite. Considering in particular B_2 - *a.p.*, we may define the inner product of two elements f and g of this space by

$$(f, g) = \lim_{T\to\infty} \frac{1}{2T} \int_{-T}^{T} f(x)\, \overline{g(x)}\, dx.$$

By § 6, Example D with $p = q = 2$, this limit exists and is finite. It is easily seen that Axiom BH of Hilbert space is satisfied, so that the functionspace B_2 - *a.p.* is a complete non-separable Hilbert space. The system $\varphi_\lambda(x) = e^{i\lambda x}$ (λ real) is orthonormal since, as we have found, $(\varphi_\lambda, \varphi_\lambda) = (\| \varphi_\lambda \|_2)^2 = 1$ and $(\varphi_\lambda, \varphi_\mu) = 0$ for $\lambda \neq \mu$. Furthermore, every $f(x) \in B_2$ - *a.p.* being a limit (in the sense of the B_2 - *a.p.* norm) of finite linear combinations of functions $\varphi_\lambda(x)$, this system is complete. We shall say now that the series $\Sigma_1^\infty f_k(x)$ of functions $f_k(x) \in B_2$ - *a.p.* converges to $f(x) \in B_2$ - *a.p.* in the sense of the B_2 - *a.p.* norm when

$$\lim_{n\to\infty} (\| f - \Sigma_1^n f_k \|)^2 = \lim_{n\to\infty} \lim_{T\to\infty} \frac{1}{2T} \int_{-T}^{T} | f(x) - \Sigma_1^n f_k(x) |^2\, dx = 0,$$

and we write $f(x) \sim \Sigma f_k(x)$. Then, by the results of § 11, the convergence (relative to the B_2 - *a.p.* norm) of $\Sigma_1^\infty \alpha_n e^{i\lambda_n x}$ is equivalent with the convergence of $\Sigma_1^\infty | \alpha_n |^2$. Furthermore, for every $f(x) \in B_2$ - *a.p.*, the number of functions $\varphi_\lambda(x) = e^{i\lambda x}$ for which

$$(f, \varphi_\lambda) = \lim_{T\to\infty} \frac{1}{2T} \int_{-T}^{T} f(x) e^{-i\lambda x}\, dx \neq 0$$

is at most enumerable. If $\varphi_{\lambda_k}(x)$ is the sequence of these functions, we have, writing $\alpha_k = (f, \varphi_{\lambda_k})$,

$$\lim_{n\to\infty} \lim_{T\to\infty} \frac{1}{2T}\int_{-T}^{T} | f(x) - \Sigma_{k=1}^{n} \alpha_k e^{i\lambda_k x} |^2 \, dx = 0$$

and

$$\lim_{T\to\infty} \frac{1}{2T}\int_{-T}^{T} | f(x) |^2 \, dx = \Sigma \mid \alpha_n |^2.$$

Parseval's relation takes the form: If $f(x) \in B_2\text{-}a.p.$ and $g(x) \in B_2\text{-}a.p.$ are arbitrary, and $\varphi_{\lambda_k}(x)$ is the sequence satisfying one at least of the inequalities $(f, \varphi_\lambda) \neq 0$ and $(g, \varphi_\lambda) \neq 0$, then

$$\lim_{T\to\infty} \frac{1}{2T}\int_{-T}^{T} f(x)\, \overline{g(x)}\, dx = \Sigma\, \alpha_k \bar{\beta}_k,$$

where $\alpha_k = (f, \varphi_{\lambda_k})$, $\beta_k = (g, \varphi_{\lambda_k})$.

We finally mention the theorem which is analogous to Riesz-Fischer's Theorem in $L_2(\Delta)$.

Theorem 3 (*Besicovitch's Theorem*). *When the sequence λ_n of real numbers (different for different n) and the sequence α_n of complex numbers satisfying $\Sigma \mid \alpha_n |^2 < \infty$ are given, there exists a function $f(x) \in B_2\text{-}a.p.$ such that $\alpha_n = (f, \varphi_{\lambda_n})$ for every value of n, whereas $(f, \varphi_\lambda) = 0$ for any other value of λ.*

Proof. Since $\Sigma \mid \alpha_n |^2 < \infty$, and the space $B_2\text{-}a.p.$ is complete, the series $\Sigma\, \alpha_n \varphi_{\lambda_n}(x)$ converges (relative to the $B_2\text{-}a.p.$ norm) to a function $f(x) \in B_2\text{-}a.p.$. But $f(x) \sim \Sigma\, \alpha_n \varphi_{\lambda_n}(x)$ implies $\alpha_n = (f, \varphi_{\lambda_n})$ for every value of n and $(f, \varphi_\lambda) = 0$ for any other value of λ.

§ 14. A Complete Orthonormal System in $L_2(\Delta)$ for a Finite Interval Δ

We suppose that Δ is a finite interval in m-dimensional real Euclidean space, and that μ is Lebesgue measure. Then it is possible to give an explicit example of a system of functions, orthonormal and complete in $L_2(\Delta, \mu)$. We shall show later on (cf. Ch. 7, § 6, Th. 8) that the same system is even complete in $L_p(\Delta) = L_p(\Delta, \mu)$ for every p satisfying $1 \leqslant p < \infty$.

Lemma α. *Let Δ be the linear interval $[0, 2\pi]$, and let for $x \in \Delta$*

$\varphi_n(x) = (2\pi)^{-1/2} e^{inx} = (2\pi)^{-1/2} (\cos nx + i \sin nx)$ $(n = 0, \pm 1, \pm 2, \ldots)$.

Then the system $\varphi_n(x)$ *is orthonormal in* $L_2(\Delta)$, *and for any continuous function* $F(x)$ *the relations*

$$\int_\Delta F(x)\varphi_n(x)dx = 0 \quad (n = 0, \pm 1, \pm 2, \ldots)$$

imply $F(x) = 0$ *for every* $x \in \Delta$.

Proof. It is easily seen by direct computation that the system $\varphi_n(x)$ is orthonormal in $L_2(\Delta)$. Let now $\int_\Delta F(x)\varphi_n(x)dx = 0$ $(n = 0, \pm 1, \pm 2, \ldots)$ for a continuous $F(x)$. Then $\int_\Delta F(x)t_n(x)dx=0$ for every trigonometric polynomial $t_n(x) = \Sigma_{k=-n}^{n} \alpha_k\varphi_k(x)$ of degree n; in particular $\int_\Delta F(x)t^n(x)dx = 0$, where $t(x) = \alpha \cos x + \beta \sin x + \gamma$ $(\alpha, \beta, \gamma$ real) is an arbitrary real trigonometric polynomial of degree one. We observe at this point that it is no restriction to suppose that $F(x)$ is real since we may replace, if necessary, $F(x)$ by its real or imaginary part. Let us assume now that $F(x_0) \neq 0$ for a point $x_0 \in \Delta$. Then $F(x) \neq 0$ in a neighbourhood of x_0; we may suppose therefore that $x_0 \neq 0$, $x_0 \neq 2\pi$, and also that $F(x_0) > 0$. Under these assumptions there exist two positive numbers δ and M_1 such that the interval $\Delta_1 = [x_0 - 2\delta, x_0 + 2\delta]$ is contained in Δ, $\delta < \pi/4$ and $F(x) > M_1$ for $x \in \Delta_1$. Furthermore we shall write $M_2 = \max_{x \in \Delta} | F(x) |$.

Defining now the real trigonometric polynomial $t(x)$ of degree one by

$$t(x) = \cos (x - x_0) - \cos \delta + 1,$$

this polynomial has the following properties:

1°. $t(x) \geqslant 1$ in $\Delta_2 = [x_0 - \delta, x_0 + \delta]$,

2°. $t(x) \geqslant 0$ in Δ_1,

3°. There exists a number M_3 such that $0 < M_3 < 1$ and $| t(x) | < M_3$ in $\Delta - \Delta_1$.

From 3° follows immediately the existence of an index n_0 such that, for $n \geqslant n_0$ and $x \in \Delta - \Delta_1$,

$$| t^n(x) | \leqslant M_1\delta/M_2(2\pi - 4\delta).$$

Then, for $n \geqslant n_0$,

$$\int_{\Delta_1} F(x)t^n(x)dx \geqslant \int_{\Delta_2} F(x)t^n(x)dx \geqslant \int_{\Delta_2} F(x)dx > 2M_1\delta,$$

$$|\int_{\Delta-\Delta_1} F(x)t^n(x)dx | \leqslant M_2 \frac{M_1\delta}{M_2(2\pi - 4\delta)} (2\pi - 4\delta) = M_1\delta,$$

hence $\int_\Delta F(x)t^n(x)dx > M_1\delta$, in contradiction with $\int_\Delta F(x)t^n(x)dx = 0$. We conclude therefore that $F(x) = 0$ for every $x \in \Delta$.

Theorem 1. *If* $\Delta = [0, 2\pi]$ *and* $\varphi_n(x) = (2\pi)^{-1/2} e^{inx} (n = 0, \pm 1, \pm 2, \ldots)$, *the relations*

$$\int_\Delta f(x)\varphi_n(x)dx = 0 \ (n = 0, \pm 1, \pm 2, \ldots)$$

for a summable $f(x)$ *imply* $f(x) = 0$ *almost everywhere on* Δ.

Proof. Let $f(x)$ be summable over Δ, and $\int_\Delta f(x)\varphi_n(x)dx = 0$ $(n = 0, \pm 1, \pm 2, \ldots)$. Writing $F(x) = \int_0^x f(y)dy$, the function $F(x)$ is continuous in Δ on account of Ch. 3, § 4, Th. 5, where it is proved that the integral of a summable function over an interval tends to zero with the measure of this interval. Furthermore

$$\Phi_n(x) = \int_0^x \varphi_n(x)dx = (2\pi)^{-1/2} \int_0^x e^{inx}\, dx = (in)^{-1}(2\pi)^{-1/2} (e^{inx} - 1)$$
$$= (in)^{-1} \{\varphi_n(x) - \varphi_0(x)\} \ (n = \pm 1, \pm 2, \ldots);$$

in particular $\Phi_n(2\pi) = 0$ $(n = \pm 1, \pm 2, \ldots)$. Hence, integrating by parts (cf. Ch. 3, § 8, Th. 1),

$$\int_\Delta F(x)\varphi_n(x)dx = F(2\pi)\Phi_n(2\pi) - \int_\Delta f(x)\Phi_n(x)dx =$$
$$- (in)^{-1} \int_\Delta f(x)\{\varphi_n(x) - \varphi_0(x)\}\, dx = 0 \ (n = \pm 1, \pm 2, \ldots).$$

Writing now $F_1(x) = F(x) - C$, where $2\pi C = \int_0^{2\pi} F(x)dx$, it may be readily verified that

$$\int_\Delta F_1(x)\varphi_n(x)dx = 0 \ (n = 0, \pm 1, \pm 2, \ldots),$$

so that by the preceding lemma $F_1(x) = 0$, or $F(x) = C$ for every $x \in \Delta$. Since $F(0) = 0$, this implies $F(x) = 0$ for every $x \in \Delta$.

Having thus established that $F(x) = \int_0^x f(y)dy = 0$ for every $x \in \Delta$, we see that $\int_A f(x)dx = F(b) - F(a) = 0$ for any cell $A = (a, b]$, contained in Δ, so that, in virtue of Ch. 3, § 4, Th. 3, we have $f(x) = 0$ almost everywhere on Δ.

Lemma β. *If* Δ *is the linear interval* $[a, b]$, *the system*

$$\tilde{\varphi}_n(x) = (b - a)^{-1/2}\, e^{2\pi in(x-a)/(b-a)} \ (n = 0, \pm 1, \pm 2, \ldots)$$

is orthonormal in $L_2(\Delta)$, *and the relations*

$$\int_\Delta f(x)\tilde{\varphi}_n(x)dx = 0 \ (n = 0, \pm 1, \pm 2, \ldots)$$

for a summable $f(x)$ *imply* $f(x) = 0$ *almost everywhere on* Δ.

Proof. By direct computation it is easily seen that the system $\tilde{\varphi}_n(x)$ is orthonormal in $L_2(\Delta)$. Furthermore, for any summable $f(x)$,

$$\int_a^b f(x)\tilde{\varphi}_n(x)dx = c \int_0^{2\pi} f\left(a + \frac{b-a}{2\pi} y\right) \varphi_n(y)dy,$$

where c is a suitable constant, and $\varphi_n(y)$ is, in the interval $0 \leqslant y \leqslant 2\pi$, the orthonormal system of the preceding theorem. Our statement is therefore an immediate consequence of the preceding theorem.

Theorem 2. *Given the systems of bounded functions $\varphi_i(x)$ and $\psi_i(y)$ $(i = 1, 2, \ldots)$, orthonormal in the spaces $L_2(\Delta_1)$ and $L_2(\Delta_2)$ respectively, where Δ_1 is a p-dimensional interval and Δ_2 a q-dimensional interval, while moreover*

$$\int_{\Delta_1} f(x)\varphi_i(x)dx = 0, \int_{\Delta_2} g(y)\psi_i(y)dy = 0 \quad (i = 1, 2, \ldots)$$

for any $f(x)$ and $g(y)$, summable over Δ_1 and Δ_2 respectively, implies $f(x) = 0$, $g(y) = 0$ (almost everywhere), the system $\chi_{ij}(x, y) = \varphi_i(x)\psi_j(y)$ is orthonormal in the space $L_2(\Delta_1 \times \Delta_2)$, and

$$\int_{\Delta_1 \times \Delta_2} f(x, y)\chi_{ij}(x, y)dx\, dy = 0 \quad (i, j = 1, 2, \ldots)$$

for any $f(x, y)$, summable over $\Delta_1 \times \Delta_2$, implies $f(x, y) = 0$ (almost everywhere on $\Delta_1 \times \Delta_2$).

Proof. By direct computation it is easily seen that the system $\chi_{ij}(x, y)$ is orthonormal in $L_2(\Delta_1 \times \Delta_2)$. Let us suppose now that

$$\int_{\Delta_1 \times \Delta_2} f(x, y)\chi_{ij}(x, y)\, dx\, dy = 0 \quad (i, j = 1, 2, \ldots)$$

for a function $f(x, y) \in L(\Delta_1 \times \Delta_2)$. By Fubini's Theorem we have

$$\int_{\Delta_1} \{\int_{\Delta_2} f(x, y)\psi_j(y)dy\}\, \varphi_i(x)dx = \int_{\Delta_1 \times \Delta_2} f(x, y)\chi_{ij}(x, y)dx\, dy = 0;$$

it follows therefore from our hypothesis on the system $\varphi_i(x)$ that

$$\int_{\Delta_2} f(x, y)\psi_j(y)dy = 0 \quad (j = 1, 2, \ldots)$$

for almost every $x \in \Delta_1$, and this in its turn, by our hypothesis on $\psi_j(y)$, implies $f(x, y) = 0$ almost everywhere on $\Delta_1 \times \Delta_2$.

Theorem 3. *Given the orthonormal system $\varphi_n(x)$ $(n = 1, 2, \ldots)$ in $L_2(\Delta)$, where Δ is an interval of arbitrary dimension, which system has the property that*

$$\int_{\Delta} f(x)\varphi_n(x)dx = 0 \quad (n = 1, 2, \ldots)$$

for any $f(x) \in L_2(\Delta)$ implies $f(x) = 0$ almost everywhere on Δ, this system $\varphi_n(x)$ is complete in $L_2(\Delta)$.

Proof. Denoting the system $\varphi_n(x)$ by S, and supposing that the linear subspace $[L(S)]$ is not identical with the whole space $L_2(\Delta)$, there exists an element $g(x)$ not belonging to $[L(S)]$. Then $g(x) = h(x) + f(x)$, weher $h(x) \in [L]$, $f(x) \in L_2 \ominus [L]$, and $f(x)$ is not identical with the null element of L_2. From $f(x) \in L_2 \ominus [L]$ follows however

$$\int_\Delta \overline{f(x)}\, \varphi_n(x)dx = (\varphi_n, f) = 0 \quad (n = 1, 2, \ldots),$$

hence $\overline{f(x)} = 0$ (almost everywhere on Δ) by hypothesis. Then $f(x) = 0$ as well, in contradiction with what we have just found. It results that $[L(S)] = L_2(\Delta)$, so that the system $\varphi_n(x)$ is complete in $L_2(\Delta)$.

The preceding arguments enable us now to construct a complete orthonormal system in $L_2(\Delta)$, where Δ is an arbitrary finite m-dimensional interval.

Theorem 4. *Let $\Delta = [a_1, b_1;\ a_2, b_2;\ \ldots;\ a_m, b_m]$ be an arbitrary finite m-dimensional interval, and let, for $j = 1, 2, \ldots, m$,*

$$\varphi_{n,j}(x_j) = (b_j - a_j)^{-1/2} e^{2\pi i n(x_j - a_j)/(b_j - a_j)} \quad (n = 0, \pm 1, \pm 2, \ldots).$$

Then the system $\varphi_{n_1, n_2 \ldots n_m}(x_1, x_2, \ldots, x_m) = \Pi_{j=1}^m \varphi_{n_j,j}(x_j)$, where the indices $n_1, n_2, \ldots, n_m$ run through the values $0, \pm 1, \pm 2, \ldots$ independently of each other, is orthonormal and complete in $L_2(\Delta)$. It has moreover the property that if

$$\int_\Delta f(x_1, \ldots, x_m)\varphi_{n_1 \ldots n_m}(x_1, \ldots, x_m)dx_1 \ldots dx_m = 0$$

for a function $f(x_1, \ldots, x_m) \in L(\Delta)$ and for all $\varphi_{n_1 \ldots n_m}$, then $f(x_1, \ldots, x_m) = 0$ almost everywhere on Δ.

Proof. By Lemma β and Theorem 2 the system $\varphi_{n_1 \ldots n_m}(x_1, \ldots, x_m)$ is orthonormal in $L_2(\Delta)$, and possesses the property stated in the last part of our theorem. By Theorem 3 it is therefore complete in $L_2(\Delta)$.

§ 15. Productspace

If E_1 and E_2 are two Banach spaces, the elements of which will be denoted by $f^1, g^1, \ldots$ and $f^2, g^2, \ldots$ respectively (the numbers $1, 2, \ldots$ are therefore indices and not exponents), we may consider the set $E_1 \times E_2$ of all pairs of elements $\{f^1, f^2\}$ where f^1 runs through E_1 and f^2 through E_2. Defining in $E_1 \times E_2$ addition and multiplication by complex numbers α by

$$\{f^1, f^2\} + \{g^1, g^2\} = \{f^1 + g^1, f^2 + g^2\},$$

$$\alpha\{f^1, f^2\} = \{\alpha f^1, \alpha f^2\},$$

$E_1 \times E_2$ evidently satisfies Axiom A of Banach space with $\{0, 0\}$ as null element. Defining now a norm $\| \{f^1, f^2\} \| \geqslant 0$ in such a way that

Axiom B of Banach space is satisfied, and that

$$\lim_{i\to\infty} \| \{f_i^1 - f^1, f_i^2 - f^2\} \| = 0$$

if and only if $\lim \| f_i^1 - f^1 \| = \lim \| f_i^2 - f^2 \| = 0$, we see easily that $E_1 \times E_2$ is a Banach space, complete if and only if E_1 and E_2 are both complete. Indeed, there exist constants M_1, M_2 and M_3 such that $\| f^1 \| \leqslant M_1 \| \{f^1, f^2\} \|$, $\| f^2 \| \leqslant M_2 \| \{f^1, f^2\} \|$ and $\| \{f^1, f^2\} \| \leqslant M_3 .\max [\| f^1 \|, \| f^2 \|]$ for arbitrary f^1, f^2. We shall prove the first of these inequalities, the other proofs being analogous. Supposing that $M_1 > 0$ with the desired property does not exist, we have $\| f_n^1 \| > n \| \{f_n^1, f_n^2\} \|$ for a certain sequence $\{f_n^1, f_n^2\}$, where it is no restriction to take $\| f_n^1 \| = 1$, because we may always replace f_n^1 and f_n^2 by $f_n^1/\| f_n^1 \|$ and $f_n^2/\| f_n^1 \|$. Then however $\lim \| \{f_n^1, f_n^2\} \| = 0$, hence $\lim \| f_n^1 \| = 0$ in contradiction with $\| f_n^1 \| = 1$.

Definition. *$E_1 \times E_2$ is called the productspace of E_1 and E_2. If moreover $\| \{f^1, 0\} \| = \| f^1 \|$, $\| \{0, f^2\} \| = \| f^2 \|$ for arbitrary $f^1 \in E_1$, $f^2 \in E_2$, the subspace of all elements $\{f^1, 0\}$ may and will be identified with E_1 and the subspace of all elements $\{0, f^2\}$ with E_2. In this case we may say that $E_1 \times E_2$ is the direct sum of E_1 and E_2.*

It is not difficult to satisfy all these conditions, e.g. by taking $\| \{f^1, f^2\} \| = \max (\| f^1 \|, \| f^2 \|)$ or $\| \{f^1, f^2\} \| = (\| f^1 \|^p + \| f^2 \|^p)^{1/p}$ for $1 \leqslant p < \infty$.

In the special case that E_1 and E_2 are Hilbert spaces, an inner product in $E_1 \times E_2$ is defined by

$$(\{f^1, f^2\}, \{g^1, g^2\}) = (f^1, g^1) + (f^2, g^2),$$

hence $\| \{f^1, f^2\} \| = (\| f^1 \|^2 + \| f^2 \|^2)^{1/2}$. With this definition $E_1 \times E_2$ is evidently also a Hilbert space.

The extension to the case of a finite number of Banach spaces or Hilbert spaces $E_1, \ldots, E_n$ $(n > 2)$ is immediate.

EXAMPLES

1) Let $[L_1]$ and $[L_2]$ be linear subspaces of a Banach space E (complete or not) such that $[L_1]$ is of finite dimension and $[L_1]$ is a proper subspace of $[L_2]$. Then there exists an element $g \in [L_2]$ such that $\| g \| = 1$ and $\| g - f \| \geqslant 1$ for every $f \in [L_1]$ (cf. § 4, Th. 6).

(Let $h \in [L_2]$ but not $h \in [L_1]$, and let d be the distance of h and $[L_1]$. Evidently $d > 0$. If now the sequence $f_n \in [L_1]$ is such that $\lim \| h - f_n \| = d$, this sequence

f_n is bounded. It is therefore compact by § 4, Th. 3, and the limit f_0 of its converging subsequence belongs to $[L_1]$. Writing $g = (h - f_0)/\| h - f_0 \|$, this element g has the desired properties).

2) The statement in § 4, Th. 7 may be extended: Let $f_1, f_2, \ldots$ be linearly independent, and let $[L_n]$ be the subspace of all linear combinations $\Sigma_{i=1}^n \alpha_i f_i$ (α_i complex). Then there exists a sequence $g_1, g_2, \ldots$ such that, for $n = 1, 2, \ldots$, we have $g_n \in [L_n]$, $\| g_n \| = 1$ and $\| g_{n+1} - f \| \geqslant 1$ for every $f \in [L_n]$.

3) The following inverse of § 4, Th. 3 holds: If every bounded subset of the Banach space E is compact, then E is of finite dimension.

(If E were not of finite dimension, it would be possible by § 4, Th. 7 to construct a sequence g_n such that $\| g_n \| = 1$ and $\| g_m - g_n \| \geqslant 1/2$ for $m > n$. This sequence would be bounded but not compact).

4) In a complete Hilbert space the statement in § 4, Th. 6 may be extended: Let $[L_1]$ and $[L_2]$ be linear subspaces of a complete Hilbert space such that $[L_1]$ is a proper subspace of $[L_2]$. Then there exists an element $g \in [L_2]$ such that $\| g \| = 1$ and $\| g - f \| \geqslant 1$ for every $f \in [L_1]$.

(Any element g satisfying $\| g \| = 1$, and belonging to the orthogonal complement $[L_2] \ominus [L_1]$, has the desired properties).

5) The following inverse of § 8, Th. 6 holds: If the set S in the complete Hilbert space R has the property that $(f, h) = (g, h)$ for every $h \in S$ implies $f = g$, then S is a complete set in R.

(Assuming S to be not complete in R, there exists an element $f \neq 0$ orthogonal to $[L(S)]$ (cf. § 12, Th. 3), hence $(f, h) = 0 = (0, h)$ for all $h \in S$, so that by hypothesis $f = 0$. This is a contradiction).

6) If the Banach space E is complete and $[L]$ is a linear subspace, the completeness of the factorspace $E/[L]$ may also be proved by observing that, if $\lim \| [f]_m - [f]_n \| = 0$ as $m, n \to \infty$, then it is no restriction of the generality to suppose that $\Sigma_{n=1}^{\infty} \| [f]_{n+1} - [f]_n \| < \infty$.

(Choose $f_1 \in [f]_1$. There exist elements $f_1' \in [f]_1$, and $f_2' \in [f]_2$ such that $\| f_2' - f_1' \| \leqslant 2 \| [f_2' - f_1'] \| = 2 \| [f]_2 - [f]_1 \|$. Then $f_2 = f_2' + (f_1 - f_1') \in [f]_2$ and $\| f_2 - f_1 \| = \| f_2' - f_1' \|$. In this way we find the sequence $f_n \in [f]_n$ $(n = 1, 2, \ldots)$ such that $\| f_{n+1} - f_n \| \leqslant 2 \| [f]_{n+1} - [f]_n \|$, hence $\Sigma_{n=1}^{\infty} \| f_{n+1} - f_n \| < \infty$. It follows that $\lim [f]_n = [f_0]$, where $f_0 = \lim f_n$).

7) Let $[L]$ be a linear subspace of finite dimension of the complete Banach space E. Then, for any element $[f]$ of the factorspace $E/[L]$, there exists an element $f \in E$ such that f belongs to $[f]$ and $\| f \| = \| [f] \|$.

(The class $[f]$ consists of all $f^* + g$, where f^* is fixed and g runs through $[L]$. Then $\lim \| f^* + g_n \| = \| [f] \|$ for a certain sequence $g_n \in [L]$. This sequence is bounded and therefore compact, hence $\lim g_i = g_0 \in [L]$ for a subsequence g_i. The element $f = f^* + g_0$ has the desired property).

8) If the function $\Phi(u)$ which occurs in the definition of the Orlicz space $L_\Phi(\Delta, \mu)$ (cf. § 6, Ex. B), satisfies $\Phi(2u) \leqslant M\Phi(u)$ for all $u \geqslant 0$, if μ is Lebesgue measure in Euclidean space R_m, and if Δ is a finite interval in R_m, then the continuous functions in Δ all belong to L_Φ, and form a non-complete Banach space which is dense in L_Φ. If Δ is an infinite interval, the continuous functions $f(x)$ in Δ such that $f(x) = 0$ outside a finite subinterval Δ_f (which may depend on f) have the stated property.

(Follows from Ch. 5, Ex. 15).

9) The continuous functions $f(x)$ in a finite interval Δ in R_m form a complete Banach space $C(\Delta)$ if addition and multiplication by complex α are defined in the usual way, and $\| f \| = \max | f(x) |$ for $x \in \Delta$.

10) Let $1 \leqslant p \leqslant \infty$, $f(x) \in B_p$ - *a.p.*, and $\varphi_\lambda(x) = e^{i\lambda x}$ for real λ. Then the number of $\varphi_\lambda(x)$ for which $(f, \varphi_\lambda) \neq 0$ is at most enumerable.

(There is a sequence s_n of trigonometric polynomials such that $\lim s_n = f$; if therefore $(s_n, \varphi_\lambda) = 0$ for all n, then $(f, \varphi_\lambda) = 0$. Now, the number of φ_λ occurring in all s_n together is at most enumerable, and for all other φ_λ we have $(s_n, \varphi_\lambda) = 0$ $(n = 1, 2, \ldots)$).

11) Let the set S in Banach space be convex, and let $d =$ lower bound $\| f \|$ for all $f \in S$. Then, if $f_n \in S$ and $\lim \| f_n \| = d$ as $n \to \infty$, we have $\lim \| (f_m + f_n)/2 \| = d$ as $m, n \to \infty$. Also, if we write $\bar{f}_n = f_n/\| f_n \|$, then $\lim \| (\bar{f}_m + \bar{f}_n)/2 \| = 1$.

(The elements $(f_m + f_n)/2$ belong to S, hence $d \leqslant \| (f_m + f_n)/2 \| \leqslant (\| f_m \| + \| f_n \|)/2$, which tends to d. The second statement follows easily).

12) A Banach space E is called *uniformly convex* if $\| f_n \| = 1$, $\| g_n \| = 1$, $\lim \| (f_n + g_n)/2 \| = 1$ imply $\lim \| f_n - g_n \| = 0$. Let now the set S in the uniformly convex Banach space E be convex, and let $d =$ lower bound $\| f \|$ for all $f \in S$. Then, if $f_n \in S$ and $\lim \| f_n \| = d$ as $n \to \infty$, we have $\lim \| f_m - f_n \| = 0$ as $m, n \to \infty$.

(Adopting the notations of the preceding example, we have $\| \bar{f}_m \| = 1$, $\| \bar{f}_n \| = 1$, hence $\lim \| (\bar{f}_m + \bar{f}_n)/2 \| = 1$, so that $\lim \| \bar{f}_m - \bar{f}_n \| = 0$ by the uniform convexity, which implies $\lim \| f_m - f_n \| = 0$).

13) Let $a_i \geqslant 0$ $(i = 1, 2, \ldots)$, $0 < r \leqslant s$, and $\Sigma_i a_i^r < \infty$. Then $(\Sigma_i a_i^s)^{1/s} \leqslant (\Sigma_i a_i^r)^{1/r}$ (Jensen's inequality).

(It is no restriction of the generality to suppose that $\Sigma a_i^r = 1$. Then $a_i \leqslant 1$ for every i, so that $\Sigma a_i^s \leqslant \Sigma a_i^r = 1$. Hence $(\Sigma a_i^s)^{1/s} \leqslant 1 = (\Sigma a_i^r)^{1/r}$).

14) The following analogue of Ch. 5, § 1, Th. 2 holds: Let $p > 1$, $a_i \geqslant 0$, $b_i \geqslant 0$ $(i = 1, 2, \ldots)$. Then $(\Sigma a_i^p)^{1/p} \leqslant M$ if and only if $\Sigma a_i b_i \leqslant M$ for every sequence b_i satisfying $\Sigma b_i^q \leqslant 1$, $1/p + 1/q = 1$.

(If $(\Sigma a_i^p)^{1/p} \leqslant M$ and $\Sigma b_i^q \leqslant 1$, then $\Sigma a_i b_i \leqslant M$ by Hölder's inequality in the sequence-space l_p. If, conversely, $\Sigma a_i b_i \leqslant M$ for every sequence b_i satisfying $\Sigma b_i^q \leqslant 1$, we consider the sequence $c_i = a_i^{p-1}$. Then $c_i^q = a_i^p$, so that, supposing that $\Sigma a_i^p > M^p$, we should have $\Sigma_{i=1}^N c_i^q = \Sigma_{i=1}^N a_i^p = A > M^p$ for a certain index N. Defining now $b_i = c_i/A^{1/q}$ for $i = 1, \ldots, N$, and $b_i = 0$ for $i > N$, the result would be that $\Sigma b_i^q = 1$, but $\Sigma a_i b_i = \Sigma_1^N a_i c_i/A^{1/q} = \Sigma_1^N a_i^p/A^{1/q} = A/A^{1/q} = A^{1/p} > M$, in contradiction with the hypothesis).

15) Let $k > 1$, and $f_1(x), f_2(x) \in L(\Delta, \mu)$. Then

$$[\{\int_\Delta | f_1 | \, d\mu\}^k + \{\int_\Delta | f_2 | \, d\mu\}^k]^{1/k} \leqslant \int_\Delta (| f_1 |^k + | f_2 |^k)^{1/k} \, d\mu.$$

(Since $(| f_1 |^k + | f_2 |^k)^{1/k} \leqslant | f_1 | + | f_2 |$ almost everywhere on Δ by Jensen's inequality, the integral on the right side is finite. Write $a_i = \int_\Delta | f_i | \, d\mu$ $(i = 1, 2)$, and let $b_i \geqslant 0$ $(i = 1, 2)$ be such that $b_1^l + b_2^l \leqslant 1$, where $1/k + 1/l = 1$. Then

$$\Sigma_{i=1}^2 a_i b_i = \int_\Delta (\Sigma | f_i | \, b_i) \, d\mu \leqslant \int_\Delta (\Sigma | f_i |^k)^{1/k} . (\Sigma b_i^l)^{1/l} \, d\mu$$
$$\leqslant \int_\Delta (| f_1 |^k + | f_2 |^k)^{1/k} \, d\mu = M.$$

But then, by the preceding example, $\Sigma a_i^k \leqslant M^k$, which is the desired result. We observe that the extension to a finite number of functions $f_1(x), \ldots, f_n(x)$ is evident).

16) Let $2 \leqslant p < \infty$, and $f_1(x), f_2(x) \in L_p(\Delta, \mu)$. Then

$$\| f_1 + f_2 \|^p + \| f_1 - f_2 \|^p \leqslant 2^{p-1}(\| f_1 \|^p + \| f_2 \|^p).$$

(Using first Jensen's inequality and then Hölder's inequality, we have almost everywhere on Δ

$$(| f_1 + f_2 |^p + | f_1 - f_2 |^p)^{1/p} \leqslant (| f_1 + f_2 |^2 + | f_1 - f_2 |^2)^{1/2} =$$
$$(2 | f_1 |^2 + 2 | f_2 |^2)^{1/2} \leqslant 2^{1/2} \{(\Sigma | f_i |^p)^{2/p}. (\Sigma\, 1)^{(p-2)/p}\}^{1/2}$$
$$= 2^{1/2} . 2^{(p-2)/2p} (| f_1 |^p + | f_2 |^p)^{1/p} = 2^{(p-1)/p} (| f_1 |^p + | f_2 |^p)^{1/p},$$

from which the result follows immediately).

17) The Lebesgue space $L_p(\Delta, \mu)$ is uniformly convex for $2 \leqslant p < \infty$ [15]. (Let $\| f_n \| = 1$, $\| g_n \| = 1$, $\lim \| f_n + g_n \| = 2$. Then, from

$$\| f_n + g_n \|^p + \| f_n - g_n \|^p \leqslant 2^{p-1}(\| f_n \|^p + \| g_n \|^p),$$

it follows that $\lim \| f_n - g_n \| = 0$).

18) Let $1 < p \leqslant 2$, $1/p + 1/q = 1$. Then, if x and y are arbitrary complex numbers, we have

$$(1) \qquad | x + y |^q + | x - y |^q \leqslant 2(| x |^p + | y |^p)^{q-1}.$$

(Writing $x + y = 2\alpha$ and $x - y = 2\beta$, the inequality (1) can be written as $2^q(| \alpha |^q + | \beta |^q) \leqslant 2(| \alpha + \beta |^p + | \alpha - \beta |^p)^{q-1}$ or $| \alpha + \beta |^p + | \alpha - \beta |^p \geqslant 2(| \alpha |^q + | \beta |^q)^{1/(q-1)} = 2(| \alpha |^q + | \beta |^q)^{p-1}$. Since this is obviously true for $\alpha = \beta = 0$, we may suppose that $\max [| \alpha |, | \beta |]$, say $| \alpha |$, is $\neq 0$. Dividing by $| \alpha |^p = | \alpha |^{q(p-1)}$, and setting $\beta/\alpha = z$, we see that (1) is equivalent with $| 1 + z |^p + | 1 - z |^p \geqslant 2(1 + | z |^q)^{p-1}$, where $z = \rho e^{i\varphi}$, $0 \leqslant \rho \leqslant 1$. Now, since it is easily seen that $| 1 + z |^p + | 1 - z |^p$ attains its minimum for $\varphi = 0$, it will be sufficient to prove that

$$f(\rho) = \tfrac{1}{2}[(1 + \rho)^p + (1 - \rho)^p] - (1 + \rho^q)^{p-1} \geqslant 0$$

for $0 \leqslant \rho \leqslant 1$. For $\rho = 0$ and $\rho = 1$ this is trivial; let therefore $0 < \rho < 1$. Then

$$\tfrac{1}{2}[(1 + \rho)^p + (1 - \rho)^p] = 1 + \frac{p(p-1)}{2!} \rho^2 + \frac{p(p-1)(2-p)(3-p)}{4!} \rho^4$$
$$+ \ldots + \frac{p(p-1)(2-p)\ldots(2k-1-p)}{(2k)!} \rho^{2k} + \ldots$$

and

$$(1 + \rho^q)^{p-1} = 1 + (p-1)\rho^q - \frac{(p-1)(2-p)}{2!} \rho^{2q} + \ldots$$
$$+ \frac{(p-1)(2-p)\ldots(2k-1-p)}{(2k-1)!} \rho^{(2k-1)q} - \frac{(p-1)(2-p)\ldots(2k-p)}{(2k)!} \rho^{2kq} + \ldots.$$

Hence

$$f(\rho) = \Sigma_{k=1}^{\infty} \Big[\frac{p(p-1)(2-p)\ldots(2k-1-p)}{(2k)!} \rho^{2k}$$
$$- \frac{(p-1)(2-p)\ldots(2k-1-p)}{(2k-1)!} \rho^{(2k-1)q} + \frac{(p-1)(2-p)\ldots(2k-p)}{(2k)!} \rho^{2kq} \Big] =$$
$$\Sigma_{k=1}^{\infty} \frac{(2-p)\ldots(2k-p)}{(2k-1)!} \rho^{2k} \Big[\frac{1 - \rho^{(2k-p)/(p-1)}}{(2k-p)/(p-1)} - \frac{1 - \rho^{2k/(p-1)}}{2k/(p-1)} \Big].$$

But $(1-\rho^t)/t$, for $t > 0$ and $0 < \rho < 1$, is a decreasing function of t; all terms in the series for $f(\rho)$ are therefore non-negative, so that $f(\rho) \geqslant 0$).

19) The Lebesgue space $L_p(\Delta, \mu)$ is uniformly convex for $1 < p \leqslant 2$ [15].

(Let $f(x), g(x) \in L_p(\Delta, \mu)$. Then, using Ex. 15 with $k = q/p$, where $1/p + 1/q = 1$, we have

$$\| f + g \|^q + \| f - g \|^q = \{\textstyle\int_\Delta | f + g |^p d\mu\}^{q/p} + \{\textstyle\int_\Delta | f - g |^p d\mu\}^{q/p}$$
$$\leqslant [\textstyle\int_\Delta (| f + g |^q + | f - g |^q)^{p/q} d\mu]^{q/p},$$

hence, by the preceding example,

$$\| f + g \|^q + \| f - g \|^q \leqslant 2[\textstyle\int_\Delta (| f |^p + | g |^p)^{p(q-1)/q} d\mu]^{q/p}$$
$$= 2[\textstyle\int_\Delta (| f |^p + | g |^p) d\mu]^{q-1} = 2(\| f \|^p + \| g \|^p)^{q-1}.$$

If therefore $\| f_n \| = 1$, $\| g_n \| = 1$, $\lim \| f_n + g_n \| = 2$, we have $\lim \| f_n - g_n \| = 0$).

20) Any Hilbert space R is uniformly convex.

(Follows from $\| f + g \|^2 + \| f - g \|^2 = 2 \| f \|^2 + 2 \| g \|^2$ for all $f, g \in R$).

21) A Banach space of finite dimension is not necessarily uniformly convex.

(Let E be the two-dimensional Banach space $E_{\infty,2}$; hence, if $f \in E$, then $f = \{f_1, f_2\}$ (f_1, f_2 complex) with $\| f \| = \max (| f_1 |, | f_2 |)$. Taking now $f = \{1, 1\}$, $g = \{1, 0\}$, we have $f + g = \{2, 1\}$, $f - g = \{0, 1\}$, so that $\| f \| = 1$, $\| g \| = 1$, $\| f + g \| = 2$, $\| f - g \| = 1$).

REFERENCES

[1] D. Hilbert, Grundzüge einer allgemeinen Theorie der linearen Integralgleichungen, Göttinger Nachrichten (1906), 4. Mitt., 157—227, and 5. Mitt., 439—480. These papers are also contained in the book of the same title, Leipzig (1912, 1924).

[2] J. von Neumann, Allgemeine Eigenwerttheorie Hermitescher Funktionaloperatoren, Math. Annalen 102 (1929), 49—131.

[3] F. Riesz published several papers on Hilbert space in Acta Sci. Math. Szeged 5(1930), 6(1933), 7(1934).

[4] M. H. Stone, Linear transformations in Hilbert space, New York (1932).

[5] S. Banach, Théorie des Opérations linéaires, Warsaw (1932).

[6] E. Hille, Functional Analysis and Semi-groups, New York (1948).

[7] B. von Sz. Nagy, Spektraldarstellung linearer Transformationen des Hilbertschen Raumes, Berlin (1942).

[8] The space B_p - *a.p.*, which we consider here, is identical with the space of all functions that are B_p-almost periodic in the sense of Besicovitch. The proof may be found in: A. S. Besicovitch, Almost periodic functions, Cambridge (1932).

[9] We give B. Jessen's arrangement of the proof, as reproduced in: H. Bohr and E. Følner, On some types of functional spaces, Acta Math. 76(1944), 31—155.

[10] Non-separable Hilbert spaces were considered for the first time in: F. Rellich, Spektraltheorie in nicht-separablen Räumen, Math. Annalen 110

(1934), 342—356, and H. Löwig, Komplexe euklidische Räume von beliebiger endlicher oder unendlicher Dimensionszahl, Acta Sci. Math. Szeged 7(1934), 1—33.

[11] E. Schmidt, Entwicklung willkürlicher Funktionen nach Systemen vorgeschriebener, Diss. Göttingen (1905) and Math. Annalen 63(1907), 433—476.

[12] F. Riesz, Zur Theorie des Hilbertschen Raumes, Acta Sci. Math. Szeged 7(1934), 34—38. The proof is based on the same principle as B. Levi's proof of a theorem on Dirichlet's principle.

[13] F. Riesz, Sur les systèmes orthogonaux de fonctions, C.R. Acad. Sc. Paris 144(1907), 615—619.
E. Fischer, Sur la convergence en moyenne, C.R. Acad. Sc. Paris 144 (1907), 1022—1024.

[14] P. R. Halmos, Introduction to Hilbert space, New York (1951).

[15] J. A. Clarkson, Uniformly convex spaces, Transactions Amer. Math. Soc. 40 (1936), 396—414.

CHAPTER 7

BOUNDED LINEAR TRANSFORMATIONS

§ 1. Definitions

Let E_1 and E_2 be two Banach spaces, identical or distinct. Let furthermore $g = Tf$ be a function defined on the set $D \subset E_1$, that is, with every element f in D corresponds a uniquely determined element $g \in E_2$. Then T is said to be a *transformation* on D to W or a *mapping* of D on W, where $W \subset E_2$ is the set of all g such that $g = Tf$ for at least one $f \in D$. The set D is called the *domain* of T, and W is called the *range* of T.

If F is a subset of D, then $T(F)$ denotes the set of all $g = Tf$ with $f \in F$, and the set $T(F)$ is called the *image* of F.

The transformation αT (α complex) is defined by $(\alpha T)f = \alpha Tf$ for every $f \in D$. If T_1 and T_2 have the same domain D, then the transformation $T_1 + T_2$ is defined by $(T_1 + T_2)f = T_1 f + T_2 f$ for every $f \in D$.

Definition. *The transformation T is called continuous for $f = f_0$ if $\lim f_n = f_0$ implies $\lim Tf_n = Tf_0$. The transformation T is called continuous if it is continuous for all elements of its domain.*

Definition. *The transformation T, defined on the Banach space E, is called additive if $T(f_1 + f_2) = Tf_1 + Tf_2$ for all $f_1, f_2 \in E$.*

This definition implies that $T0 = 0$, $T(-f) = -Tf$.

Theorem 1. *An additive transformation, which is continuous for one element, is continuous everywhere.*

Proof. Let T be additive and continuous for $f = f_0$, let $\bar{f}_0 \neq f_0$ and $\lim f_n = \bar{f}_0$. Then $\lim \{f_n + (f_0 - \bar{f}_0)\} = f_0$, hence $\lim T\{f_n + (f_0 - \bar{f}_0)\} = Tf_0$ or $\lim Tf_n + Tf_0 - T\bar{f}_0 = Tf_0$, so that $\lim Tf_n = T\bar{f}_0$. This shows that T is continuous for $f = \bar{f}_0$.

Definition. *The transformation T, defined on the Banach space E, is called homogeneous if $T(\alpha f) = \alpha T f$ for all complex α and all $f \in E$.*

An additive and homogeneous transformation is said to be linear.

Definition. *The transformation T, defined on the Banach space E, is said to be bounded if there exists a fixed $M \geqslant 0$ such that $\| Tf \| \leqslant M \| f \|$ for all $f \in E$. The smallest number M satisfying this inequality is called the norm or bound of T and is denoted by $\| T \|$.*

We observe that if T is bounded there exists certainly a smallest M for which $\| Tf \| \leqslant M \| f \|$, because it is easily seen that the lower bound of all M satisfying this inequality has the desired property. Furthermore, if T is linear and bounded, we have evidently

$$\| T \| = \text{upper bound } \| Tf \| \text{ for all } f \text{ satisfying } \| f \| \leqslant 1.$$

Theorem 2. *An additive transformation is continuous if and only if it is bounded.*

Proof. If T is bounded the continuity follows from

$$\| Tf - Tf_0 \| = \| T(f - f_0) \| \leqslant \| T \| . \| f - f_0 \|.$$

Let us suppose now that T is continuous but not bounded. Then there is a sequence of elements $\bar{f}_n \neq 0$ such that $\| T\bar{f}_n \| > 2n \| \bar{f}_n \|$. Since the additivity implies $T(\rho f) = \rho T f$ for rational ρ, it follows, taking $\| \bar{f}_n \| \leqslant \rho_n < 2 \| \bar{f}_n \|$ (ρ_n rational) and $f_n = \bar{f}_n/\rho_n$, that $\| f_n \| \leqslant 1$ and $\| Tf_n \| = \| T\bar{f}_n \|/\rho_n > 2n \| \bar{f}_n \|/\rho_n > n$. Then, if $g_n = f_n/n$, we have $\lim g_n = 0$ and $\| Tg_n \| > 1$, in contradiction with the continuity of T for $g = 0$.

Theorem 3. *Every bounded linear transformation T, defined on the non-complete Banach space E_1, and with its range in the complete Banach space E_2, can be extended onto the closure $\bar{E}_1$ in such a way that it remains linear and bounded with the same bound.*

Proof. Let $\| T \|$ be the bound of T in E_1, and let $\bar{f} \in \bar{E}_1$ be the limit of the fundamental sequence $f_n \in E_1$. Then, since $\| Tf_n - Tf_m \| = \| T(f_n - f_m) \| \leqslant \| T \| . \| f_n - f_m \|$, the sequence Tf_n converges in E_2. If $g_n \in E_1$ is a different sequence converging to $\bar{f}$, then $f_1, g_1, f_2, g_2, \ldots$ also converges to $\bar{f}$, hence $\lim Tf_n = \lim Tg_n$. Defining $T\bar{f} = \lim Tf_n$, the transformation T is therefore uniquely determined for every $\bar{f} \in \bar{E}_1$. Evidently the extended transformation T is linear, and since $\| Tf_n \| \leqslant \| T \| . \| f_n \|$ implies $\| T\bar{f} \| \leqslant \| T \| . \| \bar{f} \|$, it has the same bound as the original transformation.

§ 2. The Banach-Steinhaus Theorem on Uniform Boundedness

Theorem 1 (BANACH-STEINHAUS, 1927, [1]). *Let $\{T\}$ be a set of linear bounded transformations, defined on the complete Banach space E. Then, if $\| Tf \|$ is bounded for each $f \in E$ separately when T runs through $\{T\}$, the transformations T are uniformly bounded, that is, there exists a number $M \geqslant 0$ such that $\| Tf \| \leqslant M \| f \|$ for all $T \in \{T\}$ and all $f \in E$.*

Proof. We consider first the case that the set $\{T\}$ is enumerable, $\{T\} = \{T_1, T_2, \ldots\}$. If we can show that $\| T_n f \| < M_1$ for all n and all f contained in the sphere K with centre f_0, defined by $\| f - f_0 \| \leqslant \delta$, the theorem will be proved, since then, if $\| f \| \leqslant \delta$, we have $\| T_n f \| = \| T_n(f + f_0) - T_n f_0 \| < 2M_1$; hence, for an arbitrary f,

$$\| T_n f \| = \left\| \frac{\| f \|}{\delta} T_n \left(\frac{\delta f}{\| f \|} \right) \right\| < \frac{2M_1}{\delta} \| f \|.$$

Writing $M = 2M_1/\delta$, we have the desired result.

Supposing the theorem not to be true, the sequence $\| T_n f \|$ is therefore not bounded in any sphere K, that is, if $a > 0$ is arbitrarily given, there exists an element $f_0 \in K$ and an index n_0 such that $\| T_{n_0} f_0 \| > a$. By the continuity of T_{n_0} the inequality $\| T_{n_0} f \| > a$ even holds in a whole sphere K_1 contained in K. Let now the sphere K be arbitrary. Then, by what we have seen, there is a sphere $K_1 \subset K$ with diameter < 1 such that $\| T_{n_1} f \| > 1$ for all $f \in K_1$. Next, by the same argument, there is a sphere $K_2 \subset K_1$ with diameter $< 1/2$ such that $\| T_{n_2} f \| > 2$ for $f \in K_2$, and so on. Evidently the centres of the spheres $K_1, K_2, \ldots$ form a fundamental sequence, so that, the space E being complete, this sequence has a limit $\bar{f}$ contained in all spheres K_n. But then we should have $\| T_{n_k} \bar{f} \| > k$ $(k = 1, 2, \ldots)$, in contradiction with the hypothesis that the sequence $\| T_n \bar{f} \|$ is bounded. The theorem is therefore true for enumerable sets $\{T\}$.

Supposing now the theorem to be false for some non-enumerable set $\{T\}$, there exists an enumerable subset $\{T_n\} \subset \{T\}$ such that $\lim \| T_n \| = \infty$, which leads immediately to a contradiction with the enumerable case.

Remark. The completeness of the space E is essential. Indeed, let $\bar{R}$ be a complete Hilbert space of enumerably infinite dimension, φ_n a complete orthonormal system in $\bar{R}$, and R the non-complete Hilbert space of all finite linear combinations $\Sigma\, \alpha_i \varphi_i$ (α_i complex). Defining now the transformations T_n on R into the space of all complex numbers (which is also a Banach space, $E_{2,1}$ by the notation of Ch. 6, § 13, Ex. B) by $T_n f = (f, n\varphi_n)$, we see that $\| T_n \| = n$, since $\| T_n f \| \leqslant \| n\varphi_n \| . \| f \| = n \| f \|$ and $T_n(n\varphi_n) = (n\varphi_n, n\varphi_n) = n^2 = n \| n\varphi_n \|$. Hence $\lim \| T_n \| = \infty$, and yet $\lim T_n f = 0$ for each $f \in R$ separately.

§ 3. An Inverse of Hölder's Inequality

We have already discussed Hölder's inequality and some of its extensions. In Ch. 5, § 1, Th. 1 we have proved that if $1 \leqslant p \leqslant \infty$, $1/p + 1/q = 1$, $f(x) \in L_p = L_p(\Delta, \mu)$, $g(x) \in L_q$, then $f(x)g(x)$ is summable over Δ, and $\int_\Delta | fg | \, d\mu \leqslant \| f \|_p . \| g \|_q$. Next, in Ch. 5, § 5, Th. 3, we have seen that if L_Φ and L_Ψ are complementary Orlicz spaces, and $f(x) \in L_\Phi$, $g(x) \in L_\Psi$, then $f(x)g(x)$ is summable over Δ, and $\int_\Delta | fg | \, d\mu \leqslant \| f \|_\Phi . \| g \|_\Psi$. Furthermore, in Ch. 6, § 6, Ex. C, where we discussed the sequence-spaces l_p $(1 \leqslant p \leqslant \infty)$, we proved that if $1 \leqslant p \leqslant \infty$, $1/p + 1/q = 1$, $f = \{f_i\} \in l_p$, $g = \{g_i\} \in l_q$, then $\Sigma f_i g_i$ converges and $\Sigma | f_i g_i | \leqslant \| f \|_p . \| g \|_q$.

It is interesting that the Banach-Steinhaus Theorem allows us to prove an inverse theorem in all these cases.

Theorem 1. *Let $\Phi(u)$ and $\Psi(v)$ be complementary in the sense of Young. Then, if the complex, μ-measurable function $f(x)$, defined on the set Δ, has the property that $f(x)g(x)$ is μ-summable over Δ for every $g(x) \in L_\Psi(\Delta, \mu)$, we have $f(x) \in L_\Phi(\Delta, \mu)$. In the same way, if $f(x)g(x)$ is summable over Δ for every $f(x) \in L_\Phi$, then $g(x) \in L_\Psi$.*

Proof. Let us assume that fg is summable over Δ for all $g(x) \in L_\Psi$. In order to show now that $f(x) \in L_\Phi$, we have to prove that $\| f \|_\Phi < \infty$, where

$$\| f \|_\Phi = \text{upper bound} \int_\Delta | fg | \, d\mu \text{ for } \int_\Delta \Psi | g | \, d\mu \leqslant 1.$$

Writing $\Delta = \lim \Delta_n$, where the sequence of sets Δ_n is ascending and each Δ_n is of finite measure, we define

$$f_n(x) = f(x) \text{ when } | f(x) | \leqslant n \text{ and } x \in \Delta_n,$$
$$f_n(x) = 0 \text{ elsewhere on } \Delta.$$

Then $f_n(x) \in L_\Phi$ and $\lim f_n(x) = f(x)$ almost everywhere on Δ. The transformations $f_n^*(g) = \int_\Delta f_n(x)g(x)d\mu$, defined on L_Ψ and with their ranges in the space of complex numbers, are therefore bounded and linear as may be seen from $| f_n^*(g) | \leqslant \| f_n \|_\Phi . \| g \|_\Psi$. Furthermore the sequence $| f_n^*(g) |$ $(n = 1, 2, \ldots)$ is bounded for every $g(x) \in L_\Psi$. Indeed, we have $\lim f_n g = fg$ almost everywhere, $| f_n g | \leqslant | fg |$, and fg is summable by hypothesis, so that by Lebesgue's Theorem $\lim f_n^*(g) = \lim \int_\Delta f_n g \, d\mu = \int_\Delta fg \, d\mu$. Hence, by the Banach-Steinhaus Theorem, $| f_n^*(g) | = | \int_\Delta f_n g \, d\mu |$

$\leqslant M \| g \|_\Psi$ for a fixed M. Taking now $g(x)$ such that $\int_\Delta \Psi | g | d\mu \leqslant 1$, so that $\| g \|_\Psi \leqslant \int_\Delta \Psi | g | d\mu + 1 \leqslant 2$ (cf. Ch. 5, § 5, Th. 1), we have therefore $| \int_\Delta f_n g \, d\mu | \leqslant 2M$, hence also $| \int_\Delta fg \, d\mu | \leqslant 2M$. But then, replacing g by $| g |/\text{sgn} f$, which does not affect $| g |$, we find $\int_\Delta | fg | d\mu \leqslant 2M$, and this shows that $\| f \|_\Phi \leqslant 2M$ is finite.

The proof that $g(x) \in L_\Psi$ if $f(x)g(x)$ is summable for every $f(x) \in L_\Phi$ is similar. The important point to observe is that the functions $g_n(x)$, equal to $g(x)$ when $| g(x) | \leqslant n$ and $x \in \Delta_n$, and vanishing elsewhere on Δ, all belong to L_Ψ, even in the case that $\lim_{u \to \infty} \varphi(u)$ is finite.

Theorem 2. *Let* $1 \leqslant p \leqslant \infty$, $1/p + 1/q = 1$. *Then, if the complex, μ-measurable function $f(x)$, defined on the set Δ, has the property that $f(x)g(x)$ is summable over Δ for every $g(x) \in L_q(\Delta, \mu)$, we have $f(x) \in L_p(\Delta, \mu)$.*

Proof. Follows from the preceding theorem by taking $\Phi(u) = u^p/p$ for $1 \leqslant p < \infty$, because then $L_\Phi = L_p$ and $L_\Psi = L_q$. If $p = \infty$, we take $\Phi(u) = u$. Then $L_\Phi = L_q$ and $L_\Psi = L_p$, so that by hypothesis $f(x)g(x)$ is summable for every $g(x) \in L_\Phi$, which implies $f(x) \in L_\Psi = L_p$.

Theorem 3. *Let* $1 \leqslant p \leqslant \infty$, $1/p + 1/q = 1$. *Then, if the sequence of complex numbers $f = \{f_1, f_2, \ldots\}$ has the property that the partial sums $f_n^*(g) = \Sigma_{k=1}^n f_k g_k$ form a bounded sequence for every sequence $g = \{g_1, g_2, \ldots\} \in l_q$, we have $f = \{f_k\} \in l_p$.*

Proof. The transformations $f_n^*(g) = \Sigma_{k=1}^n f_k g_k$, defined on l_q and with range in the space of all complex numbers, are now linear and bounded, and in a similar way as in Theorem 1 we find again that they are uniformly bounded, hence $| f_n^*(g) | \leqslant M \| g \|_q$ for a fixed M. Then $\| f \|_p \leqslant M$. To prove this statement we may suppose that $1 < p < \infty$, since for $p = 1$ and $p = \infty$ it is immediately evident. We consider the sequence $c_k = | f_k |^{p-1}/\text{sgn} f_k$. Then $| c_k |^q = | f_k |^p$, so that, supposing that $\Sigma | f_k |^p > M^p$, we should have $\Sigma_{k=1}^N | c_k |^q = \Sigma_{k=1}^N | f_k |^p = A > M^p$ for a certain index N. Defining now $g_k = c_k/A^{1/q}$ for $k = 1, \ldots, N$, and $g_k = 0$ for $k > N$, the result would be that $\Sigma | g_k |^q = 1$, so $\| g \|_q = 1$, but

$$| \Sigma f_k g_k | = | \Sigma f_k c_k |/A^{1/q} = \Sigma | f_k |^p/A^{1/q} \geqslant$$
$$A/A^{1/q} = A^{1/p} > M = M \| g \|_q,$$

which is a contradiction. Hence $\| f \|_p \leqslant M$, so $f = \{f_k\} \in l_p$.

§ 4. Bounded Linear Functionals and their Form in Several Spaces

We have already seen that the set of all complex numbers may be considered as a Banach space ($E_{2,1}$ in the terminology of Ch. 6, § 13, Ex. B). Any transformation on a Banach space E which has its range in the set of complex numbers is called a *functional*. The functional $f^*(f)$ is therefore *linear* if

$$f^*(\alpha f + \beta g) = \alpha f^*(f) + \beta f^*(g)$$

for arbitrary complex α, β and $f, g \in E$; it is *bounded* if there exists a number $M \geqslant 0$ such that $| f^*(f) | \leqslant M \| f \|$ for all $f \in E$, and its norm $\| f^* \|$ has the value $\| f^* \| =$ upper bound $| f^*(f) |$ for all f with $\| f \| \leqslant 1$.

In some of the Banach spaces which we have already met as examples any arbitrarily given bounded linear functional may be written in a very simple form. We shall consider first the case of a Hilbert space, and after that the spaces L_Φ, L_p and l_p.

Theorem 1 (*Bounded linear functional in Hilbert space*). *Let R be a complete Hilbert space and $f^*(f)$ a bounded linear functional on R. Then there exists a uniquely determined element g such that $f^*(f) = (f, g)$ for every $f \in R$. The norm of $f^*(f)$ is $\| g \|$* [2].

Proof. The set of all $f \in R$ for which $f^*(f) = 0$ is a subspace $[L]$. This subspace is either identical with the whole space R, and then $f^*(f) = (f, 0)$, or we may determine by Ch. 6, § 12, Th. 3 an element $h \neq 0$ orthogonal to every $f \in [L]$. Writing $g = \overline{f^*(h)}\, h/(h, h)$, we have $f^*(f) = (f, g)$ for $f = h$, and also for all elements $f \in [L]$. Furthermore, for an arbitrary $f \in R$, if $\alpha = f^*(f)/f^*(h)$, the element $f_1 = f - \alpha h$ belongs to $[L]$ since $f^*(f_1) = f^*(f) - \alpha f^*(h) = 0$. Hence $f^*(f) = f^*(f_1 + \alpha h) = f^*(f_1) + \alpha f^*(h) = (f_1, g) + \alpha(h, g) = (f, g)$.

The thus determined element g is unique since $(f, g) = (f, g_1)$, holding for every $f \in R$, implies $g - g_1 = 0$ as may be seen by taking $f = g - g_1$.

Finally the norm of $f^*(f)$ is $\| g \|$ because $| f^*(f) | = | (f, g) | \leqslant \| g \| . \| f \|$ for every $f \in R$, and $| f^*(g) | = | (g, g) | = \| g \| . \| g \|$.

Theorem 2 (*Bounded linear functional in $L_\Phi(\Delta, \mu)$ if $\Phi(2u) \leqslant M\Phi(u)$*, [3]). *Let $L_\Phi(\Delta, \mu)$ be the Orlicz space introduced in Ch.* 5, § 5, *and let $\Phi(u)$ satisfy $\Phi(2u) \leqslant M\Phi(u)$ for a fixed $M > 0$ and all $u \geqslant 0$. The complementary function in the sense of Young will be denoted by $\Psi(v)$. Then, if $f^*(f)$ is a bounded linear functional in L_Φ, there is a uniquely determined function $g(x) \in L_\Psi$ such that*

$$f^*(f) = \int_\Delta f(x)g(x)d\mu$$

for every $f \in L_\Phi$. The norm of $f^*(f)$ satisfies

$$\| g \|_\Psi/2 \leqslant \| f^* \| \leqslant \| g \|_\Psi.$$

Proof. Let A_1 be a subset of Δ of finite measure, and let $f(x)$ run through the characteristic functions of all measurable subsets X of A_1. For $X \subset A_1$ the corresponding characteristic function $f(x)$ satisfies $\rho(f) = \int_\Delta \Phi \mid f \mid d\mu = \int_X \Phi(1) d\mu = \Phi(1) . \mu(X) \leqslant \Phi(1) . \mu(A_1)$, hence $f(x) \in L_\Phi$. If now $X = \Sigma_{k=1}^n X_k$ ($X, X_k \subset A_1$), where no two of the sets X_k have common points, so that the corresponding characteristic functions $f(x)$, $f_k(x)$ satisfy $f(x) = \Sigma_{k=1}^n f_k(x)$, we have $f^*(f) = \Sigma_{k=1}^n f^*(f_k)$. Furthermore, if $\lim \mu(X_n) = 0$, we have $\lim \rho(f_n) = 0$, hence $\lim \| f_n \|_\Phi = 0$ by Ch. 5, § 7, Lemma α, so that also $\lim f^*(f_n) = 0$. We see therefore that $X = \Sigma_{k=1}^\infty X_k$ (X, $X_k \subset A_1$, no two of the sets X_k have common points) implies $f^*(f) = \Sigma_{k=1}^\infty f^*(f_k)$ for the characteristic functions $f(x), f_k(x)$. Finally, if the measure $\mu(X) = 0$, we have $\| f \|_\Phi = 0$, hence $f^*(f) = 0$. Restricting $f(x)$ to these characteristic functions of sets $X \subset A_1$, $f^*(f)$ is therefore an additive and absolutely continuous function $F(X)$ of a set on A_1. Then, by Ch. 4, § 3, Th. 3 (Theorem of Radon-Nikodym), there exists a function $g(x)$, summable over A_1, such that

$$f^*(f) = F(X) = \int_X g(x) d\mu = \int_\Delta f(x) g(x) d\mu$$

for every measurable set $X \subset A_1$.

Since Δ may be written in the form $\Delta = \Sigma_{n=1}^\infty A_n$, where no two of the sets A_n of finite measure have common points, the function $g(x)$ may be extended onto all the sets A_n, hence

$$f^*(f) = \int_\Delta f(x) g(x) d\mu$$

for the characteristic function $f(x)$ of any measurable set $X \subset \Delta$ of finite measure.

Every simple function on Δ, vanishing outside a set of finite measure, is a finite linear combination of these characteristic functions, so that also for a simple function $f(x)$ of this kind we have

$$f^*(f) = \int_\Delta f(x) g(x) d\mu.$$

Let now $f(x)$ be measurable, vanishing outside a set $\Delta_1 \subset \Delta$ of finite measure, and bounded; $| f(x) | \leqslant A$ on Δ. Then, as we have seen in Ch. 5, § 7, Th. 1, there exists a sequence of simple functions $f_n(x)$, vanishing outside Δ_1 and satisfying $| f_n(x) | \leqslant A$, $\lim \| f - f_n \|_\Phi = 0$. This implies $\lim \int_{\Delta_1} | f - f_n | . | h | d\mu = 0$ for every $h(x)$ with $\int_\Delta \Psi \mid h \mid d\mu \leqslant 1$. Let now the positive number p be such that $\mu(\Delta_1)\Psi(p) \leqslant 1$. Taking $h(x) = p$ on Δ_1 and $h(x) = 0$ elsewhere in Δ, we have $\int_\Delta \Psi \mid h \mid d\mu \leqslant 1$, hence $\lim p \int_{\Delta_1} | f - f_n | d\mu = 0$; there exists therefore a subsequence $f_k(x)$ ($k = n_1, n_2, \ldots$) satisfying $\lim f_k(x) = f(x)$ almost everywhere on Δ_1 (cf. the proof of Ch. 5, § 2, Th. 1). From $\lim f_k(x) g(x) = f(x) g(x)$ almost everywhere on Δ_1 and $| f_k(x)g(x) | \leqslant A | g(x) |$ follows now by Lebesgue's Theorem

$$f^*(f) = \lim f^*(f_k) = \lim \int_{\Delta_1} f_k(x)g(x)d\mu =$$
$$\int_{\Delta_1} f(x)g(x)d\mu = \int_\Delta f(x)g(x)d\mu.$$

We shall prove next that $g(x) \in L_\Psi$ and that $\| g \|_\Psi/2 \leqslant \| f^* \|$. Defining, if $f(x) \in L_\Phi = L_\Phi^*$ is given, the functions $f_n(x)$ $(n = 1, 2, \ldots)$ by

$$f_n(x) = | f(x) |/\text{sgn}\, g(x) \quad \text{for } | f(x) | \leqslant n,\ x \in \Delta_n,$$
$$f_n(x) = 0 \qquad \text{elsewhere in } \Delta,$$

where $\Delta = \lim \Delta_n$, Δ_n ascending, and $\mu(\Delta_n)$ finite, we have

$$\| f_n \|_\Phi = \text{upper bound} \int_\Delta | f_n h | d\mu \leqslant \text{upper bound} \int_\Delta | fh | d\mu = \| f \|_\Phi,$$

where $\int_\Delta \Psi | h | d\mu \leqslant 1$, hence

$$| f^*(f_n) | \leqslant \| f^* \| . \| f_n \|_\Phi \leqslant \| f^* \| . \| f \|_\Phi \text{ for all } n.$$

Observing now that $f^*(f_n) = \int_\Delta f_n g d\mu = \int_\Delta | f_n g | d\mu$ and that $\lim | f_n(x)g(x) | = | f(x)g(x) |$ almost everywhere on Δ, we find by Fatou's Theorem

$$\int_\Delta | fg | d\mu \leqslant \liminf \int_\Delta | f_n g | d\mu = \liminf f^*(f_n) \leqslant \| f^* \| . \| f \|_\Phi,$$

which shows that $f(x)g(x)$ is summable over Δ for every $f(x) \in L_\Phi = L_\Phi^*$. Hence $g(x) \in L_\Psi$.

Furthermore, if $\int_\Delta \Phi | f | d\mu \leqslant 1$, so that $\| f \|_\Phi \leqslant 2$, we have $\int_\Delta | fg | d\mu \leqslant 2 \| f^* \|$, hence $\| g \|_\Psi \leqslant 2 \| f^* \|$.

We have still to show that $f^*(f) = \int_\Delta fg\, d\mu$ for every $f \in L_\Phi$, and that $\| f^* \| \leqslant \| g \|_\Psi$. If $f(x) \in L_\Phi$ is given, we define now

$$f_n(x) = f(x) \quad \text{for } | f(x) | < n,\ x \in \Delta_n,$$
$$f_n(x) = 0 \quad \text{elsewhere in } \Delta.$$

Then, as we have seen in the proof of the separability of L_Φ, we have $\lim \| f - f_n \|_\Phi = 0$, hence $f^*(f) = \lim f^*(f_n)$. From $\lim f_n(x)g(x) = f(x)g(x)$ almost everywhere on Δ, $| f_n g | \leqslant | fg |$ and the summability of $| fg |$ follows therefore

$$f^*(f) = \lim f^*(f_n) = \lim \int_\Delta f_n g\, d\mu = \int_\Delta fg\, d\mu.$$

Then $| f^*(f) | \leqslant \int_\Delta | fg | d\mu \leqslant \| f \|_\Phi . \| g \|_\Psi$, hence $\| f^* \| \leqslant \| g \|_\Psi$.

It remains to prove that $g(x)$ is uniquely determined. Supposing that $\int_\Delta f(x)\{g(x) - g_1(x)\}\, d\mu = 0$ holds for every $f(x) \in L_\Phi$, we have $\| g - g_1 \|_\Psi = 0$, hence $g(x) - g_1(x) = 0$ almost everywhere on Δ (cf. Ch. 5, § 5, Th. 1).

Theorem 3 (*Bounded linear functional in $L_p(\Delta, \mu)$, $1 \leqslant p < \infty$,* [4]). *Let $1 \leqslant p < \infty$ and $1/p + 1/q = 1$. Then, if $f^*(f)$ is a bounded linear functional in $L_p(\Delta, \mu)$, there is a uniquely determined function $g(x) \in L_q(\Delta, \mu)$ such that*

$$f^*(f) = \int_\Delta f(x)g(x)\, d\mu$$

for every $f \in L_p$. The norm of $f^*(f)$ is $\| g \|_q$.

Proof. We take $\Phi(u) = u^p/p$ so that $L_\Phi = L_p$ and $L_\Psi = L_q$. Then, by the preceding theorem, there exists a uniquely determined function $g(x) \in L_q$ such that $f^*(f) = \int_\Delta fg\, d\mu$, and $\| g \|_\Psi/2 \leqslant \| f^* \| \leqslant \| g \|_\Psi$. In this particular case however it is possible to determine $\| f^* \|$ exactly. Indeed, if $1 < p < \infty$, hence $1 < q < \infty$, we have by Ch. 5, § 1, Th. 2

$$\| g \|_q = \max | \int_\Delta fg\, d\mu | \text{ for all } f \in L_p \text{ with } \| f \|_p \leqslant 1,$$

and if $p = 1$, hence $q = \infty$,

$$\| g \|_q = \text{upper bound } | \int_\Delta fg\, d\mu | \text{ for all } f \in L_p \text{ with } \| f \|_p \leqslant 1.$$

Hence $\| f^* \| = \| g \|_q$ for $1 \leqslant p < \infty$.

Theorem 4 (*Bounded linear functional in l_p, $1 \leqslant p < \infty$*). *Let $1 \leqslant p < \infty$, $1/p + 1/q = 1$. Then, if $f^*(f)$ is a bounded linear functional in l_p, there is a uniquely determined element $g = \{g_k\} \in l_q$ such that*

$$f^*(f) = \Sigma_k f_k g_k$$

for every $f \in l_p$. The norm of $f^*(f)$ is $\| g \|_q$.

Proof. Defining the elements $e_n \in l_p$ $(n = 1, 2, \ldots)$ by $e_n = \{e_{n1}, e_{n2}, \ldots\}$, where $e_{ni} = 1$ for $i = n$ and $e_{ni} = 0$ for $i \neq n$, we have, if $f = \{f_k\} \in l_p$ is arbitrarily given, $f - \Sigma_{k=1}^n f_k e_k = \{0, 0, \ldots, 0, f_{n+1}, f_{n+2}, \ldots\}$, hence $\lim_{n\to\infty} \| f - \Sigma_{k=1}^n f_k e_k \|_p = 0$ or $f = \Sigma_{k=1}^\infty f_k e_k$. Writing $f^*(e_n) = g_n$, we find therefore

$$f^*(f) = \Sigma f_k g_k.$$

From $| \Sigma f_k g_k | = | f^*(f) | \leqslant \| f^* \| . \| f \|_p$, holding for every $f \in l_p$, we conclude as in § 3, Th. 3 (p and q are interchanged) that $g = \{g_k\} \in l_q$ and $\| g \|_q \leqslant \| f^* \|$. On the other hand, $| f^*(f) | = | \Sigma f_k g_k | \leqslant \| f \|_p . \| g \|_q$ implies $\| f^* \| \leqslant \| g \|_q$. Hence $\| f^* \| = \| g \|_q$.

In the subspaces $E_{p,n}$ of finite dimension n (cf. Ch. 6, § 6, Ex. C) we have obviously:

Let $1 \leqslant p \leqslant \infty$, $1/p + 1/q = 1$ (the case $p = \infty$, $q = 1$ is therefore included here). Then the set of all bounded linear functionals $f^*(f)$ in

$E_{p,n}$ is identical with the set of all expressions $f^*(f) = \Sigma_{k=1}^n f_k g_k$, where $g = \{g_1, \ldots, g_n\} \in E_{q,n}$ is uniquely determined by f^*, and $\| f^* \| = \| g \|_q$.

Remark. We observe finally that, conversely, the following statements are obviously true:

1°. Every functional $f^*(f) = (f, g)$ in Hilbert space is linear and bounded with $\| f^* \| = \| g \|$.

2°. Every functional $f^*(f) = \int_\Delta fg \, d\mu$ with $g(x) \in L_\Psi$ is linear and bounded in L_Φ with $\| g \|_\Psi/2 \leqslant \| f^* \| \leqslant \| g \|_\Psi$, also if $\Phi(2u) \leqslant M\Phi(u)$ for all $u \geqslant 0$ is not satisfied.

3°. Every functional $f^*(f) = \int_\Delta fg \, d\mu$ with $g(x) \in L_q$ is linear and bounded in L_p, $1 \leqslant p \leqslant \infty$, $1/p + 1/q = 1$, with $\| f^* \| = \| g \|_q$ ($p = \infty$, $q = 1$ is therefore included here).

4°. Every functional $f^*(f) = \Sigma f_k g_k$ with $g = \{g_k\} \in l_q$ is linear and bounded in l_p, $1 \leqslant p \leqslant \infty$, $1/p + 1/q = 1$, with $\| f^* \| = \| g \|_q$ ($p = \infty$, $q = 1$ is therefore included here).

§ 5. Real Banach Space

Sometimes sets are considered which satisfy all axioms of Banach space except that instead of multiplication of the elements f by arbitrary complex numbers α only multiplication by arbitrary real numbers a is supposed to be defined. A set of this category is called a *real Banach space*. An example is the subset of L_p, $1 \leqslant p \leqslant \infty$, consisting of all functions $f(x) \in L_p$, assuming only real values. To avoid confusion a Banach space allowing all complex numbers as multipliers is then sometimes called a complex Banach space.

In the same way we distinguish between complex linear bounded functionals and real linear bounded functionals. A real linear bounded functional is therefore a linear bounded transformation on a real Banach space into the real Banach space of all real numbers.

If E is a complex Banach space, there is associated to E a uniquely determined real Banach space E_r the elements of which are the elements of E, and whose addition is also that in E; if a is real and $f \in E$, the product af in E_r is the complex product $(a + 0i)f$ in E. If $\| f \|$ is the norm in E, then the same norm is to be used in E_r.

We shall now denote the set of all complex bounded linear functionals in E by E^*, and the set of all real bounded linear functionals in E_r by E_r^*. Furthermore, if $f^* \in E^*$, we define $R(f^*)$, the real part of f^*, by

$f_r^* = R(f^*)$ if $f_r^*(f) = R(f^*(f))$, the real part of $f^*(f)$, for all $f \in E$. Evidently $f_r^*(f)$ is a real bounded linear functional in E_r, hence $f_r^* \in E_r^*$.

Theorem 1. *The relation $f_r^* = R(f^*)$, defined by $f_r^*(f) = R(f^*(f))$ for all $f \in E$, is a one-to-one, norm-preserving correspondence between the whole set E^* and the whole set E_r^** [5].

Proof. Writing $f^*(f) = R(f^*(f)) + iI(f^*(f))$, we have $f^*(if) = R(if^*(f)) + iI(if^*(f)) = -I(f^*(f)) + iR(f^*(f))$, hence $f^*(f) = R(f^*(f)) - iR(f^*(if))$. This shows that, $f_r^* = R(f^*)$ being the transformation on E^* to E_r^*, $f^*(f) = f_r^*(f) - if_r^*(if)$ is the inverse transformation on E_r^* to E^*.

To prove that $\| f^* \| = \| f_r^* \|$, we observe first that $| f_r^*(f) | = | R(f^*(f)) | \leqslant | f^*(f) |$ for every f, hence $\| f_r^* \| \leqslant \| f^* \|$. On the other hand, if $f^*(f) = re^{i\varphi}$, then $f^*(fe^{-i\varphi}) = r = | f^*(f) |$ is real, so that $f_r^*(fe^{-i\varphi}) = f^*(fe^{-i\varphi}) = | f^*(f) |$. But $\| fe^{-i\varphi} \| = \| f \|$, hence

$$\| f^* \| = \text{upper bound}_{\| f \| \leq 1} | f^*(f) | \leqslant$$
$$\text{upper bound}_{\| f \| \leq 1} | f_r^*(f) | = \| f_r^* \|.$$

It follows that $\| f^* \| = \| f_r^* \|$.

Remark. Observe the analogy between the second part of the present proof and the proof of $| \int f \, d\mu | \leqslant \int | f | \, d\mu$ (Ch. 3, § 5, Th. 2).

§ 6. Extension of Linear Functionals

In the present paragraph we shall discuss the following question: Given a bounded linear functional on a linear subspace $[L]$ of the Banach space E, is it possible to extend this functional onto the whole space E in such a way that it remains linear and bounded with the same norm? A related question is whether there are bounded linear functionals vanishing on a preassigned linear subspace without vanishing identically. We shall consider first two simple cases:

1°. E is a Hilbert space.

2°. E is the direct sum of two linear subspaces one at least of which is of finite dimension.

Theorem 1. *Let $[L]$ be a proper linear subspace of the Hilbert space R. Then, if $F(f)$ is a bounded linear functional on $[L]$ with norm $\| F \|$, there exists a bounded linear functional $f^*(f)$ on R such that $f^*(f) = F(f)$ for $f \in [L]$ and $\| f^* \| = \| F \|$.*

Proof. $[L]$ itself is a Hilbert space so that there exists a unique element

$g \in \overline{[L]}$ (the closure of $[L]$) such that $F(f) = (f, g)$ for all $f \in [L]$. We define $f^*(f) = (f, g)$ for all $f \in R$. Then f^* is bounded and linear on R, $f^*(f) = F(f)$ for $f \in [L]$ and $\| f^* \| = \| g \| = \| F \|$.

Theorem 2. *Let the Banach space E (complete or non-complete) be the direct sum of the linear subspaces $[L_1]$ and $[L_2]$, where $[L_1]$ is of finite dimension. Then, if $F(f)$ is a bounded linear functional on $[L_1]$, there exists a bounded linear functional $f^*(f)$ on E such that $f^*(f) = F(f)$ for $f \in [L_1]$ and $f^*(f) = 0$ for $f \in [L_2]$.*

Proof. For every $f \in E$ there is a unique decomposition $f = g + h$, $g \in [L_1]$, $h \in [L_2]$. We define $f^*(f) = F(g)$. Then $f^*(f)$ is obviously linear, $f^*(f) = F(f)$ for all $f \in [L_1]$ and $f^*(f) = 0$ for all $f \in [L_2]$. Let us suppose now that $f^*(f)$ is not bounded. Then there exists a sequence f_n for which $| f^*(f_n) | > n \| f_n \|$, or $| F(g_n) | > n \| f_n \|$, where $f_n = g_n + h_n$. It is permitted to suppose here that $\| g_n \| = 1$ (f_n may be replaced by $f_n / \| g_n \|$). Since F is bounded on $[L_1]$, the sequence $F(g_n)$ is bounded so that $\lim \| f_n \| = 0$. We find therefore $\lim (g_n + h_n) = 0$ with $\| g_n \| = 1$. As we have seen in the proof of Ch. 6, § 4, Th. 4, this however leads to a contradiction. The functional $f^*(f)$ is therefore bounded.

Remark. We shall prove later (cf. § 14, Th. 2, Remark) that if E is complete, the condition that $[L_1]$ be of finite dimension may be left out.

We shall now consider more general cases.

Theorem 3 (*Hahn-Banach Extension Theorem in real Banach space*). *Let $[L]$ be a proper linear subspace of the real separable Banach space E_r (complete or non-complete). Then, if $F(f)$ is a real bounded linear functional on $[L]$ with norm $\| F \|$, there exists a real bounded linear functional $f^*(f)$ on E_r such that $f^*(f) = F(f)$ for $f \in [L]$ and $\| f^* \| = \| F \|$ [6].*

Proof. We write $p(f) = \| F \| . \| f \|$ for all $f \in E_r$, so that we have $| F(f) | \leqslant p(f)$ for all $f \in [L]$. Let $f_0 \in E_r - [L]$. Then, for $g', g'' \in [L]$,

$$F(g'') - F(g') = F(g'' - g') \leqslant p(g'' - g') =$$

$$p\{(g'' + f_0) + (-g' - f_0)\} \leqslant p(g'' + f_0) + p(g' + f_0),$$

hence

$$-p(g' + f_0) - F(g') \leqslant p(g'' + f_0) - F(g'').$$

The numbers

$$m = \text{upper bound}_{g \in [L]} \{-p(g + f_0) - F(g)\},$$

$$M = \text{lower bound}_{g \in [L]} \{\ \ p(g + f_0) - F(g)\}$$

are therefore finite and $m \leqslant M$, so that, if $m \leqslant r_0 \leqslant M$, we have

$$-p(g+f_0)-F(g) \leqslant r_0 \leqslant p(g+f_0)-F(g)$$

for all $g \in [L]$. Replacing g by g/a, where a is arbitrarily real, and multiplying by a, we obtain

$$-p(g+af_0)-F(g) \leqslant ar_0 \leqslant \quad p(g+af_0)-F(g) \text{ for } a \geqslant 0,$$

$$p(g+af_0)-F(g) \geqslant ar_0 \geqslant -p(g+af_0)-F(g) \text{ for } a < 0,$$

hence

$$-p(g+af_0) \leqslant F(g)+ar_0 \leqslant p(g+af_0) \tag{1}$$

for every real a. Considering now the set $[L_0]$ of all elements $f = g + af_0$, where g runs through $[L]$ and a through all real numbers, every element of this set admits exactly one representation of the form $f = g + af_0$, so that $[L_0]$ is a linear subspace (cf. Ch. 6, § 4, Th. 4) and, if we define $f^*(f) = F(g) + ar_0$ on $[L_0]$, the functional $f^*(f)$ is linear and uniquely determined. By (1) we have $| f^*(f) | \leqslant p(f) = \| F \| . \| f \|$ for all $f \in [L_0]$; the norm of $f^*(f)$ on $[L_0]$ is therefore $\| F \|$.

Using now the hypothesis that E_r is separable it is evident that, by repeating the just described process of extension an at most enumerable number of times, we may define $f^*(f)$ on a set which is dense in E_r. But then, by § 3, Th. 1, it may be extended onto the whole of E_r in such a way that it remains linear and bounded with the same norm $\| f^* \| = \| F \|$. We finally observe that already by the first extension $f^*(f) = F(f)$ for all $f \in [L]$.

Theorem 4 (*Bohnenblust-Sobczyk Extension Theorem in complex Banach space*). *Let $[L]$ be a proper linear subspace of the complex separable Banach space E (complete or non-complete). Then, if $F(f)$ is a complex bounded linear functional on $[L]$ with norm $\| F \|$, there exists a bounded linear functional $f^*(f)$ on E such that $f^*(f) = F(f)$ for $f \in [L]$ and $\| f^* \| = \| F \|$* [7].

Proof. We write $F(f) = F_r(f) + iF_i(f)$ for $f \in [L]$, where $F_r(f)$ and $F_i(f)$ are real-valued. Then, by § 5, Th. 1, $F_r(f)$ is a real functional on the real Banach space $[L]_r$ associated to $[L]$, linear and bounded with norm $\| F_r \| = \| F \|$. By the preceding theorem F_r may be extended onto the whole of E_r (the real Banach space associated to E), so that we obtain a real bounded linear functional f_r^* on E_r satisfying $f_r^*(f) = F_r(f)$ on $[L]$ and $\| f_r^* \| = \| F_r \| = \| F \|$. Writing now $f^*(f) = f_r^*(f) - if_r^*(if)$, we see, once again by § 5, Th. 1, that $f^*(f)$ has all the desired properties.

Theorem 5. *To each element f_0 of the space E, E being a Banach space in which the Extension Theorem holds, there exists a bounded linear functional $f^*(f)$ on E such that $f^*(f_0) = \| f_0 \|$ and $\| f^* \| = 1$.*

Proof. We may assume $f_0 \neq 0$. Then the set of all elements αf_0 (α complex) is a linear subspace $[L]$ on which we define $F(\alpha f_0) = \alpha \| f_0 \|$, so that $\| F \| = 1$. The result follows then by the Extension Theorem.

Remark. In Hilbert space the following direct proof may be given: Write $f^*(f) = (f, g)$, where $g = f_0/\| f_0 \|$.

Theorem 6. *Let $[L]$ be a linear subspace of the space E, E being a Banach space in which the Extension Theorem holds. Then, if the element $f_0 \in E$ has a positive distance d from $[L]$, there exists a bounded linear functional f^* on E such that $f^*(f) = 0$ for $f \in [L]$, $f^*(f_0) = 1$ and $\| f^* \| = 1/d$.*

Proof. We consider the set $[L_0]$ of all elements $f = g + \alpha f_0$, where g runs through $[L]$ and α through all complex numbers. Since $d > 0$, the representation $f = g + \alpha f_0$ is unique, so that $[L_0]$ is a linear subspace. We define $F(f) = \alpha$ for $f = g + \alpha f_0$. Then F is linear on $[L_0]$, $F(f) = 0$ on $[L]$, $F(f_0) = 1$ and $\| f \| = \| g + \alpha f_0 \| = | \alpha | . \| g/\alpha + f_0 \| \geqslant | \alpha | d$, hence $| F(f) | = | \alpha | \leqslant \| f \|/d$, so that $\| F \| \leqslant 1/d$. On the other hand $\lim \| g_n - f_0 \| = d$ for $g_n \in [L]$ implies $| F(g_n - f_0) | = | F(f_0) | = 1 \leqslant \| F \| . \| g_n - f_0 \|$, hence $1 \leqslant d \| F \|$ or $\| F \| \geqslant 1/d$. This shows that $\| F \| = 1/d$. The Extension Theorem may now be used to complete the proof.

Remark. If $E = R$ is a Hilbert space, the following direct proof may be given: We have $f_0 = g_0 + h_0$, $g_0 \in \overline{[L]}$, $h_0 \in \bar{R} \ominus \overline{[L]}$ with $\| h_0 \| = d$. The functional $f^*(f) = (f, h_1)$ with $h_1 = h_0/\| h_0 \|^2$ has now the desired properties.

Theorem 7. *Let E be a Banach space in which the Extension Theorem holds. Then the set $S \subset E$ is complete in E if and only if every bounded linear functional which vanishes on S is vanishing identically.*

Proof. Let S be complete, $f_0 \in E$ and $f_0 = \lim f_n$ where $f_n \in L(S)$, that is, every f_n is a finite linear combination of elements of S. If now f^* is a bounded linear functional, vanishing on S, then $f^*(f_n) = 0$, hence $f^*(f_0) = \lim f^*(f_n) = 0$. This shows that f^* vanishes identically.

Let now, conversely, every bounded linear functional which vanishes on S vanish identically. Then, supposing that S is not complete, there is an element f_0 having a positive distance from the subspace $[L(S)]$, so that from the preceding theorem we infer the existence of a bounded linear functional $f^*(f)$, vanishing on S, for which $f^*(f_0) = 1$. This is a contradiction; S is therefore complete.

We are now in a position to show that the system of functions $\varphi_{n_1 \ldots n_m}(x_1, \ldots, x_m)$, defined on the finite m-dimensional interval $\Delta = [a_1, b_1; \ldots; a_m, b_m]$, which we have introduced in Ch. 6, § 14, Th. 4, is not only complete in $L_2(\Delta) = L_2(\Delta, \mu)$ with μ Lebesgue measure, as we have proved there, but even in the space $L_\Phi(\Delta)$ for any $\Phi(u)$ satisfying $\Phi(2u) \leqslant M\Phi(u)$. In particular it is complete in the spaces $L_p(\Delta)$, $1 \leqslant p < \infty$.

Theorem 8. *Let* $\Delta = [a_1, b_1; \ldots; a_m, b_m]$ *be an arbitrary finite* m-*dimensional interval, and let the function* $\Phi(u)$ *which occurs in the definition of the Orlicz space* $L_\Phi(\Delta)$ *satisfy* $\Phi(2u) \leqslant M\Phi(u)$ *for all* $u \geqslant 0$. *Then the system of functions* $\varphi_{n_1, \ldots n_m}(x_1, \ldots, x_m)$ *of Ch.* 6, § 14, *Th.* 4 *is complete in* $L_\Phi(\Delta)$.

Proof. We may replace, by renumbering in some way, the sequence $\varphi_{n_1, \ldots n_m}$ by a single sequence $\psi_n(x)$ which contains the same functions. Evidently $\psi_n(x) \in L_\Phi(\Delta)$, since all $\psi_n(x)$ are bounded on Δ and Δ is finite. Furthermore, on account of $\Phi(2u) \leqslant M\Phi(u)$, the space $L_\Phi(\Delta)$ is separable, and every bounded linear functional $f^*(f)$ on $L_\Phi(\Delta)$ has the form $f^*(f) = \int_\Delta f(x)g(x)dx$, where $g(x) \in L_\Psi(\Delta)$, the complementary space. By the preceding theorem the system $\psi_n(x)$ is therefore complete in $L_\Phi(\Delta)$ if and only if

$$\int_\Delta \psi_n(x)g(x)dx = 0 \quad (n = 1, 2, \ldots)$$

for any $g(x) \in L_\Psi(\Delta)$ implies $g(x) = 0$ identically. If however $g(x) \in L_\Psi(\Delta)$, then $| f(x)g(x) |$ is summable over Δ for every $f(x) \in L_\Phi(\Delta)$, in particular for $f(x) = 1$. It follows that $g(x) \in L_\Psi(\Delta)$ implies $g(x) \in L(\Delta)$; it is therefore sufficient to prove that $\int_\Delta \psi_n g\, dx = 0$ $(n = 1, 2, \ldots)$ for any $g(x) \in L$ implies $g(x) = 0$ identically. But this we have already proved in Ch. 6, § 14, Th. 4.

For future use we give now the following definition.

Definition. *Any Banach space in which the Hahn-Banach-Bohnenblust-Sobczyk Extension Theorem holds will be said to possess the property* (*Ext.*).

Hilbert space (whether separable or not) and separable Banach spaces have therefore, as we have proved, the property (Ext.). If one admits the truth of a certain theorem, the "Wellordering theorem", it may even be proved that any Banach space has the property (Ext.). To make clear what this Wellordering theorem asserts, some introductory explanation is necessary. A set X with elements $x, y, \ldots$ is said to be *ordered* if:

1°. Between every two arbitrary different elements x and y there is defined an order relation which says that x precedes y (written $x < y$) or y precedes x (written $y < x$ or $x > y$).

2°. If $x < y$, $y < z$, then $x < z$.

Furthermore the ordered set X is said to be *wellordered* if every subset Y contains a first element, that is, if $Y \subset X$, there exists an element $y \in Y$ such that $y < z$ for any other element $z \in Y$.

The Wellordering theorem asserts now that every arbitrary set can be wellordered. Since however the proof is founded upon an axiom about the truth of which there exist controversial opinions depending upon one's attitude towards the foundations of mathematics, we shall make no use of this theorem.

Theorem 9. *If E has the property (Ext.) and $[L]$ is a linear subspace of E, then the factorspace $E/[L]$ has also the property (Ext.).*

Proof. The elements of $E/[L]$ are denoted by $[f]$ (cf. Ch. 6, § 5). The element $[f]$ contains therefore the element $f \in E$ and all $g \in E$ such that $f - g \in [L]$. Let now $[L]'$ be a linear subspace of $E/[L]$. Then the elements $f \in E$ contained in the elements $[f] \in [L]'$ form a set $H \subset E$. We shall prove that H is a linear subspace of E. Indeed, if $f_1, f_2 \in H$, then $[f_1], [f_2] \in [L]'$, hence $[\alpha_1 f_1 + \alpha_2 f_2] = [\alpha_1 f_1] + [\alpha_2 f_2] = \alpha_1[f_1] + \alpha_2[f_2] \in [L]'$, which shows that $\alpha_1 f_1 + \alpha_2 f_2 \in H$. Furthermore, if $f_n \in H$ $(n = 1, 2, \ldots)$ and $\lim \| f - f_n \| = 0$ for an element $f \in E$, then $\lim \| [f] - [f_n] \| = 0$ on account of $\| [f] - [f_n] \| = \| [f - f_n] \| \leqslant \| f - f_n \|$; hence $[f] \in [L]'$ or $f \in H$.

We suppose now that $[F]$ is an arbitrary bounded linear functional on $[L]'$. Then, by $F(f) = [F]\,[f]$, the linear functional F is defined on H. Evidently $F(f) = 0$ for all $f \in [L]$. Furthermore $| F(f) | = | [F]\,[f] | \leqslant \| [F] \| . \| [f] \| \leqslant \| [F] \| . \| f \|$, hence $\| F \| \leqslant \| [F] \|$. On the other hand, if $[f] \in [L]'$ is arbitrary, there is a sequence $f_n \in [f]$ such that $\| [f] \| = \lim \| f_n \|$ so that $| [F]\,[f] | = | F(f_n) | \leqslant \| F \| . \| f_n \|$ implies $| [F]\,[f] | \leqslant \| F \| . \| [f] \|$, hence $\| [F] \| \leqslant \| F \|$. It follows that $\| F \| = \| [F] \|$. The bounded linear functional F on H is now extended onto the whole space E. The resulting linear functional f^* on E satisfies $f^*(f) = F(f)$ for all $f \in H$, $f^*(f) = 0$ for all $f \in [L]$, and $\| f^* \| = \| F \| = \| [F] \|$. Defining then finally the linear functional $[f^*]$ on $E/[L]$ by $[f^*]\,[f] = f^*(f)$, it is easily seen that $[f^*]$ is an extension of $[F]$ and $\| [f^*] \| = \| [F] \|$.

§ 7. The Adjoint Space

We suppose that E is a Banach space, complete or non-complete, and we consider the set E^* of all bounded linear functionals $f^*(f)$ on E. In E^* addition and multiplication by complex numbers α are defined in a natural way by

$$(f_1^* + f_2^*)(f) = f_1^*(f) + f_2^*(f) \quad \text{for all } f \in E,$$
$$(\alpha f^*)(f) = \alpha f^*(f) \quad \text{for all } f \in E.$$

Then it is easily verified that Axiom A of Banach space is satisfied in E^*. The null element is the functional which vanishes for all $f \in E$. Defining now the norm $\| f^* \|$ as the smallest number M for which $| f^*(f) | \leqslant M \| f \|$ for all $f \in E$, the same definition therefore as that which we introduced in § 4, we see that $\| f^* \|$ fulfils the conditions imposed upon the norm in Axiom B of Banach space. It follows that with these definitions the set E^* is a Banach space, called the *adjoint space* of E. It is evident that, if E is not complete, E and its closure $\bar{E}$ have the same adjoint space.

Theorem 1. *The adjoint space E^* of any Banach space E is complete.*

Proof. Let $\lim \| f_m^* - f_n^* \| = 0$ as $m, n \to \infty$; $f_m^*, f_n^* \in E^*$. Since $| f_m^*(f) - f_n^*(f) | \leqslant \| f_m^* - f_n^* \| . \| f \|$, we have $\lim | f_m^*(f) - f_n^*(f) | = 0$ for every $f \in E$, that is, $\lim f_n^*(f) = f^*(f)$ exists. It is trivial that $f^*(f)$ is linear. It follows from $\| f_n^* \| \leqslant \| f_m^* \| + \| f_m^* - f_n^* \|$ that the sequence of numbers $\| f_n^* \|$ is bounded, so that there exists a number M for which $\| f_n^* \| \leqslant M$. Then $| f_n^*(f) | \leqslant M \| f \|$ for every value of n, hence also $| f^*(f) | \leqslant M \| f \|$, which shows that $f^*(f)$ is bounded. Finally, if $\varepsilon > 0$ is given, the inequality $| f_m^*(f) - f_n^*(f) | \leqslant \| f_m^* - f_n^* \| . \| f \| \leqslant \varepsilon \| f \|$, holding for sufficiently large m and n, implies $| f_m^*(f) - f^*(f) | \leqslant \varepsilon \| f \|$; hence $\lim \| f_m^* - f^* \| = 0$ as $m \to \infty$. This completes the proof.

Theorem 2. *If E is of finite dimension n, then E^* is of dimension n.*

Proof. Let $f_1, \ldots, f_n$ be a complete set in E. We define the linear functionals $f_i^*(f)$ $(i = 1, \ldots, n)$ by $f_i^*(f_j) = 1$ for $i = j$ and $f_i^*(f_j) = 0$ for $i \neq j$. Then all $f_i^*(f)$ are continuous for $f = 0$ (if $\lim f = \lim \Sigma\, \alpha_i f_i = 0$, then $\lim \alpha_i = 0$ for $i = 1, \ldots, n$ by the proof of Ch. 6, § 4, Th. 1), hence for all $f \in E$, so that they are bounded. Furthermore $f_1^*, \ldots, f_n^*$ are obviously linearly independent as elements of E^*. Let now $f^*(f)$ be an arbitrary element of E^*. If $f^*(f_i) = \alpha_i (i = 1, \ldots, n)$, then $f^*(f) = \Sigma_{i=1}^n \alpha_i f_i^*(f)$ for $f = f_1, \ldots, f_n$, hence for all $f \in E$. It follows that $f^* = \Sigma_{i=1}^n \alpha_i f_i^*$ which shows that the set $f_1^*, \ldots, f_n^*$ is complete in E^*. The space E^* is therefore n-dimensional.

Theorem 3. *If R is a Hilbert space, then R^* is also a Hilbert space, and there is a norm-preserving one-to-one correspondence $f^* \leftrightarrow f$ between R^* and $\bar{R}$, the closure of R.*

Proof. If $f^*(g)$ is a bounded linear functional on R, we know that there exists a unique element $f \in \bar{R}$ such that $f^*(g) = (g, f)$ for all $g \in R$ and $\| f^* \| = \| f \|$. It follows that $f^* \leftrightarrow f$ is a norm-preserving one-to-one correspondence between the whole space R^* and the whole space $\bar{R}$. It is not allowed however to identify R^* and $\bar{R}$ because, if $f_1^* \leftrightarrow f_1$ and $f_2^* \leftrightarrow f_2$, we have not $\alpha_1 f_1^* + \alpha_2 f_2^* \leftrightarrow \alpha_1 f_1 + \alpha_2 f_2$ (α_1, α_2 complex), but $\alpha_1 f_1^* + \alpha_2 f_2^* \leftrightarrow \bar{\alpha}_1 f_1 + \bar{\alpha}_2 f_2$. It is easily verified that R^* is made into a Hilbert space by defining $(f_1^*, f_2^*) = (f_2, f_1)$.

Theorem 4. *If E is the Orlicz space $L_\Phi(\Delta, \mu)$, and $\Phi(2u) \leqslant M\Phi(u)$ for all $u \geqslant 0$, there is a one-to-one correspondence $f^* \leftrightarrow f$ between $(L_\Phi)^*$ and the complementary space $L_\Psi(\Delta, \mu)$, which preserves addition and multiplication by complex numbers.*

Proof. If $f^*(g)$ is a bounded linear functional in L_Φ, we know that there exists a unique element $f \in L_\Psi$ such that $f^*(g) = \int_\Delta gf \, d\mu$ for all $g \in L_\Phi$ and $\| f \|_\Psi / 2 \leqslant \| f^* \| \leqslant \| f \|_\Psi$. It follows that $f^* \leftrightarrow f$ has the stated properties (but is not necessarily norm-preserving).

Theorem 5. *If E is the Lebesgue space $L_p(\Delta, \mu)$ $(1 \leqslant p < \infty)$, there is a one-to-one correspondence $f^* \leftrightarrow f$ between $(L_p)^*$ and the complementary space $L_q(\Delta, \mu)$ $(1/p + 1/q = 1)$, which preserves norm, addition and multiplication by complex numbers. The spaces $(L_p)^*$ and L_q may therefore be identified.*

Proof. If $f^*(g)$ is a bounded linear functional in L_p $(1 \leqslant p < \infty)$, we know that there exists a unique element $f \in L_q$ $(1/p + 1/q = 1)$ such that $f^*(g) = \int_\Delta gf \, d\mu$ for all $g \in L_p$ and $\| f^* \| = \| f \|_q$. It follows that $f^* \leftrightarrow f$ has the stated properties.

Theorem 6. *If E is the sequence-space l_p $(1 \leqslant p < \infty)$, there is a one-to-one correspondence $f^* \leftrightarrow f$ between $(l_p)^*$ and the complementary space l_q $(1/p + 1/q = 1)$, which preserves norm, addition and multiplication by complex numbers. The spaces $(l_p)^*$ and l_q may therefore be identified.*

Proof. Similar to the proof of the preceding theorem.

Theorem 7. *If E is the sequence-space $E_{p,n}$ $(1 \leqslant p \leqslant \infty)$ of finite dimension n, there is a one-to-one correspondence $f^* \leftrightarrow f$ between $(E_{p,n})^*$ and the complementary space $E_{q,n}$ $(1/p + 1/q = 1)$, which preserves norm, addition and multiplication by complex numbers. The spaces $(E_{p,n})^*$ and $E_{q,n}$ may therefore be identified.*

Proof. As in the preceding theorem with the only difference that the case $p = \infty$, $q = 1$ is now also included.

Theorem 8. *If the bounded linear functionals $f_1^*, \ldots, f_n^*$ on E are linearly independent (considered as elements of E^*), there exist elements $f_1, \ldots, f_n$ of E such that $f_i^*(f_j) = 1$ for $i = j$ and $f_i^*(f_j) = 0$ for $i \neq j$.*

Proof. It is evidently sufficient to prove the existence of an element f_n such that $f_n^*(f_n) = 1$, $f_i^*(f_n) = 0$ for $i = 1, \ldots, n-1$. Let us suppose first that $n = 1$. Then, since $f_1^* \neq 0$, there is an element $f_1 \in E$ for which $f_1^*(f_1) = 1$. Let us suppose now that $n > 1$ and that the theorem for $n-1$ has already been established. Then there exist elements $f_1, \ldots, f_{n-1}$ of E satisfying $f_k^*(f_k) = 1$ whereas $f_l^*(f_k) = 0$ for $l \neq k$ $(k, l = 1, \ldots, n-1)$. If now S is the set of all $f \in E$ satisfying $f_1^*(f) = \ldots = f_{n-1}^*(f) = 0$, and $f \in E$ is arbitrary, we have $\bar{f} = f - \Sigma_{i=1}^{n-1} f_i^*(f).f_i \in S$ on account of $f_k^*(\bar{f}) = f_k^*(f) - \Sigma_{i=1}^{n-1} f_i^*(f).f_k^*(f_i) = 0$ for $k = 1, \ldots, n-1$. If therefore $f_n^*(f) = 0$ would hold for every $f \in S$, and if $f_n^*(f_i) = \alpha_i$ $(i = 1, \ldots, n-1)$, so that we should have $(f_n^* - \alpha_1 f_1^* - \ldots - \alpha_{n-1} f_{n-1}^*)(f) = 0$ for all $f \in S$ and for $f = f_i$ $(i = 1, \ldots, n-1)$, it would follow that this relation is true for every $f \in E$. But then $f_n^* - \Sigma_{i=1}^{n-1} \alpha_i f_i^* = 0$, in contradiction with the linear independence of $f_1^*, \ldots, f_n^*$. We may conclude therefore that there exists an element $f_n \in S$ for which $f_n^*(f_n) = 1$.

The next theorem may be considered as a dual of Theorem 8.

Theorem 9. *Let E be the direct sum of the linear subspaces $[L_1]$ and $[L_2]$, where $[L_1]$ is of finite dimension. Then, if the elements $f_1, \ldots, f_n$ all belong to $[L_1]$ and are linearly independent, there exist bounded linear functionals $f_1^*, \ldots, f_n^*$ on E such that $f_i^*(f_j) = 1$ for $i = j$ and $f_i^*(f_j) = 0$ for $i \neq j$.*

Proof. Since the linearly independent elements $f_1, \ldots, f_n$ all belong to $[L_1]$, the dimension of $[L_1]$ is $n + k$ $(k \geqslant 0)$. Arguing now as in Ch. 6, § 4, Th. 2, it is easily seen that there exists a set $f_1, \ldots, f_n, g_1, \ldots, g_k$

which is complete in $[L_1]$. Then, defining the linear functionals f_i^* ($i = 1, \ldots, n$) on $[L_1]$ by $f_i^*(f_j) = 0$ for $i \neq j$, $f_i^*(f_i) = 1$, $f_i^*(g_l) = 0$ ($l = 1, \ldots, k$), these functionals are bounded on $[L_1]$ by § 6, Th. 2. By the same theorem the extension of all f_i^* onto the whole space E is possible.

Remark. We shall prove later (cf. § 14, Th. 2, Remark) that if E is complete, the condition that $[L_1]$ be of finite dimension may be left out. In the next paragraph we shall prove a similar theorem, dropping the condition that E is a direct sum, but supposing instead that E has the property (Ext.) (cf. § 8, Th. 4).

Theorem 10. *If E has the property (Ext.) and E^* is separable, then E is separable.*

Proof. On account of the separability of E^* there exists an enumerable set $\{g_n^*\}$ dense in E^*. Then, if we define $f_n^* = g_n^*/\| g_n^* \|$, the set $\{f_n^*\}$ is dense in the set $\| f^* \| = 1$ (the surface of the unit sphere of E^*). Since $\| f_n^* \| = 1$, there corresponds with every f_n^* an element $f_n \in E$ such that $\| f_n \| = 1$ and $| f_n^*(f_n) | \geqslant 1/2$. We shall prove that the set $\{f_n\}$ is complete in E. If this were not true there would exist an $f^* \in E^*$ with $\| f^* \| = 1$, $f^*(f_n) = 0$ for all n. Then $\| f^* - f_n^* \| \geqslant | (f^* - f_n^*)(f_n) | = | f_n^*(f_n) | \geqslant 1/2$, which is a contradiction since $\{f_n^*\}$ is dense on $\| f^* \| = 1$. It follows that $\{f_n\}$ is complete; the set of all finite linear combinations $\Sigma\, \alpha_i f_i$ with α_i rational complex is therefore dense in E. Then E is separable.

§ 8. The Second Adjoint Space. Reflexive Spaces

If E is a Banach space, complete or non-complete, and if $f^*(f)$ is a bounded linear functional on E, then the value of $f^* \in E^*$ for the element $f \in E$ is a complex number $f^*(f) = B(f, f^*)$. We may consider $B(f, f^*)$ as a bilinear functional, that is,

$$(1) \qquad B(\alpha_1 f_1 + \alpha_2 f_2, f^*) = \alpha_1 B(f_1, f^*) + \alpha_2 B(f_2, f^*),$$

$$(2) \qquad B(f, \alpha_1 f_1^* + \alpha_2 f_2^*) = \alpha_1 B(f, f_1^*) + \alpha_2 B(f, f_2^*).$$

Furthermore

$$(3) \qquad | B(f, f^*) | \leqslant \| f \| . \| f^* \|.$$

Since E^* is a Banach space, it has an adjoint space E^{**}, called the *second adjoint space* of E, the elements of which are the bounded linear functionals on E^*. It follows from (2) and (3) that for fixed f we have $B(f, f^*) \in E^{**}$, that is, there exists an $f^{**} \in E^{**}$ such that

$$(4) \qquad f^{**}(f^*) = f^*(f) \text{ for all } f^* \in E^*.$$

Theorem 1. *The bounded linear functional $f^{**} \in E^{**}$, defined by* (4), *satisfies $\| f^{**} \| \leqslant \| f \|$. If E has the property* (*Ext.*), *then $\| f^{**} \| = \| f \|$.*
Proof. From (3) follows $| f^{**}(f^*) | = | B(f, f^*) | \leqslant \| f \| . \| f^* \|$ for all $f^* \in E^*$, hence $\| f^{**} \| \leqslant \| f \|$. If E has the property (Ext.), there exists by § 6, Th. 5 a functional $f^* \in E^*$ such that $\| f^* \| = 1$ and $f^*(f) = \| f \|$, hence $f^{**}(f^*) = \| f \| = \| f \| . \| f^* \|$ for this element f^*, so that $\| f^{**} \| \geqslant \| f \|$. It follows that $\| f^{**} \| = \| f \|$.

Theorem 2. *If E has the property* (*Ext.*) *and $f^*(f) = f^*(g)$ for all $f^* \in E^*$, then $f = g$. In other words, if f and g are different elements of E, there is at least one functional f^* such that $f^*(f) \neq f^*(g)$.*
Proof. It is evidently sufficient to prove that if $f^*(f) = 0$ for a fixed $f \in E$ and all $f^* \in E^*$, then $f = 0$. This follows immediately from § 6, Th. 5.

As a consequence of Th. 1 and Th. 2 we may say now that if E has the property (Ext.), there exists a one-to-one correspondence $f \leftrightarrow f^{**}$ between the elements of E and a subset E_2 of E^{**}.

Theorem 3. *If E has the property* (*Ext.*), *then E and the just defined set $E_2 \subset E^{**}$ may be identified; hence $E \subset E^{**}$.*
Proof. The correspondence $f \leftrightarrow f^{**}$ between E and E_2 has the properties:
1°. If $f_1 \leftrightarrow f_1^{**}$, $f_2 \leftrightarrow f_2^{**}$, then $\alpha_1 f_1 + \alpha_2 f_2 \leftrightarrow \alpha_1 f_1^{**} + \alpha_2 f_2^{**}$ (α_1, α_2 arbitrarily complex).
2°. $\| f \| = \| f^{**} \|$.
This shows that E and E_2 may be identified.

Theorem 4. *If E has the property* (*Ext.*) *and the elements $f_1, \ldots, f_n$ of E are linearly independent, then there exist elements $f_1^*, \ldots, f_n^*$ of E^* such that $f_i^*(f_j) = 1$ for $i = j$ and $f_i^*(f_j) = 0$ for $i \neq j$.*
Proof. With the elements $f_1, \ldots, f_n$ of E correspond elements $f_1^{**}, \ldots, f_n^{**}$ of E^{**} such that $f_i^{**}(f^*) = f^*(f_i)$ for all $f^* \in E^*$ $(i = 1, \ldots, n)$. These elements $f_1^{**}, \ldots, f_n^{**}$ are linearly independent since $\| \alpha_1 f_1^{**} + \ldots + \alpha_n f_n^{**} \| = 0$ implies $\| \alpha_1 f_1 + \ldots + \alpha_n f_n \| = 0$ by Th. 1, hence $\alpha_1 = \ldots = \alpha_n = 0$. It follows then from § 7, Th. 8 that there exist elements $f_1^*, \ldots, f_n^*$ of E^* such that $f_j^{**}(f_i^*) = 1$ for $i = j$ and $f_j^{**}(f_i^*) = 0$ for $i \neq j$. Hence $f_i^*(f_j) = 1$ for $i = j$ and $f_i^*(f_j) = 0$ for $i \neq j$.

Theorem 5. *If E has the property* (*Ext.*) *and the set $\{f\}$ of elements $f \in E$ is such that the set of numbers $| f^*(f) |$ is bounded for each $f^* \in E^*$ separately when f runs through $\{f\}$, then the set $\{\| f \|\}$ is bounded.*

Proof. With every $f \in \{f\}$ corresponds an element $f^{**} \in E^{**}$ such that $f^{**}(f^*) = f^*(f)$ for all $f^* \in E^*$ and $\| f^{**} \| = \| f \|$. The set $\{f^{**}(f^*)\}$ of bounded linear transformations on the complete space E^*, with their ranges in the space of complex numbers, satisfies the conditions of the Banach-Steinhaus Theorem (cf. § 2, Th. 1). It follows that the set $\{\| f^{**} \|\} = \{\| f \|\}$ is bounded.

We have already proved that if E has the property (Ext.), then $E \subset E^{**}$. We shall consider now the case that $E = E^{**}$.

Definition. *If $E = E^{**}$, then E is called a reflexive Banach space* [8].

Theorem 6. *The Banach space E is reflexive in each of the following cases:*

1°. *E is of finite dimension.*

2°. *E is a complete Hilbert space.*

3°. *E is the Orlicz space $L_\Phi(\Delta, \mu)$, where $\Phi(u)$ and its complementary function $\Psi(v)$ satisfy $\Phi(2u) \leqslant M\Phi(u)$ for all $u \geqslant 0$ and $\Psi(2v) \leqslant M\Psi(v)$ for all $v \geqslant 0$, and μ is separable.*

4°. *E is the Lebesgue space L_p $(1 < p < \infty)$.*

5°. *E is the sequence-space l_p $(1 < p < \infty)$.*

Proof. 1°. If E has the dimension n, then E^* and E^{**} also have the dimension n by § 7, Th. 2. If therefore $f_1, \ldots, f_n$ is a complete set in E, the corresponding set $f_1^{**}, \ldots, f_n^{**}$ is complete in E^{**}.

2°. Follows upon inspecting the proof of § 7, Th. 3.

3°. Follows from § 7, Th. 4 and from the fact that L_Φ has the property (Ext.).

4°. Follows from § 7, Th. 5. Observe that it is not necessary to assume that μ is separable.

5°. Follows from § 7, Th. 6.

Theorem 7. *If the reflexive space E has the property (Ext.) and $[L]$ is a linear subspace of E, then $[L]$ (considered as a Banach space on its own) is also reflexive* [9].

Proof. We consider in E^* the set of all f^* such that $f^*(f) = 0$ for all $f \in [L]$. This set obviously is a linear subspace G of E^*. Every element $[f^*]$ of the factorspace E^*/G is therefore a class of functionals f^*; all $f^* \in [f^*]$ are equal on $[L]$ and $\| [f^*] \| =$ lower bound $\| f^* \|$ for $f^* \in [f^*]$. It follows that there exists a one-to-one correspondence between the space $[L]^*$ of all bounded linear functionals F^* on $[L]$ and the space

E^*/G. This correspondence $F^* \leftrightarrow [f^*]$ is defined by $F^*(f) = f^*(f)$ for all $f \in [L]$, in other words, every $f^* \in [f^*]$ is an extension of F^*. Then we have evidently $\| F^* \| \leqslant \| f^* \|$ for all these f^*, so that $\| F^* \| \leqslant \| [f^*] \|$. On the other hand we have $\| f^* \| = \| F^* \|$ for one f^* at least, so that $\| [f^*] \| \leqslant \| F^* \|$. Hence $\| F^* \| = \| [f^*] \|$; the spaces $[L]^*$ and E^*/G may therefore be identified; $[L]^* = E^*/G$.

Let now F^{**} be a bounded linear functional on $[L]^* = E^*/G$. The bounded linear functional f^{**} on E^* is then defined by $f^{**}(f^*) = F^{**}[f^*] = F^{**}(F^*)$. On account of the reflexivity of E there exists an element $f \in E$ such that $f^{**}(f^*) = f^*(f)$ for all $f^* \in E^*$, hence $F^{**}(F^*) = f^*(f)$. It remains to prove that $f \in [L]$. Supposing this to be false there would exist a functional $f^* \in E^*$ such that $f^*(g) = 0$ for all $g \in [L]$ and $f^*(f) = 1$. But $f^*(g) = 0$ for all $g \in [L]$ implies $[f^*] = 0$, hence $f^*(f) = f^{**}(f^*) = F^{**}[f^*] = 0$ in contradiction with $f^*(f) = 1$. It follows that $f \in [L]$, hence $f^*(f) = F^*(f)$ for every $f^* \in E^*$. The final result is that

$$F^{**}(F^*) = f^{**}(f^*) = f^*(f) = F^*(f)$$

for all $F^* \in [L]^*$, and this shows that $[L]$ is reflexive.

§ 9. Weak Convergence

Let E be a Banach space, complete or non-complete.

Definition. *The sequence of elements $f_n \in E$ is said to be converging weakly to the element $f \in E$ when $f^*(f) = \lim f^*(f_n)$ for every $f^* \in E^*$, and f is then called the weak limit of f_n.*

The sequence of elements $f_n \in E$ is called a weakly fundamental sequence if $\lim f^*(f_n)$ exists (as a finite number) for every $f^* \in E^*$.

It is evident that every sequence having a weak limit is a weakly fundamental sequence. Furthermore, if E has the property (Ext.) and f_n converges weakly to f, then f is uniquely determined since $f^*(f) = f^*(g)$ for all $f^* \in E^*$ implies $f = g$ by § 8, Th. 2. To avoid misunderstandings, ordinary convergence in E is sometimes called *strong convergence.*

Theorem 1. *If E has the property (Ext.), every weakly fundamental sequence in E is bounded. More generally, if the set $S \subset E$ has the property that every subset of S contains a weakly fundamental sequence, then S is bounded.*

Proof. Let f_n be a weakly fundamental sequence in E. Then the sequence of numbers $| f^*(f_n) |$ is bounded for every $f^* \in E^*$, so that by § 8, Th. 5 the set $\| f_n \|$ is bounded.

Let now $S \subset E$ have the property that every subset of S contains a weakly fundamental sequence. Supposing that S is not bounded it contains a sequence of elements f_k such that $\lim \| f_k \| = \infty$. By hypothesis f_k contains a weakly fundamental subsequence f_n ($n = k_1, k_2, \ldots$). But then $\lim \| f_n \| = \infty$, in contradiction with the first part of our proof.

Theorem 2. *If E has the property (Ext.) and E is reflexive, then every weakly fundamental sequence f_n has a weak limit f.*

Proof. With every f_n corresponds an element $f_n^{**} \in E^{**}$ such that $f_n^{**}(f^*) = f^*(f_n)$ for all $f^* \in E^*$. The sequence $f_n^{**}(f^*)$ converges therefore for every $f^* \in E^*$, and we shall call the limit $f^{**}(f^*)$. Obviously f^{**} is a linear functional on E^*, and since the sequence $\| f_n^{**} \| = \| f_n \|$ is bounded by the preceding theorem, f^{**} is also bounded. On account of the reflexivity of E there exists then an element $f \in E$ such that $f^{**}(f^*) = f^*(f)$ for all $f^* \in E^*$, hence

$$\lim f^*(f_n) = \lim f_n^{**}(f^*) = f^{**}(f^*) = f^*(f)$$

for all $f^* \in E^*$, which shows that f is the weak limit of f_n.

Remark. Considering in particular the case of a Hilbert space R, the sequence f_n converges weakly to f when $\lim (f_n, g) = (f, g)$ for all $g \in \bar{R}$, the closure of R. If R is not complete, and we should only require $\lim (f_n, g) = (f, g)$ for every $g \in R$, Theorem 1 is no longer true. Indeed, if $\bar{R}$ is a complete separable Hilbert space and the sequence φ_n is orthonormal and complete in $\bar{R}$, then $\lim_{n\to\infty} (n\varphi_n, g) = 0 = (0, g)$ for every $g \in R$, where R is the space of all finite linear combinations $\Sigma\, \alpha_i \varphi_i$ (α_i complex), but $\| n\varphi_n \| = n$ is not bounded.

Theorem 3. *Every sequence f_n, converging strongly to f, is also converging weakly to f.*

Proof. $| f^*(f) - f^*(f_n) | \leqslant \| f^* \| . \| f - f_n \|$ for every $f^* \in E^*$.

Theorem 4. *In a space of finite dimension n every weakly fundamental sequence g_i converges strongly to an element g.*

Proof. Let $f_1, \ldots, f_n$ be complete in E, and let $f_1^*, \ldots, f_n^*$ be the bounded linear functionals satisfying $f_i^*(f_j) = 1$ for $i = j$ and $f_i^*(f_j) = 0$ for $i \neq j$ (cf. § 7, Th. 2). If now $g_i = \Sigma_{k=1}^n \alpha_k^i f_k$ ($i = 1, 2, \ldots$), then $f_k^*(g_i) = \alpha_k^i$ ($k = 1, \ldots, n$; $i = 1, 2, \ldots$). By hypothesis $\alpha_k = \lim_{i\to\infty} f_k^*(g_i) = \lim \alpha_k^i$ exists ($k = 1, \ldots, n$), so that $g_i = \Sigma_{k=1}^n \alpha_k^i f_k$ converges strongly to $g = \Sigma_{k=1}^n \alpha_k f_k$.

We now come to a theorem which may be considered as an inverse of Th. 1.

Theorem 5. *If E and E^* have the property (Ext.) and E is reflexive, then every bounded infinite set $S \subset E$ contains a weakly fundamental sequence* [9].

Proof. It is no loss of generality to suppose that S is a sequence of elements f_n, where $\| f_n \| \leqslant M$. Furthermore it will be interesting to consider first the relatively simple case that E is a complete Hilbert space R. The reader will then be able to see more clearly how the proof in the general case is modelled on that for Hilbert space.

Hilbert space. On account of $| (f_n, f_1) | \leqslant M \| f_1 \|$ the sequence (f_n, f_1) $(n = 1, 2, \ldots)$ is bounded; it follows that there exists a subsequence f_{n1} of f_n such that (f_{n1}, f_1) converges. In the same way we see that there exists a subsequence f_{n2} of f_{n1} such that also (f_{n2}, f_2) converges, and so on. Then, for $g_n = f_{nn}$, the sequence (g_n, f_k) converges for every $f_k \in S$, and (g_n, f) converges therefore also for every $f \in L(S)$. We shall prove that (g_n, f) converges for every $f \in [L(S)]$. Let $f \in [L(S)]$, $f = \lim f_k$, $f_k \in L(S)$. Then, since

$$| (g_n, f) - (g_m, f) | \leqslant$$

$$| (g_n, f_k) - (g_m, f_k) | + | (g_n, f - f_k) | + | (g_m, f - f_k) | \leqslant$$

$$| (g_n, f_k) - (g_m, f_k) | + 2M \| f - f_k \|,$$

we see that $\lim (g_n, f)$ exists. Finally, since $g_n \in [L(S)]$ for all n, we have $(g_n, h) = 0$ for every $h \in R \ominus [L(S)]$; hence, every $f \in R$ being expressible in the form $f = g + h$, $g \in [L(S)]$, $h \in R \ominus [L(S)]$, the convergence of (g_n, f) for every $f \in R$ has been proved.

General case. We again consider the linear subspace $[L] = [L(S)]$. It is evidently separable. Since E is reflexive and has the property (Ext.) we have $[L] = [L]^{**}$ by § 8, Th. 7, so that $[L]^{**}$ is also separable. Furthermore, in the proof of § 8, Th. 7, we have seen that $[L]^*$ may be identified with a certain factorspace E^*/G of E^*. Since E^* has the property (Ext.), the same is true of $E^*/G = [L]^*$ by § 6, Th. 9. It follows therefore from § 7, Th. 10 that $[L]^*$ is separable, because $[L]^{**}$ is separable and $[L]^*$ has the property (Ext.). Let the sequence F_n^* be dense in $[L]^*$. Then, on account of $| F_1^*(f_n) | \leqslant M \| F_1^* \|$, there exists a subsequence f_{n1} of f_n such that $F_1^*(f_{n1})$ converges. In the same way we see that there exists a subsequence f_{n2} of f_{n1} such that also $F_2^*(f_{n2})$ converges, and so on. Then, for $g_n = f_{nn}$, the sequence $F_k^*(g_n)$ converges for all F_k^*. We shall prove that $F^*(g_n)$ converges for every $F^* \in [L]^*$. Let

$F^* \in [L]^*$, $F^* = \lim G_k^*$ ($G_1^* = F_{k_1}^*$, $G_2^* = F_{k_2}^*$, ...). Then, since

$$| F^*(g_n) - F^*(g_m) | \leqslant | G_k^*(g_n) - G_k^*(g_m) | + | (F^* - G_k^*)(g_n) |$$
$$+ | (F^* - G_k^*)(g_m) | \leqslant | G_k^*(g_n) - G_k^*(g_m) | + 2M \| F^* - G_k^* \|,$$

we see that $\lim F^*(g_n)$ exists. Finally, since every $f^* \in E^*$ is an extension of an $F^* \in [L]^*$, it is evident that $\lim f^*(g_n)$ exists for every $f^* \in E^*$.

One might ask whether Theorem 4 (the statement that in a space of finite dimension weak convergence implies strong convergence) may be extended to the general case. The following example shows that, at least in Hilbert space, a sequence may converge weakly without converging strongly.

Let φ_n $(n = 1, 2, \ldots)$ be an orthonormal system in the complete Hilbert space R. Then, if $g \in R$ is arbitrary and $\alpha_n = (g, \varphi_n)$, we have $\Sigma_1^\infty | \alpha_n |^2 \leqslant \| g \|^2$ by Bessel's inequality, hence $\lim \bar{\alpha}_n = \lim(\varphi_n, g) = 0$. This shows that φ_n converges weakly to 0. But $\| \varphi_m - \varphi_n \| = 2^{1/2}$ for $m \neq n$, so that there is no question of strong convergence.

Adding however one extra hypothesis, weak convergence in Hilbert space implies strong convergence.

Theorem 6. *If in Hilbert space f_n converges weakly to f and $\lim \| f_n \| = \| f \|$, then f_n converges strongly to f.*

Proof. We have $\lim (f_n, g) = (f, g)$ for all $g \in R$, hence in particular $\lim (f_n, f) = (f, f)$ and $\lim (f, f_n) = (f, f)$. But then

$$\lim \| f - f_n \|^2 = \lim \{(f, f) - (f_n, f) - (f, f_n) + (f_n, f_n)\}$$
$$= (f, f) - (f, f) - (f, f) + (f, f) = 0.$$

Remark. A similar theorem holds in the spaces $L_p(\Delta)$ $(1 < p < \infty)$ and l_p $(1 \leqslant p < \infty)$.

The reader will be able to apply for himself the theorems on weak convergence to the spaces L_Φ, L_p and l_p. We shall restrict ourselves here to the spaces L_Φ.

Theorem 7. *If $\Phi(u)$ and $\Psi(v)$ are complementary in the sense of Young where $\Phi(2u) \leqslant M\Phi(u)$ for all $u \geqslant 0$, if the measure μ is separable, and if the sequence $f_n(x)$ of functions belonging to $L_\Phi(\Delta, \mu)$ has the property that*

$$\lim_{n\to\infty} \int_\Delta f_n(x)g(x)d\mu$$

exists for every $g(x) \in L_\Psi(\Delta, \mu)$, *then* $\| f_n \|_\Phi$ *is bounded. If moreover* $\Psi(2v) \leqslant M\Psi(v)$ *for all* $v \geqslant 0$, *there exists a function* $f(x) \in L_\Phi$ *such that*

$$lim_{n\to\infty} \int_\Delta f_n(x)g(x)d\mu = \int_\Delta f(x)g(x)d\mu$$

for all $g(x) \in L_\Psi$. *Furthermore, under the same hypothesis on* $\Psi(v)$, *every set* $\{f(x)\}$ *of functions belonging to* L_Φ *with the property that* $\| f \|_\Phi \leqslant A$ *for a fixed* A *and all* $f \in \{f\}$ *contains a sequence* $f_n(x)$ *such that*

$$lim_{n\to\infty} \int_\Delta f_n(x)g(x)d\mu$$

exists for every $g(x) \in L_\Psi$.

Proof. Follows from the definition of weak convergence, from Theorem 1, Theorem 2 and Theorem 5.

As we see, the case that $L_\Phi = L_\infty$ falls outside the scope of Theorem 7. There is nevertheless an analogue of Theorem 7 in this case, which is a consequence of the next theorem.

Theorem 8. *If* E *is separable, every bounded infinite set* $S \subset E^*$ *contains a subsequence* f_n^* *such that there exists an element* $f^* \in E^*$ *with* $lim\, f_n^*(f) = f^*(f)$ *for all* $f \in E$.

Proof. It is no loss of generality to suppose that S is a sequence of elements $g_n^* \in E^*$, where $\| g_n^* \| \leqslant M$. Let now f_n $(n = 1, 2, \ldots)$ be dense in E. Then, on account of $| g_n^*(f_1) | \leqslant M \| f_1 \|$, there exists a subsequence g_{n1}^* of g_n^* such that $g_{n1}^*(f_1)$ converges. In the same way we see that there exists a subsequence g_{n2}^* of g_{n1}^* such that also $g_{n2}^*(f_2)$ converges, and so on. Then, for $f_n^* = g_{nn}^*$, the sequence $f_n^*(f_k)$ converges for all f_k. In a similar way as in Th. 5 it is proved now that $f_n^*(f)$ converges for all $f \in E$. The limit $f^*(f)$ is evidently a linear functional on E, and $| f_n^*(f) | \leqslant M \| f \|$ implies $| f^*(f) | \leqslant M \| f \|$ for all $f \in E$. It follows that $f^* \in E^*$.

Theorem 9. *If* $\Phi(u)$ *and* $\Psi(v)$ *are complementary in the sense of Young, where* $\Phi(2u) \leqslant M\Phi(u)$ *for all* $u \geqslant 0$, *and if the measure* μ *is separable, every set* $\{g(x)\}$ *of functions belonging to* $L_\Psi(\Delta, \mu)$ *with the property that* $\| g \|_\Psi \leqslant A$ *for a fixed* A *and all* $g \in \{g\}$ *contains a sequence* $g_n(x)$ *such that there exists a function* $g(x) \in L_\Psi$ *with*

$$lim_{n\to\infty} \int_\Delta f(x)g_n(x)d\mu = \int_\Delta f(x)g(x)d\mu$$

for every $f(x) \in L_\Phi(\Delta, \mu)$.

Proof. Follows from the preceding theorem by observing that $L_\Phi(\Delta, \mu)$ is separable.

§ 10. Metric Space. Baire's Category Theorem

A set Z with elements $f, g, \ldots$ is called a *metric space* and its elements are called *points* if for each pair of elements $f, g \in Z$ there is defined a real-valued function $d(f, g)$, called the *distance* from f to g, such that

1°. $d(f, g) = 0$ if and only if $f = g$.

2°. $d(f, g) \leqslant d(h, f) + d(h, g)$ for any three elements f, g and h.

Taking $h = g$ in 2°, we find $d(f, g) \leqslant d(g, f)$, and taking $h = f$ in $d(g, f) \leqslant d(h, g) + d(h, f)$ we find in the same way $d(g, f) \leqslant d(f, g)$. Hence

3°. $d(f, g) = d(g, f)$ for arbitrary $f, g \in Z$.

Furthermore, taking $g = f$ in 2°, we find $0 \leqslant d(h, f) + d(h, f)$, hence

4°. $d(f, g) \geqslant 0$ for arbitrary f, g.

Evidently every Banach space is a metric space if we define, as we have already done, $d(f, g) = \| f - g \|$. The usual definitions introduced already for Euclidean spaces and Banach spaces apply without change to the present case of a metric space Z, e.g. diameter of a set $X \subset Z$, boundedness of a set, distance from a point to a set, distance between two sets, spherical neighbourhood of a point, point of accumulation and isolated point, derived set X^+ of a set X, closed and open sets, limit of a sequence of points. Furthermore, if $X \subset Z$ and X^+ is the derived set, then $\overline{X} = X + X^+$ is called the *closure* of X. Evidently X is closed if and only if $X = \overline{X}$, and X is dense in Z if and only if $\overline{X} = Z$.

Theorem 1. *If X and Y are subsets of the metric space Z, then $\overline{XY} \subset \overline{X} . \overline{Y}$.*
Proof. Since $XY \subset X$ and $XY \subset Y$, we have $\overline{XY} \subset \overline{X}$ and $\overline{XY} \subset \overline{Y}$, hence $\overline{XY} \subset \overline{X} . \overline{Y}$.

Definition. *If Z is a metric space and $X \subset Z$, then X is called a boundary set when $Z - X$ is dense, that is, when $\overline{Z - X} = Z$.*

The set $Y \subset Z$ is called nowhere dense when $\overline{Y}$ is a boundary set, that is, when $\overline{Z - \overline{Y}} = Z$.

Theorem 2. 1.° *If X is nowhere dense, then X is a boundary set.*

2°. *If X is closed and a boundary set, then X is nowhere dense.*

3°. *X is a boundary set if and only if X contains no sphere.*

Proof. 1°. Suppose that X is nowhere dense. Since $Z - X \supset Z - \overline{X}$, we have $\overline{Z - X} \supset \overline{Z - \overline{X}} = Z$, hence $\overline{Z - X} = Z$ which shows that X is a boundary set.

2°. Evident.

3°. Suppose that X is a boundary set. If X would contain a sphere, the centre of this sphere would not belong to $\overline{Z-X}$, in contradiction with $\overline{Z-X}=Z$.

Let now, conversely, X contain no sphere. Then every point of Z belongs to $\overline{Z-X}$, hence $\overline{Z-X}=Z$.

Definition. *If Z is a metric space and $X \subset Z$, then X is called of the first category if X is the sum of an at most enumerable number of nowhere dense sets. Any set which is not of the first category is said to be of the second category.*

Definition. *The metric space Z is called complete if $\lim d(f_m, f_n) = 0$ as $m, n \to \infty$, $f_n \in Z$ $(n = 1, 2, \ldots)$, implies the existence of a point $f \in Z$ such that $\lim d(f, f_n) = 0$ as $n \to \infty$.*

Theorem 3. *The metric space Z is complete if and only if for every sequence $X_1 \supset X_2 \supset X_3 \supset \ldots$ of closed non-empty subsets, the diameters of which tend to 0, the set $\Pi_{n=1}^{\infty} X_n$ contains one single point.*

Proof. Let Z be complete, and suppose that the sequence $X_1 \supset X_2 \supset \ldots$ satisfies $X_n = \overline{X}_n$, X_n non-empty, $\lim \delta(X_n) = 0$, where $\delta(X_n)$ is the diameter of X_n. Taking in every X_n one point f_n we have $\lim d(f_m, f_n) = 0$ as $m, n \to \infty$. The limitpoint f belongs to every $X_n = \overline{X}_n$, hence $f \in \Pi_{n=1}^{\infty} X_n$. But f is the only point of $\Pi_{n=1}^{\infty} X_n$ on account of $\lim \delta(X_n) = 0$.

Let now conversely every sequence $X_1 \supset X_2 \supset \ldots$ of closed non-empty subsets satisfy the mentioned hypothesis, and let $\lim d(f_m, f_n) = 0$ as $m, n \to \infty$. Then, defining Y_n as the set consisting of the points $f_n, f_{n+1}, \ldots$ we have $\lim \delta(Y_n) = 0$, hence also $\lim \delta(X_n) = 0$ for $X_n = \overline{Y}_n$. It follows that $\Pi_{n=1}^{\infty} X_n$ contains one single point f, so that $\lim d(f, f_n) = 0$ on account of $d(f, f_n) \leqslant \delta(X_n)$.

Theorem 4. *In a complete metric space Z every set X of the first category is a boundary set.*

Proof. Let $X = \Sigma X_n$, where X_n $(n = 1, 2, \ldots)$ is nowhere dense. We have to prove that $Z - X$ is dense, that is, if S_0 is an arbitrary closed sphere, we have to prove that S_0 contains points of $Z - X$, in other words, that $S_0 - X$ is non-empty.

Given the closed sphere S_0, we want to define a sequence $S_0 \supset S_1 \supset S_2 \supset \ldots$ of closed spheres satisfying $S_n \subset S_{n-1} - X_n$, $\delta(S_n) < 1/n$ $(n = 1, 2, \ldots)$. To show that this is possible it is sufficient to prove that $S_{n-1} - X_n$ $(n = 1, 2, \ldots)$ is not a boundary set. Supposing that

$S_{n-1} - X_n$ is a boundary set, the set $P_n = \overline{Z - (S_{n-1} - X_n)}$ would satisfy $P_n = Z$. But $P_n = \overline{(Z - S_{n-1}) + S_{n-1}X_n} = \overline{Z - S_{n-1}} + \overline{S_{n-1}X_n}$ $\subset \overline{Z - S_{n-1}} + S_{n-1}\overline{X}_n$. The set $\overline{X}_n$ contains no sphere, which shows that every sphere concentric with S_{n-1} contains points belonging neither to $\overline{Z - S_{n-1}}$ nor to $S_{n-1}\overline{X}_n$. Hence $P_n = Z$ is impossible.

Having shown thus the existence of the spheres S_n $(n = 1, 2, \ldots)$, the preceding theorem asserts that there exists one single point $f \in \Pi_{n=0}^{\infty} S_n$, hence $f \in \Pi_{n=1}^{\infty} S_n \subset \Pi_{n=1}^{\infty} (Z - X_n) = Z - \Sigma_{n=1}^{\infty} X_n = Z - X$. It follows that $f \in S_0$ and $f \in Z - X$, hence $f \in S_0 - X$, so that $S_0 - X$ is not empty, which is what we were out to prove.

Theorem 5 (*Baire's Category Theorem*). *Every complete metric space Z is of the second category, in other words, if $Z = \Sigma X_n$, then $\overline{X}_n$ contains a sphere for at least one value of n.*

Proof. Z is evidently no boundary set, so that Z is not of the first category.

§ 11. Closed Linear Transformations on Banach Space

Let E_1 and E_2 be two complete Banach spaces, identical or distinct.

Definition. *A linear transformation T with domain $D \subset E_1$ and range $W \subset E_2$ is said to be closed when $\lim f_n = f_0$ and $\lim Tf_n = g_0$, where $f_n \in D$, implies that $f_0 \in D$ and $Tf_0 = g_0$.*

Theorem 1. *If the linear transformation T is defined on the whole space E_1 and it is bounded, then T is closed.*

Proof. Evident, since $\lim f_n = f_0$ implies $\lim Tf_n = Tf_0$.

Definition. *If the transformation $g = Tf$ with domain $D \subset E_1$ and range $W \subset E_2$ has the property that the correspondence between D and W is one-to-one, then the inverse transformation $f = T^{-1}g$ with domain W and range D is defined by $f = T^{-1}(Tf)$ for all $Tf \in W$.*

Theorem 2. *If T is linear, then T^{-1} exists if and only if $Tf = 0$ only for $f = 0$. In this case T^{-1} is also linear.*

Proof. T^{-1} exists if and only if $f_1 \neq f_2$ implies $Tf_1 \neq Tf_2$, and on account of the linearity of T this is equivalent to the statement that $Tf = 0$ if and only if $f = 0$. The proof of the second part is trivial.

Theorem 3. *If T is linear, then T^{-1} exists as a bounded linear transformation if and only if there exists a number $m > 0$ such that $\| Tf \| \geqslant m \| f \|$ for all $f \in D$. The largest admissable value of m is $1/\| T^{-1} \|$.*
Proof. If T^{-1} is bounded, then $\| f \| = \| T^{-1}g \| \leqslant M \| g \|$ for all $g \in W$, so that $\| g \| = \| Tf \| \geqslant (1/M) \| f \|$. Evidently, if $M = \| T^{-1} \|$, then $1/M$ is the largest value of m for which $\| Tf \| \geqslant m \| f \|$ holds for all $f \in D$.
Conversely, if $\| Tf \| \geqslant m \| f \|$ for all $f \in D$, then $Tf = 0$ only for $f = 0$, so that T^{-1} exists and $\| f \| = \| T^{-1}g \| \leqslant (1/m) \| g \|$ for all $g = Tf \in W$.

If T is a transformation with domain $D \subset E_1$ and range $W \subset E_2$, then the set of elements $\{f, Tf\}$, $f \in D$, in the productspace $E_1 \times E_2$ (cf. Ch. 6, § 15) is called the *graph* of the transformation T. We suppose that in $E_1 \times E_2$ the norm is defined as described in Ch. 6, § 15, e.g. $\| \{f, g\} \| = \| f \| + \| g \|$ or $\| \{f, g\} \| = (\| f \|^2 + \| g \|^2)^{1/2}$.

Theorem 4. *A linear transformation is closed if and only if its graph is a closed set in $E_1 \times E_2$.*
Proof. Follows immediately from the definition of a closed transformation.

Theorem 5. *If a closed linear transformation T has an inverse T^{-1}, then T^{-1} is also closed.*
Proof. If W is the range of T and T^{-1} exists, the graph of T may also be written in the form $\{T^{-1}g, g\}$, $g \in W$.

Theorem 6. *If $g = Tf$ is a closed linear transformation with domain $D \subset E_1$, and if its range W is of the second category in E_2, then*
1°. $W = E_2$.
2°. *There exists a number $m > 0$ such that with every $g \in E_2$ corresponds an element $f \in D$ satisfying $g = Tf$ and $\| f \| \leqslant m \| g \|$.*
3°. *If T^{-1} exists, then it is bounded.*
Proof. 1°. Let $S(n)$ be the sphere $\| f \| < n$ (n arbitrarily positive) in E_1, and let $D(n) = D.S(n)$, hence $D = \Sigma_{n=1}^{\infty} D(n)$. Writing $W(n) = T(D(n))$, we have then $W = \Sigma_{n=1}^{\infty} W(n)$. Since W is of the second category in E_2, one at least of the sets $\overline{W(n)}$ ($n = 1, 2, \ldots$), say $\overline{W(n_0)}$, contains a sphere with centre μ and radius ρ. But then $\overline{W(1)}$ contains the sphere with centre μ/n_0 and radius ρ/n_0, which implies that $\overline{W(1)}$ also contains a sphere with centre μ_1 and radius $\rho_1 = \rho/2n_0$ such that $\mu_1 \in W(1) = T(D(1))$. Let $\mu_1 = T\varphi$, $\varphi \in D(1)$. In the space E_1 we consider now the set

P of elements $f - \varphi$ where f runs through $D(1)$. Since $\| f - \varphi \| \leqslant \| f \| + \| \varphi \| < 2$, we have $P \subset D(2)$, hence $T(P) \subset W(2)$. Furthermore $\overline{T(P)}$ evidently contains the sphere $\| g \| < \rho_1$ in E_2. It follows that $\overline{W(2)}$ contains the sphere $\| g \| < \rho_1$, so that generally $\overline{W(n)} \supset K(n)$, where $K(n)$ is the sphere $\| g \| < n\rho_1/2$ in E_2. In particular

$$(1) \qquad \overline{W(2^{-k})} \supset K(2^{-k}) \quad (k = 0, 1, 2, \ldots),$$

where $K(2^{-k})$ has radius $\rho_1/2^{k+1}$.

Let g be an arbitrary element of $K(1)$. Using (1) with $k = 0$, we see that there exists an element $f_1 \in D(1)$ such that

$$\| g - Tf_1 \| < \rho_1/2^2, \quad \| f_1 \| < 1.$$

Since $g - Tf_1 \in K(2^{-1})$, we can use (1) with $k = 1$ to see that there exists an element $f_2 \in D(2^{-1})$ such that

$$\| g - Tf_1 - Tf_2 \| < \rho_1/2^3, \quad \| f_2 \| < 1/2.$$

Proceeding in this way we obtain a sequence f_n such that

$$\| g - Tf_1 - \ldots - Tf_n \| = \| g - T(\Sigma_1^n f_k) \| < \rho_1/2^{n+1},$$
$$\| f_n \| < 1/2^{n-1}.$$

Writing $s_n = \Sigma_1^n f_k$, we see that $\| s_n \| \leqslant \Sigma_1^n \| f_k \| < 2$, hence $s_n \in D(2)$. Furthermore, since $\lim \| s_m - s_n \| = 0$ as $m, n \to \infty$, $\lim s_n = f$ exists and $f \in S(2)$. Finally $\lim Ts_n = g$. Since T is closed it follows that $f \in D(2)$ and $g = Tf$. We have shown thus that the sphere $K(1)$ is contained in $W(2) = T(D(2))$.

If now $g \in E_2$ is arbitrary, there is a number $a > 0$ such that $ag \in K(1)$. This implies the existence of an element $f_0 \in D(2)$ such that $Tf_0 = ag$, hence $Tf = g$ for $f = f_0/a$.

2°. We repeat the last sentences of 1°. If $g \in E_2$ is arbitrary and $a = \rho_1/4 \| g \|$, then $\| ag \| = \rho_1/4$, hence $ag \in K(1)$ since $K(1)$ has radius $\rho_1/2$. This implies the existence of an element $f_0 \in D(2)$ such that $Tf_0 = ag$, hence $Tf = g$ for $f = f_0/a$ and

$$\| f \| = \| f_0 \|/a < 2/a = (8/\rho_1) \| g \|.$$

3°. Follows from 2° and Theorem 3.

Corollary. *If $g = Tf$ is a closed linear transformation whose domain is the whole space E_1, and if T^{-1} exists, then T is bounded.*

Proof. The closed linear transformation T^{-1} satisfies the conditions of our theorem so that $T = (T^{-1})^{-1}$ is bounded.

Theorem 7. *If a Banach space E_1 with norm $\| f \|_1$ can be made into a different Banach space E_2 by introducing a second norm $\| f \|_2$ in such a way that $\lim \| f_n \|_1 = 0$ implies $\lim \| f_n \|_2 = 0$, then conversely $\lim \| f_n \|_2 = 0$ always implies $\lim \| f_n \|_1 = 0$, and for $f \neq 0$ we have $0 < m \leqslant \| f \|_2/\| f \|_1 \leqslant M < \infty$, where m and M are independent of f.*

Proof. Follows from the corollary of the preceding theorem by taking $Tf = f$, because then, if $\lim \| f_n - f_0 \|_1 = 0$ and $\lim \| Tf_n - g_0 \|_2 = 0$, we have also $\lim \| f_n - f_0 \|_2 = 0$ and $\lim \| f_n - g_0 \|_2 = 0$, hence $g_0 = f_0 = Tf_0$, so that T is closed. Both T and T^{-1} are therefore bounded.

We come now to an extension of the corollary of Theorem 6.

Theorem 8. *If $g = Tf$ is a closed linear transformation whose domain is the whole space E_1, then T is bounded.*

Proof. We introduce two different norms in E_1; $\| f \|_1 = \| f \|$ and $\| f \|_2 = \| f \| + \| Tf \|$. We shall prove first that E_1 is a complete space with the norm $\| f \|_2$. Let $\lim \| f_m - f_n \|_2 = 0$. Then $\lim \| f_m - f_n \|_1 = 0$ and $\lim \| Tf_m - Tf_n \| = 0$, so that there exist elements $f_0 \in E_1$ and $g_0 \in E_2$ such that $\lim \| f_n - f_0 \|_1 = 0$ and $\lim \| Tf_n - g_0 \| = 0$. Since T is closed, we have $Tf_0 = g_0$. But then

$$\lim \| f_n - f_0 \|_2 = \lim \| f_n - f_0 \|_1 + \lim \| Tf_n - Tf_0 \| = 0,$$

which proves the completeness. Evidently $\lim \| f_n \|_2 = 0$ implies $\lim \| f_n\|_1 = 0$; the preceding theorem may therefore be applied, and $\| f \|_2 \leqslant M \| f \|_1$ shows that T is bounded.

Second proof. The following alternative proof of the same theorem has some interest of its own. It does not depend on Theorem 7 but uses instead the factorspace $E_1/[L]$, where $[L]$ is the linear subspace of all $f \in E_1$ such that $Tf = 0$. That $[L]$ is indeed a subspace follows immediately from the closedness of T. We define $[T]\,[f] = Tf$ on $E_1/[L]$. Then $[T]$ is evidently uniquely determined on the whole space $E_1/[L]$ and linear. To show that $[T]$ is closed, we suppose that $\lim [f]_n = [f]$, $\lim g_n = \lim [T]\,[f]_n = g$. Writing $\| [f] - [f]_n \| = \varepsilon_n$, there exist elements $f^{(n)} \in [f]$ and $f_n' \in [f]_n$ such that $\| f^{(n)} - f_n' \| < 2\varepsilon_n$. The elements $f^{(n)}$ may be different for different n; observing however that $f^{(1)} - f^{(n)} \in [L]$, so that $f_n = f_n' + (f^{(1)} - f^{(n)}) \in [f]_n$ for all n, we find $\| f^{(1)} - f_n \| = \| f^{(n)} - f_n' \| < 2\varepsilon_n$. Hence $\lim f_n = f^{(1)}$, $\lim g_n = \lim [T]\,[f]_n = \lim Tf_n = g$. Since T is closed we conclude that $g = Tf^{(1)} = [T]\,[f]$, which shows that $[T]$ is also closed. Furthermore $[T]^{-1}$ exists, because $[T]\,[f] = 0$ only for

$[f] = 0$. It follows from the corollary of Theorem 6 that $[T]$ is bounded. But then T is also bounded on account of

$$\| Tf \| = \| [T] [f] \| \leqslant \| [T] \| . \| [f] \| \leqslant \| [T] \| . \| f \| .$$

We shall now derive two applications of the theorem which we have thus proved.

Theorem 9. *If $g = Tf$ is a linear transformation whose domain is the whole complete Hilbert space R and whose range is contained in the same space R, and if $(Tf, g) = (f, Tg)$ holds for arbitrary $f, g \in R$, then T is bounded* [10].

Proof. Let $\lim f_n = f_0$, $\lim Tf_n = g_0$. Then $(Tf_n, g) = (f_n, Tg)$ implies $(g_0, g) = (f_0, Tg)$, hence $(g_0, g) = (Tf_0, g)$ for all $g \in R$. It follows that $g_0 = Tf_0$. This shows that T is closed, so that T is bounded by Theorem 8.

Theorem 10. *If E_1, E_2 and E_3 are complete Banach spaces, and*

1°. *B is a bounded linear transformation with domain E_1 and range E_2,*

2°. *C is a bounded linear transformation with domain E_1 and range contained in E_3,*

3°. *$Bf = 0$ implies $Cf = 0$, $f \in E_1$,*

then there exists a bounded linear transformation A with domain E_2 and range contained in E_3 such that $Cf = A(Bf) = ABf$ for all $f \in E_1$ [11].

Proof. Let $[L]$ be the linear subspace of all $f \in E_1$ such that $Bf = 0$. We define the linear transformation $[B]$ on $E_1/[L]$ by $[B] [f] = Bf$. Then $[B]$ is bounded since $\| [B] [f] \| = \| Bf \| \leqslant \| B \| . \| f \|$ for all $f \in [f]$, hence $\| [B] [f] \| \leqslant \| B \| . \| [f] \|$. Furthermore $[B] [f] = 0$ only for $[f] = [0]$, so that $[B]^{-1}$ exists. Observing that $[B]$, and therefore also $[B]^{-1}$, is closed, and that the domain of $[B]^{-1}$ is the whole space E_2, we see that $[B]^{-1}$ is bounded.

We now define the linear transformation $[C]$ on $E_1/[L]$ by $[C] [f] = Cf$. This is possible since by hypothesis $Cf = 0$ for all $f \in [L]$. Evidently, by the arguments used already for $[B]$, $[C]$ is bounded, so that $Ag = [C] ([B]^{-1}g) = [C] [B]^{-1}g$ is a bounded linear transformation with domain E_2 and range in E_3. Finally, for all $f \in E_1$, we have

$$A(Bf) = [C] [B]^{-1}Bf = [C] [f] = Cf.$$

§ 12. Some Definitions and Simple Properties

We suppose that E_1 and E_2 are Banach spaces, identical or distinct, complete or non-complete, and we shall consider transformations with domain $D \subset E_1$ and range $W \subset E_2$.

Definition. *If T, T_1 and T_2 are bounded linear transformations with domain E_1 and range contained in E_2, then αT (α complex) and $T_1 + T_2$ are defined for all $f \in E_1$ by*

$$(\alpha T)f = \alpha Tf,$$

$$(T_1 + T_2)f = T_1 f + T_2 f.$$

The null transformation O on E_1 to E_2 is defined by

$$Of = 0 \text{ for all } f \in E_1.$$

If E_1 and E_2 are identical, every bounded linear transformation on E_1 into itself is called an endomorphism of E_1. In this case the identical transformation I is defined by

$$If = f \text{ for all } f \in E_1,$$

and, if T_1 and T_2 are endomorphisms of E_1, the transformation $T_1 T_2$ is defined for all $f \in E_1$ by

$$(T_1 T_2)f = T_1(T_2 f).$$

Furthermore, if $T_1 T_2 f = T_2 T_1 f$ for all $f \in E_1$, the transformations T_1 and T_2 are called permutable, and we shall denote this by $T_1 \, v \, T_2$.

Theorem 1. *We have $\| \alpha T \| = | \alpha | . \| T \|$, $\| T_1 + T_2 \| \leqslant \| T_1 \| + \| T_2 \|$, $\| O \| = 0$, $\| I \| = 1$, $\| T_1 T_2 \| \leqslant \| T_1 \| . \| T_2 \|$.*

Proof. Evident.

Definition. *If T_1 and T_2 are linear transformations with domains D_1 and D_2 both contained in E_1, then $T_1 = T_2$ if and only if $D_1 = D_2$ and $T_1 f = T_2 f$ for all $f \in D_1 = D_2$. If $D_1 \subset D_2$ and $T_1 f = T_2 f$ for all $f \in D_1$, then T_2 is called an extension of T_1.*

Definition. *The sequence T_n of transformations with domain E_1 and ranges in E_2 is said to converge strongly if $\lim \| T_m f - T_n f \| = 0$ for all $f \in E_1$ as $m, n \to \infty$. The sequence is said to converge strongly to the transformation T_0, and this is denoted by $\lim T_n = T_0$, if $\lim T_n f = T_0 f$ for all $f \in E_1$.*

Theorem 2. *If E_1 and E_2 are complete Banach spaces, and the sequence of linear transformations T_n with domain E_1 and ranges in E_2 converges strongly, there exists a number $M > 0$ such that $\| T_n \| \leqslant M$, and T_n converges strongly to a bounded linear transformation T_0 such that $\| T_0 \| \leqslant M$.*

Proof. Since the sequence $\| T_n f \|$ is bounded for each $f \in E_1$ separately and E_1 is complete, the Banach-Steinhaus Theorem shows the existence of a number $M > 0$ such that $\| T_n \| \leqslant M$. Furthermore, since E_2 is complete, $\lim \| T_m f - T_n f \| = 0$ implies the existence of a $T_0 f$ such that $\lim \| T_0 f - T_n f \| = 0$. Evidently T_0 is linear, and from $\| T_n f \| \leqslant M \| f \|$ follows $\| T_0 f \| \leqslant M \| f \|$ for all $f \in E_1$, hence $\| T_0 \| \leqslant M$.

Remark. If $\lim T_n f = Tf$ for all $f \in E_1$, where E_1 is non-complete, and we know already that all T_n are linear and $\| T_n \| \leqslant M$, then $\lim T_n = T$, $\| T_n \| \leqslant M$, $\| T \| \leqslant M$ remain true after extension of T_n and T on the closure $\bar{E}_1$. Indeed, $\| T_n \| \leqslant M$ and $\| T \| \leqslant M$ follow from § 1, Th. 3, and, if $\bar{f} \in \bar{E}_1$, $\bar{f} = \lim f_k$ where $f_k \in E_1$, then $\lim T_n \bar{f} = T\bar{f}$ follows from

$$\| T\bar{f} - T_n\bar{f} \| \leqslant \| Tf_k - T_n f_k \| + \| T(\bar{f} - f_k) \| + \| T_n(\bar{f} - f_k) \|$$
$$\leqslant \| Tf_k - T_n f_k \| + 2M \| \bar{f} - f_k \|.$$

Theorem 3. *If the Banach space E_1 is of finite dimension n, then every linear transformation T with domain E_1 is bounded.*

Proof. Let $f_1, \ldots, f_n$ be a complete system in E_1, hence $f = \Sigma_1^n \alpha_i f_i$ for any $f \in E_1$. We recall that in Ch. 6, § 4, Th. 1 we have proved the impossibility of $\Sigma_1^n | \alpha_i | = 1$ for arbitrarily small $\| f \|$. It follows that there exists a number $A > 0$ such that $\Sigma_1^n | \alpha_i | \leqslant A \| f \|$ for all $f = \Sigma_1^n \alpha_i f_i$. Then, if $M = \max [\| Tf_1 \|, \ldots, \| Tf_n \|]$ and $f = \Sigma_1^n \alpha_i f_i$, we have

$$\| Tf \| = \| \Sigma \alpha_i T f_i \| \leqslant \Sigma | \alpha_i | . \| Tf_i \| \leqslant$$
$$M \Sigma | \alpha_i | \leqslant MA \| f \|.$$

The transformation T is therefore bounded.

Theorem 4. *If the linear transformation T is defined on the Hilbert space R, complete or non-complete, and its range is contained in R, and if moreover $(Tf, f) = 0$ for every $f \in R$, then T is identical with the null transformation.*

Proof. From $(T(f + g), f + g) = (Tf, f) + (Tf, g) + (Tg, f) + (Tg, g)$ follows on account of $(T(f + g), f + g) = (Tf, f) = (Tg, g) = 0$ that

(1) $$0 = (Tf, g) + (Tg, f) \text{ for all } f, g \in R.$$

Replacing g by ig in (1), we obtain $0 = (Tf, ig) + (iTg, f) = - i(Tf, g) + i(Tg, f)$, hence

(2) $$0 = - (Tf, g) + (Tg, f) \text{ for all } f, g \in R.$$

From (1) and (2) we derive $(Tf, g) = 0$ for arbitrary $f, g \in R$. Taking now $g = Tf$, we find $(Tf, Tf) = 0$, or $Tf = 0$ for all $f \in R$.

§ 13. The Adjoint Transformation

We suppose that E_1 and E_2 are Banach spaces, identical or distinct, complete or non-complete.

Definition. *Let $g = Tf$ be a bounded linear transformation with domain E_1 and range in E_2, and let E_1^* and E_2^* be the adjoint spaces of E_1 and E_2 respectively. Now, for any $g^* \in E_2^*$, we write $f^*(f) = g^*(Tf)$. Then, by $f^* = T^*g^*$, the transformation T^* with domain E_2^* and range in E_1^* is defined. This transformation T^* is called the Banach-adjoint (B-adjoint) of T. Hence*

$$(T^*g^*)(f) = g^*(Tf)$$

for all $f \in E_1$ and $g^* \in E_2^*$.

We observe that $|g^*(Tf)| \leqslant \|g^*\|.\|T\|.\|f\|$ for every $g^* \in E_2^*$ and all $f \in E_1$ so that it is justified to say that $g^*(Tf) = f^*(f)$ with $f^* \in E_1^*$.

Theorem 1. *T^* is a bounded linear transformation and $\|T^*\| \leqslant \|T\|$. If E_2 has the property (Ext.), then $\|T^*\| = \|T\|$.*

Proof. T^* is linear, for if $g^* = \alpha_1 g_1^* + \alpha_2 g_2^*$, then

$$(T^*g^*)(f) = g^*(Tf) = \alpha_1 g_1^*(Tf) + \alpha_2 g_2^*(Tf) =$$

$$\alpha_1(T^*g_1^*)(f) + \alpha_2(T^*g_2^*)(f) = (\alpha_1 T^*g_1^* + \alpha_2 T^*g_2^*)(f).$$

T^* is bounded since $|(T^*g^*)(f)| = |g^*(Tf)| \leqslant \|g^*\|.\|T\|.\|f\|$ for all $f \in E_1$, hence $\|T^*g^*\| \leqslant \|T\|.\|g^*\|$. This shows also that $\|T^*\| \leqslant \|T\|$.

Let now E_2 have the property (Ext.). By the definition of the norm $\|T\|$ there exists an element $f_0 \in E_1$ with $\|f_0\| = 1$ and $\|Tf_0\| \geqslant \|T\| - \varepsilon$, if $\varepsilon > 0$ is arbitrarily given. If $Tf_0 = g_0 \in E_2$, we take the functional $g^* \in E_2^*$ such that $g^*(g_0) = \|g_0\|$, $\|g^*\| = 1$, which is possible by § 6, Th. 5. Then $(T^*g^*)(f_0) = g^*(Tf_0) = g^*(g_0) = \|g_0\| = \|Tf_0\| \geqslant \|T\| - \varepsilon = (\|T\| - \varepsilon)\|f_0\|$, so that $\|T^*g^*\| \geqslant \|T\| - \varepsilon = (\|T\| - \varepsilon)\|g^*\|$. Hence $\|T^*\| \geqslant \|T\| - \varepsilon$, which, together with $\|T^*\| \leqslant \|T\|$, implies $\|T^*\| = \|T\|$.

Theorem 2. *We have $O^* = O$, $(T_1 + T_2)^* = T_1^* + T_2^*$, $(\alpha T)^* = \alpha T^*$. Furthermore, if the spaces E_1 and E_2 are identical, $I^* = I$ and $(T_1 T_2)^* = T_2^* T_1^*$. Finally, if T^{-1} exists as a bounded linear transformation with the whole space E_2 as domain, $(T^*)^{-1}$ exists and $(T^{-1})^* = (T^*)^{-1}$.*

Proof. We have $(O^*g^*)(f) = g^*(Of) = g^*(0) = 0 = (Og^*)(f)$, hence $O^* = O$;

$$[(T_1 + T_2)^*g^*](f) = g^*[(T_1 + T_2)f] =$$

$$g^*(T_1f) + g^*(T_2f) = (T_1^*g^*)(f) + (T_2^*g^*)(f) =$$

$$[(T_1^* + T_2^*)g^*](f), \text{ hence } (T_1 + T_2)^* = T_1^* + T_2^*;$$

$$[(\alpha T)^*g^*](f) = g^*[(\alpha T)f] = \alpha g^*(Tf) =$$

$$\alpha(T^*g^*)(f) = [(\alpha T^*)g^*](f), \text{ hence } (\alpha T)^* = \alpha T^*.$$

If $E_1 = E_2$ so that also $E_1^* = E_2^*$, then

$$(I^*g^*)(f) = g^*(If) = g^*(f) = (Ig^*)(f),$$

hence $I^* = I$;

$$[(T_1T_2)^*g^*](f) = g^*(T_1T_2f) = (T_1^*g^*)(T_2f) =$$

$$(T_2^*T_1^*g^*)(f), \text{ hence } (T_1T_2)^* = T_2^*T_1^*.$$

Let now T^{-1} exist as a bounded linear transformation with the whole space E_2 as domain. $(T^{-1})^*$ exists therefore; it has E_1^* as domain and range in E_2^*. From $T^{-1}(Tf) = f$ for all $f \in E_1$ and $T(T^{-1}g) = g$ for all $g \in E_2$ follows now easily $T^*[(T^{-1})^*f^*] = f^*$ for all $f^* \in E_1^*$ and $(T^{-1})^*(T^*g^*) = g^*$ for all $g^* \in E_2^*$. This shows that the transformation T^* on E_2^* to E_1^* is one-to-one, so that $(T^*)^{-1}$ exists and $(T^*)^{-1} = (T^{-1})^*$.

Theorem 3. *Let E_1 and E_2 have the property (Ext.). If $g = Tf$ is a bounded linear transformation on E_1 with range in E_2, then its second adjoint $T^{**} = (T^*)^*$ is an extension of T defined on E_1^{**} and with range in E_2^{**}, and $\| T^{**} \| = \| T \|$. If in particular E_1 is reflexive, then $T^{**} = T$.*

Proof. Since E_1 and E_2 have the property (Ext.), we have $E_1 \subset E_1^{**}$ and $E_2 \subset E_2^{**}$ by § 8, Th. 3. Let now $f^{**} = f \in E_1$ and $g^{**} = T^{**}f$. We shall prove that g^{**} belongs to E_2, hence $g^{**} = g$, and that $g = Tf$. Taking an arbitrary $g^* \in E_2^*$, we have

$$g^{**}(g^*) = (T^{**}f^{**})(g^*) = f^{**}(T^*g^*) =$$

$$(T^*g^*)(f) = g^*(Tf),$$

hence $g^{**} \in E_2$, and $g^{**} = Tf$. This shows that T^{**} is identical with T on E_1, so that T^{**} is an extension of T. But then $\| T^{**} \| \geqslant \| T \|$. Since on the other hand $\| T^{**} \| \leqslant \| T^* \| \leqslant \| T \|$ by Theorem 1, we have $\| T^{**} \| = \| T \|$.

If moreover E_1 is reflexive, then $E_1^{**} = E_1$, hence $T^{**} = T$.

§ 14. Bounded Linear Functionals and Transformations on Direct Sums. Annihilators. Projections. Reducibility

Definition. *If E' is a linear subspace of the Banach space E, the set $(E')^\circ$ of all bounded linear functionals $f^* \in E^*$ such that $f^*(g) = 0$ for all $g \in E'$ is sometimes called the annihilator of E'. Evidently $(E')^\circ$ is a linear subspace of E^*.*

Theorem 1. *If E has the property (Ext.), and E', E'' are different linear subspaces, then $(E')^\circ$ and $(E'')^\circ$ are different, in other words, E' is exactly the set of all $f \in E$ having the property that $f^*(f) = 0$ for all $f^* \in (E')^\circ$.*

Proof. Since E' and E'' are different, one of them, say E'', contains an element f_0 not contained in the other. Then f_0 has positive distance from E' so that by § 6, Th. 6 there exists an $f^* \in E^*$ such that $f^*(f_0) = 1$ and $f^*(g) = 0$ for all $g \in E'$. Hence $f^* \in (E')^\circ$, whereas f^* does not belong to $(E'')^\circ$ on account of $f^*(f_0) = 1$. It follows that $(E')^\circ$ and $(E'')^\circ$ are different.

If the Banach space E is the direct sum of the linear subspaces E' and E'', so that we have $f = g + h$, $g \in E'$, $h \in E''$, for every $f \in E$, where g and h are uniquely determined, we may define a transformation P on E by $Pf = g$. Evidently P is linear. P is called the *projection* on E' along E''. The linear transformation $I - P$ is then the projection on E'' along E', since $(I - P)f = f - Pf = f - g = h$. Writing $PP = P^2$, we observe that $P^2 = P$. Indeed, since $Pg = g$ for every $g \in E'$, we have $P^2f = P(Pf) = Pg = g = Pf$ for every $f \in E$.

We may ask now under what conditions P, and therefore also $I - P$, is bounded. This is obviously the case when E is the productspace $E' \times E''$ of the Banach spaces E' and E'', and the norm in E is defined in such a way that E may be considered as the direct sum of E' and E'' (cf. Ch. 6, § 15). In particular this is true whenever E is a Hilbert space and E', E'' are orthogonal subspaces, because then $f = g + h$, $g \in E'$, $h \in E''$, $(g, h) = 0$ implies $\| f \|^2 = \| g \|^2 + \| h \|^2$. Furthermore, an inspection of the proof of Ch. 6, § 4, Th. 4 shows that P is also bounded if E' is of finite dimension. In all these cases E may be non-complete. If E is complete, it is not necessary to distinguish between all kinds of cases, for then P is always bounded as shown by the next theorem.

Theorem 2. *If the complete Banach space E is the direct sum of the linear subspaces E' and E'', which therefore are also complete, then the projection P on E' along E'' is bounded.*

Proof. It is easily seen that the correspondence $g \leftrightarrow [g]$ between the elements $g \in E'$ and $[g] \in E/E''$ is one-to-one. The transformation T, defined by $[g] = Tg$, has therefore E' as its domain, the complete factor-space E/E'' as its range, and T^{-1} exists. Obviously T is linear. Since $\| [g] \| =$ lower bound $\| g + h \|$ for all $h \in E''$, we have $\| [g] \| \leqslant \| g \|$, which shows that T is bounded. By § 11, Th. 6, 3°, T^{-1} is then also bounded, $\| g \| \leqslant M \| [g] \|$, so that $\| g \| \leqslant M \| g + h \|$ for all $h \in E''$. Hence $\| g \| = \| Pf \| \leqslant M \| f \|$ for all $f = g + h$, $g \in E'$, $h \in E''$.

Second proof. For every $f \in E$ we have $f = Pf + (f - Pf)$. Let now $\lim f_n = f_0$, $\lim Pf_n = g_0$. To prove that P is closed, we have to show that $g_0 = Pf_0$. Since all $Pf_n \in E'$ and E' is complete, we have $g_0 \in E'$. Furthermore $\lim (f_n - Pf_n) = f_0 - g_0 = h_0$ exists, and since all $f_n - Pf_n \in E''$, we have $h_0 \in E''$. Hence $f_0 = g_0 + h_0$, $g_0 \in E'$, $h_0 \in E''$, and this shows that $g_0 = Pf_0$. The transformation P is therefore closed, so that by § 11, Th. 8 it is also bounded.

Remark. In § 6, Th. 2 we proved that if E is the direct sum of $[L_1]$ and $[L_2]$, where $[L_1]$ is of finite dimension, then every bounded linear functional $F(f)$ on $[L_1]$ can be extended onto E in such a way that it remains bounded. The proof rests essentially upon the fact that the projection P on $[L_1]$ along $[L_2]$ is bounded. We see now that, if E is complete, the condition that $[L_1]$ be of finite dimension may be left out. The same remark applies to § 7, Th. 9, which is a consequence of § 6, Th. 2.

Theorem 3. *If the Banach space E is the direct sum of the linear subspaces E', E'', and if the projection P on E' along E'' is bounded, then the adjoint space E^* is the direct sum of the annihilators $(E')^\circ$ and $(E'')^\circ$.*

Proof. For every $f \in E$ we have $f = g + h$, $g \in E'$, $h \in E''$, where g and h are uniquely determined, and $\| g \| = \| Pf \| \leqslant M \| f \|$ for a fixed positive M. If now $f^* \in E^*$ is arbitrarily given, we define the linear functional g^* by $g^*(f) = f^*(g)$ for every $f \in E$. Then $g^* \in E^*$ because $| g^*(f) | = | f^*(g) | \leqslant \| f^* \| . \| g \| \leqslant M \| f^* \| . \| f \|$. Furthermore, if $f = h \in E''$, then $g = 0$, hence $g^*(h) = f^*(0) = 0$ or $g^* \in (E'')^\circ$. The bounded linear functional h^* is finally defined by $h^* = f^* - g^*$, hence $h^*(f) = f^*(f) - g^*(f) = f^*(f) - f^*(g) = f^*(h)$. If now $f = g \in E'$, then $h = 0$, hence $h^*(g) = f^*(0) = 0$, or $h^* \in (E')^\circ$. It follows that $f^* = g^* + h^*$, $g^* \in (E'')^\circ$, $h^* \in (E')^\circ$.

It remains to prove that $(E')^\circ$ and $(E'')^\circ$ have only the null element in common. Supposing that f^* belongs to both $(E')^\circ$ and $(E'')^\circ$, we have

$f^*(f) = f^*(g) + f^*(h) = 0$ for every $f = g + h$, $g \in E'$, $h \in E''$; hence $f^* = 0$.

Theorem 4. *A bounded linear transformation P on a Banach space E which has its range in E as well (P is therefore an endomorphism of E), and which satisfies $P^2 = P$, is a projection.*

Proof. Let E'' be the subset of all elements $h \in E$ satisfying $Ph = 0$; let E' be the subset of all $g \in E$ satisfying $Pg = g$. Obviously E' and E'' are linear subspaces on account of the linearity and boundedness of P. We shall prove that E is the direct sum of E' and E''.

If $f \in E'$, then $Pf = f$; if $f \in E''$, then $Pf = 0$; hence, if f belongs to both E' and E'', then $f = 0$. For an arbitrary f we have $f = Pf + (I - P)f$, and $P(Pf) = P^2f = Pf$, so that $Pf \in E'$. Furthermore $P(I - P)f = Pf - P^2f = Pf - Pf = 0$, so that $(I - P)f \in E''$. This proves that E is the direct sum of E' and E'', and that P is the projection on E' along E''.

Theorem 5. *If the Banach space E is the direct sum of the linear subspaces E' and E'', and if the projection P on E' along E'' is bounded, then the Banach-adjoint P^* of P is the projection on $(E'')^\circ$ along $(E')^\circ$.*

Proof. We know already that E^* is the direct sum of $(E'')^\circ$ and $(E')^\circ$. Furthermore P^* is bounded since $\| P^* \| \leqslant \| P \|$, and $(P^*)^2 = P^*P^* = (PP)^* = P^*$, which shows that P^* is the projection on the set of all solutions of $P^*f^* = f^*$ along the set of all solutions of $P^*f^* = 0$. We have:

1°. If $f^* \in (E'')^\circ$, then

$$f^*(f) = f^*(Pf) + f^*[(I - P)f] = f^*(Pf) = (P^*f^*)(f)$$

for all $f \in E$, so that $P^*f^* = f^*$.

Conversely, if $P^*f^* = f^*$ and $f \in E''$, then

$$f^*(f) = (P^*f^*)(f) = f^*(Pf) = f^*(0) = 0,$$

so that $f^* \in (E'')^\circ$.

2°. If $f^* \in (E')^\circ$, then

$$(P^*f^*)(f) = f^*(Pf) = 0$$

for all $f \in E$, so that $P^*f^* = 0$.

Conversely, if $P^*f^* = 0$ and $f \in E'$, then

$$f^*(f) = f^*(Pf) = (P^*f^*)(f) = 0,$$

so that $f^* \in (E')^\circ$.

We have shown therefore in 1° that the set of solutions of $P^*f^* = f^*$ is exactly $(E'')^\circ$, and in 2° that the set of solutions of $P^*f^* = 0$ is exactly $(E')^\circ$, which is precisely what was to be proved.

Definition. *Let E' be a linear subspace of the Banach space E, and let T be a linear transformation with domain E and range in E. Then, if $f \in E'$ implies $Tf \in E'$, we say that E' is invariant under T, or also that E' reduces T.*

If E is the direct sum of the linear subspaces E' and E'', and both E' and E'' reduce the linear transformation T, we say that T is completely reduced by (E', E'').

In the case that T is completely reduced by (E', E''), we may consider T to be split up into two transformations T' and T'' with domains E' and E'' and ranges in E' and E'' respectively. Hence, if $f = g + h$, $g \in E'$, $h \in E''$, we have $Tf = T'g + T''h$. The transformation T is sometimes called the direct sum of T' and T''.

Theorem 6. *If the Banach space E is the direct sum of the linear subspaces E' and E'', and the projection P on E' along E'' is bounded, the linear transformation T with domain E and range in E is completely reduced by (E', E'') if and only if $PT = TP$.*

Proof. By Theorem 4, E' is the set of all solutions of $Pg = g$ and E'' is the set of all solutions of $Ph = 0$.

Let now $PT = TP$. If $g \in E'$, then $Tg = TPg = PTg$, so that $Tg \in E'$; if $h \in E''$, then $Ph = 0$, and $PTh = TPh = 0$, so that $Th \in E''$. This shows that T is completely reduced by (E', E'').

Let now conversely T be completely reduced by (E', E''). For an arbitrary $f = g + h$, $g \in E'$, $h \in E''$, we have then $TPf = Tg$, and $PTPf = PTg = Tg$ since $Tg \in E'$. Hence $TPf = Tg = PTPf$ for all $f \in E$, or $PTP = TP$. In the same way, since T is also reduced by E'', we find $(I - P)T(I - P) = T(I - P)$, or $T - TP - PT + PTP = T - TP$, so that $PTP = PT$. Hence $TP = PTP = PT$.

Theorem 7. *If E' is a linear subspace of the Banach space E, and if the bounded linear transformation T (with domain E and range in E) is reduced by E', then the adjoint T^* is reduced by the annihilator $(E')^\circ$. If E is the direct sum of E', E'' and T is completely reduced by (E', E''), while moreover the projection P on E' along E'' is bounded, then T^* is completely reduced by $((E')^\circ, (E'')^\circ)$.*

Proof. We suppose that T is reduced by E', hence $f \in E'$ implies $Tf \in E'$.

Let now $f^* \in (E')^\circ$. Then, for every $f \in E'$, we have $(T^*f^*)(f) = f^*(Tf) = 0$, hence $T^*f^* \in (E')^\circ$. This shows that T^* is reduced by $(E')^\circ$.

Taking into account Theorem 3, the second statement follows now immediately.

Theorem 8. *If the reflexive Banach space E has the property (Ext.), and E' is a linear subspace, then $(E')^{\circ\circ} = [(E')^\circ]^\circ = E'$.*

Proof. $f^{**} \in (E')^{\circ\circ}$ is equivalent with $f^{**}(f^*) = 0$ for all $f^* \in (E')^\circ$. Since however $f^{**} = f \in E$, this is equivalent with $f^*(f) = 0$ for all $f^* \in (E')^\circ$, and on account of Theorem 1 the set of all $f \in E$ with this property is exactly E'.

Let E be a Banach space. We consider the product space $E^n = E \times E \times \ldots \times E$ (n factors), and we suppose that the norm in E^n is defined in such a way that E^n may be considered as the direct sum of the n spaces E. The elements $\{f^1, \ldots, f^n\}$, where $f^i \in E$ $(i = 1, \ldots, n)$, of E^n will shortly be denoted by $\{f\}$. For $\{f\} = \{f^1, \ldots, f^n\}$ we have therefore $\| \{f\} \| \leqslant \Sigma_{i=1}^n \| f^i \|$ and $\| f^i \| \leqslant A \, \| \{f\} \|$ $(i = 1, \ldots, n)$, where A is fixed (cf. Ch. 6, § 15).

Let now the n^2 linear transformations $T_{ij} (i, j = 1, \ldots, n)$ all have E as their domain, and let their ranges be contained in E. Then, by $g^i = \Sigma_{j=1}^n T_{ij} f^j$ $(i = 1, \ldots, n)$, a linear transformation $\{g\} = T\{f\}$ is defined with domain E^n and range in E^n. We shall say that T has the matrix $\{T_{ij}\}$.

Theorem 9. *T is bounded if and only if all T_{ij} are bounded.*

Proof. Let first $\| T_{ij} \| \leqslant M$ for all T_{ij}. Then

$$\| g^i \| = \| \Sigma \, T_{ij} f^j \| \leqslant \Sigma \, \| T_{ij} f^j \| \leqslant M \, \Sigma \, \| f^j \| \leqslant MnA \, \| \{f\} \|,$$

hence

$$\| \{g\} \| \leqslant \Sigma \, \| g^i \| \leqslant AMn^2 \, \| \{f\} \|,$$

which shows that T is bounded.

Let now conversely $\| T \| \leqslant M$, and suppose that for one at least of the T_{ij} there exists an $f_0 \in E$ such that $\| T_{ij} f_0 \| > AM \, \| f_0 \|$. Then $\{f_0\} = \{f_0^1, \ldots, f_0^n\}$ is defined by $f_0^j = f_0$ and $f_0^k = 0$ for $k \neq j$. For $\{g_0\} = T\{f_0\}$ we have now

$$\begin{aligned} \| \{g_0\} \| \geqslant A^{-1} \| g_0^i \| &= A^{-1} \| \Sigma_k \, T_{ik} f_0^k \| = A^{-1} \| T_{ij} f_0 \| \\ &> A^{-1} AM \, \| f_0 \| = M \, \Sigma_k \, \| f_0^k \| \geqslant M \, \| \{f_0\} \|, \end{aligned}$$

in contradiction with $\| T \| \leqslant M$. Hence $\| T_{ij} \| \leqslant AM$ for all T_{ij}.

Theorem 10. *$T \neq O$ (the null transformation in E^n) if and only if $T_{ij} \neq O$ (the null transformation in E) for one at least of the T_{ij}.*

Proof. It is trivial that $T \neq O$ implies $T_{ij} \neq O$ for one at least of the T_{ij}.

Let now conversely $T_{ij} \neq O$ for a certain T_{ij}, so that $T_{ij}f_0 \neq 0$ for one $f_0 \in E$ at least. Then $\{f\} = \{f^1, \ldots, f^n\}$ is defined by $f^j = f_0$ and $f^k = 0$ for $k \neq j$. For $\{g\} = T\{f\}$ we have now $g^i = T_{ij}f_0 \neq 0$, hence $\{g\} \neq 0$, which shows that $T \neq O$.

In a similar way as in Th. 3 it is easily proved that the adjoint space $(E^n)^*$ satisfies $(E^n)^* = (E^*)^n = E^* \times E^* \times \ldots \times E^*$, where $(E^*)^n$ may be considered as a direct sum.

Theorem 11. *If T is bounded, the adjoint transformation $\{f^*\} = T^*\{g^*\}$ with domain $(E^*)^n$ and range in $(E^*)^n$ is given by $(f^*)^i = \Sigma_{j=1}^n (T^*)_{ij} (g^*)^j$, where $(T^*)_{ij} = (T_{ji})^*$.*

Proof. We have

$$\{f^*\} (\{f\}) = (T^*\{g^*\}) (\{f\}) = \{g^*\} (T\{f\}) = \{g^*\} (\{g\}) =$$
$$\Sigma_j (g^*)^j(g^j) = \Sigma_j(g^*)^j(\Sigma_i T_{ji}f^i) = \Sigma_{ij}[(T_{ji})^*(g^*)^j](f^i),$$

hence

$$(f^*)^i = \Sigma_j (T_{ji})^*(g^*)^j.$$

Remark. If the linear transformations S and T with domains E^n and ranges in E^n have the matrices $\{S_{ij}\}$ and $\{T_{ij}\}$ respectively, an immediate computation shows that the linear transformation ST has the matrix $\{(ST)_{ij}\}$ where $(ST)_{ij} = \Sigma_k S_{ik}T_{kj}$.

§ 15. Examples of Bounded Linear Transformations

Example A. *Multiplication by a bounded function*

Let $\Phi(u)$ and $\Psi(v)$ be complementary in the sense of Young, and let Δ be a μ-measurable set. Then, if $t(x) \in L_\infty(\Delta, \mu)$ (that is, $|t(x)| \leqslant A$ almost everywhere on Δ, where A does not depend on x), the transformation T, defined by

$$Tf = t(x)f(x)$$

is a bounded linear transformation on $L_\Phi(\Delta, \mu)$ with range in $L_\Phi(\Delta, \mu)$. We have $T = O$ (the null transformation) if and only if $t(x) = 0$ almost everywhere on Δ.

To prove the first statement we have only to observe that the summability of $f(x)h(x)$ for $f \in L_\Phi$, $h \in L_\Psi$ implies the summability of

$t(x)f(x)h(x)$, hence $t(x)f(x) \in L_\Phi$. Furthermore $\int_\Delta |\, tfh \,|\, d\mu \leqslant A \int_\Delta |\, fh \,|\, d\mu$, hence $\| tf \|_\Phi \leqslant A \| f \|_\Phi$.

It is trivial that $t(x) = 0$ (almost everywhere) implies $T = O$. If conversely $T = O$, then $\| t(x)f(x) \|_\Phi = 0$ or $t(x)f(x) = 0$ (almost everywhere) for all $f(x) \in L_\Phi$, hence $t(x) = 0$ (almost everywhere).

Let now $\Phi(2u) \leqslant M\Phi(u)$ for all $u \geqslant 0$, so that every $g^* \in (L_\Phi)^*$ may be represented by a uniquely determined function $g^*(x) \in L_\Psi(\Delta, \mu)$ (cf. § 7, Th. 4). Then, if T^* is the Banach-adjoint transformation of T and $f^* = T^*g^*$, the functional f^* is represented by $f^*(x) = t(x)g^*(x)$. Indeed,

$$(T^*g^*)(f) = g^*(Tf) = \int_\Delta tfg^* d\mu = \int_\Delta f \cdot tg^* d\mu,$$

hence, since $f^*(x)$ is uniquely determined, $f^*(x) = t(x)g^*(x)$.

We observe that it is not allowed to consider as identical the transformations $f^* = T^*g^*$ with $f^*, g^* \in (L_\Phi)^*$ and $f^*(x) = t(x)g^*(x)$ with $f^*(x), g^*(x) \in L_\Psi$, because the norms in $(L_\Phi)^*$ and L_Ψ are not necessarily identical. Obviously, however, $f^*(x) = t(x)g^*(x)$ is also bounded when considered as a transformation with domain L_Ψ and range in L_Ψ.

Considering now in particular the spaces $L_p(\Delta, \mu)$ $(1 \leqslant p \leqslant \infty)$, $Tf = t(x)f(x)$ is a bounded linear transformation with domain L_p and range in L_p, and for $1 \leqslant p < \infty$ the B-adjoint T^*g^* may be identified with the transformation $t(x)g^*(x)$ with domain L_q and range in L_q, where $1/p + 1/q = 1$. The identifying is now permitted because the spaces $(L_p)^*$ and L_q may be identified (cf. § 7, Th. 5).

Example B. *Integral transformation of finite double-norm*

Let $T(x, y)$ be a $\mu \times \mu$-measurable function on $\Delta \times \Delta$, where Δ is a μ-measurable set. Let furthermore $\Phi(u)$ and $\Psi(v)$ be complementary in the sense of Young. Then, if $T(x, y)$ considered as a function of y belongs to $L_\Psi(\Delta, \mu)$ for almost every $x \in \Delta$, and if $t(x) = \| T(x, y) \|_\Psi$ belongs to $L_\Phi(\Delta, \mu)$, the transformation T, defined by

$$g(x) = Tf = \int_\Delta T(x, y)f(y)d\mu,$$

is a bounded linear transformation on $L_\Phi(\Delta, \mu)$ into $L_\Phi(\Delta, \mu)$. We have $T = O$ (the null transformation) if and only if $T(x, y) = 0$ almost everywhere on $\Delta \times \Delta$.

The transformation $g = Tf$, thus defined, is called an *integral transformation* with *kernel* $T(x, y)$. The number

$$\| t(x) \|_\Phi = \| \, \| T(x, y) \|_\Psi \|_\Phi$$

is called the *double-norm* of T, and it is sometimes denoted by $|||\, T \,|||$.

To prove that T is bounded on L_Φ, we observe first that $T(x, y)h(x)f(y)$ is measurable on $\Delta \times \Delta$ for arbitrary $h(x) \in L_\Psi$, $f(y) \in L_\Phi$, hence

$$\int_{\Delta\times\Delta} | T(x, y)h(x)f(y) | d(\mu \times \mu) = \int_\Delta (\int_\Delta | T(x, y)f(y) | d\mu) | h(x) | d\mu$$
$$\leqslant \int_\Delta \| T(x, y) \|_\Psi \| f \|_\Phi | h(x) | d\mu = \| f \|_\Phi \int_\Delta t(x) | h(x) | d\mu$$
$$\leqslant \| f \|_\Phi \| t \|_\Phi \| h \|_\Psi,$$

which shows that $T(x, y)h(x)f(y)$ is summable over $\Delta \times \Delta$. On account of Fubini's Theorem we have therefore

$$\int_{\Delta\times\Delta} T(x, y)h(x)f(y)d(\mu \times \mu) = \int_\Delta (\int_\Delta T(x, y)f(y)d\mu)h(x)d\mu,$$

where $g(x) = \int_\Delta T(x, y)f(y)d\mu$ is on Δ a measurable function of x. Furthermore, since $g(x)h(x)$ is summable for every $h(x) \in L_\Psi$, we find $g(x) \in L_\Phi$ (cf. § 3, Th. 1).

We have already seen that

$$\int_\Delta | gh | d\mu \leqslant \| f \|_\Phi \int_\Delta t | h | d\mu;$$

if therefore $\int_\Delta \Psi | h | d\mu \leqslant 1$, it follows that $\int_\Delta t | h | d\mu \leqslant \| t \|_\Phi$, so that $\int_\Delta | gh | d\mu \leqslant \| f \|_\Phi \| t \|_\Phi$ or $\| g \|_\Phi \leqslant \| t \|_\Phi \| f \|_\Phi$. This shows that T is bounded with

$$\| T \| \leqslant ||| T |||.$$

It is trivial that $T(x, y) = 0$ almost everywhere on $\Delta \times \Delta$ implies $||| T ||| = 0$, hence $\| T \| = 0$ or $T = O$. If conversely $T = O$, we have $g(x) = \int_\Delta T(x, y)f(y)d\mu = 0$ almost everywhere on Δ for every $f(y) \in L_\Phi$ (where the set of exceptional x, however, may depend on $f(y)$), hence $\int_\Delta g(x)h(x)d\mu = \int_{\Delta\times\Delta} T(x,y)h(x)f(y)d(\mu \times \mu) = 0$ for all $h(x) \in L_\Psi$, $f(y) \in L_\Phi$. In particular $\int_{\Delta_1\times\Delta_2} T(x, y)d(\mu \times \mu) = 0$ for arbitrary sets $\Delta_1, \Delta_2 \subset \Delta$ of finite measure, which implies $T(x, y) = 0$ almost everywhere on $\Delta \times \Delta$ (cf. Ch. 3, § 4, Th. 3).

Let now $\Phi(2u) \leqslant M\Phi(u)$ for all $u \geqslant 0$, so that every $g^* \in (L_\Phi)^*$ may be represented by a uniquely determined function $g^*(y) \in L_\Psi(\Delta, \mu)$. Then, if T^* is the Banach-adjoint transformation of T, and $f^* = T^*g^*$, the functional f^* is represented by

$$f^*(x) = \int_\Delta T(y, x)g^*(y)d\mu.$$

Indeed,

$$(T^*g^*)(f) = g^*(Tf) = \int_{\Delta\times\Delta} T(y, x)f(x)g^*(y)d(\mu \times \mu) =$$
$$\int_\Delta (\int_\Delta T(y, x)g^*(y)\, d\mu)f(x)\, d\mu,$$

hence, since $f^*(x)$ is uniquely determined,

$$f^*(x) = \int_\Delta T(y, x)g^*(y)d\mu.$$

We observe once more that the transformation $f^* = T^*g^*$ with f^*, $g^* \in (L_\Phi)^*$ may not be considered as identical with the transformation $f^*(x) = \int_\Delta T(y, x)g^*(y)d\mu$, where $f^*(x), g^*(x) \in L_\Psi$. Obviously however this last transformation is also bounded, since on account of $\| f^*(x) \|_\Psi/2 \leqslant \| f^* \| \leqslant \| f^*(x) \|_\Psi$ we have

$$\| f^*(x) \|_\Psi \leqslant 2 \| f^* \| = 2 \| T^*g^* \| \leqslant 2 \| T \| . \| g^* \| \leqslant 2 \| T \| . \| g^*(x) \|_\Psi .$$

Considering now in particular the spaces $L_p(\Delta, \mu)$ $(1 \leqslant p \leqslant \infty)$, the double-norm of T is usually defined as

$$||| T ||| = [\int_\Delta (\int_\Delta | T(x, y) |^q d\mu)^{p/q} d\mu]^{1/p},$$

where $1/p + 1/q = 1$, and where the interpretation in the boundary cases $p = 1$ and $p = \infty$ is evident. The difference with the case L_Φ, $\Phi(u) = u^p/p$, is a constant factor (cf. Ch. 6, § 6, Ex. B). If now $||| T ||| < \infty$, the transformation

$$g(x) = Tf = \int_\Delta T(x, y)f(y)d\mu$$

on $L_p(\Delta, \mu)$ into $L_p(\Delta, \mu)$ is bounded, and in the same way as in the general case we may prove that $\| T \| \leqslant ||| T |||$. For $1 \leqslant p < \infty$ the B-adjoint T^*g^* may be identified with the transformation $\int_\Delta T(y, x) g^*(y)d\mu$ on L_q into L_q, where $1/p + 1/q = 1$.

Example C. *An integral transformation which is a projection*

The reader, after having seen the preceding example, might have the idea that for a linear integral transformation, in order to be bounded, it is necessary to be of finite double-norm. We shall show that this is not the case. We shall, in fact, give an example of a bounded linear integral transformation P of infinite double-norm on the space $L_2(\Delta)$, where Δ is the linear interval $[0, 1]$, which has its range in the same space. It will be proved that this transformation P is a projection on E' along E'', where E' and E'' are orthogonal linear subspaces.

Let Δ be the linear interval $[0, 1]$, and let $P(x, y)$ be defined on $\Delta \times \Delta$ by

$$P(x, y) = 2 \text{ on } 0 \leqslant x, y < 1/2,$$

$$P(x, y) = 2^2 \text{ on } 1/2 \leqslant x, y < 3/4,$$

$$\cdots\cdots\cdots$$

$$P(x, y) = 2^n \text{ on } 1 - (1/2)^{n-1} \leqslant x, y < 1 - (1/2)^n,$$

$$\cdots\cdots\cdots$$

$$P(x, y) = 0 \text{ at all other points of } \Delta \times \Delta.$$

Then, if the linear transformation P on $L_2(\Delta)$ is defined by

$$g(x) = Pf = \int_\Delta P(x, y)f(y)dy,$$

where the integral is a Lebesgue integral, we shall prove that P has the stated properties. In the first place, the double-norm of P is ($p = q = 2$)

$$|||\, P \,||| = [\int_{\Delta\times\Delta} |\, P(x, y)|^2 \, dx\, dy]^{1/2} =$$

$$[\Sigma_{n=1}^{\infty} \int_{\Delta_n\times\Delta_n} |\, P(x, y)\,|^2\, dx\, dy]^{1/2} = [\Sigma_{n=1}^{\infty} 1]^{1/2} = \infty,$$

where Δ_n denotes the interval $1-(1/2)^{n-1} \leqslant x < 1-(1/2)^n$. Furthermore, for $x \in \Delta_n$,

$$|\, g(x)\,|^2 = |\int_\Delta P(x, y)f(y)dy\,|^2 = |\int_{\Delta_n} P(x, y)f(y)dy\,|^2$$

$$\leqslant \int_{\Delta_n} P^2(x, y)\, dy \,.\, \int_{\Delta_n} |\, f\,|^2\, dy = 2^n \int_{\Delta_n} |\, f\,|^2\, dy,$$

hence

$$\int_\Delta |\, g\,|^2\, dx = \Sigma_{n=1}^{\infty} \int_{\Delta_n} |\, g\,|^2\, dx \leqslant \Sigma_{n=1}^{\infty} \int_{\Delta_n} |\, f\,|^2\, dy \,.\, \int_{\Delta_n} 2^n dx$$

$$= \Sigma_{n=1}^{\infty} \int_{\Delta_n} |\, f\,|^2\, dy = \int_\Delta |\, f\,|^2\, dy,$$

which shows that $\|\, g\,\| = \|\, Pf\,\| \leqslant \|\, f\,\|$.

Let now E' be the set of all $g(x) \in L_2(\Delta)$ that are constant in every interval Δ_n. From the definition of $P(x, y)$ it follows immediately that $Pg = g$ for $g \in E'$. Furthermore, for an arbitrary $f(x) \in L_2(\Delta)$, we have $Pf \in E'$, hence $PPf = Pf$ for all $f \in L_2$ or $P^2 = P$. By § 14, Th. 4, P is therefore the projection on E' along E'' where E'' is the set of all solutions h of $Ph = 0$. It remains to prove that $Pg = g$, $Ph = 0$ implies $(g, h) = 0$.

We observe first that $u(x) = \int_\Delta P(x, y) \,|\, f(y)\,|\, dy \in L_2$ for every $f \in L_2$, so that $u(x)v(x)$ is summable over Δ for every $v \in L_2$. Hence

$$\int_\Delta |\, uv\,|\, dx = \int_\Delta (\int_\Delta P(x, y)\,|\, f(y)\,|\, dy)\,|\, v(x)\,|\, dx =$$

$$\int_{\Delta\times\Delta} |\, P(x, y)f(y)v(x)\,|\, dx\, dy < \infty.$$

This shows that $P(x, y)f(y)v(x)$ is summable over $\Delta \times \Delta$, so that

$$(Pf, v) = \int_\Delta (\int_\Delta P(x, y)f(y)dy)\, \overline{v(x)}\, dx =$$

$$\int_{\Delta\times\Delta} P(x, y)\, \overline{v(x)}\, f(y)\, dx\, dy = \int_{\Delta\times\Delta} \overline{P(y, x)v(x)}\, f(y)\, dx\, dy$$

$$= \int_\Delta f(y)\, (\overline{\int_\Delta P(y, x)v(x)\, dx})\, dy = (f, Pv).$$

Let now $Pg = g$, $Ph = 0$. Then $(g, h) = (Pg, h) = (g, Ph) = (g, 0) = 0$, which was to be proved.

EXAMPLES

1) If Δ is the linear interval $0 \leqslant x \leqslant 1$, then every bounded linear functional $f^*(f)$ in the Banach space $C(\Delta)$ of all continuous functions $f(x)$ in Δ (cf. Ch. 6, Ex. 9) is of the form

$$f^*(f) = \int_0^1 f(x)dg(x),$$

where the integral is a Stieltjes integral, and $g(x)$ is of bounded variation on Δ. The norm $\| f^* \|$ of $f^*(f)$ satisfies $\| f^* \| = V(g)$, where $V(g)$ is the total variation of $g(x)$ over Δ [12].

(For rational x in $0 \leqslant x \leqslant 1$ the function $h_x(y)$ is defined in $0 \leqslant y \leqslant 1$ by $h_x(y) = 1$ for $0 \leqslant y \leqslant x$, and $h_x(y) = 0$ for $x < y \leqslant 1$. Since the set of all $h_x(y)$ is enumerable, $f^*(f)$ may be extended without change of norm onto all $f = h_x(y)$, considering $h_x(y)$ as belonging to $L_\infty(\Delta)$ (hence $\| h_x \| = 1$). Writing $g(x) = f^*(h_x)$, we have, if $0 = x_0 < x_1 < \ldots < x_n = 1$, all x_i are rational, and $1/\varepsilon_i = \operatorname{sgn} \{g(x_i) - g(x_{i-1})\}$,

$$\Sigma_1^n \mid g(x_i) - g(x_{i-1}) \mid = \Sigma_1^n \{g(x_i) - g(x_{i-1})\}\varepsilon_i =$$

$$f^*[\Sigma_1^n (h_{x_i} - h_{x_{i-1}})\varepsilon_i] \leqslant \| f^* \| . \| \Sigma_1^n (h_{x_i} - h_{x_{i-1}})\varepsilon_i \| = \| f^* \|.$$

This shows that $g(x)$ (x rational) is of bounded variation, and that $V(g) \leqslant \| f^* \|$. Defining $g(x)$ for irrational x in $0 \leqslant x \leqslant 1$ by $g(x) = \lim g(y)$, where y tends to x through rational values $y > x$, the total variation $V(g)$ remains unchanged.

Let now $f(x) \in C(\Delta)$, and write $\varphi_n(x) = \Sigma_{r=1}^n f(r/n)[h_{r/n}(x) - h_{(r-1)/n}(x)]$. Then $\lim \| f - \varphi_n \| = 0$, hence $\lim f^*(\varphi_n) = f^*(f)$. But $f^*(\varphi_n) = \Sigma_{r=1}^n f(r/n) [g(r/n) - g\{(r-1)/n\}]$, hence $f^*(f) = \lim f^*(\varphi_n) = \int_0^1 f(x)dg(x)$. Finally $\mid f^*(f) \mid \leqslant V(g) \| f \|$, so that $\| f^* \| \leqslant V(g)$. This together with $V(g) \leqslant \| f^* \|$, shows that $\| f^* \| = V(g)$).

2) The following extension of § 6, Th. 3 holds: Let E be a real separable Banach space E_r (complete or non-complete), and let the continuous real functional $p(f)$, defined on E_r, satisfy

$$p(f + g) \leqslant p(f) + p(g), \quad p(\alpha f) = \alpha p(f) \text{ for } \alpha \geqslant 0.$$

Then, if $[L]$ is a proper linear subspace of E_r, and $F(f)$ is a real linear functional on $[L]$ such that $F(f) \leqslant p(f)$ for all $f \in [L]$, there exists a bounded real linear functional $f^*(f)$ on E_r such that

$$f^*(f) \leqslant p(f) \text{ on } E_r, \text{ and } f^*(f) = F(f) \text{ on } [L].$$

(The proof is very similar to that of § 6, Th. 3).

3) Let E be a Banach space and E^* its adjoint space. The subset $G \subset E^*$ is said to be *regularly closed* if for every $f_0^* \in E^*$, but not belonging to G, there exists an element $f_0 \in E$ such that $f_0^*(f_0) = 1$ and $f^*(f_0) = 0$ for all $f^* \in G$. Let now the set $X \subset E$ be arbitrary. Then the set $G \subset E^*$ of all f^* for which $f^*(f) = 0$ for all $f \in X$ is regularly closed.

4) Let E be a Banach space and E^* its adjoint space. The subset $G \subset E^*$ is said to be *weakly closed* if $f_n^* \in G$ ($n = 1, 2, \ldots$) and $\lim f_n^*(f) = f_0^*(f)$ for all $f \in E$ imply $f_0^* \in G$. Then, if $G \subset E^*$ is regularly closed, G is weakly closed.

(Let $f_n^* \in G$ ($n = 1, 2, \ldots$) and $\lim f_n^*(f) = f_0^*(f)$ for all $f \in E$. Then, if f_0^* should not belong to G, there would exist an element $f_0 \in E$ such that $f_0^*(f_0) = 1$ and

$f^*(f_0) = 0$ for all $f^* \in G$. Hence $f_n^*(f_0) = 0$ for all n, so that also $f_0^*(f_0) = \lim f_n^*(f_0) = 0$, which is a contradiction).

5) If $G \subset E^*$ is weakly closed, then it is closed.

(Let $\lim \| f_n^* - f_0^* \| = 0$, where $f_n^* \in G$ $(n = 1, 2, \ldots)$. Then, since $| f_n^*(f) - f_0^*(f) | \leqslant \| f_n^* - f_0^* \| . \| f \|$, we have $\lim f_n^*(f) = f_0^*(f)$ for all $f \in E$. Hence $f_0^* \in G$).

6) Let the reflexive Banach space E have the property (Ext.). Then, if E^* has also the property (Ext.), every linear subspace $G \subset E^*$ is regularly closed, that is, every linear closed set $G \subset E^*$ is regularly closed.

(Let $G \subset E^*$ be a linear subspace, and let $f_0^* \in E^*$ not belong to G. Then, since E^* has the property (Ext.), there exists an $f_0^{**} \in E^{**}$ such that $f_0^{**}(f_0^*) = 1$ and $f_0^{**}(f^*) = 0$ for all $f^* \in G$ (cf. § 6, Th. 6). Hence, on account of the reflexivity of E, there exists an $f_0 \in E$ such that $f_0^*(f_0) = 1$ and $f^*(f_0) = 0$ for all $f^* \in G$).

7) Let the Banach space E have the property (Ext.), and let, in E^{**}, every weakly closed linear subspace be regularly closed. Then, if every weakly fundamental sequence of elements $f_n \in E$ has a weak limit f, E is reflexive.

(By § 8, Th. 3, E may be identified with a linear subspace $E_2 \subset E^{**}$. Since, in E, every weakly fundamental sequence has a weak limit, E_2 is weakly closed, hence regularly closed. Supposing now that E_2 is a proper subspace of E^{**}, there exists an element $f_0^{**} \in E^{**}$, not belonging to E_2. Then there also exists an element $f_0^* \in E^*$ such that $f_0^{**}(f_0^*) = 1$ and $f^{**}(f_0^*) = 0$ for all $f^{**} \in E_2$. This implies $f_0^*(f) = 0$ for all $f \in E$, hence $f_0^* = 0$, in contradiction with $f_0^{**}(f_0^*) = 1$).

8) Let E and E^* have the property (Ext.). Then E is reflexive if and only if both the following properties hold:

1°. Every weakly fundamental sequence in E has a weak limit.

2°. Every weakly closed linear subspace of E^{**} is regularly closed.

(The reflexivity of E follows from 1° and 2° by the preceding example. If, conversely, E is reflexive, then 1° holds by § 9, Th. 2, while 2° follows from Ex. 6 by observing that E^* is also reflexive).

9) The Banach-Steinhaus Theorem (cf. § 2, Th. 1) may be extended as follows: Let T_n be a sequence of bounded linear transformations, defined on the complete Banach space E. Then, if $G \subset E$ is of the second category in E (cf. § 10), and the sequence $\| T_n f \|$ is bounded for each $f \in G$, the transformations T_n are uniformly bounded, that is, there exists a number $M \geqslant 0$ such that $\| T_n \| \leqslant M$ for all n. In other words, if there exists a sequence of elements f_n such that $\| f_n \| \leqslant 1$ and $\lim\sup \| T_n f_n \| = \infty$, the set X of all f for which the sequence $\| T_n f \|$ is bounded is of the first category in E (hence $X \neq E$ by § 10, Th. 5).

(Let $X_i (i = 1, 2, \ldots)$ be the set of all f satisfying $\| T_n f \| \leqslant i$ for all n. Then all X_i are closed, and $X = \Sigma_{i=1}^{\infty} X_i$. Supposing that X is of the second category, one at least of the $X_i = \overline{X}_i$ contains a sphere K (centre f_0, radius ρ). If therefore $g = f - f_0$, $\| g \| \leqslant \rho$, then $f \in K$, so that $\| T_n g \| \leqslant \| T_n f \| + \| T_n f_0 \| \leqslant 2i$ for all n. In particular $\| \rho f_n \| \leqslant \rho$, hence $\| T_n(\rho f_n) \| \leqslant 2i$ or $\| T_n f_n \| \leqslant 2i/\rho$ for all n, in contradiction with $\lim\sup \| T_n f_n \| = \infty$).

10) Let $1 \leqslant p < \infty$, $1/p + 1/q = 1$, Δ μ-measurable, and $f_n(x) \in L_p(\Delta, \mu)$ $(n = 1, 2, \ldots)$. Then, if $\lim\sup \| f_n \|_p = \infty$, there exists a function $g(x) \in L_q(\Delta, \mu)$ such that $\lim\sup | \int_\Delta f_n(x) g(x)\, d\mu | = \infty$.

(Let $h_n(x) = | f_n(x) |^{p-1} / \| f_n \|^{p/q} \operatorname{sgn} f_n(x)$. Then $h_n(x) \in L_q$ and $\| h_n \|_q = 1$.

Defining T_n on L_q by $T_n h = \int_\Delta f_n(x)h(x)\,d\mu$, we have $T_n h_n = \int_\Delta |f_n|^p\,d\mu/\|f_n\|^{p/q} = \|f_n\|^p/\|f_n\|^{p/q} = \|f_n\|$, hence $\limsup \|T_n h_n\| = \infty$. It follows from the preceding example that there exists a set $L_q - X$ (of the second category) such that for every $g(x) \in L_q - X$ we have $\limsup |\int_\Delta f_n g\,d\mu| = \infty$).

11) Let Δ be μ-measurable and $f_n(x) \in L_\infty(\Delta, \mu)$ $(n = 1, 2, \ldots)$. Then, if $\limsup \|f_n\|_\infty = \infty$, there exists a function $g(x) \in L(\Delta, \mu)$ such that $\limsup |\int_\Delta f_n(x)g(x)\,d\mu| = \infty$.

(Let $E_n \subset \Delta$ be a set of finite positive measure $\mu(E_n)$ such that $|f_n(x)| > \|f_n\|_\infty/2$ for $x \in E_n$. Defining $h_n(x) = 1/\mu(E_n)\,\mathrm{sgn}\, f_n(x)$ for $x \in E_n$, and $h_n(x) = 0$ elsewhere, we have $h_n(x) \in L$ and $\|h_n\|_1 = 1$. Defining now T_n on L by $T_n h = \int_\Delta f_n(x)h(x)d\mu$, we see that $T_n h_n = \int_{E_n} |f_n|\,d\mu/\mu(E_n) \geqslant \|f_n\|_\infty/2$, hence $\limsup \|T_n h_n\| = \infty$. It follows that there exists a set $L - X$ (of the second category) such that every $g(x) \in L - X$ satisfies $\limsup |\int_\Delta f_n g\,d\mu| = \infty$).

12) For $p = 1$ and μ Lebesgue measure in a Euclidean space, the statement of Ex. 10 may be extended: Let Δ be a finite interval, and $f_n(x) \in L(\Delta)$ $(n = 1, 2, \ldots)$. Then, if $\limsup \|f_n\| = \infty$, there exists a continuous $g(x)$ on Δ such that $\limsup |\int_\Delta f_n(x)g(x)dx| = \infty$.

(To every f_n may be assigned a bounded function g_n such that $\|f_n - g_n\| \leqslant 1/4$. Let $|g_n(x)| \leqslant N$ in Δ. Then there exists a continuous $h_n(x)$ such that $\int_\Delta |h_n - 1/\mathrm{sgn}\, g_n|\,dx < 1/4N$ (cf. Ch. 6, Ex. 8).

Evidently we may suppose that $|h_n(x)| \leqslant 2$. Then $|\int_\Delta (f_n - g_n)h_n\,dx| \leqslant 1/2$ and $|\int_\Delta g_n(h_n - 1/\mathrm{sgn}\, g_n)\,dx| \leqslant 1/4$. Observing that $\int_\Delta f_n h_n\,dx = \int_\Delta (f_n - g_n)h_n\,dx + \int_\Delta g_n(h_n - 1/\mathrm{sgn}\, g_n)\,dx + \int_\Delta |g_n|\,dx$, we see that $|\int_\Delta f_n h_n\,dx| \geqslant \|g_n\| - 1/2 - 1/4$. Since moreover $\|g_n\| \geqslant \|f_n\| - 1/4$, we find $|\int_\Delta f_n h_n\,dx| \geqslant \|f_n\| - 1$. Defining now T_n on the Banach space $C(\Delta)$, the space of all continuous functions in Δ (cf. Ch. 6, Ex. 9), by $T_n h = \int_\Delta f_n h dx$, we have shown that $\|T_n h_n\| \geqslant \|f_n\| - 1$, hence $\limsup \|T_n h_n\| = \infty$. It follows that there exists a set $C(\Delta) - X$ (of the second category) such that every $g(x) \in C(\Delta) - X$ satisfies $\limsup |\int_\Delta f_n g\,dx| = \infty$).

13) For $p = 1$ and μ Lebesgue measure in a Euclidean space, the statement in § 3, Th. 2 may be extended: Let Δ be a finite interval. Then, if the measurable function $f(x)$ has the property that $f(x)g(x)$ is summable over Δ for every continuous $g(x)$, we have $f(x) \in L(\Delta)$.

(Let $f_n(x) = f(x)$ for $|f(x)| \leqslant n$, and $f_n(x) = 0$ elsewhere in Δ. Supposing that $f(x)$ is not summable, we have $\lim \|f_n\| = \infty$, so that, by the preceding example, there exists a continuous $g(x)$ such that $\limsup |\int_\Delta f_n g\,dx| = \infty$. But $\lim f_n g = fg$, $|f_n g| \leqslant |fg|$, hence $\lim \int_\Delta f_n g\,dx = \int_\Delta fg dx$).

14) Let T_{pq} be a double sequence of bounded linear transformations, defined on the complete Banach space E (the range of T_{pq} may be different for different p). Then, if $\limsup_{q\to\infty} \|T_{pq}\| = \infty$ for all p, there exists a set $X \subset E$ of the second category such that $\limsup_{q\to\infty} \|T_{pq} f\| = \infty$ $(p = 1, 2, \ldots)$ for all $f \in X$.

(For given p the set H_p of all $f \in E$ for which $\limsup_{q\to\infty} \|T_{pq} f\|$ is finite, is of the first category by Ex. 9. The same is therefore true of $\Sigma_{p=1}^\infty H_p$, so that $X = E - \Sigma_{p=1}^\infty H_p$ has the desired property).

15) Let T_{pq} be a double sequence of bounded linear transformations, defined on the complete Banach space E (the range of T_{pq} may be different for different p). Then, if with every p $(p = 1, 2, \ldots)$ there corresponds an element f_p such that the sequence $T_{pq} f_p$ diverges, there exists a set $X \subset E$ of the second category such that $T_{p1} f, T_{p2} f, \ldots$ diverges for $p = 1, 2, \ldots$ and all $f \in X$.

(For given p we denote by H_p the set of all $f \in E$ such that $T_{p1}f, T_{p2}f, \ldots$ converges. If $\limsup_{q\to\infty} \| T_{pq} \| = \infty$, then H_p is of the first category by Ex. 9; if $\| T_{pq} \| < A_p < \infty$ for all q, we shall prove that H_p is even nowhere dense. Indeed, supposing that $\overline{H}_p$ contains a sphere K, there exists, if $f \in K$ and $\varepsilon > 0$ are given, an element $f' \in H_p$ satisfying $\| f - f' \| < \varepsilon/3A_p$. Observing now that $\| T_{pq}f' - T_{pr}f' \| < \varepsilon/3$ for $q, r > q(\varepsilon, f)$ and $\| T_{pq}(f - f') \| < A_p \| f - f' \| < \varepsilon/3$ for all q, we find $\| T_{pq}f - T_{pr}f \| < \varepsilon$ for $q, r > q(\varepsilon, f)$. The thus established convergence in K is easily extended onto the whole space E, in contradiction with our hypothesis. H_p is therefore in any case of the first category. The same is then true of $\Sigma_{p=1}^{\infty} H_p$, so that $X = E - \Sigma_{p=1}^{\infty} H_p$ has the desired property).

16) If P_1 and P_2 are bounded projections, P_1 on M_1 along N_1 and P_2 on M_2 along N_2, then P_1P_2 is a projection if and only if the following condition is satisfied: If $f \in M_2$, then $P_1f = g + h$, where $g \in M_2$ and $h \in N_1N_2$.

(Note that P_1P_2 is bounded in any case. Let now P_1P_2 be a projection. If $f \in M_2$, we have $P_1f = g + h$ with $g = P_2P_1f \in M_2$ and $h \in N_2$. It remains to prove that $h \in N_1$ as well. Since $P_1f = P_1P_2f = P_1P_2P_1P_2f = P_1P_2P_1f = P_1g$, it follows that $P_1h = P_1(P_1f - g) = P_1P_1f - P_1g = P_1f - P_1g = 0$, hence $h \in N_1$.

Let now for all $f \in M_2$ the decomposition $P_1f = g + h$, $g \in M_2$, $h \in N_1N_2$ hold. Then $P_1P_2P_1P_2f = P_1P_2P_1f = P_1g = P_1(g + h) = P_1f = P_1P_2f$, hence $(P_1P_2)^2f = P_1P_2f$ for all $f \in M_2$. If $f \in N_2$, then $(P_1P_2)^2f = 0$ and $P_1P_2f = 0$. An appeal to § 14, Th. 4 completes the proof).

17) Under the same hypothesis as in the preceding example, $P_1 + P_2$ is a projection if and only if $P_1P_2 = P_2P_1 = O$.

(If $P_1P_2 = P_2P_1 = O$, then it is trivial that $(P_1 + P_2)^2 = P_1 + P_2$. Let now conversely $P_1 + P_2$ be a projection, hence $(P_1 + P_2)^2 = P_1 + P_2$ or $P_1P_2 + P_2P_1 = O$. If $f \in N_1$, then $P_2P_1f = 0$, hence also $P_1P_2f = 0$. If $f \in M_1$, then $P_1P_2f + P_2f = P_1P_2f + P_2P_1f = 0$. Writing $P_2f = g + h$, $g \in M_1$, $h \in N_1$, we have $0 = P_1P_2f + P_2f = P_1(g + h) + g + h = 2g + h$, hence $h = -2g$, so that $g = h = 0$. This shows that $P_2f = 0$, hence $P_1P_2f = P_2P_1f = 0$).

18) Under the same hypothesis as in the preceding examples, we write $P_1 > P_2$ whenever $M_1 \supset M_2$ and $N_1 \subset N_2$. Then we have

1°. If $P_1 > P_2$ and $P_2 > P_3$, then $P_1 > P_3$.

2°. If $P_1 > P_2$, then $P_1^* > P_2^*$.

3°. If $P_1 > P_2$, then $P_1P_2 = P_2P_1 = P_2$.

(The first part is trivial. The second part follows from § 14, Th. 5. To prove the last part, let $f = g + h$, $g \in M_2$, $h \in N_2$, for an arbitrary $f \in E$. Then $P_1P_2f = P_1g = g = P_2f$. Finally $P_2f - P_2P_1f = P_2(f - P_1f) = 0$, since $f - P_1f \in N_1 \subset N_2$).

19) If P_1 and P_2 are bounded permutable projections (that is, $P_1P_2 = P_2P_1$), P_1 on M_1 along N_1 and P_2 on M_2 along N_2, then P_1P_2 is the projection on M along N, where $M = M_1M_2$ and N is the set of all $g + h$, $g \in N_1$, $h \in N_2$.

($P_1P_2 = (P_1P_2)^2$ is trivial. Evidently $M \subset M_1$, since $f \in M$ implies $f = P_1P_2f = P_1(P_2f) \in M_1$. Similarly $M \subset M_2$, hence $M \subset M_1M_2$. Let now $f \in M_1M_2$. Then $P_1P_2f = f$, hence $M_1M_2 \subset M$.

Obviously $N \supset N_1$ and $N \supset N_2$, so that N contains all $g + h$, $g \in N_1$, $h \in N_2$. Let now conversely $f \in N$, hence $P_1P_2f = 0$. Writing $f = g + h$, $g \in M_2$, $h \in N_2$, we have $0 = P_1P_2f = P_1g$, hence $g \in N_1$).

20) Let P_1 and P_2 be bounded projections, P_1 on M_1 along N_1 and P_2 on M_2 along N_2. Then, if $P_1 > P_2$, $Q = P_1 - P_2$ is a projection on M along N, where $M = M_1N_2$ and N is the set of all $g + h$, $g \in M_2$, $h \in N_1$.

($P_1 > P_2$ implies $P_1P_2 = P_2P_1 = P_2$, hence $(P_1 - P_2)^2 = P_1^2 - P_1P_2 - P_2P_1 + P_2^2 = P_1 - P_2$. If $f \in M_1N_2$, then $P_1f = f$ and $P_2f = 0$, hence $(P_1 - P_2)f = f$, so that $M \supset M_1N_2$. If conversely $f \in M$, then $(P_1 - P_2)f = f$, so that $P_1f = P_1(P_1 - P_2)f = (P_1^2 - P_1P_2)f = (P_1 - P_2)f = f$, hence $f \in M_1$. Also $P_2f = P_2(P_1 - P_2)f = 0$, hence $f \in N_2$. This shows that $M = M_1N_2$.

Observe now that $Qf = 0$ for $f \in M_2$ and $f \in N_1$, so that N contains all $g + h$, $g \in M_2$, $h \in N_1$. Let now conversely $Qf = 0$, hence $P_1f = P_2f$. Then $f = P_2f + (f - P_2f) = P_2f + (f - P_1f)$ with $P_2f \in M_2$ and $f - P_1f \in N_1$).

21) Let M and N be linear subspaces of the Banach space E with the property (Ext.). Then, if the annihilators M° and N° have only the null element in common, E is the closure of the set of all $g + h$, $g \in M$, $h \in N$.

(Supposing that there is an $f_0 \in E$ not belonging to this closure, there exists an $f^* \in E^*$ such that $f^*(f_0) = 1$, $f^*(f) = 0$ for all $f \in M$ and all $f \in N$. Then $f^* \neq 0$ belongs to both M° and N°, which is a contradiction).

22) Let the complete reflexive Banach space E have the property (Ext.), and let P_n be a sequence of projections for which $P_n < P_{n+1}$, $\| P_n \| \leqslant K$ ($n = 1, 2, \ldots$). P_n is the projection on M_n along N_n, so that P_n^* is the projection on $(M)_n = N_n^\circ$ along $(N)_n = M_n^\circ$. Let M be the smallest linear subspace containing all M_n, and let $N = \Pi_{n=1}^{\infty} N_n$. The subspaces (M) and (N) of E^* are defined similarly. Then

1°. $(M) = N^\circ$, $(N) = M^\circ$, $M = (N)^\circ$, $N = (M)^\circ$.

2°. E is the direct sum of M and N; E^* is the direct sum of (M) and (N).

3°. The projection P on M along N is bounded, $\| P \| \leqslant K$; the projection P^* on (N) along (M) is bounded, $\| P^* \| \leqslant K$ [8].

(Since $(N)_n = M_n^\circ$ and $(N) \subset (N)_n$, we have $(N) \subset M_n^\circ$ ($n = 1, 2, \ldots$). Hence $(N) \subset M^\circ$. Let now $f^* \in M^\circ$. Then $f^* \in M_n^\circ = (N)_n$ ($n = 1, 2, \ldots$) so that $f^* \in (N)$. Hence $(N) = M^\circ$, and, by § 14, Th. 8, $M = M^{\circ\circ} = (N)^\circ$.

Since $(M)_n = N_n^\circ$, so that $(M)_n \subset N^\circ$ ($n = 1, 2, \ldots$), we have $(M) \subset N^\circ$ which implies $(M)^\circ \supset N^{\circ\circ} = N$. Let now $f \in (M)^\circ$. Then $f \in (M)_n^\circ = N_n^{\circ\circ} = N_n$ ($n = 1, 2, \ldots$), so that $f \in N$. Hence $(M)^\circ = N$, and, by § 14, Th. 8, $(M) = (M)^{\circ\circ} = N^\circ$.

Let now $f \in M$, $g \in N$. Then there exist elements $f_n \in M_n$ such that $f = \lim f_n$, so that $\| f_n \| = \| P_n(f_n + g) \| \leqslant K \| f_n + g \|$, which involves $\| f \| \leqslant K \| f + g \|$. If therefore f belongs to both M and N, we have $f \in M$, $g = -f \in N$, hence $\| f \| \leqslant K \| f - f \| = 0$, or $f = 0$. Furthermore the direct sum of M and N is closed. Indeed, if $f_n + g_n$ ($f_n \in M$, $g_n \in N$) converges, then f_n converges by $\| f_m - f_n \| \leqslant K \| f_m + g_m - (f_n + g_n) \|$, hence $\lim f_n = f_0 \in M$. Then also $\lim g_n = g_0 \in N$, so that $\lim (f_n + g_n) = f_0 + g_0$. Since $\| P_n^* \| = \| P_n \| \leqslant K$ and $P_{n+1}^* > P_n^*$, the same facts hold for (M) and (N).

Having thus proved that $M^\circ = (N)$ and $N^\circ = (M)$ have only the null element in common, the preceding example shows that E is the closure of the direct sum of M and N. But, this direct sum being closed itself, E must be identical with the direct sum of M and N. A similar argument applies to (M) and (N).

If $f \in M$, $g \in N$, we have already seen that $\| P(f + g) \| = \| f \| \leqslant K \| f + g \|$, hence $\| P \| \leqslant K$. Finally $\| P^* \| = \| P \| \leqslant K$).

23) With the notations of the preceding example, the projection P has the following properties:

1°. $\lim \| Pf - P_n f \| = 0$ for any $f \in E$.

2°. $P > P_n$ $(n = 1, 2, \ldots)$. If Q is a bounded projection such that $Q > P_n$ $(n = 1, 2, \ldots)$, then $Q > P$.

3°. If T is a bounded linear transformation on E with range in E, and if $P_n T = T P_n$ $(n = 1, 2, \ldots)$, then $PT = TP$.

($P > P_n$ follows from $M \supset M_n$, $N \subset N_n$; hence $P_n P = P_n$. Let now $f \in E$. Then $Pf \in M$, and there exist elements $g_n \in M_n$ with $\lim g_n = Pf$. This implies $\| Pf - P_n f \| \leqslant \| Pf - g_n \| + \| g_n - P_n f \| = \| Pf - g_n \| + \| P_n(g_n - Pf) \|$, which converges to zero on account of $\| P_n \| \leqslant K$.

If $Q > P_n$, then $M_Q \supset M_n$ and $N_Q \subset N_n$ $(n = 1, 2, \ldots)$, hence $M_Q \supset M$ and $N_Q \subset N$, so that $Q > P$.

Since $P_n Tf = TP_n f$, $\lim P_n Tf = PTf$, $\lim TP_n f = TPf$, we have $PTf = TPf$.

The last statement is evident).

24) If the complete Banach space E is uniformly convex, and $f^* \in E^*$ satisfies $\| f^* \| \neq 0$, then there exists a unique $f_0 \in E$ such that $\| f_0 \| = 1$ and $f^*(f_0) = \| f^* \|$.

(We may suppose $\| f^* \| = 1$. Then there exists a sequence $f_n \in E$ with $\| f_n \| = 1$ and $\lim f^*(f_n) = 1$. It follows that $\lim \| f_m + f_n \| = 2$ as $m, n \to \infty$, on account of $\| f_m + f_n \| \geqslant f^*(f_m + f_n)$. Hence, by the uniform convexity, $\lim \| f_m - f_n \| = 0$. Let $f_0 = \lim f_n$. Then $\| f_0 \| = 1$ and $f^*(f_0) = \lim f^*(f_n) = 1 = \| f^* \|$. If there is a second element f_1 with $\| f_1 \| = 1$ and $f^*(f_1) = 1$, we have $2 = f^*(f_0 + f_1) \leqslant \| f_0 + f_1 \|$, hence $\| f_0 + f_1 \| = 2$, which implies $\| f_0 - f_1 \| = 0$. It follows that $f_1 = f_0$).

25) Let E_i $(i = 1, 2, \ldots)$ be a sequence of complete Banach spaces and let $1 < p < \infty$. Let $E = l_p(E_i)$ be the class of all sequences $f = \{f_1, f_2, \ldots\}$ with $f_i \in E_i$ and $\| f \| = (\Sigma_{i=1}^{\infty} \| f_i \|^p)^{1/p}$. Then, with the obvious definitions of addition and multiplication by a complex α, E is a complete Banach space.

26) With the notations of the preceding example, $E^* = \{l_p(E_i)\}^* = l_q(E_i^*)$, where $1/p + 1/q = 1$ [13].

(Let $f^* \in E^*$; let $(f)_i \in E$ have the form $\{0, 0, \ldots, 0, f_i, 0, \ldots\}$, and define $f_i^* \in E_i^*$ by $f_i^*(f_i) = f^*\{(f)_i\}$. Then there exist $f_i \in E_i$ such that $\| f_i \| = 1$ and $\| f_i^* \|/2 \leqslant f_i^*(f_i) \leqslant \| f_i^* \|$. Since $\| f_i \| = 1$, the sequence $\{\alpha_i f_i\}$ belongs to E if and only if $\Sigma \, | \alpha_i |^p < \infty$. Furthermore, if $f^j = \{\alpha_1 f_1, \ldots, \alpha_j f_j, 0, 0, \ldots\}$ and $f = \{\alpha_i f_i\} \in E$, then $\lim f^j = f$, hence $\lim f^*(f^j) = f^*(f)$. But $f^*(f^j) = \Sigma_{i=1}^{j} \alpha_i f_i^*(f_i)$, so that $\Sigma_{i=1}^{\infty} \alpha_i f_i^*(f_i)$ converges if $\Sigma \, | \alpha_i |^p < \infty$. This shows that $\Sigma \, | f_i^*(f_i) |^q < \infty$ (cf. § 3, Th. 3), hence also $\Sigma \, \| f_i^* \|^q < \infty$. With every $f^* \in E^*$ corresponds therefore an element $\{f_1^*, f_2^*, \ldots\} \in l_q(E_i^*)$ such that for any $f = \{f_i\} \in E$ we have $f^*(f) = \Sigma f_i^*(f_i)$. Conversely, if $\{f_i^*\} \in l_q(E_i^*)$ and $f = \{f_i\} \in l_p(E_i)$, then

$$\Sigma \, | f_i^*(f_i) | \leqslant \Sigma \, \| f_i^* \| . \| f_i \| \leqslant (\Sigma \, \| f_i^* \|^q)^{1/q} . \| f \|,$$

which shows that this sequence $\{f_i^*\}$ defines an $f^* \in E^*$ with $f^*(f) = \Sigma f_i^*(f_i)$. Evidently $\| f^* \| = (\Sigma \, \| f_i^* \|^q)^{1/q}$ (compare the proof of § 3, Th. 3)).

27) With the notations of the preceding example, E is reflexive if and only if all E_i are reflexive.

(Follows from $E = l_p(E_i)$, $E^{**} = l_p(E_i^{**})$).

REFERENCES

[1] S. BANACH and H. STEINHAUS, Sur le principe de la condensation de singularités, Fundamenta Math. 9 (1927), 50—61.

[2] F. RIESZ, Zur Theorie des Hilbertschen Raumes, Acta sci. Math. Szeged 7 (1934), 34—38.

[3] A. C. ZAANEN, On a certain class of Banach spaces, Annals of Math. 47 (1946), 654—666.

[4] For $p = 2$ by M. FRÉCHET, Sur les ensembles de fonctions et les opérations linéaires, C.R. Acad. Sc., Paris 144 (1907), 1414—1416.
For $1 < p < \infty$ by F. RIESZ, Untersuchungen über Systeme integrierbarer Funktionen, Math. Annalen 69 (1910), 449—497.
For $p = 1$ by H. STEINHAUS, Additive und stetige Funktionaloperationen, Math. Zeitschrift 5 (1918), 186—221.

[5] M. M. DAY, Inner-product spaces, Transactions Amer. Math. Soc. 62 (1947), 320—337, in particular § 7.

[6] H. HAHN, Über lineare Gleichungen in linearen Räumen, Journal für reine und angew. Math. 157 (1927), 214—229.
S. BANACH, Sur les fonctionnelles linéaires I, II, Studia Math. 1 (1929), 211—216, 223—239.

[7] H. F. BOHNENBLUST and A. SOBCZYK, Extension of functionals on complex linear spaces, Bulletin Amer. Math. Soc. 44 (1938), 91—93.

[8] E. R. LORCH, On a calculus of operators in reflexive vector spaces, Transactions Amer. Math. Soc. 45 (1939), 217—234.

[9] B. J. PETTIS, A note on regular Banach spaces, Bulletin Amer. Math. Soc. 44 (1938), 420—428.

[10] A different proof may be found in M. H. STONE, Linear transformations in Hilbert space, New York (1932) p. 59.

[11] A. SARD, Integral representation of remainders, Duke Math. Journal 15 (1948), 333—345.

[12] F. RIESZ, Sur les opérations fonctionnelles linéaires, C. R. Acad. Sc., Paris 149 (1909), 974—977.

[13] M. M. DAY, Reflexive Banach spaces not isomorphic to uniformly convex spaces, Bulletin Amer. Math. Soc. 47 (1941), 313—317.

Chapter 8

BANACH SPACES OF FINITE DIMENSION

§ 1. Recapitulation

In the present chapter we consider Banach spaces of finite dimension [1]. For the sake of completeness we recapitulate here the properties which have already been proved for spaces of this kind in the preceding chapters.

In Ch. 6, § 4 it was shown that every Banach space E of finite dimension n is a complete space, and that every set $f_1, \ldots, f_n$ of n linearly independent elements is a complete set in E. A set $\{f\} = \{f_1, \ldots, f_n\}$ of this kind is sometimes called a *coordinate system* in E, and if $f = \sum_{i=1}^n \alpha_i f_i$, the complex numbers α_i $(i = 1, \ldots, n)$ are called the *coordinates* of f in the coordinate system $\{f\}$. From the proof of Ch. 6, § 4, Th. 2 it follows that, given the linearly independent elements $g_1, \ldots, g_m$ $(m < n)$, there exist elements $g_{m+1}, \ldots, g_n$ such that $\{g\} = \{g_1, \ldots, g_n\}$ is a coordinate system. In other words, if E' is a linear subspace of dimension $m < n$, there exists a linear subspace E'' of dimension $n - m$ such that E is the direct sum of E' and E''. If, conversely, it is known that E is the direct sum of the linear subspaces E' and E'', the sum of the dimensions of E' and E'' is n.

From Ch. 6, § 5, where we discussed factorspaces, it is clear that if E is the direct sum of E' and E'', there is a one-to-one correspondence between E' and the factorspace E/E''.

In Ch. 7, § 7, Th. 2 we have proved that, given the coordinate system $\{f\} = \{f_1, \ldots, f_n\}$ in E, there exists a coordinate system $\{f^*\} = \{f_1^*, \ldots, f_n^*\}$ in E^* such that $f_i^*(f_j) = 1$ for $i = j$ and $f_i^*(f_j) = 0$ for $i \neq j$. The systems $\{f\}$ and $\{f^*\}$ are sometimes called dual coordinate systems.

Since E is obviously separable, it has the property (Ext.). Furthermore, by Ch. 7, § 8, Th. 6, E is reflexive. By Ch. 7, § 9, Th. 4, strong and weak convergence in E are equivalent, and by Ch. 7, § 12, Th. 3 every linear transformation with domain E is bounded.

If T is a linear transformation with domain E, the linear transfornation T^{-1} exists by Ch. 7, § 11, Th. 2 if and only if $Tf = 0$ implies $f = 0$, in other words, if and only if the elements $Tf_1, \ldots, Tf_n$ are linearly independent whenever $\{f_1, \ldots, f_n\}$ is a coordinate system. If the range of T is contained in E, the statement that $Tf_1, \ldots, Tf_n$ are linearly independent is equivalent with the statement that

$$(\text{domain of } T^{-1}) = (\text{range of } T) = E.$$

Hence:

Theorem 1. *If the range of the linear transformation T on E is contained in E, then T^{-1} exists if and only if the range of T is identical with the whole space E.*

Corollary. *If the range of the linear transformation T of E is contained in E, and T^{-1} exists, then $(T^*)^{-1}$ exists and $(T^{-1})^* = (T^*)^{-1}$.*
Proof. Follows from Ch. 7, § 13, Th. 2.

Definition. *If T is a linear transformation on E into E, then T is called non-singular whenever T^{-1} exists. If T^{-1} does not exist, T is said to be singular.*

We finally observe that if E' is a linear subspace of dimension $m < n$, and if the coordinate system $\{f\} = \{f_1, \ldots, f_n\}$ in E has the property that $\{f_1, \ldots, f_m\}$ is a coordinate system in E', then it follows from Ch. 7, § 14 that the annihilator $(E')^\circ$ of E' has $\{f^*_{m+1}, \ldots, f^*_n\}$ as one of its coordinate systems, where $\{f^*\}$ is the dual system of $\{f\}$. The dimension of $(E')^\circ$ is therefore $n - m$.

§ 2. Matrix of a Linear Transformation

Let $\{f\} = \{f_1, \ldots, f_n\}$ be a coordinate system in E, and T a linear transformation on E into E. Then, for $i = 1, \ldots, n$, Tf_i is a linear combination of $f_1, \ldots, f_n$, hence

$$Tf_i = \Sigma_j \tau_{ji} f_j \ (i = 1, \ldots, n).$$

The set of n^2 complex numbers $\tau_{ij}(i, j = 1, \ldots, n)$, written in the form

$$\text{mat}\,(T) = \{\tau_{ij}\} = \left\| \begin{matrix} \tau_{11} & \tau_{12} & \cdots & \tau_{1n} \\ \tau_{21} & \tau_{22} & \cdots & \tau_{2n} \\ \vdots & & & \vdots \\ \tau_{n1} & \tau_{n2} & \cdots & \tau_{nn} \end{matrix} \right\|,$$

is called the *matrix* of T in the coordinate system $\{f\}$. The numbers $\tau_{i1}, \tau_{i2}, \ldots, \tau_{in}$ form the i-th row; the numbers $\tau_{1j}, \tau_{2j}, \ldots, \tau_{nj}$ form the j-th column; the numbers $\tau_{11}, \tau_{22}, \ldots, \tau_{nn}$ form the principal diagonal of mat (T).

The connection between T, the coordinate system $\{f\}$ and the matrix $\{\tau_{ij}\}$ is therefore given by the following rule: The coefficients of Tf_i, written as a linear combination of $f_1, \ldots, f_n$, form the i-th column of $\{\tau_{ij}\}$.

We observe that, if the coordinate system $\{f\}$ is fixed, mat (T) is completely determined by T, and T is completely determined by mat (T).

If T is non-singular, we shall also say that mat (T) is a non-singular matrix.

If $\{\tau_{ij}\}$ and $\{\sigma_{ij}\}$ are two matrices and α is a complex number, we define addition of matrices and multiplication of a matrix by α by

$$\{\tau_{ij}\} + \{\sigma_{ij}\} = \{\tau_{ij} + \sigma_{ij}\},$$

$$\alpha\{\tau_{ij}\} = \{\alpha\tau_{ij}\}.$$

The *null matrix* is defined to be the matrix for which $\tau_{ij} = 0$ for all $i, j = 1, \ldots, n$, and the *identical matrix* is the matrix which has numbers 1 on the principal diagonal and zeros elsewhere, hence $\tau_{ij} = 1$ for $i = j$ and $\tau_{ij} = 0$ for $i \neq j$. Any matrix $\{\tau_{ij}\}$ for which $\tau_{ij} = 0$ whenever $i \neq j$ is called a *diagonal matrix*. Finally, the *product* $\{\sigma_{ij}\}.\{\tau_{ij}\}$ of the matrices $\{\sigma_{ij}\}$ and $\{\tau_{ij}\}$ is defined by

$$\{\sigma_{ij}\}.\{\tau_{ij}\} = \{\gamma_{ij}\},$$

where

$$\gamma_{ij} = \Sigma_{k=1}^{n} \sigma_{ik}\tau_{kj}.$$

Theorem 1. *If S and T are linear transformations on E into E, if α and β are complex, if O is the null transformation and I is the identical transformation, then*

$$\begin{aligned} &\textit{mat}\ (\alpha S + \beta T) = \alpha\ \textit{mat}\ (S) + \beta\ \textit{mat}\ (T), \\ &\textit{mat}\ (O) \quad = \textit{null matrix}, \\ &\textit{mat}\ (I) \quad = \textit{identical matrix}, \\ &\textit{mat}\ (ST) = \textit{mat}\ (S).\textit{mat}\ (T). \end{aligned}$$

Proof. It is only the last statement which needs a proof, the other statements being evident. Now

$$(ST)f_i = S(Tf_i) = S(\Sigma_k\, \tau_{ki}\, f_k) = \Sigma_k\, \tau_{ki}\, Sf_k =$$

$$\Sigma_{kj}\, \tau_{ki}\sigma_{jk}f_j = \Sigma_j\, (\Sigma_k\, \sigma_{jk}\tau_{ki})f_j = \Sigma_j\, \gamma_{ji}f_j,$$

hence mat $(ST) = \{\gamma_{ij}\} =$ mat (S).mat (T).

Theorem 2. *If* $\{\tau_{ij}\}$ *is the matrix of* T *in the coordinate system* $\{f\}$; $f = \Sigma\, \alpha_i f_i$ *and* $Tf = \Sigma\, \beta_i f_i$ *for an arbitrary* $f \in E$, *then*

$$\beta_i = \Sigma_j\, \tau_{ij}\alpha_j \ (i = 1, \ldots, n).$$

Proof. $\Sigma\, \beta_i f_i = Tf = T(\Sigma\, \alpha_j f_j) = \Sigma\, \alpha_j T f_j =$

$$\Sigma_{ij}\, \alpha_j \tau_{ij} f_i = \Sigma_i\, (\Sigma_j\, \tau_{ij}\alpha_j) f_i.$$

If the linear subspace E' of dimension $m < n$ reduces the linear transformation T, and if the coordinate system $\{f\} = \{f_1, \ldots, f_n\}$ has the property that $\{f_1, \ldots, f_m\}$ is a coordinate system in E', then $Tf_i = \Sigma_j\, \tau_{ji} f_j \in E'$ for $1 \leqslant i \leqslant m$, hence $Tf_i = \Sigma_{j=1}^{m}\, \tau_{ji} f_j$ and $\tau_{ji} = 0$ for $m + 1 \leqslant j \leqslant n$. It follows that the matrix of T in the coordinate system $\{f\}$ has the form

$$\text{mat}\ (T) = \left\| \begin{matrix} [T_1] & [T_3] \\ [0] & [T_2] \end{matrix} \right\|,$$

where $[T_1]$ is a matrix of m rows and m columns, $[T_2]$ a matrix of $n - m$ rows and $n - m$ columns, $[T_3]$ an array of m rows and $n - m$ columns, and $[0]$ an array of $n - m$ rows and m columns consisting only of zeros.

If T is completely reduced by (E', E''), and if $\{f_1, \ldots, f_m\}$ and $\{f_{m+1}, \ldots, f_n\}$ are coordinate systems in E' and E'' respectively, then $[T_3]$ as well contains only zeros.

We add a remark about the matrix of a projection. Let E be the direct sum of E' and E'', and let the coordinate system $\{f\}$ have the property that $\{f_1, \ldots, f_m\}$ and $\{f_{m+1}, \ldots, f_n\}$ are coordinate systems in E' and E'' respectively. If the projection P on E' along E'' has the matrix $\{p_{ij}\}$ in the system $\{f\}$, then $p_{ij} = 0$ for $i \neq j$, $p_{ii} = 1$ for $1 \leqslant i \leqslant m$, and $p_{ii} = 0$ for $m + 1 \leqslant i \leqslant n$.

Theorem 3. *If* $\{f\}$ *and* $\{f^*\}$ *are dual coordinate systems in* E *and* E^* *respectively, and if* mat $(T) = \{\tau_{ij}\}$ *in the system* $\{f\}$, *then* mat $(T^*) = \{\tau_{ij}^*\} = \{\tau_{ji}\}$ *in the system* $\{f^*\}$.

Proof. From $Tf_j = \Sigma_k\, \tau_{kj} f_k$ follows $f_i^*(Tf_j) = \tau_{ij}$, hence

$$(T^* f_i^*)(f_j) = f_i^*(Tf_j) = \tau_{ij} =$$

$$\Sigma_k\, \tau_{ik} f_k^*(f_j) = (\Sigma_k\, \tau_{ik} f_k^*)(f_j).$$

This holds for $j = 1, \ldots, n$, so that $T^* f_i^* = \Sigma_k\, \tau_{ik} f_k^* = \Sigma_j\, \tau_{ij} f_j^*$. But $T^* f_i^* = \Sigma_j\, \tau_{ji}^* f_j^*$, hence $\tau_{ji}^* = \tau_{ij}$ or $\tau_{ij}^* = \tau_{ji}$.

§ 3. Change of Coordinate System

In § 1 we have seen that if the range of the linear transformation T on E is also contained in E, then T is non-singular if and only if T transforms every coordinate system $\{f\}$ into a system $\{g\}$ which is a coordinate system as well. If therefore $\{f\}$ and $\{g\}$ are two coordinate systems, and we write $g_i = Tf_i = \Sigma_j \tau_{ji} f_j$ $(i = 1, \ldots, n)$, then T is non-singular.

Let now S be a linear transformation on E into E. The relation between the matrix $\{\sigma_{ij}\} = \text{mat}\ (S; f)$ in the coordinate system $\{f\}$ and the matrix $\{s_{ij}\} = \text{mat}\ (S; g)$ in the coordinate system $\{g\}$ is then determined by the statement in the following theorem:

Theorem 1. *mat* $(S; g) =$ *mat* (T^{-1}).*mat* $(S; f)$.*mat* (T).

Proof. We have $Sg_i = STf_i = \Sigma_j(\Sigma_k \sigma_{jk}\tau_{ki})f_j$.

On the other hand,

$$Sg_i = \Sigma_k s_{ki} g_k = \Sigma_k s_{ki} Tf_k =$$

$$\Sigma_{kj} s_{ki}\tau_{jk} f_j = \Sigma_j (\Sigma_k \tau_{jk} s_{ki}) f_j.$$

Hence $\Sigma_k \tau_{jk} s_{ki} = \Sigma_k \sigma_{jk}\tau_{ki}$ for $i, j = 1, \ldots, n$, or

$$\text{mat}\ (T).\text{mat}\ (S; g) = \text{mat}\ (S; f).\text{mat}\ (T).$$

Since T^{-1} exists and $T^{-1}T = I$, we have mat (T^{-1}). mat(T) = mat (I), hence

$$\text{mat}\ (S; g) = \text{mat}\ (T^{-1}).\text{mat}\ (S; f).\text{mat}\ (T).$$

§ 4. Range and Null Space. Rank and Nullity

If T is a linear transformation on E into E, its range, denoted by $W(T)$, is a linear subspace of E. By the *null space* $N(T)$ of T we shall mean the set of all $f \in E$ satisfying $Tf = 0$. Evidently $N(T)$ is also a linear subspace of E.

Theorem 1. $(W(T))^\circ = N(T^*)$ *and* $(N(T))^\circ = W(T^*)$.

Proof. If $f^* \in (W(T))^\circ$, then $0 = f^*(Tf) = (T^*f^*)(f)$ for all $f \in E$, hence $T^*f^* = 0$ or $f^* \in N(T^*)$.

If conversely $f^* \in N(T^*)$, then $T^*f^* = 0$, hence $0 = (T^*f^*)(f) = f^*(Tf)$ for all $f \in E$ or $f^* \in (W(T))^\circ$.

This shows that $(W(T))^\circ = N(T^*)$. Then also $(W(T^*))^\circ = N(T^{**}) = N(T)$ since E is reflexive, hence $(N(T))^\circ = (W(T^*))^{\circ\circ} = W(T^*)$.

Definition. *If T is a linear transformation on E into E, the rank $\rho(T)$ of T is the dimension of $W(T)$; the nullity $\nu(T)$ of T is the dimension of $N(T)$.*

Theorem 2. $\rho(T) = \rho(T^*)$ *and* $\nu(T) = n - \rho(T)$.

Proof. Since $N(T^*) = (W(T))^\circ$, and the dimension of $(W(T))^\circ$ is $n - \rho(T)$, we find

$$\nu(T^*) = n - \rho(T).$$

If now $\{f_1, \ldots, f_n\}$ is a coordinate system in E such that $\{f_1, \ldots, f_\nu\}$ is a coordinate system in $N(T)$, and $f = \Sigma \alpha_i f_i$ is arbitrary, then $Tf = \Sigma \alpha_i T f_i = \Sigma_{i=\nu+1}^{n} \alpha_i T f_i$, hence $\rho(T) \leqslant n - \nu(T)$, or

$$\nu(T) \leqslant n - \rho(T) = \nu(T^*).$$

On the other hand, replacing T by T^*, we find

$$\nu(T^*) \leqslant \nu(T^{**}) = \nu(T).$$

This shows that $\nu(T) = \nu(T^*)$. Hence $n - \nu(T^*) = n - \nu(T) = n - \nu(T^{**})$ or $\rho(T) = \rho(T^*)$, and also $\nu(T) = \nu(T^*) = n - \rho(T)$.

Evidently, if $\{f\}$ is a coordinate system in E, $\rho(T)$ is the maximal number of linearly independent Tf_i, or, expressed in terms of the coordinates $\{\tau_{1i}, \tau_{2i}, \ldots, \tau_{ni}\}$ of Tf_i, $\rho(T)$ is the maximal number of linearly independent columns of mat $(T) = \{\tau_{ij}\}$. Since $\rho(T^*) = \rho(T)$ and mat $(T^*) = \{\tau_{ij}^*\} = \{\tau_{ji}\}$, it follows that $\rho(T)$ is also the maximal number of linearly independent rows of mat (T).

Theorem 3. *If T is a linear transformation on E into E, and if E' is an m-dimensional linear subspace of E, then the dimension m' of $T(E')$ (the linear subspace of all Tf with $f \in E'$) satisfies $m' \geqslant m - \nu(T)$.*

Proof. Let E'' be any linear subspace for which E is the direct sum of E' and E'', so that the dimension of E'' is $n - m$. Then the dimension of $T(E'')$ is $\leqslant n - m$. Since the dimension of $T(E)$ is $n - \nu(T)$, and since this dimension at most equals the sum of the dimensions of $T(E')$ and $T(E'')$, we have

$$n - \nu(T) \leqslant m' + n - m,$$

hence

$$m' \geqslant m - \nu(T).$$

Theorem 4. *If A and B are linear transformations on E into E, then*

$$\rho(A + B) \leqslant \rho(A) + \rho(B), \tag{1}$$

$$\rho(AB) \leqslant \min\,[\rho(A), \rho(B)] \tag{2}$$

and

$$\nu(AB) \leqslant \nu(A) + \nu(B). \tag{3}$$

If B is non-singular, then

(4) $$\rho(AB) = \rho(BA) = \rho(A).$$

Proof. Formula (1) is a consequence of the fact that the dimension of the subspace of all $(A + B)f$ equals at most the sum of the dimensions of the subspaces of all Af and all Bf.

We now shall prove (2) and (4). Since $(AB)f = A(Bf)$, the range $W(AB)$ is contained in the range $W(A)$; hence $\rho(AB) \leqslant \rho(A)$. Applying this to B^*A^*, we obtain $\rho(AB) = \rho(AB)^* = \rho(B^*A^*) \leqslant \rho(B^*) = \rho(B)$. Hence

$$\rho(AB) \leqslant \min [\rho(A), \rho(B)].$$

If B is non-singular, then

$$\rho(A) = \rho(AB.B^{-1}) \leqslant \rho(AB)$$

and

$$\rho(A) = \rho(B^{-1}.BA) \leqslant \rho(BA),$$

so that, in virtue of (2),

$$\rho(AB) = \rho(BA) = \rho(A).$$

Finally, to prove (3), we observe that the dimension of $W(B)$ is $n - \nu(B)$ by Theorem 2, so that the dimension of $W(AB)$ is $\geqslant n - \nu(B) - \nu(A)$ by Theorem 3. Hence $n - \nu(AB) \geqslant n - \nu(B) - \nu(A)$, or $\nu(AB) \leqslant \nu(A) + \nu(B)$.

Theorem 5. *If T is a linear transformation on E into E, there exist two non-singular linear transformations T_1 and T_2 such that T_1T and TT_2 are projections.*

Proof. Let $\{f_1, \ldots, f_n\}$ be a coordinate system in E such that $\{f_1, \ldots, f_\rho\}$ is a coordinate system in the range $W(T)$. Then, for $i = 1, \ldots, \rho$, there exist elements g_i such that $Tg_i = f_i$. Let now $g_{\rho+1}, \ldots, g_n$ be a coordinate system in the null space $N(T)$ of T. We shall prove that $g_1, \ldots, g_n$ is a coordinate system in E. Indeed, let $\Sigma_{i=1}^n \alpha_i g_i = 0$. Then

$$0 = T(\Sigma_{i=1}^n \alpha_i g_i) = \Sigma_{i=1}^\rho \alpha_i f_i,$$

hence $\alpha_1 = \ldots = \alpha_\rho = 0$. But then also $\Sigma_{i=\rho+1}^n \alpha_i g_i = 0$, hence $\alpha_{\rho+1} = \ldots = \alpha_n = 0$.

The non-singular linear transformation T_1 is now defined by $T_1 f_i = g_i$ $(i = 1, \ldots, n)$. Then T_1T is a projection, since $T_1Tg_i = T_1f_i = g_i$ for $i = 1, \ldots, \rho$, and $T_1Tg_i = T_10 = 0$ for $i = \rho + 1, \ldots, n$.

Let now T^* be the adjoint transformation of T. Then, by what we have just proved, there exists a non-singular linear transformation A (on E^* into E^*) such that AT^* is a projection. It follows that $(AT^*)^*$ is a projection in $E^{**} = E$. But $(AT^*)^* = T^{**}A^* = TA^*$, so that, writing $A^* = T_2$, and observing that A^* is non-singular since A is non-singular ($\rho(A^*) = \rho(A) = n$), we see that TT_2 is a projection with non-singular T_2.

Corollary. *Given the matrix $\{\tau_{ij}\}$, there exist two non-singular matrices $\{p_{ij}\}$ and $\{q_{ij}\}$ such that the product $\{p_{ij}\}.\{\tau_{ij}\}.\{q_{ij}\}$ is a diagonal matrix.*

Proof. Considering $\{\tau_{ij}\}$ as the matrix (on a certain coordinate system $\{f\}$) of a linear transformation T on E, there exists a non-singular T_1 with matrix $\{t_{ij}\}$ such that T_1T is a projection. We observe that

$$\text{mat}\,(T_1T;f) = \{t_{ij}\}.\{\tau_{ij}\}.$$

Introducing now the coordinate system $\{g\}$ on which mat (T_1T) is a diagonal matrix (cf. § 2), we have by § 3, Th. 1

$$\text{mat}\,(T_1T;g) = \text{mat}\,(Q^{-1}).\{t_{ij}\}.\{\tau_{ij}\}.\text{mat}\,(Q),$$

where Q is non-singular. Hence, writing mat $(Q) = \{q_{ij}\}$ and mat $(Q^{-1}).\{t_{ij}\} = \{p_{ij}\}$, we see that $\{p_{ij}\}.\{\tau_{ij}\}.\{q_{ij}\}$ is a diagonal matrix with non-singular $\{p_{ij}\}$ and $\{q_{ij}\}$.

§ 5. Determinants. The Spectrum of a Linear Transformation

If T is a linear transformation on E into E, we shall write $\Delta(T;f)$ for the determinant of mat (T) on the coordinate system $\{f\}$. The following properties of $\Delta(T;f)$ will be used:

1°. $\Delta(O;f) = 0$, where O is the null transformation.

2°. $\Delta(I;f) = 1$, where I is the identical transformation.

3°. $\Delta(T_1T_2;f) = \Delta(T_1;f).\Delta(T_2;f)$.

4°. $\Delta(T;f) = \Delta(T^*;f)$.

5°. T is singular if and only if $\Delta(T;f) = 0$.

6°. $\Delta(T - \lambda I;f)$ is a polynomial of degree n in the complex variable λ; the coefficient of λ^n is $(-1)^n$.

Theorem 1. *If $\{f\}$ and $\{g\}$ are two different coordinate systems in E, then $\Delta(T;f) = \Delta(T;g)$ for every T.*

Proof. By § 3, Th. 1 there exists a non-singular transformation Q such that mat $(T;g) = \text{mat}\,(Q^{-1}).\text{mat}\,(T;f).\text{mat}\,(Q)$, hence

$$\Delta(T;g) = \Delta(Q^{-1};f).\Delta(T;f).\Delta(Q;f) =$$
$$\Delta(T;f).\Delta(Q^{-1}Q;f) = \Delta(T;f).\Delta(I;f) = \Delta(T;f).$$

Since, as a consequence of this theorem, $\Delta(T; f)$ is independent of any coordinate system $\{f\}$, we shall write $\Delta(T)$ instead of $\Delta(T; f)$.

Definition. *If T is a linear transformation on E into E, the polynomial $\Delta(T - \lambda I)$ in λ is called the characteristic polynomial of T; the equation $\Delta(T - \lambda I) = 0$ is called the characteristic equation of T.*

If there exists an element $f \neq 0$ and a complex number λ such that $Tf = \lambda f$, this element is called a characteristic element of T, and λ is said to be the corresponding characteristic value.

Theorem 2. *The complex number λ is a characteristic value of T if and only if λ is a root of the characteristic equation $\Delta(T - \lambda I) = 0$. Every linear transformation T of the kind considered here has therefore n characteristic values (multiplicities properly counted).*

Proof. We have $Tf = \lambda f$, $f \neq 0$, if and only if $(T - \lambda I)f = 0$, $f \neq 0$. This however means that $T - \lambda I$ is singular, which is equivalent to $\Delta(T - \lambda I) = 0$.

Definition. *The multiplicity of the root λ of the characteristic equation of T is called the algebraic multiplicity of the characteristic value λ; if λ is a simple root, then λ is said to be a simple characteristic value. The set of n characteristic values, with multiplicities properly counted, is the spectrum of T.*

Theorem 3. *The complex number λ does not belong to the spectrum of T if and only if $(T - \lambda I)^{-1}$ exists.*

Proof. The complex number λ does not belong to the spectrum of T if and only if $\Delta(T - \lambda I) \neq 0$, in other words, if and only if $T - \lambda I$ is non-singular. The non-singularity of $T - \lambda I$ however is equivalent to the existence of $(T - \lambda I)^{-1}$.

We observe that if $Tf = \lambda f$, then

$$T^2 f = T(Tf) = \lambda Tf = \lambda^2 f;$$

more generally (by induction) $T^n f = \lambda^n f$ for any integer $n \geqslant 2$, where $T^n f$ is defined to be $T(T^{n-1} f)$.

Furthermore, if P is a projection (so that $P^2 = P$), and $Pf = \lambda f$, $f \neq 0$, then $\lambda^2 f = P^2 f = Pf = \lambda f$, hence $\lambda^2 = \lambda$. This implies that any characteristic value of a projection is either 0 or 1.

Definition. *If λ is a characteristic value of T, then the set of all elements f satisfying $Tf = \lambda f$ is a linear subspace of E. The dimension of this subspace is called the geometric multiplicity of the characteristic value λ.*

Theorem 4. *The geometric multiplicity of any characteristic value λ_0 of T is at most equal to its algebraic multiplicity.*

Proof. Let $m \leqslant n$ be the geometric multiplicity of the characteristic value λ_0. If E' is the linear subspace of dimension m, consisting of all f satisfying $Tf = \lambda_0 f$, then T is reduced by E'. Choosing now a coordinate system in E', extending it onto the whole space E and expressing mat $(T) = \{\tau_{ij}\}$ in this extended coordinate system, we have $\tau_{ii} = \lambda_0$ for $i = 1, \ldots, m$, whereas $\tau_{ij} = 0$ for all other elements in the first m columns. It follows that $\Delta(T - \lambda I)$ contains the factor $(\lambda_0 - \lambda)^m$, which shows that the algebraic multiplicity of λ_0 is at least m.

To show that the geometric multiplicity of a characteristic value may actually be smaller than its algebraic multiplicity, we consider the Banach space E of dimension n consisting of all polynomials $f \equiv f(x) = \alpha_0 + \alpha_1 x + \ldots + \alpha_{n-1}x^{n-1}$ in the linear interval $0 \leqslant x \leqslant 1$, where we suppose that $n \geqslant 2$. Addition and multiplication by a complex number α are defined in the usual way, and $\| f \| = \max | f(x) |$ on $0 \leqslant x \leqslant 1$. The elements $\{1, x, x^2, \ldots, x^{n-1}\}$ form a coordinate system. Defining the linear transformation D on E by

$$Df = D(\alpha_0 + \alpha_1 x + \ldots + \alpha_{n-1}x^{n-1}) = \alpha_1 + 2\alpha_2 x + 3\alpha_3 x^2 + \ldots + (n-1)\alpha_{n-1}x^{n-2},$$

the element $f \neq 0$ is a characteristic element of D if $Df = \lambda f$ for some λ, that is, if

$$\alpha_1 + 2\alpha_2 x + \ldots + (n-1)\alpha_{n-1}x^{n-2} = \lambda(\alpha_0 + \alpha_1 x + \ldots + \alpha_{n-1}x^{n-1}).$$

Supposing that $\lambda \neq 0$, we should find $\alpha_{n-1} = \alpha_{n-2} = \ldots = \alpha_0 = 0$ in succession; hence $\lambda = 0$. But then $f = \alpha_0$. The transformation D has therefore only the characteristic value $\lambda = 0$, so that the algebraic multiplicity of this characteristic value is $n \geqslant 2$. The geometric multiplicity however is only one.

§ 6. The Superdiagonal Form of a Matrix

Theorem 1. *If T is a linear transformation on E into E, there exist n linear subspaces $E_1, E_2, \ldots, E_n$ such that:*

1°. *Every* E_i $(i = 1, \ldots, n)$ *reduces* T.
2°. *The dimension of* E_i *is* i.
3°. $E_1 \subset E_2 \subset \ldots \subset E_{n-1} \subset E_n = E$.

Proof. For $n = 1$ the theorem is trivial; let us suppose now that the statement is true for $n - 1$. Considering the transformation T^* on E^*, we observe that it has at least one characteristic element f^*; T^* is therefore reduced by the one-dimensional subspace of all multiples of f^*. Denoting by E_{n-1} the annihilator of this subspace in $E^{**} = E$, we see that E_{n-1} has dimension $n - 1$ (cf. § 2), and that E_{n-1} reduces T (cf. Ch. 7, § 14, Th. 7). It follows that we may consider T as a transformation on E_{n-1} alone, so that by our induction hypothesis there exist subspaces $E_1, E_2, \ldots, E_{n-1}$ satisfying the conditions of our theorem. Setting $E_n = E$ the theorem is proved completely.

Definition. *A matrix* $\{\tau_{ij}\}$ *is said to have the superdiagonal form if all matrixelements below the principal diagonal vanish, hence* $\tau_{ij} = 0$ *for* $i > j$.

Theorem 2. *If* T *is a linear transformation on* E *into* E, *there exists a coordinate system* $\{f\}$ *in* E *such that mat* $(T; f)$ *has the superdiagonal form, or, in other words, given any matrix* $\{\tau_{ij}\}$, *there exists a non-singular linear transformation* Q *such that mat* $(Q^{-1}).\{\tau_{ij}\}.$*mat* (Q) *is superdiagonal. The numbers on the principal diagonal of the superdiagonal matrix are the characteristic values of* T, *each one of them appearing with the proper algebraic multiplicity.*

Proof. We use the same notations as in the preceding theorem. The coordinate system $\{f\} = \{f_1, \ldots, f_n\}$ is determined in such a way that, for $j = 1, \ldots, n$, $\{f_1, \ldots, f_j\}$ is a coordinate system in E_j. Then, since E_j reduces T,

$$Tf_j = \Sigma_{i=1}^{j} \tau_{ij} f_i,$$

so that $\tau_{ij} = 0$ for $i > j$. This means that mat $(T; f) = \{\tau_{ij}\}$ has the superdiagonal form.

Since $\Delta(T - \tau_{ii} I) = 0$ for $i = 1, \ldots, n$, the numbers τ_{ii} are the characteristic values of T.

Remark. Since sum and product of two matrices having the superdiagonal form have also the superdiagonal form, we see that the characteristic values of $p(T) = \alpha_0 I + \alpha_1 T + \alpha_2 T^2 + \ldots + \alpha_n T^n$ (α_i complex) are exactly (that is, with the proper algebraic multiplicities) the numbers

$p(\lambda) = \alpha_0 + \alpha_1\lambda + \alpha_2\lambda^2 + \ldots + \alpha_n\lambda^n$, where λ runs through the characteristic values of T.

§ 7. Nilpotent Transformations

We consider once again linear transformations T on E into E.

Definition. *T is called nilpotent of index p (p integer and $\geqslant 1$) whenever $T^p = O$ and $T^{p-1} \neq O$. For $p = 1$ it is understood that $T^{p-1} = I$.*

From this definition it follows that whenever T is nilpotent of index p, the dimension $\nu(T^p)$ of the null space $N(T^p)$ satisfies $\nu(T^p) = n$, whereas $\nu(T^{p-1}) < n$. Evidently $N(T) \subset N(T^2) \subset \ldots \subset N(T^{p-1}) \subset N(T^p)$, hence $\nu(T) \leqslant \nu(T^2) \leqslant \ldots \leqslant \nu(T^{p-1}) < \nu(T^p) = n$.

Theorem 1. *Let T be nilpotent of index p. Then, writing*

$$\nu(T) = \nu(T) - \nu(T^0) = d_1,$$
$$\nu(T^2) - \nu(T) = d_2,$$
$$\ldots\ldots\ldots\ldots$$
$$\nu(T^p) - \nu(T^{p-1}) = d_p,$$

we have $d_1 \geqslant d_2 \geqslant \ldots \geqslant d_p > 0$, and $\Sigma_{i=1}^p d_i = n$.

Proof. $\Sigma_{i=1}^p d_i = n$ is a trivial consequence of $\nu(T^p) = n$, and $d_p > 0$ follows from $\nu(T^{p-1}) < \nu(T^p)$. Let us choose now one of the numbers d_i $(i \geqslant 2)$, and prove that $d_i \leqslant d_{i-1}$. Since $d_i = \nu(T^i) - \nu(T^{i-1})$, there exist linearly independent elements $f_1, \ldots, f_d$ $(d = d_i)$ such that $N(T^i)$ is the direct sum of $N(T^{i-1})$ and the subspace determined by $f_1, \ldots, f_d$. Hence, observing that $Tf_1, \ldots, Tf_d$ all belong to $N(T^{i-1})$ and that $d_{i-1} = \nu(T^{i-1}) - \nu(T^{i-2})$, it will be sufficient to prove that $Tf_1, \ldots, Tf_d, g_1, \ldots, g_\nu$ are linearly independent, where $g_1, \ldots, g_\nu$ is an arbitrary coordinate system in $N(T^{i-2})$. Let us suppose on the contrary that

$$\Sigma_{r=1}^d \alpha_r Tf_r + \Sigma_{j=1}^\nu \beta_j g_j = 0, \tag{1}$$

where not all α_r and β_j vanish. Then, on account of the linear independence of $g_1, \ldots, g_\nu$, one at least of the α_r does not vanish, so that also $\Sigma_{r=1}^d \alpha_r f_r \neq 0$. Furthermore, since $T^{i-2}g_j = 0$ $(j = 1, \ldots, \nu)$, it follows from (1) that

$$0 = \Sigma_{r=1}^d \alpha_r T^{i-1} f_r = T^{i-1}(\Sigma_{r=1}^d \alpha_r f_r),$$

hence $\Sigma_{r=1}^d \alpha_r f_r \in N(T^{i-1})$. But, since $N(T^i)$ is the direct sum of $N(T^{i-1}$

and the subspace determined by $f_1, \ldots, f_d$, it is impossible that $\sum_{r=1}^{d} \alpha_r f_r \neq 0$ belongs to this subspace and to $N(T^{i-1})$ simultaneously. The elements $Tf_1, \ldots, Tf_d, g_1, \ldots, g_\nu$ are therefore linearly independent.

Theorem 2. *Let T be nilpotent of index p. Then, with the notations of the preceding theorem, there exist elements $f_1, \ldots, f_{d_1}$ such that the elements shown in the following diagram:*

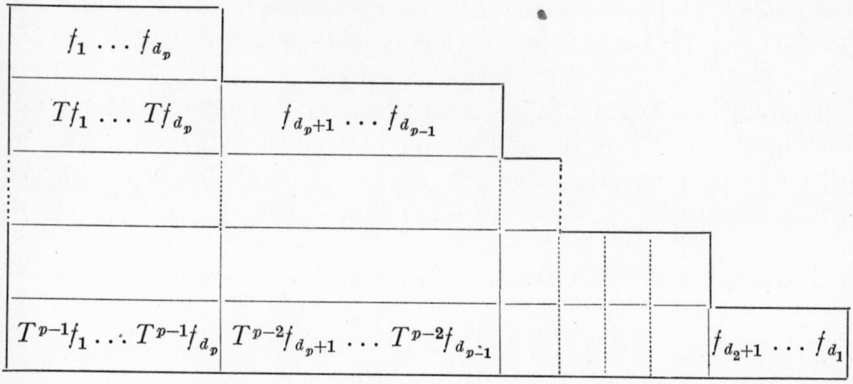

form a coordinate system in E, and such that the elements in the last i rows of the diagram ($i = 1, \ldots, p$) form a coordinate system in $N(T^i)$.

Proof. Since $d_p = \nu(T^p) - \nu(T^{p-1}) > 0$, there exist linearly independent elements $f_1, \ldots, f_{d_p}$ such that $E = N(T^p)$ is the direct sum of $N(T^{p-1})$ and the linear subspace determined by $f_1, \ldots, f_{d_p}$. Then, by what we have proved in the preceding theorem, $N(T^{p-1})$ is the direct sum of $N(T^{p-2})$ and a linear subspace determined by $Tf_1, \ldots, Tf_{d_p}$ and (if $d_{p-1} > d_p$) suitable elements $f_{d_p+1}, \ldots, f_{d_{p-1}}$. Continuing in this way we find our diagram with the stated properties.

Remark. Using the elements in the diagram as a coordinate system (beginning with the first column from top), the matrix $\{\tau_{ij}\}$ of T has a very simple form. Every matrixelement not on the diagonal just below the principal diagonal vanishes (that is, $\tau_{ij} \neq 0$ implies $i = j + 1$), and the elements below the principal diagonal begin (at the top) with a string of $p - 1$ numbers one followed by a single zero, then go on with another string of numbers one followed by a single zero, and continue thus to the end, the lengths of the strings not increasing (in fact, the length of the last strings may be 0). Since the characteristic equation of T is $(-\lambda)^n = 0$, T has only the characteristic value 0 with algebraic multiplicity n. The geometric multiplicity is $\nu(T) = d_1$.

§ 8. Canonical Form of a Matrix. Elementary Divisors

We consider once more linear transformations T on E into E.

Theorem 1. *Every linear transformation T is the direct sum of a nilpotent transformation and a non-singular transformation.*

Proof. The subspaces $N(T^i)$ $(i = 1, 2, \ldots)$ satisfy $N(T) \subset N(T^2) \subset \ldots$. If, for some k, we have $N(T^k) = N(T^{k+1})$, then $N(T^k) = N(T^{k+j})$ for all positive integers j. Indeed, if $T^{k+j}f = 0$, then $T^{k+1}T^{j-1}f = 0$, hence on account of $N(T^k) = N(T^{k+1})$, also $T^kT^{j-1}f = 0$ or $T^{k+j-1}f = 0$. It follows that $N(T^{k+j-1}) = N(T^{k+j})$; proceeding in this way we find $N(T^k) = N(T^{k+j})$.

Since E is of finite dimension, the subspaces $N(T^i)$ $(i = 1, 2, \ldots)$ cannot go on to increase indefinitely; let q be the smallest positive integer for which $N(T^q) = N(T^{q+1})$. If $f \in N(T^q)$, hence $T^qf = 0$, then $T^q(Tf) = 0$; this shows that $N(T^q)$ reduces T.

Let now $W(T^q)$ be the range of T^q. If $f \in W(T^q)$, hence $f = T^qg$, then $Tf = T^q(Tg)$; this shows that $W(T^q)$ reduces T. We shall prove that E is the direct sum of $N(T^q)$ and $W(T^q)$, and that on $N(T^q)$ the transformation T is nilpotent, whereas on $W(T^q)$ it is non-singular. Indeed, if f belongs to both $N(T^q)$ and $W(T^q)$, then $T^qf = 0$ and $f = T^qg$, hence $T^{2q}g = 0$, so that, by what we have already proved, also $T^qg = 0$ or $f = 0$. Furthermore the sum of the dimensions of $N(T^q)$ and $W(T^q)$ is n (cf. § 4, Th. 2). It follows that E is the direct sum of $N(T^q)$ and $W(T^q)$. Evidently T is nilpotent of index q on $N(T^q)$. Finally, if $f \in W(T^q)$, hence $f = T^qg$, and $Tf = 0$, then $T^{q+1}g = 0$, hence also $T^qg = 0$ or $f = 0$. This shows that T is non-singular on $W(T^q)$.

Theorem 2. *Let $\lambda_1, \ldots, \lambda_p$ be the different characteristic values of T with algebraic multiplicities $m_1, \ldots, m_p$ respectively. Then E is the direct sum of p linear subspaces $E_1, \ldots, E_p$ of dimensions $m_1, \ldots, m_p$ such that*

1°. *T is reduced by each E_j.*

2°. *On E_j the transformation T has the form $B_j + \lambda_jI$, where B_j is nilpotent.*

Proof. Consider the linear transformation $T_j = T - \lambda_jI$. By the preceding theorem there exist subspaces E_j and W_j such that T_j is nilpotent on E_j and non-singular on W_j. Furthermore E_j and W_j reduce T_j, so that they also reduce $T = T_j + \lambda_jI$, and also $T - \lambda I$ for every λ. The determinant $\Delta(T - \lambda I)$ is therefore the product of the two corresponding determinants which we obtain when we consider $T - \lambda I$ on E_j and W_j separately. Since on E_j the only characteristic value of T is λ_j, and since T

does not have the characteristic value λ_j on W_j on account of the non-singularity of $T_j = T - \lambda_j I$ on W_j, the dimension of E_j is m_j. Let us suppose now that $i \neq j$, and that E_i and E_j have an element $f \neq 0$ in common. Then the common part P of E_i and E_j is a linear subspace of dimension $\geqslant 1$. Since E_i and E_j both reduce T, the same is true of P. But $P \subset E_i$ implies that T on P can only have the characteristic value λ_i, and $P \subset E_j$ implies in the same way that T on P can only have the characteristic value λ_j. This is a contradiction. Hence, for $i \neq j$, E_i and E_j have only the null element in common.

Finally $\Sigma_{i=1}^{p} m_i = n$, the dimension of E. This shows that E is the direct sum of $E_1, \ldots, E_p$. Denoting by B_j the transformation T_j on E_j, the theorem is completely proved.

The result is that, given a linear transformation T, there exists a coordinate system $\{f\}$ in E such that every element not on or immediately below the principal diagonal of mat $(T; f)$ vanishes. On the principal diagonal are the characteristic values of T, every one of them appearing a number of times equal to its algebraic multiplicity. If $\lambda_1, \ldots, \lambda_p$ are the different characteristic values with algebraic multiplicities $m_1, \ldots, m_p$, the whole matrix may be "split up" into p square blocks, the principal diagonal of each block being a part of the principal diagonal of the given matrix, and such that the i-th block has m_i rows and columns, and has only numbers λ_i on its principal diagonal. In each block there are only numbers one and zero below the principal diagonal, in the following way: there are strings of numbers one followed by a single zero, with the lengths of the strings decreasing from top to bottom. This form of mat (T) is called the *canonical form.*

Let now the number of strings of numbers one under λ_i be r_i, and let the lengths of these strings be $q_{i1} - 1, q_{i2} - 1, \ldots, q_{ir_i} - 1$ (hence $\Sigma_{j=1}^{r_i} q_{ij} = m_i$). The polynomial $(\lambda - \lambda_i)^{q_{ij}}$ is called an *elementary divisor* of T of multiplicity q_{ij}, belonging to the characteristic value λ_i. An elementary divisor is said to be *simple* if $q_{ij} = 1$; a linear transformation T has therefore (in a suitable coordinate system) a diagonal matrix if and only if all elementary divisors are simple.

Definition. *The polynomial* $(\lambda - \lambda_1)^{q_{11}}(\lambda - \lambda_2)^{q_{21}} \ldots (\lambda - \lambda_p)^{q_{p1}}$ *is called the minimal polynomial of T. It is therefore the product of all elementary divisors of the highest multiplicities.*

Theorem 3. *The linear transformation T is annulled by its minimal* *polynomial, in other words,* $(T - \lambda_1 I)^{q_{11}}(T - \lambda_2 I)^{q_{21}} \ldots (T - \lambda_p I)^{q_{p1}} = O$ *(the null transformation).*

Proof. The linear transformation B_j on E_j, which we discussed in Theorem 2, is evidently nilpotent of index q_{j1}, in other words,

$$(T - \lambda_j I)^{q_{j1}} = O \text{ on } E_j.$$

Theorem 4 (*Theorem of Hamilton-Cayley*). *The linear transformation T is annulled by its characteristic polynomial.*

Proof. Since the characteristic polynomial of T is the product of all elementary divisors, it is a multiple of the minimal polynomial of T.

Theorem 5. *The canonical form of mat* (T^*) *is the same as that of mat* (T).

Proof. If $\{f\}$ is the coordinate system on which mat(T) has its canonical form, and $\{f^*\}$ is the dual coordinate system, then (since $\tau^*_{ij} = \tau_{ji}$) mat (T^*) on $\{f^*\}$ has a form very much like the canonical form of mat (T). The difference is that the strings of numbers one are on the diagonal immediately above the principal diagonal. Let now $f^*_i, f^*_{i+1}, \ldots, f^*_{i+k-1}, f^*_{i+k}$ be those elements f^* connected with a particular elementary divisor. Then, writing $g^*_i = f^*_{i+k}, g^*_{i+1} = f^*_{i+k-1}, \ldots, g^*_{i+k} = f^*_i$, and doing this for all elementary divisors, mat (T^*) on $\{g^*\}$ has the same form as mat (T) on $\{f\}$; in other words, mat (T) and mat (T^*) have the same canonical form.

EXAMPLES

1) If A and B are linear transformations on the n-dimensional Banach space E with their ranges in E, and $AB = O$ (the null transformation), then the ranks $\rho(A)$ and $\rho(B)$ satisfy $\rho(A) + \rho(B) \leqslant n$. If A is given, there exists a linear transformation B such that $AB = O$, $\rho(A) + \rho(B) = n$.

(The nullities satisfy $n = \nu(AB) \leqslant \nu(A) + \nu(B)$ (cf. § 4, Th. 4), hence $n \leqslant 2n - \rho(A) - \rho(B)$. If A is given and the nullspace $N(A)$ has dimension $\nu(A) = m \leqslant n$, we take the coordinate system $\{f_1, \ldots, f_n\}$ such that $\{f_1, \ldots, f_m\}$ is a coordinate system in $N(A)$. Defining now B by $Bf_i = f_i$ $(i = 1, \ldots, m)$, $Bf_i = 0$ $(i = m + 1, \ldots, n)$, we have evidently $AB = O$, $\rho(A) = n - m$ and $\rho(B) = m$).

2) If A and B are linear transformations on E into E, then $\nu(AB) \geqslant \max [\nu(A), \nu(B)]$.

(Since $\max [\nu(A), \nu(B)] = n - \min [\rho(A), \rho(B)]$, we have $\nu(AB) = n - \rho(AB) \geqslant n - \min [\rho(A), \rho(B)] = \max [\nu(A), \nu(B)]$).

3) If A, B and C are linear transformations on E into E, then $\rho(AB) + \rho(BC) \leqslant \rho(B) + \rho(ABC)$.

(The statement in § 4, Th. 3 may be interpreted as follows: The nullity of a linear transformation T on a linear subspace never exceeds the nullity of T on the whole space. Observing now that the range $W(BC)$ is a linear subspace of the range $W(B)$, that $\rho(BC)-\rho(ABC)$ is the nullity of A on $W(BC)$, and that $\rho(B)-\rho(AB)$ is the nullity of A on $W(B)$, we have $\rho(BC)-\rho(ABC)\leqslant\rho(B)-\rho(AB)$).

4) If A and B are linear transformations on E with range in E, then AB and BA have the same characteristic equation.

(Suppose first that A is non-singular. Then

$$\rho(AB-\lambda I)=\rho[A(B-\lambda A^{-1})]=\rho[(B-\lambda A^{-1})A]=\rho(BA-\lambda I)$$

for every complex λ. Generally $\rho[(AB-\lambda I)^p]=\rho[A\{(B-\lambda A^{-1})A(B-\lambda A^{-1})\ldots A(B-\lambda A^{-1})\}]=\rho[\{(B-\lambda A^{-1})A\ldots(B-\lambda A^{-1})\}A]=\rho[(BA-\lambda I)^p]$ for every positive integer p. It follows that for every complex λ and every positive integer p the dimension of the null space $N[(AB-\lambda I)^p]$ is equal to the dimension of the null space $N[(BA-\lambda I)^p]$. The transformations AB and BA have therefore the same characteristic values with the same algebraic multiplicities, in other words, the characteristic equations of AB and BA are identical. Since the coefficients in these equations are certain polynomials in the elements α_{ij} and β_{ij} of mat (A) and mat (B), the form of these polynomials being independent of the singularity or non-singularity of A, the characteristic equations are identical as well in the case that A is singular).

REFERENCES

[1] A more detailed discussion may be found in P. R. Halmos, Finite dimensional vector spaces (Annals of Math. Studies, 7), Princeton (1942, 1948).

CHAPTER 9

BOUNDED LINEAR TRANSFORMATIONS IN HILBERT SPACE

§ 1. The Hilbert-Adjoint Transformation

Let R be a complete Hilbert space. Then, as we have proved in Ch. 7, § 7, Th. 3, there exists a norm-preserving one-to-one correspondence $f \leftrightarrow f^*$ between R and the adjoint space R^*. This correspondence is defined by $f^*(g) = (g, f)$, holding for all $g \in R$. We observe once more that R and R^* cannot be identified since $f_1 \leftrightarrow f_1^*$, $f_2 \leftrightarrow f_2^*$ implies $\alpha_1 f_1 + \alpha_2 f_2 \leftrightarrow \bar{\alpha}_1 f_1^* + \bar{\alpha}_2 f_2^*$.

Let now T be a bounded linear transformation on R into R, and let T_B^* be the Banach-adjoint of T, hence $(T_B^* f^*)(g) = f^*(Tg)$ for all $g \in R$ and all $f^* \in R^*$. But $h^* = T_B^* f^*$ is an element of R^*, corresponding therefore with a unique element $h_f \in R$ (where $\| h_f \| = \| h^* \| = \| T_B^* f^* \|$), so that $(T_B^* f^*)(g) = f^*(Tg)$ may also be written in the form $(g, h_f) = (Tg, f)$. It follows that to every $f \in R$ there is assigned a unique $h_f \in R$ such that $(Tg, f) = (g, h_f)$ for all $g \in R$. We write $h_f = T_H^* f$, and the transformation T_H^*, thus defined, is called the *Hilbert-adjoint* of T. When speaking about Hilbert space, we shall write T^* instead of T_H^*. Hence

$$(Tg, f) = (g, T^*f)$$

for all $f, g \in R$. If necessary, the Banach-adjoint will be denoted by T_B^*.

Theorem 1. *If T is linear and bounded on R into R, then T^* is linear and bounded with $\| T^* \| = \| T \|$.*

Proof. If $f_1 \leftrightarrow f_1^*$ and $f_2 \leftrightarrow f_2^*$, then $T^*(\alpha_1 f_1 + \alpha_2 f_2) \leftrightarrow T_B^*(\bar{\alpha}_1 f_1^* + \bar{\alpha}_2 f_2^*) = \bar{\alpha}_1 T_B^* f_1^* + \bar{\alpha}_2 T_B^* f_2^* \leftrightarrow \alpha_1 T^* f_1 + \alpha_2 T^* f_2$. This shows that T^* is linear.

Observing that $f \leftrightarrow f^*$ implies $T^*f \leftrightarrow T_B^* f^*$, and that the correspondence $f \leftrightarrow f^*$ is norm-preserving, we find $\| T^* \| = \| T_B^* \|$. But $\| T_B^* \| = \| T \|$ by Ch. 7, § 13, Th. 1, hence $\| T^* \| = \| T \|$.

Corollary. $T^{**} = (T^*)^*$ *exists and* $T^{**} = T$.

Proof. The existence of T^{**} follows from the linearity and boundedness of T^*. We have therefore $(T^*g, f) = (g, T^{**}f)$ for all $f, g \in R$. But also $(T^*g, f) = (g, Tf)$, hence $(g, Tf) = (g, T^{**}f)$ for all $f, g \in R$, which implies $Tf = T^{**}f$.

Theorem 2. $\| T^*T \| = \| T \|^2$.

Proof. We have $\| T^*T \| \leqslant \| T^* \| . \| T \| = \| T \|^2$. On the other hand, for every element f with $\| f \| = 1$, we have $\| T^*Tf \| = \| T^*Tf \| . \| f \| \geqslant (T^*Tf, f) = (Tf, Tf) = \| Tf \|^2$, hence, taking upper bounds, $\| T^*T \| \geqslant \| T \|^2$. It follows that $\| T^*T \| = \| T \|^2$.

Theorem 3. *We have* $O^* = O$, $I^* = I$, $(T_1 + T_2)^* = T_1^* + T_2^*$, $(\alpha T)^* = \bar{\alpha}T^*$ *and* $(T_1T_2)^* = T_2^*T_1^*$. If T^{-1} *exists as a bounded linear transformation with* R *as domain, then* $(T^*)^{-1}$ *exists and* $(T^{-1})^* = (T^*)^{-1}$.

Proof. All statements follow easily from the corresponding statements for the Banach-adjoint (cf. Ch. 7, § 13, Th. 2). Independent proofs of $(\alpha T)^* = \bar{\alpha}T^*$ and $(T_1T_2)^* = T_2^*T_1^*$ follow here:

$$(\alpha Tf, g) = \alpha(Tf, g) = \alpha(f, T^*g) = (f, \bar{\alpha}T^*g),$$

$$(T_1T_2f, g) = (T_2f, T_1^*g) = (f, T_2^*T_1^*g).$$

If T^{-1} is bounded with domain R, then $(T^{-1})^*$ exists as a bounded linear transformation. Hence $(f, T^*(T^{-1})^*g) = (Tf, (T^{-1})^*g) = (T^{-1}Tf, g) = (f, g)$ for all $f, g \in R$, so that $T^*(T^{-1})^* = I$. Furthermore $(f, (T^{-1})^*T^*g) = (TT^{-1}f, g) = (f, g)$, hence $(T^{-1})^*T^* = I$. It follows that $(T^{-1})^* = (T^*)^{-1}$.

Theorem 4. *If* T *is linear and bounded on* R *into* R, *and if the linear subspace* $[L]$ *reduces both* T *and* T^*, *then* T (*and also* T^*) *is completely reduced by* $([L], R \ominus [L])$.

Proof. We have to prove that $f \in R \ominus [L]$ implies $Tf \in R \ominus [L]$. If $g \in [L]$, then $(Tf, g) = (f, T^*g) = 0$, since $T^*g \in [L]$. Hence $Tf \in R \ominus [L]$.

§ 2. Matrix Representation of Bounded Linear Transformations in Separable Hilbert Space

Let R be a separable Hilbert space, and let the orthonormal sequence φ_n be complete in R. Given the bounded linear transformation T on R into R, we define by $\tau_{ij} = (T\varphi_j, \varphi_i)$ a finite or infinite matrix of complex numbers τ_{ij}. The matrix is finite if and only if R is of finite dimension.

In virtue of Parseval's relation we have $\Sigma_i \mid \tau_{ij} \mid^2 = \Sigma_i \mid (T\varphi_j, \varphi_i) \mid^2 = \| T\varphi_j \|^2$. Since T may be extended onto the closure $\bar{R}$, the adjoint T^* is defined on $\bar{R}$; hence $\tau_{ij} = (T\varphi_j, \varphi_i) = (\varphi_j, T^*\varphi_i)$, so that, once again by Parseval's relation, $\Sigma_j \mid \tau_{ij} \mid^2 = \Sigma_j \mid (T^*\varphi_i, \varphi_j) \mid^2 = \| T^*\varphi_i \|^2$.

For an arbitrary $f = \Sigma_i \alpha_i\varphi_i$ we have $Tf = \Sigma_i \beta_i\varphi_i$, where $\beta_i = (Tf, \varphi_i) = (T \Sigma \alpha_j\varphi_j, \varphi_i) = (\Sigma \alpha_j T\varphi_j, \varphi_i) = \Sigma \alpha_j(T\varphi_j, \varphi_i) = \Sigma_j \alpha_j\tau_{ij}$. Hence

$$f = \Sigma \alpha_i\varphi_i, \quad Tf = \Sigma_i (\Sigma_j \tau_{ij}\alpha_j)\varphi_i.$$

In particular $T\varphi_i = \Sigma_j \tau_{ji}\varphi_j$. Furthermore $\| Tf \|^2 = \Sigma_j \mid (Tf, \varphi_j) \mid^2 = \Sigma_j \mid \Sigma_i \tau_{ji}\alpha_i \mid^2$. But $\| Tf \|^2 \leqslant \| T \|^2 . \Sigma \mid \alpha_i \mid^2$, hence

$$\Sigma_j \mid \Sigma_i \tau_{ji}\alpha_i \mid^2 \leqslant \| T \|^2 \Sigma \mid \alpha_i \mid^2.$$

Theorem 1. *If the orthonormal sequence φ_n is complete in the separable complete Hilbert space R, then $\tau_{ij} = (T\varphi_j, \varphi_i)$ defines a one-to-one correspondence between the set of all bounded linear transformations T on R (into R) and the set of all matrices $\{\tau_{ij}\}$ the elements τ_{ij} of which satisfy, for a number $M > 0$ (depending upon the matrix) and for all sequences $\{\alpha_i\} \in l_2$, the condition*

$$\Sigma_j \mid \Sigma_i \tau_{ji}\alpha_i \mid^2 \leqslant M \Sigma \mid \alpha_i \mid^2.$$

Proof. With every bounded linear transformation T corresponds, as we have seen, a uniquely defined matrix $\{\tau_{ij}\} = \{(T\varphi_j, \varphi_i)\}$ satisfying the stated condition with $M = \| T \|^2$. Let now conversely the matrix $\{\tau_{ij}\}$ satisfy $\Sigma_j \mid \Sigma_i \tau_{ji}\alpha_i \mid^2 \leqslant M \Sigma \mid \alpha_i \mid^2$ for all $\{\alpha_i\} \in l_2$. Then, taking $\alpha_i = 1$ for one particular value of i and $\alpha_i = 0$ for all other values of i, we see that $\Sigma_j \mid \tau_{ji} \mid^2 \leqslant M$ for every i; $\Sigma \tau_{ji}\varphi_j$ is therefore an element of R. Writing $T\varphi_i = \Sigma_j \tau_{ji}\varphi_j$, the linear transformation T is defined in the set (dense in R) of all finite linear combinations $f = \Sigma \alpha_i\varphi_i$, and $\tau_{ij} = (T\varphi_j, \varphi_i)$. Since for these f we have $\| Tf \|^2 = \Sigma_j \mid \Sigma_i \tau_{ji}\alpha_i \mid^2 \leqslant M \Sigma \mid \alpha_i \mid^2 = M \| f \|^2$, we see that T is bounded on this set, and that $\| T \| \leqslant M$. It follows that T may be extended with the same bound onto the whole space R. The uniqueness of T follows by observing that $(T_1\varphi_i, \varphi_j) = (T_2\varphi_i, \varphi_j)$ for all i, j implies $T_1 = T_2$.

A matrix $\{\tau_{ij}\}$ satisfying $\Sigma_j \Sigma_i \mid \tau_{ji} \mid^2 = M < \infty$ corresponds with a bounded linear transformation T since, supposing that $\Sigma \mid \alpha_i \mid^2 < \infty$, we have $\mid \Sigma_i \tau_{ji}\alpha_i \mid^2 \leqslant \Sigma_i \mid \alpha_i \mid^2 . \Sigma_i \mid \tau_{ji} \mid^2$, hence $\Sigma_j \mid \Sigma_i \tau_{ji}\alpha_i \mid^2 \leqslant \Sigma_j \Sigma_i \mid \tau_{ji} \mid^2 . \Sigma_i \mid \alpha_i \mid^2 = M \Sigma \mid \alpha_i \mid^2$. It follows that $\| T \|^2 \leqslant M = \Sigma_j \Sigma_i \mid \tau_{ji} \mid^2$. We observe moreover that, by an evident application of Fubini's Theorem, $M = \Sigma_j \Sigma_i \mid \tau_{ji} \mid^2 = \Sigma_i \Sigma_j \mid \tau_{ji} \mid^2 = \lim_{m\to\infty,\, n\to\infty} \Sigma_{j=1}^{m} \Sigma_{i=1}^{n} \mid \tau_{ji} \mid^2$.

Theorem 2. *If the matrix* $\{\tau_{ij}\}$ *of* T *on the complete orthonormal system* φ_n *satisfies* $\Sigma_{ij} \mid \tau_{ji} \mid^2 = M < \infty$, *and* $\{t_{ij}\}$ *is the matrix of* T *on the complete orthonormal system* ψ_n, *then* $\Sigma_{ij} \mid t_{ji} \mid^2 = M$. *The expression* $\Sigma_{ij} \mid \tau_{ji} \mid^2$ *is therefore independent of the complete orthonormal system which serves to compute it.*

Proof. We have $M = \Sigma_{ij} \mid \tau_{ji} \mid^2 = \Sigma_{ij} \mid (T\varphi_i, \varphi_j) \mid^2 = \Sigma_i \| T\varphi_i \|^2 = \Sigma_{ij} \mid (T\varphi_i, \psi_j) \mid^2 = \Sigma_{ij} \mid (\varphi_i, T^*\psi_j) \mid^2 = \Sigma_j \| T^*\psi_j \|^2 = \Sigma_{ij} \mid (\psi_i, T^*\psi_j) \mid^2 = \Sigma_{ij} \mid (T\psi_i, \psi_j) \mid^2 = \Sigma_{ij} \mid t_{ji} \mid^2$ by repeated application of Parseval's relation.

Definition. *A linear transformation* T (*on* R *into* R) *with matrix* $\{\tau_{ij}\}$ *satisfying* $\Sigma_{ij} \mid \tau_{ji} \mid^2 = \Sigma_j \Sigma_i \mid \tau_{ji} \mid^2 = \Sigma_i \Sigma_j \mid \tau_{ji} \mid^2 < \infty$, *is said to be of finite double-norm* $\Sigma_{ij} \mid \tau_{ji} \mid^2 = ||| T |||^2$.

Hence, by what we have already proved:

Theorem 3. *A linear transformation* T *of finite double-norm* $||| T |||$ *is bounded;* $\| T \| \leqslant ||| T |||$.

Theorem 4. *If* S, T *with matrices* $\{S_{ij}\}$, $\{T_{ij}\}$ *are bounded linear transformations on* R *into* R, *if* α, β *are complex, if* O *is the null transformation and* I *is the identical transformation, then*

$$(\alpha S + \beta T)_{ij} = \alpha S_{ij} + \beta T_{ij},$$

$$O_{ij} = 0,$$

$$I_{ij} = 1 \text{ for } i = j \text{ and } I_{ij} = 0 \text{ for } i \neq j,$$

$$(ST)_{ij} = \Sigma_k S_{ik} T_{kj}.$$

Furthermore, if R *is complete,*

$$(T^*)_{ij} = \overline{T_{ji}}.$$

Proof. Only the last two statements need a proof. Now

$$(ST)_{ij} = (ST\varphi_j, \varphi_i) = (S \, \Sigma_k T_{kj}\varphi_k, \varphi_i) =$$

$$(\Sigma_k T_{kj} S\varphi_k, \varphi_i) = \Sigma_k T_{kj}(S\varphi_k, \varphi_i) = \Sigma_k S_{ik} T_{kj},$$

and, if R is complete (so that $T^*f \in R$ for $f \in R$),

$$(T^*)_{ij} = (T^*\varphi_j, \varphi_i) = (\varphi_j, T\varphi_i) = \overline{T_{ji}}.$$

Finally, it will hardly be necessary to draw attention to the resemblance between the theorems on finite matrices in Ch. 8, § 2 and those in the present paragraph.

§ 3. Unitary Transformations

Let R be a complete Hilbert space.

Definition. *A bounded linear transformation U (on R into R) is said to be unitary when $UU^* = U^*U = I$ (the identical transformation), in other words, whenever the inverse transformation U^{-1} exists with domain R, and satisfies $U^{-1} = U^*$.*

We observe that every unitary transformation U is *isometric*, that is, $\| Uf \| = \| f \|$ for every $f \in R$. Indeed, $U^*U = I$ implies $(Uf, Uf) = (f, U^*Uf) = (f, f)$. Hence $\| U \| = 1$. Furthermore, if U is isometric, then $(Uf, Ug) = (f, g)$ for arbitrary $f, g \in R$ on account of

$$(f, g) = 4^{-1} [\| f + g \|^2 - \| f - g \|^2 + i \| f + ig \|^2 - i \| f - ig \|^2] =$$
$$4^{-1} [\| Uf + Ug \|^2 - \| Uf - Ug \|^2 + i \| Uf + iUg \|^2 - i \| Uf - iUg \|^2] =$$
$$= (Uf, Ug).$$

It follows that an isometric transformation transforms an orthonormal system into an orthonormal system.

Theorem 1. *If the linear transformation U is isometric and has its range $W(U)$ dense in R, then U is unitary.*

Proof. Since $\| Uf \| = \| f \|$, we have $Uf = 0$ if and only $f = 0$, which involves the existence of U^{-1}. Evidently $\| U^{-1}g \| = \| g \|$ for all $g \in W(U)$, hence $\| U^{-1} \| = 1$. But then, since U^{-1} is bounded, $W(U)$, the domain of U^{-1}, is not only dense in R but identical with R.

Observing now that $0 = (Uf, Ug) - (f, g) = (U^*Uf, g) - (f, g) = (U^*Uf - f, g)$ for all $f, g \in R$, we find $U^*Uf = f$ for all $f \in R$, hence $U^*U = I$.

Furthermore, if $f \in R$ is arbitrary, there exists an element $g \in R$ such that $f = Ug$, hence $U^*f = U^*Ug = g$. But then $f = Ug = U(U^*f) = UU^*f$ for all $f \in R$, hence $UU^* = I$.

Remark. If R is of finite dimension n, and the linear transformation U is isometric, then $W(U) = R$ is automatically satisfied. Indeed, if $f_1, \ldots, f_n$ is a coordinate system in R, then $Uf_1, \ldots, Uf_n$ is also a coordinate system in R, since $Uf_1, \ldots, Uf_n$ are linearly independent.

On the other hand, if R is of enumerably infinite dimension, and φ_n $(n = 1, 2, \ldots)$ is a complete orthonormal system in R, then the linear transformation U, defined by $U(\Sigma_1^\infty \alpha_n\varphi_n) = \Sigma_1^\infty \alpha_n\varphi_{n+1}$, is isometric but not unitary, since φ_1 does not belong to $W(U)$.

Theorem 2. *Let the space R be complete and separable, and let the sequences φ_n and ψ_n be complete and orthonormal in R. Then, if the linear transformation U is defined by $U(\Sigma_1^\infty \alpha_i\varphi_i) = \Sigma_1^\infty \alpha_i\psi_i$, this transformation is unitary.*

Proof. U is isometric on account of $\| U(\Sigma_1^\infty \alpha_i\varphi_i) \|^2 = \| \Sigma_1^\infty \alpha_i\psi_i \|^2 = \Sigma_1^\infty | \alpha_i |^2 = \| \Sigma_1^\infty \alpha_i\varphi_i \|^2$. Furthermore the range $W(U)$ is identical with R, since the system ψ_n is complete. Our statement is therefore an immediate consequence of the preceding theorem.

As regards the matrix representation of a unitary transformation U in the case that the space R is separable, we observe that $(UU^*)_{ij} = (U^*U)_{ij} = I_{ij}$ implies $\Sigma_k U_{ik}U^*_{kj} = \Sigma_k U^*_{ik}U_{kj} = I_{ij}$, or, since $U^*_{kj} = \overline{U_{jk}}$, $\Sigma_k U_{ik}\overline{U_{jk}} = \Sigma_k \overline{U_{ki}}U_{kj} = I_{ij}$. Hence, distinguishing between the cases $i = j$ and $i \neq j$,

$$\Sigma_k | U_{ik} |^2 = \Sigma_k | U_{ki} |^2 = 1,$$

$$\Sigma_k U_{ik}\overline{U_{jk}} = \Sigma_k U_{ki}\overline{U_{kj}} = 0 \text{ for } i \neq j.$$

Theorem 3. *Given the complex numbers u_{ij} $(i, j = 1, 2, \ldots)$, satisfying the relations*

$$(1) \quad \begin{cases} \Sigma_k | u_{ik} |^2 = \Sigma_k | u_{ki} |^2 = 1 \text{ for } i = 1, 2, \ldots, \\ \Sigma_k u_{ik}\overline{u_{jk}} = \Sigma_k u_{ki}\overline{u_{kj}} \;\; = 0 \text{ for } i, j = 1, 2, \ldots; \; i \neq j, \end{cases}$$

there exists, in the case that the orthonormal system φ_n is complete in the complete Hilbert space R, a unitary transformation U such that $u_{ij} = (U\varphi_j, \varphi_i)$ $(i, j = 1, 2, \ldots)$.

Proof. Since $\Sigma_k | u_{ki} |^2 = 1$, the element $\psi_i = \Sigma_k u_{ki}\varphi_k$ exists, and $\| \psi_i \| = 1$. Furthermore $(\psi_i, \psi_j) = (\Sigma_k u_{ki}\varphi_k, \Sigma_k u_{kj}\varphi_k) = \Sigma_k u_{ki}\overline{u_{kj}} = 0$ for $i \neq j$. The system ψ_n is therefore orthonormal, so that, defining the linear transformation U by $U(\Sigma_1^\infty \alpha_i\varphi_i) = \Sigma_1^\infty \alpha_i\psi_i$, U is isometric, and therefore bounded. It follows that U^* exists.

The relation $U\varphi_j = \psi_j = \Sigma_k u_{kj}\varphi_k$ shows that $U_{ij} = (U\varphi_j, \varphi_i) = u_{ij}$ for $i, j = 1, 2, \ldots$; hence $U^*_{ij} = \overline{U_{ji}} = \overline{u_{ji}}$, so that

$$(UU^*)_{ij} = \Sigma_k U_{ik}U^*_{kj} = \Sigma_k u_{ik}\overline{u_{jk}} = I_{ij},$$

$$(U^*U)_{ij} = \Sigma_k U^*_{ik}U_{kj} = \Sigma_k \overline{u_{ki}}u_{kj} = I_{ij}.$$

It follows that $UU^* = U^*U = I$, which shows that U is unitary.

Definition. *Any matrix* $\{u_{ij}\}$ $(i, j = 1, 2, \ldots)$ *satisfying the conditions* (1) *will be called a unitary matrix.*

We observe that if $\{u_{ij}\}$ is a unitary matrix, the adjoint matrix $\{u^*_{ij}\}$ $(u^*_{ij} = \overline{u_{ji}})$ is at the same time the inverse matrix of $\{u_{ij}\}$.

Theorem 4. *Given an arbitrary matrix* $\{\tau_{ij}\}$ *of n rows and n columns, there exists a unitary matrix* $\{u_{ij}\}$ *of n rows and n columns such that the matrixproduct* $\{u^*_{ij}\}.\{\tau_{ij}\}.\{u_{ij}\}$ *has the superdiagonal form.*

Proof. The matrix $\{\tau_{ij}\}$ may be considered as the matrix of a linear transformation T on n-dimensional Hilbert space with respect to an orthonormal coordinate system $\{\varphi\} = \{\varphi_1, \ldots, \varphi_n\}$. Now, in Ch. 8, § 6, Th. 2, we have proved that there exists a coordinate system $\{\psi\} = \{\psi_1, \ldots, \psi_n\}$ such that mat $(T; \psi)$ has the superdiagonal form, and, upon inspecting this proof, it is easily seen that the system $\{\psi\}$ may be chosen such that it is orthonormal (Schmidt's orthogonalization process). Writing $\psi_i = U\varphi_i$ $(i = 1, \ldots, n)$, U is unitary by Theorem 2, so that mat $(U) = \{u_{ij}\}$ is a unitary matrix. Since

$$\text{mat}\,(T; \psi) = \{u^*_{ij}\}.\{\tau_{ij}\}.\{u_{ij}\}$$

(cf. Ch. 8, § 3, Th. 1), our proof is complete.

§ 4. Bounded Self-Adjoint Transformations

Let R be a Hilbert space, complete or non-complete.

Definition. *The bounded linear transformation* A*, on* R *into* R*, is called self-adjoint whenever* $(Af, g) = (f, Ag)$ *holds for all* $f, g \in R$.

If, therefore, A is self-adjoint, and the extension of A onto the closure $\bar{R}$ is also denoted by A, then $(Af_n, g_n) = (f_n, Ag_n)$ for all $f_n, g_n \in R$, together with $\lim f_n = f$, $\lim g_n = g$, implies $(Af, g) = (f, Ag)$ for all $f, g \in \bar{R}$, so that A remains self-adjoint. It follows that the extended transformation A satisfies $A = A^*$.

If A, A_1, A_2 and all transformations of the converging sequence A_n are self-adjoint, and if a is an arbitrary real number, then aA, $A_1 + A_2$ and $\lim A_n$ are self-adjoint. If A_1 and A_2 are self-adjoint, then A_1A_2 is self-adjoint if and only if $A_1 \, v \, A_2$, that is, if and only if $A_1A_2 = A_2A_1$ (cf. Ch. 7, § 12), as follows from $(A_1A_2f, g) = (A_2f, A_1g) = (f, A_2A_1 g)$

Since $A \, v \, A$, the transformations $A^2 = AA$, $A^3 = AAA, \ldots$ are self-adjoint if A is self-adjoint. Finally, we observe that the null transformation O and the identical transformation I are self-adjoint.

Theorem 1. *The bounded linear transformation A is self-adjoint if and only if (Af, f) is real for all $f \in R$.*

Proof. If A is self-adjoint, then $(Af, f) = (f, Af) = \overline{(Af, f)}$. If conversely (Af, f) is real, then $(Af, f) = \overline{(Af, f)} = (f, Af)$. Hence $(A(f + \lambda g), f + \lambda g) = (f + \lambda g, A(f + \lambda g))$ for all, $f, g \in R$ and all complex λ. This involves $\lambda(Ag, f) + \bar{\lambda}(Af, g) = \lambda(g, Af) + \bar{\lambda}(f, Ag)$, so that, taking $\lambda = 1$, $\lambda = i$ and adding, we find $(Af, g) = (g, Af)$ (compare the proof of Ch. 7, § 12, Th. 4, where it was proved that $(Tf, f) = 0$ for all $f \in R$ implies $Tf = 0$ for all $f \in R$).

Theorem 2. *If T is a bounded linear transformation (on the complete Hilbert space R into R), then $T = A + iB$, where A and B are self-adjoint. A and B are uniquely determined by T.*

Proof. Since $(T + T^*)/2$ and $(T - T^*)/2i$ are self-adjoint, we may take $A = (T + T^*)/2$ and $B = (T - T^*)/2i$. To prove the uniqueness, let us suppose that $A_1 + iB_1 = A_2 + iB_2$ (A_1, B_1, A_2, B_2 self-adjoint). Then $A_1 - A_2 = i(B_2 - B_1)$, so that $i((B_2 - B_1)f, f)$ is real for all $f \in R$. But $((B_2 - B_1)f, f)$ is real as well, hence $((B_2 - B_1)f, f) = 0$ for all $f \in R$. It follows from Ch. 7, § 12, Th. 4 that $B_2 - B_1 = O$ (the null transformation). Hence $B_1 = B_2$ and $A_1 = A_2$.

Definition. *If A and B are bounded and self-adjoint, and $(Af, f) \geqslant (Bf, f)$ for all $f \in R$, we write $A \geqslant B$ or $B \leqslant A$. The sequence of bounded self-adjoint transformations A_n is called ascending if $A_1 \leqslant A_2 \leqslant \ldots$, it is called descending if $A_1 \geqslant A_2 \geqslant \ldots$.*

Theorem 3. *If the bounded transformations A and B are self-adjoint, and the relations $A \geqslant B$, $A \leqslant B$ hold simultaneously, then $A = B$.*

Proof. From $A \geqslant B$, $A \leqslant B$ follows $(Af, f) = (Bf, f)$ or $((A - B)f, f) = 0$ for all $f \in R$. Hence, by Ch. 7, § 12, Th. 4, $A - B = O$ or $A = B$.

Theorem 4. *Let A be self-adjoint, and let the real numbers m_1 and m_2 be such that $m_1 I \leqslant A \leqslant m_2 I$, where m_1 is the largest number and m_2 the smallest number having this property. Then, if $m = \max(|m_1|, |m_2|)$, we have $\|A\| = m$.*

Proof. Evidently $m =$ upper bound $|(Af, f)|/\|f\|^2$ for all $f \neq 0$. Since $|(Af, f)| \leqslant \|Af\| . \|f\| \leqslant \|A\| . \|f\|^2$, we have therefore $m \leqslant \|A\|$. To prove the inverse inequality, we observe that $(A(g+h), g+h) - (A(g-h), g-h) = 2(Ag, h) + 2(Ah, g)$; hence $2(Ag, h) + 2(h, Ag) = 2(Ag, h) + 2(Ah, g) \leqslant m \| g+h \|^2 + m \| g-h \|^2 = 2m(\| g \|^2 + \| h \|^2)$. Taking now $g = af$, $h = Af/a$, where $a \neq 0$ is real and $f \neq 0$, we obtain $4 \| Af \|^2 = 4(Af, Af) = 2(Aaf, \ Af/a) + 2(Af/a, \ Aaf) \leqslant 2m(a^2 \| f \|^2 + \| Af \|^2/a^2)$, or, choosing $a^2 = \| Af \| / \| f \|$,

$$4 \| Af \|^2 \leqslant 2m(\| Af \| . \| f \| + \| Af \| . \| f \|) = 4m \| Af \| . \| f \|.$$

It follows that $\| Af \| \leqslant m \| f \|$, so that $\| A \| \leqslant m$.

Theorem 5. *If the space R is complete, and the linear transformation A satisfies $(Af, g) = (f, Ag)$ for all $f, g \in R$, then A is a bounded self-adjoint transformation.*

Proof. The present theorem is essentially identical with Ch. 7, § 11, Th. 9.

Definition. *If the bounded self-adjoint transformation H satisfies $H \geqslant O$, that is, if $(Hf, f) \geqslant 0$ for all $f \in R$, then H is called positive or of positive type.*

Evidently the null transformation O and the identical transformation I are both positive. Furthermore, if $O \leqslant H \leqslant I$, then H and $I - H$ are both positive.

Theorem 6. *Let A and T be bounded linear transformations on the complete space R into R. Then:*

1°. *If A is self-adjoint, T^*AT is self-adjoint. If A is positive, T^*AT is positive.*

2°. *If the range of T is dense in R and T^*AT is self-adjoint, then A is self-adjoint. If moreover T^*AT is positive, then A is positive.*

Proof. 1°. If A is self-adjoint, then $(T^*ATf, f) = (ATf, Tf)$ is real for all $f \in R$, which shows that T^*AT is self-adjoint. If A is positive, then $(T^*ATf, f) = (ATf, Tf) \geqslant 0$, so that T^*AT is also positive.

2°. For every $f = Tg$ in the range of T we have $(Af, f) = (ATg, Tg) = (T^*ATg, g)$, so that, supposing T^*AT to be self-adjoint and the range of T to be dense in R, (Af, f) is real in a set $\{f\}$ which is dense in R. But then (Af, f) is real for all $f \in R$, in other words, A is self-adjoint. If moreover T^*AT is positive, we have $(Af, f) \geqslant 0$ in a dense set, hence $(Af, f) \geqslant 0$ for all $f \in R$.

Corollary. *T^*T and TT^* are positive.*
Proof. $T^*T = T^*IT$ and $TT^* = (T^*)^*IT^*$, and I is positive.

Theorem 7. *If the bounded linear transformations H_1 and H_2 are self-adjoint, and if moreover $H_2 \geqslant O$ and $H_1 \, v \, H_2$, then the self-adjoint transformation $H_1^2 H_2$ is positive.*
Proof. $(H_1^2 H_2 f, f) = (H_1 H_2 f, H_1 f) = (H_2 H_1 f, H_1 f) \geqslant 0$ for every $f \in R$.

Theorem 8. *If the bounded linear transformations H and G are positive and permutable, then the self-adjoint transformation $HG = GH$ is also positive* [1].
Proof. Evidently we may suppose that $H \neq O$, hence $\| H \| > 0$. We define the sequence H_n $(n = 1, 2, \ldots)$ of self-adjoint transformations by

$$H_1 = H/\| H \|,$$

$$H_2 = H_1 - H_1^2,\ H_3 = H_2 - H_2^2,\ \ldots,\ H_{n+1} = H_n - H_n^2,\ \ldots,$$

and we shall prove that $O \leqslant H_n \leqslant I$ for every value of n. For $n = 1$ we have $0 \leqslant (H_1 f, f) = (Hf, f)/\| H \| \leqslant (f, f)$, hence $O \leqslant H_1 \leqslant I$. Furthermore

$$I - H_{n+1} = (I - H_n) + H_n^2,$$

and, on account of $H_{n+1} = H_n - H_n^2 = H_n^2 - H_n^3 + H_n - 2H_n^2 + H_n^3$,

$$H_{n+1} = H_n^2(I - H_n) + H_n(I - H_n)^2.$$

Supposing that $H_n \geqslant O$ and $I - H_n \geqslant O$ have already been proved, we find therefore, using the preceding theorem, that $I - H_{n+1} \geqslant O$ and $H_{n+1} \geqslant O$, hence $O \leqslant H_{n+1} \leqslant I$.

It follows next from $H_1 = H_1^2 + H_2^2 + \ldots + H_n^2 + H_{n+1}$ and $H_{n+1} \geqslant O$ that $\Sigma_1^n (H_k f, H_k f) = \Sigma_1^n (H_k^2 f, f) = (H_1 f, f) - (H_{n+1} f, f) \leqslant (H_1 f, f)$; the series $\Sigma \| H_k f \|^2$ converges therefore, so that $\lim \| H_n f \| = 0$. Then $\lim (\Sigma_1^n H_k^2) f = \lim (H_1 f - H_{n+1} f) = H_1 f$.

Since $G \, v \, H$ by hypothesis, we see readily that $G \, v \, H_k$ for every value of k; hence $(GHf, f)/\| H \| = (GH_1 f, f) = \lim \Sigma_1^n (GH_k^2 f, f) = \lim \Sigma_1^n (H_k G H_k f, f) = \lim \Sigma_1^n (GH_k f, H_k f) \geqslant 0$, and this shows that GH is positive.

Theorem 9. *Let the space R be complete. Then, if all transformations of the ascending sequence A_n of self-adjoint transformations are mutually permutable, and if there exists a self-adjoint transformation B such that $A_n \, v \, B$ and $A_n \leqslant B$ for all n, the sequence A_n converges to a self-adjoint transformation A satisfying $A_n \, v \, A$ and $A_n \leqslant A \leqslant B$.*

A similar statement holds for descending sequences [1].

Proof. We consider the descending sequence of positive transformations $H_n = B - A_n$. They are mutually permutable; for $m > n$, the transformations $H_m(H_n - H_m)$ and $(H_n - H_m)H_n$ are therefore positive by the preceding theorem. Hence, for every $f \in R$,

$$(H_m^2 f, f) \leqslant (H_m H_n f, f) \leqslant (H_n^2 f, f),$$

from which we infer that the non-ascending sequence of non-negative numbers $(H_m^2 f, f) = \| H_m f \|^2$ has a limit (depending on f), and that $(H_m H_n f, f)$ has the same limit for $m, n \to \infty$. Consequently,

$$\lim \| (H_m - H_n)f \|^2 = \lim ((H_m - H_n)^2 f, f)$$
$$= \lim [(H_m^2 f, f) - 2(H_m H_n f, f) + (H_n^2 f, f)] = 0.$$

The sequence $H_n f$ converges therefore for every $f \in R$, so that the same is true of the sequence $A_n f$. By $Af = \lim A_n f$ (here the completeness of the space R is used) we define a transformation A, which is evidently linear and self-adjoint. The relations $A_n \leqslant A_{n+1}$, $A_n \leqslant B$ (for all n) imply $A_n \leqslant A \leqslant B$, and the relations $A_n \, v \, A_k$, $\lim A_k = A$ imply $A_n \, v \, A$.

Theorem 10. *Let the space R be complete. Then, if H is bounded and positive, there exists a unique bounded and positive transformation B such that $B^2 = H$* [2].

Proof. Evidently we may suppose that $H \leqslant I$, since we may always replace H by $H/\| H \|$. The sequence of self-adjoint transformations B_n is now defined by

$$B_0 = O, \; B_{n+1} = B_n + \tfrac{1}{2}(H - B_n^2) \; (n = 0, 1, 2, \ldots).$$

It is easily seen by induction that if a bounded self-adjoint transformation C is permutable with H, then it is permutable with all B_n, hence, since $H \, v \, H$, we have $H \, v \, B_n$. Next, $B_m \, v \, H$ (for all m) implies $B_m \, v \, B_n$ (for all m and n).

We find now $I - B_{n+1} = I - B_n - \frac{1}{2}(H - B_n^2) = \frac{1}{2}I - B_n + \frac{1}{2}B_n^2 + \frac{1}{2}I - \frac{1}{2}H = \frac{1}{2}(I - B_n)^2 + \frac{1}{2}(I - H)$, hence $I - B_n \geqslant O$ for all n. Furthermore, in view of $B_n \, v \, B_{n-1}$, we have

$$B_{n+1} - B_n = B_n + \tfrac{1}{2}(H - B_n^2) - B_{n-1} - \tfrac{1}{2}(H - B_{n-1}^2) =$$
$$B_n - B_{n-1} - \tfrac{1}{2}(B_n^2 - B_{n-1}^2) = (B_n - B_{n-1}) [I - \tfrac{1}{2}(B_n + B_{n-1})]$$
$$= \tfrac{1}{2}[(I - B_n) + (I - B_{n-1})] (B_n - B_{n-1}),$$

which implies $B_{n+1} \geqslant B_n$. Indeed, for $n = 0$ we have $B_1 = \frac{1}{2}H \geqslant O = B_0$, if therefore we have already proved that $B_n - B_{n-1} \geqslant O$, we find by

Theorem 8 that $B_{n+1} - B_n \geqslant O$ as well, since $B_{n+1} - B_n$ is the product of the permutable and positive transformations $\frac{1}{2}[(I - B_n) + (I - B_{n-1})]$ and $B_n - B_{n-1}$.

The sequence B_n, satisfying therefore $O = B_0 \leqslant B_1 \leqslant B_2 \leqslant \dots \leqslant I$, converges now by the preceding theorem to a positive transformation B; hence, making $n \to \infty$ in $B_{n+1} = B_n + \frac{1}{2}(H - B_n^2)$, we obtain $B = B + \frac{1}{2}(H - B^2)$ or $B^2 = H$.

To show that B is uniquely determined, we observe first that every bounded self-adjoint transformation C, permutable with H, is also permutable with B since $C \, v \, H$ implies $C \, v \, B_n$, and this in its turn implies $C \, v \, B$. If therefore C is bounded and positive, and $C^2 = H$, we see, since $HC = CH = C^3$, that $C \, v \, B$. Let now $B^{1/2}$ and $C^{1/2}$ be two positive transformations satisfying $(B^{1/2})^2 = B$ and $(C^{1/2})^2 = C$ (their existence follows from the first part of the present proof), let $f \in R$ be arbitrary, and $g = (B - C)f$. Then, on account of $C \, v \, B$, we have $\| B^{1/2}g \|^2 + \| C^{1/2}g \|^2 = (Bg, g) + (Cg, g) = ((B + C)(B - C)f, g) = ((B^2 - C^2)f, g) = 0$; hence $B^{1/2}g = C^{1/2}g = 0$, so that also $Bg = B^{1/2}B^{1/2}g = 0$ and $Cg = C^{1/2}C^{1/2}g = 0$. But this implies $\| (B - C)f \|^2 = ((B - C)^2 f, f) = ((B - C)g, f) = 0$ or $Bf = Cf$. It follows, since f is arbitrary, that $B = C$.

Definition. *If H is a bounded positive transformation, defined on the complete Hilbert space R, we shall denote by $H^{1/2}$ the bounded positive transformation satisfying $(H^{1/2})^2 = H$. As we have seen, $H^{1/2}$ is uniquely determined by H. Since $(H^{1/2})^* = H^{1/2}$, we find by § 1, Th. 2 that $\| H \| = \| H^{1/2}H^{1/2} \| = \| H^{1/2} \|^2$, hence $\| H^{1/2} \| = \| H \|^{1/2}$.*

Theorem 11. *If H is a bounded positive transformation on the space R (complete or non-complete), then*

1°. $| (Hf, g) | \leqslant (Hf, f)^{1/2} . (Hg, g)^{1/2}$ *for all* $f, g \in R$.

2°. $\| Hf \| \leqslant \| H \|^{1/2} (Hf, f)^{1/2}$ *for all* $f \in R$.

3°. $(Hf, f) = 0$ *if and only if* $Hf = 0$.

Proof. We extend H onto the closure $\bar{R}$. Then, by the preceding theorem, $H^{1/2}$ is defined on $\bar{R}$, so that, for all $f, g \in \bar{R}$, we have

$| (Hf, g) | = | (H^{1/2}f, H^{1/2}g) | \leqslant \| H^{1/2}f \| . \| H^{1/2}g \| \doteq (Hf, f)^{1/2} . (Hg, g)^{1/2}$.

Taking $g = Hf$ in this inequality, we find $\| Hf \|^2 \leqslant (Hf, f)^{1/2} . (H^2 f, Hf)^{1/2}$. But $(H^2 f, Hf) \leqslant \| H^2 f \| . \| Hf \| \leqslant \| H \| . \| Hf \|^2$, hence $\| Hf \|^2 \leqslant \| H \|^{1/2} (Hf, f)^{1/2} \| Hf \|$, or $\| Hf \| \leqslant \| H \|^{1/2} (Hf, f)^{1/2}$. Finally it is evident that $Hf = 0$ implies $(Hf, f) = 0$, and conversely, if $(Hf, f) = 0$, we see from $\| Hf \| \leqslant \| H \|^{1/2} (Hf, f)^{1/2}$ that $Hf = 0$.

Hence, since 1°, 2° and 3° hold for $f, g \in \bar{R}$, they certainly hold for $f, g \in R$.

Remark. It is possible to give a proof of 1°, analogous to the proof of Schwarz's inequality $|(f, g)| \leqslant \|f\|.\|g\|$, without having to refer to the existence of $H^{1/2}$. From

$$(Hf, f) + \lambda(Hg, f) + \bar{\lambda}(Hf, g) + \lambda\bar{\lambda}(Hg, g) = (H(f + \lambda g), f + \lambda g) \geqslant 0$$

for arbitrary complex λ follows, if $(Hg, g) \neq 0$, by taking $\lambda = -(Hf, g)/(Hg, g)$, that

$$(Hf, f) - (Hf, g)\,(Hg, f)/(Hg, g) \geqslant 0$$

or $|(Hf, g)| \leqslant (Hf, f)^{1/2}.(Hg, g)^{1/2}$. If $(Hg, g) = 0$ but $(Hf, f) \neq 0$, the same inequality is proved in a similar way. In the case that $(Hf, f) = (Hg, g) = 0$, we have $\lambda(Hg, f) + \bar{\lambda}(Hf, g) = 0$, and, by taking $\lambda = 1$, $\lambda = i$, we see that $(Hf, g) = 0$, so that again $|(Hf, g)| \leqslant (Hf, f)^{1/2}.(Hg, g)^{1/2}$.

Theorem 12. *Let R be separable, and let φ_n be a complete orthonormal system in R. Then, if $\{\alpha_{ij}\}$ is the matrix of the bounded linear transformation A in the system φ_n, hence $\alpha_{ij} = (A\varphi_j, \varphi_i)$, A is self-adjoint if and only if $\alpha_{ij} = \overline{\alpha_{ji}}$ for all i, j.*

Proof. Let A be self-adjoint. Then $\alpha_{ij} = (A\varphi_j, \varphi_i) = (\varphi_j, A\varphi_i) = \overline{(A\varphi_i, \varphi_j)} = \overline{\alpha_{ji}}$ for all i, j. We observe that in particular $\alpha_{ii} = \overline{\alpha_{ii}}$ for all i, so that all numbers α_{ii} are real.

Let now $\alpha_{ij} = \overline{\alpha_{ji}}$ for all i, j; hence $(A\varphi_j, \varphi_i) = (\varphi_j, A\varphi_i)$. Then, by the completeness of the orthonormal system φ_n, we have $(Af, g) = (f, Ag)$ for all $f, g \in R$.

Theorem 13. *If $\{h_{ij}\}$ is the matrix of the bounded transformation H, then H is positive if and only if all sums $\sum_{i=1}^n \sum_{j=1}^n h_{ij}\overline{\alpha}_i\alpha_j \geqslant 0$ for $\alpha_1, \alpha_2, \ldots$ arbitrarily complex.*

Proof. If H is positive, then $\sum_{i=1}^n \sum_{j=1}^n h_{ij}\overline{\alpha}_i\alpha_j = \sum\sum (H\varphi_j, \varphi_i)\overline{\alpha}_i\alpha_j = (H \sum_1^n \alpha_j\varphi_j, \sum_1^n \alpha_i\varphi_i) \geqslant 0$. If, conversely, $(H \sum_1^n \alpha_j\varphi_j, \sum_1^n \alpha_i\varphi_i) \geqslant 0$ for all n and all sequences $\{\alpha_i\}$, then $(Hf, f) \geqslant 0$ for all $f \in R$ by the completeness of the orthonormal system φ_n. Since, in particular, (Hf, f) is real for all $f \in R$, H is self-adjoint by Theorem 1; since $(Hf, f) \geqslant 0$, H is positive.

Theorem 14. *If A is a self-adjoint transformation on the complete space*

R, and A is reduced by the linear subspace $[L]$, then A is completely reduced by $([L], R \ominus [L])$.

Proof. Follows from § 1, Th. 4, since $A^* = A$.

§ 5. Factorspace Relative to a Positive Transformation

Let R be a Hilbert space, complete or non-complete, and let H be a bounded linear transformation on R into R. If $H \neq O$, the set of all elements f satisfying $Hf = 0$ is a linear subspace $[L]$, not identical with the whole space R. The orthogonal complement $R \ominus [L]$ will be denoted by $[M]$. We shall suppose that R is the direct sum of $[L]$ and $[M]$. By Ch. 6, § 12, Th. 3 this will certainly be the case if either $[L]$ or $[M]$, considered as a Hilbert space on its own, is complete; hence in particular if R itself is complete. Since $[L]$ and R are not identical, $[M]$ contains not only the null element but other elements as well. If therefore P is the projection on $[M]$ along $[L]$, we have $P \neq O$. The projection on $[L]$ along $[M]$ is $I - P$.

Theorem 1. *We have $H = HP$.*

Proof. Since $Hh = 0$ for every $h \in [L]$, we have $H(I - P)f = 0$ for every $f \in R$, hence $Hf = HPf$ or $H = HP$.

We shall, in what follows, suppose now that H is self-adjoint.

Theorem 2. $H = HP = PH$.

Proof. We have $H = HP$ by Theorem 1. Let now $h \in [L]$ and $f \in R$. Then $(h, Hf) = (Hh, f) = 0$, hence $Hf \in [M]$ for every $f \in R$. It follows that $PHf = Hf$, or $PH = H$.

Definition. *Two elements f and g will be called H-orthogonal when $(Hf, g) = 0$, and the system Q of elements is called H-orthonormal when, for $\varphi \in Q$, $\psi \in Q$, we have*

$$(H\varphi, \psi) = \begin{cases} 1 \text{ for } \varphi = \psi, \\ 0 \text{ for } \varphi \neq \psi. \end{cases}$$

The elements $f_1, \ldots, f_n$ will be called H-independent when $H \sum_1^n \alpha_i f_i = 0$ implies $\alpha_1 = \ldots = \alpha_n = 0$.

Evidently every subset of an H-orthonormal system is also H-orthonormal, and every H-independent set is a linearly independent set.

Theorem 3. *If the elements $\varphi_1, \ldots, \varphi_n$ form an H-orthonormal system, they are H-independent.*

Proof. $H \Sigma_1^n \alpha_i \varphi_i = \Sigma_1^n \alpha_i H\varphi_i = 0$ implies $\Sigma_{i=1}^n \alpha_i (H\varphi_i, \varphi_k) = 0$ for $k = 1, \ldots, n$; hence $\alpha_1 = \ldots = \alpha_n = 0$.

We shall, in what follows, suppose now that H is positive. The non-negative number $(Hf, f)^{1/2}$ will be denoted by $N(f)$.

Theorem 4. *Given the finite or enumerable set V of H-independent elements, there exists an H-orthonormal system Q such that $L(Q) = L(V)$, that is, the set of all finite linear combinations of elements from Q is identical with the set of all finite linear combinations of elements from V.*

Proof. Let $f_1, f_2, \ldots$ be the elements of V. The H-orthonormal system Q with elements $\varphi_1, \varphi_2, \ldots$ is now defined by a process, wholly similar to Schmidt's orthogonalization process, in the following way:

$$\varphi_1 = f_1/N(f_1), \quad g_2 = f_2 - (Hf_2, \varphi_1)\varphi_1, \quad \varphi_2 = g_2/N(g_2), \ldots.$$

Generally, if $\varphi_1, \ldots, \varphi_{n-1}$ are already defined,

$$g_n = f_n - \Sigma_{k=1}^{n-1} (Hf_n, \varphi_k)\varphi_k, \quad \varphi_n = g_n/N(g_n).$$

To justify this definition it is necessary to show that $(Hg_n, g_n) \neq 0$, assuming that the existence of $\varphi_1, \ldots, \varphi_{n-1}$ has already been established. Every φ_k is however a linear combination of $f_1, \ldots, f_k$, so that g_n may be written in the form $g_n = f_n - \Sigma_{k=1}^{n-1} \alpha_k f_k$; the H-independence of $f_1, \ldots, f_n$ guarantees therefore that $Hg_n \neq 0$, hence $(Hg_n, g_n) \neq 0$ by § 4, Th. 11. The existence of the system Q being thus established, we see easily that it is H-orthonormal. Moreover, every φ_n is a linear combination of $f_1, \ldots, f_n$, and every f_n is a linear combination of $\varphi_1, \ldots, \varphi_n$; hence $L(Q) = L(V)$. This completes the proof.

We consider now the factorspace $R/[L]$. If $f \in R$ and $[f]$ is the element of $R/[L]$ which contains f, then the following three statements hold (cf. § 4, Th. 11 for the equivalence of 2° and 3°):

1°. $[f]$ consists of all $g \in R$ satisfying $Pg = Pf$.

2°. $[f]$ consists of all $g \in R$ satisfying $Hg = Hf$.

3°. $[f]$ consists of all $g \in R$ satisfying $N(f - g) = 0$.

In particular $[f]$ contains Pf since $P(Pf) = Pf$. The null element $[0]$ of $R/[L]$ consists of all g satisfying $Hg = 0$.

Definition. *The factorspace Z of R relative to the bounded positive transformation H contains the same elements as the ordinary factorspace $R/[L]$,* *where* $[L]$ *is the linear subspace of all* f *satisfying* $Hf = 0$. *Addition and multiplication by complex* α *are defined as in* $R/[L]$, *but the inner product* $([f], [g])$ *of* $[f]$ *and* $[g]$ *is defined to be* (Hf, g), *where* $f \in [f]$ *and* $g \in [g]$.

To show that no contradiction arises we have to prove that $f, f_1 \in [f]$ and $g, g_1 \in [g]$ implies $(Hf_1, g_1) = (Hf, g)$. This however is an easy consequence of $Hf_1 = Hf$ and $Hg_1 = Hg$, which involves $(Hf_1, g_1) = (Hf, g_1) = (f, Hg_1) = (f, Hg) = (Hf, g)$.

Observing that moreover $([f], [f]) = (Hf, f) \geqslant 0$, and that $\| [f] \|^2 = ([f], [f]) = (Hf, f) = N^2(f) = 0$ if and only if $Hf = 0$, that is, if and only if $[f] = [0]$, we see that Z satisfies the Axioms A and BH of Hilbert space (cf. Ch. 6, § 7); Z is therefore a Hilbert space. We shall see in Theorem 9 that Z is not necessarily complete even in the case that R is complete.

Theorem 5. *Two elements* f *and* g *from the space* R *are* H*-orthogonal if and only if the elements* $[f]$ *and* $[g]$ *from* Z *are orthogonal.*
Proof. $(Hf, g) = 0$ is equivalent with $([f], [g]) = 0$.

Theorem 6. *The elements* $f_1, \ldots, f_n$ *from* R *are* H*-independent if and only if the elements* $[f_1], \ldots, [f_n]$ *from* Z *are linearly independent.*
Proof. $H \sum_1^n \alpha_i f_i = 0$ is equivalent with $\sum_1^n \alpha_i [f_i] = [0]$; if therefore one of these relations implies $\alpha_1 = \ldots = \alpha_n = 0$, the same is true of the other.

A certain class of linear transformations T on R (into R) corresponds now with the class of all linear transformations $[T]$ on Z (into Z) in such a way that if T and $[T]$ are corresponding we have $[T]\,[f] = [Tf]$ for all $f \in R$. If the linear transformation T on R is given, and we define $[T]$ on Z by $[T]\,[f] = [Tf]$, this definition is without contradiction if and only if $[f] = [g]$ implies $[Tf] = [Tg]$; in other words, if and only if $Hf = 0$ implies $HTf = 0$, or, stated differently once more, if and only if T is reduced by the linear subspace $[L]$. Conversely, given the linear transformation $[T]$ on Z, there exists at least one linear transformation T on R such that $[Tf] = [T]\,[f]$ for all $f \in R$. Indeed, if $[T]\,[f] = [g]$, we define $TPf = Pg$ for all elements $Pf \in [M]$, whereas on the orthogonal complement $[L] = R \ominus [M]$ the transformation T may be defined as an arbitrary linear transformation with its range in $[L]$.

Theorem 7. *We have* $[T_1] = [T_2]$ *for two linear transformations of the considered class if and only if* $HT_1 = HT_2$, *or, which is equivalent, if and only if* $PT_1 = PT_2$.

Proof. $[T_1] = [T_2]$ is equivalent with $[T_1f] = [T_2f]$ for every $f \in R$, and therefore with $HT_1f = HT_2f$ or with $HT_1 = HT_2$.

Theorem 8. *If the linear transformations T_1 and T_2 are reduced by $[L]$, then T_1T_2 is reduced by $[L]$, and $[T_1T_2] = [T_1][T_2]$.*

Proof. $Hf = 0$ implies $HT_2f = 0$, and this in its turn implies $HT_1T_2f = 0$. It follows that $[T_1T_2]$ exists, and that $[T_1T_2][f] = [T_1T_2f] = [T_1][T_2f] = [T_1][T_2][f]$.

Theorem 9. *Even if R is a complete Hilbert space, Z is not necessarily complete.*

Proof. Let φ_n be a complete orthonormal system in R, and $\lambda_n = 1/n!$ $(n = 1, 2, \ldots)$. The bounded positive transformation H is defined by $H\varphi_n = \lambda_n^2\varphi_n$ $(n = 1, 2, \ldots)$, hence $Hf = \Sigma\, \lambda_n^2\alpha_n\varphi_n$ for an arbitrary $f = \Sigma\, \alpha_n\varphi_n$. Evidently $\| H \| = 1$, $(Hf, f) = \Sigma\, \lambda_n^2 \mid \alpha_n \mid^2$ and $H^{1/2}f = \Sigma\, \lambda_n\alpha_n\varphi_n$. Let now $f_n = \Sigma_1^n\, \varphi_i$. Then, for $m > n$, we have $\| [f_m] - [f_n] \|^2 = \| [f_m - f_n] \|^2 = \| H^{1/2}(f_m - f_n) \|^2 = \Sigma_{n+1}^m\, \lambda_i^2$, which tends to zero as $m, n \to \infty$. It follows that the sequence $[f_n]$ is a fundamental sequence in Z. Supposing now that it has a limit element $[f]$ in Z, where $f = \Sigma\, \alpha_i\varphi_i$ $(\Sigma \mid \alpha_i \mid^2 < \infty)$, we have $\lim \| [f_n] - [f] \| = 0$, hence $\lim \| H^{1/2}(f_n - f) \| = 0$ or $\lim \Sigma_1^n\, \lambda_i\varphi_i = \Sigma\, \lambda_i\alpha_i\varphi_i$. But $\lim \Sigma_1^n\, \lambda_i\varphi_i = \Sigma\, \lambda_i\varphi_i$, so that we should have $\alpha_i = 1$ $(i = 1, 2, \ldots)$ or $f = \Sigma\, \varphi_i$. This however is a contradiction because $\Sigma \mid \alpha_i \mid^2 = \Sigma\, 1^2 = \infty$. It follows that $[f_n]$ has no limit in Z.

Theorem 10. *Even if the linear transformation T on R, reduced by $[L]$, is bounded, the corresponding transformation $[T]$ on Z is not necessarily bounded.*

Proof. With the same definitions for the space R, the system φ_n, the sequence λ_n and the transformation H as in the preceding theorem, we define $T\varphi_1 = 0$, $T\varphi_n = \varphi_{n-1}$ $(n = 2, 3, \ldots)$, hence $Tf = \Sigma_2^\infty\, \alpha_n\varphi_{n-1}$ for $f = \Sigma_1^\infty\, \alpha_n\varphi_n$. Then $\| T \| = 1$, and, since $[L]$ contains only the null element, T is reduced by $[L]$. Furthermore, for $n = 2, 3, \ldots$, we have $\| [T][\varphi_n] \| = \| [T\varphi_n] \| = \| H^{1/2}T\varphi_n \| = \| H^{1/2}\varphi_{n-1} \| = \lambda_{n-1}$ and $\| [\varphi_n] \| = \| H^{1/2}\varphi_n \| = \lambda_n$, so that $\| [T][\varphi_n] \| / \| [\varphi_n] \| = \lambda_{n-1}/\lambda_n = n \to \infty$. It follows that $[T]$ is unbounded.

Remark. A condition upon T which is sufficient to ensure the boundedness of $[T]$ may be found in Ch. 12, Ex. 22.

Theorem 11. *Even if the linear transformation* $[T]$ *on* Z *is bounded, all corresponding transformations* T *on* R *may be unbounded.*

Proof. With the same notations as in the preceding theorem R is now the space of all finite linear combinations $\Sigma\, \alpha_i \varphi_i$. The linear transformation T on R is defined by $T\varphi_n = (n+1)\varphi_{n+1}$ $(n = 1, 2, \ldots)$. Then, for $f = \Sigma\, \alpha_n \varphi_n$, we have $H^{1/2} f = \Sigma\, \lambda_n \alpha_n \varphi_n$ and $H^{1/2} T f = H^{1/2}(\Sigma (n+1) \alpha_n \varphi_{n+1}) = \Sigma \lambda_{n+1} (n+1)\, \alpha_n \varphi_{n+1} = \Sigma \lambda_n \alpha_n \varphi_{n+1}$, hence $\| [T]\, [f] \| = \| H^{1/2} T f \| = \| H^{1/2} f \| = \| [f] \|$, or $\| [T] \| = 1$, whereas T itself is unbounded. Observing that the correspondence between T and $[T]$ is one-to-one, our proof is complete.

§ 6. Multiplication by Bounded Functions

Let $\Phi(u)$ and $\Psi(v)$ be complementary in the sense of Young, and let Δ be a finite or infinite interval in real m-dimensional Euclidean space. Furthermore, let μ be Lebesgue measure in this space. Then, if $t(x) \in L_\infty(\Delta) = L_\infty(\Delta, \mu)$, we have proved in Ch. 7, § 15, Ex. A that the transformation T, defined by $Tf = t(x) f(x)$, is a bounded linear transformation on $L_\Phi(\Delta)$ into $L_\Phi(\Delta)$. Furthermore $T = O$ (the null transformation) if and only if $t(x) = 0$ almost everywhere on Δ. In the case that $\Phi(2u) \leqslant M\Phi(u)$ for all $u \geqslant 0$, so that every $g^* \in (L_\Phi)^*$ is represented by a unique $g^*(x) \in L_\Psi(\Delta)$, the functional $f^* = T^* g^*$ is represented by $f^*(x) = t(x) g^*(x)$. Here T^* is the Banach-adjoint of T.

In the present paragraph we shall consider in particular the case that $L_\Phi(\Delta)$ is the Hilbert space $L_2(\Delta)$. First, however, we shall generalize the obtained results to the productspace $[L_\Phi(\Delta)]^n$ (n a positive integer). This is possible on account of Ch. 7, § 14, Th. 9, 10, 11. In the same way as in these theorems we suppose that the norm in L_Φ^n is such that L_Φ^n is the direct sum of the n spaces L_Φ. The element $\{f^1(x), \ldots, f^n(x)\}$ of L_Φ^n, where $f^i(x) \in L_\Phi$, will shortly be denoted by $\{f\}$.

Theorem 1. *Let* $t_{ij}(x) \in L_\infty(\Delta)$ $(i, j = 1, \ldots, n)$. *Then the transformation* $\{g\} = T\{f\}$, *defined by*

$$g^i(x) = \Sigma_{j=1}^n\, t_{ij}(x) f^j(x) \quad (i = 1, \ldots, n),$$

is a bounded linear transformation on L_Φ^n *into* L_Φ^n. *We have* $T = O$ *if and only if all* $t_{ij}(x) = 0$ *almost everywhere on* Δ. *In the case that* $\Phi(2u) \leqslant M\Phi(u)$ *for all* $u \geqslant 0$, *so that every functional* $\{g^*\} \in (L_\Phi^n)^*$ *is represented by a unique element* $\{g^{*1}(x), \ldots, g^{*n}(x)\} \in L_\Psi^n$, *the functional* $\{f^*\} = T^*\{g^*\}$ *is represented by* $\{f^{*1}(x), \ldots, f^{*n}(x)\} \in L_\Psi^n$, *where*

$$f^{*i}(x) = \Sigma_{j=1}^n\, t_{ji}(x) g^{*j}(x) \quad (i = 1, \ldots, n).$$

Proof. Follows immediately from Ch. 7, § 14, Th. 9, 10, 11.

We shall consider now the case that $L_\Phi(\Delta)$ is the Hilbert space $L_2(\Delta)$. It will be useful to define first the concepts of Hermitian matrix and Hermitian function of two variables.

Definition. *The matrix* $\{\tau_{ij}\}$ $(i, j = 1, .., n)$ *of complex numbers* τ_{ij} *is said to be Hermitian when* $\tau_{ij} = \overline{\tau_{ji}}$ $(i, j = 1, \ldots, n)$. *In the case that all* τ_{ij} *depend on a parameter* x, *running through an interval* Δ, *it is only required that* $\tau_{ij}(x) = \overline{\tau_{ji}(x)}$ *almost everywhere on* Δ.

The measurable function $T(x, y)$, *defined on* $\Delta \times \Delta$, *is said to be Hermitian when* $T(x, y) = \overline{T(y, x)}$ *for almost every point* $(x, y) \in \Delta \times \Delta$.

The matrix $\{T_{ij}(x, y)\}$ $(i, j = 1, \ldots, n)$ *of measurable functions, defined on* $\Delta \times \Delta$, *is called Hermitian when* $T_{ij}(x, y) = \overline{T_{ji}(y, x)}$ *almost everywhere on* $\Delta \times \Delta$.

We formulate now the analogue of Theorem 1 for $[L_2(\Delta)]^n$.

Theorem 2. *Let* $t_{ij}(x) \in L_\infty(\Delta)$ $(i, j = 1, \ldots, n)$. *Then the transformation* $\{g\} = T\{f\}$, *defined by*

$$g^i(x) = \Sigma_{j=1}^n t_{ij}(x) f^j(x) \quad (i = 1, \ldots, n),$$

is a bounded linear transformation on L_2^n *into* L_2^n. *We have* $T = O$ *if and only if all* $t_{ij}(x) = 0$ *almost everywhere on* Δ. *The Hilbert-adjoint transformation* $\{h\} = T^*\{f\}$ *is given by*

$$h^i(x) = \Sigma_{j=1}^n \overline{t_{ji}(x)}\, f^j(x) \quad (i = 1, \ldots, n).$$

The transformation T *is self-adjoint if and only if the matrix* $\{t_{ij}(x)\}$ *is Hermitian, that is, if and only if* $t_{ij}(x) = \overline{t_{ji}(x)}$ *almost everywhere on* Δ. *The transformation* T *is positive if and only if*

$$\Sigma_{ij=1}^n t_{ij}(x) \overline{\alpha_i} \alpha_j \geqslant 0$$

almost everywhere on Δ *for every system of complex numbers* $\alpha_1, \ldots, \alpha_n$ *(where the set of exceptional* x *is independent of the system* $\alpha_1, \ldots, \alpha_n$*).*

Proof. The first two statements follow from Theorem 1. To prove the statement on T^*, we suppose first that $n = 1$, hence simply $g(x) = T.f(x) = t(x)f(x)$. Then

$$(f, T^*g) = (Tf, g) = \int_\Delta t(x)f(x)\,\overline{g(x)}\,dx =$$

$$\int_\Delta f(x)\,.\,\overline{\overline{t(x)}g(x)}\,dx,$$

hence $T^*g = \overline{t(x)}\, g(x)$. For $n > 1$, we write $\{h\} = T\{f\}$ in the form $h^i = \Sigma_{j=1}^n T_{ij} f^j$ $(i = 1, \ldots, n)$. Then, observing that the inner product $(\{f\}, \{g\})$ in L_2^n is defined as $\Sigma_{i=1}^n (f^i, g^i)$, we find

$$(\{f\}, T^*\{g\}) = (T\{f\}, \{g\}) = \Sigma_{j=1}^n (\Sigma_{i=1}^n T_{ji} f^i, g^j)$$
$$= \Sigma_{ij=1}^n (f^i, (T_{ji})^* g^j) = \Sigma_{i=1}^n (f^i, \Sigma_{j=1}^n (T_{ji})^* g^j),$$

hence $(T^*)_{ij} = (T_{ji})^*$. It follows that $(T^*)_{ij}$ is represented by $\overline{t_{ji}(x)}$.

T is self-adjoint if and only if $T - T^* = O$, that is, if and only if $t_{ij}(x) = \overline{t_{ji}(x)}$ almost everywhere on Δ. For $n = 1$, this means that $t(x) = t_{11}(x)$ is real for almost every $x \in \Delta$.

Finally, the statement that the bounded transformation T is positive means that

$$\Sigma_{ij=1}^n \int_\Delta t_{ij}(x)\, \overline{f^i(x)}\, f^j(x) dx = (T\{f\}, \{f\}) \geqslant 0$$

for every $\{f\} \in L_2^n$. This however is equivalent with $\Sigma_{ij=1}^n t_{ij}(x)\, \overline{f^i(x)}\, f^j(x) \geqslant 0$ almost everywhere on Δ for every $\{f\} \in L_2^n$. If therefore $\Sigma_{ij=1}^n t_{ij}(x) \overline{\alpha}_i \alpha_j \geqslant 0$ almost everywhere on Δ for every system $\alpha_1, \ldots, \alpha_n$, then T is positive. If conversely T is positive, $\alpha_1, \ldots, \alpha_n$ are rational complex, and Δ_1 is an arbitrary finite subset of Δ, we define $\{f\} = \{f^1(x), \ldots, f^n(x)\} \in L_2^n$ by $f^i(x) = \alpha_i$ on Δ_1 and $f^i(x) = 0$ elsewhere on Δ. Then $\Sigma_{ij=1}^n t_{ij}(x) \overline{\alpha}_i \alpha_j \geqslant 0$ almost everywhere on Δ_1, or, since Δ_1 is arbitrary, almost everywhere on Δ. We denote the set of exceptional x corresponding with this rational system $\{\alpha\}_1$ by E_1. Letting now $\alpha_1, \ldots, \alpha_n$ run through all rational complex numbers, we obtain an enumerable set of systems $\{\alpha\}_k$ with corresponding exceptional sets E_k. Hence, for $x \in \Delta - \Sigma_1^\infty E_k$, we have $\Sigma_{ij=1}^n t_{ij}(x)\, \overline{\alpha}_i \alpha_j \geqslant 0$ for all rational systems $\alpha_1, \ldots, \alpha_n$. A continuity argument shows now that $\Sigma_{ij=1}^n t_{ij}(x) \overline{\alpha}_i \alpha_j \geqslant 0$ for all systems $\alpha_1, \ldots, \alpha_n$ if only $x \in \Delta - \Sigma_1^\infty E_k$, that is, almost everywhere on Δ.

For $n = 1$, T is positive if and only if $t(x) = t_{11}(x) \geqslant 0$ almost everywhere on Δ.

Theorem 3. 1°. *If the matrix $\{h_{ij}\}$ $(i, j = 1, \ldots, n)$ of complex numbers is Hermitian and of positive type (that is, $h_{ij} = \overline{h_{ji}}$ and $\Sigma_{ij=1}^n h_{ij} \overline{\alpha}_i \alpha_j \geqslant 0$ for every system $\alpha_1, \ldots, \alpha_n$ of complex numbers), there exists a uniquely determined matrix $\{h_{ij}^{(1/2)}\}$, which is also Hermitian and of positive type, such that*

$$\{h_{ij}^{(1/2)}\} . \{h_{ij}^{(1/2)}\} = \{h_{ij}\}.$$

2°. *If now the numbers h_{ij} depend on the parameter x, running through the interval Δ, and all $h_{ij}(x)$ belong to $L_\infty(\Delta)$, then all $h_{ij}^{(1/2)}(x)$ belong to $L_\infty(\Delta)$ as well.*

3°. *If all $h_{ij}(x)$ are continuous on Δ, the same holds for all $h_{ij}^{(1/2)}(x)$.*

Proof. 1°. Let us consider an n-dimensional Hilbert space with orthonormal coordinate system $\varphi_1, \ldots, \varphi_n$, and let us define the linear transformation H on this space by $H\varphi_j = \Sigma_i h_{ij}\varphi_i$, hence mat $(H) = \{h_{ij}\}$. Then, for $f = \Sigma \alpha_j\varphi_j$, we have $(Hf, f) = (\Sigma_j \alpha_j \Sigma_i h_{ij}\varphi_i, \Sigma \alpha_i\varphi_i) = \Sigma_{ij} h_{ij}\overline{\alpha}_i\alpha_j \geqslant 0$, which shows that H is positive. The positive transformation $H^{1/2}$ such that $(H^{1/2})^2 = H$ is therefore uniquely determined. Writing $(H^{1/2}\varphi_j, \varphi_i) = h_{ij}^{(1/2)}$ $(i, j = 1, \ldots, n)$, the matrix $\{h_{ij}^{(1/2)}\}$ is then Hermitian and of positive type, and, since $H^{1/2}H^{1/2} = H$, we have $\{h_{ij}^{(1/2)}\}.\{h_{ij}^{(1/2)}\} = \{h_{ij}\}$. Any other matrix $\{l_{ij}\}$, Hermitian and of positive type, such that $\{l_{ij}\}.\{l_{ij}\} = \{h_{ij}\}$, is identical with $\{h_{ij}^{(1/2)}\}$ since, introducing the transformation L by $L\varphi_j = \Sigma_i l_{ij}\varphi_i$, we see that L is positive and satisfies $L^2 = H$, hence $L = H^{1/2}$.

2°. Using the same notations as in 1°, we observe that by the proof of § 3, Th. 4 there exists an orthonormal system $\psi_1, \ldots, \psi_n$ such that mat $(H; \psi) = \{k_{ij}\}$ has the superdiagonal form, hence $k_{ij} = 0$ for $i > j$. But then, on account of $k_{ij} = \overline{k_{ji}}$ (H is self-adjoint), $k_{ij} = 0$ for $j > i$ as well, so that mat $(H; \psi)$ is a diagonal matrix. Writing $k_{ii} = \lambda_i$, we have $H\psi_i = \lambda_i\psi_i$ $(i = 1, \ldots, n)$ with $\lambda_i = \lambda_i(\psi_i, \psi_i) = (H\psi_i, \psi_i) \geqslant 0$. Evidently $H^{1/2}$ is given by $H^{1/2}\psi_i = \lambda_i^{1/2}\psi_i$. The transformation from the system $\{\varphi\}$ to the system $\{\psi\}$ is unitary by § 3, Th. 2, hence $\varphi_i = \Sigma_j \beta_{ji}\psi_j$ with $\Sigma_j |\beta_{ji}|^2 = 1$ $(i = 1, \ldots, n)$. For every integer $p \geqslant 0$ we have now

$$(H^p\varphi_j, \varphi_i) = \Sigma_{k=1}^n (H^p\varphi_j, \psi_k)\overline{(\varphi_i, \psi_k)} = \Sigma_{k=1}^n \lambda_k^p\beta_{kj}\overline{\beta_{ki}},$$

hence, if $P(\lambda)$ is an arbitrary polynomial,

$$(P(H)\varphi_j, \varphi_i) = \Sigma_{k=1}^n P(\lambda_k)\beta_{kj}\overline{\beta_{ki}}.$$

Furthermore, in the same way,

$$h_{ij}^{(1/2)} = (H^{1/2}\varphi_j, \varphi_i) = \Sigma_{k=1}^n \lambda_k^{1/2}\beta_{kj}\overline{\beta_{ki}}.$$

Let now all $h_{ij} = (H\varphi_j, \varphi_i)$ belong to $L_\infty(\Delta)$. Then there exists a set $\Delta_1 \subset \Delta$ such that $\Delta - \Delta_1$ has measure zero and $|h_{ij}(x)| \leqslant A$ $(i, j = 1, \ldots, n)$ for all $x \in \Delta_1$, where A is a constant. The transformation H, depending on x, is now also bounded, uniformly for $x \in \Delta_1$. It follows that there exists a constant $B > 0$ such that, for all $x \in \Delta_1$, all $\lambda_i(x)$ $(i = 1, \ldots, n)$ are contained in $0 \leqslant \lambda \leqslant B$. Let now $\varepsilon > 0$ be arbitrarily given. Then there exists a polynomial $P(\lambda)$ such that $|P(\lambda) - \lambda^{1/2}| < \varepsilon$ in $0 \leqslant \lambda \leqslant B$. Writing $p_{ij} = (P(H)\varphi_j, \varphi_i)$, we have therefore

$$(1) \quad \begin{cases} |p_{ij} - h_{ij}^{(1/2)}| = |\Sigma_{k=1}^n \{P(\lambda_k) - \lambda_k^{1/2}\}\beta_{kj}\overline{\beta_{ki}}| \leqslant \varepsilon \Sigma_{k=1}^n |\beta_{kj}\overline{\beta_{ki}}| \\ \qquad \leqslant \varepsilon (\Sigma_k |\beta_{kj}|^2)^{1/2} (\Sigma_k |\beta_{ki}|^2)^{1/2} = \varepsilon, \end{cases}$$

uniformly for $x \in \Delta_1$. In other words, the functions $h_{ij}^{(1/2)}(x)$ may be approximated by functions $p_{ij}(x)$, uniformly on Δ_1. Since every $p_{ij}(x)$, being a polynomial in the $h_{ij}(x)$, is evidently measurable, the same holds then for $h_{ij}^{(1/2)}(x)$. Furthermore, for $x \in \Delta_1$,

$$| h_{ij}^{(1/2)}(x) | = | \Sigma_{k=1}^{n} \lambda_k^{1/2} \beta_{kj} \overline{\beta_{ki}} | \leqslant B^{1/2} \Sigma_{k=1}^{n} | \beta_{kj} \overline{\beta_{ki}} | \leqslant B^{1/2}.$$

Hence $h_{ij}^{(1/2)}(x) \in L_\infty(\Delta)$.

3°. If all $h_{ij}(x)$ are continuous on Δ, the same holds for all $p_{ij}(x)$, hence by (1), which is valid now for all $x \in \Delta$, also for all functions $h_{ij}^{(1/2)}(x)$.

Remark. The theorem is trivial for $n = 1$.

We return to the space $[L_2(\Delta)]^n$.

Theorem 4. *Let $h_{ij}(x) \in L_\infty(\Delta)$ $(i, j = 1, \ldots, n)$ and $\Sigma_{ij=1}^{n} h_{ij}(x)\overline{\alpha_i}\alpha_j \geqslant 0$ almost everywhere on Δ for every system of complex numbers $\alpha_1, \ldots, \alpha_n$, so that the transformation $\{g\} = H\{f\}$, defined by*

$$g^i(x) = \Sigma_j h_{ij}(x) f^j(x) \quad (i = 1, \ldots, n),$$

is bounded and positive on L_2^n. Then the uniquely determined bounded positive transformation $\{h\} = H^{1/2}\{f\}$ is given by

$$h^i(x) = \Sigma_j h_{ij}^{(1/2)}(x) f^j(x) \quad (i = 1, \ldots, n),$$

where the functions $h_{ij}^{(1/2)}(x)$ are defined as in the preceding theorem.

Proof. Follows immediately from the preceding theorem.

Remark. All statements, except Theorem 3, 3°, may immediately be extended to the case that μ is an arbitrary measure, and Δ is an arbitrary μ-measurable set.

§ 7. Integral Transformations

We assume that Δ is a finite or infinite interval in real m-dimensional Euclidean space, that μ is Lebesgue measure in this space, and that $\Phi(u)$, $\Psi(v)$ are complementary in the sense of Young. In Ch. 7, § 15, Ex. B we have considered integral transformations $Tf = \int_\Delta T(x, y) f(y) dy$ of finite double-norm on $L_\Phi(\Delta)$. In the present paragraph we shall adopt a more general point of view, and drop the condition that T is of finite double-norm. In the next paragraph we shall then apply the obtained results to the case that $L_\Phi(\Delta)$ is the Hilbert space $L_2(\Delta)$.

Definition. *We shall say that the function $T(x, y)$, measurable on $\Delta \times \Delta$, has the property (P) relative to $L_\Phi(\Delta)$ when*

$$\int_\Delta | T(x, y)f(y) | dy \in L_\Phi$$

for every $f \in L_\Phi$.

Theorem 1. *If $T(x, y)$ has the property (P), then*

$$Tf = \int_\Delta T(x, y)f(y)dy$$

defines a linear transformation T on L_Φ into L_Φ. The function $T(x, y)$ is therefore the kernel of T (cf. Ch. 7, § 15, Ex. B). We have $T = O$ (the null transformation) if and only if $T(x, y) = 0$ almost everywhere on $\Delta \times \Delta$.

If $T_1(x, y)$ and $T_2(x, y)$ both have the property (P), and if they determine the linear transformations T_1 and T_2 respectively, then $T_3 = T_1T_2$ has the kernel $T_3(x, y) = \int_\Delta T_1(x, z)\, T_2(z, y)dz$, and $T_3(x, y)$ has the property (P).

Proof. Let $T(x, y)$ have the property (P). Then our hypothesis implies that, for arbitrary $f \in L_\Phi$, $g \in L_\Psi$,

$$\int_{\Delta\times\Delta} | T(x, y)f(y)g(x) | dx\, dy = \int_\Delta (\int_\Delta | T(x, y)f(y) | dy) | g(x) | dx < \infty.$$

It follows that $T(x, y)f(y)g(x)$ is summable over $\Delta \times \Delta$, so that

$$\int_{\Delta\times\Delta} T(x, y)f(y)g(x)dx\, dy = \int_\Delta (\int_\Delta T(x, y)f(y)dy)g(x)dx$$

exists as a finite number. This however implies $\int_\Delta T(x, y)f(y)dy \in L_\Phi$, which shows that $g(x) = \int_\Delta T(x, y)f(y)dy$ determines a linear transformation $g = Tf$ on L_Φ into L_Φ.

If $T(x, y) = 0$ almost everywhere on $\Delta \times \Delta$, then, for almost every $x \in \Delta$, we have $g(x) = \int_\Delta T(x, y)f(y)dy = 0$, hence $T = O$. If conversely $T = O$, then $g(x) = \int_\Delta T(x, y)f(y)dy = 0$ almost everywhere on Δ for every $f(y) \in L_\Phi$ (where the set of exceptional x, however, may depend on $f(y)$), hence $\int_\Delta g(x)h(x)dx = \int_{\Delta\times\Delta} T(x, y)h(x)f(y)dx\, dy = 0$ for all $h(x) \in L_\Psi$, $f(y) \in L_\Phi$. In particular $\int_{\Delta_1\times\Delta_2} T(x, y)dx\, dy = 0$ for arbitrary finite intervals $\Delta_1, \Delta_2 \subset \Delta$, which implies $T(x, y) = 0$ almost everywhere in $\Delta \times \Delta$ (cf. Ch. 3, § 4, Th. 3).

If $T_1(x, y)$ and $T_2(x, y)$ both have the property (P), then

$$(1) \qquad \int_\Delta | T_1(x, z) | (\int_\Delta | T_2(z, y) | . | f(y) | dy)dz \in L_\Phi$$

for every $f \in L_\Phi$, hence

$$\int_\Delta [\int_\Delta | T_1(x, z) | (\int_\Delta | T_2(z, y) | . | f(y) | dy)dz] . | g(x) | dx < \infty$$

for arbitrary $f \in L_\Phi$, $g \in L_\Psi$. If now Δ_1 is an arbitrary bounded subset of Δ, we take $f(x) = g(x) = 1$ on Δ_1 and $f(x) = g(x) = 0$ elsewhere on Δ, and we find

$$\int_{\Delta_1\times\Delta_1\times\Delta} | T_1(x, z)\, T_2(z, y) |\, dx\, dy\, dz =$$

$$\int_{\Delta_1} [\int_\Delta | T_1(x, z) |\, (\int_{\Delta_1} | T_2(z, y) |\, dy) dz] dx < \infty.$$

Hence

$$\int_{\Delta_1\times\Delta_1\times\Delta} T_1(x, z)\, T_2(z, y) dx\, dy\, dz = \int_{\Delta_1\times\Delta_1} (\int_\Delta T_1(x, z) T_2(z, y) dz) dx\, dy,$$

where $T_3(x, y) = \int_\Delta T_1(x, z)\, T_2(z, y) dz$ is measurable on $\Delta_1 \times \Delta_1$. But $\Delta_1 \subset \Delta$ is arbitrary, so that $T_3(x, y)$ is measurable on $\Delta \times \Delta$.

The relation (1) shows moreover that $| T_1(x, z) T_2(z, y) f(y) |$, and therefore also $T_1(x, z) T_2(z, y) f(y) = A_x(y, z)$, is summable over $\Delta \times \Delta$ for almost every $x \in \Delta$. Hence, for these values of x,

$$(2) \quad \begin{cases} \int_{\Delta\times\Delta} A_x(y, z) dy\, dz = \int_\Delta T_1(x, z)\, (\int_\Delta T_2(z, y) f(y) dy) dz = \\ \int_\Delta (\int_\Delta T_1(x, z) T_2(z, y) dz) f(y) dy = \int_\Delta T_3(x, y) f(y) dy \end{cases}$$

and

$$(3) \quad \int_\Delta (\int_\Delta | T_1(x, z) T_2(z, y) | dz) | f(y) | dy = \int_\Delta | T_1(x, z) | (\int_\Delta | T_2(z, y) f(y) | dy) dz.$$

By (2) we find now

$$T_1 T_2 f = \int_\Delta T_1(x, z)\, (\int_\Delta T_2(z, y) f(y) dy) dz = \int_\Delta T_3(x,y) f(y) dy.$$

Furthermore, observing that $| T_3(x, y) | \leqslant \int_\Delta | T_1(x, z) T_2(z, y) |\, dz$, (3) and (1) imply

$$\int_\Delta | T_3(x, y) f(y) |\, dy \leqslant \int_\Delta (\int_\Delta | T_1(x, z) T_2(z, y) |\, dz)\, | f(y) |\, dy \in L_\Phi,$$

which shows that $T_3(x, y)$ has the property (P).

Corollary. *If the measurable function $T(x, y)$ has the property (P), so that $T(x, y)$ is the kernel of a linear transformation T, then, defining*

$$T_1(x, y) = T(x, y),$$

$$T_n(x, y) = \int_\Delta T(x, z) T_{n-1}(z, y) dz \ (n = 2, 3, \ldots),$$

all kernels $T_n(x, y)$ have the property (P) and

$$T^n f = \int_\Delta T_n(x, y) f(y) dy \quad (n = 1, 2, \ldots).$$

Definition. *The kernels $T_n(x, y)$ $(n = 2, 3, \ldots)$, defined in the above Corollary, are called the iterated kernels of $T_1(x, y) = T(x, y)$.*

Theorem 2. *If $T(x, y)$ has the property (P), the linear transformation T which has $T(x,y)$ as its kernel is bounded.*

Proof. The summability of $T(x, y)f(y)g(x)$ over $\Delta \times \Delta$ for arbitrary $f \in L_\Phi$, $g \in L_\Psi$ implies

$$\int_{\Delta\times\Delta} T(x, y)f(y)g(x)dx\,dy = \int_\Delta f(y)\,(\int_\Delta T(x, y)g(x)dx)dy.$$

This shows that

$$h(y) = \int_\Delta T(x, y)g(x)dx \in L_\Psi \text{ for } g \in L_\Psi.$$

Let now $\lim \| f_n - f \|_\Phi = 0$, $\lim \| Tf_n - k \|_\Phi = 0$. We shall prove that $k = Tf$, in other words, that T is a closed transformation. Indeed, for every $g(x) \in L_\Psi$ we have

$$\int_\Delta k(x)g(x)dx = \lim \int_\Delta (\int_\Delta T(x, y)f_n(y)dy)g(x)dx$$

$$= \lim \int_\Delta f_n(y)\,(\int_\Delta T(x, y)g(x)dx)dy =$$

$$\int_\Delta f(y)\,(\int_\Delta T(x, y)g(x)dx)dy = \int_\Delta (\int_\Delta T(x, y)f(y)dy)g(x)dx,$$

hence

$$\int_\Delta [k(x) - \int_\Delta T(x, y)f(y)dy]g(x)dx = 0.$$

It follows that $k(x) = \int_\Delta T(x, y)f(y)dy$ for almost every $x \in \Delta$, or $k = Tf$.

The transformation T is therefore closed, and it has the complete space $L_\Phi(\Delta)$ as its domain. Then, by Ch. 7, § 11, Th. 8, it is bounded.

Theorem 3. *Let $\Phi(2u) \leqslant M\Phi(u)$ for all $u \geqslant 0$, and let $T(x, y)$ have the property (P), so that $T(x, y)$ is the kernel of a bounded linear transformation T. Then, if $g^* \in (L_\Phi)^*$ is represented by $g^*(x) \in L_\Psi$, and T^* is the Banach-adjoint of T, the functional $f^* = T^*g^*$ is represented by*

$$f^*(x) = \int_\Delta T(y, x)g^*(y)dy.$$

The kernel $T^*(x, y) = T(y, x)$ has the property (P) relative to $L_\Psi(\Delta)$.

If T_1 and T_2 have the kernels $T_1(x, y)$ and $T_2(x, y)$ with the property (P), and $T_3 = T_1T_2$, then T_3^* has the kernel $T_3^*(x, y) = T_3(y, x) = \int_\Delta T_1(y, z)\,T_2(z, x)dz$.

Proof. We have

$$(T^*g^*)\,(f) = g^*(Tf) = \int_{\Delta\times\Delta} T(y, x)f(x)g^*(y)dx\,dy$$

$$= \int_\Delta (\int_\Delta T(y, x)g^*(y)dy)f(x)dx,$$

hence, since $f^*(x)$ is uniquely determined,

$$f^*(x) = \int_\Delta T(y, x)g^*(y)dy.$$

Furthermore, for arbitrary $f(x) \in L_\Phi$, $g^*(y) \in L_\Psi$,

$$\int_\Delta (\int_\Delta | T(y, x)g^*(y) | dy) | f(x) | dx = \int_{\Delta\times\Delta} | T(y, x)f(x)g^*(y) | dx\,dy < \infty,$$

and this shows that

$$\int_\Delta | T(y, x)g^*(y) | dy \in L_\Psi \text{ for } g^* \in L_\Psi.$$

It follows that $T^*(x, y) = T(y, x)$ has the property (P) relative to $L_\Psi(\Delta)$.
The last statement follows now immediately from what we have proved in Theorem 1 about $T_3 = T_1T_2$.

The extension to the productspace L^n_Φ is now easy.

Theorem 4. *Let $T_{ij}(x, y)$ $(i, j = 1, \ldots, n)$ all have the property (P) relative to $L_\Phi(\Delta)$. Then the transformation $\{g\} = T\{f\}$, defined by*

$$g^i(x) = \Sigma^n_{j=1} \int_\Delta T_{ij}(x, y)f^j(y)dy \quad (i = 1, \ldots, n)$$

is a bounded linear transformation on L^n_Φ into L^n_Φ. This transformation T has therefore the matrix kernel $\{T_{ij}(x, y)\}$. We have $T = O$ if and only if all $T_{ij}(x, y) = 0$ almost everywhere on $\Delta \times \Delta$. In the case that $\Phi(2u) \leqslant M\Phi(u)$ for all $u \geqslant 0$, so that every functional $\{g^*\} \in (L^n_\Phi)^*$ is represented by a unique element $\{g^{*1}(x), \ldots, g^{*n}(x)\} \in L^n_\Psi$, the functional $\{f^*\} = T^*\{g^*\}$ is represented by $\{f^{*1}(x), \ldots, f^{*n}(x)\} \in L^n_\Psi$, where

$$f^{*i}(x) = \Sigma^n_{j=1} \int_\Delta T_{ji}(y, x)g^{*j}(y)dy \quad (i = 1, \ldots, n).$$

If S and T have the matrix kernels $\{S_{ij}(x, y)\}$ and $\{T_{ij}(x, y)\}$ with property (P), and $V = ST$, then V has the matrix kernel $\{V_{ij}(x, y)\}$ with property (P), where

$$V_{ij}(x, y) = \Sigma^n_{k=1} \int_\Delta S_{ik}(x, z)T_{kj}(z, y)dz.$$

Proof. Follows from the preceding theorems by application of Ch. 7, § 14, Th. 9, 10, 11.

Remark. All statements may immediately be extended to the case that μ is an arbitrary measure, and Δ is an arbitrary μ-measurable set.

§ 8. Integral Transformations in $L_2(\Delta)$

We consider now the case that $L_\Phi(\Delta)$ is the Hilbert space $L_2(\Delta)$.

Theorem 1. *If $T(x, y)$ has the property (P) relative to $L_2(\Delta)$, the transformation T, defined by*

$$g(x) = Tf = \int_\Delta T(x, y)f(y)dy,$$

is a bounded linear transformation on $L_2(\Delta)$ into $L_2(\Delta)$. We have $T = O$

if and only if $T(x, y) = 0$ *almost everywhere on* $\Delta \times \Delta$. *The Hilbert-adjoint transformation* $h = T^*f$ *is given by*

$$h(x) = T^*f = \int_\Delta \overline{T(y, x)}f(y)dy.$$

The transformation T *is self-adjoint if and only if* $T(x, y)$ *is Hermitian, that is, if and only if* $T(x, y) = \overline{T(y, x)}$ *almost everywhere on* $\Delta \times \Delta$. *If the transformation* T *is positive, then*

$$\int_{\Delta_1 \times \Delta_1} T(x, y)dx\, dy \geqslant 0$$

for every bounded set $\Delta_1 \subset \Delta$. *If, moreover,* $T(x, y)$ *is continuous at every point* $(x, x) \in \Delta \times \Delta$, *then* $T(x, x) \geqslant 0$ *for every* $x \in \Delta$.

Proof. The first two statements follow from Theorem 1 of the preceding paragraph. To prove the statement on T^*, we observe that

$$(T^*f, g) = (f, Tg) = \int_{\Delta \times \Delta} \overline{T(y, x)}f(y)\overline{g(x)}dx\, dy =$$
$$\int_\Delta \left(\int_\Delta \overline{T(y, x)}f(y)dy\right)\overline{g(x)}dx.$$

Hence

$$T^*f = \int_\Delta \overline{T(y, x)}f(y)dy.$$

In Theorem 3 of the preceding paragraph we have already proved that $T(y, x)$ has the property (P); the same is therefore true of $\overline{T(y, x)}$.

T is self-adjoint if and only if $T - T^* = O$, that is, if and only if $T(x, y) = \overline{T(y, x)}$ almost everywhere on $\Delta \times \Delta$.

Let now T be positive, and let Δ_1 be an arbitrary bounded subset of Δ. Taking $f(x) = 1$ for $x \in \Delta_1$, and $f(x) = 0$ elsewhere on Δ, the function $f(x)$ belongs to $L_2(\Delta)$, and we find

$$\int_{\Delta_1 \times \Delta_1} T(x, y)dx\, dy = \int_{\Delta \times \Delta} T(x, y)\, \overline{f(x)}\, f(y)dx\, dy = (Tf, f) \geqslant 0.$$

Finally we shall suppose that T is positive and that $T(x, y)$ is continuous at every point $(x, x) \in \Delta \times \Delta$. Then $T(x, y) - \overline{T(y, x)} = 0$ almost everywhere in a neighbourhood of (x_0, x_0) for every $x_0 \in \Delta$; hence in particular $T(x_0, x_0) - \overline{T(x_0, x_0)} = 0$, so that $T(x_0, x_0)$ is real. If there exists a point $x_0 \in \Delta$ with $T(x_0, x_0) < 0$, we may take a finite interval $\Delta_1 \subset \Delta$ such that $x_0 \in \Delta_1$ and $T(x, y) < 0$ for $(x, y) \in \Delta_1 \times \Delta_1$. This implies $\int_{\Delta_1 \times \Delta_1} T(x, y)dx\, dy < 0$, which is a contradiction. It follows that $T(x, x) \geqslant 0$ for every $x \in \Delta$.

Theorem 2. *If the measurable functions* $T_{ij}(x, y)$ $(i, j = 1, \ldots, n)$ *all have the property* (P) *relative to* $L_2(\Delta)$, *the transformation* $\{g\} = T\{f\}$, *defined by*

$$g^i(x) = \Sigma_{j=1}^n \int_\Delta T_{ij}(x, y)f^j(y)dy \quad (i = 1, \ldots, n),$$

is a bounded linear transformation on L_2^n into L_2^n. The Hilbert-adjoint transformation $\{h\} = T^*\{f\}$ is given by

$$h^i(x) = \Sigma_{j=1}^n \int_\Delta \overline{T_{ji}(y, x)} f^j(y)dy \quad (i = 1, \ldots, n).$$

We have $T = O$ if and only if all $T_{ij}(x, y) = 0$ almost everywhere on $\Delta \times \Delta$.

The transformation T is self-adjoint if and only if the matrix kernel $\{T_{ij}(x, y)\}$ is Hermitian, that is, if and only if $T_{ij}(x, y) = \overline{T_{ji}(y, x)}$ almost everywhere on $\Delta \times \Delta$. If T is positive, then

$$\int_{\Delta_i \times \Delta_i} T_{ii}(x, y)dx\, dy \geqslant 0 \quad (i = 1, \ldots, n)$$

for every bounded subset $\Delta_i \subset \Delta$. If moreover $T_{ii}(x, y)$ is continuous at every point $(x, x) \in \Delta \times \Delta$, then $T_{ii}(x, x) \geqslant 0$ for every $x \in \Delta$.

Proof. Only the statement on positive T needs a proof. If T is positive, then

$$(T\{f\}, \{f\}) = \Sigma_{ij=1}^n \int_{\Delta \times \Delta} T_{ij}(x, y)\, \overline{f^i(x)}\, f^j(y)dx\, dy \geqslant 0$$

for every $\{f\} \in L_2^n$. If now Δ_i is an arbitrary bounded subset of Δ, we take $\{f\} = \{0, \ldots, 0, f^i(x), 0, \ldots, 0\}$, where $f^i(x) = 1$ on Δ_i and $f^i(x) = 0$ elsewhere on Δ. It follows that

$$\int_{\Delta_i \times \Delta_i} T_{ii}(x, y)dx\, dy \geqslant 0.$$

The last statement is proved as in the preceding theorem.

Remark. All statements, except those on continuity, may immediately be extended to the case that μ is an arbitrary measure, and Δ an arbitrary μ-measurable set.

§ 9. Examples of Integral Transformations in $L_2(\Delta)$

We shall discuss some examples.

Example A. *A bounded integral transformation which is a projection*

For the sake of completeness we shortly mention here again the example discussed already in Ch. 7, § 15, Ex. C. Let Δ be the linear interval $0 \leqslant x \leqslant 1$, and let $P(x, y)$ be defined on $\Delta \times \Delta$ by

$$P(x, y) = 2^n \text{ on } 1 - (1/2)^{n-1} \leqslant x, y < 1 - (1/2)^n \quad (n = 1, 2, \ldots),$$

$$P(x, y) = 0 \text{ at all other points of } \Delta \times \Delta.$$

Then we have proved that the integral transformation

$$g = Pf = \int_0^1 P(x, y)f(y)dy$$

is bounded on $L_2(\Delta)$ into $L_2(\Delta)$. More precisely, we have proved that P

is the projection on E' along E'', where E' and E'' are orthogonal linear subspaces of $L_2(\Delta)$. Hence, observing that $\| Pf \| \leqslant \| f \|$ for all $f \in L_2$ and $Pf = f$ for all $f \in E'$, we have $\| P \| = 1$. Evidently, since $P(x, y) \geqslant 0$ for all $(x, y) \in \Delta \times \Delta$, the kernel $P(x, y)$ has the property (P). Since $P^n = P$ $(n = 1, 2, \ldots)$, all iterated kernels $P_n(x, y)$ (cf. the definition of iterated kernel in § 7) are identical with $P(x, y)$ itself.

A somewhat different definition of the same kernel $P(x, y)$ may be given. If the functions $\varphi_1(x), \varphi_2(x), \ldots$ are defined on Δ by

$$\varphi_1(x) = 2^{1/2} \quad \text{on } \Delta_1[0 \leqslant x < 1/2], \quad \text{and } = 0 \text{ elsewhere in } \Delta,$$

$$\varphi_2(x) = (2^{1/2})^2 \text{ on } \Delta_2[1/2 \leqslant x < 3/4], \text{ and } = 0 \text{ elsewhere in } \Delta,$$

$$\ldots\ldots\ldots\ldots$$

$$\varphi_n(x) = (2^{1/2})^n \text{ on } \Delta_n[1 - (1/2)^{n-1} \leqslant x < 1 - (1/2)^n], \text{ and } = 0 \text{ elsewhere in } \Delta,$$

$$\ldots\ldots\ldots\ldots,$$

then the system $\varphi_n(x)$ is orthonormal in Δ. Obviously it is not complete, since e.g. $\psi(x)$, where $\psi(x) = 2^{1/2}$ on $0 \leqslant x < 1/4$, $\psi(x) = -2^{1/2}$ on $1/4 \leqslant x < 1/2$ and $\psi(x) = 0$ elsewhere in Δ, is orthogonal to all $\varphi_n(x)$. Comparing the definitions of $P(x, y)$ and $\varphi_n(x)$, we see that

$$P(x, y) = \Sigma_{n=1}^{\infty} \varphi_n(x)\varphi_n(y) = \Sigma_{n=1}^{\infty} \varphi_n(x)\overline{\varphi_n(y)},$$

where for every point $(x, y) \in \Delta \times \Delta$ one term at most of this series differs from zero. The convergence in the whole interval $\Delta \times \Delta$ is therefore guaranteed. It is immediately verified that

$$g(x) = Pf = \Sigma_{n=1}^{\infty} (f, \varphi_n)\varphi_n(x)$$

for every $f \in L_2(\Delta)$, which shows that P is the orthogonal projection on the subspace determined by the system $\varphi_n(x)$.

Example B. *A bounded integral transformation T which has the property that $T^p = O$ for a prescribed positive integer p, whereas $T^q \neq O$ for $1 \leqslant q < p$*

We shall, to simplify notations, first construct a bounded integral transformation $T \neq O$ satisfying $T^2 = O$. For this purpose we consider the same system $\varphi_n(x)$ as in the preceding example, and we define

$$T(x, y) = \varphi_2(x)\varphi_3(y) + \varphi_4(x)\varphi_5(y) + \ldots =$$

$$\Sigma_{n=1}^{\infty} \varphi_{2n}(x)\varphi_{2n+1}(y) = \Sigma_{n=1}^{\infty} \varphi_{2n}(x)\overline{\varphi_{2n+1}(y)}.$$

The convergence in $\Delta \times \Delta$ is guaranteed, since for every $(x, y) \in \Delta \times \Delta$ one term at most of the series differs from zero. For $x \in \Delta_{2n}$ $(n = 1, 2, \ldots)$

and $f(x) \in L_2(\Delta)$ we have

$$g(x) = Tf = \int_\Delta T(x, y)f(y)dy =$$

$$\varphi_{2n}(x) \int_\Delta f(y)\overline{\varphi_{2n+1}(y)}dy = (f, \varphi_{2n+1})\varphi_{2n}(x),$$

and for $x \in \Delta_{2n-1}$ ($n = 1, 2, \ldots$) we have obviously $g(x) = 0$. Hence, for all $x \in \Delta$,

$$g(x) = Tf = \Sigma_{n=1}^{\infty} (f, \varphi_{2n+1})\varphi_{2n}(x).$$

Since $\| Tf \|^2 = \Sigma \mid (f, \varphi_{2n+1}) \mid^2 \leqslant \| f \|^2$ (Bessel's inequality), T is bounded.

Observing now that $(g, \varphi_{2n+1}) = (Tf, \varphi_{2n+1}) = \Sigma_{k=1}^{\infty} (f, \varphi_{2k+1})(\varphi_{2k}, \varphi_{2n+1}) = 0$ for $n = 1, 2, \ldots$, we find

$$T^2f = Tg = \Sigma_{n=1}^{\infty} (g, \varphi_{2n+1})\, \varphi_{2n}(x) = 0,$$

hence $T^2 = O$.

The extension from $p = 2$ to arbitrary p follows by defining

$$T(x, y) = \{\varphi_p(x)\varphi_{p+1}(y) + \varphi_{p+1}(x)\varphi_{p+2}(y) + \ldots + \varphi_{2p-2}(x)\varphi_{2p-1}(y)\}$$

$$+ \{\varphi_{2p}(x)\varphi_{2p+1}(y) + \ldots + \varphi_{3p-2}(x)\varphi_{3p-1}(y)\} + \{\varphi_{3p}(x)\varphi_{3p+1}(y) + \ldots =$$

$$\Sigma_{n=1}^{\infty} [\varphi_{np}(x)\varphi_{np+1}(y) + \varphi_{np+1}(x)\varphi_{np+2}(y) + \ldots + \varphi_{np+p-2}(x)\varphi_{np+p-1}(y)].$$

In the same way as for $p = 2$ it is easily seen that $T, T^2, \ldots, T^{p-1} \neq O$, and $T^p = O$.

We make one final remark. If $g(x) \in L_2(\Delta)$ has the property that $g(x) = 0$ on $1/2 < x \leqslant 1$, then $(g, \varphi_n) = 0$ ($n = 2, 3, \ldots$), hence $Tg = 0$. If therefore $S(x, y)$ is the kernel of a bounded integral transformation S, and $S(x, y) = 0$ outside $0 < x, y \leqslant 1/2$, so that $g(x) = Sf = 0$ for $1/2 < x \leqslant 1$, then $TSf = Tg = 0$ for all $f \in L_2$. Since on the other hand $h(x) = Tf = 0$ in $0 \leqslant x < 1/2$, we have also $STf = 0$. It follows that

$$(S + T)^2 = S^2 + ST + TS + T^2 = S^2 + T^2,$$

$$(S + T)^3 = (S^2 + T^2)\,(S + T) = S^3 + S.ST + T.TS + T^3 = S^3 + T^3,$$

and so on. Generally $(S + T)^q = S^q + T^q$, so that for $q \geqslant p$ we have $(S + T)^q = S^q$.

Example C. *The kernel* $A(x, y) = \mid x - y \mid^{-\alpha}$ $(\alpha < 1)$

We shall consider the linear transformation A, defined by

$$g(x) = Af = \int_0^1 A(x, y)f(y)dy,$$

where $A(x, y)$ is defined on $0 \leqslant x, y \leqslant 1$ by $A(x, y) = \mid x - y \mid^{-\alpha}$ $(\alpha < 1)$.

Lemma 1. *The integral* $\int_0^1 x^{-\alpha} dx$ *is finite for* $\alpha < 1$, *and it is the limit of the Riemann integral* $\int_\delta^1 x^{-\alpha} dx$ *for* δ *tending to* 0; *hence* $\int_0^1 x^{-\alpha} dx = 1/(1-\alpha)$. *For* $\alpha \geqslant 1$ *we have* $\int_0^1 x^{-\alpha} dx = \infty$.

Proof. Follows by considering the integrals $\int_0^1 f_n(x)dx$, where $f_n(x) = n$ for $x^{-\alpha} > n$ and $f_n(x) = x^{-\alpha}$ for $x^{-\alpha} \leqslant n$, and then making $n \to \infty$.

Lemma 2. *Let* $A(x, y) = |x - y|^{-\alpha}$ *for* $0 \leqslant x, y \leqslant 1$. *Then* $\int_0^1 \int_0^1 |A(x,y)|^2 dx\, dy = (1-\alpha)^{-1}(1-2\alpha)^{-1}$ *for* $\alpha < 1/2$ *and* $= \infty$ *for* $\alpha \geqslant 1/2$.

Proof. We observe first that $\int_0^1 \int_0^1 |A|^2 dx\, dy = 2\int_0^1 (\int_0^x |A|^2 dy)dx$. For $\alpha < 1/2$ we have by Lemma 1 $\int_0^x |A|^2 dy = \int_0^x (x - y)^{-2\alpha} dy = (1 - 2\alpha)^{-1} x^{1-2\alpha}$, hence

$$\int_0^1 \int_0^1 |A|^2 dx\, dy = 2(1 - 2\alpha)^{-1} \int_0^1 x^{1-2\alpha} dx = (1 - \alpha)^{-1}(1 - 2\alpha)^{-1}.$$

For $\alpha \geqslant 1/2$ we have by Lemma 1 $\int_0^x |A|^2 dy = \infty$, hence $\int_0^1 \int_0^1 |A|^2 dx\, dy = \infty$.

Lemma 3. *Let* $f(x)$ *and* $\varphi(x)$ *be defined in the one-dimensional interval* $-\infty < x < \infty$, *and let us suppose that they both have the period* 1, *hence* $f(x+1) = f(x)$, $\varphi(x+1) = \varphi(x)$ *for all* x. *Then, if* $f(x)$ *and* $\varphi(x)$ *are both summable over* (0, 1), *the composition*

$$h(x) = \int_0^1 \varphi(x - y) f(y) dy$$

of φ *and* f *is summable over* (0, 1).

Proof. Since $\varphi(x)$ is measurable on $-1 \leqslant x \leqslant 1$, we see easily that $\varphi(x - y)$, considered as a function of two variables, is measurable on the parallelogram bounded by $x - y = \pm 1$, $y = 0$, $y = 1$, and therefore also on the interval $0 \leqslant x, y \leqslant 1$. Observing that $\varphi(x)$ is periodic, we find therefore

$$\int_0^1 \int_0^1 |\varphi(x - y) f(y)| dx\, dy = \int_0^1 (\int_0^1 |\varphi(x - y)| dx) |f(y)| dy$$

$$= \int_0^1 |\varphi(x)| dx . \int_0^1 |f(y)| dy < \infty,$$

which shows that $\varphi(x - y)f(y)$ is summable over $0 \leqslant x, y \leqslant 1$. Then, by Fubini's Theorem, $h(x)$ is a summable function of x.

Lemma 4. *Let* $f(x)$ *and* $\varphi(x)$ $(-\infty < x < \infty)$ *have the period* 1; *let* $\varphi(x)$ *be summable over* (0, 1) *and* $f(x) \in L_p[0, 1]$ $(1 \leqslant p \leqslant \infty)$. *Then the composition* h *of* φ *and* f *belongs to* $L_p[0, 1]$ *and*

$$\| h \|_p \leqslant \int_0^1 |\varphi(x)| dx . \| f \|_p.$$

Proof. If $1 \leqslant p < \infty$, we have

$$(1) \begin{cases} \int_0^1 |\varphi(x)|\,dx . \|f\|^p = \int_0^1 (\int_0^1 |\varphi(x)|\,dx)\,|f(y)|^p\,dy = \\ \int_0^1 (\int_0^1 |\varphi(x-y)|\,dx)\,|f(y)|^p\,dy = \int_0^1 \int_0^1 |\varphi(x-y)|.|f(y)|^p\,dx\,dy = \\ \int_0^1 (\int_0^1 |\varphi(x-y)|.|f(y)|^p\,dy)dx. \end{cases}$$

Observing now that $|h(x)| \leqslant \int_0^1 |\varphi(x-y)f(y)|\,dy = \int_0^1 |\varphi|^{1/p}.|f|.|\varphi|^{1/q}\,dy$ $(1/p + 1/q = 1)$, we find by Hölder's inequality

$$|h(x)|^p \leqslant \int_0^1 |\varphi(x-y)|.|f(y)|^p\,dy.[\int_0^1 |\varphi(x-y)|\,dy]^{p/q}$$
$$= \int_0^1 |\varphi(x-y)|.|f(y)|^p\,dy.[\int_0^1 |\varphi(y)|\,dy]^{p/q},$$

hence, by (1),

$$\int_0^1 |h|^p\,dx \leqslant [\int_0^1 |\varphi|\,dy]^{p/q}\,[\int_0^1 (\int_0^1 |\varphi(x-y)|.|f(y)|^p\,dy)dx]$$
$$= (\int_0^1 |\varphi|\,dx)^{1+p/q}\,\|f\|^p,$$

so that, since $1 + p/q = p(1/p + 1/q) = p$, we have

$$\|h\| \leqslant \int_0^1 |\varphi|\,dx.\|f\|.$$

If $p = \infty$, hence $|f(y)| \leqslant \|f\|$ almost everywhere on $0 \leqslant y \leqslant 1$, we have

$$|h(x)| \leqslant \int_0^1 |\varphi(x-y)|\,dy.\|f\| = \int_0^1 |\varphi(y)|\,dy.\|f\|$$

almost everywhere on $0 \leqslant x \leqslant 1$, hence

$$\|h\| \leqslant \int_0^1 |\varphi|\,dx.\|f\|.$$

This completes the proof.

We shall show now that the transformation A, defined by

$$g(x) = Af = \int_0^1 A(x,y)f(y)dy = \int_0^1 |x-y|^{-\alpha} f(y)dy \quad (\alpha < 1),$$

is a bounded linear transformation on $L_p[0, 1]$ $(1 \leqslant p \leqslant \infty)$ into $L_p[0, 1]$, and that

$$\|A\| \leqslant \begin{cases} 2^\alpha/(1-\alpha) & (0 \leqslant \alpha < 1), \\ (2-2^\alpha)/(1-\alpha) & (\alpha < 0). \end{cases}$$

Let, for this purpose [3], $\varphi(t)$ $(-\infty < t < \infty)$ be defined by $\varphi(-t) = \varphi(t)$, $\varphi(t+1) = \varphi(t)$ for all t, and

$$\varphi(t) = \begin{cases} t^{-\alpha} \text{ for } 0 \leqslant t \leqslant 1/2, \text{ if } 0 \leqslant \alpha < 1, \\ t^{-\alpha} \text{ for } 1/2 \leqslant t \leqslant 1, \text{ if } \alpha < 0. \end{cases}$$

Then $|t|^{-\alpha} \leqslant \varphi(t)$ for $|t| \leqslant 1$, and

$$\int_0^1 |\varphi| \, dt = 2\int_0^{1/2} \varphi(t)dt = 2\int_0^{1/2} t^{-\alpha}\, dt = 2^\alpha/(1-\alpha) \quad (0 \leqslant \alpha < 1),$$

$$\int_0^1 |\varphi| \, dt = 2\int_{1/2}^{1} \varphi(t)dt = 2\int_{1/2}^{1} t^{-\alpha}\, dt = (2-2^\alpha)/(1-\alpha) \quad (\alpha < 0).$$

Writing $h(x) = \int_0^1 \varphi(x-y)\,|f(y)|\,dy$, if $f(x) \in L_p[0, 1]$ is given, we have by Lemma 4

$$\begin{cases} \| h \|_p \leqslant \{2^\alpha/(1-\alpha)\}\, \| f \|_p & (0 \leqslant \alpha < 1), \\ \| h \|_p \leqslant \{(2-2^\alpha)/(1-\alpha)\}\, \| f \|_p & (\alpha < 0), \end{cases}$$

so that, since

$$| g(x) | = | \int_0^1 |x-y|^{-\alpha} f(y)dy | \leqslant \int_0^1 \varphi(x-y)\,|f(y)|\,dy = h(x),$$

also

$$\begin{cases} \| g \|_p \leqslant \{2^\alpha/(1-\alpha)\}\, \| f \|_p & (0 \leqslant \alpha < 1), \\ \| g \|_p \leqslant \{(2-2^\alpha)/(1-\alpha)\}\, \| f \|_p & (\alpha < 0). \end{cases}$$

Evidently, if $A(x, y) = B(x, y)\,|x-y|^{-\alpha}$, where $B(x, y)$ is measurable and bounded almost everywhere on $0 \leqslant x, y \leqslant 1$, the same result is obtained. We note that the kernel $A(x, y) = B(x, y)\,|x-y|^{-\alpha}$ has the property (P), since $|x-y|^{-\alpha} \geqslant 0$.

Let us consider now in particular the case $p = 2$. Then, by Lemma 2, the transformation $Af = \int_0^1 |x-y|^{-\alpha} f(y)dy$ is of finite double-norm $|||\, A \,|||$ for $\alpha < 1/2$, and $|||\, A \,||| = (\int_0^1\int_0^1 |x-y|^{-2\alpha}\, dx\, dy)^{1/2} = (1-\alpha)^{-1/2} (1-2\alpha)^{-1/2}$. As we know, $\| A \| \leqslant |||\, A \,|||$ (cf. Ch. 7, § 15, Ex. A), hence

$$\| A \| \leqslant \min\,[(2-2^\alpha)/(1-\alpha),\ |||\, A \,|||] \text{ for } \alpha < 0,$$

$$\| A \| \leqslant \min\,[2^\alpha/(1-\alpha),\ |||\, A \,|||] \qquad \text{for } 0 \leqslant \alpha < 1/2.$$

For $\alpha < 0$ we have $|||\, A \,||| = (1-\alpha)^{-1/2}(1-2\alpha)^{-1/2} < (1-\alpha)^{-1} < (2-2^\alpha)/(1-\alpha)$, so that $|||\, A \,|||$ gives the better value. For $\alpha = 0$ we have $|||\, A \,||| = 1 = 2^0/(1-0)$. For small positive α the value of $|||\, A \,|||$ is once again better than $2^\alpha/(1-\alpha)$, but if α exceeds a certain value α_0 (it is easily verified that $\alpha_0 < 1/4$), then $2^\alpha/(1-\alpha)$ is the smaller value. Hence, and this is an important fact to note,

$$\| A \| < |||\, A \,|||$$

for $\alpha_0 < \alpha < 1/2$.

The most interesting case, however, is $1/2 \leqslant \alpha < 1$. Then, although $|||\, A \,||| = \infty$, the value of $\| A \|$ is finite, so that in this case A is a bounded transformation of infinite double-norm. In Example A we also discussed a bounded transformation P of infinite double-norm, and since $P^n = P (n = 1, 2, \ldots)$, P^n has infinite double-norm for all values of n. We shall see that our transformation A $(1/2 \leqslant \alpha < 1)$ has different properties. More precisely, we shall prove that A^n is of finite double-norm for $n > 1/2(1-\alpha)$.

Lemma 5. *The integral* $\int_1^\infty x^{-\alpha}dx = \lim_{T\to\infty}\int_1^T x^{-\alpha}dx$ *is finite for* $\alpha > 1$, *and* $= \infty$ *for* $\alpha \leqslant 1$.

Proof. Follows by direct computation.

Lemma 6. *The integral* $\int_{-\infty}^{\infty} |\sigma|^{-\alpha} |1-\sigma|^{-\beta}d\sigma$ *is finite for* $\alpha < 1$, $\beta < 1$, $\alpha + \beta > 1$, *and it is the limit of the sum of Riemann integrals* $\int_{-T}^{-\delta} + \int_{\delta}^{1-\delta} + \int_{1+\delta}^{T}$ for $T \to \infty$ *and* $\delta \to 0$.

Proof. Follows from Lemma 1 and Lemma 5.

Lemma 7. *Let* $0 \leqslant x \leqslant 1, 0 \leqslant y \leqslant 1, x \neq y, \alpha < 1, \beta < 1, \alpha + \beta > 1$. *Then*

$$J = \int_0^1 |x-z|^{-\alpha} |y-z|^{-\beta}dz \leqslant$$

$$|x-y|^{-(\alpha+\beta-1)} \int_{-\infty}^{\infty} |\sigma|^{-\alpha} |1-\sigma|^{-\beta}d\sigma = M_{\alpha\beta} |x-y|^{-(\alpha+\beta-1)}$$

Proof. By Lemma 1 the integral J is the limit of the Riemann integral which is obtained by excluding two small intervals around x and y from the interval of integration $[0, 1]$. In this Riemann integral we introduce a new variable σ by $z = x + \sigma(y-x)$. Then $|x-z| = |\sigma|.|x-y|$, $|y-z| = |1-\sigma|.|x-y|$, $dz = (y-x)d\sigma$. Substituting this and taking the limit we obtain the desired result.

Lemma 8. *Let* $0 \leqslant \alpha < 1$, $0 \leqslant \beta < 1$, $\alpha + \beta < 1$, $A(x, y) = B(x, y) |x-y|^{-\alpha}$ *and* $A^*(x, y) = B^*(x, y) |x-y|^{-\beta}$ *for* $0 \leqslant x, y \leqslant 1$, *where* $B(x, y)$ *and* $B^*(x, y)$ *are measurable and bounded (almost everywhere). Then* $C(x, y) = \int_0^1 A(x, z)A^*(z, y)dz$ *is measurable and bounded (almost everywhere) on* $0 \leqslant x, y \leqslant 1$.

Proof. Since both $A(x, y)$ and $A^*(x, y)$ have the property (P) relative to $L_2[0, 1]$, it follows from § 7, Th. 1 that $C(x, y)$ has the property (P). In particular $C(x, y)$ is measurable.

Supposing now that both $|B(x, y)|$ and $|B^*(x, y)| \leqslant M$ almost everywhere on $[0, 1; 0, 1]$, we have, for almost every x and almost every y, the inequalities $|B(x, z)| \leqslant M$, $|B^*(z, y)| \leqslant M$ for almost every z. If x and y have this property, and $x \leqslant y$, we split up $\int_0^1$ into $\int_0^x + \int_x^y + \int_y^1$. Then $|\int_0^x AA^*dz| = |\int_0^x BB^* |x-z|^{-\alpha} |y-z|^{-\beta} dz| \leqslant M^2 \int_0^x |x-z|^{-(\alpha+\beta)} dz \leqslant M_1$ and $|\int_y^1 AA^*dz| \leqslant M^2 \int_y^1 |y-z|^{-(\alpha+\beta)} |dz \leqslant M_2$. Furthermore

$| \int_x^y AA^*dz | = | \int_x^{(x+y)/2} + \int_{(x+y)/2}^y | \leqslant M^2(\int_x^{(x+y)/2} | x - z |^{-(\alpha+\beta)} dz + \int_{(x+y)/2}^y | y - z |^{-(\alpha+\beta)}dz) \leqslant M_3$. Adding these results, we find $| C(x, y) | \leqslant M_1 + M_2 + M_3$, which shows that $C(x, y)$ is bounded almost everywhere for $x \leqslant y$. For $x > y$ the proof is similar.

Lemma 9. *Let* $\alpha < 1, \beta < 1, \alpha + \beta > 1$ *(hence* $\alpha > 0, \beta > 0$*),* $A(x, y) = B(x, y) \, | x - y |^{-\alpha}$ *and* $A^*(x, y) = B^*(x, y) \, | x - y |^{-\beta}$ *for* $0 \leqslant x, y \leqslant 1$, *where* $B(x, y)$ *and* $B^*(x, y)$ *are measurable and bounded (almost everywhere). Then* $C(x, y) = \int_0^1 A(x, z)A^*(z, y)dz$ *is measurable, and* $C(x, y) \, | x - y |^{\alpha+\beta-1}$ *is bounded (almost everywhere).*

Proof. The measurability of $C(x, y)$ is proved as in the preceding lemma. By Lemma 7 we have (for almost every x and almost every y) $| C(x, y) | \leqslant \int_0^1 | AA^* | \, dz \leqslant M^2 \int_0^1 | x - z |^{-\alpha} \, | y - z |^{-\beta} \, dz \leqslant M^2 . M_{\alpha\beta} \, | x - y |^{-(\alpha+\beta-1)}$, and this shows that $C(x, y) \, | x - y |^{\alpha+\beta-1}$ is bounded (almost everywhere). We may write therefore $C(x, y) = D(x, y) \, | x - y |^{-(\alpha+\beta-1)}$, where $D(x, y)$ is bounded (almost everywhere).

Lemma 10. *Let* $\alpha < 1, \beta < 1, \alpha + \beta = 1$ *(hence* $\alpha > 0, \beta > 0$*),* $A(x, y) = B(x, y) \, | x - y |^{-\alpha}$ *and* $A^*(x, y) = B^*(x, y) \, | x - y |^{-\beta}$ *for* $0 \leqslant x, y \leqslant 1$, *where* $B(x, y)$ *and* $B^*(x, y)$ *are measurable and bounded (almost everywhere). Then* $C(x, y) = \int_0^1 A(x, z)A^*(z, y)dz$ *is measurable, and* $C(x, y) \, | x - y |^{\varepsilon}$ *is bounded (almost everywhere) for every* $\varepsilon > 0$.

Proof. It is no restriction to suppose that $\varepsilon < \min(1 - \alpha, 1 - \beta)$. By Lemma 7 we have then (for almost every x and almost every y) $| C(x, y) | \leqslant M^2 \int_0^1 | x - z |^{-\alpha} \, | y - z |^{-\beta}dz \leqslant M^2 \int_0^1 | x - z |^{-(\alpha+\varepsilon)} . | y - z |^{-\beta}dz \leqslant M^2 . M_{\alpha+\varepsilon,\beta} \, | x - y |^{-\varepsilon}$. We may write therefore $C(x, y) = D(x, y) \, | x - y |^{-\varepsilon}$, where $D(x, y)$ is bounded (almost everywhere).

Lemma 11. *Let* $0 < \alpha < 1$, *and* $A(x, y) = B(x, y) \, | x - y |^{-\alpha}$ *for* $0 \leqslant x, y \leqslant 1$, *where* $B(x, y)$ *is measurable and bounded (almost everywhere). Then the iterated kernels*

$$A_1(x, y) = A(x, y),$$

$$A_n(x, y) = \int_0^1 A_1(x, z)A_{n-1}(z, y)dz \quad (n = 2, 3, \ldots)$$

are measurable; for $n > 1/2(1 - \alpha)$ *the double-norm* $||| A_n ||| = \int_0^1 \int_0^1 | A_n |^2 dx \, dy$ *is finite, and for* $n > 1/(1 - \alpha)$ *the kernel* $A_n(x, y)$ *is bounded (almost everywhere).*

Proof. The measurability of the iterated kernels follows once again from § 7, Th. 1. Let first $0 < \alpha < 1/2$, so that $1 < 1/(1 - \alpha) < 2$ and $0 < 1/2(1 - \alpha) < 1$. We have to prove therefore that $A_n(x, y)$ is bounded for $n \geqslant 2$, and that $||| A_n |||$ is finite for $n \geqslant 1$. The first statement follows from Lemma 8. Indeed, taking $\beta = \alpha$ in this lemma, we first find that $A_2(x, y)$ is bounded. Next, taking $\alpha = \alpha$, $\beta = 0$, we see that $A_n(x, y)$ $(n \geqslant 3)$ is also bounded. The second statement is a consequence of Lemma 2, by which $||| A_1 ||| = ||| A |||$ is finite, and the boundedness of $A_n(x, y)$ for $n \geqslant 2$.

Let now $\alpha = 1/2$. Denoting by $B_n(x, y)$ $(n = 1, 2, \ldots)$ bounded functions, we find, on account of Lemma 10 and Lemma 8,

$$A_1(x, y) = B_1(x, y) \mid x - y \mid^{-1/2},$$

$$A_2(x, y) = B_2(x, y) \mid x - y \mid^{-\varepsilon},$$

$$A_n(x, y) = B_n(x, y) \qquad (n \geqslant 3);$$

hence $||| A_n ||| < \infty$ for $n > 1 = 1/2(1 - 1/2) = 1/2(1 - \alpha)$, and $A_n(x, y)$ is bounded for $n > 2 = 1/(1 - 1/2) = 1/(1 - \alpha)$.

For $1/2 < \alpha < 1$ we have by Lemma 9

$$A_1(x, y) = B_1(x, y) \mid x - y \mid^{-\alpha},$$

$$A_2(x, y) = B_2(x, y) \mid x - y \mid^{-(2\alpha-1)},$$

$$A_3(x, y) = B_3(x, y) \mid x - y \mid^{-(3\alpha-2)},$$

and so on. Generally

$$A_n(x, y) = B_n(x, y) \mid x - y \mid^{-\{n\alpha-(n-1)\}} \qquad (n = 1, 2, \ldots),$$

as long as $1 - n(1 - \alpha) = n\alpha - (n - 1) > 0$. Hence $||| A_n ||| < \infty$ for $1 - n(1 - \alpha) < 1/2$ or $n > 1/2(1 - \alpha)$.

If there exists a value of n for which $1 - n(1 - \alpha) = 0$ or $n = 1/(1 - \alpha)$, the Lemmas 9, 10, and 8 show that, for this particular value of n and arbitrary $\varepsilon > 0$, we have

$$A_{n-1}(x, y) = B_{n-1}(x, y) \mid x - y \mid^{-(1-\alpha)},$$

$$A_n(x, y) = B_n(x, y) \mid x - y \mid^{-\varepsilon},$$

$$A_{n+j}(x, y) = B_{n+j}(x, y) \quad (j = 1, 2, \ldots),$$

which involves boundedness of $A_n(x, y)$ for $n > 1/(1 - \alpha)$. If there exists no integer n for which $1 - n(1 - \alpha) = 0$, but if n_0 is the largest integer n for which $1 - n(1 - \alpha) > 0$, Lemma 8 shows that $A_n(x, y)$ is bounded for $n > n_0$. In other words, $A_n(x, y)$ is bounded for $1 - n(1 - \alpha) < 0$ or $n > 1/(1 - \alpha)$. This completes the proof.

As a consequence of the last lemma we see now that the bounded linear integral transformation A on $L_2[0, 1]$, defined by

$$Af = \int_0^1 A(x, y)f(y)dy = \int_0^1 B(x, y) \mid x - y \mid^{-\alpha} f(y)dy,$$

where $1/2 \leqslant \alpha < 1$ and $B(x, y)$ is measurable and bounded (almost everywhere), has the property that A^n is of finite double-norm for $n > 1/2(1 - \alpha)$.

We finally note that A is self-adjoint if and only if $A(x, y)$ is Hermitian, that is, if and only if $A(x, y) = \overline{A(y, x)}$ almost everywhere. This condition however is satisfied if and only if $B(x, y) = \overline{B(y, x)}$ almost everywhere.

Example D. *Kernel of finite double-norm*

Let $\Phi(u)$ and $\Psi(v)$ be complementary functions in the sense of Young, and let Δ be a finite or infinite interval. Then, if $T(x, y)$ is of finite double-norm on $\Delta \times \Delta$, that is, if $T(x, y)$ as a function of y belongs to $L_\Psi(\Delta)$ for almost every $x \in \Delta$, and $t(x) = \| T(x, y) \|_\Psi \in L_\Phi(\Delta)$, we have proved in Ch. 7, § 15, Ex. B that the linear transformation T on $L_\Phi(\Delta)$ (into $L_\Phi(\Delta)$), defined by

$$Tf = \int_\Delta T(x, y)f(y)dy,$$

is bounded, and that $\| T \| \leqslant ||| T ||| = \| t(x) \|_\Phi$.

In the case that $\Phi(2u) \leqslant M\Phi(u)$ for all $u \geqslant 0$, we have also proved that the linear transformation T^* on $L_\Psi(\Delta)$ (into $L_\Psi(\Delta)$), defined by

$$T^*f = \int_\Delta T(y, x)f(y)dy,$$

is bounded as well.

Before examining more in detail the case that $L_\Phi(\Delta)$ and $L_\Psi(\Delta)$ are both identical with the Hilbert space $L_2(\Delta)$, we make two remarks. In the first place we note that it may occur that $\| T \| < ||| T |||$, as was shown in the preceding example (transformation A on $L_2[0, 1]$ with kernel $A(x, y) = \mid x - y \mid^{-\alpha}$, $1/4 < \alpha < 1/2$; $\| A \| \leqslant 2^\alpha/(1 - \alpha) < (1 - \alpha)^{-1/2}(1 - 2\alpha)^{-1/2} = ||| A |||$). In the second place it may be asked whether $||| T ||| < \infty$ implies $||| T^* ||| < \infty$. More precisely, if we restrict ourselves to the spaces $L_p(\Delta)$ $(1 < p < \infty)$, we ask whether $\int_\Delta (\int_\Delta \mid T(x, y) \mid^q dy)^{p/q} dx < \infty$ implies $\int_\Delta (\int_\Delta \mid T(x, y) \mid^p dx)^{q/p} dy < \infty$ $(1/p + 1/q = 1)$. That this is not so, is shown by the example $T(x, y) = \mid x - y \mid^{-1/2}$, $\Delta = [0, 1]$, $p = 4$ (hence $q = 4/3$). Then

$$\int_0^1 (\int_0^1 \mid T(x, y) \mid^q dy)^{p/q} dx = \int_0^1 (\int_0^1 \mid x - y \mid^{-2/3} dy)^3 dx < \infty,$$

$$\int_0^1 (\int_0^1 \mid T(x, y) \mid^p dx)^{q/p} dy = \int_0^1 (\int_0^1 \mid x - y \mid^{-2} dx)^{1/3} dy = \infty.$$

§ 10. Integral Transformations of Finite Double-Norm in $L_2(\Delta)$

We consider first a separable Hilbert space R, and we assume the orthonormal system $\varphi_n (n = 1, 2, \ldots)$ to be complete in R. According to the definition in § 2 the linear transformation T, on R into R, will be said to be of finite double-norm whenever the expression $|||\, T \,|||^2 = \Sigma_{ij} \mid \tau_{ji} \mid^2$ is finite, where $\tau_{ji} = (T\varphi_i, \varphi_j)$ $(i, j = 1, 2, \ldots)$. We have already proved that in this case T is bounded, $\| T \| \leqslant |||\, T \,|||$, and that the value of $|||\, T \,|||$ is independent of the particular orthonormal system which is used in its definition.

Theorem 1. *If T and S are of finite double-norm, and α is arbitrarily complex, then $T + S$ and αT are of finite double-norm, and $|||\, T + S \,||| \leqslant |||\, T \,||| + |||\, S \,|||$, $|||\, \alpha T \,||| = | \alpha | . |||\, T \,|||$.*

If the space R is complete, so that T^* exists, T^* is of finite double-norm, and $|||\, T^* \,||| = |||\, T \,|||$.

Proof. The statement about $T + S$ follows immediately from

$$(\Sigma_{ij} \mid \tau_{ij} + \sigma_{ij} \mid^2)^{1/2} \leqslant (\Sigma_{ij} \mid \tau_{ij} \mid^2)^{1/2} + (\Sigma_{ij} \mid \sigma_{ij} \mid^2)^{1/2},$$

and $|||\, \alpha T \,||| = | \alpha | . |||\, T \,|||$ follows from $(\alpha T\varphi_i, \varphi_j) = \alpha(T\varphi_i, \varphi_j)$.

If T^* exists, we have $(T^*\varphi_i, \varphi_j) = (\varphi_i, T\varphi_j) = \overline{(T\varphi_j, \varphi_i)} = \overline{\tau_{ij}}$, hence $\Sigma_{ij} \mid (T^*\varphi_i, \varphi_j) \mid^2 = \Sigma_{ij} \mid \tau_{ij} \mid^2$.

Theorem 2. *If A is an arbitrary bounded linear transformation and T is of finite double-norm, then AT and TA are of finite double-norm, and*

$$|||\, AT \,||| \leqslant \| A \| . |||\, T \,|||, \qquad |||\, TA \,||| \leqslant \|A\| . |||\, T \,||| \quad [4].$$

Proof. We have

$$\Sigma_j \mid (AT\varphi_i, \varphi_j) \mid^2 = \| AT\varphi_i \|^2 \leqslant \| A \|^2 . \| T\varphi_i \|^2 =$$
$$\| A \|^2 \Sigma_j \mid (T\varphi_i, \varphi_j) \mid^2 = \| A \|^2 \Sigma_j \mid \tau_{ji} \mid^2,$$

hence

$$\Sigma_{ij} \mid (AT\varphi_i, \varphi_j) \mid^2 \leqslant \| A \|^2 \Sigma_{ij} \mid \tau_{ji} \mid^2$$

or $|||\, AT \,||| \leqslant \| A \| . |||\, T \,|||$.

Furthermore

$$|||\, TA \,||| = |||\, (TA)^* \,||| = |||\, A^*T^* \,||| \leqslant \| A^* \| . |||\, T^* \,||| = \| A \| . |||T|||,$$

where, if the space R is not complete of itself, A^*, T^* and $(TA)^*$ are considered as transformations on the closure $\bar{R}$ into $\bar{R}$.

Corollary. *If T_1 and T_2 are of finite double-norm, then T_1T_2 is of finite double-norm, and $|||\, T_1T_2 \,||| \leqslant \| T_1 \| . |||\, T_2 \,||| \leqslant |||\, T_1 \,||| . |||\, T_2 \,|||$. In* *particular, if T is of finite double-norm,* $|||\,T^n\,||| \leqslant |||\,T\,|||^n$ $(n = 1, 2, \ldots)$.

Theorem 3. *If* T_n $(n = 1, 2, \ldots)$ *is a sequence of linear transformations of finite double-norm such that* $\lim |||\,T - T_n\,||| = 0$, *then* T *is a linear transformation of finite double-norm.*

Proof. Follows from Theorem 1 by observing that $T = T_n + (T - T_n)$.

Definition. *If* T_n $(n = 1, 2, \ldots)$ *is a sequence of linear transformations of finite double-norm such that* $\lim |||\,T - T_n\,||| = 0$, *then the sequence* T_n *is said to converge in double-norm to* T.

We observe that $\lim |||\,T - T_n\,||| = 0$ implies $\lim \|\,T - T_n\,\| = 0$, and this in its turn implies $\lim \|\,Tf - T_nf\,\| = 0$ for every $f \in R$. If therefore T_n converges in double-norm to T, then T_n converges to T in the ordinary sense (cf. Ch. 7, § 12).

Theorem 4. *If* T_n $(n = 1, 2, \ldots)$ *is a sequence of linear transformations of finite double-norm such that* $\lim |||\,T_m - T_n\,||| = 0$ *as* $m, n \to \infty$, *then there exists a linear transformation* T *of finite double-norm such that* $\lim |||\,T - T_n\,||| = 0$.

Proof. Since

$$\lim_{m,n\to\infty} \Sigma_{ij} \,|\, (T_m\varphi_i, \varphi_j) - (T_n\varphi_i, \varphi_j) \,|^2 = 0,$$

the numbers $\tau_{ji} = \lim_{n\to\infty} (T_n\varphi_i, \varphi_j)$ exist, and $\lim_{n\to\infty} \Sigma_{ij} \,|\, \tau_{ji} - (T_n\varphi_i, \varphi_j) \,|^2 = 0$. Defining therefore T by $(T\varphi_i, \varphi_j) = \tau_{ji}$, we have $\lim |||\,T - T_n\,||| = 0$.

Theorem 5. *If* A *is an arbitrary bounded linear transformation, and* T_n *converges to* T *in double-norm, then* AT_n *converges to* AT *in double-norm, and* T_nA *converges to* TA *in double-norm.*

Proof. Follows from Theorem 2.

Definition. *If the bounded linear transformation* A *with matrix* $\{\alpha_{ij}\}$ *has the property that* $\Sigma\, \alpha_{ii}$ *converges, then* $\tau(A) = \Sigma_i\, \alpha_{ii}$ *is called the trace of* A.

Theorem 6. *If* $A = BC$, *where* B *and* C *are of finite double-norm, then* $\tau(A)$ *exists and* $|\,\tau(A)\,| \leqslant |||\,B\,|||\,.\,|||\,C\,|||$.

Proof. Denoting the matrices of A, B, C by $\{\alpha_{ij}\}, \{\beta_{ij}\}, \{\gamma_{ij}\}$ respectively, we have $\alpha_{ii} = \Sigma_j\, \beta_{ij}\gamma_{ji}$, hence $(\Sigma \,|\, \alpha_{ii} \,|)^2 \leqslant \Sigma_{ij} \,|\, \beta_{ij} \,|^2 . \Sigma_{ij} \,|\, \gamma_{ij} \,|^2 = |||\,B\,|||^2 \,.\, |||\,C\,|||^2$. It follows that $\tau(A) = \Sigma_i\, \alpha_{ii}$ converges, and that

$$|\,\tau(A)\,| \leqslant |||\,B\,|||\,.\,|||\,C\,|||.$$

Corollary. *If A is of finite double-norm, then $\tau(A^n)$ exists for $n \geqslant 2$, and* $|\tau(A^n)| \leqslant ||| A^{n-1} |||.||| A ||| \leqslant ||| A |||^n$.

Theorem 7. *If $A = BC$, where B and C are of finite double-norm, then $\tau(A)$ is independent of the particular orthonormal system φ_n used in its definition.*

Proof. We note first that $\Sigma_i \| B\varphi_i \|^2 = \Sigma_{ij} | (B\varphi_i, \varphi_j) |^2 = ||| B |||^2 < \infty$ and $\Sigma_i \| C^*\varphi_i \|^2 = \Sigma_{ij} | (\varphi_j, C^*\varphi_i) |^2 = \Sigma_{ij} | (C\varphi_j, \varphi_i) |^2 = ||| C |||^2 < \infty$, hence $\Sigma_i \| B\varphi_i \|.\| C^*\varphi_i \| < \infty$, so that also $\Sigma_{ij} | (B\varphi_i, \psi_j) \overline{(C^*\varphi_i, \psi_j)} | \leqslant \Sigma_i \{\Sigma_j | (B\varphi_i, \psi_j) |^2\}^{1/2} \{\Sigma_j | (C^*\varphi_i, \psi_j) |^2\}^{1/2} = \Sigma_i \| B\varphi_i \|.\| C^*\varphi_i \| < \infty$, where ψ_n is a different complete orthonormal system. Hence $\Sigma_i \Sigma_j (B\varphi_i, \psi_j) \overline{(C^*\varphi_i, \psi_j)} = \Sigma_j \Sigma_i (B\varphi_i, \psi_j) \overline{(C^*\varphi_i, \psi_j)}$. Furthermore $\tau(A) = \tau(BC) = \Sigma_{ij} \beta_{ij} \gamma_{ji}$ since $\Sigma_{ij} | \beta_{ij}\gamma_{ji} | < \infty$ (cf. Theorem 6), so that $\tau(BC) = \Sigma_{ij} \beta_{ij}\gamma_{ji} = \tau(CB)$. It follows that

$$\tau(A) = \Sigma_i (A\varphi_i, \varphi_i) = \Sigma_i (BC\varphi_i, \varphi_i) = \Sigma_i (CB\varphi_i, \varphi_i) = \Sigma_i (B\varphi_i, C^*\varphi_i)$$
$$= \Sigma_i\Sigma_j (B\varphi_i, \psi_j) \overline{(C^*\varphi_i, \psi_j)} = \Sigma_j\Sigma_i (B\varphi_i, \psi_j) \overline{(C^*\varphi_i, \psi_j)} =$$
$$\Sigma_j\Sigma_i (C\psi_j, \varphi_i) \overline{(B^*\psi_j, \varphi_i)} = \Sigma_j(C\psi_j, B^*\psi_j) = \Sigma_j(BC\psi_j, \psi_j) = \Sigma_i(A\psi_i, \psi_i).$$

Theorem 8. 1°. *If B and C are of finite double-norm, then $\tau(BC) = \tau(CB)$.*

2°. *If $\tau(A)$ exists, then $\tau(A^*)$ exists, and $\tau(A^*) = \overline{\tau(A)}$.*

3°. *If A_n converges to A in double-norm and B_n converges to B in double-norm, then $\lim \tau(A_nB_n) = \tau(AB)$.*

Proof. 1°. We have $\Sigma_{ij} | \beta_{ij}\gamma_{ji} | < \infty$ (cf. Theorem 6), hence $\tau(BC) = \Sigma_{ij} \beta_{ij}\gamma_{ji} = \tau(CB)$.

2°. $\tau(A) = \Sigma_i(A\varphi_i, \varphi_i) = \Sigma_i(\varphi_i, A^* \varphi_i) = \overline{\tau(A^*)}$.

3°. Follows from $| \tau(A_nB_n) - \tau(AB) | = | \tau[(A_n - A)(B_n - B)] + \tau[A(B_n - B)] + \tau[(A_n - A)B] | \leqslant |||A_n - A |||.||| B_n - B ||| + ||| A |||.||| B_n - B ||| + ||| A_n - A |||.||| B |||$.

We suppose now that the Hilbert space R is the separable Lebesgue space $L_2(\Delta, \mu)$, where μ is a separable measure, and Δ is a μ-measurable set. Then it might seem at first as if we have two different definitions for a linear transformation T to be of finite double-norm:

1°. $Tf = \int_\Delta T(x, y)f(y)d\mu$, where the measurable function $T(x, y)$ satisfies $||| T |||^2 = \int_{\Delta\times\Delta} | T |^2 d(\mu \times \mu) < \infty$.

2°. $||| T |||^2 = \Sigma_{ij} | (T\varphi_i, \varphi_j) |^2 < \infty$, where φ_n is a complete orthonormal system.

Theorem 9. *The definitions* 1° *and* 2° *are equivalent.*

Proof. 1° → 2°. We have

$$\Sigma_{ij} \mid (T\varphi_i, \varphi_j) \mid^2 = \Sigma_i \parallel T\varphi_i \parallel^2 = \Sigma_i \int_\Delta \mid \int_\Delta T(x, y)\varphi_i(y)d\mu \mid^2 d\mu =$$
$$\int_\Delta [\Sigma_i \mid \int_\Delta \overline{\overline{T(x, y)}} \, . \overline{\varphi_i(y)}d\mu \mid^2]d\mu = \int_\Delta [\Sigma_i \mid (\overline{T(x, y)}, \quad \varphi_i(y)) \mid^2]d\mu =$$
$$\int_\Delta [\int_\Delta \mid T(x, y) \mid^2 d\mu]d\mu = \int_{\Delta\times\Delta} \mid T \mid^2 d(\mu \times \mu) = \mid\mid\mid T \mid\mid\mid^2 < \infty.$$

2° → 1°. The system $\psi_{ij}(x, y) = \varphi_i(x)\overline{\varphi_j(y)}$ ($i, j = 1, 2, \ldots$) is complete and orthonormal in $L_2(\Delta \times \Delta)$ (cf. Ch. 6, § 14, Th. 2, 3). Writing now $\tau_{ji} = (T\varphi_i, \varphi_j)$, and observing that $\Sigma_{ij} \mid \tau_{ji} \mid^2 < \infty$, we see that $\Sigma_{ij} \tau_{ij}\varphi_i(x) \overline{\varphi_j(y)}$ converges in mean (cf. Ch. 6, § 13, Ex. A) to a limitfunction $T(x, y)$,

$$T(x, y) \sim \Sigma_{ij} \tau_{ij}\varphi_i(x)\overline{\varphi_j(y)}.$$

Since $T(x, y) \in L_2(\Delta \times \Delta)$, we have $\int_{\Delta\times\Delta} \mid T \mid^2 d(\mu \times \mu) < \infty$, so that the linear transformation T_1, defined by

$$T_1 f = \int_\Delta T(x, y)f(y)d\mu,$$

is of finite double-norm according to the first definition. It remains to prove that $T_1 = T$. This follows from

$$(T_1\varphi_i, \varphi_j) = \int_{\Delta\times\Delta} T(x, y)\varphi_i(y)\overline{\varphi_j(x)}d(\mu \times \mu) = (T(x, y), \varphi_j(x)\overline{\varphi_i(y)}) =$$
$$\Sigma_{kl} \tau_{kl}(\varphi_k(x)\overline{\varphi_l(y)}, \varphi_j(x)\overline{\varphi_i(y)}) = \tau_{ji} = (T\varphi_i, \varphi_j)$$

for all $i, j = 1, 2, \ldots.$

Theorem 10. *If* S *and* T *with kernels* $S(x, y)$ *and* $T(x, y)$ *are of finite double-norm, then*

$$\tau(ST) = \int_{\Delta\times\Delta} S(x, y)T(y, x)d(\mu \times \mu).$$

Proof. Since $\Sigma_{ij} \mid (T\varphi_i, \varphi_j) (S^*\varphi_i, \varphi_j) \mid < \infty$, we have

$$\tau(ST) = \Sigma_i(ST\varphi_i, \varphi_i) = \Sigma_i (T\varphi_i, S^*\varphi_i) = \Sigma_{ij} (T\varphi_i, \varphi_j) \overline{(S^*\varphi_i, \varphi_j)} =$$
$$\Sigma_{ij} (T(x, y), \varphi_j(x)\overline{\varphi_i(y)}) . \overline{(S^*(x, y), \varphi_j(x) \overline{\varphi_i(y)})} = (T(x, y), S^*(x, y)) =$$
$$\int_{\Delta\times\Delta} T(x, y)\overline{S^*(x, y)}d(\mu\times\mu) = \int_{\Delta\times\Delta} T(x, y)S(y, x)d(\mu\times\mu) =$$
$$\int_{\Delta\times\Delta} S(x, y)T(y, x) \, d(\mu \times \mu).$$

Theorem 11. *If* T *with kernel* $T(x, y)$ *is of finite double-norm, so that* $T(x, y)$ *as a function* $t_y(x)$ *of* x *belongs to* $L_2(\Delta)$ *for almost every* $y \in \Delta$, *and* A *is an arbitrary bounded linear transformation, then* AT *has the kernel* $p(x, y) = At_y(x)$.

Proof. AT is of finite double-norm by Th. 2, so that it has a kernel $P(x, y) \in L_2(\Delta \times \Delta)$ by Theorem 9. Let $f, g \in L_2(\Delta)$, and write $A^*g = h$. Then

$$(ATf, g) = (Tf, A^*g) = (Tf, h) = \int_{\Delta\times\Delta} T(x, y)\overline{h(x)}f(y)d(\mu \times \mu)$$
$$= \int_\Delta (\int_\Delta t_y(x)\overline{h(x)}d\mu)f(y)d\mu.$$

But, for those values of y for which $t_y(x) \in L_2(\Delta)$, we have

$$\int_\Delta t_y(x)\overline{h(x)}d\mu = (t_y, h) = (t_y, A^*g) = (At_y, g) = \int_\Delta p(x, y)\overline{g(x)}d\mu,$$

hence

$$(ATf, g) = \int_\Delta (\int_\Delta p(x, y)\overline{g(x)}d\mu)f(y)d\mu.$$

Also

$$(ATf, g) = \int_\Delta (\int_\Delta P(x, y)\overline{g(x)}d\mu)f(y)d\mu,$$

hence

$$\int_\Delta (\int_\Delta \{p(x, y) - P(x, y)\}\overline{g(x)}d\mu)f(y)d\mu = 0$$

for all $f, g \in L_2(\Delta)$. Let now Δ_1 and Δ_2 be arbitrary subsets of Δ of finite measure. Then, taking $g(x)$ and $f(y)$ such that $g(x) = 1$ on Δ_1, $f(y) = 1$ on Δ_2, and that $g(x)$ and $f(y)$ vanish elsewhere on Δ, we find

$$\int_{\Delta_2} (\int_{\Delta_1} \{p(x, y) - P(x, y)\}d\mu)d\mu = 0.$$

Keeping first Δ_1 fixed, it follows that $\int_{\Delta_1} \{p(x, y) - P(x, y)\}d\mu = 0$ for almost every $y \in \Delta$ (cf. Ch. 3, § 4, Th. 3). The set of exceptional y, however, may depend on Δ_1. Nevertheless, observing that the measure μ is separable, we may assert that, for almost every $y \in \Delta$,

$$\int_F \{p(x, y) - P(x, y)\}d\mu = 0$$

for all sets F of the enumerable collection Z, introduced in Ch. 5, § 3. Approximating an arbitrary set E of finite measure by a sequence $F_n \in Z$ in such a way that $\mu(\Sigma F_n) < \infty$, an appeal to the absolute continuity of the integral shows that $\int_E \{p - P\}d\mu = 0$. Hence $p(x, y) - P(x, y) = 0$ almost everywhere on $\Delta \times \Delta$. It follows that the kernel of AT is $p(x, y)$.

Remark. In the middle part of the present proof it is not allowed to write

$$(ATf, g) = \int_\Delta (\int_\Delta p(x, y)\overline{g(x)}d\mu)f(y)d\mu = \int_{\Delta\times\Delta} p(x, y)\overline{g(x)}f(y)d(\mu \times \mu),$$

since we do not even know in that stage of the proof whether $p(x, y)$ is $\mu \times \mu$-measurable or not.

Theorem 12. *If S and T with kernels $S(x, y)$ and $T(x, y)$ are of finite double-norm, and A is an arbitrary bounded linear transformation, then $Q = SAT$ is of finite double-norm, and its kernel $Q(x, y)$ satisfies*

$$| Q(x, y) | \leqslant \| A \| s(x)t(y)$$

almost everywhere on $\Delta \times \Delta$, where

$$s(x) = (\int_\Delta | S(x, y) |^2 d\mu)^{1/2}, \ t(y) = (\int_\Delta | T(x, y) |^2 d\mu)^{1/2} \ [4].$$

Proof. By the preceding theorem AT has the kernel $p(x, y) \in L_2(\Delta \times \Delta)$, where $p(x, y) = At_y(x)$. Then $Q = SAT$ has the kernel

$$Q(x, y) = \int_\Delta S(x, z)p(z, y)d\mu$$

and we have, almost everywhere on $\Delta \times \Delta$,

$$| Q(x, y) | \leqslant (\int_\Delta | S(x, z) |^2 d\mu)^{1/2} (\int_\Delta | p(z, y) |^2 d\mu)^{1/2} = s(x) \| At_y(x) \|$$
$$\leqslant \| A \| s(x) \| t_y(x) \| = \| A \| s(x) (\int_\Delta | T(x, y) |^2 d\mu)^{1/2} = \| A \| s(x)t(y).$$

Finally, we add two theorems on the productspace $L_2^n(\Delta)$.

Theorem 13. *If $\{\varphi_i\} = \{\varphi_i^1, \varphi_i^2, \ldots, \varphi_i^n\}$ $(i = 1, 2, \ldots)$ is a complete orthonormal system in L_2^n, then $||| T |||^2 = \Sigma_{ij} | (T\{\varphi_i\}, \{\varphi_j\}) |^2 < \infty$ if and only if $\{g\} = T\{f\}$ is defined by*

$$g^k(x) = \Sigma_l \int_\Delta T_{kl}(x, y)f^l(y)d\mu \ (k = 1, \ldots, n),$$

where $\Sigma_{kl} \int_{\Delta \times \Delta} | T_{kl} |^2 \, d(\mu \times \mu) = ||| T |||^2 < \infty$.

Proof. The proof is of course similar to that of Theorem 9, the notations being only somewhat more complicated. We shall indicate the main points. If $\Sigma_{kl} \int_{\Delta \times \Delta} | T_{kl} |^2 \, d(\mu \times \mu) < \infty$, then

$$\Sigma_{ij} | (T\{\varphi_i\}, \{\varphi_j\}) |^2 = \Sigma_i \| T\{\varphi_i\} \|^2 = \Sigma_i \Sigma_k \int_\Delta | \Sigma_l \int_\Delta T_{kl}(x, y)\varphi_i^l(y)d\mu |^2 \, d\mu$$
$$= \Sigma_k \int_\Delta [\Sigma_i | \Sigma_l \overline{(T_{kl}(x, y)}, \varphi_i^l(y)) |^2]d\mu = \Sigma_k \int_\Delta [\Sigma_l \int_\Delta | T_{kl}(x, y) |^2 \, d\mu]d\mu =$$
$$= \Sigma_{kl} \int_{\Delta \times \Delta} | T_{kl} |^2 d(\mu \times \mu).$$

If conversely $\Sigma_{ij} | \tau_{ji} |^2 = \Sigma_{ij} | (T\{\varphi_i\}, \{\varphi_j\}) |^2 < \infty$, we observe that $\psi_{ij}^{kl}(x, y) = \varphi_i^k(x)\overline{\varphi_j^l(y)}$ $(i, j = 1,2, \ldots)$ is complete and orthonormal in $L_2^{n^2}(\Delta \times \Delta)$, so that $\Sigma_{ij} \tau_{ij}\varphi_i^k(x)\overline{\varphi_j^l(y)}$ converges in mean to a limitfunction $T_{kl}(x, y) \in L_2(\Delta \times \Delta)$. Defining $\{h\} = T_1\{f\}$ by $h^k(x) = \Sigma_l \int_\Delta T_{kl}(x, y)f^l(y)d\mu$, we have

$$(T_1\{\varphi_i\}, \{\varphi_j\}) = \Sigma_{kl} \int_{\Delta \times \Delta} T_{kl}(x, y)\overline{\varphi_j^k(x)}\varphi_i^l(y)d(\mu \times \mu) = \Sigma_{kl} (T_{kl}(x, y),$$
$$\varphi_j^k(x)\overline{\varphi_i^l(y)}) = \Sigma_{pq} \tau_{pq} \Sigma_{kl} (\varphi_p^k(x)\overline{\varphi_q^l(y)}, \ \varphi_j^k(x)\overline{\varphi_i^l(y)}) = \tau_{ji} = (T\{\varphi_i\}, \{\varphi_j\}),$$

hence $T_1 = T$.

Theorem 14. *If S and T with matrix kernels $\{S_{kl}(x, y)\}$ and $\{T_{kl}(x, y)\}$ are of finite double-norm, then*

$$\tau(ST) = \Sigma_{kl} \int_{\Delta\times\Delta} S_{kl}(x, y) T_{lk}(y, x) d(\mu \times \mu).$$

Proof. Similar to the proof of Theorem 10.

§ 11. Orthogonal Projections

Let $[L]$ be a linear subspace of the Hilbert space R, and let R be the direct sum of $[L]$ and its orthogonal subspace $R \ominus [L]$. We know already that this last condition is automatically satisfied if either $[L]$ or $R \ominus [L]$ is complete, when considered as a Hilbert space on its own. In particular it is satisfied whenever R is complete. The projection P on $[L]$ along $R \ominus [L]$ is now called an *orthogonal projection*. It is bounded, since $f = Pf + (f - Pf)$, $Pf \in [L]$, $f - Pf \in R \ominus [L]$ implies $\| f \|^2 = \| Pf \|^2 + \| f - Pf \|^2$, hence $\| Pf \|^2 \leqslant \| f \|^2$ or $\| P \| \leqslant 1$.

Theorem 1. *The bounded linear transformation P is an orthogonal projection if and only if $P = P^2$ and P is self-adjoint.*

Proof. Let P be an orthogonal projection. Then $P = P^2$, since every projection satisfies this equality (cf. Ch. 7, § 14). Furthermore, if $f = f_1 + f_2$, $g = g_1 + g_2$ are the decompositions of two arbitrary elements $f, g \in R$, then $(Pf, g) = (f_1, g_1 + g_2) = (f_1, g_1) = (f_1 + f_2, g_1) = (f, Pg)$, which shows that P is self-adjoint.

Let now conversely $P = P^2$ and $(Pf, g) = (f, Pg)$ for arbitrary $f, g \in R$. The relation $P = P^2$ implies that P is the projection on the subspace of all solutions of $Pf = f$ along the subspace of all solutions of $Pg = 0$ (cf. Ch. 7, § 14, Th. 4). It remains to show that $Pf = f$, $Pg = 0$ implies $(f, g) = 0$. This follows from $(f, g) = (Pf, g) = (f, Pg) = (f, 0) = 0$.

Theorem 2. *The bounded linear transformation P is an orthogonal projection if and only if $P = P^2$ and $\| Pf \| \leqslant \| f \|$ for all $f \in R$.*

Proof. If P is an orthogonal projection we know already that $P = P^2$ and $\| Pf \| \leqslant \| f \|$ for all $f \in R$. Let now conversely $P = P^2$ and $\| Pf \| \leqslant \| f \|$ for all $f \in R$. Then P is a projection, and it remains to prove that the range $W(P)$ of all elements Pf is orthogonal to the null space $N(P)$ of all solutions of $Pg = 0$. For this purpose we observe that, for every $f \in R$, we have $g = Pf - f \in N(P)$; hence, if in particular $f \in R \ominus N(P)$, then $Pf = f + g$ with $(f, g) = 0$. It follows that in this case $\| f \|^2 \geqslant \| Pf \|^2 = \| f \|^2 + \| g \|^2$, so that $g = 0$. Hence $Pf = f$, which shows that

$R \ominus N(P) \subset W(P)$. Let now conversely $f \in W(P)$, so that $Pf = f$. We have $f = g + h$, $g \in R \ominus N(P)$, $h \in N(P)$, hence $f = Pf = Pg + Ph = Pg = g$. It follows that $W(P) \subset R \ominus N(P)$. The final result is therefore that $W(P) = R \ominus N(P)$, which is even more than was to be proved.

Theorem 3. *An orthogonal projection P is not only self-adjoint, but even positive.*

Proof. We have $(Pf, f) = (P^2f, f) = (Pf, Pf) \geqslant 0$ for every $f \in R$.

Theorem 4. *Let P_1 and P_2 be orthogonal projections on $[L]$ and $[M]$ respectively. Then $[L]$ and $[M]$ are orthogonal if and only if $P_1P_2 = O$. In this case we have also $P_2P_1 = O$.*

Proof. If $[L]$ and $[M]$ are orthogonal, then $P_2f \in [M] \subset R \ominus [L]$ for every f, hence $P_1P_2f = 0$. In the same way $P_2P_1f = 0$.

If conversely $P_1P_2f = 0$ for every f, then $P_2f \in R \ominus [L]$, hence $[M] \subset R \ominus [L]$, which shows that $[L]$ and $[M]$ are orthogonal.

Theorem 5. *If $P_1, \ldots, P_n$ are orthogonal projections, then $P = P_1 + \ldots + P_n$ is an orthogonal projection if and only if $P_iP_j = O$ for $i \neq j$ $(i, j = 1, \ldots, n)$.*

Proof. Let $P_iP_j = O$ for $i \neq j$. Then it is trivial that $P^2 = P$ and $(Pf, g) = (f, Pg)$, so that P is an orthogonal projection by Theorem 1. If conversely P is an orthogonal projection, and f belongs to the range of P_i, then $\| f \|^2 \geqslant \| Pf \|^2 = (Pf, f) = (\Sigma P_jf, f) = \Sigma \| P_jf \|^2 \geqslant \| P_if \|^2 = \| f \|^2$, hence $\Sigma \| P_jf \|^2 = \| P_if \|^2$ or $P_jf = 0$ for $j \neq i$. It follows that $P_jP_i = O$ for $i \neq j$.

Theorem 6. *If $P_1, P_2, \ldots$ are orthogonal projections, then $P = \Sigma_{i=1}^{\infty} P_i$ is an orthogonal projection if and only if $P_iP_j = O$ for $i \neq j$ $(i, j = 1, 2, \ldots)$.*

Proof. Let $P_iP_j = O$ for $i \neq j$. Then, by the preceding theorem, all $S_n = \Sigma_{i=1}^{n} P_i$ are orthogonal projections. Furthermore $(S_{n+1}f, f) = (S_nf, f) + (P_{n+1}f, f) \geqslant (S_nf, f)$ and $(S_nf, f) \leqslant (f, f)$. The sequence S_n of self-adjoint and permutable transformations is therefore ascending, bounded by the identical transformation I, and permutable with I. It follows by § 4, Th. 9 that $P = \lim S_n = \Sigma_{i=1}^{\infty} P_i$ exists, and that P is self-adjoint. Furthermore $(P^2f, g) = (Pf, Pg) = \lim (S_nf, S_ng) = \lim (S_n^2f, g) = \lim (S_nf, g) = (Pf, g)$, hence $P^2 = P$. This shows that P is an orthogonal projection.

If conversely $P = \Sigma_{i=1}^{\infty} P_i$ is an orthogonal projection, the same argument as in the preceding proof shows that $P_iP_j = O$ for $i \neq j$.

Theorem 7. *Let P_1 and P_2 be orthogonal projections on $[L]$ and $[M]$ respectively. Then the following statements are equivalent:*

1°. $P_1 \leqslant P_2$.

2°. $\| P_1 f \| \leqslant \| P_2 f \|$ *for all* $f \in R$.

3°. $[L] \subset [M]$.

4°. $P_1 P_2 = P_2 P_1 = P_1$.

Proof. 1° → 2°. We have $0 \leqslant (P_2 f - P_1 f, f) = (P_2 f, f) - (P_1 f, f) = \| P_2 f \|^2 - \| P_1 f \|^2$ for all $f \in R$.

2° → 3°. For $f \in [L]$ we have $\| f \| \geqslant \| P_2 f \| \geqslant \| P_1 f \| = \| f \|$, hence $\| f \|^2 = \| P_2 f \|^2$ or $(f, f) - (P_2 f, f) = 0$. Then also $\| (I - P_2) f \|^2 = ((I - P_2) f, f) = 0$, so that $f = P_2 f$, or $f \in [M]$.

3° → 4°. $[L] \subset [M]$ implies $P_1 f \in [M]$ for all f, hence $P_2 P_1 f = P_1 f$ or $P_2 P_1 = P_1$. Then also $P_1 P_2 = P_1^* P_2^* = (P_2 P_1)^* = P_1^* = P_1$.

4° → 1°. $P_2 P_1 = P_1$ implies that $Q = P_2 - P_1$ is an orthogonal projection, since Q is self-adjoint and $Q^2 = P_2^2 - P_1 P_2 - P_2 P_1 + P_1^2 = P_2 - P_1 - P_1 + P_1 = Q$. Hence $(P_2 f, f) - (P_1 f, f) = (Qf, f) = \| Qf \|^2 \geqslant 0$.

§ 12. Symmetrisable Transformations

In the present paragraph the conception of a bounded self-adjoint transformation is extended into a certain direction. In the next paragraph we shall deal with a second extension into a different direction.

Let R be a Hilbert space, complete or non-complete, and let $H \neq O$ be a bounded self-adjoint transformation on R. Then $[L]$, the subspace of all solutions of $Hf = 0$, is not identical with R. In the same way as in § 5 we assume that R is the direct sum of $[L]$ and its orthogonal subspace $[M] = R \ominus [L]$. The orthogonal projection on $[M]$ is called P. By § 5 we have $P \neq O$ and $H = HP = PH$.

Definition. *If the bounded linear transformation K has the property that $S = HK$ is self-adjoint, then K is called symmetrisable (to the left, and relative to H).*

Remark. The notion of a symmetrisable transformation was introduced by J. Marty [5] for the special case of integral transformations.

Theorem 1. *If K is symmetrisable relative to the self-adjoint transformation H, then*

1°. $T = PK$ *is symmetrisable.*

2°. $T = TP$ *and* $S = SP$.

3°. $Tf = 0$ *if and only if* $Sf = 0$.

Proof. 1°. We have $HT = H(PK) = (HP)K = HK = S$, and S is self-adjoint by hypothesis. T is therefore symmetrisable.

2°. We have to prove that $T(I - P) = S(I - P) = O$, which is equivalent to the statement that $Hf = 0$ implies $Tf = Sf = 0$. Since $(Tg, Hf) = (HTg, f) = (g, HTf)$ for arbitry f, g, the relation $Hf = 0$ implies $(g, HTf) = 0$ for arbitrary g, hence $Sf = HTf = 0$. Then however $Tf \in [L]$. But also $Tf = PKf \in [M]$. Hence $Tf = 0$.

3°. We have already seen in 2° that $Sf = 0$ implies $Tf = 0$. Conversely $Tf = 0$ implies $Sf = HTf = 0$.

Theorem 2. *If A is a bounded linear transformation satisfying $HAH = HA^*H$, then $K = AH$ is symmetrisable. In particular this is true whenever A is self-adjoint.*

Proof. $HAH = HA^*H$ is equivalent to $S = S^*$, where $S = HK$.

In view of this result it may be asked under what conditions a bounded linear transformation K symmetrisable relative to H, may be written in the form $K = AH$. In this direction we have:

Theorem 3. *If the space R is complete, if the range $W(H)$ is a subspace of R (and therefore also complete), and if the bounded linear transformation K satisfies the condition that $Hf = 0$ implies $Kf = 0$, then $K = AH$, where A is bounded and linear.*

Proof. Follows from Ch. 7, § 11, Th. 10 by taking $E_1 = E_3 = R$, $E_2 = W(H)$, $B = H$, $C = K$ in this theorem. Then, according to this theorem, there exists a bounded linear transformation A with domain E_2 such that $Cf = ABf$ for all $f \in E_1$. Hence, in our case, there exists a bounded linear transformation A with domain $W(H)$ such that $Kf = AHf$ for all $f \in R$. Defining A to be the null transformation on $R \ominus W(H)$, our proof is complete.

Theorem 4. *If the space R is complete, if the range $W(H)$ is a subspace of R, and if the symmetrisable transformation K satisfies the condition that $Hf = 0$ implies $Kf = 0$, there exists a bounded transformation A such that $K = AH$ and $HAH = HA^*H$. If $W(H) = R$, then A is self-adjoint.*

Proof. Defining A as in the preceding theorem, we have $K = AH$ where A is bounded and linear. Since $S = HK$ is self-adjoint, we have $HAH = HA^*H$. If $W(H) = R$, then A is self-adjoint by § 4, Th. 6, 2°.

Theorem 5. *If K is symmetrisable relative to H, then $K^n (n = 2, 3, \ldots)$ is also symmetrisable relative to H. Stated in other words, if K is symmetris-*

able relative to H, then K is also symmetrisable relative to HK, HK^2, HK^3, ...

Proof. Let us suppose that it has already been proved that HK^{n-1} is self-adjoint. Then $(HK^n f, f) = (HK^{n-1}Kf, f) = (Kf, HK^{n-1}f) = (HKf, K^{n-1}f) = (f, HKK^{n-1}f) = (f, HK^n f)$, which shows that HK^n is also self-adjoint.

Remark. Taking in particular for the bounded self-adjoint transformation H the identical transformation I, we observe that a transformation K which is symmetrisable relative to this $H = I$, is nothing else but a self-adjoint transformation. In this case $H = P = I$ and $S = T = K$. It is in this sense, therefore, that the notion of a symmetrisable transformation is an extension of that of a self-adjoint transformation.

We shall give now some examples of symmetrisable transformations in the functionspaces $L_2(\Delta)$ and $L_2^n(\Delta)$.

Example A. Let $h(x)$ be a measurable, bounded (almost everywhere) and non-negative function on Δ, and let the function $A(x, y)$, measurable on $\Delta \times \Delta$, be Hermitian (hence $A(x, y) = \overline{A(y, x)}$ almost everywhere on $\Delta \times \Delta$), and have the property (P) relative to $L_2(\Delta)$ (hence $\int_\Delta | A(x, y) f(y) | d\mu \in L_2$ for every $f \in L_2$). Then, by § 6, Th. 2, the linear transformation H, defined by $Hf = h(x)f(x)$, is bounded and positive on L_2, and by § 8, Th. 1 the linear integral transformation A with kernel $A(x, y)$ is bounded and self-adjoint. The linear transformation $K = AH$ is therefore symmetrisable (relative to H). Evidently K is an integral transformation with kernel $K(x, y) = A(x, y)h(y)$, where $K(x, y)$ has the property (P). If A is of finite double-norm (hence $\int_{\Delta\times\Delta} | A |^2 d(\mu \times \mu) < \infty$), the same holds for K.

The extension to the productspace $L_2^n(\Delta)$ is immediate. If the functions $h_{ij}(x)$ $(i, j = 1, \ldots, n)$ are measurable on Δ and bounded almost everywhere on Δ, and if

$$\Sigma_{ij=1}^n h_{ij}(x)\overline{\alpha_i}\alpha_j \geqslant 0$$

almost everywhere on Δ for every system of complex numbers $\alpha_1, \ldots, \alpha_n$ (where the set of exceptional x is independent of $\alpha_1, \ldots, \alpha_n$), then the transformation $\{g\} = H\{f\}$, defined by

$$g^i(x) = \Sigma_{j=1}^n h_{ij}(x) f^j(x) \quad (i = 1, \ldots, n),$$

is bounded and positive on L_2^n (cf. § 6, Th. 2). Furthermore, if the functions $A_{ij}(x, y)$ $(i, j = 1, \ldots, n)$, measurable on $\Delta \times \Delta$, are such that the matrix kernel $\{A_{ij}(x, y)\}$ is Hermitian (hence $A_{ij}(x, y) = \overline{A_{ji}(y, x)}$ almost everywhere on $\Delta \times \Delta$), and that every $A_{ij}(x, y)$ has the property (P), then the integral transformation A with matrix kernel $\{A_{ij}(x, y)\}$ is bounded and self-adjoint on L_2^n (cf. § 8, Th. 2). The linear transformation $K = AH$ is therefore symmetrisable (relative to H). Evidently K is an integral transformation with matrix kernel $\{K_{ij}(x, y)\}$, where $\{K_{ij}(x, y)\}$ is the matrixproduct of $\{A_{ij}(x, y)\}$ and $\{h_{ij}(y)\}$, and where every $K_{ij}(x, y) = \Sigma_{k=1}^n A_{ik}(x, y)h_{kj}(y)$ has the property (P). If A is of finite double-norm, the same holds for K.

Example B (*Garbe kernel* [6]). Let H be an integral transformation on $L_2(\Delta)$ with kernel $H(x, y)$. We suppose that $H(x, y)$ has the property (P), and that $\int_{\Delta \times \Delta} H(x, y)\overline{f(x)}f(y)d(\mu \times \mu) \geqslant 0$ for every $f(x) \in L_2(\Delta)$. The transformation H is therefore bounded and positive. Let furthermore $A(x)$ be a measurable function, bounded almost everywhere on Δ, and assuming only real values. The transformation A, defined by $Af = A(x)f(x)$, is then bounded and self-adjoint. It follows that $K = AH$ is symmetrisable (relative to H). Evidently K is an integral transformation with kernel $K(x, y) = A(x)H(x, y)$, where $K(x, y)$ has the property (P). If H is of finite double-norm, the same holds for K.

The extension to $L_2^n(\Delta)$ is evident.

Example C (*Pell kernel* [7]). Let H be defined as in the preceding example, whereas A is now a self-adjoint integral transformation with Hermitian kernel $A(x, y)$, having the property (P). Then $K = AH$ is symmetrisable (relative to H). Evidently K is an integral transformation with kernel $K(x, y) = \int_\Delta A(x, z)H(z, y)d\mu$, where $K(x, y)$ has the property (P) (cf. § 7, Th. 1). If either H or A is of finite double-norm, K is of finite double-norm.

The extension to $L_2^n(\Delta)$ is evident.

§ 13. Normal Transformations

Let R be a complete Hilbert space.

Definition. *The bounded linear transformation A on R is said to be normal when $AA^* = A^*A$.*

Evidently every bounded self-adjoint transformation is normal. The same holds for every unitary transformation.

Theorem 1. *The bounded linear transformation A is normal if and only if $\| Af \| = \| A^*f \|$ for every $f \in R$.*

Proof. If $AA^* = A^*A$, then $\| Af \|^2 = (Af, Af) = (A^*Af, f) = (AA^*f, f) = (A^*f, A^*f) = \| A^*f \|^2$; if conversely $\| Af \| = \| A^*f \|$ for every f, then $(A^*Af, f) = \| Af \|^2 = \| A^*f \|^2 = (AA^*f, f)$ for every f, hence $AA^* = A^*A$ by Ch. 7, § 12, Th. 4.

Corollary. *If A is normal, then $\| A^2 \| = \| A \|^2$.*

Proof. $\| A^2f \| = \| A(Af) \| = \| A^*(Af) \|$ for every f, so that $\| A^2 \| = \| A^*A \|$. But $\| A^*A \| = \| A \|^2$ by § 1, Th. 2, hence $\| A^2 \| = \| A \|^2$.

Theorem 2. *The bounded linear transformation A is normal if and only if $A = B + iC$, where B and C are self-adjoint and permutable.*

Proof. If B and C are self-adjoint and permutable, then $A = B + iC$ is normal because $A^* = B - iC$ implies $AA^* = A^*A = B^2 + C^2$. If conversely A is normal, we have $A = B + iC$, where $B = (A + A^*)/2$ and $C = (A - A^*)/2i$ are self-adjoint and permutable.

§ 14. Range and Null Space. Factorisation

Let R be a complete Hilbert space. If T is an arbitrary bounded linear transformation, the set of all elements $f \in R$ satisfying $Tf = 0$ is a linear subspace which, in accordance with Ch. 8, § 4, we shall call the *null space* of T, and denote by $N(T)$. The range $W(T)$ of T is a linear manifold (that is, $f, g \in W(T)$ implies $\alpha f + \beta g \in W(T)$ for arbitrary complex α, β), but it need not be a subspace since $f_n \in W(T)$, $f = \lim f_n$ need not imply $f \in W(T)$. Adding however to $W(T)$ all its points of accumulation, we obtain a subspace $[W(T)]$. Evidently $W(T)$ is dense in $[W(T)]$.

We shall prove now for Hilbert space the analogue of Ch. 8, § 4, Th. 1 on the range and null space of a bounded linear transformation T. In the next chapter (Ch. 10, § 3) we shall prove a more general theorem in an arbitrary Banach space.

Theorem 1. *If T is a bounded linear transformation (on R into R), then*

$$N(T^*) = R \ominus [W(T)] \text{ and } [W(T^*)] = R \ominus N(T).$$

Proof. If $g \in R \ominus [W(T)]$, then $0 = (Tf, g) = (f, T^*g)$ for all $f \in R$, hence $T^*g = 0$ or $g \in N(T^*)$. If conversely $g \in N(T^*)$, so that $T^*g = 0$, then $0 = (f, T^*g) = (Tf, g)$ for all $f \in R$, hence $g \in R \ominus [W(T)]$. It follows that $N(T^*) = R \ominus [W(T)]$.

Applying this to T^*, we find $R \ominus [W(T^*)] = N(T^{**}) = N(T)$.

Corollary. *If A is a bounded normal transformation, $N(A)$ and $[W(A)]$ are orthogonal complements.*

Proof. We have $N(A) = N(A^*)$, since $\| Af \| = \| A^*f \|$ (for all $f \in R$) shows that $Af = 0$ if and only if $A^*f = 0$. Hence $N(A) = N(A^*) = R \ominus [W(A)]$.

Theorem 2. *If T is a bounded linear transformation, then $[W(T)] = [W(TT^*)]$.*

Proof. We observe first that TT^* is self-adjoint, since $(TT^*)^* = T^{**}T^* = TT^*$. We have therefore to prove that $N(T^*) = N(TT^*)$. It is trivial that $T^*f = 0$ implies $TT^*f = 0$. Conversely, if $TT^*f = 0$, we have $\| T^*f \|^2 = (T^*f, T^*f) = (TT^*f, f) = 0$.

Corollary. *If A is bounded and self-adjoint, then $[W(A)] = [W(A^2)]$.*

Theorem 3. *If A is a bounded normal transformation, and the positive transformation H is defined by $H = (A^*A)^{1/2}$, then $[W(A)] = [W(H)]$.*

Proof. The transformation A^*A is positive, since $(A^*Af, f) = \| Af \|^2 \geqslant 0$ for every $f \in R$. If therefore A is normal, we have by the preceding theorem (and its corollary)

$$[W(A)] = [W(AA^*)] = [W(A^*A)] = [W(A^*A)^{1/2}] = [W(H)].$$

Theorem 4. *If T is a bounded linear transformation, there exists a positive transformation H with domain R and an isometric transformation U with domain $[W(H)]$ such that $T = UH$. The transformation H is uniquely determined by T; in fact, $H = (T^*T)^{1/2}$. The transformation U is uniquely determined on $[W(H)]$.*

Proof. Since T^*T is positive, the same holds for the square root $H = (T^*T)^{1/2}$. Furthermore $\| Hf \|^2 = (Hf, Hf) = (H^2f, f) = (T^*Tf, f) = \| Tf \|^2$, so that $Hf = 0$ if and only if $Tf = 0$. If now $g \in W(H)$, there exists at least one f such that $g = Hf$. In the case that $g = Hf_1 = Hf_2$, we have also $Tf_1 = Tf_2$. We may define therefore the transformation U on $W(H)$ by $Ug = Tf$. Evidently U is linear, and $\| Ug \| = \| Tf \| = \| Hf \| = \| g \|$, which shows that U is isometric on $W(H)$. Extending U as a linear bounded transformation onto $[W(H)]$, U is isometric on $[W(H)]$. Since $UHf = Ug = Tf$ for all $f \in R$, we have $UH = T$.

Let us suppose now that also $T = U_1H_1$, where H_1 is positive and U_1 is isometric on $W(H_1)$. Then $\| Tf \|^2 = \| U_1H_1f \|^2 = \| H_1f \|^2$, hence $(T^*Tf, f) = (H_1^2f, f)$ for all $f \in R$. This implies $T^*T = H_1^2$, so that $H_1 = (T^*T)^{1/2} = H$. Then also $U_1 = U$ on $[W(H)]$.

Remark. If the space R is of finite dimension, U may be extended onto the whole space R as an isometric transformation, so that in this case U is even unitary. Indeed, the original domain of U is then $W(H) = W(T^*T) = W(T^*)$, and its range is $W(T)$. Since the dimensions of $W(T^*)$ and $W(T)$ are equal by Ch. 8, § 4, Th. 2, it is easily seen that U may be extended in the stated way.

The next two theorems give sufficient conditions for U to be unitary in the case that R is of infinite dimension.

Theorem 5. *If T is a bounded linear transformation such that*

1°. *$W(T)$ is dense in R,*

2°. *$N(T)$ contains only the null element,*

then $T = UH$ with positive H and unitary U. The transformations H and U are uniquely determined.

Proof. Defining H and U as in the preceding theorem, we have $T = UH$ with $[W(H)] = [W(T^*T)] = [W(T^*)] = R \ominus N(T) = R$ and $[W(T)]=R$. Both the domain and the range of the isometric transformation U are therefore identical with the whole space R. But then U is uniquely determined on R (by the preceding theorem) and unitary (by § 3, Th. 1).

Theorem 6. *If A is normal, then $A = UH$ with positive H and unitary U. The transformation H is uniquely determined, and U is uniquely determined on $[W(H)] = [W(A)]$.*

Proof. Determining once more H and U as in Theorem 4, both the domain and the range of the unique isometric transformation U are identical with $[W(H)] = [W(A)]$ (cf. Theorem 3). Setting $U = U_0$ on $R \ominus [W(A)]$, where U_0 is an arbitrary unitary transformation with domain and range $R \ominus [W(A)]$, U is unitary on the whole space R by § 3, Th. 1.

Theorem 7. *If A is a bounded linear transformation, and $A = UH$ with positive H and unitary U, then A is normal if and only if $UH = HU$ (that is, if A is normal, then $UH = HU$ for every U, and if $UH = HU$ for one single U, then A is normal).*

Proof. If A is normal, so that $A = UH$ with positive $H = (A^*A)^{1/2}$ and unitary U, then $H^2U = A^*AU = AA^*U = (UH)(HU^*)U = UH^2$. This shows that U is permutable with H^2. But then, as the proof of § 4, Th. 10 shows, U is also permutable with H.

If conversely $UH = HU$, then $AA^* = UHHU^* = H^2UU^* = H^2 = A^*A$.

§ 15. Characteristic Values

Let R be a Hilbert space, complete or non-complete. If T is a linear transformation on R into R, we shall denote the transformation $T - \lambda I$ (λ complex, I the identical transformation) by T_λ. The set $N(T_\lambda)$ of all $f \in R$ satisfying $T_\lambda f = 0$, is a linear manifold; if T is bounded, $N(T_\lambda)$ is even a linear subspace of R. If $N(T_\lambda)$ contains other elements besides the null element, that is, if there exists at least one element $f \neq 0$ such that $Tf = \lambda f$, the complex number λ is called a *characteristic value* of T, and all elements $f \neq 0$ for which $Tf = \lambda f$ are said to be *characteristic elements* of T belonging to the characteristic value λ.

Theorem 1. *Let the space R be complete, and let A be a bounded normal transformation. Then*

1°. *$Af = \lambda f$ if and only if $A^*f = \bar{\lambda}f$; in other words, f is a characteristic element of A with characteristic value λ if and only if it is at the same time a characteristic element of A^* with characteristic value $\bar{\lambda}$.*

2°. *Characteristic elements of A, belonging to different characteristic values, are orthogonal. In other words, if $\lambda \neq \mu$, then $N(A_\lambda)$ and $N(A_\mu)$ are orthogonal subspaces.*

3°. *A is completely reduced by $(N(A_\lambda), R \ominus N(A_\lambda))$ for every complex λ.*

Proof. 1°. Since $A_\lambda = A - \lambda I$ is normal if and only if A is normal, we have $\| Af - \lambda f \| = \| A_\lambda f \| = \| (A_\lambda)^* f \| = \| (A^* - \bar{\lambda} I) f \| = \| A^* f - \bar{\lambda} f \|$ for all $f \in R$. It follows that $Af = \lambda f$ if and only if $A^*f = \bar{\lambda} f$.

2°. Let $Af = \lambda f$, $Ag = \mu g$, $\lambda \neq \mu$. We have to prove that $(f, g) = 0$. This follows from $\lambda(f, g) = (\lambda f, g) = (Af, g) = (f, A^*g) = (f, \bar{\mu} g) = \mu(f, g)$, since $\lambda \neq \mu$ and $A^*g = \bar{\mu} g$ by 1°.

3°. If $f \in N(A_\lambda)$, that is, if $Af = \lambda f$, then $Af \in N(A_\lambda)$, so that A is reduced by $N(A_\lambda)$. Furthermore, if $f \in N(A_\lambda)$, then $A(A^*f) = A^*(Af) = A^*(\lambda f) = \lambda(A^*f)$. This shows that $A^*f \in N(A_\lambda)$, so that A^* is also reduced by $N(A_\lambda)$. Then however A (and also A^*) is completely reduced by $(N(A_\lambda), R \ominus N(A_\lambda))$ (cf. § 1, Th. 4).

Theorem 2. 1°. *If the space R is complete or non-complete, and A is self-adjoint, the characteristic values of A are real, and characteristic elements, belonging to different characteristic values, are orthogonal. If A is positive, the characteristic values of A are non-negative.*

2°. *If R is complete and U is unitary, the characteristic values of U have absolute value one, and characteristic elements, belonging to different characteristic values, are orthogonal.*

Proof. 1°. Let R be complete and A self-adjoint. If $Af = \lambda f$, $f \neq 0$, then $A^*f = \bar{\lambda}f$ by the preceding theorem, hence $\lambda f = Af = A^*f = \bar{\lambda}f$, which implies $\lambda = \bar{\lambda}$ since $f \neq 0$. The orthogonality of characteristic elements, belonging to different characteristic values, follows from the corresponding fact for normal transformations. If the space R is not complete, we extend A onto the closure $\bar{R}$. This extended transformation A has the stated properties, so that the same holds for the original transformation A. If A is positive, and $Af = \lambda f$, $f \neq 0$, then $\lambda \| f \|^2 = (\lambda f, f) = (Af, f) \geqslant 0$, hence $\lambda \geqslant 0$.

2°. If U is unitary and $Uf = \lambda f$, $f \neq 0$, then $\| f \| = \| Uf \| = \| \lambda f \| = | \lambda | . \| f \|$, hence $| \lambda | = 1$ since $\| f \| \neq 0$. The orthogonality of characteristic elements, belonging to different characteristic values, follows from the corresponding fact for normal transformations.

We now consider symmetrisable transformations on a Hilbert space R, complete or non-complete. The notations of § 12 are adopted; $H \neq O$ is therefore a fixed bounded self-adjoint transformation; $[L]$ is the null space of H, $[M]$ is the orthogonal complement of $[L]$, and R is supposed to be the direct sum of $[L]$ and $[M]$. The orthogonal projection on $[M]$ is denoted by P. If the bounded linear transformation K is symmetrisable relative to H, so that $S = HK$ is self-adjoint, we have proved in § 12, Th. 1 that $T = PK$ is also symmetrisable, that $T = TP$, $S = SP$, and that $Tf = 0$ if and only if $Sf = 0$.

Theorem 3. *If K is symmetrisable, the characteristic elements, belonging to characteristic values λ and μ such that $\lambda \neq \bar{\mu}$, are H-orthogonal and S-orthogonal. In other words, $Kf = \lambda f$, $Kg = \mu g$, $\lambda \neq \bar{\mu}$ implies $(Hf, g) = (Sf, g) = 0$.*

Proof. We have $\lambda(Hf, g) = (HKf, g) = (f, HKg) = (Hf, Kg) = \bar{\mu}(Hf, g)$, hence $(Hf, g) = 0$ since $\lambda \neq \bar{\mu}$. Furthermore $(Sf, g) = (HKf, g) = \lambda(Hf, g) = 0$.

Corollary. *If $Kf = \lambda f$, λ non-real, then $(Hf, f) = (Sf, f) = 0$.*

Proof. Writing $f = g$, $\lambda = \mu$, we have $Kf = \lambda f$, $Kg = \mu g$, $\lambda \neq \bar{\mu}$, hence $(Hf, g) = (Sf, g) = 0$ or $(Hf, f) = (Sf, f) = 0$.

We now come to the definition of two properties, one at least of which most of the symmetrisable transformations which we shall discuss will be supposed to satisfy.

Definition. *Full symmetrisability. The transformation K will be called fully symmetrisable if $Hf \neq 0$ for every $f \in R$ such that $Kf = \lambda f \neq 0$.*

Strong symmetrisability. The transformation K will be called strongly symmetrisable if $Hf = 0$ implies $Kf = 0$, in other words, if $K(I - P) = O$ or $K = KP$.

We observe that K is fully symmetrisable whenever it is strongly symmetrisable, so that strong symmetrisability is a stronger condition upon K.

Theorem 4. *If K is fully symmetrisable, and $Kf_i = \lambda f_i \neq 0$ $(i = 1, \ldots, n)$, where $f_1, \ldots, f_n$ are linearly independent, then $K^*Hf_i = \lambda Hf_i$ $(i = 1, \ldots, n)$, where $Hf_1, \ldots, Hf_n$ are linearly independent* [8].

Proof. Since $S = HK$ is self-adjoint, we have $HK = (HK)^* = K^*H$, hence $K^*Hf_i = HKf_i = \lambda Hf_i$ $(i = 1, \ldots, n)$. Suppose now that $\Sigma_{i=1}^{n} \alpha_i Hf_i = 0$ (α_i complex). Then $H(\Sigma \alpha_i f_i) = 0$ and $K(\Sigma \alpha_i f_i) = \lambda(\Sigma \alpha_i f_i)$ simultaneously, hence $\Sigma \alpha_i f_i = 0$ by hypothesis. This implies $\alpha_1 = \ldots = \alpha_n = 0$, so that $Hf_1, \ldots, Hf_n$ are linearly independent.

Remark. Even if K is not fully symmetrisable, then $T = PK$ is fully symmetrisable (even strongly symmetrisable since $T = TP$). Hence the next theorem.

Theorem 5. *If $Tf_i = \lambda f_i \neq 0$ $(i = 1, \ldots, n)$, where $f_1, \ldots, f_n$ are linearly independent, then $K^*Hf_i = T^*Hf_i = \lambda Hf_i$ $(i = 1, \ldots, n)$, where $Hf_1, \ldots, Hf_n$ are linearly independent.*

Proof. Only $K^*H = T^*H$ remains to be proved. Now $HK = HPK = HT$, hence $K^*H = (HK)^* = (HT)^* = T^*H$.

Theorem 6. *In case K is fully symmetrisable, and either H or $S = HK$ is positive, all characteristic values of K are real.*

Proof. Suppose that $Kf = \lambda f \neq 0$, λ non-real. Then, by Theorem 3, Corollary, $(Hf, f) = (Sf, f) = 0$. If therefore H is positive, we should have $\| H^{1/2} f \|^2 = (Hf, f) = 0$, hence $Hf = 0$, in contradiction with the full symmetrisability. If S is positive, we should have in the same way $Sf = 0$, which implies $\lambda Hf = HKf = Sf = 0$ or $Hf = 0$ (since $\lambda \neq 0$), once more in contradiction with the full symmetrisability.

Remarks. 1°. Even if K is not fully symmetrisable, then $T = PK$ has this property, so that all characteristic values of T are real if either H or S is positive.

2°. Under the conditions of the present theorem we may assert that characteristic elements of K, belonging to different characteristic values, are H-orthogonal and S-orthogonal.

Theorem 7. *If A is a bounded normal transformation on the complete space R, and $(A - \lambda I)^p f = 0$ for an integer $p \geqslant 1$, then $(A - \lambda I)f = 0$.*
Proof. For $p = 1$ the theorem is trivial, so that we may suppose $p \geqslant 2$. Considering the elements $A_\lambda f, A_\lambda^2 f, \ldots, A_\lambda^p f$, and supposing that $A_\lambda f \neq 0$, there exists an integer q $(2 \leqslant q \leqslant p)$ such that $A_\lambda^q f = 0$ but $g = A_\lambda^{q-1} f \neq 0$. Then $A_\lambda g = 0$, so that g belongs to the null space $N(A_\lambda)$. At the same time $g = A_\lambda h$, which shows that g belongs to the range $W(A_\lambda)$. Since however $A_\lambda = A - \lambda I$ is normal simultaneously with A, the null space $N(A_\lambda)$ and the range $W(A_\lambda)$ are orthogonal (cf. § 14, Th. 1, Corollary). Hence $g = 0$, in contradiction with $g = A_\lambda^{q-1} f \neq 0$. The final result is therefore that $(A - \lambda I)f = A_\lambda f = 0$.

Theorem 8. *If the bounded linear transformation K is symmetrisable relative to the bounded self-adjoint transformation H, the null space $N(K)$ and the range $W(K)$ are H-orthogonal.*
Proof. Let $f \in N(K)$ and $g \in W(K)$, hence $Kf = 0$, and $g = Kh$. Then $(Hf, g) = (Hf, Kh) = (f, HKh) = (HKf, h) = 0$.

Theorem 9. *Let the bounded linear transformation K be fully symmetrisable relative to the bounded self-adjoint transformation H, and let either H or $S = HK$ be positive. Then, if $\lambda \neq 0$ and $(K - \lambda I)^p f = 0$ for an integer $p \geqslant 1$, we have $(K - \lambda I)f = 0$.*
Proof. As in Theorem 7 the hypothesis that $K_\lambda f = (K - \lambda I)f \neq 0$ leads to the existence of an integer q $(2 \leqslant q \leqslant p)$ such that $K_\lambda^q f = 0$ but $g = K_\lambda^{q-1} f \neq 0$. Then $K_\lambda g = 0$, which shows that λ is a characteristic value of K. The hypothesis of Theorem 6 being satisfied, λ is therefore real. Furthermore, $K_\lambda g = 0$ shows that $g \in N(K_\lambda)$. At the same time $g = K_\lambda h$, hence $g \in W(K_\lambda)$. Since $K_\lambda = K - \lambda I$ (λ real) is symmetrisable simultaneously with K, the null space $N(K_\lambda)$ and the range $W(K_\lambda)$ are H-orthogonal by the preceding theorem. Hence $(Hg, g) = 0$. If H is positive, this implies $Hg = 0$, a result which is in contradiction with our hypothesis that K is fully symmetrisable. $(Hg, g) = 0$ implies $(Sg, g) = (HKg, g) = \lambda(Hg, g) = 0$; if therefore S is positive, we have $Sg = 0$, which implies $\lambda Hg = HKg = Sg = 0$ or $Hg = 0$, once again in contradiction with the full symmetrisability of K. The final result is therefore that $(K - \lambda I)f = K_\lambda f = 0$.

Remark. The present theorem does not include the case $\lambda = 0$. It is however easily proved that if K is symmetrisable relative to the positive transformation H, and if $Hf = 0$ only for $f = 0$ (so that the symmetrisability is automatically full), then $K^p f = 0$ for an integer $p \geqslant 1$ implies $Kf = 0$.

Theorem 10. *If A is a normal transformation on the Hilbert space R of finite dimension, the geometric multiplicity of every characteristic value of A is equal to its algebraic multiplicity. In other words, the canonical form of the matrix of A is a diagonal matrix.*

Proof. We have to prove that all elementary divisors of A are simple. Now, if there exists an elementary divisor of A which is not simple, but has the multiplicity $p > 1$, we have $(A - \lambda I)^p f = 0$ for a certain element $f \neq 0$, whereas $(A - \lambda I)f \neq 0$. This is in contradiction with Theorem 7.

Theorem 11. *If the space R is of finite dimension, H is a self-adjoint transformation on R, K is fully symmetrisable relative to H, and either H or $S = HK$ is positive, then the geometric multiplicity of every characteristic value $\lambda \neq 0$ of K is equal to its algebraic multiplicity. If H is positive and non-singular, the statement holds for all characteristic values of K.*

Proof. Follows from Theorem 9.

We finally observe that we do not assert that a bounded linear transformation T on a Hilbert space of infinite dimension really possesses any characteristic values. Indeed, we shall discuss an integral transformation which is even of finite double-norm (a particular example of a transformation with Volterra kernel), having no characteristic values at all. We shall also prove however, that for a rather general class of normal or symmetrisable transformations (including those of finite double-norm) there exists at least one characteristic value (cf. Ch. 12, § 3).

§ 16. Solution of a Functional Equation in a Space of Finite Dimension

Let R be a p-dimensional Hilbert space, and let $\varphi_1, \ldots, \varphi_p$ be a fixed orthonormal system in R. Since R is of finite dimension, every linear transformation T on R (into R) is bounded and of finite double-norm. If T has the matrix $\{t_{ij}\}$ in the coordinate system $\{\varphi\}$, the trace of $T = IT$ is

$$\sigma_1 = \tau(T) = \Sigma_{i=1}^{p} t_{ii}.$$

Since both I and T are of finite double-norm, σ_1 is independent of the orthonormal system (cf. § 10, Th. 7). We shall write det T for the determinant of $\{t_{ij}\}$. Then $\varphi(\mu) = \det(T - \mu I)$, considered as a polynomial in μ, is the characteristic polynomial of T. Both det T and $\varphi(\mu)$ are independent of the orthonormal system $\{\varphi\}$. The roots $\mu_1, \ldots, \mu_p$ of $\varphi(\mu) = 0$ are the characteristic values of T. By Ch. 8, § 6, Th. 2 there exists a coordinate system $\{\psi\}$ in R such that mat $(T; \psi)$ has the superdiagonal form, and, upon inspecting the proof, it is easily seen that the system $\{\psi\}$ may be chosen such that it is orthonormal. The elements on the principal diagonal of mat $(T; \psi)$ are exactly the characteristic values $\mu_1, \ldots, \mu_p$. It follows that the trace σ_1 satisfies $\sigma_1 = \Sigma_{i=1}^{p} \mu_i$. Since the transformations $T^n (n = 1, 2, \ldots)$ have the characteristic values $\mu_1^n, \ldots, \mu_p^n$ (cf. Ch. 8, § 6, Th. 2), their traces σ_n satisfy $\sigma_n = \tau(T^n) = \Sigma_{i=1}^{p} \mu_i^n$.

If $\varphi(\mu) = \det(T - \mu I) \neq 0$, that is, if μ does not belong to the spectrum of T, the linear transformation $(T - \mu I)^{-1}$ exists. In other words, if λ is not the reciprocal of one of the numbers $\mu_1, \ldots, \mu_p$, the equation

$$(I - \lambda T)f = g$$

has a unique solution $f \in R$, if $g \in R$ is given. If $f = \Sigma_{i=1}^{p} f_i \varphi_i$, $g = \Sigma_{i=1}^{p} g_i \varphi_i$, the equation $(I - \lambda T)f = g$ is equivalent to

$$f_i - \lambda \Sigma_{j=1}^{p} t_{ij} f_j = g_i \quad (i = 1, \ldots, p).$$

Writing $d(\lambda) = \det(I - \lambda T)$, the solution can be written in the form

$$f_i = [d(\lambda)]^{-1} \Sigma_{j=1}^{p} d_{ij}(\lambda) g_j \quad (i = 1, \ldots, p),$$

where $d_{ij}(\lambda)$ is the coefficient of the (j, i)-element in $d(\lambda)$. This shows that $d_{ij}(\lambda)$ is a polynomial in λ. The solution can therefore be written more shortly as $f = [d(\lambda)]^{-1} D(\lambda) g$, where $D(\lambda)$ is the linear transformation with matrix $\{d_{ij}(\lambda)\}$. The transformation $D(\lambda)$ is therefore a polynomial in λ with fixed linear transformations as coefficients.

Theorem 1. *For arbitrary $f, g \in R$ we have*

$$(D(\lambda)g, f) = -\det \begin{vmatrix} 0 & \bar{f}_1 \; - \; - \; - \; \bar{f}_p \\ g_1 & \\ \vdots & I - \lambda T \\ g_p & \end{vmatrix}.$$

Proof. Expanding the determinant in terms of its first row, we see that the coefficient of $\bar{f}_i$ if $(-1)^{i+2}(-1)^{i+1}$ times the determinant which we obtain by replacing the i-th column of $d(\lambda) = \det(I - \lambda T)$ by $g_1, \ldots, g_p$. This coefficient is therefore $-\Sigma_{j=1}^{p} d_{ij}(\lambda) g_j$, which was to be proved.

Since $d(\lambda)$ and $D(\lambda)$ are polynomials in λ, we may write them formally as power series

$$d(\lambda) = \Sigma_{n=0}^{\infty} d_n \lambda^n, \quad D(\lambda) = \Sigma_{n=0}^{\infty} D_n \lambda^n,$$

where the coefficients d_n are complex numbers and the coefficients D_n are linear transformations on R.

Theorem 2. *We have* ([4])

$$d_0 = 1, \quad d_n = (-1)^n P_n / n! \ (n = 1, 2, \ldots),$$

where

$$P_n = \det \begin{vmatrix} \sigma_1 & n-1 & 0 & - & - & - & 0 & 0 \\ \sigma_2 & \sigma_1 & n-2 & - & - & - & 0 & 0 \\ \cdot\cdot & \cdot\cdot & \cdot\cdot & - & - & - & \cdot\cdot & \cdot\cdot \\ \sigma_{n-1} & \sigma_{n-2} & \sigma_{n-3} & - & - & - & \sigma_1 & 1 \\ \sigma_n & \sigma_{n-1} & \sigma_{n-2} & - & - & - & \sigma_2 & \sigma_1 \end{vmatrix}.$$

Proof. Since $d(0) = \det(I) = 1$, it follows that $d_0 = 1$. Writing $P_0 = 1$, $0! = 1$, we find by successive expansions

$$P_n = \sigma_1 P_{n-1} - (n-1)\sigma_2 P_{n-2} + (n-1)(n-2)\sigma_3 P_{n-3} - \ldots \\ \ldots + (-1)^{n-1}(n-1)!\sigma_n P_0,$$

so that, writing for a moment $d_n' = (-1)^n P_n / n!$, we have

(1) $$nd_n' = -\sigma_1 d_{n-1}' - \sigma_2 d_{n-2}' - \ldots - \sigma_n d_0' = \\ -\Sigma_{m=0}^{n-1} d_m' \sigma_{n-m} \ (n = 1, 2, \ldots).$$

Now we observe that $d(\lambda) = \Pi_{i=1}^{p}(1 - \mu_i \lambda)$, so that, for $|\lambda|$ sufficiently small,

$$d'(\lambda)/d(\lambda) = -\Sigma_{i=1}^{p} \mu_i/(1 - \mu_i \lambda) = \\ -\Sigma_{i=1}^{p} \Sigma_{n=0}^{\infty} \mu_i^{n+1} \lambda^n = -\Sigma_{n=0}^{\infty} \sigma_{n+1} \lambda^n.$$

Combining this with $d(\lambda) = \Sigma_{n=0}^{\infty} d_n \lambda^n$, $d'(\lambda) = \Sigma_{n=0}^{\infty} (n+1) d_{n+1} \lambda^n$, we find

$$\Sigma_{n=0}^{\infty}(n+1) d_{n+1} \lambda^n = -\Sigma_{m=0}^{\infty} d_m \lambda^m \Sigma_{q=0}^{\infty} \sigma_{q+1} \lambda^q,$$

hence, comparing the coefficients of λ^{n-1} on both sides,

(2) $$nd_n = -\Sigma_{m=0}^{n-1} d_m \sigma_{n-m}.$$

Observing now that $d_0 = d'_0 = 1$, and that the recurrence relations (1) and (2) are identical, we find $d_n = d'_n = (-1)^n P_n/n!\ (n = 0, 1, 2, \ldots)$.

Theorem 3. *We have* ([4])

$$D_0 = I,\ D_n = D'_n \ (n = 1, 2, \ldots),$$

where

$$D'_n = \frac{(-1)^n}{n!}\, det \begin{vmatrix} I & n \quad 0 \quad - \quad - \quad - \quad 0 \\ T & \\ T^2 & P_n \\ \vdots & \\ T^n & \end{vmatrix}.$$

Proof. For those values of λ for which $d(\lambda) \neq 0$, we have $f = [d(\lambda)]^{-1}D(\lambda)g$ as the unique solution of $(I - \lambda T)f = g$; hence, substituting this in $(I - \lambda T)f = g$, we find

$$D(\lambda)g - \lambda TD(\lambda)g = d(\lambda)g.$$

This holds for arbitrary $g \in R$, hence $D(\lambda) = d(\lambda)I + \lambda TD(\lambda)$ or $\Sigma_{n=0}^{\infty} \lambda^n D_n = \Sigma_{n=0}^{\infty} \lambda^n d_n I + \Sigma_{n=0}^{\infty} \lambda^{n+1} TD_n$. Comparing the coefficients of λ^n on both sides, we obtain

(3) $$D_0 = I,\ D_n = d_n I + TD_{n-1} \ (n = 1, 2, \ldots).$$

Writing now $D'_0 = I$, we have for $n \geqslant 1$, by expanding the determinant D'_n in terms of its first row,

(4) $$D'_n = d_n I - n(-1/n)TD'_{n-1} = d_n I + TD'_{n-1} \ (n = 1, 2, \ldots).$$

Observing that $D_0 = D'_0 = I$, and that the recurrence relations (3) and (4) are identical, we find therefore $D_n = D'_n \ (n = 0, 1, 2, \ldots)$.

To extend these results to transformations T of finite double-norm in a Hilbert space of infinite dimension, it will be necessary to modify the formulas, since in a space of infinite dimension $\sigma_1 = \Sigma_{i=1}^{\infty} t_{ii}$ does not necessarily exist. For this purpose we observe that in our p-dimensional space R the solution f of $(I - \lambda T)f = g$ may be written in the form

$$f = [\delta(\lambda)]^{-1}\Delta(\lambda)g,$$

where

$$\delta(\lambda) = e^{\sigma_1 \lambda} d(\lambda),\ \Delta(\lambda) = e^{\sigma_1 \lambda} D(\lambda).$$

Both $\delta(\lambda)$ and $\Delta(\lambda)$ are power series in λ;

$$\delta(\lambda) = \Sigma_{n=0}^{\infty} \delta_n \lambda^n,\ \Delta(\lambda) = \Sigma_{n=0}^{\infty} \Delta_n \lambda^n,$$

both series being convergent for all complex λ. The coefficients δ_n are complex numbers and the coefficients Δ_n are linear transformations on R.

Theorem 4. *We have*

$$\delta_0 = 1,\ \delta_n = (-1)^n Q_n/n!\ (n = 1, 2, \ldots),$$

where Q_n is the determinant which is obtained by replacing all numbers σ_1 on the principal diagonal of the determinant P_n by zeros.

Proof It follows from $\delta(\lambda) = e^{\sigma_1\lambda}d(\lambda)$ that, for $|\lambda|$ sufficiently small,

$$\delta'(\lambda)/\delta(\lambda) = \sigma_1 + d'(\lambda)/d(\lambda) =$$

$$\sigma_1 - \Sigma_{n=0}^{\infty} \sigma_{n+1}\lambda^n = -\Sigma_{n=1}^{\infty} \sigma_{n+1}\lambda^n.$$

This differs from the corresponding formula for $d'(\lambda)/d(\lambda)$ only by the disappearance of the term in σ_1. We obtain therefore the coefficients δ_n simply by replacing σ_1 by 0 in the formulas for d_n.

Theorem 5. *We have*

$$\Delta_0 = I,\ \Delta_n = \Delta_n'\ (n = 1, 2, \ldots),$$

where the transformations Δ_n' are obtained by replacing all σ_1 by zeros in the formulas for D_n' in Theorem 3.

Proof. As in Theorem 3.

Theorem 6. *For $n = 1, 2, \ldots$ we have*

$$\tau(T\Delta_n - \delta_n T) = -(n+1)\delta_{n+1}.$$

Proof. Since $\Delta_n = \delta_n I + T\Delta_{n-1}$ $(n = 1, 2, \ldots)$ by (4), we find

$$\Delta_n = \delta_n I + \delta_{n-1}T + \delta_{n-2}T^2 + \ldots + \delta_0 T^n,$$

hence

$$T\Delta_n - \delta_n T = \delta_{n-1}T^2 + \delta_{n-2}T^3 + \ldots + \delta_0 T^{n+1},$$

so that by (2), with d_i replaced by δ_i and σ_1 replaced by 0,

$$\tau(T\Delta_n - \delta_n T) = \delta_0\sigma_{n+1} + \delta_1\sigma_n + \ldots + \delta_{n-1}\sigma_2 = -(n+1)\delta_{n+1}.$$

Remark. The same device which has led to the elimination of σ_1 from our formulas may be used to eliminate any finite number of successive traces $\sigma_1, \ldots, \sigma_n$ of T. Indeed, instead of $\delta(\lambda) = e^{\sigma_1\lambda}d(\lambda)$, $\Delta(\lambda) = e^{\sigma_1\lambda}D(\lambda)$, it is sufficient to consider then $\delta(\lambda) = e^{p(\lambda)}d(\lambda)$, $\Delta(\lambda) = e^{p(\lambda)}D(\lambda)$, where $p(\lambda) = \sigma_1\lambda + 2^{-1}\sigma_2\lambda^2 + \ldots + n^{-1}\sigma_n\lambda^n$. In fact, it is possible by a similar procedure to replace in our formulas any finite number $\sigma_{i_1}, \sigma_{i_2}, \ldots, \sigma_{i_n}$ of the traces by arbitrary complex numbers.

Lemma α. *Let* $f(z) = \Sigma_{n=0}^{\infty} a_n z^n$ *be a power series in the complex variable* $z = re^{i\varphi}$, *converging for all* z, *and let* $|f(z)| \leqslant g(|z|) = g(r)$ *for all* z. *Then, for all* $r \geqslant 0$, *we have*

$$|a_n| \leqslant r^{-n} g(r) \quad (n = 0, 1, 2, \ldots).$$

Proof. We choose $r_0 > 0$ arbitrarily. Then, since the power series converges uniformly in the circle $|z| \leqslant r_0$, there exists to every preassigned $\varepsilon > 0$ an index $N_0 = N_0(\varepsilon, r_0)$ such that for $N \geqslant N_0$

$$|f(z)\overline{f(z)} - (\Sigma_{m=0}^{N} a_m z^m)(\Sigma_{n=0}^{N} \overline{a_n z^n})| \leqslant \varepsilon$$

or

$$||f(z)|^2 - \Sigma_{m=0}^{N} a_m r^m e^{im\varphi} \Sigma_{n=0}^{N} \bar{a}_n r^n e^{-in\varphi}| \leqslant \varepsilon.$$

Integrating over $0 \leqslant \varphi \leqslant 2\pi$, we find

$$|\int_0^{2\pi} |f(z)|^2 d\varphi - \Sigma_{n=0}^{N} |a_n|^2 r^{2n} \int_0^{2\pi} d\varphi| \leqslant 2\pi\varepsilon.$$

This shows that

$$\Sigma_{n=0}^{\infty} |a_n|^2 r^{2n} = (2\pi)^{-1} \int_0^{2\pi} |f(z)|^2 d\varphi \leqslant [g(r)]^2,$$

hence $|a_n|^2 r^{2n} \leqslant [g(r)]^2$ for $n = 0, 1, 2, \ldots$. Finally

$$|a_n| \leqslant r^{-n} g(r) \quad (n = 0, 1, 2, \ldots).$$

Lemma β (*Hadamard's inequality*). *If* $\{t_{ij}\}$ *is a matrix with* p *rows and* p *columns, then*

$$|\det|t_{ij}||^2 \leqslant \Pi_{i=1}^{p} \Sigma_{j=1}^{p} |t_{ij}|^2.$$

Proof. We first prove a fundamental inequality between the geometric and the arithmetic means of p non-negative numbers $a_1, \ldots, a_p$; in formula

$$\Pi_{i=1}^{p} a_i \leqslant A^p, \text{ where } A = \Sigma_{i=1}^{p} a_i/p.$$

We have

$$a_1 a_2 = [(a_1 + a_2)/2]^2 - [(a_1 - a_2)/2]^2 \leqslant [(a_1 + a_2)/2]^2,$$

with equality if and only if $a_1 = a_2$. Hence

$$a_1 a_2 a_3 a_4 \leqslant [(a_1 + a_2)/2]^2 [(a_3 + a_4)/2]^2 \leqslant [(a_1 + a_2 + a_3 + a_4)/4]^4,$$

with equality if and only if $a_1 = a_2 = a_3 = a_4$. After m steps

$$\Pi_{i=1}^{2^m} a_i \leqslant [\Sigma_{i=1}^{2^m} a_i/2^m]^{2^m},$$

with equality if and only if $a_1 = a_2 = \ldots = a_{2m}$. If p is not a power of 2, we take m such that $2^m > p$, and we define

$$b_1 = a_1, \ldots, b_p = a_p, b_{p+1} = \ldots = b_{2m} = A.$$

Then

$$a_1 a_2 \ldots a_p A^{2^m - p} \leqslant [\Sigma_1^{2^m} b_i/2^m]^{2^m} = [\{pA + (2^m - p)A\}/2^m]^{2^m} = A^{2^m},$$

hence

$$\Pi_{i=1}^p a_i \leqslant A^p,$$

with equality if and only if all b_i, and therefore all a_i, are equal.

We now come to the proof of Hadamard's inequality. We may suppose $\Sigma_{j=1}^p |t_{ij}|^2 > 0$ for $i = 1, \ldots, p$, since in the opposite case both sides of the inequality vanish. The matrix $\{t_{ij}\}$ may be considered as the matrix of a linear transformation T in the orthonormal coordinate system $\varphi_1, \ldots, \varphi_p$. Then mat $(T^*; \varphi) = \{\overline{t_{ji}}\}$, hence mat $(TT^*; \varphi) = \{c_{ij}\}$ with $c_{ij} = \Sigma_{k=1}^p t_{ik} \overline{t_{jk}}$. In particular $c_{ii} = \Sigma_{k=1}^p |t_{ik}|^2 > 0$. Furthermore $\det(TT^*) = \det(T)$. $\det(T^*) = |\det(T)|^2$. Defining now the linear transformation C by $(C\varphi_j, \varphi_i) = \gamma_{ij} = c_{ij}/(c_{ii}c_{jj})^{1/2}$, we see that $\gamma_{ii} = 1$ and that, for an arbitrary $f = \Sigma \alpha_i \varphi_i$,

$$(Cf, f) = (\Sigma \alpha_j C\varphi_j, \Sigma \alpha_i \varphi_i) = \Sigma_{ij} c_{ij}(\overline{\alpha_i}\, c_{ii}^{-1/2})\ (\alpha_j c_{jj}^{-1/2}) \geqslant 0,$$

since TT^* with matrix $\{c_{ij}\}$ is positive. Furthermore

$$\det(C) = \det(TT^*)/\Pi_1^p c_{ii} = |\det(T)|^2/\Pi_1^p c_{ii}.$$

The transformation C has p non-negative characteristic values with $\Sigma \gamma_{ii} = \Sigma 1 = p$ as sum and $\det(C)$ as product. Hence, by the theorem on geometric and arithmetic means,

$$\det(C) \leqslant [\Sigma \gamma_{ii}/p]^p = [p/p]^p = 1,$$

or

$$|\det(T)|^2 \leqslant \Pi c_{ii} = \Pi_{i=1}^p \Sigma_{j=1}^p |t_{ij}|^2.$$

Theorem 7. *For $n = 1, 2, \ldots$ we have* ([4])

$$|\delta_n| \leqslant e^{n/2}\, |||\, T\, |||^n / n^{n/2},$$

where δ_n and T have the same meaning as in Theorem 4.

Proof. We observe first that this formula for δ_n also holds for $n = 0$, if we write $n^{n/2} = 1$ for $n = 0$. If $|||\, T\, ||| = 0$, the theorem is trivial since then $\delta_n = 0$ $(n \geqslant 1)$. We suppose therefore that $|||\, T\, ||| \neq 0$. We have

$$\delta(\lambda) = e^{\sigma_1 \lambda} d(\lambda) = e^{\lambda \Sigma t_{ii}} \det(I - \lambda T),$$

hence, by Hadamard's inequality,

$$| \delta(\lambda) |^2 \leqslant [| e^{\lambda t_{11}} |^2 (| 1 - \lambda t_{11} |^2 + | \lambda t_{12} |^2 + \dots + | \lambda t_{1p} |^2)] \dots$$
$$\dots [| e^{\lambda t_{pp}} |^2 (| \lambda t_{p1} |^2 + | \lambda t_{p2} |^2 + \dots + | 1 - \lambda t_{pp} |^2)] =$$
$$\Pi_{i=1}^p e^{\lambda t_{ii} + \overline{\lambda t_{ii}}} (1 - (\lambda t_{ii} + \overline{\lambda t_{ii}}) + | \lambda |^2 \Sigma_{j=1}^p | t_{ij} |^2).$$

Using the inequality $1 + a \leqslant e^a$, holding for all real a, we obtain

$$| \delta(\lambda) |^2 \leqslant \Pi_{i=1}^p e^{| \lambda |^2 \Sigma_{j=1}^p | t_{ij} |^2} = e^{| \lambda |^2 ||| T |||^2}$$

or

$$| \delta(\lambda) | \leqslant e^{| \lambda |^2 ||| T |||^2/2}.$$

Application of Lemma α shows that

$$| \delta_n | \leqslant r^{-n} e^{r^2 ||| T |||^2/2} \quad (n = 0, 1, 2, \dots)$$

for all $r \geqslant 0$. Taking $r = n^{1/2} ||| T |||^{-1}$ (hence $r^2 ||| T |||^2 = n$), we find

$$| \delta_n | \leqslant e^{n/2} ||| T |||^n / n^{n/2} \quad (n = 1, 2, \dots).$$

Lemma γ. *If T is a linear transformation on the Hilbert space R, and $| (Tf, g) | \leqslant A \| f \| . \| g \|$ for all $f, g \in R$, then T is bounded, and $\| T \| \leqslant A$.*

Proof. Suppose that there exists an element $f_0 \in R$ such that $\| Tf_0 \| > A \| f_0 \|$. Then, taking $f = f_0$, $g = Tf_0$, we have $(Tf, g) = \| Tf_0 \|^2 = \| Tf_0 \| . \| Tf_0 \| > A \| f \| . \| g \|$, in contradiction with our hypothesis. It follows that $\| Tf \| \leqslant A \| f \|$ for all $f \in R$.

Theorem 8. *For $n = 1, 2, \dots$ the norm $\| \Delta_n \|$ of the linear transformation Δ_n satisfies* ([4])

$$\| \Delta_n \| \leqslant e^{(n+1)/2} ||| T |||^n / n^{n/2},$$

where Δ_n and T have the same meaning as in Theorem 5.

Proof. We observe first that this formula for $\| \Delta_n \|$ also holds for $n = 0$, if we write $n^{n/2} = 1$ for $n = 0$. We may once again assume that $||| T ||| \neq 0$. For arbitrary $f, g \in R$ we have, by Theorem 1,

$$(\Delta(\lambda)g, f) = e^{\sigma_1 \lambda} (D(\lambda)g, f) = - e^{\lambda \Sigma_{i=1}^p t_{ii}} \det \begin{vmatrix} 0 & \bar{f}_1 & - & - & - & \bar{f}_p \\ g_1 & & & & & \\ \vdots & & & I - \lambda T & & \\ g_p & & & & & \end{vmatrix}.$$

Let first $\| f \| = \| g \| = 1$. Then, using Hadamard's inequality, and following the same procedure as in the preceding theorem, we obtain

$$| (\Delta(\lambda)g, f) |^2 \leqslant e^{1 + | \lambda |^2 ||| T |||^2},$$

so that, for arbitrary $f, g \in R$,

$$|(\Delta(\lambda)g, f)| \leqslant e^{\{1+|\lambda|^2 |||T|||^2\}/2} \|f\| \cdot \|g\|.$$

Applying Lemma α, we find

$$|(\Delta_n g, f)| \leqslant [e^{(n+1)/2} |||T|||^n / n^{n/2}] \cdot \|f\| \cdot \|g\|$$

for $n = 1, 2, \ldots$, hence, by Lemma γ,

$$\|\Delta_n\| \leqslant e^{(n+1)/2} |||T|||^n / n^{n/2} \quad (n = 1, 2, \ldots).$$

§ 17. Fredholm Theory in a Hilbert Space of Enumerable Dimension

We now suppose that R is a complete Hilbert space of enumerable dimension. The system $\varphi_1, \varphi_2, \ldots$ is a fixed orthonormal system in R. If p is a positive integer, we define the orthogonal projection P_p by $P_p(\Sigma_1^\infty \alpha_i \varphi_i) = \Sigma_1^p \alpha_i \varphi_i$. P_p is therefore the orthogonal projection on the p-dimensional space R_p determined by $\varphi_1, \ldots, \varphi_p$. Let now T be a linear transformation of finite double-norm on R, hence

$$|||T|||^2 = \Sigma_{ij} |t_{ij}|^2 < \infty,$$

where $t_{ij} = (T\varphi_j, \varphi_i)$. The traces $\sigma_n = \tau(T^n)$ exist for $n \geqslant 2$, and $|\sigma_n| \leqslant |||T|||^n$ (cf. § 10, Th. 6). Writing $P_p T P_p = T_p$ $(p = 1, 2, \ldots)$, we have

$$(T_p \varphi_j, \varphi_i) = \begin{cases} t_{ij} & \text{for } i, j = 1, \ldots, p, \\ 0 & \text{for } i > p \text{ or } j > p. \end{cases}$$

The trace $\tau(T_p^n)$ is denoted by σ_{np}. The transformation T_p may be considered as a linear transformation with domain R_p and range in R_p, and this makes no difference to the values of $|||T_p^n|||$ or σ_{np}.

Theorem 1. *We have*

1°. $\lim_{p\to\infty} |||T_p^n - T^n||| = 0 \qquad (n = 1, 2, \ldots).$

2°. $\lim_{p\to\infty} |||T_p^n||| = |||T^n||| \qquad (n = 1, 2, \ldots).$

3°. $\lim_{p\to\infty} \sigma_{np} = \sigma_n \qquad (n = 2, 3, \ldots).$

4°. $\lim_{p\to\infty} (T_p^n f, g) = (T^n f, g) \qquad (n = 1, 2, \ldots).$

Proof. 1°. We have $\lim_{p\to\infty} |||T - T_p|||^2 = \lim_{p\to\infty} \Sigma_{ij=p+1}^\infty |t_{ij}|^2 = 0$. Furthermore, since $|||T_p|||^2 = \Sigma_{ij=1}^p |t_{ij}|^2 \leqslant \Sigma_{ij=1}^\infty |t_{ij}|^2 = |||T|||^2$, we find $|||T_p^n||| \leqslant |||T_p|||^n \leqslant |||T|||^n$ for all n.

Let now $\lim_{p\to\infty} ||| T^{n-1} - T_p^{n-1} ||| = 0$. Then, on account of

$$||| T^n - T_p^n ||| \leqslant ||| T^n - T^{n-1}T_p ||| + ||| T^{n-1}T_p - T_p^n |||$$
$$\leqslant ||| T^{n-1} |||.||| T - T_p ||| + ||| T^{n-1} - T_p^{n-1} |||.||| T_p |||$$

and $||| T_p ||| \leqslant ||| T |||$, we see that $\lim_{p\to\infty} ||| T^n - T_p^n ||| = 0$.

2°. We have $| \, ||| T^n ||| - ||| T_p^n ||| \, | \leqslant ||| T^n - T_p^n |||$.

3°. For $n \geqslant 2$ we have $| \sigma_n - \sigma_{np} | = | \tau(T^n) - \tau(T_p^n) | = | \tau(T^n - T_p^n) | \leqslant ||| T^n - T_p^n |||$.

4°. $| (T^n f, g) - (T_p^n f, g) | \leqslant \| T^n - T_p^n \|.\| f \|.\| g \| \leqslant ||| T^n - T_p^n |||. \| f \|.\| g \|$.

Theorem 2. *Let T be of finite double-norm, and let $\sigma_n = \tau(T^n)$ $(n = 2, 3, \ldots)$. Then, defining δ_n and Δ_n $(n = 0, 1, 2, \ldots)$ by the formulas of Theorem 4 and Theorem 5 of the preceding paragraph, we have*

$$\delta_0 = 1, \ \Delta_0 = I,$$

$$\Delta_n = \delta_n I + T\Delta_{n-1} = \delta_n I + \Delta_{n-1} T \ \ (n = 1, 2, \ldots),$$

$$\tau(T\Delta_n - \delta_n T) = \tau(\Delta_n T - \delta_n T) = -(n+1)\delta_{n+1} \ \ (n = 1, 2, \ldots),$$

$$| \delta_n | \leqslant e^{n/2} ||| T |||^n / n^{n/2}, \ \| \Delta_n \| \leqslant e^{(n+1)/2} ||| T |||^n / n^{n/2}.$$

Proof. Only the inequalities need a proof. Considering T_p as a transformation on the p-dimensional space R_p, we may define δ_{np} and Δ_{np} $(n = 0, 1, 2, \ldots)$ for T_p as in the preceding paragraph. The domain of Δ_{np} is extended to the whole space R by

$$\Delta_{np} = P_p \Delta_{np} P_p = \Delta_{np} P_p,$$

where Δ_{np} on the left is the extended Δ_{np}. Hence $(\Delta_{np} f, g) = (\Delta_{np} P_p f, P_p g)$ for arbitrary $f, g \in R$, where Δ_{np} on the left is again the extended Δ_{np}.

We now observe that, by § 16, Th. 7,

$$| \delta_{np} | \leqslant e^{n/2} ||| T_p |||^n / n^{n/2} \leqslant e^{n/2} ||| T |||^n / n^{n/2} \ \ (n = 1, 2, \ldots),$$

and that $\lim_{p\to\infty} \delta_{np} = \delta_n$ on account of $\lim_{p\to\infty} \sigma_{ip} = \sigma_i$ $(i = 2, 3, \ldots)$. Hence

$$| \delta_n | \leqslant e^{n/2} ||| T |||^n / n^{n/2} \ \ (n = 1, 2, \ldots).$$

Furthermore, for arbitrary $f, g \in R$, by § 17, Th. 8,

$$| (\Delta_{np} f, g) | = | (\Delta_{np} P_p f, P_p g) | \leqslant \| \Delta_{np} \|.\| P_p f \|.\| P_p g \| \leqslant$$
$$[e^{(n+1)/2} ||| T_p |||^n / n^{n/2}].\| f \|.\| g \| \leqslant [e^{(n+1)/2} ||| T |||^n / n^{n/2}].\| f \|.\| g \|$$

and $\lim_{p\to\infty} (\Delta_{np}f, g) = (\Delta_n f, g)$ on account of $\lim_{p\to\infty} ||| T^i - T_p^i ||| = 0$ $(i = 1, 2, \ldots)$ and $\lim_{p\to\infty} \sigma_{jp} = \sigma_j$ $(j = 2, 3, \ldots)$. Hence

$$| (\Delta_n f, g) | \leqslant [e^{(n+1)/2} ||| T |||^n/n^{n/2}].\| f \|.\| g \| \quad (n = 1, 2, \ldots)$$

for arbitrary $f, g \in R$, or

$$\| \Delta_n \| \leqslant e^{(n+1)/2} |||T|||^n/n^{n/2} \quad (n = 1, 2, \ldots).$$

Lemma α. *Let $f(z) = \Sigma_{n=0}^{\infty} a_n z^n$ be a power series in the complex variable z, converging for all z, and such that not all coefficients a_n vanish. Then, if $r_0 > 0$ is arbitrary, the equation $f(z) = 0$ has only a finite number of solutions in the circle $| z | \leqslant r_0$.*

Proof. Let α be arbitrarily complex, and $A > | \alpha |$. Consider now those z for which $| z - \alpha | \leqslant A - | \alpha |$, hence $| z - \alpha | + | \alpha | \leqslant A$. We have $a_n z^n = a_n\{(z - \alpha) + \alpha\}^n = \Sigma_{k=0}^{n} b_{nk}(z - \alpha)^k$, where $\Sigma_{k=0}^{n} | b_{nk} |.| z - \alpha |^k = | a_n |\{| z - \alpha | + | \alpha |\}^n \leqslant | a_n | A^n$. Since $\Sigma_{n=0}^{\infty} | a_n | A^n < \infty$, we find $\Sigma_{n=0}^{\infty} \Sigma_{k=0}^{n} | b_{nk} |.| z - \alpha |^k < \infty$, so that, as a consequence of Fubini's theorem, $f(z) = \Sigma_{n=0}^{\infty} \Sigma_{k=0}^{n} b_{nk}(z - \alpha)^k = \Sigma_{k=0}^{\infty} c_k(z - \alpha)^k$ in $| z - \alpha | \leqslant A - | \alpha |$, where $c_k = \Sigma_{n=k}^{\infty} b_{nk}$. Since $A > | \alpha |$ is arbitrary, this holds for all z. It follows that $f(z)$ can be written as an everywhere converging power series in $z - \alpha$.

By hypothesis not all coefficients a_n of $f(z) = \Sigma\, a_n z^n$ vanish. Let $a_0 = \ldots = a_{q-1} = 0$, $a_q \neq 0$. Then $f(z) = z^q(a_q + r_q(z))$, and there exists a circle $| z | \leqslant B$ such that $| a_q + r_q(z) | > | a_q |/2$ for all z in this circle. Hence $| f(z) | > | a_q |.| z |^q/2 \neq 0$ for $0 < | z | \leqslant B$, which shows in particular that $f(z)$ does not vanish identically.

Let us suppose now that $f(z) = 0$ has an infinity of solutions in $| z | \leqslant r_0$. Then there exists a sequence $z_1, z_2, \ldots$ such that $f(z_n) = 0$ $(n = 1, 2, \ldots)$, $\lim z_n = \alpha$, $\alpha \leqslant r_0$. Writing $f(z) = \Sigma_{n=0}^{\infty} c_n(z - \alpha)^n$, the same proof as before shows that $| f(z) | \neq 0$ for $0 < | z - \alpha | \leqslant B$, unless all c_n vanish. All c_n do not vanish, since then $f(z)$ would vanish identically. The other possibility $| f(z) | \neq 0$ for $0 < | z - \alpha | \leqslant B$ is in contradiction with the existence of the sequence z_n. It follows that such a sequence does not exist. In other words, $f(z) = 0$ has only a finite number of solutions in $| z | \leqslant r_0$.

Theorem 3. *Let T be of finite double-norm, and let δ_n and $\Delta_n (n = 0, 1, 2, \ldots)$ be defined as in the preceding theorem. Then the power series*

$$\delta(\lambda) = \Sigma_{n=0}^{\infty} \delta_n \lambda^n$$

converges for all complex λ, and the power series

$$\Delta(\lambda) = \Sigma_{n=0}^{\infty} \Delta_n \lambda^n$$

even satisfies

$$\lim_{n\to\infty} \| \Delta(\lambda) - \Sigma_{i=0}^{n} \Delta_i \lambda^i \| = 0$$

for all λ, *so that* $\Delta(\lambda)$ *is a bounded linear transformation.*

Furthermore, if $\delta(\lambda_0) \neq 0$, *the equation*

$$(I - \lambda_0 T)f = g$$

has the unique solution ([4])

$$f = [\delta(\lambda_0)]^{-1} \Delta(\lambda_0)g.$$

Proof. The statements on convergence are immediate consequences of the inequalities for δ_n and $\| \Delta_n \|$ in the preceding theorem. From

$$\Delta_0 = I,\ \Delta_n = \delta_n I + T\Delta_{n-1} = \delta_n I + \Delta_{n-1} T \quad (n = 1, 2, \ldots)$$

follows

$$(I - \lambda T)\, \Delta(\lambda) = \Sigma_{n=0}^{\infty}(I - \lambda T)\Delta_n \lambda^n =$$

$$\Sigma_{n=0}^{\infty} (\Delta_n - \lambda\Delta_{n+1} + \lambda\delta_{n+1} I)\lambda^n = I(1 + \Sigma_{n=1}^{\infty} \delta_n \lambda^n) = \delta(\lambda)I.$$

Similarly $\Delta(\lambda)\,(I - \lambda T) = \delta(\lambda)I$.

Let us suppose now that $\delta(\lambda_0) \neq 0$. Then, if $f = [\delta(\lambda_0)]^{-1} \Delta(\lambda_0)g$, we have $(I - \lambda_0 T)f = (I - \lambda_0 T)\Delta(\lambda_0)g/\delta(\lambda_0) = g$, which shows that f is a solution of $(I - \lambda_0 T)f = g$. Supposing that f_1 is also a solution, we find $f_1 = \delta(\lambda_0)f_1/\delta(\lambda_0) = \Delta(\lambda_0)\ (I - \lambda_0 T)f_1/\delta(\lambda_0) = \Delta(\lambda_0)g/\delta(\lambda_0) = f$, and this shows that $f = [\delta(\lambda_0)]^{-1}\Delta(\lambda_0)g$ is the unique solution of $(I - \lambda_0 T)f = g$.

We finally observe that, in any circle $|\lambda| \leqslant r$ (r arbitrarily positive), the equation $\delta(\lambda) = 0$ has only a finite number of solutions by Lemma α. If therefore λ is not one of these solutions, our theorem shows that $I - \lambda T$ has a bounded inverse $(I - \lambda T)^{-1} = \Delta(\lambda)/\delta(\lambda)$.

Corollary. *If* $\delta(\lambda) \neq 0$, *the equation*

$$(I - \bar{\lambda} T^*)f = g$$

has the unique solution

$$f = [\overline{\delta(\lambda)}]^{-1}\{\Delta(\lambda)\}^* g.$$

Proof. Since $I - \lambda T$ has a bounded inverse $\Delta(\lambda)/\delta(\lambda)$, the transformation $I - \bar{\lambda}T^* = (I - \lambda T)^*$ has also a bounded inverse $(I - \bar{\lambda}T^*)^{-1}$, and $(I - \bar{\lambda}T^*)^{-1} = \{(I - \lambda T)^{-1}\}^* = [\overline{\delta(\lambda)}]^{-1}\{\Delta(\lambda)\}^*$ (cf. § 1, Th. 3). We observe that $\overline{\delta(\lambda)} = \Sigma_{n=0}^{\infty} \bar{\delta}_n \bar{\lambda}^n$ and $\{\Delta(\lambda)\}^* = \Sigma_{n=0}^{\infty} \Delta_n^* \bar{\lambda}^n$, and this makes it clear that we could also derive a proof by repeating for T^* the argument which led for T to $(I - \lambda T)^{-1} = \Delta(\lambda)/\delta(\lambda)$. Indeed, observing that $(T^*)^n = (T^n)^*$, we find $\sigma_n^* = \tau[(T^*)^n] = \bar{\sigma}_n$ for all n, so that δ_n and Δ_n for T^* are equal to $\bar{\delta}_n$ and Δ_n^* respectively. It follows that $\delta^*(\bar{\lambda}) = \Sigma_{n=0}^{\infty} \bar{\delta}_n \bar{\lambda}^n = 0$ if and only if $\delta(\lambda) = 0$, and that for $\delta(\lambda) \neq 0$ the equation $(I - \bar{\lambda}T^*)f = g$ has the unique solution $f = [\delta^*(\bar{\lambda})]^{-1}(\Sigma_0^{\infty} \Delta_n^* \bar{\lambda}^n)g = [\overline{\delta(\lambda)}]^{-1} \{\Delta(\lambda)\}^* g$.

Theorem 4. *For all values of λ we have*

$$\Delta(\lambda) = \delta(\lambda)I + \lambda H(\lambda),$$

where

$$H(\lambda) = \Sigma_{n=0}^{\infty} H_n \lambda^n, \; H_n = T\Delta_n = \Delta_n T \; (n = 0, 1, 2, \ldots).$$

Every H_n is of finite double-norm, $H(\lambda)$ is of finite double-norm, and the series for $H(\lambda)$ converges in double-norm.

Proof. From $\Delta_n = \delta_n I + T\Delta_{n-1}$ $(n = 1, 2, \ldots)$ follows

$$\Delta(\lambda) = \Sigma_{n=0}^{\infty} \Delta_n \lambda^n = \Delta_0 + \Sigma_1^{\infty}(\delta_n I + T\Delta_{n-1})\lambda^n$$

$$= I + (\Sigma_1^{\infty} \delta_n \lambda^n)I + \Sigma_1^{\infty} T\Delta_{n-1}\lambda^n =$$

$$\delta(\lambda)I + \lambda \Sigma_0^{\infty} T\Delta_n \lambda^n = \delta(\lambda)I + \lambda \Sigma_0^{\infty} H_n \lambda^n.$$

Furthermore, by § 10, Th. 2,

$$|||\, \lambda^n H_n \,||| = |||\, \lambda^n T\Delta_n \,||| \leqslant |\lambda|^n . \|\Delta_n\| . |||\, T \,|||$$

$$\leqslant e^{(n+1)/2} \, |||\, T \,|||^{n+1} \, |\lambda|^n / n^{n/2},$$

so that $\Sigma_0^{\infty} |||\, \lambda^n H_n \,|||$ converges. It follows that $\Sigma_0^{\infty} H_n \lambda^n$ converges in double-norm. But then $H(\lambda)$ is also of finite double-norm.

Theorem 5. *We have $\delta(\lambda) = 0$ if and only if $\mu = \lambda^{-1}$ is a characteristic value of T.*

Proof. Let $\mu = \lambda^{-1}$, $Tf = \mu f$, $f \neq 0$. Then $\lambda T f = f$, hence $(I - \lambda T)f = 0$. From $\Delta(\lambda)(I - \lambda T) = \delta(\lambda)I$, holding for all λ, follows now $\delta(\lambda)If = 0$, hence $\delta(\lambda) = 0$.

Let us suppose now that $\delta(\lambda_0) = 0$. Since, by Lemma α, $\delta(\lambda) = \Sigma_0^{\infty} c_n (\lambda - \lambda_0)^n$, this means that $c_0 = 0$. Let $c_0 = \ldots c_{q-1} = 0$, but $c_q \neq 0$; in other words, let $\delta(\lambda)$ contain the factor $(\lambda - \lambda_0)^q$, but not $(\lambda - \lambda_0)^{q+1}$. Then the derivative $\delta'(\lambda)$ contains the factor $(\lambda - \lambda_0)^{q-1}$, but not $(\lambda - \lambda_0)^q$. By the preceding theorem $\lambda H(\lambda)$ is the limit in double-norm (for $N \to \infty$) of $\Sigma_0^N H_n \lambda^{n+1} = \Sigma_0^N T\Delta_n \lambda^{n+1} = \Sigma_0^N (\Delta_{n+1} - \delta_{n+1} I)\lambda^{n+1} = \Sigma_1^{N+1} (\Delta_n - \delta_n I)\lambda^n$, so that by § 10, Th. 6

$$\tau(T.\lambda H(\lambda)) = \lim \tau(\Sigma_1^{N+1} (\Delta_n T - \delta_n T)\lambda^n) =$$

$$\lim \Sigma_1^{N+1} \tau(\Delta_n T - \delta_n T)\lambda^n = - \lim \Sigma_1^{N+1} (n+1)\delta_{n+1}\lambda^n$$

$$= -(2\delta_2\lambda + 3\delta_3\lambda^2 + \ldots) = -\delta'(\lambda).$$

We have used here that $\tau(\Delta_n T - \delta_n T) = -(n+1)\delta_{n+1}$ $(n = 1, 2, \ldots)$ by Theorem 2, and that $\delta_1 = 0$ by the definition given in § 16, Th. 4.

Supposing now that $\mu_0 = \lambda_0^{-1}$ is not a characteristic value of T, we have $(I - \lambda_0 T)f \neq 0$ for every $f \neq 0$. Nevertheless $(I - \lambda_0 T)\Delta(\lambda_0)f = \delta(\lambda_0)f = 0$ for every f, hence $\Delta(\lambda_0) = O$ (the null transformation). By an argument which is wholly similar to that in Lemma α it follows that $\Delta(\lambda)$ may be written as a power series in $\lambda - \lambda_0$, so that $\Delta(\lambda_0) = O$ implies that $\Delta(\lambda)$ contains the factor $\lambda - \lambda_0$. Hence $(I - \lambda T)\Delta(\lambda)/(\lambda - \lambda_0) = \delta(\lambda)I/(\lambda - \lambda_0)$ for every λ. If now q, the number of factors $\lambda - \lambda_0$ contained in $\delta(\lambda)$, is > 1, we may repeat the argument. Proceeding in this way, we find that $\Delta(\lambda)$ contains $(\lambda - \lambda_0)^q$. Then $\lambda H(\lambda) = \Delta(\lambda) - \delta(\lambda)I$ also contains $(\lambda - \lambda_0)^q$, so that the same is true of $\delta'(\lambda) = -\tau(T.\lambda H(\lambda))$. This however is in contradiction with our former result that $\delta'(\lambda)$ contains $(\lambda - \lambda_0)^{q-1}$, but not $(\lambda - \lambda_0)^q$. It follows that $\mu_0 = \lambda_0^{-1}$ is a characteristic value of T.

We now suppose that the Hilbert space R is the Lebesgue space $L_2(\Delta, \mu)$, where Δ is a finite or infinite interval in real m-dimensional Euclidean space ,and μ is Lebesgue measure in this space. Every linear transformation T of finite double-norm is therefore an integral transformation whose kernel $T(x, y)$ satisfies $|||T|||^2 = \int_{\Delta\times\Delta} |T(x, y)|^2 \,dx\,dy < \infty$.

Theorem 6. ([4]). *If T is of finite double-norm, and $\delta(\lambda_0) \neq 0$, the solution of the equation*

$$f(x) - \lambda_0 \int_\Delta T(x, y)f(y)dy = g(x)$$

can be written in the form

$$f(x) = g(x) + \lambda_0[\delta(\lambda_0)]^{-1} \int_\Delta H(x, y; \lambda_0)g(y)dy,$$

where

$$H(x, y; \lambda) = \Sigma_{n=0}^{\infty} \lambda^n H_n(x, y).$$

The kernels $H_n(x, y)$ are of finite double-norm; for every λ the series for

$H(x, y; \lambda)$ converges in mean in $L_2(\Delta \times \Delta)$, and it also converges in the ordinary sense for almost every point $(x, y) \in \Delta \times \Delta$.

Moreover, writing

$$s(x) = (\int_\Delta | T(x, y) |^2 dy)^{1/2}, \; t(y) = (\int_\Delta | T(x, y) |^2 dx)^{1/2},$$

we have for almost every $(x, y) \in \Delta \times \Delta$

$$H_0(x, y) = T(x, y),$$

$$| H_1(x, y) | \leqslant e^{1/2} ||| T |||.| T(x, y) | + s(x)t(y),$$

$$| H_n(x, y) | \leqslant e^{n/2} ||| T |||^n n^{-n/2} |T(x, y)| + e^{n/2} ||| T |||^{n-1}(n-1)^{-(n-1)/2} s(x)t(y)$$

$$(n = 2, 3, \ldots).$$

Proof. The first statements are immediate consequences of Theorem 4; the statement about the convergence in mean of $H(x, y; \lambda) = \Sigma_0^\infty \lambda^n H_n(x, y)$ is equivalent to the statement in Theorem 4 that $H(\lambda) = \Sigma_0^\infty H_n \lambda^n$ converges in double-norm. Since

$$H_0 = T\Delta_0 = T, \; H_n = T\Delta_n = \delta_n T + T\Delta_{n-1}T \;\; (n = 1, 2, \ldots),$$

we have

$$H_n(x, y) = \delta_n T(x, y) + g_n(x, y),$$

where $g_0(x, y) = 0$, and, for $n \geqslant 1$, $g_n(x, y)$ is the kernel of $T\Delta_{n-1}T$. Hence, by § 10, Th. 12,

$$| g_n(x, y) | \leqslant \| \Delta_{n-1} \| . s(x)t(y)$$

for almost every point $(x, y) \in \Delta \times \Delta$. The inequalities for $H_n(x, y)$ follow now immediately from the inequalities for δ_n and $\| \Delta_n \|$ in Theorem 2. The partial sums of $\Sigma_0^\infty \lambda^n H_n(x, y)$ satisfy therefore

$$\Sigma_0^N | \lambda^n H_n(x, y) | \leqslant A[| T(x, y) | + s(x)t(y)]$$

almost everywhere, where A depends only on λ. This shows that the series converges for almost all (x, y).

A solution $f(x)$ of the equation

$$f(x) - \lambda \int_\Delta T(x, y) f(y) dy = g(x) \tag{1}$$

was given for the first time by FREDHOLM [9] for the particular case that Δ is a finite interval and $T(x, y)$ is continuous on $\Delta \times \Delta$. This solution had the form

$$f(x) = g(x) + \lambda[d(\lambda)]^{-1} \int_\Delta D(x, y; \lambda) g(y) dy, \tag{2}$$

the same form therefore as our solution in Theorem 6. To describe what $d(\lambda)$ and $D(x, y; \lambda)$ mean, we denote by M_n ($n = 1, 2, \ldots$) the determinant with elements $T(z_i, z_j)$ ($i, j = 1, \ldots, n$), and by $M_n^*(x, y)$ the determinant

$$\begin{vmatrix} T(x, y) & T(x, z_1) & - & - & - & T(x, z_n) \\ T(z_1, y) & & & & & \\ \vdots & & & M_n & & \\ T(z_n, y) & & & & & \end{vmatrix}.$$

Then

$$d(\lambda) = 1 - \lambda \int_\Delta M_1 dz_1 + \frac{\lambda^2}{2!} \int_\Delta \int_\Delta M_2 \, dz_1 \, dz_2 - \ldots,$$

$$D(x, y; \lambda) = T(x, y) - \lambda \int_\Delta M_1^*(x, y) dz_1 + \frac{\lambda^2}{2!} \int_\Delta \int_\Delta M_2^*(x, y) \, dz_1 \, dz_2 - \ldots;$$

both series converge for all complex λ, and (2) is the solution of (1) in case $d(\lambda) \neq 0$. If $T(x, y)$ is no longer supposed to be continuous, the diagonal terms $T(z_i, z_i)$ in M_n need not be measurable functions, so that some modification of the formulas is necessary. For this purpose we denote by N_n ($n = 1, 2, \ldots$) the determinant which is obtained by replacing the elements $T(z_i, z_i)$ on the principal diagonal of M_n by zeros, and by $N_n^*(x, y)$ the determinant which is obtained by replacing M_n by N_n in $M_n^*(x, y)$. For some special discontinuous kernels (in particular $T(x, y) = | x - y |^{-\alpha}$, $0 < \alpha < 1/2$) Hilbert [10] has shown that (2) is still the solution of (1) if M_n and $M_n^*(x, y)$ are replaced by N_n and $N_n^*(x, y)$ respectively. It was proved by Carleman [11] that the thus modified formula (2) gives the solution of (1) in the general case that $|||\, T \,|||^2 = \int_{\Delta \times \Delta} | T(x, y) |^2 \, dx \, dy < \infty$. His method of proof supposes the theory for continuous kernels to be already known, whereas the method of Smithies [4], explained in the preceding theorems, can be applied directly to kernels $T(x, y)$ of finite double-norm. It remains to show now that Smithies' solution in Theorem 6 is the same as Carleman's solution.

Theorem 7. ([4]). *With the notations of Theorem* 6 *we have* $\delta_n = \varepsilon_n$, $H_n(x, y) = k_n(x, y)$, *where*

$$\varepsilon_n = \frac{(-1)^n}{n!} \int_\Delta \cdots \int_\Delta N_n \, dz_1 \ldots dz_n,$$

$$k_n(x, y) = \frac{(-1)^n}{n!} \int_\Delta \cdots \int_\Delta N_n^*(x, y) \, dz_1 \ldots dz_n \quad (n = 1, 2, \ldots).$$

Proof. We denote the transformation with kernel $k_n(x, y)$ by K_n $(n = 1, 2, \ldots)$. Then, since $k_1(x, y) = -\int_\Delta N_1^*(x, y)\, dz_1 = \int_\Delta T(x, z_1) T(z_1, y) dz_1$ and $H_1 = T\Delta_1 = TT = T^2$, we have $k_1(x, y) = H_1(x, y)$. Furthermore $\varepsilon_1 = -\int_\Delta N_1\, dz_1 = 0 = \delta_1$.

For $n > 1$ we have for δ_n and H_n the recurrence formulas

$$H_n = T\Delta_n = T(\delta_n I + T\Delta_{n-1}) = \delta_n T + TH_{n-1}, \tag{3}$$

$$-n\delta_n = \tau(T\Delta_{n-1} - \delta_{n-1}T) = \tau(H_{n-1} - \delta_{n-1}T). \tag{4}$$

We shall show that ε_n and K_n satisfy the same recurrence formulas. Since $K_{n-1} - \varepsilon_{n-1}T$ has the kernel

$$\frac{(-1)^{n-1}}{(n-1)!} \int_\Delta \cdots \int_\Delta N_{n-1}^{**}(x, y)\, dz_1 \ldots dz_{n-1},$$

where $N_{n-1}^{**}(x, y)$ is obtained from $N_{n-1}^*(x, y)$ by replacing the element $T(x, y)$ in the "north-west" corner by zero, we find

$$(4')\quad \left\{\begin{aligned} &\tau(K_{n-1} - \varepsilon_{n-1}T) = \\ &\frac{(-1)^{n-1}}{(n-1)!} \int_\Delta\int_\Delta \cdots \int_\Delta \begin{vmatrix} 0 & T(x, z_1) \ldots T(x, z_{n-1}) \\ T(z_1, x) & \\ \vdots & N_{n-1} \\ T(z_{n-1}, x) & \end{vmatrix} dx\, dz_1 \ldots dz_{n-1} \\ &= -n\varepsilon_n \ (n = 2, 3, \ldots). \end{aligned}\right.$$

Furthermore $k_n(x, y) = \varepsilon_n T(x, y) + g_n(x, y)$ with

$$g_n(x, y) = \frac{(-1)^n}{n!} \int_\Delta \cdots \int_\Delta N_n^{**}(x, y)\, dz_1 \ldots dz_n.$$

We expand $N_n^{**}(x, y)$ in terms of its top row. Then all the n terms in the expansion of $g_n(x, y)$ are equal, and we obtain

$$k_n(x, y) = \varepsilon_n T(x, y) + \int_\Delta T(x, z) k_{n-1}(z, y) dz,$$

hence

$$K_n = \varepsilon_n T + TK_{n-1} \ (n = 2, 3, \ldots). \tag{3'}$$

The recurrence formulas (3′) and (4′) for ε_n and K_n are the same as (3) and (4) for δ_n and H_n. Since moreover $\varepsilon_1 = \delta_1$, $K_1 = H_1$, we have $\delta_n = \varepsilon_n$, $H_n = K_n$ for all $n \geqslant 1$. This completes the proof.

Remark. The Theorems 6 and 7 may immediately be extended to the case that μ is a separable measure, and Δ a μ-measurable set.

In Ch 13 we shall discuss more fully equations of the form

$$f(x) - \lambda \int_\Delta T(x, y) f(y) dy = g(x).$$

In fact, we shall prove that, provided $T(x, y)$ satisfies certain conditions, the Carleman-Smithies solution retains its validity in case the equation is understood as a functional relation in a Lebesgue space $L_p(\Delta)$ $(1 \leqslant p < \infty)$ or an Orlicz space $L_\Phi(\Delta)$ (with $\Phi(2u) \leqslant M\Phi(u)$ for all $u \geqslant 0$).

EXAMPLES

1) In § 1, Th. 1 the existence of T^* and the relation $\| T^* \| = \| T \|$ for a bounded linear transformation on a complete Hilbert space R are proved by making use of the Banach-adjoint T_B^*. It is possible to give a direct proof.

(The inner product (Tg, f) for fixed f and variable g defines a linear functional $h_f^*(g)$, which is bounded on account of $| h_f^*(g) | = | (Tf, g) | \leqslant \| T \| . \| f \| . \| g \|$. Hence, by Ch. 7, § 4, Th. 1, there exists an element h_f such that $(Tg, f) = (g, h_f)$ for all $g \in R$. Writing $h_f = T^*f$, it is easily seen that T^* is linear. From $\| T^*f \|^2 = (T^*f, T^*f) = (TT^*f, f) \leqslant \| T \| . \| T^*f \| . \| f \|$ follows $\| T^* \| \leqslant \| T \|$, and, since $(Tg, f) = (g, T^*f)$ is symmetric, also $\| T \| \leqslant \| T^* \|$).

2) If $[L]$ is a linear subspace of the Hilbert space R, and $[L]$ reduces the self-adjoint transformation A, then A is completely reduced by $([L], R \ominus [L])$ (cf. § 4, Th. 14). The same need not be true for a normal transformation A; it is even not necessarily true for a unitary transformation U. If however R is of finite dimension, and $[L]$ reduces the normal transformation A, then A is completely reduced by $([L], R \ominus [L])$.

(Let R be of enumerably infinite dimension, and let $\ldots, \varphi_{-1}, \varphi_0, \varphi_1, \ldots$ be a complete orthonormal system in R. The unitary transformation U is defined by $U(\Sigma_{-\infty}^{\infty} \alpha_i \varphi_i) = \Sigma_{-\infty}^{\infty} \alpha_i \varphi_{i+1}$. Then U is reduced by the linear subspace $[L]$ determined by $\varphi_0, \varphi_1, \varphi_2, \ldots$, but not by $R \ominus [L]$ since $U\varphi_{-1} = \varphi_0$.

If the normal transformation A is reduced by the linear k-dimensional subspace $[L]$ of the finite dimensional space R, we consider A on $[L]$. By § 15, Th. 10 there exists a coordinate system $\{\varphi\} = \{\varphi_1, \ldots, \varphi_k\}$ in $[L]$ such that mat $(A; \varphi)$ is a diagonal matrix. Hence $A\varphi_i = \lambda_i \varphi_i (i = 1, \ldots, k)$. But then $A^*\varphi_i = \bar{\lambda}_i \varphi_i$ (cf. § 15, Th. 1), so that A^* is reduced by $[L]$).

3) The metric space Z (cf. Ch. 7, § 10) is called *separable* in case there exists an enumerable subset $X \subset Z$ such that X is dense in Z. If Z is a separable metric space, and Y is an arbitrary subset of Z, then Y is separable.

(We adopt the notations of Ch. 7, § 10, so that the distance between the elements f and g of Z is denoted by $d(f, g)$. Let $X = \{g_1, g_2, \ldots\}$ be dense in Z. Then, if n is a positive integer and R_{in} is the sphere $d(f, g_i) < (2n)^{-1}$, every $f \in Z$ is contained in one at least of the spheres $R_{1n}, R_{2n}, \ldots$. If R_{in} contains points of Y, we denote one of these points by h_{in}. It follows that for every $f \in Y$ there exists one h_{in} at least such that $d(f, h_{in}) < n^{-1}$. The set of points $\{h_{in}\}$ $(i, n = 1, 2, \ldots)$ is now dense in Y).

4) Let the Hilbert space R be complete and separable, and let $\{T\}$ be a set of bounded linear transformations on R into R. Then $\{T\}$ contains a sequence $T_n (n = 1, 2, \ldots)$ such that every $T \in \{T\}$ is the limit of a suitable subsequence $T_i (i = n_1, n_2, \ldots,$ where $n_1, n_2, \ldots$ depends on T), and at the same time $T^* = \lim T_i^*$.

(We suppose first that $\| T \| \leqslant A$ for a fixed A and all $T \in \{T\}$. We consider the Hilbert space R^∞, the elements of which are the sequences $\{f_1, f_2, \ldots\}$, where $f_i \in R$ and $\Sigma_{i=1}^\infty \| f_i \|^2 < \infty$. The rules of addition and multiplication in R^∞, and the inner product are defined in an obvious way. Let $g_1, g_2, \ldots$ be dense in R. Then the elements $\{g_{n_1}, g_{n_2}, \ldots, g_{n_p}, 0, 0, \ldots\}$ (with arbitrary p) are dense in R^∞, which shows that R^∞ is separable. To every $T \in \{T\}$ we assign now

$$\varphi_T = \left\{\frac{Tg_1}{\| g_1 \|}, \frac{T^*g_1}{\| g_1 \|}, \frac{Tg_2}{2\| g_2 \|}, \frac{T^*g_2}{2\| g_2 \|}, \ldots, \frac{Tg_n}{2^{n-1}\| g_n \|}, \frac{T^*g_n}{2^{n-1}\| g_n \|}, \ldots\right\}.$$

It is easily verified that $\varphi_T \in R^\infty$. Since R^∞ is separable, the same is true of the set $\varphi_T (T \in \{T\})$ by the preceding example. It follows that there exists a sequence φ_{T_n} $(n = 1, 2, \ldots)$ such that every φ_T is the limit of a suitable subsequence $\varphi_{T_i} (i = n_1, n_2, \ldots)$. Then

$$Tg_n = \lim_i T_i g_n, \; T^*g_n = \lim_i T_i^* g_n \; (n = 1, 2, \ldots),$$

which implies by a well-known argument

$$Tf = \lim_i T_i f, \; T^*f = \lim_i T_i^* f$$

for every $f \in R$. Finally we free ourselves from the restriction $\| T \| \leqslant A$ by considering successively the subsets $\{T\}_n$ $(n = 1, 2, \ldots)$ of $\{T\}$, where $\{T\}_n$ contains all $T \in \{T\}$ satisfying $\| T \| \leqslant n$).

5) If $\{\alpha_{ij}\}$ is a matrix of n rows and n columns, and $\lambda_i (i = 1, \ldots, n)$ are the roots of the characteristic equation of this matrix, then $\Sigma_i \mid \lambda_i \mid^2 \leqslant \Sigma_{ij} \mid \alpha_{ij} \mid^2$, with equality if and only if the matrixproducts $\{\alpha_{ij}\}.\{\alpha_{ij}^*\}$ and $\{\alpha_{ij}^*\}.\{\alpha_{ij}\}$ are equal, where $\alpha_{ij}^* = \overline{\alpha_{ji}}$ $(i, j = 1, \ldots, n)$.

(Let $\varphi_1, \ldots, \varphi_n$ be an arbitrary orthonormal system in n-dimensional Hilbert space. The transformation A is defined by $A\varphi_i = \Sigma_j \alpha_{ji}\varphi_j$, hence mat $(A; \varphi) = \{\alpha_{ij}\}$. There exists an orthonormal system $\psi_1, \ldots, \psi_n$ such that mat $(A; \psi)$ has the superdiagonal form. The elements on the principal diagonal of mat $(A; \psi)$ are then $\lambda_1, \ldots, \lambda_n$ (cf. Ch. 8, § 6, Th. 2 and Ch. 9, § 2, Th. 4). Observing that the double-norm is invariant under a change of orthonormal coordinate system, we find $\Sigma_i \mid \lambda_i \mid^2 \leqslant \Sigma_{ij} \mid \alpha_{ij} \mid^2$, with equality if and only if mat $(A; \psi)$ has the diagonal form. The statement however that there exists an orthonormal coordinate system $\{\psi\}$ such that mat $(A; \psi)$ has the diagonal form is equivalent to the statement that A is normal).

6) If $\varphi_n(x)$ $(n = 1, 2, \ldots)$ is the orthonormal system in $L_2[0, 1]$, defined in § 9, Ex. A, and $A(x, y) = \varphi_1(x)\varphi_2(y) + \varphi_2(x)\varphi_1(y) + \varphi_3(x)\varphi_4(y) + \varphi_4(x)\varphi_3(y) + \ldots$, then the transformation A on $L_2[0, 1]$ with kernel $A(x, y)$ is bounded and self-adjoint with $\lambda = 0$, $\lambda = 1$ and $\lambda = -1$ as its only characteristic values. Furthermore $A^2 = P$, where P is the transformation of § 9, Ex. A. Generally $A^n = A$ for odd n and $A^n = P$ for even n.

(Observe that $A(x, y)$ is Hermitian and that, introducing the orthonormal system $\psi_1 = 2^{-1/2}(\varphi_1 + \varphi_2)$, $\psi_2 = 2^{-1/2}(\varphi_1 - \varphi_2)$, $\psi_3 = 2^{-1/2}(\varphi_3 + \varphi_4)$, $\psi_4 = 2^{-1/2}(\varphi_3 - \varphi_4), \ldots$, we have $A\psi_{2n-1} = \psi_{2n-1}$, $A\psi_{2n} = -\psi_{2n}$ $(n = 1, 2, \ldots)$, whereas $A\chi = 0$ for every $\chi(x)$ which is orthogonal to all $\varphi_n(x)$).

7) If $\varphi_n(x)$ $(n = 1, 2, \ldots)$ is the same orthonormal system in $L_2[0, 1]$ as in the preceding example, and $T(x, y) = \varphi_2(x)\varphi_1(y) + \varphi_4(x)\varphi_2(y) + \varphi_6(x)\varphi_3(y) + \ldots$, then the transformation T on $L_2[0, 1]$ with kernel $T(x, y)$ is bounded. It has no characteristic values but $\lambda = 0$. All powers $T^n (n = 1, 2, \ldots)$ are of infinite double-norm.

(Every $f \in L_2[0, 1]$ may be represented in the form $f = \Sigma_i \alpha_i\varphi_i + h$, where $(h, \varphi_i) = 0$ for all i. Obviously $Tf = \Sigma\alpha_i\varphi_{2i}$, hence $\| Tf \| \leqslant \| f \|$. If $Tf = \lambda f$, $\lambda \neq 0$, then $\Sigma\, \alpha_i\varphi_{2i} = \Sigma\, \lambda\alpha_i\varphi_i + \lambda h$; hence $h = 0$ and $\alpha_i = 0$ for all i. If $Tf = 0f$, then $\Sigma\, \alpha_i\varphi_{2i} = 0$, hence $\alpha_i = 0$ for all i, so that f is a characteristic element belonging to the characteristic value $\lambda = 0$ if and only if $(f, \varphi_i) = 0$ for all i. It follows that T has only the characteristic value $\lambda = 0$. Finally, it is easily seen that T^n has the kernel $T_n(x, y) = \varphi_{2^n}(x)\varphi_1(y) + \varphi_{2.2^n}(x)\varphi_2(y) + \varphi_{3.2^n}(x)\varphi_3(y) + \ldots$, so that $||| T^n ||| = \infty$).

8) The kernel $T(x, y) = | x - y |^{-\alpha}$, defined in $0 \leqslant x, y \leqslant 1$, is of finite double-norm in $L_p[0, 1]$ $(1 \leqslant p \leqslant \infty)$ if $\alpha < 1 - 1/p$.

9) If the linear integral transformation T with kernel $T(x, y)$ is of finite double-norm on $L_2(\Delta)$, so hat $T(x, y)$ as a function $t_x(y)$ of y belongs to $L_2(\Delta)$ for almost every $x \in \Delta$, and A is an arbitrary bounded linear transformation, then TA has the kernel $q(x, y) = \overline{A^*\overline{t_x(y)}}$.

(Let $f, g \in L_2(\Delta)$, and write $Af = \overline{h(x)}$. Then $(TAf, g) = \int_\Delta (\int_\Delta t_x(y)\overline{h(y)}dy)\overline{g(x)}dx$. But, for almost every $x \in \Delta$, $\int_\Delta t_x(y)\overline{h(y)}dy = (t_x, h) = (t_x, \overline{Af}) = (Af, \overline{t_x}) = (f, A^*\overline{t_x}) = \int_\Delta q(x, y)f(y)dy$. It follows as in § 10, Th. 11 that $q(x, y)$ is the kernel of TA. A different proof may be given by observing that $TA = (A^*T^*)^*$, and that A^*T^* has the kernel $A^*\overline{t_x(y)}$ by § 10, Th. 11).

10) Let R be a complete Hilbert space. If T is a linear transformation with domain R and range in R, and T_1 is a linear transformation with domain D dense in R and range in R, and if $(Tf, g) = (f, T_1g)$ for all $f \in R$, $g \in D$, then T is bounded and T_1 is identical with T^* on D.

(Let $f_0 = \lim f_n$, $h_0 = \lim Tf_n$. From $(Tf_n, g) = (f_n, T_1g)$ for all $g \in D$ follows $(h_0, g) = (f_0, T_1g)$. But also $(Tf_0, g) = (f_0, T_1g)$. Hence $(h_0, g) = (Tf_0, g)$ for all $g \in D$. Since D is dense in R, we have then $h_0 = Tf_0$. This shows that T is closed, so that, by Ch. 7, § 11, Th. 8, T is bounded. The rest is trivial).

11) Let the sequence of complex numbers $\lambda_1, \lambda_2, \ldots$ have $\lambda = 0$ as a point of accumulation (the case that $\lambda_i = 0$ for an infinity of values of i is permitted). Then there exists a linear transformation T with its domain D dense in $L_2[0, \infty]$ and its range in $L_2[0, \infty]$ such that T has all λ_i as characteristic values, and

$$Tf = \int_0^\infty T(x, y)f(y)dy$$

for all $f \in D$, with $\int_0^\infty | T(x, y)|^2\, dy < \infty$ for every x $(0 \leqslant x < \infty)$ [12].

(There exists a subsequence $\lambda_{m_1}, \lambda_{m_2}, \ldots$ satisfying $| \lambda_{m_i} | < i^{-1}$. The remaining subsequence is $\lambda_{n_1}, \lambda_{n_2}, \ldots$, and we may suppose that it still contains an infinity of terms. We now make a double sequence of indices

n_1	m_1	m_2	m_4	m_8	$\ldots$
n_2	m_3	m_6	m_{12}	m_{24}	$\ldots$
n_3	m_5	m_{10}	m_{20}	m_{40}	$\ldots$
$\ldots\ldots$					
n_i	m_{2i-1}	$m_{2(2i-1)}$	$m_{4(2i-1)}$	$m_{8(2i-1)}$	$\ldots$
$\ldots\ldots$					

The $(i, 1)$-element is therefore n_i, and, for $j \geqslant 2$, the (i, j)-element is $m_{2^{j-2}(2i-1)}$. Bij λ_{ij} we denote the λ with index equal to the (i, j)-element. Then all λ are represented exactly one time in the double sequence λ_{ij}, and on account of $|\lambda_{ij}| \leqslant 2^{-(j-2)}$ for $j \geqslant 2$, we have $\Sigma_{j=1}^{\infty} |\lambda_{ij}| < \infty$ for $i = 1, 2, \ldots$.

Let now $\psi_1(x), \psi_2(x), \ldots$ be a complete orthonormal system in $L_2[0, 1]$, having the property that all $\psi_i(x)$ are uniformly bounded, hence $|\psi_i(x)| \leqslant M$ for a fixed M and all i and x. The existence of a system with these properties was proved in Ch. 6, § 14. Defining $\varphi_{ij}(x)$ $(i, j = 1, 2, \ldots)$ in $0 \leqslant x < \infty$ by

$$\varphi_{ij}(x) = \begin{cases} \psi_j\{x - (i-1)\} & \text{for } i - 1 \leqslant x < i, \\ 0 & \text{elsewhere,} \end{cases}$$

it is easily seen that the system $\{\varphi_{ij}\}$ is complete and orthonormal in $L_2[0, \infty]$. Finally $T(x, y)$ is defined on $0 \leqslant x, y < \infty$ by

$$T(x, y) = \Sigma_{ij=1}^{\infty} \lambda_{ij}\varphi_{ij}(x)\overline{\varphi_{ij}(y)}.$$

This double series converges absolutely for every point (x, y) in $0 \leqslant x, y < \infty$, since for $i_1 - 1 \leqslant x < i_1$, $i_2 - 1 \leqslant y < i_2$, $i_1 \neq i_2$, all terms vanish, and, if $i_1 = i_2$, all terms with $i \neq i_1 = i_2$ vanish, so that in this case the summation is only over the index j. Then $|T(x, y)| \leqslant \Sigma_{j=1}^{\infty} |\lambda_{i_1j}| . M^2$, hence

$$\int_0^\infty |T|^2 dy = \int_{i_1-1}^{i_1} |T|^2 dy \leqslant M^4 \Sigma_{j=1}^{\infty} |\lambda_{i_1j}|^2 < \infty.$$

It follows that by $g(x) = Tf = \int_0^\infty T(x, y)f(y)dy$ there is assigned to every $f \in L_2[0, \infty]$ a function $g(x)$. Evidently $T\varphi_{ij} = \lambda_{ij}\varphi_{ij}$, so that, if D is the set of all finite linear combinations $\Sigma\, \alpha_{ij}\varphi_{ij}$, we may say that T is a linear transformation on D (dense in $L_2[0, \infty]$) with range in $L_2[0, \infty]$. Evidently every λ_{ij}, that is, every λ_i from the original sequence $\lambda_1, \lambda_2, \ldots$, is a characteristic value of T).

12) If, with the same notations and definitions as in the preceding example, the sequence $\lambda_1, \lambda_2, \ldots$ is bounded, the transformation T has the whole space $L_2[0, \infty]$ as its domain, and T is a bounded normal transformation on $L_2[0, \infty]$. If all λ_i are real, T is a bounded self-adjoint transformation.

(T is defined on the space $L_2[0, \infty]$ by $Tf = T(\Sigma_{ij=1}^{\infty} \alpha_{ij}\varphi_{ij}) = \Sigma\, \lambda_{ij}\alpha_{ij}\varphi_{ij} = g$. We have to prove that $g(x) = \int_0^\infty T(x, y)f(y)dy$, also if $f(x)$ does not belong to the original domain D. Writing $f_n(x) = \Sigma_{ij=1}^{n} \alpha_{ij}\varphi_{ij}(x)$ and $g_n(x) = Tf_n = \int_0^\infty T(x, y)f_n(y)$ dy, we have

$$|g_n(x) - \int_0^\infty T(x, y)f(y)dy|^2 \leqslant \int_0^\infty |T|^2 dy . \int_0^\infty |f_n - f|^2 dy \to 0,$$

hence $\int_0^\infty T(x, y)f(y)dy = \lim g_n(x)$ for every $x \in [0, \infty]$. But, since $f_n(x)$ converges in mean to $f(x)$, $g_n(x)$ converges in mean to $g(x)$. It follows (cf. Ch. 5, Ex. 9) that $g(x) = \int_0^\infty T(x, y)f(y)dy$. The boundedness of T is a consequence of $\| Tf \|^2 =$

$\Sigma \mid \lambda_{ij}\alpha_{ij} \mid^2 \leqslant B^2 \Sigma \mid \alpha_{ij} \mid^2 = B^2 \| f \|^2$, where B is the upper bound of the sequence $\lambda_1, \lambda_2, \ldots$. Since evidently $T^*(\Sigma \alpha_{ij}\varphi_{ij}) = \Sigma \overline{\lambda_{ij}}\alpha_{ij}\varphi_{ij}$, T is normal. If all λ_i are real, we have $T = T^*$).

13) Let $0 \leqslant x < 1$ and $0 \leqslant y < \infty$. Then there exists a one-to-one correspondence between all $F(x) \in L_2[0, 1]$ and all $f(y) \in L_2[0, \infty]$ which leaves the inner product invariant.

(If $f(y) \in L_2[0, \infty]$, we assign to $f(y)$ the function $F(x)$ $(0 \leqslant x < 1)$ such that $F(x) = (1 - x)^{-1}f(y)$, where $y = x/(1 - x)$).

14) The statements in the Examples 11, 12 remain true if $L_2[0, \infty]$ is replaced by $L_2[0, 1]$.

REFERENCES

[1] F. RIESZ, Über die linearen Transformationen des komplexen Hilbertschen Raumes, Acta Sci. Math. Szeged 5 (1930), 23—54.

[2] C. VISSER, Note on linear operators, Proc. Akad. Amsterdam 40 (1937), 270—272.

B. VON SZ. NAGY, On semi-groups of self-adjoint transformations in Hilbert space, Proc. Nat. Acad. Sci. U.S.A. 24 (1938), 559—560.

[3] The proof in its present form is essentially due to N. G. DE BRUYN.

[4] F. SMITHIES, The Fredholm theory of integral equations, Duke Math. Journal 8 (1941), 107—130.

[5] J. MARTY, Valeurs singulières d'une équation de Fredholm, C.R. Acad. Sc., Paris 150 (1910), 1499—1502.

[6] E. GARBE, Zur Theorie der Integralgleichung dritter Art, Math. Annalen 76 (1915), 527—547.

[7] A. J. PELL, Applications of biorthogonal systems of functions to the theory of integral equations, Transactions Amer. Math. Soc. 12 (1911), 165—180.

[8] H. J. ZIMMERBERG, Definite integral systems, Duke Math. Journal 15 (1948), 371—388, in particular Lemma 2.1.

[9] I. FREDHOLM, Sur une classe d'équations fonctionnelles, Acta Math. 27 (1903), 365—390.

[10] D. HILBERT, Grundzüge einer allgemeinen Theorie der linearen Integralgleichungen, Göttinger Nachrichten (1904), 1. Mitt., 49—91. This paper is also contained in the book of the same title, Leipzig (1912, 1924).

[11] T. CARLEMAN, Zur Theorie der linearen Integralgleichungen, Math. Zeitschrift 9 (1921), 196—217.

[12] J. VON NEUMANN, Charakterisierung des Spektrums eines Integraloperators, Actualités Sci. et Ind. 229, Paris (1935).

CHAPTER 10

RANGE, NULL SPACE AND SPECTRAL PROPERTIES OF BOUNDED LINEAR TRANSFORMATIONS

§ 1. Introduction

Let E_1 and E_2 be two Banach spaces, identical or distinct, complete or non-complete, and let T be a bounded linear transformation with domain E_1 and range $W(T)$ contained in E_2. In accordance with our previous definitions (cf. Ch. 8, § 4 and Ch. 9, § 14), the null space $N(T)$ of T is the linear subspace of all $f \in E_1$ satisfying $Tf = 0$. The adjoint spaces of E_1 and E_2 are E_1^* and E_2^*. They are complete by Ch. 7, § 7, Th. 1. The adjoint transformation T^* has E_2^* as its domain and its range is contained in E_1^* (cf. Ch. 7, § 13). The mutual relations between the ranges $W(T)$, $W(T^*)$ and the null spaces $N(T)$, $N(T^*)$ have already been considered in the simple case that E_1 and E_2 are identical, and that moreover $E = E_1 = E_2$ is either of finite dimension or a Hilbert space (cf. Ch. 8, § 4 and Ch. 9, § 14). Here we shall consider the general case, which is much more complicated. Practically all the results which we shall obtain are due to S. BANACH [1].

In the second part of the present chapter we shall generalize some of the results in Ch. 8, § 5 on the spectral properties of a linear transformation T, defined on a space of finite dimension, to the case of a bounded linear transformation T, which has as its domain an arbitrary Banach space E, and the range of which is contained in the same space E.

§ 2. The Functional of Minkowski

Let E be a Banach space, complete or non-complete. By Ch. 6, § 12 a set $S \subset E$ is called convex when $f_1 \in S$, $f_2 \in S$ implies $(f_1 + f_2)/2 \in S$. Sometimes S is said to be convex in the restricted sense in this case, and a set $S \subset E$ is then called convex in the general sense when $f_1 \in S$, $f_2 \in S$ implies $\alpha f_1 + (1 - \alpha) f_2 \in S$ for all real α satisfying $0 \leqslant \alpha \leqslant 1$. Any set which is convex in the general sense is certainly convex in the restricted sense, and any closed set which is convex in the restricted sense is also convex in the general sense. A closed set S which is convex, and which contains at least one interior point (f_0 is an interior point of S if there exists a neighbourhood $\| f - f_0 \| \leqslant r$ which belongs to S), is called a *convex body*.

Definition. *Let $K \subset E$ be a convex body with $f = 0$ as an interior point. Then, for every $f \in E$, the functional $M(f)$, assuming only non-negative values, is defined as the lower bound of all $a > 0$ for which $a^{-1}f \in K$. This functional $M(f)$ is called the functional of Minkowski of the body K.*

We observe that, since $f = 0$ is an interior point of K, there exists a finite number a such that $a^{-1}f \in K$, hence $M(f) < \infty$ for every $f \in E$.

Theorem 1. *Let $K \subset E$ be a convex body with $f = 0$ as an interior point, and let $M(f)$ be the functional of Minkowski of K. Then:*

1°. *If f is an interior point of K, we have $M(f) < 1$; if f is on the boundary of K, we have $M(f) = 1$.*

2°. *$M(f + g) \leqslant M(f) + M(g)$ for arbitrary $f, g \in E$.*

3°. *$M(bf) = bM(f)$ for arbitrary $f \in E$ and $b \geqslant 0$.*

4°. *$M(f) \leqslant A \| f \|$ for all $f \in E$, where $A \geqslant 0$ does not depend on f.*

Proof. 1°. If f is an interior point of K, there exists a non-negative number $a < 1$ satisfying $a^{-1}f \in K$, hence $M(f) < 1$. If f is on the boundary of K, we have $f \in K$, since K is closed. It follows that $a^{-1}f \in K$ for every $a \geqslant 1$ (K is convex), hence $M(f) \leqslant 1$. Let us suppose now that $a^{-1}f \in K$ for a certain $a < 1$. Observing that every f' with $\| f' \| \leqslant r$ belongs to K for a certain $r > 0$, we find that $a(a^{-1}f) + (1 - a)f' \in K$, hence $f + f'' \in K$ for all f'' satisfying $\| f'' \| \leqslant (1 - a)r$. But then f is an interior point of K, in contradiction with our hypothesis that f is on the boundary of K. It follows that $a^{-1}f \in K$ for $a < 1$ is impossible. Hence $M(f) = 1$.

2°. If $a_1^{-1}f \in K$ and $a_2^{-1}g \in K$, then

$$\frac{a_2^{-1}}{a_1^{-1} + a_2^{-1}} a_1^{-1}f + \frac{a_1^{-1}}{a_1^{-1} + a_2^{-1}} a_2^{-1}g \in K$$

by the convexity of K, hence, if $a_3 = a_1 + a_2$, so that $a_3^{-1} = (a_2 + a_1)^{-1} = a_1^{-1}a_2^{-1}/(a_1^{-1} + a_2^{-1})$, we have $a_3^{-1}(f + g) \in K$. It follows that the lower bound of all admissable a_3 does not surpass the sum of the lower bounds of all admissable a_1 and all admissable a_2, which implies $M(f + g) \leqslant M(f) + M(g)$.

3°. We have $a^{-1}f \in K$ if and only if $(ab)^{-1}(bf) \in K$ for all $b \geqslant 0$.

4°. If $f = 0$, then $M(f) = 0$, hence $M(0) \leqslant A \| 0 \|$ for every $A \geqslant 0$. If $f_0 \neq 0$, we observe that there exists a neighbourhood $\| f \| \leqslant r$ of $f = 0$ which is contained in K. For $a \geqslant r^{-1} \| f_0 \|$, that is, for $\| a^{-1} f_0 \| \leqslant r$, we have therefore $a^{-1} f_0 \in K$. It follows that the lower bound of all admissable a does not surpass $r^{-1} \| f_0 \|$. Hence $M(f_0) \leqslant r^{-1} \| f_0 \|$ for all $f_0 \in E$, which shows that $A = r^{-1}$ has the required property.

Theorem 2. *Let E be a separable Banach space, and let $K \subset E$ be a convex body with $f = 0$ as an interior point, which has the additional property that $f \in K$ implies $e^{i\varphi} f \in K$ for all real φ. Then, if f_0 is on the boundary of K, there exists a bounded linear functional $f^*(f)$ on E such that $f^*(f_0) = 1$ and $| f^*(f) | \leqslant 1$ for $f \in K$.*

Proof. We start by observing that our special hypothesis on K implies $M(e^{i\varphi} f) = M(f)$ for all real φ, where $M(f)$ is the functional of Minkowski of K. Let $[L]$ be the set of all elements αf_0 (α arbitrarily complex). Writing $F^*(\alpha f_0) = \alpha$, F^* is a linear functional on $[L]$. The real part of F^* is denoted by F_r^*. Then, for $\alpha = | \alpha | e^{i\varphi}$, we have $F_r^*(\alpha f_0) = | \alpha | \cos \varphi \leqslant | \alpha | = M(| \alpha | f_0) = M(\alpha f_0)$, in other words, $F_r^*(f) \leqslant M(f)$ for all $f \in [L]$. By an argument which is very similar to that used in Ch. 7, § 6, Th. 3 (cf. also Ch. 7, Ex. 2) we may extend F_r^* onto the whole space E. It follows that there exists a real bounded linear functional $f_r^*(f)$ on E such that $f_r^*(f) = F_r^*(f)$ for $f \in [L]$ and $f_r^*(f) \leqslant M(f)$ for all $f \in E$. As in Ch. 7, § 6, Th. 4 the complex bounded linear functional $f^*(f)$ is now defined by $f^*(f) = f_r^*(f) - i f_r^*(if)$. Then $f^*(f) = F^*(f)$ for $f \in [L]$, hence in particular $f^*(f_0) = F^*(f_0) = 1$. Finally, if $f \in E$ is arbitrary, and $f^*(f) = re^{i\psi}$ ($r \geqslant 0$, ψ real), then $| f^*(f) | = r = f^*(fe^{-i\psi}) = f_r^*(fe^{-i\psi}) \leqslant M(fe^{-i\psi}) = M(f)$. In particular $| f^*(f) | \leqslant 1$ for $f \in K$.

§ 3. Range and Null Space

Let E_1 and E_2 be two Banach spaces, identical or distinct, complete or non-complete, and let T be a bounded linear transformation with domain E_1 and range $W(T)$ contained in E_2. Then T^* has E_2^* as its domain, and its range $W(T^*)$ is contained in E_1^*. We recall that if L is a linear manifold in the Banach space E (that is, $f_1, f_2 \in L$ implies $\alpha_1 f_1 + \alpha_2 f_2 \in L$ for arbitrary complex α_1, α_2), and we add to L all its points of accumulation, the resulting linear subspace is denoted by $[L]$ (cf. Ch. 6, § 3).

Theorem 1. *We have $[W(T)]^\circ = N(T^*)$, where $[W(T)]^\circ$ is the annihilator* *of* $[W(T)]$. *If* E_2 *has the property* (*Ext.*), $[W(T)]$ *is the only linear subspace of* E_2 *having* $N(T^*)$ *as its annihilator.*

Proof. If $g^* \in [W(T)]^\circ$, then $0 = g^*(Tf) = (T^*g^*)(f)$ for all $f \in E_1$, hence $T^*g^* = 0$ or $g^* \in N(T^*)$.

If conversely $g^* \in N(T^*)$, then $T^*g^* = 0$, hence $0 = (T^*g^*)(f) = g^*(Tf)$ for all $f \in E_1$, or $g^* \in [W(T)]^\circ$.

This shows that $[W(T)]^\circ = N(T^*)$.

To prove the last statement of the present theorem, we recall that we have seen in Ch. 7, § 14, Th. 1 that if E_2 has the property (Ext.), and E', E'' are different linear subspaces of E_2, then $(E')^\circ$ and $(E'')^\circ$ are different. It follows that if E_2 has the property (Ext.), $[W(T)]$ is the only linear subspace of E_2 having $N(T^*)$ as its annihilator.

Although $[W(T)]^\circ = N(T^*)$ holds without any restriction, the dual relation $(N(T))^\circ = [W(T^*)]$ seems to be true only under rather severe restrictions. The next two theorems throw some light upon this problem.

Theorem 2. *If* E_1, E_2 *and* E_1^* *have the property* (*Ext.*), *and* E_1 *is reflexive, then* $(N(T))^\circ = [W(T^*)]$.

Proof. We observe first that, since E_1 and E_1^{**} are identical, the same holds for E_1^* and E_1^{***}, which shows that E_1^* is also reflexive. Furthermore $T^{**} = T$ by Ch. 7, § 13, Th. 3. Hence, by the preceding theorem, $[W(T^*)]^\circ = N(T^{**}) = N(T)$, which implies $[W(T^*)]^{\circ\circ} = (N(T))^\circ$. But, since the reflexive Banach space E_1^* has the property (Ext.), we have $[W(T^*)]^{\circ\circ} = [W(T^*)]$ by Ch. 7, § 14, Th. 8, hence $(N(T))^\circ = [W(T^*)]$.

Theorem 3. 1°. *We have always* $[W(T^*)] \subset (N(T))^\circ$.

2°. *If* $W(T)$, *considered on its own, is a complete Banach space, and if* E_2 *has the property* (*Ext.*), *then* $(N(T))^\circ = W(T^*)$. *In the particular case that* E_2 *is complete and* $W(T) = E_2$, *the condition that* E_2 *has the property* (*Ext.*) *may be omitted.*

Proof. 1°. Let $f^* \in W(T^*)$, hence $f^* = T^*g^*$ for a certain $g^* \in E_2^*$. Then, for every $f \in N(T)$, we have $f^*(f) = (T^*g^*)(f) = g^*(Tf) = 0$, hence $f^* \in (N(T))^\circ$. It follows that $[W(T^*)] \subset (N(T))^\circ$.

2°. We have to prove that $(N(T))^\circ \subset W(T^*)$ under the mentioned conditions. Let $f^* \in (N(T))^\circ$, that is, let $Tf = 0$ imply $f^*(f) = 0$. Then $Tf_1 = Tf_2$ implies $f^*(f_1) = f^*(f_2)$, so that the linear functional G^*, defined on $W(T)$ by $G^*(Tf) = f^*(f)$, is uniquely determined. We assert that G^* is bounded. Indeed, since $W(T)$ is a complete Banach space, there exists, on account of Ch. 7, § 11, Th. 6, to every $g \in W(T)$ an element $f \in E_1$

such that $g = Tf$ and $\| f \| \leqslant m \| g \|$, where m does not depend on g. Then $| G^*(Tf) | = | f^*(f) | \leqslant \| f^* \| . \| f \| \leqslant m \| f^* \| . \| Tf \|$ for all $g = Tf \in W(T)$, hence $\| G^* \| \leqslant m \| f^* \|$. By the property (Ext.) of E_2 there exists now an element $g^* \in E_2^*$ such that $g^*(Tf) = G^*(Tf)$ for all $g = Tf \in W(T)$. We have therefore $(T^*g^*)(f) = g^*(Tf) = G^*(Tf) = f^*(f)$ for all $f \in E_1$, which shows that $f^* = T^*g^*$, hence $f^* \in W(T^*)$. The desired result $(N(T))^\circ \subset W(T^*)$ follows now.

Evidently, if we have already $W(T) = E_2$ (E_2 complete), the extension of G^* to g^* is not necessary.

We examine more closely the case that $W(T) = E_2$ (E_2 complete).

Theorem 4. 1°. *If E_2 is a complete Banach space and $W(T) = E_2$, then T^* has a bounded inverse $(T^*)^{-1}$.*

2°. *If E_1 is a complete Banach space, E_2 is separable and T^* has a bounded inverse $(T^*)^{-1}$, then E_2 is complete and $W(T) = E_2$.*

Proof. 1°. By Ch. 7, § 11, Th. 6 there exists to every $g \in E_2$ an element $f \in E_1$ such that $g = Tf$ and $\| f \| \leqslant m \| g \|$, where m does not depend on g. Hence, for every $g^* \in E_2^*$,

$$| g^*(g) | = | g^*(Tf) | = | (T^*g^*)(f) | \leqslant m \| T^*g^* \| . \| g \|.$$

It follows that $\| g^* \| \leqslant m \| T^*g^* \|$ for all $g^* \in E_2^*$, which shows that T^* has a bounded inverse $(T^*)^{-1}$.

Incidentically, we observe that the domain of $(T^*)^{-1}$ is $W(T^*) = (N(T))^\circ$ by the preceding theorem.

2°. It is obviously no restriction of the generality to suppose from the beginning that E_2 is complete, since this makes no difference for E_2^*. We shall denote the image in E_2 of the sphere $\| f \| \leqslant r$ in E_1 by $W(r)$, and we shall prove first that the closure $\overline{W(r)}$ contains a sphere $\| g \| \leqslant \sigma(r)$. The set $\overline{W(r)}$ is closed and convex, and it has the property that $g \in \overline{W(r)}$ implies $e^{i\varphi} g \in \overline{W(r)}$ for all real φ. If now $\overline{W(r)}$ does not contain a sphere $\| g \| \leqslant \sigma(r)$, there exists a sequence g_n of elements not belonging to $\overline{W(r)}$ such that $\lim \| g_n \| = 0$. Denoting the distance between g_n and $\overline{W(r)}$ by δ_n ($\delta_n > 0$), every point of $\overline{W(r)}$ is considered as the centre of a sphere with radius $\delta_n/2$, and the closure of the sum of all these spheres is called S_n. Then S_n is a convex body, containing $g = 0$ as an interior point, and having the property that $g \in S_n$ implies $e^{i\varphi} g \in S_n$ for all real φ. Let θ_n be the upper bound of all $a > 0$ for which $ag_n \in S_n$. Then $\theta_n < 1$, and $z_n = \theta_n g_n$ is on the boundary of S_n. By § 2, Th. 2 there exists now a bounded linear functional $g^*(g)$ on E_2 such that $g^*(z_n) = 1$ and $|g^*(g)| \leqslant 1$ for $g \in S_n$. In particular $|g^*(Tf)| \leqslant 1$ for every $f \in E_1$ satisfying $\|f\| \leqslant r$, since $\|f\| \leqslant r$ implies $Tf \in W(r) \subset S_n$. It follows that $|(T^*g^*)(f)| = |g^*(Tf)| \leqslant 1$ for $\|f\| \leqslant r$, hence $\|T^*g^*\| \leqslant r^{-1}$. But then $\|g^*\| \leqslant \|(T^*)^{-1}\|.\|T^*g^*\| \leqslant r^{-1}\|(T^*)^{-1}\|$, so that $1 = g^*(z_n) \leqslant \|g^*\|.\|z_n\|$ or $\|z_n\| \geqslant \|g^*\|^{-1} \geqslant r\|(T^*)^{-1}\|^{-1}$. This holds for $n = 1, 2, \ldots$. But we have already seen that $z_n = \theta_n g_n$ with $0 < \theta_n < 1$ and $\lim \|g_n\| = 0$, hence $\lim \|z_n\| = 0$. This is a contradiction. It follows therefore that $\overline{W(r)}$ contains a sphere $\|g\| \leqslant \sigma(r)$.

If g_0 belongs to the sphere $\|g\| \leqslant \sigma(1)$, there exists now a point $g_1 \in W(1)$ such that $\|g_0 - g_1\| \leqslant \sigma(2^{-1})$; next, there exists a point $g_2 \in W(2^{-1})$ such that $\|g_0 - g_1 - g_2\| \leqslant \sigma(2^{-2})$, and so on. Generally, $g_n \in W(2^{-n+1})$ and $\|g_0 - \Sigma_{i=1}^n g_i\| \leqslant \sigma(2^{-n})$. But $g_n \in W(2^{-n+1})$ implies the existence of an element $f_n \in E_1$ such that $g_n = Tf_n$ and $\|f_n\| \leqslant 2^{-n+1}$. Since E_1 is complete, $f_0 = \Sigma_{i=1}^\infty f_i$ exists. Observing that, in virtue of $\lim r = 0$, the diameter of the image $W(r)$ tends to zero, so that also $\lim \sigma(r) = 0$, we find $Tf_0 = \Sigma\, Tf_i = \Sigma\, g_i = g_0$. The result is therefore that every g_0 belonging to the sphere $\|g\| \leqslant \sigma(1)$ belongs to the range $W(T)$. But then every $g \in E_2$ belongs to $W(T)$, hence $W(T) = E_2$.

We shall now prove a theorem which is the dual of Theorem 3, 2°. The dual of Theorem 3, 1° is of course $[W(T)]^\circ = N(T^*)$, which we have already proved in Theorem 1.

Theorem 5. *If $W(T^*)$, considered on its own, is a complete Banach space, if E_1 is complete and if E_2 is separable, then $W(T)$ is a complete Banach space; hence, by Theorem 1, $(W(T))^\circ = N(T^*)$.*

Proof. Let G^* be an arbitrary bounded linear functional on $[W(T)]$. Then the bounded linear functional $f^* \in E_1^*$ is defined by $f^*(f) = G^*(Tf)$ for all $f \in E_1$. We write $f^* = T_1^* G^*$. Obviously T_1^* is linear and bounded. For every $g^* \in E_2^*$ which is an extension of G^* we have $g^*(Tf) = G^*(Tf)$, hence $T^*g^* = T_1^*G^*$. Conversely every G^* may be extended onto the whole space E_2, since E_2 has the property (Ext.). It follows that the ranges $W(T^*)$ and $W(T_1^*)$ are identical. Furthermore $T_1^*G^* = 0$ implies $0 = (T_1^*G^*)(f) = G^*(Tf)$ for all $Tf \in W(T)$, so that also $G^*(g) = 0$ for all $g \in [W(T)]$, hence $G^* = 0$. The relation $f^* = T_1^*G^*$ establishes therefore a one-to-one correspondence between complete Banach spaces (indeed, $W(T_1^*) = W(T^*)$ is complete by hypothesis); by Ch. 7, § 11, Th. 6 the bounded linear transformation T_1^* has then a bounded inverse $(T_1^*)^{-1}$. We now apply Theorem 4, 2° with E_2 replaced by $[W(T)]$ and T^* replaced by T_1^*. This is possible since $[W(T)] \subset E_2$ is also separable, and since $(T_1^* G^*)(f) = G^*(Tf)$ for all $f \in E_1$, $G^* \in [W(T)]^*$. It follows that $W(T) = [W(T)]$ is a complete Banach space.

We examine more closely the case that $W(T^*) = E_1^*$.

Theorem 6. 1°. *If E_1 has the property (Ext.), and $W(T^*) = E_1^*$, then T has a bounded inverse T^{-1}.*

2°. *If E_2 has the property (Ext.), and T has a bounded inverse T^{-1}, then $W(T^*) = E_1^*$.*

Proof. 1°. By Ch. 7, § 11, Th. 6 there exists to every $f^* \in E_1^*$ an element $g^* \in E_2^*$ such that $f^* = T^* g^*$ and $\| g^* \| \leqslant m \| f^* \|$, where m does not depend on f^*. If now $f \in E_1$ is arbitrary, there exists, since E_1 has the property (Ext.), an element $f^* \in E_1^*$ satisfying $\| f^* \| = 1$, $| f^*(f) | = \| f \|$. Assigning to this element f^* an element g^* in the way described, we find $\| g^* \| \leqslant m \| f^* \| = m$, hence

$$\| f \| = | f^*(f) | = | (T^* g^*)(f) | = | g^*(Tf) | \leqslant$$
$$\| g^* \| . \| Tf \| \leqslant m \| Tf \|,$$

which shows that T has a bounded inverse T^{-1}.

2°. Now T^{-1} is bounded; if therefore $f^* \in E_1^*$ is given, the linear functional G^* on $W(T)$, defined by $G^*(g) = f^*(T^{-1}g)$ for all $g \in W(T)$, is bounded. Since E_2 has the property (Ext.), there exists an element $g^* \in E_2^*$ such that $g^*(g) = G^*(g)$ for all $g \in W(T)$, hence

$$(T^* g^*)(f) = g^*(Tf) = G^*(Tf) = f^*(T^{-1}Tf) = f^*(f)$$

for all $f \in E_1$. It follows that $f^* = T^* g^*$, and, since $f^* \in E_1^*$ is arbitrary, this shows that $W(T^*) = E_1^*$.

Theorem 7. 1°. *If E_2 is a complete Banach space, and $g = Tf$ has a unique solution $f \in E_1$ for every $g \in E_2$, then $f^* = T^* g^*$ has a unique solution $g^* \in E_2^*$ for every $f^* \in E_1^*$.*

2°. *If both E_1 and E_2 have the property (Ext.), and $f^* = T^* g^*$ has a unique solution $g^* \in E_2^*$ for every $f^* \in E_1^*$, then $g = Tf$ has a unique solution $f \in E_1$ for every $g \in E_2$.*

Proof. 1°. Our hypothesis implies $W(T) = E_2$, whereas $N(T)$ contains only the null element. Since E_2 is complete and $W(T) = E_2$, T^* has a bounded inverse by Theorem 4, 1°, and, by Theorem 3, 2°, $W(T^*) = (N(T))^\circ = E_1^*$. It follows that $f^* = T^* g^*$ has a unique solution $g^* \in E_2^*$ for every $f^* \in E_1^*$.

2°. Our hypothesis implies $W(T^*) = E_1^*$, whereas $N(T^*)$ contains only the null element. Since E_1 has the property (Ext.) and $W(T^*) = E_1^*$, T has a bounded inverse by Theorem 6, 1°, and by Theorem 1, $(W(T))^\circ = N(T^*)$, so that $(W(T))^\circ$ contains only the null element of E_2^*. But E_2 has the property (Ext.), which implies that $W(T)$ is uniquely determined by $(W(T))^\circ$. It follows that $W(T) = E_2$, so that, on account of the existence of T^{-1}, $g = Tf$ has a unique solution $f \in E_1$ for every $g \in E_2$.

Theorem 8. *Let E_1 be complete, and E_2 separable. Then, if T and T^* have bounded inverses T^{-1} and $(T^*)^{-1}$, the equations $g = Tf$ and $f^* = T^*g^*$ have uniquely determined solutions f and g^* for every $g \in E_2$ and every $f^* \in E_1^*$.*

Proof. Since E_2 has the property (Ext.), and T^{-1} is bounded, we have $W(T^*) = E_1^*$ by Theorem 6, 2°. Since E_1 is complete, E_2 is separable, and $(T^*)^{-1}$ is bounded, we have $W(T) = E_2$ by Theorem 4, 2° (moreover, E_2 is complete). The relations $W(T) = E_2$, $W(T^*) = E_1^*$, together with the existence of T^{-1} and $(T^*)^{-1}$, yield the desired result.

Theorem 9. *Let E_2 be complete, and let E_1 have the property (Ext.). Then, if $g = Tf$ and $f^* = T^*g^*$ have solutions f and g^* for every $g \in E_2$ and every $f^* \in E_1^*$, these solutions are uniquely determined.*

Proof. Since E_2 is complete and $W(T) = E_2$, the inverse $(T^*)^{-1}$ exists and is bounded by Theorem 4, 1°. Since E_1 has the property (Ext.) and $W(T^*) = E_1^*$, the inverse T^{-1} exists and is bounded by Theorem 6, 1°. The desired result follows now.

In the case that both E_1 and E_2 are complete and separable, our results may be summed up in a more convenient form.

Theorem 10. *Let the Banach spaces E_1 and E_2 be complete and separable. Then, if T is a bounded linear transformation on E_1 into E_2, we have:*

1°. *$W(T) = E_2$ if and only if T^* has a bounded inverse $(T^*)^{-1}$.*

2°. *$W(T^*) = E_1^*$ if and only if T has a bounded inverse T^{-1}.*

3°. *If $W(T)$ is a linear subspace of E_2, then $W(T^*) = (N(T))^\circ$.*

4°. *If $W(T^*)$ is a linear subspace of E_1^*, then $W(T)$ is a linear subspace of E_2, and it is determined by $(W(T))^\circ = N(T^*)$.*

Remark. If both E_1 and E_2 are identical with the same Hilbert space R, the relation between the Banach adjoint T_B^* and the Hilbert adjoint $T_H^* = T^*$, as defined in Ch. 9, § 1, shows that $(N(T))^\circ$ and $(W(T))^\circ$ may be replaced in the present theorem by $R \ominus N(T)$ and $R \ominus W(T)$ respectively.

§ 4. The Space of Endomorphisms of a Banach Space

We suppose that E is a Banach space, complete or non-complete. If T is a bounded linear transformation on E into E, we know already (cf. Ch. 7, § 12) that T is called an endomorphism of E. Also, if T, T_1 and T_2 are endomorphisms of E, and $f \in E$ is arbitrary, we have $(T_1 + T_2)f = T_1 f + T_2 f$, $(\alpha T)f = \alpha(Tf)$ for every complex α, and $(T_1 T_2)f = T_1(T_2 f)$. This implies $\| T_1 + T_2 \| \leqslant \| T_1 \| + \| T_2 \|$, $\| \alpha T \| = | \alpha | . \| T \|$ and $\| T_1 T_2 \| \leqslant \| T_1 \| . \| T_2 \|$. Evidently the set of all endomorphisms of E may therefore be considered as a Banach space, where the norm of the element T is taken to be $\| T \|$. This Banach space will be denoted by $B(E)$.

Theorem 1. *If the space E is complete, then the space $B(E)$ is complete.*
Proof. Let $\lim \| T_m - T_n \| = 0$ as $m, n \to \infty$; $T_m, T_n \in B(E)$. Since $\| T_m f - T_n f \| \leqslant \| T_m - T_n \| . \| f \|$, we have $\lim \| T_m f - T_n f \| = 0$ for every $f \in E$, which implies on account of the completeness of E that $\lim T_n f = Tf$ exists. Evidently T is linear. It follows from $\| T_n \| \leqslant \| T_m \| + \| T_m - T_n \|$ that the sequence of numbers $\| T_n \|$ is bounded, hence $\| T_n \| \leqslant M$ for a fixed M. Then $\| T_n f \| \leqslant M \| f \|$ for every n, so that also $\| Tf \| \leqslant M \| f \|$, which shows that T is bounded. Finally, if $\varepsilon > 0$ is given, the inequality $\| T_m f - T_n f \| \leqslant \| T_m - T_n \| . \| f \| \leqslant \varepsilon \| f \|$, holding for sufficiently large m and n, implies $\| T_m f - Tf \| \leqslant \varepsilon \| f \|$, hence $\lim \| T_m - T \| = 0$ as $m \to \infty$. This completes the proof.

Definition. *If the sequence $T_n \in B(E)$ satisfies $\lim \| T_n - T_0 \| = 0$ as $n \to \infty$, we say that T_n converges uniformly to T_0.*

Evidently uniform convergence implies strong convergence ($\lim T_n f = T_0 f$ for all $f \in E$). If E is a separable Hilbert space, and all $T_n (n = 0, 1, 2, \ldots)$ are of finite double-norm, then uniform convergence stands between strong convergence and convergence in double-norm, since $\| T_n f - T_0 f \| \leqslant \| T_n - T_0 \| . \| f \| \leqslant ||| T_n - T_0 ||| . \| f \|$ for all $f \in E$.

§ 5. The Resolvent and Spectrum of a Linear Transformation

We consider a linear transformation, not necessarily bounded, whose domain D and range W are contained in the same Banach space E. The transformation $T - \lambda I = T_\lambda$ (λ complex, I the identical transformation) is also defined on D.

Definition. *The values of λ for which T_λ has a bounded inverse $R_\lambda = R(\lambda, T)$ with domain dense in E form the resolvent set $\rho(T)$ of T. The set of all these $R(\lambda, T)$ is called the resolvent of T. The values of λ for which T_λ has an unbounded inverse with domain dense in E form the continuous spectrum $C\sigma(T)$ of T. The values of λ for which T_λ has an inverse with domain not dense in E form the residual spectrum $R\sigma(T)$ of T. The values of λ for which T_λ has no inverse form the point spectrum $P\sigma(T)$ of T. The sum of $C\sigma(T)$, $R\sigma(T)$ and $P\sigma(T)$ is the spectrum $\sigma(T)$ of T.*

The next theorems are direct consequences of this definition.

Theorem 1. *No two of the four sets $\rho(T)$, $C\sigma(T)$, $R\sigma(T)$ and $P\sigma(T)$ have common points, and their sum is the whole complex λ-plane.*

Theorem 2. *The equation $Tf = \lambda_0 f$ has a solution $f \neq 0$ if and only if $\lambda_0 \in P\sigma(T)$.*

Definition. *If $\lambda_0 \in P\sigma(T)$, then λ_0 is called a characteristic value of T, and the solutions $f \neq 0$ of $Tf = \lambda_0 f$ are called characteristic elements of T, belonging to λ_0. The set of all solutions of $Tf = \lambda_0 f$ is a linear manifold $M(\lambda_0, T)$, and its closure $[M(\lambda_0, T)]$ is called the characteristic subspace of λ_0 (cf. Ch. 9, § 15).*

We observe that, whenever T is bounded, $M(\lambda_0, T) = [M(\lambda_0, T)]$.

§ 6. Examples

Example A. We assume that R is a separable complete Hilbert space of infinite dimension, and that the orthonormal system $\varphi_n (n = 1, 2, \ldots)$ is complete in R. The linear transformation T is defined by

$$T\varphi_1 = \varphi_2/2,\ T\varphi_2 = \varphi_3/3,\ \ldots,\ T\varphi_n = \varphi_{n+1}/(n+1),\ \ldots.$$

Evidently $\| T \| = 1/2$. The range of T is dense in the subspace determined by $\varphi_2, \varphi_3, \ldots,$ since it contains all finite linear combinations $\Sigma_2\, \beta_i \varphi_i$. Furthermore $Tf = 0$ implies $f = 0$. It follows that T^{-1} exists with domain dense in the subspace $[L(\varphi_2, \varphi_3, \ldots)]$, which shows that $\lambda = 0$ is in the residual spectrum of T.

For $f = \Sigma_1^\infty \alpha_i \varphi_i$, $\lambda \neq 0$, we have

$$T_\lambda f = (T - \lambda I) f = \Sigma_1^\infty [\alpha_i/(i+1)]\varphi_{i+1} - \lambda \Sigma_1^\infty \alpha_i \varphi_i =$$
$$- \lambda \alpha_1 \varphi_1 + \Sigma_2^\infty (\alpha_{i-1}/i - \lambda \alpha_i)\varphi_i,$$

from which it is immediately evident that $T_\lambda f = 0$ implies $f = 0$. The inverse T_λ^{-1} exists therefore. A direct computation shows that

$$T_\lambda^{-1}\varphi_1 = - \Sigma_1^\infty (\lambda^{-i}/i!)\varphi_i,\ T_\lambda^{-1}\varphi_2 = - 2!\lambda \Sigma_2^\infty (\lambda^{-i}/i!)\varphi_i, \ldots,$$

generally

$$T_\lambda^{-1}\varphi_n = - n!\lambda^{n-1} \Sigma_n^\infty (\lambda^{-i}/i!)\varphi_i,$$

so that in any case the domain of T_λ^{-1} is dense in R. We shall prove that T_λ^{-1} is bounded. If $|\lambda| > 1/2$, we have immediately

$$\| T_\lambda f \| = \| \lambda f - Tf \| \geqslant \| \lambda f \| - \| Tf \| \geqslant (|\lambda| - 1/2) \| f \|$$

for all $f \in R$, hence $\| T_\lambda^{-1} \| \leqslant (|\lambda| - 1/2)^{-1}$. If $n^{-1} \geqslant |\lambda| > (n+1)^{-1}$ for a certain n ($n = 2, 3, \ldots$), we split up $f = \Sigma_1^\infty \alpha_i\varphi_i$ into $\Sigma_1^{n-1} + \Sigma_n^\infty = f' + f''$, and we write $g = T_\lambda f = T_\lambda f' + T_\lambda f'' = g' + g''$. Then

$$g'' = T_\lambda f'' = \Sigma_n^\infty [\alpha_i/(i+1)]\varphi_{i+1} - \lambda \Sigma_n^\infty \alpha_i\varphi_i =$$
$$- \lambda\alpha_n\varphi_n + \Sigma_{n+1}^\infty (\alpha_{i-1}/i - \lambda\alpha_i)\varphi_i,$$

hence $\| g'' \|^2 = |\lambda\alpha_n|^2 + \Sigma_{n+1}^\infty |\lambda\alpha_i - \alpha_{i-1}/i|^2$, whereas $\| g \|^2 = |\lambda\alpha_1|^2 + \Sigma_2^\infty |\lambda\alpha_i - \alpha_{i-1}/i|^2$. Now

$$|\lambda\alpha_n| \leqslant |\lambda\alpha_n - \alpha_{n-1}/n| + \frac{1}{n|\lambda|}|\lambda\alpha_{n-1}| \leqslant$$

$$|\lambda\alpha_n - \alpha_{n-1}/n| + \frac{1}{n|\lambda|}|\lambda\alpha_{n-1} - \alpha_{n-2}/(n-1)| + \frac{1}{n(n-1)|\lambda|^2}|\lambda\alpha_{n-2}| \leqslant$$
$$\ldots\ldots \leqslant$$
$$p_1 |\lambda\alpha_1| + \Sigma_2^n p_i |\lambda\alpha_i - \alpha_{i-1}/i|,$$

where $p_n = 1$, and $p_1, \ldots, p_{n-1}$ depend only on λ, but not on $\alpha_1, \ldots, \alpha_n$. Hence, by Schwarz's inequality,

$$|\lambda\alpha_n|^2 \leqslant (\Sigma_1^n p_i^2)[|\lambda\alpha_1|^2 + \Sigma_2^n |\lambda\alpha_i - \alpha_{i-1}/i|^2].$$

Writing $\Sigma_1^n p_i^2 = A_\lambda^2 (A_\lambda \geqslant 1)$, we find $\| g'' \|^2 \leqslant A_\lambda^2 \| g \|^2$, hence $\| g'' \| \leqslant A_\lambda \| g \|$, which implies $\| g' \| = \| g - g'' \| \leqslant (A_\lambda + 1) \| g \|$. Now

$$\| g'' \| \geqslant |\lambda| . \| \Sigma_n^\infty \alpha_i\varphi_i \| - \| \Sigma_n^\infty [\alpha_i/(i+1)]\varphi_{i+1} \| =$$
$$|\lambda| (\Sigma_n^\infty |\alpha_i|^2)^{1/2} - (\Sigma_n^\infty |\alpha_i/(i+1)|^2)^{1/2} \geqslant$$
$$[|\lambda| - 1/(n+1)](\Sigma_n^\infty |\alpha_i|^2)^{1/2} = [|\lambda| - 1/(n+1)] \| f'' \|,$$

hence

(1) $\| f'' \| \leqslant [| \lambda | - 1/(n+1)]^{-1} \| g'' \| \leqslant A_\lambda [| \lambda | - 1/(n+1)]^{-1} \| g \|$.

Since T_λ transforms the $(n-1)$-dimensional space $L(\varphi_1, \ldots, \varphi_{n-1})$ into the $(n-1)$-dimensional space $L(T_\lambda \varphi_1, \ldots, T_\lambda \varphi_{n-1})$, T_λ^{-1} is certainly bounded on $L(T_\lambda \varphi_1, \ldots, T_\lambda \varphi_{n-1})$, hence

(2) $$\| f' \| = \| T_\lambda^{-1} g' \| \leqslant M_\lambda \| g' \| \leqslant M_\lambda (A_\lambda + 1) \| g \|.$$

Finally, from (1) and (2),

$$\| f \| = \| f' + f'' \| \leqslant \| f' \| + \| f'' \| \leqslant C_\lambda \| g \|$$

for all g belonging to the range of T_λ. This shows that T_λ^{-1} is bounded.

The result is therefore that $\lambda = 0$ forms the residual spectrum of T, and that all $\lambda \neq 0$ form the resolvent set of T.

Example B. We assume that R is a separable complete Hilbert space of infinite dimension, and that the orthonormal system $\psi_n (n = 1, 2, \ldots)$ is complete in R. The linear transformation T is defined by

$$T\psi_1 = \lambda_1 \psi_1, \ldots, T\psi_n = \lambda_n \psi_n, \ldots,$$

where λ_n is a sequence of complex numbers satisfying $\lambda_n \neq 1$, $\lim \lambda_n = 1$. Evidently T is bounded, and all numbers λ_n belong to the point spectrum $P\sigma(T)$ of T. Let us consider $T_\lambda = T - \lambda I$ for $\lambda = 1$. Since $(T - I)f = 0$ only for $f = 0$, the inverse T_1^{-1} exists. Since $\| (T-I)\psi_n \| = \| (\lambda_n - 1) \psi_n \| = | \lambda_n - 1 |$ tends to zero as $n \to \infty$, T_1^{-1} is not bounded. Finally, since all ψ_n belong to the range of $T - I$, the domain of T_1^{-1} is dense in R. It follows that $\lambda = 1$ belongs to the continuous spectrum $C\sigma(T)$ of T.

If $\lambda \neq 1$ and $\lambda \neq \lambda_i (i = 1, 2, \ldots)$, there exists a positive number C_λ such that $| \lambda - \lambda_i | > C_\lambda$ for all λ_i. Hence, if $f = \Sigma\, \alpha_i \psi_i$ is arbitrary,

$$\| T_\lambda f \|^2 = \| \Sigma\, (\lambda_i - \lambda) \alpha_i \psi_i \|^2 = \Sigma\, | \lambda_i - \lambda |^2 . | \alpha_i |^2 \geqslant$$
$$C_\lambda^2\, \Sigma\, | \alpha_i |^2 = C_\lambda^2 \| f \|^2,$$

and this shows that T_λ^{-1} is bounded. The domain of T_λ^{-1} is evidently the whole space R. It follows that λ belongs to the resolvent set $\rho(T)$ of T.

The result is therefore that the points $\lambda = \lambda_i$ form the point spectrum, $\lambda = 1$ forms the continuous spectrum, and all other values of λ belong to the resolvent set.

Example C. We assume that R is a separable complete Hilbert space of infinite dimension, and that R is the direct sum of the orthogonal subspaces R_1 and R_2, both of infinite dimension. The orthonormal systems φ_n

$(n = 1, 2, \ldots)$ and $\psi_n (n = 1, 2, \ldots)$ are complete in R_1 and R_2 respectively. The linear transformation T_1 on R_1 is defined as T was defined in Example A, the linear transformation T_2 on R_2 is defined as T was defined in Example B. The linear transformation on R, identical with T_1 on R_1 and with T_2 on R_2, is called T. Evidently T is completely reduced by (R_1, R_2), and the same is true of $T_\lambda = T - \lambda I$ for arbitrary complex λ. Then, supposing moreover that $\lambda_i \neq 0$ for all λ_i, the numbers $\lambda_i (i = 1, 2, \ldots)$ form the point spectrum of T, $\lambda = 1$ forms the continuous spectrum, $\lambda = 0$ forms the residual spectrum, and all other λ form the resolvent set of T.

Example D. We assume that R is a separable complete Hilbert space, and that the linear transformation T on R (into R) is of finite double-norm. Then, in Ch. 9, § 17, Th. 3, we have seen that the equation

$$(I - \lambda T)f = g$$

has the unique solution $f = [\delta(\lambda)]^{-1}\Delta(\lambda)g$, where $\Delta(\lambda)$ is bounded, except for those values of λ satisfying $\delta(\lambda) = 0$. For those values of λ for which $\delta(\lambda) = 0$ the number $\mu = \lambda^{-1}$ is a characteristic value of T (cf. Ch. 9, § 17, Th. 5). Since, writing $\mu = \lambda^{-1}$ for $\lambda \neq 0$, the equation $(I - \lambda T)f = g$ is equivalent to $(T - \mu I)f = -\mu g$, we see that all $\mu \neq 0$, satisfying $\delta(\mu^{-1}) = 0$, belong to the point spectrum of T, whereas all $\mu \neq 0$, satisfying $\delta(\mu^{-1}) \neq 0$, belong to the resolvent set of T. Since $\delta(\mu^{-1}) = 0$ has only a finite number of solutions for which $|\mu| \geqslant r_0$ (if $r_0 > 0$ is given), the number of different characteristic values $\mu_1, \mu_2, \ldots$ of T is at most enumerably infinite, and if it is infinite, then $\lim \mu_n = 0$.

Example E. We assume that the complete Banach space E is the direct sum of the linear subspaces L and M, both subspaces containing other elements besides the null element. Since E is complete, the projection P on L along M is bounded (cf. Ch. 7, § 14, Th. 2). Hence, if $f = g + h$, $g \in L$, $h \in M$, there exists a positive A (not depending on f) such that $\| g \| \leqslant A \| f \|$, $\| h \| \leqslant A \| f \|$.

The numbers $\lambda = 0$ and $\lambda = 1$ evidently belong to the point spectrum of P. Let now $\lambda \neq 0$, $\lambda \neq 1$. Then, if again $f = g + h$, $g \in L$, $h \in M$, the equation $P_\lambda f_1 = Pf_1 - \lambda f_1 = f$ has the unique solution $f_1 = (1 - \lambda)^{-1}g - \lambda^{-1}h$, and $\| f_1 \| \leqslant |1 - \lambda|^{-1} \| g \| + |\lambda|^{-1} \| h \| \leqslant [A |1 - \lambda|^{-1} + A |\lambda|^{-1}] \| f \|$. This shows that P_λ^{-1} exists with domain E, and is bounded.

The result is that $\lambda = 0$ and $\lambda = 1$ form the point spectrum of P, and that all other values of λ belong to the resolvent set of P.

§ 7. The Resolvent of a Closed Linear Transformation

We assume that T is a closed linear transformation, whose domain D and range W are contained in the same complete Banach space E.

Theorem 1. *If the complex number μ belongs to the resolvent set $\rho(T)$ of T, then all λ satisfying $|\lambda - \mu| < 1/\|T_\mu^{-1}\|$ have the property that T_λ^{-1} exists, and is bounded.*

Proof. If $f \in D$, then $T_\lambda f = T_\mu f - (\lambda - \mu)f$. Hence, for $|\lambda - \mu| < 1/\|T_\mu^{-1}\|$,

$$\|Tf - \lambda f\| \geqslant \|T_\mu f\| - |\lambda - \mu| . \|f\| \geqslant (1/\|T_\mu^{-1}\| - |\lambda - \mu|) \|f\|.$$

This shows that $T_\lambda f = 0$ implies $f = 0$, so that T_λ^{-1} exists. Furthermore $\|T_\lambda^{-1}\| \leqslant (1/\|T_\mu^{-1}\| - |\lambda - \mu|)^{-1} = \|T_\mu^{-1}\|/(1 - |\lambda - \mu| . \|T_\mu^{-1}\|)$.

We observe that we may not conclude that $\lambda \in \rho(T)$ for $|\lambda - \mu| < 1/\|T_\mu^{-1}\|$, since we have not yet proved that the domain of T_λ^{-1} is dense in E.

Theorem 2. *If $\lambda \in \rho(T)$, the domain of $R_\lambda = T_\lambda^{-1}$ is the whole space E.*

Proof. We know that $W(T_\lambda)$ is dense in E, and that R_λ with domain $W(T_\lambda)$ is bounded. We have to prove that $W(T_\lambda) = E$. Let $g \in E$ be arbitrary, $g = \lim g_n$, $g_n \in W(T_\lambda)$. Then there exist elements $f_n \in D$ such that $g_n = T_\lambda f_n$, hence $f_n = R_\lambda g_n$. Since R_λ is bounded and $g = \lim g_n$, the sequence f_n converges to an element f. But then $Tf_n = T_\lambda f_n + \lambda f_n = g_n + \lambda f_n$ converges to $g + \lambda f$. Since T is closed, it follows that $f \in D$ and $Tf = g + \lambda f$, hence $T_\lambda f = g$ or $g \in W(T_\lambda)$. The element $g \in E$ being arbitrary, we find that $W(T_\lambda) = E$.

Corollary. *If $\lambda \in \rho(T)$ and $R_\lambda f = 0$ for an element $f \in E$, then $f = 0$.*

Proof. The correspondence between the domain D and the range $E = W(T_\lambda)$ is one-to-one.

Theorem 3. *If $\lambda, \mu \in \rho(T)$, then*

$$R_\lambda - R_\mu = (\lambda - \mu)R_\lambda R_\mu = (\lambda - \mu)R_\mu R_\lambda.$$

Proof. We have $R_\lambda T_\mu R_\mu = R_\lambda$, $R_\lambda T_\lambda R_\mu = R_\mu$, and, on the domain D, $T_\mu - T_\lambda = (\lambda - \mu)I$. Hence $R_\lambda - R_\mu = R_\lambda(T_\mu - T_\lambda)R_\mu = (\lambda - \mu)R_\lambda R_\mu$. Then also $R_\mu - R_\lambda = (\mu - \lambda)R_\mu R_\lambda$, hence $R_\lambda - R_\mu = (\lambda - \mu)R_\mu R_\lambda$.

Theorem 4. *If X_λ is a set of bounded linear transformations with domain E, defined for every point λ in a set Σ of the complex λ-plane, such that*

$X_\lambda - X_\mu = (\lambda - \mu)X_\lambda X_\mu$ for every pair of points $\lambda, \mu \in \Sigma$, and if $X_\lambda f = 0$ implies $f = 0$ for at least one λ in Σ, then there exists a unique closed linear transformation T whose resolvent exists, and is identical with X_λ for every $\lambda \in \Sigma$.

Proof. There exists at least one value of λ, say $\lambda = \mu$, such that $X_\mu f = 0$ implies $f = 0$. Let now $\lambda \in \Sigma$ be arbitrary, and let $X_\lambda f = 0$. Then

$$X_\mu f = X_\lambda f + (\mu - \lambda)X_\mu X_\lambda f = 0,$$

hence $f = 0$. The correspondence between the domain E of X_λ and the range $W(X_\lambda)$ is therefore one-to-one. If f is an arbitrary element of $W(X_\lambda)$, hence $f = X_\lambda g$, we assign to f the unique element $g + \lambda f = g + \lambda X_\lambda g$. We shall prove that this correspondence is independent of λ. For this purpose it is necessary to show that, if $\lambda, \mu \in \Sigma$ and $g \in E$ are given, there exists an element $g' \in E$ such that $X_\lambda g = X_\mu g'$ and $g + \lambda X_\lambda g = g' + \mu X_\mu g'$. Evidently, if one element g' exists such that $X_\lambda g = X_\mu g'$, it is uniquely determined. The element g' is defined by $g' = g + (\lambda - \mu)X_\lambda g$, since then $X_\mu g' = X_\mu g + (\lambda - \mu)X_\mu X_\lambda g = X_\lambda g$, and also $g' + \mu X_\mu g' = g' + \mu X_\lambda g = g + \lambda X_\lambda g$. The desired independence of λ is thus proved. We now take D to be the range $W(X_\lambda)$, and the linear transformation T, defined on D, transforms the element $f = X_\lambda g$ of D into $g + \lambda f = g + \lambda X_\lambda g$. If $\lambda \in \Sigma$, we have $Tf - \lambda f = g$, $f = X_\lambda g$, so that T_λ and X_λ are inverse. Since X_λ is closed (it is bounded, hence certainly closed), the same is true of T_λ (cf. Ch. 7, § 11, Th. 5), so that T is also closed. Evidently the resolvent set $\rho(T)$ contains Σ, and $R_\lambda = X_\lambda$ for every $\lambda \in \Sigma$. It is also evident that T is uniquely determined.

Theorem 5. *If $\mu \in \rho(T)$, then all points λ satisfying $|\lambda - \mu| < 1/\|R_\mu\|$ belong to $\rho(T)$ (cf. Theorem 1), and, for these values of λ,*

$$R_\lambda = \Sigma_{n=0}^{\infty} (\lambda - \mu)^n R_\mu^{n+1}.$$

Proof. If $|\lambda - \mu| < 1/\|R_\mu\|$, then $\Sigma |\lambda - \mu|^n \|R_\mu^{n+1}\| \leqslant \Sigma |\lambda - \mu|^n \|R_\mu\|^{n+1} < \infty$, which shows that the transformations $S_N = \Sigma_0^N (\lambda - \mu)^n R_\mu^{n+1}$ converge uniformly to a bounded linear transformation S. We have

$$[I - (\lambda - \mu)R_\mu]S = \Sigma_0^\infty (\lambda - \mu)^n R_\mu^{n+1} - \Sigma_1^\infty (\lambda - \mu)^n R_\mu^{n+1} = R_\mu,$$

hence

$$[T_\mu - (\lambda - \mu)I]S = I,$$

where we have used that $S_N f$ is in the domain of T_μ for every $f \in E$, and converges to Sf, and that $T_\mu S_N f$ converges as well, so that, since T_μ is closed, Sf is in the domain of T_μ. But $T_\mu - (\lambda - \mu)I = T_\lambda$, hence

$T_\lambda S = I$, which shows that T_λ has the whole space E as its range. It follows that $\lambda \in \rho(T)$ and $S = R_\lambda$.

Corollary. *The resolvent set of T is open.*

Theorem 6. *If T is a bounded linear transformation with domain E, then all λ satisfying $|\lambda| > \|T\|$ belong to the resolvent set $\rho(T)$, and for these values*

$$R_\lambda = -\Sigma_{n=1}^{\infty} \lambda^{-n} T^{n-1}.$$

Furthermore $\|R_\lambda\| \leqslant (|\lambda| - \|T\|)^{-1}$ for these λ.

Proof. If $|\lambda| > \|T\|$, then $\|T_\lambda f\| = \|\lambda f - Tf\| \geqslant (|\lambda| - \|T\|)\|f\|$, which shows that T_λ^{-1} exists, and is bounded with $\|T_\lambda^{-1}\| \leqslant (|\lambda| - \|T\|)^{-1}$. Furthermore, $\Sigma_1^\infty |\lambda|^{-n} \|T^{n-1}\| \leqslant \Sigma_1^\infty |\lambda|^{-n} \|T\|^{n-1} < \infty$, so that $-\Sigma_1^N \lambda^{-n} T^{n-1}$ converges uniformly to a bounded linear transformation S. We have

$$[I - \lambda^{-1}T]S = -\Sigma_1^\infty \lambda^{-n} T^{n-1} + \Sigma_2^\infty \lambda^{-n} T^{n-1} = -\lambda^{-1} I,$$

hence

$$(T - \lambda I)S = I,$$

which shows that $T - \lambda I$ has the whole space E as its range. It follows that $\lambda \in \rho(T)$ and $S = R_\lambda$.

§ 8. Integral, where the Integrand is a Variable Element of Banach Space

Let $a \leqslant x \leqslant b$ be a finite interval on the X-axis, and let $f(x)$ be a function, defined for $a \leqslant x \leqslant b$, with values in the Banach space E. The function $f(x)$ is called *continuous* at x_0 if $\lim_{x \to x_0} f(x) = f(x_0)$, that is, if $\lim \|f(x) - f(x_0)\| = 0$ as $\lim |x - x_0| = 0$.

Theorem 1. *If $f(x)$ is continuous at all x in $a \leqslant x \leqslant b$, then $f(x)$ is uniformly continuous in this interval, by which we mean that to each $\varepsilon > 0$ there exists a number $\delta > 0$, depending on ε only, such that $\|f(x_1) - f(x_2)\| < \varepsilon$ for all x_1, x_2 in $a \leqslant x \leqslant b$ satisfying $|x_1 - x_2| < \delta$.*

Proof. To every x_0 in $a \leqslant x \leqslant b$ we assign an interval $|x - x_0| < \delta(x_0)$ such that $\|f(x) - f(x_0)\| < \varepsilon/4$ for all x in this interval. By the Heine-Borel-Lebesgue Theorem the whole interval $a \leqslant x \leqslant b$ is covered by a finite number of these intervals. Let $x_1 < x_2 < \ldots < x_n$ be their centres. Supposing that unnecessary intervals are left out, we have then

$\| f(x_{i+1}) - f(x_i) \| < \varepsilon/2$ $(i = 1, 2, \ldots, n-1)$. Let δ be the smallest under the diameters of these n intervals, and suppose that $| x' - x'' | < \delta$. Then x' and x'' are either in the same interval, in which case $\| f(x') - f(x'') \| < \varepsilon/2$, or in adjoining intervals (belonging to x_i and x_{i+1}, say), in which case $\| f(x') - f(x'') \| \leqslant \varepsilon/4 + \varepsilon/4 + \| f(x_{i+1}) - f(x_i) \| < \varepsilon$. This completes the proof.

If the interval $a \leqslant x \leqslant b$ is divided into subintervals by the points $a = x_0 < x_1 < \ldots < x_n = b$, and $\max_i(x_i - x_{i-1}) \leqslant \delta$, we shall say that the points $x_0, x_1, \ldots, x_n$ form a *δ-division* of $a \leqslant x \leqslant b$. If moreover $f(x)$ is a continuous function, defined in $a \leqslant x \leqslant b$, we shall say that $S = \Sigma_{i=1}^n f(\xi_i)(x_i - x_{i-1})$, where ξ_i is an arbitrary point in $x_{i-1} \leqslant x \leqslant x_i$, is a *$\delta$-sum* of $f(x)$.

Theorem 2. *If $f(x)$ is continuous on $a \leqslant x \leqslant b$, and $\varepsilon > 0$ is given, there exists a number $\delta > 0$ such that the difference between any two δ-sums of $f(x)$ does not exceed ε in norm.*

Proof. If $\varepsilon > 0$ is given, there exists a number $\delta > 0$ such that $\| f(x_1) - f(x_2) \| < \varepsilon/2(b-a)$, if only $| x_1 - x_2 | < \delta$ (cf. the preceding theorem). If now S_1 and S_3 are two δ-sums of $f(x)$ with the special property that one of the corresponding δ-divisions is a subdivision of the other one, we have

$$\| S_1 - S_3 \| \leqslant [\varepsilon/2(b-a)] \, \Sigma \, (x_i - x_{i-1}) = \varepsilon/2.$$

If therefore S_1 and S_2 are two arbitrary δ-sums, and S_3 is the δ-sum whose δ-division is the superposition of the δ-divisions corresponding with S_1 and S_2, then $\| S_1 - S_2 \| \leqslant \| S_1 - S_3 \| + \| S_2 - S_3 \| < \varepsilon$.

As a consequence of this theorem the following definition may be given:

Definition. *If $f(x)$, having its values in the complete Banach space E, is continuous on $a \leqslant x \leqslant b$, the δ-sums $S = \Sigma f(\xi_i)(x_i - x_{i-1})$ tend to a limit, depending only on $f(x)$, as δ tends to zero. This limit is called the integral of $f(x)$ over $[a, b]$, and it is denoted by $\int_a^b f(x)dx$.*

Remark. The properties

$$\int_a^b f(x)dx = \int_a^c f(x)dx + \int_c^b f(x)dx \quad (a \leqslant c \leqslant b),$$

$$\int_a^b \alpha f(x)dx = \alpha \int_a^b f(x)dx \ \ (\alpha \text{ complex}),$$

$$\int_a^b (f_1 + f_2)dx = \int_a^b f_1 \, dx + \int_a^b f_2 \, dx,$$

$$\| \int_a^b f \, dx \| \leqslant \int_a^b \| f \| \, dx,$$

$$\int_a^b f\,dx = (b-a)f, \text{ if } f(x) \text{ is constant,}$$

are easily seen to be true. Also, if $f(x) = g(x)h$, where $g(x)$ is a complex-valued continuous function, and h is an element of E,

$$\int_a^b f(x)\,dx = \left(\int_a^b g(x)dx\right)h.$$

It will be evident to the reader that extensive generalisations are possible [2]. As an application we prove:

Theorem 3. *If T is a closed linear transformation with domain D and range W in the same complete Banach space E, and if $\mu \in \rho(T)$, so that all $\lambda = \mu + re^{i\varphi}$ (r fixed, $0 \leqslant r < 1/\| R_\mu \|$, φ real and variable) belong to $\rho(T)$, and*

$$R_\varphi = R_\lambda = \Sigma_{n=0}^{\infty} r^n e^{in\varphi} R_\mu^{n+1}$$

for these values of λ (cf. § 7, Th. 5), then

$$R_\mu f = (2\pi)^{-1} \int_0^{2\pi} R_\varphi f.d\varphi$$

for all $f \in E$.

Proof. If $\varepsilon > 0$ is given, there exists an index N_0 such that, for $N \geqslant N_0$,

$$R_\varphi f = \Sigma_0^N r^n e^{in\varphi} R_\mu^{n+1} f + q_N(f),$$

where $\| q_N(f) \| < \varepsilon \| f \|$ for all φ in $0 \leqslant \varphi \leqslant 2\pi$. Since $R_\varphi f$ is a continuous function of φ in $0 \leqslant \varphi \leqslant 2\pi$, the integral $\int_0^{2\pi} R_\varphi f.d\varphi$ exists, the same is therefore true of $\int_0^{2\pi} q_N(f)d\varphi$, and $\| \int_0^{2\pi} q_N(f)d\varphi \| \leqslant \int_0^{2\pi} \| q_N(f) \| d\varphi < 2\pi\varepsilon \| f \|$. Hence

$$\int_0^{2\pi} R_\varphi f.d\varphi = \Sigma_0^N R_\mu^{n+1} f \int_0^{2\pi} r^n e^{in\varphi} d\varphi + \int_0^{2\pi} q_N(f)d\varphi$$
$$= 2\pi R_\mu f + \int_0^{2\pi} q_N(f)d\varphi,$$

so that

$$R_\mu f = (2\pi)^{-1} \int_0^{2\pi} R_\varphi f.d\varphi.$$

Corollary. *If λ runs through $\rho(T)$, and f is a fixed element of E, the function $\| R_\lambda f \|$, defined on $\rho(T)$, has no proper maximum. Precisely stated, if the sequence $\lambda_n \in \rho(T)$, converging to $\mu \in \rho(T)$, has the property that $\| R_{\lambda_n} f \| < \| R_\mu f \|$ $(n = 1, 2, \ldots)$, then there exists a sequence ν_n, also converging to μ, such that $\| R_{\nu_n} f \| > \| R_\mu f \|$ $(n = 1, 2, \ldots)$.*

Proof. Follows immediately from

$$\| R_\mu f \| \leqslant (2\pi)^{-1} \int_0^{2\pi} \| R_\varphi f \| d\varphi,$$

where the integration is over a sufficiently small circle around μ.

§ 9. The Spectrum of a Bounded Linear Transformation

We consider here more closely some properties of the spectrum of a bounded linear transformation T, whose domain is the complete Banach space E, and whose range is contained in the same space E.

Theorem 1. *The spectrum $\sigma(T)$ of T is not empty.*

Proof. Let us suppose that all complex λ belong to the resolvent set $\rho(T)$ of T. Then, if $f \neq 0$ is a fixed element of E, $R_\lambda f \neq 0$ for all λ (cf. § 7, Th. 2, Corollary). Hence $\| R_0 f \| = A > 0$. By § 7, Th. 6 we have

$$\| R_\lambda f \| \leqslant (| \lambda | - \| T \|)^{-1} \| f \|$$

for $| \lambda | > \| T \|$; it follows that there exists a positive number C such that $\| R_\lambda f \| < A/2$ for $| \lambda | \geqslant C$. For $| \lambda | \leqslant C$ the function $\| R_\lambda f \|$ is a continuous function of λ, so that it has a finite maximum M. This maximum M is at least A, since $\| R_0 f \| = A$. The points where $\| R_\lambda f \| = M$ are therefore interior points of $| \lambda | \leqslant C$ on account of $\| R_\lambda f \| < A/2$ for $| \lambda | = C$. It follows that there exists at least one point λ_0 in $| \lambda | < C$ having the property that $\| R_{\lambda_0} f \| = M$, and that $\| R_{\lambda_n} f \| < M$ $(n = 1, 2, \ldots)$ for a certain sequence $\lambda_1, \lambda_2, \ldots$, converging to λ_0. Then, by § 8, Th. 3, Corollary, there exists also a sequence $\nu_1, \nu_2, \ldots$, converging to λ_0, such that $\| R_{\nu_n} f \| > M$ $(n = 1, 2, \ldots)$. This is a contradiction.

We may conclude therefore that the spectrum of T is not empty.

Theorem 2. *Let all λ in a neighbourhood of $\lambda = \mu$, except μ itself, belong to the resolvent set $\rho(T)$. Then, if there exist an element $f \in E$ and a number $n > 0$ such that*

$$\lim\, (\lambda - \mu)^n R_\lambda f = g \neq 0 \text{ as } \lim \lambda = \mu,$$

the point μ belongs to the point spectrum $P\sigma(T)$ of T, and g is a characteristic element, belonging to the characteristic value μ.

Proof. Observing that $T_\mu R_\lambda = T_\lambda R_\lambda + (\lambda - \mu) R_\lambda = I + (\lambda - \mu) R_\lambda$, we see that $\lim\, (\lambda - \mu)^n R_\lambda f = g$ implies $\lim\, (\lambda - \mu)^n \{f + (\lambda - \mu) R_\lambda f\} = T_\mu g$. But

$$\lim\, (\lambda - \mu)^n \{f + (\lambda - \mu) R_\lambda f\} = \lim\, \{(\lambda - \mu)^n f + (\lambda - \mu)(\lambda - \mu)^n R_\lambda f\} = 0,$$

hence $T_\mu g = 0$. Since $g \neq 0$, this shows that μ belongs to the point spectrum $P\sigma(T)$ of T, and that g is a characteristic element belonging to the characteristic value μ.

Remark. As an illustration we may consider Example E in § 6. Here the complete Banach space E is the direct sum of the linear subspaces L and M, and P is the projection on L along M. We have found that

$\lambda = 0$ and $\lambda = 1$ form the point spectrum of P, and that, for $\lambda \neq 0$, $\lambda \neq 1$, the equation $P_\lambda f_1 = f$ has the solution $f_1 = (1-\lambda)^{-1}Pf - \lambda^{-1}(I-P)f$. Hence $R_\lambda = (1-\lambda)^{-1}P - \lambda^{-1}(I-P)$. Then $\lim_{\lambda \to 1}(\lambda - 1)R_\lambda = -P$; our theorem shows therefore that every element $Pf \neq 0$ is a characteristic element of P, belonging to the characteristic value $\lambda = 1$. In the same way $\lim_{\lambda \to 0}\lambda R_\lambda = -(I-P)$; every element $(I-P)f \neq 0$ is therefore a characteristic element of P belonging to the characteristic value $\lambda = 0$. Both facts, of course, we knew already.

A more interesting example is furnished by Example D in § 6. Here we considered a linear transformation T of finite double-norm on the separable complete Hilbert space R, and we proved that every complex $\mu \neq 0$, for which $\lambda = \mu^{-1}$ is not a zero of the power series $\delta(\lambda)$ (cf. Ch. 9, § 17), belongs to the resolvent set of T. Since the values $\mu_0 \neq 0$, for which $\delta(\mu_0^{-1}) = 0$, are isolated, all values μ in a neighbourhood of such a point μ_0 belong to the resolvent set. Writing now $\lambda = \mu^{-1}$, $\lambda_0 = \mu_0^{-1}$, and using the notations of Ch. 9, § 17, we know that $R_\mu = \Delta(\lambda)/\delta(\lambda)$. Furthermore, by Ch. 9, § 17, Th. 5, if $\delta(\lambda)$ contains the factor $(\lambda - \lambda_0)^q$ (q integer, $\geqslant 1$), $\Delta(\lambda)$ contains at most a factor $(\lambda - \lambda_0)^p$ (p integer, $0 \leqslant p < q$). Hence $\Delta(\lambda) = A_p(\lambda - \lambda_0)^p + A_{p+1}(\lambda - \lambda_0)^{p+1} + \ldots$, where $A_p \neq O$ (the null transformation). It follows that $\lim_{\lambda \to \lambda_0} (\lambda - \lambda_0)^{q-p}R_\mu = A_p/c_q$, where $c_q \neq 0$ is the coefficient of $(\lambda - \lambda_0)^q$ in $\delta(\lambda) = \Sigma_{i=q}^{\infty} c_i(\lambda - \lambda_0)^i$. Every element $A_p f \in R$, satisfying $A_p f \neq 0$, is therefore a characteristic element of T belonging to the characteristic value $\mu_0 = \lambda_0^{-1}$. We observe, incidentally, that a direct consideration of the relation $(I - \lambda T)\Delta(\lambda) = \delta(\lambda)I$ gives the same result.

That not every λ_0, with the property that a neighbourhood of λ_0 belongs to the resolvent set, is always in the point spectrum is shown by Example A of § 6, where $\lambda = 0$ forms the residual spectrum of T, whereas all $\lambda \neq 0$ form the resolvent set. A second example follows here.

Let Δ be the linear interval $[0, 1]$, and let the linear transformation T on $L_2[0, 1]$ be defined by

$$Tf = \int_\Delta T(x, y)f(y)dy,$$

where the integral is a Lebesgue integral, and

$$T(x, y) = \begin{cases} 1 \text{ for } x \geqslant y, \\ 0 \text{ for } x < y. \end{cases}$$

Hence $Tf = \int_0^x f(y)dy$. Obviously T is of finite double-norm with $|||T|||^2 = 1/2$. For the iterated kernels $T_n(x, y)$ $(n = 2, 3, \ldots)$ we easily find

$$T_n(x, y) = \begin{cases} (x-y)^{n-1}/(n-1)! & \text{for } x \geqslant y, \\ 0 & \text{for } x < y, \end{cases}$$

hence $\| T^n \| \leqslant ||| T^n ||| \leqslant 1/(n-1)!$. It follows that for $\lambda \neq 0$ the series

$$-\lambda^{-1}I - \lambda^{-2}T - \lambda^{-3}T^2 - \dots$$

converges uniformly to a bounded transformation S_λ. Since $(T - \lambda I)S_\lambda = S_\lambda(T - \lambda I) = I$, we have $S_\lambda = R_\lambda$. This shows that all $\lambda \neq 0$ belong to the resolvent set of T. Furthermore, since $Tf = 0$ (that is, $\int_0^x f(y)dy = 0$ for all $x \in \Delta$) implies $f = 0$, the inverse T^{-1} exists. Considering the system $\varphi_n(x) = \sin n\pi x$ $(n = 1, 2, \dots)$, which is complete in $L_2[0, 1]$ (we shall prove this statement at the end of the present proof), we have $T(n\pi \cos n\pi x) = n\pi \int_0^x \cos n\pi y\, dy = \sin n\pi x = \varphi_n(x)$. The range of T is therefore dense in $L_2[0, 1]$. Since $\| \cos n\pi x \| = 2^{-1/2}$ $(n = 1, 2, \dots)$, and $\| T(\cos n\pi x) \| = 2^{-1/2}/n\pi$, T^{-1} is not bounded. This shows that $\lambda = 0$ forms the continuous spectrum of T.

It remains to prove that the system $\{\sin n\pi x\}$ is complete in $L_2[0, 1]$, or, in other words, that the system $\{\sin nx\}$ is complete in $L_2[0, \pi]$. Now, in Ch. 6, § 14, Th. 1 and 3, we have seen that the system $\{(2\pi)^{-1/2}, \pi^{-1/2} \cos x, \pi^{-1/2} \sin x, \dots, \pi^{-1/2} \cos nx, \pi^{-1/2} \sin nx, \dots\}$ is orthonormal and complete in $L_2[0, 2\pi]$. Then the same system is also orthonormal and complete in $L_2[-\pi, \pi]$ on account of the fact that all functions of the system have the period 2π. Let now $f(x) \in L_2[0, \pi]$. Then we extend $f(x)$ on $[-\pi, 0)$ by $f(-x) = -f(x)$, so that $f(x)$ becomes an odd function on $[-\pi, \pi]$. All inner products $(f, \cos nx)$ $(n = 0, 1, 2, \dots)$ vanish therefore. It follows that $\lim \| f - s_n \|^2 = \lim \int_0^{2\pi} | f(x) - s_n(x) |^2\, dx = 0$, where $s_n(x) = \sum_{k=1}^n \alpha_k \pi^{-1/2} \sin kx$ with $\alpha_k = (f, \pi^{-1/2} \sin kx)$. Then also $\lim \int_0^\pi | f - s_n |^2\, dx = 0$, which shows that the system $\{\pi^{-1/2} \sin nx\}$ $(n = 1, 2, \dots)$ is complete in $L_2[0, \pi]$. We observe that it may be proved in a similar way that the system $\{\cos nx\}$ $(n = 0, 1, 2, \dots)$ is complete in $L_2[0, \pi]$.

Theorem 3. *Let the sequence of complex numbers λ_n ($\lambda_m \neq \lambda_n$ for $m \neq n$) and the sequence of positive integers p_n be given. Then, if the sequence of elements $f_n \neq 0$ satisfies $(T - \lambda_n I)^{p_n} f_n = 0$, the elements f_n $(n = 1, 2, \dots)$ are linearly independent.*

Proof. It is obviously no restriction of the generality to suppose that $(T - \lambda_n I)^{q_n} f_n \neq 0$ for $0 \leqslant q_n < p_n$ (q_n integer). We proceed by induction, and we suppose that we have already proved that any elements $g_1, \ldots, g_{n-1}$, all $\neq 0$ and satisfying $(T - \lambda_i I)^{p_i} g_i = 0$ $(i = 1, \ldots, n-1)$, are linearly independent. It is easily seen that, for $i \neq n$,

$$(T - \lambda_n I)f_i = (\lambda_i - \lambda_n)f_i + (T - \lambda_i I)f_i,$$

$$(T - \lambda_n I)^2 f_i = (\lambda_i - \lambda_n)^2 f_i + 2(\lambda_i - \lambda_n)(T - \lambda_i I)f_i + (T - \lambda_i I)^2 f_i,$$

$$\cdots\cdots\cdots\cdot$$

$$(T - \lambda_n I)^{p_n} f_i = (\lambda_i - \lambda_n)^{p_n} f_i + h_i = g_i,$$

where $(T - \lambda_i I)^{p_i - 1} h_i = 0$. It is impossible that $g_i = 0$, since this would imply $(T - \lambda_i I)^{p_i - 1} f_i = 0$, against our hypothesis. Let us suppose now that $f_1, \ldots, f_n$ are not linearly independent. Then, since $f_1, \ldots, f_{n-1}$ are linearly independent by our induction hypothesis, we have $f_n = \Sigma_{i=1}^{n-1} \alpha_i f_i$. Hence

$$0 = (T - \lambda_n I)^{p_n} f_n = \Sigma_{i=1}^{n-1} \alpha_i g_i$$

with $g_i \neq 0$ and $(T - \lambda_i I)^{p_i} g_i = 0$ $(i = 1, \ldots, n-1)$. But then $g_1, \ldots, g_{n-1}$ are linearly independent by our induction hypothesis, hence $\alpha_1 = \ldots = \alpha_{n-1} = 0$. This, however, implies $f_n = \Sigma_1^{n-1} \alpha_i f_i = 0$, which is not true. It follows therefore that $f_1, \ldots, f_n$ are linearly independent.

Theorem 4. *If $\lambda \in \rho(T)$, then $\lambda \in \rho(T^*)$, where T^* is the Banach-adjoint of T.*

Proof. We observe first that the Banach-adjoint of $T_\lambda = T - \lambda I$ is $T_\lambda^* = T^* - \lambda I$. Let now $\lambda \in \rho(T)$, that is, let the domain $W(T_\lambda)$ of the bounded inverse T_λ^{-1} be identical with the whole space E. Then, by § 3, Th. 4, 1°, T_λ^* has a bounded inverse, and $W(T_\lambda^*) = (N(T_\lambda))^\circ = E^*$. This shows that $\lambda \in \rho(T^*)$.

Remark. If E is a complete Hilbert space R, the Hilbert-adjoint of $T - \lambda I$ is $T^* - \bar{\lambda} I$ (where now T^* is also the Hilbert-adjoint of T), so that in this case $\lambda \in \rho(T)$ implies $\bar{\lambda} \in \rho(T^*)$.

Theorem 5. *If E has the property (Ext.), and $\lambda \in R\sigma(T)$ (the residual spectrum of T), then $\lambda \in P\sigma(T^*)$ (the point spectrum of T^*).*

Proof. Since $\lambda \in R\sigma(T)$, the range $W(T_\lambda)$ is not dense in E, so that, on account of the property (Ext.) of E, the annihilator $[W(T_\lambda)]^\circ$ contains an element $f^* \neq 0$ of E^*. But $[W(T_\lambda)]^\circ = N(T_\lambda^*)$, hence $T_\lambda^* f^* = 0$. This shows that $\lambda \in P\sigma(T^*)$.

Remark. If E is a complete Hilbert space R, and T^* is the Hilbert-adjoint of T, then $\lambda \in R\sigma(T)$ implies $\bar{\lambda} \in P\sigma(T^*)$.

Theorem 6. *If E has the property (Ext.), and $\lambda \in P\sigma(T)$, then either $\lambda \in P\sigma(T^*)$ or $\lambda \in R\sigma(T^*)$.*

Proof. Since $N(T_\lambda)$ contains elements $\neq 0$, and E has the property (Ext.), the annihilator $(N(T_\lambda))^\circ$ is a proper subspace of E^*. By § 3, Th. 3, 1° we have $[W(T_\lambda^*)] \subset (N(T_\lambda))^\circ$; the range $W(T_\lambda^*)$ is therefore not dense in E^*. This shows that either $\lambda \in P\sigma(T^*)$ or $\lambda \in R\sigma(T^*)$.

Remark. If E is a complete Hilbert space, and T^* is the Hilbert-adjoint of T, then $\lambda \in P\sigma(T)$ implies either $\bar{\lambda} \in P\sigma(T^*)$ or $\bar{\lambda} \in R\sigma(T^*)$.

In the next three theorems we suppose that A is a bounded linear transformation on the complete Hilbert space R, whose range is contained in the same space.

Theorem 7. *If A is normal, the residual spectrum $R\sigma(A)$ is empty.*

Proof. We recall that $A_\lambda = A - \lambda I$ and A are normal simultaneously. Supposing now that the range $W(A_\lambda)$ is not dense in R for a certain λ, the null space $N(A_\lambda) = R \ominus [W(A_\lambda)]$ (cf. Ch. 9, § 14, Th. 1, Corollary) contains other elements besides the null element. It follows that $\lambda \in P\sigma(A)$ in this case, so that the residual spectrum $R\sigma(A)$ is empty.

Theorem 8. *If A is self-adjoint, the spectrum $\sigma(A)$ contains only real numbers. The residual spectrum $R\sigma(A)$ is empty.*

Proof. Since A, as a self-adjoint transformation, is also normal, the residual spectrum is empty by the preceding theorem. Let now λ be non-real, hence $\lambda = \alpha + i\beta$ with α, β real, $\beta \neq 0$. Since all characteristic values of A are real (cf. Ch. 9, § 15, Th. 2), the inverse A_λ^{-1} exists. For every element f in the domain of A_λ^{-1} we have now

$$(AA_\lambda^{-1}f, A_\lambda^{-1}f) = (A_\lambda^{-1}f, AA_\lambda^{-1}f),$$

$$(f + \lambda A_\lambda^{-1}f, A_\lambda^{-1}f) = (A_\lambda^{-1}f, f + \lambda A_\lambda^{-1}f),$$

$$(\lambda - \bar{\lambda}) \| A_\lambda^{-1}f \|^2 = (A_\lambda^{-1}f, f) - (f, A_\lambda^{-1}f),$$

hence

$$2 | \beta | . \| A_\lambda^{-1}f \|^2 \leqslant 2 \| A_\lambda^{-1}f \| . \| f \|,$$

or

$$\| A_\lambda^{-1}f \| \leqslant \| f \| / | \beta |.$$

This shows that $\lambda \in \rho(A)$. The spectrum of A contains therefore only real numbers.

Theorem 9. *If $A = U$ is unitary, the spectrum $\sigma(U)$ contains only numbers λ satisfying $|\lambda| = 1$. The residual spectrum is empty.*

Proof. Since U is also normal, its residual spectrum is empty. On account of $\| U \| = 1$, all λ with $|\lambda| > 1$ belong to the resolvent set $\rho(U)$. For $|\lambda| < 1$ we have

$$\| U_\lambda f \| \geqslant \| Uf \| - \| \lambda f \| = \| f \| - |\lambda| . \| f \| = (1 - |\lambda|) \| f \|.$$

This shows that U_λ^{-1} exists, and is bounded. Hence $\lambda \in \rho(U)$. The spectrum of U contains therefore only values of λ satisfying $|\lambda| = 1$.

As an illustration we consider some of the examples in § 6. For Example A we find

$$T^*\varphi_1 = 0,\ T^*\varphi_2 = \varphi_1/2,\ \ldots,\ T^*\varphi_n = \varphi_{n-1}/n,\ \ldots.$$

The point $\lambda = 0$ is the point spectrum of T^*, and all $\lambda \neq 0$ form the resolvent set.

For Example B we have $T^*\psi_n = \bar{\lambda}_n\psi_n$ $(n = 1, 2, \ldots)$; the points $\lambda = \bar{\lambda}_n$ form therefore the point spectrum of T^*, $\lambda = 1$ is the continuous spectrum, and all other values of λ form the resolvent set.

For transformations of finite double-norm on a separable Hilbert space R we have already seen in Ch. 9, § 17 that all complex numbers $\mu \neq 0$ belong either to the point spectrum or the resolvent set, that the number of different characteristic values $\mu_1, \mu_2, \ldots$ is finite or enumerably infinite, and that in the latter case $\lim \mu_n = 0$. The characteristic values of T^* are $\overline{\mu_1}, \overline{\mu_2}, \ldots$, and all other $\mu \neq 0$ belong to the resolvent set of T^*.

Considering once more the transformation T on $L_2[0, 1]$, defined by $Tf = \int_0^x f(y)dy$, we find easily $T^*f = \int_x^1 f(y)dy$. All $\lambda \neq 0$ form the resolvent set of T^*, and $\lambda = 0$ is the continuous spectrum of T^*.

EXAMPLES

1) If T is a bounded linear transformation on the complete Banach space E whose range is also contained in E, and if E has the property (Ext.), then $\lambda \in C\sigma(T^*)$ (the continuous spectrum of T^*) implies $\lambda \in C\sigma(T)$.

($\lambda \in \rho(T)$ is impossible by § 9, Th. 4, $\lambda \in R\sigma(T)$ is impossible by § 9, Th. 5, and $\lambda \in P\sigma(T)$ is impossible by § 9, Th. 6).

2) Under the same conditions $\lambda \in \rho(T^*)$ implies $\lambda \in \rho(T)$.

($\lambda \in \rho(T^*)$ implies that the domain $W(T_\lambda^*)$ of the bounded inverse $(T_\lambda^*)^{-1}$ is identical with E^*. Then, by § 3, Th. 6, 1°, T_λ has a bounded inverse T_λ^{-1}, and by § 3, Th. 1 we have $[W(T_\lambda)]^\circ = N(T_\lambda^*)$. Hence, since $N(T_\lambda^*)$ contains only the null element, we have $[W(T_\lambda)] = E$. This shows that $\lambda \in \rho(T)$).

3) Let R be a separable complete Hilbert space of infinite dimension, and let

the orthonormal system $\varphi_n (n = 1, 2, \ldots)$ be complete in R. In § 9 we have proved in an indirect way that the linear transformation T, defined by

$$T\varphi_1 = 0,\ T\varphi_2 = \varphi_1/2,\ \ldots,\ T\varphi_n = \varphi_{n-1}/n,\ \ldots,$$

has $\lambda = 0$ as its point spectrum, and the set of all $\lambda \neq 0$ as its resolvent set. A direct proof is of course possible.

(Since $T\varphi_1 = 0$, we see that $\lambda = 0$ belongs to the point spectrum of T. For $f = \Sigma_1^\infty \alpha_i \varphi_i$, $\lambda \neq 0$, we have

$$T_\lambda f = (T - \lambda I)f = \Sigma_2^\infty [\alpha_i/i]\varphi_{i-1} - \lambda\, \Sigma_1^\infty \alpha_i\varphi_i = \Sigma_1^\infty (\alpha_{i+1}/(i+1) - \lambda\alpha_i)\varphi_i,$$

from which it follows immediately that $T_\lambda f = 0$ only for $f = 0$. The inverse T_λ^{-1} exists therefore. A direct computation shows that

$$T_\lambda^{-1}\varphi_1 = -\lambda^{-1}\varphi_1,\ T_\lambda^{-1}\varphi_2 = (-\lambda^{-2}/2!)(\varphi_1 + 2!\lambda\varphi_2),\ \ldots,$$

generally

$$T_\lambda^{-1}\varphi_n = (-\lambda^{-n}/n!)(\Sigma_{k=1}^n k!\lambda^{k-1}\varphi_k),$$

so that the domain of T_λ^{-1} is dense in R. Since $\| T \| = 1/2$, all λ satisfying $|\lambda| > 1/2$ are in the resolvent set of T. If $n^{-1} \geqslant |\lambda| > (n+1)^{-1}$ for a certain n $(n = 2, 3, \ldots)$, we split up $f = \Sigma_1^\infty \alpha_i\varphi_i$ into $\Sigma_1^n + \Sigma_{n+1}^\infty = f' + f''$, and we write $g = T_\lambda f = T_\lambda f' + T_\lambda f'' = g' + g''$. Then

$$g' = T_\lambda f' = \Sigma_1^{n-1}(\alpha_{i+1}/(i+1) - \lambda\alpha_i)\varphi_i - \lambda\alpha_n\varphi_n,$$

hence $\| g' \|^2 = |\lambda\alpha_n|^2 + \Sigma_1^{n-1} |\lambda\alpha_i - \alpha_{i+1}/(i+1)|^2$, whereas $\| g \|^2 = \Sigma_1^\infty |\lambda\alpha_i - \alpha_{i+1}/(i+1)|^2$. Now

$$|\lambda\alpha_n| \leqslant |\lambda\alpha_n - \alpha_{n+1}/(n+1)| + \frac{1}{|\lambda|(n+1)} |\lambda\alpha_{n+1}| \leqslant \ldots$$

$$\leqslant |\lambda\alpha_n - \alpha_{n+1}/(n+1)| + \frac{1}{|\lambda|(n+1)} |\lambda\alpha_{n+1} - \alpha_{n+2}/(n+2)|$$

$$+ \frac{1}{|\lambda|^2(n+1)(n+2)} |\lambda\alpha_{n+2} - \alpha_{n+3}/(n+3)| + \ldots$$

$$+ \frac{1}{|\lambda|^p(n+1)(n+2)\ldots(n+p)} |\lambda\alpha_{n+p}|$$

for any arbitrary positive integer p. Since

$$1 + \Sigma_{p=1}^\infty [|\lambda|^{2p}(n+1)^2(n+2)^2 \ldots (n+p)^2]^{-1} = A_\lambda^2 < \infty,$$

we find by Schwarz's inequality

$$|\lambda\alpha_n|^2 \leqslant A_\lambda^2\, \Sigma_n^\infty |\lambda\alpha_i - \alpha_{i+1}/(i+1)|^2,$$

which implies $\| g' \| \leqslant A_\lambda \| g \|$, hence also $\| g'' \| \leqslant (A_\lambda + 1)\| g \|$. The rest of the argument is similar to that in § 6, Ex. A, and we conclude that all $\lambda \neq 0$ belong to the resolvent set of T).

4) Let Δ be the linear interval $[0, 1]$, and let $C(\Delta)$ be the Banach space of all continuous functions $f(x)$, defined on Δ, with $\| f \| = \max |f(x)|$ (cf. Ch. 6, Ex. 9). The linear transformation T on $C(\Delta)$ is defined by

$$g(x) = Tf = \int_0^x f(y)dy.$$

Then $\lambda = 0$ forms the residual spectrum of T, and all $\lambda \neq 0$ form the resolvent set.

(As in the example in § 9, Th. 2, Remark, we have $Tf = \int_\Delta T_1(x, y)f(y)dy$ with $T_1(x, y) = 1$ for $x \geqslant y$ and $T_1(x, y) = 0$ for $x < y$. Also $T^n f = \int_\Delta T_n(x, y)f(y)dy$ with $T_n(x, y) = (x - y)^{n-1}/(n - 1)!$ for $x \leqslant y$ and $T_n(x, y) = 0$ for $x > y$. Hence $\| T \| = 1$ and $\| T^n \| \leqslant 1/(n - 1)!$ The series

$$- \lambda^{-1}I - \lambda^{-2}T - \lambda^{-3}T^2 - \ldots$$

converges therefore uniformly for $\lambda \neq 0$, and we easily find that its sum is R_λ. All $\lambda \neq 0$ belong therefore to the resolvent set of T. Since $Tf = 0$ only for $f = 0$, the inverse T^{-1} exists. Since $g(x) = Tf$ vanishes at $x = 0$ for all f, we have $\| f_0 - Tf \| \geqslant 1$ for $f_0(x) \equiv 1$ and all $f \in C(\Delta)$. The range of T is therefore not dense in $C(\Delta)$. This shows that $\lambda = 0$ forms the residual spectrum of T).

5) Let $\lambda_n (n = 1, 2, \ldots)$ be the sequence of all rational complex numbers in $| \lambda | \leqslant 1$ (in some specified order), and let $\varphi_n (n = 1, 2, \ldots)$ be orthonormal and complete in the complete Hilbert space R of enumerably infinite dimension. The linear transformation T is defined by $T\varphi_n = \lambda_n \varphi_n$ $(n = 1, 2, \ldots)$. Then the set of all λ_n is the point spectrum of T, the set of all λ satisfying $| \lambda | > 1$ is the resolvent set, and all irrational λ in $| \lambda | \leqslant 1$ form the continuous spectrum. The same statement holds for T^*.

6) Let Δ be the interval $0 \leqslant x < \infty$, and let $C_0(\Delta)$ be the set of all functions $f(x)$, continuous at all $x \in \Delta$, and such that $\lim f(x)$ exists as a finite number for $x \to \infty$. Then, with the obvious definitions for addition and multiplication by complex numbers, and taking $\| f \| =$ upper bound $| f(x) |$ in $0 \leqslant x < \infty$, $C_0(\Delta)$ is a Banach space, and the system $e^{-nx} (n = 0, 1, 2, \ldots)$ is complete in $C_0(\Delta)$.

(The last statement is derived from the completeness of the system x^n $(n = 0, 1, 2, \ldots)$ in $C[0, 1]$).

7) The linear transformation T on the Banach space $C_0[0, \infty]$ is defined by $Tf(x) = f(x + 1)$. Then the set of all λ for which $| \lambda | < 1$, together with $\lambda = 1$, forms the point spectrum of T; all other λ with $| \lambda | = 1$ form the continuous spectrum, and all λ with $| \lambda | > 1$ form the resolvent set of T.

(Evidently $\| T \| = 1$, so that all λ satisfying $| \lambda | > 1$ belong to the resolvent set. If $0 < | \lambda | < 1$, we write $\lambda = re^{i\varphi}$ $(0 < r < 1, \varphi$ real). Then $f(x) = e^{x(\log r + i\varphi)}$ satisfies the equation $Tf = \lambda f$. If $\lambda = 0$, every $f(x) \in C_0[0, \infty]$, vanishing for $x \geqslant 1$, satisfies $Tf = \lambda f = 0$. If $\lambda = 1$, $f(x) = 1$ satisfies $Tf = \lambda f = f$. Hence all λ satisfying $| \lambda | < 1$, together with $\lambda = 1$, belong to the point spectrum of T. For $\lambda = e^{i\varphi}$ $(0 < \varphi < 2\pi)$, we have

$$(T - \lambda I)e^{-nx} = (e^{-n} - \lambda)e^{-nx} \; (n = 0, 1, 2, \ldots),$$

which shows that the range of T_λ is dense in $C_0[0, \infty]$. The relation $T_\lambda f = 0$ for an element $f \neq 0$ would imply the existence of a sequence of values $f(x_0), f(x_0 + 1), f(x_0 + 2), \ldots$, all $\neq 0$, and such that $f(x_0 + p + 1) = \lambda f(x_0 + p)$ $(p = 0, 1, 2, \ldots)$, in contradiction with the existence of $\lim f(x)$ for $x \to \infty$. The inverse T_λ^{-1} exists therefore with domain dense in $C_0[0, \infty]$. Consider now a sequence of functions $f_n(x)$, all belonging to $C_0[0, \infty]$, such that $f_n(0) = 1$, $| f_n(x) | \leqslant 1$, $\lim f_n(x) = 0$ as $x \to \infty$ for all n, and $| f_n(x + 1) - f_n(x) | < n^{-1}$ for all x. Then, writing $\varphi_n(x) = f_n(x)e^{i\varphi x}$, we have $\| \varphi_n \| = 1$ and $T_\lambda \varphi_n = [f_n(x + 1) - f_n(x)]e^{i\varphi(x+1)}$, hence $\| T_\lambda \varphi_n \| < n^{-1}$. This shows that the inverse T_λ^{-1} is not bounded. It follows that the numbers λ satisfying $| \lambda | = 1, \lambda \neq 1$, form the continuous spectrum of T).

8) Let Δ be the interval $0 \leqslant x < \infty$, and let $C(\Delta)$ be the set of all functions $f(x)$, continuous at all $x \in \Delta$, and such that $f(x)$ is bounded on Δ. Then, with the obvious definitions for addition and multiplication by complex numbers, and taking $\| f \| =$ upper bound $| f(x) |$ in $0 \leqslant x < \infty$, C(Δ) is a Banach space. The linear transformation T on $C(\Delta)$ is defined by $Tf(x) = f(x+1)$. Then the set of all λ satisfying $| \lambda | \leqslant 1$ is the point spectrum of T, and all λ satisfying $| \lambda | > 1$ form the resolvent set of T. The same statements on the spectrum of T hold if the space $C(\Delta)$ is replaced by the space $L_\infty(\Delta, \mu)$, where μ is Lebesgue measure.

9) Let $f(t) \in L(\Delta, \mu)$, where Δ is the linear interval $0 \leqslant t \leqslant 1$ and μ is Lebesgue measure, and let

$$\int_\Delta f(t) t^n dt = 0 \quad (n = 0, 1, 2, \ldots).$$

Then $f(t) = 0$ almost everywhere on $0 \leqslant t \leqslant 1$.

(We first suppose that $f(t)$ is continuous. Then, if $\varepsilon > 0$ is given, there exists a polynomial $p(t)$ such that $| f(t) - p(t) | < \varepsilon$ in $0 \leqslant t \leqslant 1$. On account of $\int_\Delta f(t)\overline{p(t)}dt = 0$ we find

$$\int_\Delta | f |^2 dt = \int_\Delta f(t)[\overline{f(t)} - \overline{p(t)}]dt \leqslant \varepsilon \int_\Delta | f(t) | dt,$$

hence, since ε is arbitrary, $f(t) = 0$ in $0 \leqslant t \leqslant 1$.

Let now $f(t) \in L(\Delta)$, so that $F(t) = \int_0^t f(y)dy$ is continuous in $0 \leqslant t \leqslant 1$. Integration by parts gives, for $n = 1, 2, \ldots$,

$$n \int_\Delta F(t) t^{n-1} dt = F(1) - \int_\Delta f(t) t^n dt = 0,$$

hence, by what we have already proved, $F(t) = 0$ for all t. It follows by a well-known argument (cf. Ch. 3, § 4, Th. 3) that $f(t) = 0$ almost everywhere on Δ).

10) Let $f(x) \in L_p[0, \infty]$ $(1 \leqslant p \leqslant \infty)$, and let

$$\int_0^\infty f(x) e^{-nx} dx = 0 \quad (n = 1, 2, \ldots).$$

Then $f(x) = 0$ almost everywhere on $0 \leqslant x < \infty$.

(If $1 \leqslant p < \infty$, then $f(x) \in L_p[0, \infty]$ implies $| f(-\log t) |^p/t \in L[0, 1]$, hence certainly $f_1(t) = f(-\log t) \in L_p[0, 1]$. If $f(x) \in L_\infty[0, \infty]$, then also $f_1(t) = f(-\log t) \in L_\infty[0, 1]$. By hypothesis

$$\int_0^1 f(-\log t) t^{n-1} dt = 0 \quad (n = 1, 2, \ldots),$$

hence $f(-\log t) = 0$ for almost every t on $0 \leqslant t \leqslant 1$. This implies $f(x) = 0$ almost everywhere on $0 \leqslant x < \infty$).

11) The system $e^{-nx} (n = 1, 2, \ldots)$ is complete in the Banach space $L_p[0, \infty]$ $(1 \leqslant p < \infty)$.

(Since for $1 \leqslant p < \infty$ the space $L_p[0, \infty]$ is separable, it has the property (Ext.). The system $S = \{e^{-nx}\}$ $(n = 1, 2, \ldots)$ will therefore be complete in $L_p[0, \infty]$ if every bounded linear functional which vanishes on S is vanishing identically (cf. Ch. 7, § 6, Th. 7). Every bounded linear functional $f^*(f)$ on $L_p[0, \infty]$ has the form $f^*(f) = \int_0^\infty f^*(x) f(x) dx$, where $f^*(x) \in L_q[0, \infty]$, $1/p + 1/q = 1$, hence $1 < q \leqslant \infty$. Since however

$$\int_0^\infty f^*(x) e^{-nx} dx = 0 \quad (n = 1, 2, \ldots)$$

implies $f^*(x) = 0$ by the preceding example, our statement is proved).

12) The linear transformation T on the Banach space $L_p[0, \infty]$ $(1 \leqslant p < \infty)$ s defined by $Tf(x) = f(x+1)$. Then the set of all λ for which $| \lambda | < 1$ is the

point spectrum of T, all λ satisfying $|\lambda| = 1$ form the continuous spectrum, and all λ satisfying $|\lambda| > 1$ form the resolvent set of T.

(Evidently $\| T \| = 1$, so that all λ satisfying $|\lambda| > 1$ belong to the resolvent set. If $0 < |\lambda| < 1$, hence $\lambda = re^{i\varphi}$ with $0 < r < 1$, then $f(x) = e^{x(\log r + i\varphi)}$ satisfies $Tf = \lambda f$. If $\lambda = 0$, every $f(x) \in L_p[0, \infty]$, vanishing for $x \geqslant 1$, satisfies $Tf = \lambda f = 0$. Hence all λ satisfying $|\lambda| < 1$ belong to the point spectrum of T. For $\lambda = e^{i\varphi}$ $(0 \leqslant \varphi < 2\pi)$ we have

$$(T - \lambda I)e^{-nx} = (e^{-n} - \lambda)e^{-nx} \ (n = 1, 2, \ldots),$$

which shows that the range of T_λ is dense in $L_p[0, \infty]$. The relation $T_\lambda f = 0$ for an element $f \in L_p[0, \infty]$ implies $f(x + 1) = \lambda f(x)$ for almost every x; hence $|f(x + 1)| = |f(x)|$, so that, for every positive integer k,

$$\int_0^k |f|^p \, dx = k \int_0^1 |f|^p \, dx.$$

This is only possible for $f = 0$. The inverse T_λ^{-1} exists therefore with domain dense in $L_p[0, \infty]$. Consider now the sequence of functions $\varphi_n(x) = f_n(x)e^{i\varphi x}$, where $f_n(x) = e^{-x/n}$. Then $\| \varphi_n \|^p = n/p$ and $\| T_\lambda \varphi_n \|^p = (n/p)\,[1 - e^{-1/n}]^p$. This shows that the inverse T_λ^{-1} is not bounded. It follows that all values of λ satisfying $|\lambda| = 1$ form the continuous spectrum of T).

13) The linear transformation T^* on the Banach space $L_p[0, \infty]$ $(1 < p < \infty)$ is defined by $T^*f(x) = 0$ for $0 \leqslant x < 1$, $T^*f(x) = f(x - 1)$ for $x \geqslant 1$. Then the set of all λ satisfying $|\lambda| < 1$ is the residual spectrum of T^*, all λ satisfying $|\lambda| = 1$ form the continuous spectrum, and the set of all λ such that $|\lambda| > 1$ is the resolvent set of T^*.

(T^* is the adjoint of the transformation T from the preceding example. Also, by the reflexiveness of $L_p (1 < p < \infty)$, $T = (T^*)^*$. Since $\| T^*f \| = \| f \|$ for all f, no value of λ satisfying $|\lambda| \neq 1$ can belong to the point spectrum of T^*. Since all λ satisfying $|\lambda| < 1$ belong to the point spectrum of T, they belong therefore to the residual spectrum of T^*. The set of all λ such that $|\lambda| = 1$ is the continuous spectrum of $T = (T^*)^*$; these values of λ belong therefore to the continuous spectrum of T^*. Finally it is evident that all λ satisfying $|\lambda| > 1$ belong to the resolvent set of T^*).

REFERENCES

[1] S. Banach, Théorie des Opérations linéaires, Warsaw (1932), in particular Ch. 10.

[2] Generalisations and references in : E. Hille, Functional Analysis and Semi-groups, New York (1948), in particular Ch. 3.

Chapter 11

COMPACT LINEAR TRANSFORMATIONS

§ 1. Definition and some Simple Properties

We shall consider linear transformations T, whose domain is the Banach space E_1 (complete or not), and whose range is contained in the Banach space E_2 (complete or not).

Definition. *The linear transformation T is called compact when every bounded infinite set of elements $f \in E_1$ contains a sequence f_n such that the element $g = \lim Tf_n$ exists, and belongs to E_2.*

Theorem 1. *Every compact linear transformation T is bounded.*

Proof. Supposing that T is not bounded, there exists a sequence $f_n \in E_1$ such that $\| Tf_n \| > n \| f_n \|$. Writing $g_n = f_n/\| f_n \|$, we find then $\| g_n \| = 1$ and $\| Tg_n \| > n$, which is a contradiction since the bounded sequence g_n contains, on account of the compactness of T, a subsequence $g_i (i = n_1, n_2, \ldots)$ for which Tg_i converges. It follows that T is bounded.

Theorem 2. *If E_1 and E_2 have the property (Ext.), and T is compact, then every weakly fundamental sequence $f_n \in E_1$ has the property that $g = \lim Tf_n$ exists, and belongs to E_2.*

Proof. By hypothesis $f^*(f_n)$ is a converging sequence for every $f^* \in E_1^*$. If therefore g^* is an arbitrary element of E_2^*, the sequence $(T^*g^*)(f_n)$ converges. But $(T^*g^*)(f_n) = g^*(Tf_n)$, so that we may conclude that the sequence Tf_n is a weakly fundamental sequence in the space E_2. It follows easily that if f_n converges weakly to f_0, then Tf_n converges weakly to Tf_0.

Since T is compact and the sequence f_n is bounded (cf. Ch. 7, § 9, Th. 1), there exists a subsequence f_k $(k = n_1, n_2, \ldots)$ such that $g = \lim Tf_k$ exists, and belongs to E_2. This implies that Tf_k, and therefore the whole sequence Tf_n, converges weakly to g. We shall prove that the whole sequence Tf_n converges strongly to g. Indeed, if this were not the case, there would exist a number $\varepsilon > 0$ and a subsequence f_l such that $\| Tf_l - g \| > \varepsilon$. But, the sequence f_l being bounded, it would contain a subsequence f_m such that $\lim Tf_m = g_1$ exists. This implies that Tf_m, and therefore the whole sequence Tf_n, would converge weakly to g_1. Since however E_2 has the property (Ext.), the weak limit of Tf_n is uniquely determined (cf. Ch. 7, § 9), hence $g = g_1$, in contradiction with $\| g_1 - g \| \geqslant \varepsilon$. It follows that $g = \lim Tf_n$.

Theorem 3. *If E_1 and E_1^* have the property (Ext.), E_1 is reflexive, and T has the property that for every weakly fundamental sequence $f_n \in E_1$ the element $g = \lim Tf_n$ exists, then T is compact.*
Proof. Let $\{f\}$ be a bounded infinite set of elements of E_1. Then, by Ch. 7, § 9, Th. 5, $\{f\}$ contains a weakly converging sequence f_n. By hypothesis $g = \lim Tf_n$ exists, and this shows that T is compact.

Remark. It follows from the Theorems 2 and 3 that, if E_1, E_1^* and E_2 have the property (Ext.), and E_1 is reflexive, then T is compact if and only if every weakly fundamental sequence $f_n \in E_1$ has the property that $g = \lim Tf_n$ exists. Since the reflexivity of E_1 implies the existence of the weak limit f_0 of the sequence f_n (cf. Ch. 7, § 9, Th. 2), we may say also that T is compact if and only if every sequence f_n, converging weakly to f_0, has the property that Tf_n converges strongly to Tf_0.

Theorem 4. *Every linear transformation T, whose domain is a Banach space E_1 of finite dimension, is compact.*
Proof. By Ch. 7, § 12, Th. 3 the linear transformation T is bounded. Furthermore, if the set $\{f\}$ of elements $f \in E_1$ is bounded, it contains a sequence f_n converging to an element f_0 (cf. Ch. 6, § 4, Th. 3). It follows that Tf_n converges to $g = Tf_0$.

Theorem 5. *Every bounded linear transformation T, whose range is contained in a Banach space E_2 of finite dimension, is compact.*
Proof. If the set $\{f\}$ of elements $f \in E_1$ is bounded, the same is true of the set $\{Tf\}$ of elements $Tf \in E_2$. It follows that $\{Tf\}$ contains a sequence Tf_n converging to an element g.

Remark. As an example we may consider the bounded linear transformation T on the arbitrary Banach space E_1, defined by $Tf = \Sigma_{i=1}^n f_i^*(f) f_i$, where $f_1, \ldots, f_n$ are n fixed elements of E_1 and $f_1^*, \ldots, f_n^*$ are n fixed elements of E_1^*.

We now come to a small interlude on metric spaces (cf. Ch. 7, § 10).

Definition. *If X is a subset of the metric space Z, the set X is called compact (sometimes it is called conditionally compact) when every infinite subset of X contains a fundamental sequence. The set X is called completely bounded when, for every $\delta > 0$, X may be considered as the sum of a finite number of sets with diameter not exceeding δ.*

Lemma α. *A subset X of the metric space Z is compact if and only if it is completely bounded.*

Proof. We suppose first that X is compact. If $\delta > 0$ is given, and $f_1 \in X$ is arbitrary, we choose $f_2 \in X$ (if possible) such that the distance $d(f_1, f_2)$ satisfies $d(f_1, f_2) \geqslant \delta/2$. We next choose $f_3 \in X$ (if possible) such that $d(f_1, f_3) \geqslant \delta/2$, $d(f_2, f_3) \geqslant \delta/2$, and so on. This process breaks off after a finite number of steps, since in the opposite case the sequence $f_n (n = 1, 2, \ldots)$ would not contain a fundamental sequence. Let therefore $f_1, \ldots, f_n$ be the sequence which we find in this way. Then, if $f \in X$ is arbitrary, there exists at least one f_k $(1 \leqslant k \leqslant n)$ such that $d(f, f_k) < \delta/2$. If now X_k $(k = 1, \ldots, n)$ is the set of all $f \in X$ satisfying $d(f, f_k) < \delta/2$, the diameter of X_k does not exceed δ, and $X = \Sigma_{k=1}^{n} X_k$.

Let now conversely X be completely bounded, so that, if $\delta > 0$ is given, there exist sets $X_1, \ldots, X_n$ with diameter $\leqslant \delta$ (where n depends of course on δ) such that $X = \Sigma_{k=1}^{n} X_k$. If, moreover, the sequence $f_n (n = 1, 2, \ldots)$ of elements belonging to X is given, one at least of the sets X_k contains an infinity of elements f_n. This shows that there exists a subsequence $f_{11}, f_{12}, \ldots$ with diameter not exceeding δ. In the same way we find that $f_{11}, f_{12}, \ldots$ contains a subsequence $f_{21}, f_{22}, \ldots$ with diameter not exceeding $\delta/2$, and so on. The diagonal sequence $f_{11}, f_{22}, \ldots$ is then a fundamental sequence.

Lemma β. *If the subset X of the metric space Z is compact, then it is separable.*

Proof. By the preceding lemma we have $X = \Sigma_{k=1}^{n_1} X_{1k}$, where the diameter of each of the sets X_{1k} does not exceed a preassigned $\delta > 0$. In each of the X_{1k} we choose an element f_{1k}. In the same way $X = \Sigma_{k=1}^{n_2} X_{2k}$, where every X_{2k} has a diameter not exceeding $\delta/2$. In each of the sets X_{2k} we choose an element f_{2k}. Proceeding in this way, the sequence of all f_{ik} is dense in X.

We return to compact linear transformations.

Theorem 6. *If T is a compact linear transformation, the range $W(T)$ is separable.*

Proof. The set $X_n \subset E_2$ of all Tf satisfying $\| f \| \leqslant n$ (n a positive integer) is compact by hypothesis, hence separable by Lemma β. The same is therefore true of $W(T) = \Sigma_{n=1}^{\infty} X_n$.

Theorem 7. *If the space E_2 is complete, and T_n ($n = 1, 2, \ldots$) is a sequence of compact linear transformations which converges uniformly to T, then T is compact.*

Proof. Let $f_n (n = 1, 2, \ldots)$ be an arbitrary bounded sequence in E_1. Then it contains a subsequence $f_{11}, f_{12}, \ldots$ such that $T_1(f_{1n})$ converges; the sequence $f_{11}, f_{12}, \ldots$ contains a subsequence $f_{21}, f_{22}, \ldots$ such that $T_2(f_{2n})$ converges, and so on. Then $T_n(f_{11}), T_n(f_{22}), T_n(f_{33}), \ldots$ converges for $n = 1, 2, \ldots$. It follows that

$$\| T(f_{pp}) - T(f_{qq}) \| \leqslant$$

$$\| T(f_{pp}) - T_n(f_{pp}) \| + \| T_n(f_{pp}) - T_n(f_{qq}) \| + \| T_n(f_{qq}) - T(f_{qq}) \|$$

$$\leqslant \| T - T_n \| (\| f_{pp} \| + \| f_{qq} \|) + \|T_n(f_{pp}) - T_n(f_{qq}) \|,$$

which shows that $T(f_{11}), T(f_{22}), T(f_{33}), \ldots$ is a fundamental sequence. Since E_2 is complete, $g = \lim T(f_{pp})$ exists. The transformation T is therefore compact.

Theorem 8. *If T is compact, then T^* is compact, that is, if $g_n^* \in E_2^*$ is a bounded sequence, there exists a subsequence g_k^* ($k = n_1, n_2, \ldots$) and an element $f^* \in E_1^*$ such that $f^* = \lim T^* g_k^*$* [1].

Proof. Let $\| g_n^* \| \leqslant M$. Since the range $W(T)$ of T is separable by Theorem 6, there exists a sequence g_n which is dense in $W(T)$. Hence, on account of $\| g_n^* \| \leqslant M$, there exists a subsequence $g_{11}^*, g_{12}^*, \ldots$ such that $g_{11}^*(g_1), g_{12}^*(g_1), \ldots$ converges. This subsequence contains a second subsequence $g_{21}^*, g_{22}^*, \ldots$ such that $g_{21}^*(g_2), g_{22}^*(g_2), \ldots$ converges, and so on. Then the diagonal sequence $g_{11}^*, g_{22}^*, \ldots$ has the property that $g_{11}^*(g_n), g_{22}^*(g_n), \ldots$ converges for $n = 1, 2, \ldots$, and it is easily seen that $g_{11}^*(g), g_{22}^*(g), \ldots$ even converges for every $g \in W(T)$. Writing $f_k^* = T^* g_{kk}^*$ ($k = 1, 2, \ldots$), the sequence $f_k^*(f) = (T^* g_{kk}^*)(f) = g_{kk}^*(Tf)$ converges therefore for every $f \in E_1$. Let $f^*(f) = \lim f_k^*(f)$. Our theorem will be proved if we show that $\lim \| f^* - T^* g_{kk}^* \| = \lim \| f^* - f_k^* \| = 0$. Let us suppose that this is not true. Then it is no restriction of the generality to suppose that $\| f^* - f_k^* \| > \eta$ for all k and a certain $\eta > 0$. If $f_k \in E_1$ is such that $\| f_k \| = 1$ and $| f^*(f_k) - f_k^*(f_k) | \geqslant \| f^* - f_k^* \|/2$, we have therefore

$$(1) \qquad |\, g_{kk}^*(Tf_k) - \lim_{p\to\infty} g_{pp}^*(Tf_k) \,| \geqslant \eta/2$$

for all k. Since $\| f_k \| = 1$, there exists a subsequence f_l $(l = k_1, k_2, \ldots)$ such that $g_0 = \lim Tf_l$ exists. Then $g_0 \in [W(T)]$, and it easily follows that $g_{11}^*(g_0), g_{22}^*(g_0), \ldots$ converges. If therefore $\varepsilon > 0$ is given, there exists an index N such that, for $l > N$, we have $\| g_0 - Tf_l \| < \varepsilon$ and $|\, g_{ll}^*(g_0) - \lim_{p\to\infty} g_{pp}^*(g_0) \,| < \varepsilon$. Hence, for $l > N$,

$$|\, g_{ll}^*(Tf_l) - \lim_{p\to\infty} g_{pp}^*(Tf_l) \,| \leqslant$$
$$|\, g_{ll}^*(Tf_l - g_0) \,| + |\, g_{ll}^*(g_0) - \lim_{p\to\infty} g_{pp}^*(g_0) \,| + |\, \lim_{p\to\infty} g_{pp}^*(Tf_l - g_0) \,|$$
$$\leqslant M\varepsilon + \varepsilon + M\varepsilon,$$

in contradiction with (1). It follows that $\lim \| f^* - T^* g_{kk}^* \| = \lim \| f^* - f_k^* \| = 0$.

Remark. If T is a compact linear transformation on the complete Hilbert space R, which has its range in R as well, the present theorem states that the Banach-adjoint T_B^* is compact. Then, obviously, the Hilbert-adjoint T_H^* is also compact.

Theorem 9. *If the space E_2 is complete and has the property (Ext.), and if T^* is compact, then T is compact* [2].

Proof. If $f \in E_1$ is given, the element $f^{**} \in E_1^{**}$ is defined by $f^{**}(f^*) = f^*(f)$ for all $f^* \in E_1^*$. Then, by Ch. 7, § 8, Th. 1, $\| f^{**} \| \leqslant \| f \|$. If therefore the sequence $f_n \in E_1$ satisfies $\| f_n \| \leqslant M (n = 1, 2, \ldots)$, the corresponding sequence f_n^{**} also satisfies $\| f_n^{**} \| \leqslant M$. Now, since T^* is compact, the same holds for T^{**} by the preceding theorem, so that $g_n^{**} = T^{**} f_n^{**}$ contains a converging subsequence $g_k^{**} (k = n_1, n_2, \ldots)$. Furthermore, if $g^* \in E_2^*$ is arbitrary,

$$g_n^{**}(g^*) = (T^{**} f_n^{**})(g^*) = f_n^{**}(T^* g^*) = (T^* g^*)(f_n) = g^*(Tf_n),$$

so that, since E_2 has the property (Ext.), $\| g_p^{**} - g_q^{**} \| = \| Tf_p - Tf_q \|$ (cf. Ch. 7, § 8, Th. 1). It follows that the sequence $Tf_k (k = n_1, n_2, \ldots)$ converges, and, since E_2 is complete, the element $g = \lim Tf_k$ exists.

Theorem 10. *If T_1 and T_2 are compact, and α, β are arbitrarily complex, then $\alpha T_1 + \beta T_2$ is compact. In particular the null transformation is compact.*

If the spaces E_1 and E_2 are identical, if T_1 is bounded and T_2 is compact, then $T_1 T_2$ and $T_2 T_1$ are compact. If $E_1 = E_2$ is of infinite dimension, *the identical transformation I is not compact. More generally, if P is the projection on E' along E'', where E' is of infinite dimension, then P is not compact.*

Proof. All statements, except the last one, are immediately evident. The last statement follows from Ch. 6, § 4, Th. 7.

Theorem 11. *If E_1 is of infinite dimension and T is an isometric linear transformation, that is, if $\| Tf \| = \| f \|$ for all $f \in E_1$, then T is not compact. In particular, if U is a unitary transformation on a complete Hilbert space, then U is not compact.*

Proof. By Ch. 6, § 4, Th. 7 the space E_1 contains an infinite sequence $g_n (n = 1, 2, \dots)$ such that $\| g_n \| = 1$ and $\| g_m - g_n \| \geqslant 1/2$ for $m \neq n$. If the linear transformation T is isometric, we have therefore $\| Tg_m - Tg_n \| \geqslant 1/2$, and this shows that the sequence Tg_n $(n = 1, 2, \dots)$ contains no converging subsequence.

For our next theorem we assume that the n^2 linear transformations $T_{ij} (i, j = 1, \dots, n)$ all have the Banach space E as their domain, and that their ranges are contained in the same space E. Then, by $g^i = \Sigma_{j=1}^n T_{ij} f^j$ $(i = 1, \dots, n)$, the linear transformation $\{g\} = T\{f\}$ with matrix $\{T_{ij}\}$ is defined on the productspace E^n, and its range is contained in the same space E^n (cf. Ch. 7, § 14, Th. 9, 10, 11). As in our former discussions on the same subject we suppose that E^n may be considered as the direct sum of the n spaces E.

Theorem 12. *T is compact if and only if all T_{ij} are compact.*

Proof. Let first all $T_{ij} (i, j = 1, \dots, n)$ be compact. Let, furthermore, $\{f\}$ be an infinite set of elements in E^n such that $\| \{f\} \| \leqslant M$ for all $\{f\}$ of this set. We observe that there exists a fixed positive A such that, if $\{f\} = \{f^1, \dots, f^n\}$ is an arbitrary element of E^n, we have $\| f^i \| \leqslant A \| \{f\} \|$ (cf. Ch. 6, § 15). It follows that the set $\{f\}$ contains a sequence $\{f_k\}$ $(k = 1, 2, \dots)$ such that $T_{11} f_k^1$ converges to an element $g^{11} \in E$; the sequence $\{f_k\}$ in its turn contains a subsequence $\{f_m\}$ $(m = k_1, k_2, \dots)$ such that $T_{12} f_m^2$ converges to an element $g^{12} \in E$, and so on. In this way we obtain a subsequence $\{f_r\}$ such that $\lim_{r \to \infty} T_{ij} f_r^j = g^{ij}$ $(i, j = 1, \dots, n)$. Writing $\Sigma_{j=1}^n g^{ij} = g^i$ and $\{g\} = \{g^1, \dots, g^n\}$, we have $\lim_{r \to \infty} T\{f_r\} = \{g\}$, which shows that T is compact.

Let now, conversely, T be compact. Let, furthermore, the infinite set of elements $f \in E$ be given, where $\| f \| \leqslant M$ for all f in this set. Defining, for a fixed j, the corresponding set of elements $\{f\} = \{f^1, \ldots, f^n\} \in E^n$ by $f^j = f$ and $f_k = 0$ for $k \neq j$, we have $\| \{f\} \| \leqslant \Sigma_{i=1}^n \| f^i \| = \| f \| \leqslant M$ for all $\{f\}$. The set $\{f\}$ contains therefore a sequence $\{f_r\}$ such that $\{g_r\} = T\{f_r\}$ converges to an element $\{g\} = \{g^1, \ldots, g^n\} \in E^n$. Then $g^i = \lim_{r\to\infty} T_{ij} f_r^j = \lim_{r\to\infty} T_{ij} f_r$, which shows that T_{ij} is compact.

In our last theorem we shall suppose that both E_1 and E_2 are identical with the same Hilbert space R.

Theorem 13. *If A is a bounded normal transformation on the complete Hilbert space R, and if there exists an integer $p > 1$ such that A^p is compact, then A itself is compact.*

Proof. We first consider the case that A is self-adjoint. Then, if $f \in R$ is arbitrary and n is an integer $\geqslant 1$, we have

$$(2) \qquad \begin{cases} \| A^n f \|^2 = (A^n f, A^n f) = (A^{2n} f, f) \leqslant \| A^{2n} f \| . \| f \|, \\ \| A^n f \|^2 = (A^n f, A^n f) = (A^{2n-1} f, Af) \leqslant \| A^{2n-1} f \| . \| Af \|. \end{cases}$$

Now, since A^p is compact, every set of elements f, satisfying $\| f \| \leqslant M$, contains a sequence f_k for which

$$(3) \qquad \lim A^p(f_k - f_l) = 0$$

as $k, l \to \infty$. We have $\| f_k - f_l \| \leqslant 2M$ and $\| A(f_k - f_l) \| \leqslant 2M \| A \|$; hence, by (2),

$$\begin{cases} \| A^n(f_k - f_l) \|^2 \leqslant 2M \| A^{2n}(f_k - f_l) \|, \\ \| A^n(f_k - f_l) \|^2 \leqslant 2M \| A \| . \| A^{2n-1}(f_k - f_l) \|, \end{cases}$$

which shows that if either $\lim A^{2n}(f_k - f_l) = 0$ or $\lim A^{2n-1}(f_k - f_l) = 0$, then $\lim A^n(f_k - f_l) = 0$. Applying this argument to (3), we conclude that either $\lim A^{p/2}(f_k - f_l) = 0$ or $\lim A^{(p+1)/2}(f_k - f_l) = 0$, according as p is even or odd. Repeating the argument, we arrive in a finite number of steps at $\lim A(f_k - f_l) = 0$; and this shows that A is compact.

Let now A be normal. Then, since $(A^*A)^p = (A^*)^p A^p$ by the permutability of A and A^*, our hypothesis implies that $(A^*A)^p$ is compact. The transformation A^*A being positive, we have $(A^*A)^p = H^{2p}$, where $H = (A^*A)^{1/2}$. The first part of our proof shows now that H is compact. By Ch. 9, § 14, Th. 6, we have $A = UH$ with unitary U. It follows that A is compact.

§ 2. Examples

We shall investigate some of the examples, discussed already before, upon compactness.

Example A. *Multiplication by a bounded function.*

Let $\Phi(u)$ and $\Psi(v)$ be complementary in the sense of Young, and let Δ be an arbitrary μ-measurable set. Then, if $t(x) \in L_\infty(\Delta, \mu)$, that is, if $| t(x) | \leqslant A$ almost everywhere on Δ, where A does not depend on x, we have proved in Ch. 7, § 15, Ex. A that the linear transformation T, defined by $Tf = t(x)f(x)$, is bounded on $L_\Phi(\Delta, \mu)$, and has its range in $L_\Phi(\Delta, \mu)$. Furthermore $T = O$ (the null transformation) if and only if $t(x) = 0$ almost everywhere on Δ. Obviously we have $T^n f = t^n(x)f(x)$ for $n = 1, 2, \ldots$.

We shall prove now that, if $t(x) \neq 0$ on a set of positive measure, and the measure μ is non-atomic (cf. Ch. 6, § 6, Ex. A), neither T nor any of its iterates $T^n (n = 2, 3, \ldots)$ is compact. For this purpose we observe that, given the positive integer n, there exists a number $\varepsilon > 0$ and a set Δ_1 of positive measure such that $| t^n(x) | \geqslant \varepsilon$ for $x \in \Delta_1$. Writing now $\Delta_1 = \Sigma_{i=1}^\infty E_i$, where all sets E_i are of finite positive measure and without common points, and defining the function $f_i(x)$ to have a constant value $\neq 0$ on E_i, and to have the value zero elsewhere, and such that $\| f_i \|_\Phi = 1$, we see that $t^n(x)f_i(x) \neq 0$ on E_i and $t^n(x)f_i(x) = 0$ elsewhere on Δ. Hence, for $i \neq j$, and for an arbitrary $g(x) \in L_\Psi$,

$$\int_\Delta | t^n(x)\{f_i(x) - f_j(x)\} g(x) | \, dx \geqslant \int_{E_i} | t^n(x)\{f_i(x) - f_j(x)\}g(x) | \, dx$$
$$= \int_{E_i} | t^n(x) | . | f_i(x)g(x) | \, dx \geqslant \varepsilon \int_\Delta | f_i(x)g(x) | \, dx,$$

which implies $\| T^n f_i - T^n f_j \|_\Phi \geqslant \varepsilon \| f_i \|_\Phi = \varepsilon$. This shows that T^n is not compact, since the bounded sequence f_i $(i = 1, 2, \ldots)$ contains no subsequence f_k for which $T^n f_k$ converges.

In Ch. 9, § 6, Th. 1 we have proved that, if $t_{ij}(x) \in L_\infty$ $(i, j = 1, \ldots, n)$, the linear transformation $\{g\} = T\{f\}$, defined by $g^i(x) = \Sigma_{j=1}^n t_{ij}(x)f^j(x)$ $(i = 1, \ldots, n)$, is bounded on L_Φ^n into L_Φ^n. Furthermore $T = O$ if and only if all $t_{ij}(x) = 0$ almost everywhere on Δ. If therefore one at least of the $t_{ij}(x) \neq 0$ on a set of positive measure, it follows from § 1, Th. 12 and from what we have just proved that T is not compact.

Example B. *A bounded integral transformation which has the property hat neither the transformation itself nor any of its iterates is compact.*

In Ch. 7, § 15, Ex. C and in Ch. 9, § 9, Ex. A we have seen that in the Hilbert space $L_2[0, 1]$ there exists an integral transformation P with kernel $P(x, y)$ such that the linear transformation P, defined by $Pf = \int_0^1 P(x, y)f(y)dy$, is an orthogonal projection on a subspace of infinite dimension. Since, by § 1, Th. 10, this transformation P is not compact, and since $P = P^n (n = 1, 2, \ldots)$, P has the mentioned property.

Example C. *A bounded integral transformation T which has the property that T^q is not compact for $1 \leqslant q < p$, where p is a prescribed positive integer, whereas T^q is compact for $q \geqslant p$.*

In Ch. 9, § 9, Ex. B we have seen that in the Hilbert space $L_2[0, 1]$ there exists a bounded integral transformation T with kernel $T(x, y)$ such that, for a prescribed positive integer p, $T^p = O$ (the null transformation), whereas $T^q \neq O$ for $1 \leqslant q < p$. In the definition of T we had to do with a certain orthonormal system $\varphi_n(x)$ $(n = 1, 2, \ldots)$, and then we wrote

$$T\varphi_1 = \ldots = T\varphi_p = 0,$$
$$T\varphi_{p+1} = \varphi_p, T\varphi_{p+2} = \varphi_{p+1}, \ldots, T\varphi_{2p-1} = \varphi_{2p-2}, T\varphi_{2p} = 0,$$
$$T\varphi_{2p+1} = \varphi_{2p}, T\varphi_{2p+2} = \varphi_{2p+1}, \ldots, T\varphi_{3p-1} = \varphi_{3p-2}, T\varphi_{3p} = 0,$$

and so on. Obviously, since T transforms the orthonormal system $\{\varphi_{2p-1}, \varphi_{3p-1}, \ldots\}$ into the orthonormal system $\{\varphi_{2p-2}, \varphi_{3p-2}, \ldots\}$, T is not compact. In the same way, since $T^q (1 \leqslant q < p)$ transforms $\{\varphi_{2p-1}, \varphi_{3p-1}, \ldots\}$ into $\{\varphi_{2p-1-q}, \varphi_{3p-1-q}, \ldots\}$, T^q is not compact. On the other hand, since $T^q = O$ for $q \geqslant p$, all transformations $T^q (q \geqslant p)$ are compact.

If we consider the transformation $S + T$, also mentioned in Ch. 9, § 9, Ex. B, and we choose the kernel $S(x, y)$ of S in such a way that S is compact and $S^q \neq O$ for all q (it is easily seen that, if S is self-adjoint and $\neq O$, then $S^q \neq O$ for all q; if therefore S is of finite double-norm, the next example shows that S satisfies the mentioned conditions), then $(S + T)^q$ is not compact for $1 \leqslant q < p$, whereas for $q \geqslant p$ the transformation $(S + T)^q$ is compact and $\neq O$.

Example D. *Integral transformations of finite double-norm.*

Let $T(x, y)$ be $\mu \times \mu$-measurable on $\Delta \times \Delta$, where Δ is an arbitrary μ-measurable set. Then, if $\Phi(u)$ and $\Psi(v)$ are complementary in the sense of Young, and $T(x, y) \in L_\Psi(\Delta, \mu)$ for almost every $x \in \Delta$, while moreover $t(x) = \| T(x, y) \|_\Psi \in L_\Phi(\Delta, \mu)$, the linear transformation T, defined by $g(x) = Tf = \int_\Delta T(x, y)f(y)d\mu$, is bounded on $L_\Phi(\Delta, \mu)$, and its range is contained in $L_\Phi(\Delta, \mu)$. In Ch. 7, § 15, Ex. B we have proved this statement, and we have called the number $||| T ||| = \| t(x) \|_\Phi = \| \| T(x, y) \|_\Psi \|_\Phi$ the double-norm of T.

We shall prove now, under the additional conditions that there exists a positive number M such that $\Phi(2u) \leqslant M\Phi(u)$, $\Psi(2v) \leqslant M\Psi(v)$ for all $u, v \geqslant 0$ and that μ is separable, that T is compact [3]. For this purpose we observe that, by Ch. 7, § 9, Th. 7, every set $\{f(x)\}$ of functions, satisfying $\| f \|_\Phi \leqslant A$ for a fixed A and all $f \in \{f\}$, contains a sequence $f_n(x)$ such that there exists a function $f_0(x) \in L_\Phi$ satisfying

$$\lim \int_\Delta f_n(y)h(y)d\mu = \int_\Delta f_0(y)h(y)d\mu$$

for every $h(y) \in L_\Psi$. Since $T(x, y) \in L_\Psi$ for almost every value of x, we may take $h(y) = T(x, y)$ for these values, hence

$$\lim g_n(x) = \lim \int_\Delta T(x, y)f_n(y)d\mu = \int_\Delta T(x, y)f_0(y)d\mu = g_0(x)$$

or $\lim \{g_n(x) - g_0(x)\} = 0$ almost everywhere on Δ. This implies, since $\Phi(u)$ is continuous, that also

(1) $$\lim \Phi \mid g_n(x) - g_0(x) \mid = 0$$

almost everywhere on Δ. Furthermore

$$\mid g_n(x) - g_0(x) \mid \leqslant \| f_n - f_0 \|_\Phi \| T(x, y) \|_\Psi \leqslant A_1 t(x),$$

where $A_1 = A + \| f_0 \|_\Phi$, so that, since $A_1 t(x) \in L_\Phi$,

(2) $$\Phi \mid g_n(x) - g_0(x) \mid \leqslant \Phi \mid A_1 t(x) \mid,$$

where $\Phi \mid A_1 t(x) \mid$ is summable over Δ. We have used here that any function $p(x) \in L_\Phi$ has, on account of $\Phi(2u) \leqslant M\Phi(u)$, the property that $\Phi \mid p(x) \mid$ is summable over Δ. From (1) and (2) follows now, by Lebesgue's well-known theorem (cf. Ch. 3, § 4, Th. 4 and Ch. 3, § 5, Th. 1),

$$\lim \int_\Delta \Phi \mid g_n - g_0 \mid dx = 0,$$

or, by Ch. 5, § 7, Lemma α,

$$\lim \| g_n - g_0 \|_\Phi = 0.$$

This shows that $\lim Tf_n = \lim g_n = g_0$, so that T is compact.

As a particular case we immediately obtain the result [4] that, if $1 < p < \infty$, $1/p + 1/q = 1$, and $\int_\Delta (\int_\Delta \mid T(x, y) \mid^q d\mu)^{p/q} d\mu < \infty$, the transformation T is compact on $L_p(\Delta, \mu)$ into $L_p(\Delta, \mu)$.

We shall also pay attention to the limitcases $p = \infty$ and $p = 1$ which are not covered by the general result, since for $p = \infty$ the function $\Phi(u)$ does not satisfy $\Phi(2u) \leqslant M\Phi(u)$ for all $u \geqslant 0$, whereas for $p = 1$ it is $\Psi(v)$ which fails to satisfy $\Psi(2v) \leqslant M\Psi(v)$ for all $v \geqslant 0$.

For $p = \infty$ the linear integral transformation T is of finite double-norm on $L_\infty(\Delta, \mu)$ when there exists a finite positive constant A such that $\int_\Delta |T(x, y)| d\mu \leqslant A$ for almost every $x \in \Delta$. An example with Lebesgue measure on the interval $\Delta = [0, 1]$ is furnished by

$$T(x, y) = x^{-1} \text{ for } 0 \leqslant y \leqslant x,$$

$$T(x, y) = 0 \quad \text{for } x < y \leqslant 1.$$

Then $\int_\Delta | T(x, y) | dy = \int_0^x x^{-1} dy = 1$ for all x in $0 < x \leqslant 1$. If now $\mu \geqslant 1$, the function $f(x) = x^{\mu-1}$ belongs to $L_\infty(\Delta)$, and

$$Tf = \int_\Delta T(x, y) f(y) dy = \int_0^x x^{-1} y^{\mu-1} dy = \mu^{-1} x^{\mu-1} = \mu^{-1} f.$$

This shows that all values $\lambda = \mu^{-1} (0 < \lambda \leqslant 1)$ are characteristic values of T. Since $Tf = \lambda f$ implies $T^n f = \lambda^n f$ $(n = 1, 2, \ldots)$, the transformation T^n has also all numbers between 0 and 1 as characteristic values. Now, as we shall soon see (§ 3, Th. 5), a compact linear transformation has at most an enumerable infinity of characteristic values. We may conclude therefore that neither T nor any of its iterates is compact on $L_\infty(\Delta)$, although T is of finite double-norm on $L_\infty(\Delta)$.

The case $p = 1$ will receive a separate treatment in the next example.

We return to the general case that T (with kernel $T(x, y)$) is of finite double-norm on $L_\Phi(\Delta, \mu)$, where $\Phi(u)$ and its complementary function $\Psi(v)$ satisfy $\Phi(2u) \leqslant M\Phi(u)$, $\Psi(2v) \leqslant M\Psi(v)$ for all $u, v \geqslant 0$. Then, as we have seen in Ch. 7, § 15, Ex. B, if the element $g^* \in (L_\Phi)^*$ is represented by the function $g^*(x) \in L_\Psi(\Delta, \mu)$ and $f^* = T^* g^*$ (where T^* is the Banach adjoint of T), the element $f^* \in (L_\Phi)^*$ is represented by $f^*(x) = \int_\Delta T(y, x) g^*(y) d\mu$. Although the transformations $f^* = T^* g^*$ $(f^*, g^* \in (L_\Phi)^*)$ and $f^*(x) = \int_\Delta T(y, x) g^*(y) d\mu$ $(f^*(x), g^*(x) \in L_\Psi)$ may not be considered as identical, there is a close connection between them. We have, for example, already proved that the latter transformation, considered as a transformation on L_Ψ into L_Ψ, is bounded with a bound which does not exceed $2 \| T \|$.

We shall prove now that this linear transformation

$$f^*(x) = \int_\Delta T(y, x) g^*(y) d\mu,$$

considered on $L_\Psi(\Delta, \mu)$, is compact, provided μ is separable.

Let, for this purpose, the bounded sequence $g_n^*(x)$ in L_Ψ be given, hence $\| g_n^* \|_\Psi \leqslant A$. Considering then the sequence $g_n^*(f) = \int_\Delta f(x)g_n^*(x)d\mu$ of bounded linear functionals on L_Φ, we have $\| g_n^* \| \leqslant \| g_n^*(x) \|_\Psi \leqslant A$. Since the linear transformation $f^* = T^*g^*$ is compact on $(L_\Phi)^*$ by § 1, Th. 8, the sequence $f_n^* = T^*g_n^*$ contains a converging subsequence, so that, for f_p^* and f_q^* belonging to this subsequence, $\lim \| f_p^* - f_q^* \| = 0$. But $f_n^*(f) = \int_\Delta f(x)f_n^*(x)d\mu$ where $f_n^*(x) = \int_\Delta T(y, x)g_n^*(y)d\mu$, and $\| f_n^*(x)\|_\Psi/2 \leqslant \| f_n^* \| \leqslant \| f_n^*(x) \|_\Psi$. Hence $\lim \| f_p^*(x) - f_q^*(x) \|_\Psi = 0$, and this shows that $f_n^*(x)$ contains a converging subsequence. The transformation $f^*(x) = \int_\Delta T(y, x)g^*(y)d\mu$ is therefore compact on L_Ψ.

We finally observe that, if the linear transformations T_{ij} $(i, j = 1, \ldots, n)$ with kernels $T_{ij}(x, y)$ are all of finite double-norm on L_Φ, then, by § 1, Th. 12, the linear transformation $\{g\} = T\{f\}$ on the productspace L_Φ^n, defined by

$$g^i(x) = \Sigma_{j=1}^n \int_\Delta T_{ij}(x, y)f^j(y)dy \quad (i = 1, \ldots, n),$$

is compact.

Example E. *Integral transformations of finite double-norm on the space of all summable functions.*

The linear integral transformation T with kernel $T(x, y)$ is of finite double-norm on the space $L(\Delta, \mu)$ when

$$\int_\Delta \| T(x, y) \|_\infty \, d\mu < \infty.$$

Here, in $\| T(x, y) \|_\infty$, $T(x, y)$ is considered as a function of y.

We shall prove first that the property to be of finite double-norm on $L(\Delta, \mu)$, where μ is Lebesgue measure, does not necessarily imply that T is compact. This is shown by the existence of bounded measurable kernels $T(x, y)$ on $0 \leqslant x, y \leqslant 1$ such that the corresponding transformation T fails to be compact. The following example is due to J. von Neumann [4].

The orthonormal system $\varphi_n(x)$ $(n = 1, 2, \ldots)$ in $0 \leqslant x \leqslant 1$ is defined by

$$\varphi_1(x) = \begin{cases} 2^{1/2} \sin 2\pi x & \text{for } 0 < x < 1/2, \\ 2 & \text{for } 3/4 < x < 7/8, \\ 0 & \text{elsewhere,} \end{cases}$$

$$\varphi_2(x) = \begin{cases} 2^{1/2} \sin 2\pi x & \text{for } \quad 0 < x < 1/2, \\ -2 & \text{for } 3/4 < x < 7/8, \\ 0 & \text{elsewhere,} \end{cases}$$

$$\varphi_3(x), \varphi_4(x) = \begin{cases} 2^{1/2} \sin 4\pi x & \text{for } \quad 0 < x < 1/2, \\ 2^2, -2^2 & \text{for } 15/16 < x < 31/32, \\ 0 & \text{elsewhere,} \end{cases}$$

generally

$$\varphi_{2n-i}(x) = \begin{cases} 2^{1/2} \sin 2n\pi x & \text{for } 0 < x < 1/2, \\ (-1)^{i+1}2^n & \text{for } 1 - 2^{-2n} < x < 1 - 2^{-2n-1}, \\ 0 & \text{elsewhere } (n = 1, 2, \ldots, i = 0,1). \end{cases}$$

We write

$$T(x, y) = \Sigma_1^\infty 2^{-n}[\varphi_{2n-1}(x)\varphi_{2n-1}(y) - \varphi_{2n}(x)\varphi_{2n}(y)].$$

For a fixed value of y $(0 < y < 1)$, there is at most one term in this series which does not vanish. Using this remark, it is readily seen that $| T(x, y) | \leqslant 2^{3/2}$, so that the kernel is bounded. Furthermore

$$T\varphi_{2n-1} = 2^{-n}\varphi_{2n-1}, \; T\varphi_{2n} = -2^{-n}\varphi_{2n},$$

hence, writing $\psi_n(x) = 2^n[\varphi_{2n-1}(x) - \varphi_{2n}(x)]$, we have $T\psi_n = \varphi_{2n-1} + \varphi_{2n}$. Now

$$\| \psi_n \|_1 = 2^n \textstyle\int_0^1 | \varphi_{2n-1}(x) - \varphi_{2n}(x) | \, dx = 1,$$

whereas, for $n \neq m$,

$$\| T\psi_m - T\psi_n \|_1 = \textstyle\int_0^1 | [\varphi_{2m-1} + \varphi_{2m}] - [\varphi_{2n-1} + \varphi_{2n}] | \, dx =$$

$$2^{3/2} \textstyle\int_0^{1/2} | \sin 2m\pi x - \sin 2n\pi x | \, dx = 2^{5/2} \textstyle\int_0^{1/2} | \sin (m - n)\pi x | .$$

$$| \cos (m + n)\pi x | \, dx \geqslant 2^{5/2} \textstyle\int_0^{1/2} \sin^2(m - n)\pi x \cos^2 (m + n)\pi x \, dx = 2^{-1/2}.$$

This shows that the bounded sequence ψ_n is transformed into the sequence $T\psi_n$ which fails to contain a converging subsequence. The transformation T is therefore not compact.

We shall prove now, however, that for any transformation T, of finite double-norm on $L(\Delta, \mu)$, where μ is a separable measure, the transformation T^2 is compact. For this purpose it will be necessary to add something to what we have said about weak convergence in Ch. 7, § 9. We have seen in Ch. 7, § 9, Th. 7 that every set $\{f(x)\}$ of functions belonging to $L_p(\Delta, \mu)(1 < p < \infty)$, with the property that $\| f \|_p \leqslant A$

for a fixed A and all $f \in \{f\}$, contains a sequence $f_n(x)$ such that there exists a function $f_0(x) \in L_p(\Delta, \mu)$ satisfying

$$\lim_{n\to\infty} \int_\Delta f_n(x)g(x)d\mu = \int_\Delta f_0(x)g(x)d\mu$$

for all $g(x) \in L_q(\Delta, \mu)$, where $1/p + 1/q = 1$. This statement is not correct for $p = 1$ without further conditions, but upon adding the extra assumption that the set functions $F_n(X) = \int_X f_n(x)d\mu (X \subset \Delta)$ are absolutely continuous, uniformly in n, the statement remains true. For simplicity we shall give the proof only for a set Δ of finite measure, the extension to a set Δ of infinite measure being immediate. Precisely stated, we prove the following lemma:

Lemma. *Let Δ be of finite measure and let $\{f(x)\}$ be a set of functions, summable over Δ, with the properties:*

1°. $\| f \|_1 \leqslant A$ *for a fixed A and all $f \in \{f\}$.*

2°. *Given an arbitrary $\varepsilon > 0$, there exists a number $\delta > 0$ such that $| \int_X f(x)d\mu | < \varepsilon$ for all sets $X \subset \Delta$ satisfying $\mu(X) < \delta$, and for all $f \in \{f\}$.*

Then this set $\{f(x)\}$ contains a sequence $f_n(x)$ such that there exists a function $f_0(x) \in L$ satisfying

$$\lim_{n\to\infty} \int_\Delta f_n(x)g(x)d\mu = \int_\Delta f_0(x)g(x)d\mu$$

for every $g(x) \in L_\infty$.

Proof. We first observe that it follows easily from 2° that, given $\varepsilon > 0$, there exists a number $\delta_1(\varepsilon) > 0$ such that $\int_X | f(x) | d\mu < \varepsilon$ for all sets $X \subset \Delta$ satisfying $\mu(X) < \delta_1$, and for all $f \in \{f\}$. In fact, we may take $\delta_1(\varepsilon) = \delta(\varepsilon/4)$.

We now consider the set $f^*(g) = \int_\Delta f(x)g(x)d\mu$ of bounded linear functionals on L_∞, where $f(x)$ runs through $\{f(x)\}$. Evidently $\| f^* \| = \| f(x) \|_1 \leqslant A$ for all f^*. Restricting now $g(x)$ to the characteristic functions of sets $F.\Delta$, where F runs through the sets of the enumerable collection Z, introduced in Ch. 5, § 3, we may find by the diagonal process a sequence $f_n(x)$ $(n = 1, 2, \ldots)$, contained in $\{f(x)\}$, such that $\int_\Delta f_n(x)g(x)d\mu = \int_{F.\Delta} f_n(x)d\mu$ converges for all $F \in Z$. If therefore X is a measurable set, contained in Δ, and $F \in Z$ is chosen such that $\mu(X - F.\Delta) < \delta_1(\varepsilon)$ and $\mu(F.\Delta - X) < \delta_1(\varepsilon)$, we have

$$| \int_X (f_n - f_m)d\mu | = | \int_{F.\Delta} + \int_{X-F.\Delta} - \int_{F.\Delta-X} | \leqslant$$

$$| \int_{F.\Delta} | + \int_{X-F.\Delta} | f_n - f_m | d\mu + \int_{F.\Delta-X} | f_n - f_m | d\mu \leqslant | \int_{F.\Delta} | + 4\varepsilon.$$

This implies that $\int_X f_n d\mu$ converges for any measurable set $X \subset \Delta$.

Writing now $F(X) = \lim \int_X f_n d\mu$, the set function $F(X)$ satisfies $F(\Sigma_{i=1}^n X_i) = \Sigma_{i=1}^n F(X_i)$ for sets X_i without common points, and, since $| \int_X f_n(x) d\mu | < \varepsilon$ for $\mu(X) < \delta$, also $| F(X) | < \varepsilon$ for $\mu(X) < \delta$. It follows that $F(X)$ is additive and absolutely continuous (cf. Ch. 4), hence, by Radon-Nikodym's Theorem (cf. Ch. 4, § 3, Th. 3), $F(X) = \int_X f_0(x) d\mu$, where $f_0(x) \in L$. If therefore $g(x)$ is a simple measurable function on Δ, that is, a measurable function assuming only a finite number of values, we have $\lim \int_\Delta (f_n - f_0) g d\mu = 0$.

Let now $g(x) \in L_\infty$. It is no restriction of the generality to suppose that $g(x)$ is real and non-negative. Then, by Ch. 2, § 8, Th. 10, there exists a non-descending sequence of measurable non-negative simple functions $g_n(x)$ such that $g(x) = \lim g_n(x)$ almost everywhere on Δ. This implies by Egoroff's Theorem (cf. Ch. 2, § 9, Th. 1) that, for a given $\varepsilon > 0$, there exists an index $N(\varepsilon)$ and a set $Q \subset \Delta$ such that $\mu(Q) < \delta_1(\varepsilon)$ and $| g_n(x) - g(x) | < \varepsilon$ for $n \geqslant N$ and $x \in \Delta - Q$. Hence, for every i $(i = 1, 2, \ldots)$,

$$| \int_\Delta (f_i - f_0)(g - g_N) d\mu | \leqslant \int_Q 2 \| g \|_\infty | f_i - f_0 | d\mu$$

$$+ \int_{\Delta - Q} \varepsilon | f_i - f_0 | d\mu \leqslant 4\varepsilon \| g \|_\infty + \varepsilon(A + \| f_0 \|_1),$$

so that, since $\lim_{i\to\infty} \int_\Delta (f_i - f_0) g_N \, d\mu = 0$, also $\lim_{i\to\infty} \int_\Delta (f_i - f_0) g \, d\mu = 0$ or

$$\lim_{i\to\infty} \int_\Delta f_i(x) g(x) d\mu = \int_\Delta f_0(x) g(x) d\mu.$$

Remark. If the set Δ is of infinite measure, we have to add the condition that to every $\varepsilon > 0$ there exists a set Δ_ε of finite measure such that $\int_{\Delta - \Delta_\varepsilon} | f | d\mu < \varepsilon$ for all $f(x) \in \{f(x)\}$.

We are now in a position to prove that if T, with kernel $T(x, y)$, is of finite double-norm on $L(\Delta, \mu)$, then T^2 is compact. Indeed, let $\{f(x)\}$ be a set of functions $f(x) \in L$ such that $\| f \|_1 \leqslant B$ for a fixed B and all $f \in \{f\}$. Then, if $\int_\Delta \| T(x, y) \|_\infty \, d\mu = C$ $(C < \infty$ by hypothesis), and T transforms the set $\{f\}$ into the set $\{h\}$, we have

$$| h(x) | = | \int_\Delta T(x, y) f(y) d\mu | \leqslant \| T(x, y) \|_\infty . B$$

for almost every $x \in \Delta$, hence $\| h \|_1 \leqslant CB = A$ for all $h \in \{h\}$. Furthermore, if $\varepsilon > 0$ is given, there exists a number $\delta > 0$ such that $\int_X \| T(x, y) \|_\infty \, d\mu < \varepsilon / B$ for all $X \subset \Delta$ satisfying $\mu(X) < \delta$, and, in the case that Δ is of infinite measure, there also exists a set Δ_ε of finite measure such that $\int_{\Delta - \Delta_\varepsilon} \| T(x, y) \|_\infty \, d\mu < \varepsilon / B$. Hence $\int_X | h(x) | d\mu < \varepsilon$ for $\mu(X) < \delta$ and $\int_{\Delta - \Delta_\varepsilon} | h(x) | d\mu < \varepsilon$ for all $h \in \{h\}$. An application of the lemma shows now the existence of a sequence $h_n(x) = Tf_n(x)$ and a function $h_0(x) \in L$ such that

$$\lim \int_\Delta h_n(y)g(y)d\mu = \int_\Delta h_0(y)g(y)d\mu$$

for all $g(y) \in L_\infty$. Since $T(x, y) \in L_\infty$ as a function of y for almost every value of $x \in \Delta$, we may choose $g(y) = T(x, y)$ for these values, hence

$$\lim k_n(x) = \lim \int_\Delta T(x, y)h_n(y)d\mu = \int_\Delta T(x, y)h_0(y)d\mu = k_0(x)$$

or

$$(1) \qquad \lim | k_n(x) - k_0(x) | = 0$$

almost everywhere on Δ. Furthermore $| k_n(x) - k_0(x) | \leqslant \| h_n - h_0 \|_1 \cdot \| T(x, y) \|_\infty \leqslant (A + \| h_0 \|_1) \| T(x, y) \|_\infty$, where the last function is a summable function of x over Δ. Hence, from (1) by Lebesgue's Theorem (cf. Ch. 3, § 4, Th. 4 and Ch. 3, § 5, Th. 1),

$$\lim \int_\Delta | k_n(x) - k_0(x) | d\mu = 0$$

or $\lim k_n = k_0$. But $k_n = Th_n = T^2 f_n$, so that $\lim T^2 f_n = k_0$. The bounded set $\{f\}$ contains therefore a sequence f_n with the property that $T^2 f_n$ converges. This shows that T^2 is compact.

Remark. A small modification of the proof shows that if T_1 and T_2 are both of finite double-norm on $L(\Delta, \mu)$, then $T_1 T_2$ is compact.

Example F. *Integral transformation with kernel* $A(x,y)=B(x,y)\,|x-y|^{-\alpha}$, *where* $B(x, y)$ *is bounded and* $0 < \alpha < 1$.

Let Δ be the linear interval $0 \leqslant x \leqslant 1$. In Ch. 9, § 9, Ex. C we have considered the integral transformation A, defined on $L_p(\Delta)$ $(1 \leqslant p \leqslant \infty)$ by

$$g(x) = Af = \int_\Delta A(x, y)f(y)dy,$$

where $A(x, y) = B(x, y) \,| x - y |^{-\alpha}$, $| B(x, y) | \leqslant M$ in $\Delta \times \Delta$, $0 < \alpha < 1$, and the integral is a Lebesgue integral, and we have proved that A is bounded and that

$$\| g \|_p \leqslant \{2^\alpha M/(1 - \alpha)\} \| f \|_p.$$

We shall prove now that for $1 < p < \infty$ the transformation A is compact. The proof will be divided into a number of lemmas.

Lemma 1. *Let* $f(x)$ *and* $\varphi(x)$ $(-\infty < x < \infty)$ *have the period* 1; *let* $\varphi(x)$ *be summable over* $\Delta = [0, 1]$ *and* $f(x) \in L_p(\Delta)$ $(1 \leqslant p < \infty)$. *Let* *furthermore* $h(x) = \int_\Delta \varphi(x-y)f(y)dy$ *and* $1/p + 1/q = 1$. *Then, given* $\varepsilon > 0$, *there exists a positive number* η, *depending only on* ε *and* $\varphi(x)$, *such that*

$$\int_E | h |^p dx \leqslant \varepsilon(\int_\Delta | \varphi(x) | dx)^{p-1} \| f \|_p^p$$

for every set E *the measure* $m(E)$ *of which satisfies* $m(E) < \eta$.

Proof. Given $\varepsilon > 0$, there exists a positive number η, depending only on ε and $\varphi(x)$, such that $\int_E | \varphi | dx < \varepsilon$ if only $m(E) < \eta$. Then

$$(1) \begin{cases} \int_E(\int_\Delta | \varphi(x-y) | . | f(y) |^p dy)dx = \int_\Delta (\int_E | \varphi(x-y) | dx) | f(y)|^p dy = \\ \int_\Delta (\int_{E-y} | \varphi(t) | dt) | f(y) |^p dy < \varepsilon \| f \|_p^p, \end{cases}$$

where $E - y$ is the set of all $t = x - y$, $x \in E$. Furthermore, by Hölder's inequality,

$$| h(x) |^p \leqslant [\int_\Delta | \varphi(x-y)f(y) | dy]^p = [\int_\Delta | \varphi |^{1/p} . | f | . | \varphi |^{1/q} dy]^p$$
$$\leqslant \int_\Delta | \varphi(x-y) | . | f(y) |^p dy . (\int_\Delta | \varphi(x-y) | dy)^{p/q} =$$
$$\int_\Delta | \varphi(x-y) | . | f(y) |^p dy . (\int_\Delta | \varphi(x) | dx)^{p/q};$$

hence, by (1) and observing that $p/q = p - 1$,

$$\int_E | h |^p dx \leqslant (\int_\Delta | \varphi | dx)^{p-1} \int_E (\int_\Delta | \varphi(x-y) | . | f(y) |^p dy)dx$$
$$< \varepsilon(\int_\Delta | \varphi | dx)^{p-1} \| f \|_p^p.$$

Lemma 2. *Let* $g(x) = Af = \int_\Delta A(x, y)f(y)dy$, $f(x) \in L_p(\Delta)$ $(1 \leqslant p < \infty)$, $A(x, y) = B(x, y) | x - y |^{-\alpha}$, $| B(x, y) | \leqslant M$, $0 < \alpha < 1$. *Then, given* $\varepsilon > 0$, *there exists a positive number* η, *depending only on* ε, M *and* α *but not on* $f(x)$, *such that*

$$\int_E | g |^p dx \leqslant \varepsilon \{2^\alpha M/(1-\alpha)\}^{p-1} \| f \|_p^p$$

for every set $E \subset \Delta$ *the measure* $m(E)$ *of which satisfies* $m(E) < \eta$.

Proof. Define a function $\varphi(t)$ $(-\infty < t < \infty)$ by $\varphi(-t) = \varphi(t)$, $\varphi(t+1) = \varphi(t)$ for all t and $\varphi(t) = Mt^{-\alpha}$ in $0 \leqslant t \leqslant 1/2$. Then $M | t |^{-\alpha} \leqslant \varphi(t)$ for $| t | \leqslant 1$ and

$$\int_\Delta | \varphi | dt = 2\int_0^{1/2} \varphi(t)dt = 2M \int_0^{1/2} t^{-\alpha}dt = 2^\alpha M/(1-\alpha).$$

Since

$$| g(x) | = | \int_\Delta B(x, y) | x - y |^{-\alpha} f(y)dy | \leqslant \int_\Delta \varphi(x-y) | f(y) | dy = h(x),$$

we conclude from the preceding lemma that to every $\varepsilon > 0$ there exists a number $\eta > 0$, depending only on ε and $\varphi(x)$, such that

$$\int_E | g |^p dx \leqslant \int_E | h |^p dx \leqslant \varepsilon \{2^\alpha M/(1-\alpha)\}^{p-1} \| f \|_p^p.$$

Lemma 3. *If* $f(x) \in L_p(\Delta)$ $(1 < p < \infty)$ *and* $1 \leqslant r < p$, *then* $\| f \|_r \leqslant \| f \|_p$.

Proof. By Hölder's inequality we have

$$\int_\Delta | f |^r dx = \int_\Delta | f |^r . 1 \, dx \leqslant (\int_\Delta | f |^p dx)^{r/p} (\int_\Delta 1 . dx)^{1-r/p} = (\int_\Delta | f |^p dx)^{r/p},$$

hence $\| f \|_r \leqslant \| f \|_p$.

Lemma 4. *The transformation A on $L_p(\Delta)$ into $L_p(\Delta)$, defined in Lemma 2, is compact for* $1/(1-\alpha) < p < \infty$.

Proof. If $1/p + 1/q = 1$, $1/(1-\alpha) < p < \infty$, then $1/p < 1 - \alpha$, hence $\alpha < 1 - 1/p = 1/q$ or $\alpha q < 1$, so that

$$\int_\Delta (\int_\Delta | A(x, y) |^q dy)^{p/q} dx \leqslant \int_\Delta (\int_\Delta M^q | x - y |^{-\alpha q} dy)^{p/q} dx < \infty.$$

This shows that A is of finite double-norm, so that it is compact (cf. Example D).

Lemma 5. *The same transformation A is compact for* $1 < p < 1/\alpha$.

Proof. If $1/p + 1/q = 1$, $p < 1/\alpha$, then $1/p > \alpha$, hence $1 - 1/q > \alpha$, $1/q < 1 - \alpha$, $q > 1/(1 - \alpha)$, so that by the preceding lemma, applied to the kernel $\tilde{A}(x, y) = B(y, x) | x - y |^{-\alpha}$, the transformation $\tilde{A}$ with kernel $\tilde{A}(x, y)$ is compact on $L_q(\Delta)$. Then, by § 1, Th. 8, the adjoint transformation is also compact, and, since this adjoint transformation is the transformation A on $L_p(\Delta)$ with kernel $A(x, y) = B(x, y) | x - y |^{-\alpha}$ (cf. Ch. 9, § 7, Th. 3), our lemma is proved.

Remark. For $0 < \alpha < 1/2$, all p for which $1 < p < \infty$ satisfy one at least of the inequalities $p > 1/(1 - \alpha)$ or $p < 1/\alpha$. For $1/2 \leqslant \alpha < 1$, however, we have $1/(1 - \alpha) \geqslant 2$ and $1/\alpha \leqslant 2$, so that in this case there remains a gap $1/\alpha \leqslant p \leqslant 1/(1 - \alpha)$.

Lemma 6. *Let* $1/2 \leqslant \alpha < 1$ *and* $1/\alpha \leqslant p \leqslant 1/(1 - \alpha)$. *Then the transformation A on $L_p(\Delta)$ into $L_p(\Delta)$, defined in Lemma 2, is compact.*

Proof. Suppose that $f_n(x) \in L_p(\Delta)$ and that $\| f_n \|_p \leqslant C$ $(n = 1, 2, \ldots)$. Then, if $1 < r < 1/\alpha$, we have $1 < r < p$, so that by Lemma 3 also $\| f_n \|_r \leqslant C$ $(n = 1, 2, \ldots)$. Since A is compact on $L_r(\Delta)$ by Lemma 5, the sequence $g_n = Af_n$ contains a subsequence $g_k = Af_k$ $(k = n_1, n_2, \ldots)$, converging according to the L_r-norm to a function $g_0(x) \in L_r(\Delta)$. It follows from the proof of the completeness of $L_r(\Delta)$ that this sequence $g_k(x)$ in its turn contains a subsequence $g_i(x)$ $(i = n_{k_1}, n_{k_2}, \ldots)$, converging almost everywhere on Δ to $g_0(x)$. Let now, if $\varepsilon > 0$ is arbitrarily given, the number $\eta > 0$ be defined as in Lemma 2. Then, by Egoroff's Theorem, there exists a set $E \subset \Delta$ such that $m(E) < \eta$ and $g_i(x)$ converges uniformly to $g_0(x)$ on $\Delta - E$. If $g_{i_1}(x)$ and $g_{i_2}(x)$ belong to the sequence $g_i(x)$ we have therefore

$$\limsup_{i_1, i_2 \to \infty} (\textstyle\int_\Delta | g_{i_1} - g_{i_2} |^p dx)^{1/p} \leqslant \limsup (\textstyle\int_{\Delta - E} + \int_E)^{1/p}$$
$$\leqslant \varepsilon^{1/p}\{2^\alpha M/(1-\alpha)\}^{1-1/p}\{ \| f_{i_1} \|_p + \| f_{i_2} \|_p\} \leqslant$$
$$2C\, \varepsilon^{1/p}\, \{2^\alpha M/(1-\alpha)\}^{1-1/p},$$

and this shows, since $\varepsilon > 0$ is arbitrary, that

$$\lim_{i_1, i_2 \to \infty} \textstyle\int_\Delta | g_{i_1} - g_{i_2} |^p dx = 0.$$

Hence the sequence $g_n = Af_n$ contains a subsequence converging according to the L_p-norm, from which we may conclude that A is compact.

Remarks. 1°. It is interesting that for the case $p = 2$ a much simpler proof exists. In this case we have to do with a linear transformation A on the Hilbert space $L_2(\Delta)$, about which it is known that A itself is of finite double-norm if $\alpha < 1/2$, and A^n is of finite double-norm for $n > 1/2(1-\alpha)$ if $1/2 \leqslant \alpha < 1$. It is only the latter subcase which needs further consideration. If $A(x, y) = B(x, y) \,|\, x - y \,|^{-\alpha}$ where $B(x, y)$ is Hermitian, that is, $B(x, y) = \overline{B(y, x)}$, the transformation A is self-adjoint, so that the compactness of A^n for $n > 1/2(1-\alpha)$ implies the compactness of A itself by § 1, Th. 13. If $B(x, y)$ is not Hermitian, we consider the Hermitian kernels $\{B(x, y) + \overline{B(y, x)}\} \,|\, x - y \,|^{-\alpha}$ and $[\{B(x, y) - \overline{B(y, x)}\}/i] \,|\, x - y \,|^{-\alpha}$, both of which are therefore kernels of compact transformations. Addition shows now that A is compact.

We observe at this point that if $q \geqslant 2$ is a given integer, and we choose α such that

$$1 - 1/(2q-2) < \alpha < 1 - 1/2q,$$

then the transformation A on $L_2(\Delta)$, defined by $Af = \int_\Delta | x - y |^{-\alpha} f(y) dy$, is an example of a compact integral transformation A such that A^r is not of finite double-norm for $1 \leqslant r < q$, whereas A^r is of finite double-norm for $r \geqslant q$.

2°. Defining $A(x, y) = B(x, y) \,|\, x - y \,|^{-\alpha}$, $B(x, y) = 1/\Gamma(1-\alpha)$ for $0 \leqslant y \leqslant x$, $B(x, y) = 0$ for $x < y \leqslant 1$, we obtain

$$g(x) = Af = \int_0^1 A(x, y) f(y) dy = \frac{1}{\Gamma(1-\alpha)} \int_0^x (x-y)^{-\alpha} f(y) dy,$$

or, writing $\beta = 1 - \alpha$,

$$g(x) = Af = \{1/\Gamma(\beta)\} \int_0^x (x - y)^{\beta-1} f(y) dy,$$

and this shows that $g(x)$ is the fractional integral of $f(x)$ of order β (cf. Ch. 3, § 9). Our theorem shows therefore that if $f_n(x)$ $(n = 1, 2, \ldots)$ is a sequence of functions belonging to $L_p(\Delta)$ $(1 < p < \infty)$, whose L_p-norms are uniformly bounded, then the sequence of fractional integrals of order β $(\beta > 0)$ contains a subsequence which converges in mean with index p.

We finally observe that by Ch. 3, § 9 the iterated transformations $A^n (n = 2, 3, \ldots)$ are given by

$$A^n f = \{1/\Gamma(n\beta)\} \int_0^x (x - y)^{n\beta-1} f(y) dy,$$

so that in this particular case it is immediately evident that A^n has a bounded kernel for $n\beta - 1 \geqslant 0$ or $n \geqslant 1/\beta = 1/(1 - \alpha)$.

§ 3. Spectral Properties. The Riesz-Schauder Theory

In Ch. 10, § 9 we have investigated the spectral properties of a bounded linear transformation T whose domain is the complete Banach space E, and whose range is contained in the same space E. In the case that T or one of its iterates T^n is compact, more detailed statements on the spectrum of T can be made. In Ch. 9, § 17 and in Ch. 10, § 6, Ex. D, where we had to do with the special case that the space E is a complete separable Hilbert space, and that T is of finite double-norm (hence compact), we have found that the number of different characteristic values λ_n of T is finite or enumerably infinite, and that in the latter case $\lim \lambda_n = 0$. Furthermore, every complex number $\lambda \neq \lambda_n$ $(n = 1, 2, \ldots)$, and $\neq 0$, belongs to the resolvent set of T. One of the main results in what follows now will be that these facts are also true in the case that E is an arbitrary Banach space, and that T or one of its iterates T^n is compact. It will moreover be shown that $\lambda \neq 0$ is a characteristic value of T if and only if λ is a characteristic value of the Banach-adjoint T^*, and that in this case the null spaces $N(T_\lambda)$ and $N(T_\lambda^*)$ have the same finite dimension. To avoid any misunderstandings the fact must be stressed that not every compact transformation T necessarily has characteristic values $\neq 0$. In fact, in Ch. 10, § 6, Ex. A ($E = R =$ separable complete Hilbert space of infinite dimension, φ_n $(n = 1, 2, \ldots)$ complete orthonormal system, $T\varphi_n = \varphi_{n+1}/(n + 1)$, T of finite double-norm since $\sum_{ij=1}^{\infty} |(T\varphi_i, \varphi_j)|^2 = \sum_i \|T\varphi_i\|^2 = \sum_i (i + 1)^{-2} < \infty$) all $\lambda \neq 0$ form the resolvent set and $\lambda = 0$ is the residual spectrum; in Ch. 10, Ex. 3 (the same space, $T\varphi_1 = 0$, $T\varphi_n = \varphi_{n-1}/n$ for $n \geqslant 2$, T of finite double-norm) all $\lambda \neq 0$ form the resolvent set and $\lambda = 0$ is the point spectrum, and in the example mentioned in Ch. 10, § 9, Th. 2, Remark ($E = L_2[0, 1]$, $Tf = \int_0^x f(y)dy$, T of finite double-norm) all $\lambda \neq 0$ form the resolvent set and $\lambda = 0$ is the continuous spectrum.

Theorem 1. *Let T be a bounded linear transformation whose domain is the Banach space E (complete or non-complete), and whose range is contained in the same space E. Let, furthermore, $\varepsilon_k = e^{2\pi ik/n}$ $(k = 0, 1, \ldots, n-1)$, where n is a given positive integer (the numbers $\varepsilon_0, \varepsilon_1, \ldots, \varepsilon_{n-1}$ are therefore the roots of the equation $\varepsilon^n = 1$). Then:*

1°. If φ is a characteristic element of T with characteristic value λ, then φ is also a characteristic element of T^n with characteristic value λ^n.

2°. If λ^n is a characteristic value of T^n, there is at least one ε_k such that $\varepsilon_k\lambda$ is a characteristic value of T.

Proof. 1°. The statement is true for $n = 1$. Assuming now that $T^{n-1}\varphi = \lambda^{n-1}\varphi$ has already been proved, we find $T^n\varphi = T(T^{n-1}\varphi) = T(\lambda^{n-1}\varphi) = \lambda^{n-1}T\varphi = \lambda^n\varphi$.

2°. Let $T^n\varphi - \lambda^n\varphi = 0$, where $\varphi \neq 0$. Then we define the elements $\varphi_1, \ldots, \varphi_n$ by

$$\varphi_1 = T\varphi - \varepsilon_0\lambda\varphi,$$

$$\varphi_2 = T\varphi_1 - \varepsilon_1\lambda\varphi_1 = T^2\varphi - (\varepsilon_0 + \varepsilon_1)\lambda T\varphi + \varepsilon_0\varepsilon_1\lambda^2\varphi,$$

$$\cdots\cdots$$

$$\varphi_n = T\varphi_{n-1} - \varepsilon_{n-1}\lambda\varphi_{n-1} = T^n\varphi - (\Sigma_k\, \varepsilon_k)\lambda T^{n-1}\varphi + (\Sigma_{kl}\, \varepsilon_k\varepsilon_l)\lambda^2 T^{n-2}\varphi$$
$$- \ldots + (-1)^n\varepsilon_0\varepsilon_1 \ldots \varepsilon_{n-1}\lambda^n\varphi = T^n\varphi - \lambda^n\varphi = 0.$$

From $\varphi_n = T\varphi_{n-1} - \varepsilon_{n-1}\lambda\varphi_{n-1} = 0$ we derive that either $\varepsilon_{n-1}\lambda$ is a characteristic value of T or that $\varphi_{n-1} = 0$. Supposing the second alternative to be true, it follows from $\varphi_{n-1} = T\varphi_{n-2} - \varepsilon_{n-2}\lambda\varphi_{n-2} = 0$ that either $\varepsilon_{n-2}\lambda$ is a characteristic value of T or $\varphi_{n-2} = 0$. Proceeding in this way we find, if neither of the numbers $\varepsilon_{n-1}\lambda, \varepsilon_{n-2}\lambda, \ldots, \varepsilon_1\lambda$ is a characteristic value of T, that $\varphi_1 = 0$. From $\varphi_1 = T\varphi = \varepsilon_0\lambda\varphi - 0$ follows then, since $\varphi \neq 0$, that $\varepsilon_0\lambda$ is a characteristic value of T. One at least of the numbers $\varepsilon_k\lambda$ is therefore a characteristic value of T.

Remark. If φ is a characteristic element of T^n with characteristic value λ^n, but φ is no characteristic element of T with characteristic value λ, our proof shows, since $\varepsilon_0 = 1$, that T possesses a characteristic value $\varepsilon_k\lambda$, where $\varepsilon_k \neq 1$.

In the remaining part of the present paragraph we shall assume that E is an arbitrary Banach space, either complete or non-complete, that T is a bounded linear transformation on E into E, and that there exists a positive integer p such that T^p is compact. If T^* is the Banach-adjoint of T, then T^* is linear and bounded on E^* into E^*. Furthermore, since $(T^n)^* = (T^*)^n$ for every positive integer n, the transformation $(T^*)^p = (T^p)^*$ is compact by § 1, Th. 8.

Of the results which follow now the greater part is due to F. RIESZ [5]; the important Th. 13 is due to J. SCHAUDER [2].

Lemma α. *If $\lambda \neq 0$ is a complex number, then $T_\lambda = T - \lambda I$ transforms every bounded closed set $G \subset E$ into a closed set. A similar statement holds for $T^*_\lambda = T^* - \lambda I$.*

Proof. Let $f_n \in G (n = 1, 2, \ldots)$ and $\lim T_\lambda f_n = g_0$. We have to prove the existence of an element $f_0 \in G$ such that $T_\lambda f_0 = g_0$. Since the sequence f_n is bounded, it contains a subsequence f_k $(k = n_1, n_2, \ldots)$ such that $\lim T^p f_k = h_0$, hence $\lim (T_\lambda + \lambda I)^p f_k = h_0$. It follows easily, on account of $\lambda \neq 0$ and $\lim T^q_\lambda f_k = T^{q-1}_\lambda g_0$ $(q = 1, 2, \ldots)$, that $f_0 = \lim f_k$ exists. Then $f_0 \in G$, since G is closed. Observing that $g_0 = \lim T_\lambda f_n = \lim T_\lambda f_k = T_\lambda f_0$, our proof is complete. The proof for T^* is similar.

Theorem 2. *If $\lambda \neq 0$ is a complex number, then $T_\lambda = T - \lambda I$ transforms every linear subspace $G \subset E$ (that is, every closed linear set $G \subset E$) into a linear subspace. A similar statement holds for $T^*_\lambda = T^* - \lambda I$.*

Proof. Let $f_n \in G$ $(n = 1, 2, \ldots)$ and $\lim T_\lambda f_n = g_0$. We have to prove the existence of an element $f_0 \in G$ such that $T_\lambda f_0 = g_0$. If the sequence f_n is bounded, the desired result is an immediate consequence of the preceding lemma. If f_n is not bounded we consider G_1, the set of all elements f that belong both to G and to the null space $N(T_\lambda)$. This set G_1 is linear and closed so that, if d_n is the distance from f_n to G_1, there exists an element $h_n \in G_1$ satisfying $d_n \leqslant \| f_n - h_n \| \leqslant (1 + n^{-1})d_n$. Furthermore $\lim T_\lambda(f_n - h_n) = g_0$. If therefore $f_n - h_n$ contains a bounded subsequence, the desired result follows from the preceding lemma. If, however, $\lim \| f_n - h_n \| = \infty$, we write $k_n = (f_n - h_n)/\| f_n - h_n \|$. Then $\lim T_\lambda k_n = 0$ and $\| k_n \| = 1$; the sequence k_n contains therefore by the proof of the preceding lemma a subsequence k_i $(i = n_1, n_2, \ldots)$, converging to an element $h_0 \in G$. Since $T_\lambda h_0 = \lim T_\lambda k_i = 0$, we find even that $h_0 \in G_1$. Writing $k_n - h_0 = \varepsilon_n$, so that $\lim \varepsilon_i = 0$, we have now $\varepsilon_n = \{(f_n - h_n)/\| f_n - h_n \|\} - h_0$ or $f_n - h_n - \| f_n - h_n \| h_0 = \varepsilon_n \| f_n - h_n \|$, hence

$$(1) \quad \| f_i - p_i \| = \| f_i - h_i - \| f_i - h_i \| h_0 \| \leqslant \varepsilon_i(1 + i^{-1})d_i \leqslant d_i/2$$

for i sufficiently large. But $p_i = h_i + \| f_i - h_i \| h_0 \in G_1$, which implies

$$(2) \qquad \| f_i - p_i \| \geqslant d_i.$$

The inequalities (1) and (2) contradict each other; $\lim \| f_n - h_n \| = \infty$ is therefore impossible. This completes the proof. The proof for T_λ^* is similar.

Theorem 3. *If $\lambda \neq 0$ is a complex number and $L_0 = E = W(T_\lambda^0)$, $L_1 = W(T_\lambda)$, $L_2 = W(T_\lambda^2)$, ..., then all L_n $(n = 0, 1, 2, \ldots)$ are linear subspaces, and $L_0 \supset L_1 \supset L_2 \supset \ldots$. A similar statement holds for T_λ^*.*
Proof. Since $L_0 = E$ is linear and closed, and since T_λ transforms L_{n-1} into L_n $(n = 1, 2, \ldots)$, all L_n are linear and closed by the preceding theorem. Obviously $L_0 \supset L_1 \supset L_2 \supset \ldots$. The proof for T_λ^* is similar.

Theorem 4. *If $\lambda \neq 0$ is a complex number and M_n $(n = 0, 1, 2, \ldots)$ is the null space $N(T_\lambda^n)$, then all M_n are of finite dimension, and $M_0 \subset M_1 \subset M_2 \subset \ldots$. A similar statement holds for T_λ^*.*
Proof. Since $M_0 = N(T_\lambda^0)$ contains only the null element, M_0 is of finite dimension. Consider now $M_1 = N(T_\lambda)$. Supposing that M_1 is not of finite dimension, there exists a linearly independent sequence f_n $(n = 1, 2, \ldots)$ of elements belonging to M_1. But then, by Ch. 6, § 4, Th. 7, there also exists a sequence g_n $(n = 1, 2, \ldots)$ of elements belonging to M_1 such that

$$\| g_n \| = 1, \ \| g_n - g_m \| \geqslant 1/2 \text{ for } n \neq m.$$

But $Tg_n = \lambda g_n$, hence $\lambda^p g_n = T^p g_n$, so that, since T^p is compact, $\lambda^p g_n$ contains a converging subsequence, in contradiction with $\| \lambda^p g_n - \lambda^p g_m \| \geqslant | \lambda |^p/2$. This shows that M_1 is of finite dimension.

To prove the same for M_n $(n = 2, 3, \ldots)$, we consider $T_\lambda^n = (T - \lambda I)^n$, and we observe that T_λ^n may be written in the form $V + (-\lambda)^n I$ with $V = ST = TS$, where S is a bounded linear transformation. It follows that $V^p = S^p T^p$, which shows that V^p is compact. Hence, by the first part of our proof, M_n is of finite dimension. Obviously we have $M_0 \subset M_1 \subset M_2 \subset \ldots$. The proof for T_λ^* is similar.

Theorem 5. *The number of different characteristic values* λ_n *of* T *is finite or enumerably infinite, and in the latter case* $\lim \lambda_n = 0$. *The same statement holds for* T^*.

Proof. It will be sufficient to prove that, if d is an arbitrary positive number, the number of different characteristic values λ, for which $|\lambda| \geqslant d$, is finite. Let us suppose therefore that λ_n is an infinite sequence of different characteristic values satisfying $|\lambda_n| \geqslant d$ $(n = 1, 2, \ldots)$. Then there exists a sequence of elements $f_n \neq 0$ such that $Tf_n = \lambda_n f_n$. By Ch. 10, § 9, Th. 3, the elements f_n are linearly independent. Denoting by E_n $(n = 1, 2, \ldots)$ the space of all finite linear combinations $\Sigma_{i=1}^n \alpha_i f_i$, we have, if $f = \Sigma_{i=1}^n \alpha_i f_i$ is arbitrary, $T_{\lambda_n} f = \Sigma_1^n \lambda_i \alpha_i f_i - \Sigma_1^n \lambda_n \alpha_i f_i = \Sigma_1^{n-1} (\lambda_i - \lambda_n)\alpha_i f_i$, hence $T_{\lambda_n} f \in E_{n-1}$ for all $f \in E_n$. Now, by Ch. 6, § 4, Th. 7, there exists a sequence g_n $(n = 1, 2, \ldots)$ of elements such that

$$g_n \in E_n, \; \| g_n \| = 1, \; \| g_n - f \| \geqslant 1/2 \text{ for all } f \in E_{n-1},$$

hence $\| \lambda_n g_n - f \| \geqslant |\lambda_n|/2 \geqslant d/2$ for all $f \in E_{n-1}$. Since, for $m > n$, we have $\| Tg_m - Tg_n \| = \| \lambda_m g_m - [\lambda_m g_m - Tg_m + Tg_n] \|$ with $\lambda_m g_m - Tg_m \in E_{m-1}$ and $Tg_n \in E_n \subset E_{m-1}$, it follows therefore that $\| Tg_m - Tg_n \| \geqslant d/2$. Supposing now first that T itself is compact, we immediately obtain a contradiction, since in this case the sequence Tg_n $(n = 1, 2, \ldots)$ should contain a converging subsequence. If not T itself but T^p is compact for a certain integer $p > 1$, our proof shows that the characteristic values of T^p have the desired properties. But then Theorem 1 shows that the same holds for the characteristic values of T. This completes the proof. The proof for T^* is similar.

Theorem 6. *If* $\lambda \neq 0$ *is a complex number, and* $M_n = N(T_\lambda^n)$ $(n = 0, 1, 2, \ldots)$ *are the linear subspaces of finite dimension considered in Theorem* 4, *there exists an index* $\nu = \nu(\lambda)$ *such that* $M_n = M_\nu$ *for* $n \geqslant \nu$, *whereas* M_n *is a proper subspace of* M_{n+1} *for* $n < \nu$. *A similar index* ν^* *exists for* T_λ^*.

Proof. We first observe that if $M_m = M_{m+1}$ for a certain index m, then $M_n = M_{n+1}$ for $n > m$. Indeed, if M_n should be a proper subspace of M_{n+1}, we should have $T_\lambda^{n+1} f = 0$, $T_\lambda^n f \neq 0$ for a certain element f. Writing $g = T_\lambda^{n-m} f$, this would imply $T_\lambda^{m+1} g = T_\lambda^{n+1} f = 0$, $T_\lambda^m g = T_\lambda^n f \neq 0$, in contradiction with $M_m = M_{m+1}$. It will be sufficient, therefore, to prove the impossibility of M_n being a proper subspace of M_{n+1} for all values of n. Supposing that M_n is a proper subspace of M_{n+1} for every n, there exists a sequence f_n $(n = 1, 2, \ldots)$ of elements such that

$$f_n \in M_n, \; \| f_n \| = 1, \; \| f_n - f \| \geqslant 1/2 \text{ for all } f \in M_{n-1}.$$

Observing now that, for $n > m$,

$$T(f_n - f_m) = \lambda f_n - (\lambda f_m - T_\lambda f_n + T_\lambda f_m) = \lambda(f_n - g_1),\ g_1 \in M_{n-1},$$

$$T^2(f_n - f_m) = \lambda T(f_n - g_1) = \lambda^2(f_n - g_2),\ g_2 \in M_{n-1},$$

generally

$$T^p(f_n - f_m) = \lambda^p(f_n - g_p),\ g_p \in M_{n-1},$$

hence $\| T^p f_n - T^p f_m \| = | \lambda |^p \| f_n - g_p \| \geqslant | \lambda |^p/2$, we obtain a contradiction since the sequence $T^p f_n$ $(n = 1, 2, \ldots)$ should contain a converging subsequence. The proof for T_λ^* is similar.

Remark. Observe that we have not yet proved that the index $\nu(\lambda)$ for T and the index $\nu^*(\lambda)$ for T^* are equal.

Theorem 7. *If $\lambda \neq 0$ is a complex number, and $L_n = W(T_\lambda^n)$ $(n = 0, 1, 2, \ldots)$ are the linear subspaces considered in Theorem 3, then $L_n = L_\nu$ for $n \geqslant \nu$, whereas L_{n+1} is a proper subspace of L_n for $n < \nu$. Here $\nu = \nu(\lambda)$ is the same index as in the preceding theorem. A similar statement holds for T_λ^*.*

Proof. It is evident that $L_m = L_{m+1}$ for a certain index m implies $L_n = L_{n+1}$ for $n > m$. Let us suppose now that L_{n+1} is a proper subspace of L_n for every value of n. Then, by Ch. 6, § 4, Th. 7, there exists a sequence f_n $(n = 1, 2, \ldots)$ of elements such that

$$f_n \in L_n,\ \| f_n \| = 1,\ \| f_n - f \| \geqslant 1/2 \text{ for all } f \in L_{n+1}.$$

Observing now that, for $n < m$,

$$T(f_n - f_m) = \lambda f_n - (\lambda f_m - T_\lambda f_n + T_\lambda f_m) = \lambda(f_n - g_1),\ g_1 \in L_{n+1},$$

hence, generally, $T^p(f_n - f_m) = \lambda^p(f_n - g_p)$, $g_p \in L_{n+1}$, we find $\| T^p f_n - T^p f_m \| = | \lambda |^p \| f_n - g_p \| \geqslant | \lambda |^p/2$, which is a contradiction since $T^p f_n$ $(n = 1, 2, \ldots)$ contains a converging subsequence. It follows that there exists an index μ such that $L_n = L_\mu$ for $n \geqslant \mu$, whereas L_{n+1} is a proper subspace of L_n for $n < \mu$. It remains to prove that $\mu = \nu$.

For this purpose we observe that, on account of $L_\mu = L_{\mu+1}$, the equation $T_\lambda f = g$ has for every $g \in L_\mu$ a solution $f \in L_\mu$. Furthermore $T_\lambda f = 0$ has in L_μ only the solution $f = 0$. Indeed, if $T_\lambda f_1 = 0$ for an element $f_1 \neq 0$, $f_1 \in L_\mu$, there exists an element $f_2 \in L_\mu$ satisfying $T_\lambda f_2 = f_1$, an element $f_3 \in L_\mu$ satisfying $T_\lambda f_3 = f_2$, and so on. But $T_\lambda f_n = f_{n-1}$ $(n = 2, 3, \ldots)$ implies $T_\lambda^n f_n = 0$, $T_\lambda^{n-1} f_n = f_1 \neq 0$, so that the null space $M_{n-1} = N(T_\lambda^{n-1})$ is a proper subspace of $M_n = N(T_\lambda^n)$ for every value of n. This is in contradiction with Theorem 6. It follows that every solution of $T_\lambda^{\mu+1}f = 0$ is already a solution of $T_\lambda^\mu f = 0$, since in the opposite case $g = T_\lambda^\mu f \neq 0$ should be a solution of $T_\lambda f = 0$ in L_μ. Hence $M_\mu = M_{\mu+1}$.

On the other hand, if $n < \mu$, there exists a solution f of $T_\lambda^{n+1}f = 0$ for which $T_\lambda^n f \neq 0$. To obtain this solution we observe that there exists an element f satisfying $T_\lambda^n f \in L_{\mu-1} - L_\mu$. Then $g = T_\lambda^{n+1} f \in L_\mu$, which implies that there exists also an element $f_1 \in L_\mu$ satisfying $T_\lambda^{n+1} f_1 = g$. It follows that $T_\lambda^{n+1}(f - f_1) = 0$, whereas $T_\lambda^n(f - f_1) = T_\lambda^n f - T_\lambda^n f_1 \neq 0$, since $T_\lambda^n f \in L_{\mu-1} - L_\mu$ and $T_\lambda^n f_1 \in L_\mu$. The element $f - f_1$ is therefore the desired solution. The result is now that M_n is a proper subspace of M_{n+1} for $n < \mu$. Together with $M_\mu = M_{\mu+1}$ this shows that $\mu = \nu$. The proof for T_λ^* is similar.

Definition. *The non-negative integer* $\nu = \nu(\lambda)$, *having the properties stated in Theorem* 6 *and Theorem* 7, *is called the index of* λ *for* T. *Similarly* $\nu^* = \nu^*(\lambda)$ *is the index of* λ *for* T^*.

Theorem 8. *The space* E *is the direct sum of* $M_\nu = N(T_\lambda^\nu)$ *and* $L_\nu = W(T_\lambda^\nu)$. *Similarly,* E^* *is the direct sum of* M_{ν^*} *and* L_{ν^*}.

Proof. Let $f \in E$ be arbitrary, and write $T_\lambda^\nu f = g$. Then $g \in L_\nu = L_{2\nu}$, so that there exists a solution f_1 of $T_\lambda^{2\nu} f_1 = g$. Writing now $T_\lambda^\nu f_1 = f_0$, we have $T_\lambda^\nu f_0 = T_\lambda^{2\nu} f_1 = g = T_\lambda^\nu f$ or $T_\lambda^\nu(f - f_0) = 0$, hence $f - f_0 \in M_\nu$. The decomposition $f = f_0 + (f - f_0)$, $f_0 \in L_\nu$, $f - f_0 \in M_\nu$, is therefore of the desired form. Supposing that $f = f_0 + (f - f_0) = f_0' + (f - f_0')$ with $f_0, f_0' \in L_\nu$ and $f - f_0$, $f - f_0' \in M_\nu$, the element $h_0 = f_0 - f_0' = (f - f_0') - (f - f_0)$ belongs to L_ν and to M_ν. Then, since $h_0 \in L_\nu$, $T_\lambda^\nu h = h_0$ has a solution h, and, since $h_0 \in M_\nu$, we have $T_\lambda^\nu h_0 = 0$. It follows that $T_\lambda^{2\nu} h = 0$, hence, on account of $M_{2\nu} = M_\nu$, also $h_0 = T_\lambda^\nu h = 0$. This shows that $f_0 = f_0'$. The decomposition $f = f_0 + (f - f_0)$, $f_0 \in L_\nu$, $f - f_0 \in M_\nu$ is therefore uniquely determined. The proof for E^* is similar.

Definition. *For every* $\lambda \neq 0$ *the dimension of* $M_{\nu(\lambda)} = N(T_\lambda^\nu)$ *is called the algebraic multiplicity of* λ, *and the dimension of* $M_1 = N(T_\lambda)$ *is called the geometric multiplicity of* λ. *If, therefore,* $\nu(\lambda) = 0$, *so that* $M_0 = M_1 = M_2 = \ldots$ *contains only the null element,* λ *has the multiplicity zero. A similar definition holds for* T_λ^*.

We observe that, by Ch. 8, § 8, Th. 2, our present definition is in accordance with the definition of algebraic and geometric multiplicities of a complex number λ given in the case that the Banach space E is of finite dimension.

Theorem 9. *If the space E is complete, if $\lambda \neq 0$ and $\nu(\lambda) = 0$, then λ belongs to the resolvent set of T. Similarly, if $\lambda \neq 0$ and $\nu^*(\lambda) = 0$, λ belongs to the resolvent set of T^*.*

Proof. If $\nu(\lambda) = 0$, then $M_0 = M_1 = N(T_\lambda)$ contains only the null element, hence $T_\lambda f = 0$ only for $f = 0$. This shows that T_λ^{-1} exists. Since, furthermore, $E = L_0 = L_1 = W(T_\lambda)$ is complete, the inverse T_λ^{-1} is bounded by Ch. 7, § 11, Th. 6. This shows that λ belongs to the resolvent set of T. Observing that E^* is always complete, even if E is not, the proof for T^* is similar.

If the space E is not complete, we know (cf. Ch. 7, § 1, Th. 3) that every bounded linear transformation T on E into E may be extended onto the complete closure $\bar{E}$ of E in such a way that its bound $\| T \|$ remains the same.

Theorem 10. *If the space E is not complete, and T^p is compact on E, then the extended transformation T^p on the complete closure $\bar{E}$ is also compact. Furthermore, if $\lambda \neq 0$, n is a positive integer and $g \in E$, every solution f of $(T - \lambda I)^n f = g$ belongs to E. In particular, every solution f of $(T - \lambda I)^n f = 0$ belongs to E.*

Proof. Let the bounded sequence f_n of elements $f_n \in \bar{E}$ be given. Then there exists a sequence g_n of elements $g_n \in E$ such that $\lim (f_n - g_n) = 0$. Since this sequence g_n is also bounded, $T^p g_k$ converges for a subsequence g_k $(k = n_1, n_2, \ldots)$ to an element $h_0 \in E$. Then also $\lim T^p f_k = h_0$, and this proves that T^p is compact on $\bar{E}$. If $f \in \bar{E}$ is arbitrary, the particular case $f_n = f$ $(n = 1, 2, \ldots)$ shows that $T^p f \in E$.

To prove our second statement, we suppose first that $(T - \lambda I)f = g$, $g \in E$. Then $\lambda f = Tf - g$, hence $\lambda T^{p-1} f = T^p f - T^{p-1} g \in E$. But then also $\lambda T^{p-2} f = T^{p-1} f - T^{p-2} g \in E$, and so on. Hence $f \in E$. Let now n be an integer > 1, and let it already be proved that $(T - \lambda I)^{n-1} f_1 = g$, $g \in E$ implies $f_1 \in E$. Then, if $(T - \lambda I)^n f = g$, $g \in E$, we have $(T - \lambda I)^{n-1}$ $(T - \lambda I)f = g$, hence $(T - \lambda I)f \in E$, which implies $f \in E$.

Corollary. *If f is an element of $\bar{E}$, not belonging to E, and $\lambda \neq 0$, then none of the elements $T_\lambda^n f$ $(n = 1, 2, \ldots)$ belongs to E. In particular, by the extension of T there are created no new characteristic values $\neq 0$.*

The next theorem, which completes Theorem 9, is now an immediate consequence.

Theorem 11. *If the space E is either complete or non-complete, if $\lambda \neq 0$ and $\nu(\lambda) = 0$, the inverse T_λ^{-1} is a bounded linear transformation with domain E.*

Theorem 12. *If E is of finite dimension, the value $\lambda = 0$ belongs either to the resolvent set or to the point spectrum of T. If E is of infinite dimension, $\lambda = 0$ belongs either to the point spectrum, the residual spectrum or the continuous spectrum of T, but never to the resolvent set.*

Proof. If E is of finite dimension, every value of λ which is a root of the characteristic equation of T belongs to the point spectrum of T (cf. Ch. 8, § 5, Th. 2). All other values of λ have the property that $(T - \lambda I)^{-1}$ exists with domain E (cf. Ch. 8, § 5, Th. 3), and belong therefore to the resolvent set of T, since on a space of finite dimension every linear transformation is bounded.

If E is of infinite dimension, we have already seen at the beginning of the present paragraph that $\lambda = 0$ may belong to the point spectrum, the residual spectrum or the continuous spectrum of T. It remains to prove that $\lambda = 0$ never belongs to the resolvent set. For this purpose we observe that by Ch. 6, § 4, Th. 7 there exists a sequence f_n ($n = 1, 2, \ldots$) of elements satisfying $\| f_n \| = 1$, $\| f_n - f_m \| \geqslant 1/2$ for $n \neq m$. Supposing now that $\lambda = 0$ belongs to the resolvent set, so that the inverse T^{-1} exists and is bounded, the bounded sequence $g_n = T^{-p} f_n$ contains a subsequence $g_k (k = n_1, n_2, \ldots)$ for which $T^p g_k = T^p T^{-p} f_k = f_k$ converges. This is in contradiction with $\| f_n - f_m \| \geqslant 1/2$ for $n \neq m$.

Theorem 13. *If $\lambda \neq 0$ is a complex number, then $M_1 = N(T_\lambda)$ and $M_1^* = N(T_\lambda^*)$ have the same dimension. In other words, a complex number $\lambda \neq 0$ is a characteristic value of T if and only if it is a characteristic value of T^*, and in this case λ has the same geometric multiplicity for T and T^*.*

Proof. Since T_λ is nilpotent with index ν on the finite-dimensional space $M_\nu = N(T_\lambda^\nu)$, Ch. 8, § 7, Th. 1 and Th. 2 show the existence of integers $d_1 \geqslant d_2 \geqslant \ldots \geqslant d_\nu > 0$ and elements $f_1, f_2, \ldots, f_{d_1}$ such that the elements in the following diagram:

$f_1 \dots f_{d_\nu}$			
$T_\lambda f_1 \dots T_\lambda f_{d_\nu}$	$f_{d_\nu+1} \dots f_{d_{\nu-1}}$		
$T_\lambda^{\nu-1} f_1 \dots T_\lambda^{\nu-1} f_{d_\nu}$	$T_\lambda^{\nu-2} f_{d_\nu+1} \dots T_\lambda^{\nu-2} f_{d_{\nu-1}}$		$f_{d_2+1} \dots f_{d_1}$

form a coordinate system in M_ν, and such that the elements in the last n rows of the diagram ($n = 1, 2, \dots, \nu$) form a coordinate system in M_n. The dimension of $M_1 = N(T_\lambda)$ is therefore d_1. The space of dimension $d = d_1$ which has $f_1, f_2, \dots, f_{d_1}$ as one of its coordinate systems we shall call P, and the space which has the remaining elements in the diagram as one of its coordinate systems will be called Q. Then every element of M_ν may be written in the form $h + k$ ($h \in Q$, $k \in P$), where h and k are uniquely determined, so that, on account of Theorem 7, every $f \in E$ admits a uniquely determined decomposition $f = g + h + k$ ($g \in L_\nu = W(T_\lambda^\nu)$, $h \in Q$, $k \in P$). Every $g \in L_\nu$, however, is of the form $T_\lambda g_1$, and every $h \in Q$ is of the form $T_\lambda h_1$, so that for every $f \in E$ we have $f = T_\lambda f' + k$. Hence, if f^* is a solution of $T_\lambda^* f^* = 0$, so that $f^*(T_\lambda f') = (T_\lambda^* f^*)(f') = 0$ for every $f' \in E$, we have $f^*(f) = f^*(k)$.

Let us suppose now that $T_\lambda^* f^* = 0$ has at least $d + 1$ linearly independent solutions $f_1^*, \dots, f_{d+1}^*$. Then, by Ch. 7, § 7, Th. 8, there exist elements $g_1, \dots, g_{d+1}$ such that $f_i^*(g_j) = 1$ for $i = j$ and $f_i^*(g_j) = 0$ for $i \neq j$ ($i, j = 1, \dots, d + 1$). Since, by what we have just proved, $f_i^*(f) = f_i^*(k)$ ($i = 1, \dots, d + 1$), we may assume that $g_1, \dots, g_{d+1}$ belong to the space P. Furthermore it is evident that $g_1, \dots, g_{d+1}$ are linearly independent. But this would imply that the d-dimensional space P contains $d + 1$ linearly independent elements, which is not possible. The maximal number of linearly independent solutions of $T_\lambda^* f^* = 0$ is therefore at most $d = d_1$. We shall prove now that this number is exactly d. For this purpose we define in the space P the linear functionals $g_1^*, \dots, g_d^*$ by $g_i^*(f_j) = 1$ for $i = j$ and $g_i^*(f_j) = 0$ for $i \neq j$ ($i, j = 1, \dots, d$). Obviously, since P is of finite dimension, these linear functionals are bounded. We now observe that the direct sum S of Q and L_ν is nothing else but L_1. Indeed, $f \in S$ implies $f \in L_1$, and, if conversely $f \in L_1$, we have $f = T_\lambda f' = T_\lambda(h + k)$, where $h \in S$, $k \in P$. But $T_\lambda k \in S$, hence $f \in S$. Our statement being thus proved, it follows that E is the direct sum of L_1 and P. Extending therefore the bounded linear functionals $g_1^*, \ldots, g_d^*$ onto the whole space E by defining $g_i^*(f) = 0$ $(i = 1, \ldots, d)$ for $f \in L_1$, they remain bounded on E by Ch. 7, § 6, Th. 2. We have $g_i^*(T_\lambda f) = 0$ $(i = 1, \ldots, d)$ for every $f \in E$, hence $T_\lambda^* g_i^* = 0$ $(i = 1, \ldots, d)$. Furthermore $g_1^*, \ldots, g_d^*$ are linearly independent on P, hence certainly on E. We may conclude therefore that $T_\lambda^* f^* = 0$ has at least, and hence exactly, d linearly independent solutions. This completes the proof.

Theorem 14. *If $\lambda \neq 0$ is a complex number and n is an arbitrary non-negative integer, then $M_n = N(T_\lambda^n)$ and $M_n^* = N[(T_\lambda^*)^n]$ have the same dimension. Furthermore the index $\nu(\lambda)$ of λ for T and the index $\nu^*(\lambda)$ of λ for T^* are equal, so that λ has the same algebraic multiplicity for T and T^*.*

Proof. Since $T_\lambda^n = V + (-\lambda)^n I$, where V^p is compact (cf. the proof of Theorem 3), and $(T_\lambda^*)^n = (T_\lambda^n)^*$, it follows immediately from the preceding theorem that M_n and M_n^* have the same dimension. If therefore $M_n = M_\nu$ for $n \geqslant \nu$ whereas M_n is a proper subspace of M_{n+1} for $n < \nu$, then also $M_n^* = M_\nu^*$ for $n \geqslant \nu$ whereas M_n^* is a proper subspace of M_{n+1}^* for $n < \nu$. Hence $\nu = \nu^*$.

Theorem 15. *If $\lambda \neq 0$ is a complex number, the following four statements are equivalent:*

1°. *T_λ has a bounded inverse on E.*
2°. *T_λ^* has a bounded inverse on E^*.*
3°. *$T_\lambda f = g$ has a solution $f \in E$ for every $g \in E$.*
4°. *$T_\lambda^* f^* = g^*$ has a solution $f^* \in E^*$ for every $g^* \in E^*$.*

Proof. By Theorem 11 the statements 1° and 3° are equivalent, and so are 2° and 4°. By Theorem 14 the statements 3° and 4° are equivalent, since $\nu = \nu^* = 0$.

On account of Ch. 10, § 3, Th. 1 the annihilator $(W(T_\lambda))^\circ$ of the linear subspace $L_1 = W(T_\lambda)$ satisfies $(W(T_\lambda))^\circ = N(T_\lambda^*)$, and, by Ch. 7, § 14, Th. 1, $W(T_\lambda)$ is uniquely determined by this relation provided the space E has the property (Ext.). Under the present hypotheses, however, we shall prove that $W(T_\lambda)$ is uniquely determined by $(W(T_\lambda))^\circ = N(T_\lambda^*)$ without assuming that E has the property (Ext.).

Theorem 16. *If $\lambda \neq 0$, then $W(T_\lambda)$ consists of those and only those elements $g \in E$ satisfying $f_i^*(g) = 0$ $(i = 1, \ldots, d)$, where $f_1^*, \ldots, f_d^*$ is a maximal system of linearly independent solutions of $T_\lambda^* f^* = 0$.*

Proof. If $g \in W(T_\lambda)$, hence $g = T_\lambda f$, then $f_i^*(g) = f_i^*(T_\lambda f) = (T_\lambda^* f_i^*)(f) = 0$ $(i = 1, \ldots, d)$. Let now conversely $f_i^*(g) = 0$ $(i = 1, \ldots, d)$, and suppose that g does not belong to $W(T_\lambda)$. By the proof of Theorem 13 the space E is the direct sum of L_1 and the d-dimensional space P, hence $g = h + k$, $h \in L_1$, $k \in P$, $k \neq 0$. Defining now a bounded linear functional g^* on P in such a way that $g^*(k) = 1$, and extending it onto the whole space E by writing $g^*(h) = 0$ for all $h \in L_1$, it remains bounded and linear (cf. Ch. 7, § 6, Th. 2). Then $g^*(T_\lambda f) = 0$ for any $f \in E$, hence $T_\lambda^* g^* = 0$ or $g^* = \Sigma_{i=1}^d \alpha_i f_i^*$. This however implies $1 = g^*(k) = g^*(h + k) = g^*(g) = (\Sigma\, \alpha_i f_i^*)(g) = 0$, which is a contradiction.

Theorem 17. *If $\lambda \neq 0$, then $(N(T_\lambda))^\circ = W(T_\lambda^*)$. In other words, $W(T_\lambda^*)$ consists of those and only those elements $g^* \in E^*$ satisfying $g^*(f_i) = 0$ $(i = 1, \ldots, d)$, where $f_1, \ldots, f_d$ is a maximal system of linearly independent solutions of $T_\lambda f = 0$.*

Proof. If $g^* \in W(T_\lambda^*)$, hence $g^* = T_\lambda^* f^*$, then $g^*(f_i) = (T_\lambda^* f^*)(f_i) = f^*(T_\lambda f_i) = 0$ $(i = 1, \ldots, d)$. Let now conversely $g^*(f_i) = 0$ $(i = 1, \ldots, d)$, and suppose first that the space E is complete. Then, if f' and f'' are any two elements of E satisfying $T_\lambda f' = T_\lambda f''$, we have $g^*(f') = g^*(f'')$, so that the linear functional f^*, defined on $W(T_\lambda)$ by $f^*(T_\lambda f) = g^*(f)$, is uniquely determined. The functional f^* is bounded on $W(T_\lambda)$. Indeed, since $W(T_\lambda)$ is a linear subspace of the complete space E, it is complete itself, which implies by Ch. 7, § 11, Th. 6 that to every $g \in W(T_\lambda)$ there is assigned an element $f \in E$ such that $g = T_\lambda f$ and $\| f \| \leqslant m \| g \|$, where m does not depend on g. Then $| f^*(T_\lambda f) | = | g^*(f) | \leqslant \| g^* \| . \| f \| \leqslant m \| g^* \| . \| T_\lambda f \|$ for all $g = T_\lambda f \in W(T_\lambda)$, hence $\| f^* \| \leqslant m \| g^* \|$. Now, since E is the direct sum of $L_1 = W(T_\lambda)$ and the d-dimensional space P, we may extend f^* onto the whole space E in such a way that it remains linear and bounded. Then $(T_\lambda^* f^*)(f) = f^*(T_\lambda f) = g^*(f)$ for all $f \in E$, hence $g^* = T_\lambda^* f^*$, and this shows that $g^* \in W(T_\lambda^*)$. It follows that $(N(T_\lambda))^\circ = W(T_\lambda^*)$, provided E is complete. If E is not complete, the same relation holds since neither $N(T_\lambda)$ nor $W(T_\lambda^*)$ is affected by the process of extending T onto the closure $\bar{E}$ of E.

Remark. The present proof is very similar to that of Ch. 10, §3, Th. 3, 2°.

In all the preceding theorems $T^* = T_B^*$ was the Banach-adjoint of T. If however the space E is a complete Hilbert space, and $T^* = T_H^*$ denotes now the Hilbert-adjoint of T, some changes have to be made. No modifications are necessary in Theorems 1—12; Theorem 13 now states that, for any $\lambda \neq 0$, the null spaces $N(T - \lambda I)$ and $N(T^* - \bar{\lambda} I)$ have the same dimension (so that λ has the same geometric multiplicity for T as the conjugate complex number $\bar{\lambda}$ has for T^*), and Theorem 14 states that, for $\lambda \neq 0$ and n a positive integer, the null spaces $N[(T - \lambda I)^n]$ and $N[(T^* - \bar{\lambda} I)^n]$ have the same dimension, and that $\nu(\lambda) = \nu^*(\bar{\lambda})$ (so that in particular λ has the same algebraic multiplicity for T as $\bar{\lambda}$ has for T^*). Finally, the statements in Theorem 16 and Theorem 17 are now special cases of Ch. 10, § 14, Th. 1, which asserts that if T is a bounded linear transformation on the complete Hilbert space R, with range in R, then $N(T^*) = R \ominus [W(T)]$ and $[W(T^*)] = R \ominus N(T)$.

Theorem 18. *If A is a compact normal transformation on the complete Hilbert space R, then every characteristic value $\lambda \neq 0$ of A has the index $\nu(\lambda) = 1$ for A.*

If K is compact and symmetrisable relative to the bounded self-adjoint transformation H, if moreover this symmetrisability is full (that is, if $Hf \neq 0$ for every characteristic element f of K, belonging to a characteristic value $\neq 0$), and either H or HK is positive, then every characteristic value $\lambda \neq 0$ of K has the index $\nu(\lambda) = 1$ for K.

Proof. Follows from Ch. 9, § 15, Th. 7 and Th. 9.

Before stating our final theorem, we make a few introductory remarks. In the proof of Theorem 13 we have seen that, if ν is the index of $\lambda \neq 0$ for T, there exist integers $d_1 \geqslant d_2 \geqslant \dots \geqslant d_\nu > 0$ and elements $f_1, \dots, f_{d_1}$ such that the elements in the following diagram I:

diagram I

$f_1 \dots f_{d_\nu}$			
$T_\lambda f_1 \dots T_\lambda f_{d_\nu}$	$f_{d_\nu+1} \dots f_{d_{\nu-1}}$		
⋮	⋮		
$T_\lambda^{\nu-1} f_1 \dots T_\lambda^{\nu-1} f_{d_\nu}$	$T_\lambda^{\nu-2} f_{d_\nu+1} \dots T_\lambda^{\nu-2} f_{d_{\nu-1}}$	⋯	$f_{d_2+1} \dots f_{d_1}$

form a coordinate system in M_ν, and such that the elements in the last n rows ($n = 1, 2, \dots, \nu$) form a coordinate system in M_n. Denoting the dimension of M_ν by q, we have therefore $q = d_1 + d_2 + \dots + d_\nu$. We shall denote now for a moment the elements in the diagram by

$g_1, \ldots, g_q$, where $g_1, \ldots, g_\nu$ are the elements in the first column from top to bottom, and so on. Hence, if g_i and g_{i+1} are in the same column, $g_{i+1} = T_\lambda g_i$. The bounded linear functionals $g_1^*, \ldots, g_q^*$ on M_ν are defined by $g_i^*(g_j) = 1$ for $i = j$ and $g_i^*(g_j) = 0$ for $i \neq j$ $(i, j = 1, \ldots, q)$. They may be extended as bounded linear functionals onto the whole space E by defining $g_i^*(h) = 0$ $(i = 1, \ldots, q)$ for all $h \in L_\nu$. We shall prove now that we may build up a diagram containing $g_1^*, \ldots, g_q^*$, which has similar properties with respect to $M_\nu^* = N[(T_\lambda^*)^\nu]$ as the original diagram I with respect to $M_\nu = N(T_\lambda^\nu)$.

Theorem 19. *Writing the elements $g_1^*, \ldots, g_q^*$ in a diagram in exactly the same way as the elements $g_1, \ldots, g_q$ in the original diagram I, and then reversing the order in every column, the thus obtained diagram II has the property that the elements in the last n rows $(n = 1, 2, \ldots, \nu)$ form a coordinate system in the null space $M_n^* = N[(T_\lambda^*)^n]$. In particular, $g_1^*, \ldots, g_q^*$ form a coordinate system in M_ν^*.*

Proof. Let g_i and g_{i+1} belong to the same column in the original diagram, hence $g_{i+1} = T_\lambda g_i$. We shall prove that $g_i^* = T_\lambda^* g_{i+1}^*$. Indeed,

$$g_i^*(g_i) = 1 = g_{i+1}^*(g_{i+1}) = g_{i+1}^*(T_\lambda g_i) = (T_\lambda^* g_{i+1}^*)(g_i);$$

for $j \neq i$ we have

$$g_i^*(g_j) = 0 = g_{i+1}^*(T_\lambda g_j) = (T_\lambda^* g_{i+1}^*)(g_j),$$

and for every $h \in L_\nu$ we have

$$g_i^*(h) = 0 = g_{i+1}^*(T_\lambda h) = (T_\lambda^* g_{i+1}^*)(h),$$

where we have used that $T_\lambda h \in L_\nu$. Hence $g_i^*(f) = (T_\lambda^* g_{i+1}^*)(f)$ for every $f \in E$, since every $f \in E$ may be written in the form $f = \Sigma_{i=1}^q \alpha_i g_i + h$, $h \in L_\nu$. It follows that $g_i^* = T_\lambda^* g_{i+1}^*$. Considering therefore, for example, the first column of the new diagram II, it contains from top to bottom the elements $g_\nu^*, g_{\nu-1}^* = T_\lambda^* g_\nu^*, g_{\nu-2}^* = (T_\lambda^*)^2 g_\nu^*, \ldots, g_1^* = (T_\lambda^*)^{\nu-1} g_\nu^*$. To complete the proof for this column we have still to show that $(T_\lambda^*)^\nu g_\nu^* = 0$. Now $[(T_\lambda^*)^\nu g_\nu^*](f) = g_\nu^*(T_\lambda^\nu f)$. For $f \in M_\nu$ this vanishes since $T_\lambda^\nu f = 0$, and for $f \in L_\nu$ it also vanishes, since then $T_\lambda^\nu f \in L_\nu$. The proof for the other columns is similar. Finally, $g_1^*, \ldots, g_q^*$ are obviously linearly independent.

Remark. Writing the new diagram II in the form

$f_1^* \dots f_{d_\nu}^*$			
$T_\lambda^* f_1^* \dots T_\lambda^* f_{d_\nu}^*$	$f_{d_\nu+1}^* \dots f_{d_{\nu-1}}^*$		
$\vdots$	$\vdots$		
$(T_\lambda^*)^{\nu-1} f_1^* \dots (T_\lambda^*)^{\nu-1} f_{d_\nu}^*$	$(T_\lambda^*)^{\nu-2} f_{d_\nu+1}^* \dots (T_\lambda^*)^{\nu-2} f_{d_{\nu-1}}^*$	$\vdots$	$f_{d_2+1}^* \dots f_{d_1}^*$

diagram II

and denoting the elements in the last row by $e_1^*, \dots, e_d^*$ $(d = d_1)$, whereas the elements in the last row of the original diagram I are denoted by $e_1, \dots, e_d$, the linear transformation V_i, defined by $V_i f = e_i^*(f) e_i$ $(i = 1, \dots, d)$, has the property that it transforms the element f_i at the top of the i-th column of diagram I into the element at the bottom of the same column, whereas every other element of diagram I, and also every element belonging to L_ν, is transformed into the null element.

§ 4. The Resolvent

In the present paragraph we restrict ourselves to the case that the Banach space E is complete. We assume that T is a bounded linear transformation on E into E, and we also assume that there exists a positive integer p such that T^p is compact. It will be our aim to investigate the behaviour of the resolvent $R_\lambda = (T - \lambda I)^{-1}$ in the neighbourhood of a characteristic value $\lambda_0 \neq 0$ of T.

We first consider the very simple case that E is of finite dimension n, that $\{g\} = \{g_1, \dots, g_n\}$ is a coordinate system in E, and that T has the matrix $\{\tau_{ij}\}$ in this coordinate system $\{g\}$, where $\tau_{ii} = \lambda_0$ $(i = 1, \dots, n)$, $\tau_{ij} = 1$ for $i = j + 1$ and $\tau_{ij} = 0$ for $i \neq j$ and $i \neq j + 1$. This matrix has therefore numbers λ_0 on the principal diagonal, numbers one immediately below the principal diagonal and numbers zero elsewhere. Hence $Tg_i = \lambda_0 g_i + g_{i+1}$ $(i = 1, \dots, n - 1)$ and $Tg_n = \lambda_0 g_n$. In other words, $(T - \lambda_0 I) g_i = g_{i+1}$ $(i = 1, \dots, n - 1)$ and $(T - \lambda_0 I) g_n = 0$. A simple computation shows that in the matrix of $(T - \lambda I)^{-1}$ all elements above the principal diagonal vanish, that the first column consists from top to bottom of $-(\lambda - \lambda_0)^{-1}, -(\lambda - \lambda_0)^{-2}, \dots, -(\lambda - \lambda_0)^{-n}$; the second column of $0, -(\lambda - \lambda_0)^{-1}, \dots, -(\lambda - \lambda_0)^{-(n-1)}$, and so on.

Let us denote now by $V_{i,j}$ $(i, j = 1, \ldots, n)$ the linear transformation which transforms g_i into g_j, and all g_k $(k \neq i)$ into the null element. The matrix of $V_{i,j}$ has therefore a number one on the (j, i)-place and zeros elsewhere. Then it is immediately evident that

$$(T - \lambda I)^{-1} = \frac{V_{1,n}}{-(\lambda - \lambda_0)^n} + \frac{V_{1,n-1} + V_{2,n}}{-(\lambda - \lambda_0)^{n-1}} + \frac{V_{1,n-2} + V_{2,n-1} + V_{3,n}}{-(\lambda - \lambda_0)^{n-2}} + \ldots + \frac{V_{1,1} + V_{2,2} + \ldots + V_{n,n}}{-(\lambda - \lambda_0)},$$

or, denoting by V_i $(i = 0, 1, 2, \ldots)$ the linear transformation which transforms every element of the sequence $g_1, g_2, \ldots, g_n, 0, 0, \ldots$ into the element which is situated i places further on in the same sequence,

$$(T - \lambda I)^{-1} = \frac{V_{n-1}}{-(\lambda - \lambda_0)^n} + \frac{V_{n-2}}{-(\lambda - \lambda_0)^{n-1}} + \ldots + \frac{V_0}{-(\lambda - \lambda_0)}.$$

But, observing that $(T - \lambda_0 I) g_i = g_{i+1}$ $(i = 1, \ldots, n-1)$ and $(T - \lambda_0 I) g_n = 0$, we see that $V_i = (T - \lambda_0 I)^i$ $(i = 0, 1, 2, \ldots)$, hence

$$(1) \quad \left\{ \begin{aligned} (T - \lambda I)^{-1} &= \frac{(T - \lambda_0 I)^{n-1}}{-(\lambda - \lambda_0)^n} + \frac{(T - \lambda_0 I)^{n-2}}{-(\lambda - \lambda_0)^{n-1}} \\ &+ \ldots + \frac{T - \lambda_0 I}{-(\lambda - \lambda_0)^2} + \frac{I}{-(\lambda - \lambda_0)}. \end{aligned} \right.$$

Note, incidentally, that we may write also $(T - \lambda I)^{-1} = -\Sigma_{k=0}^{\infty} (T - \lambda_0 I)^k/(\lambda - \lambda_0)^{k+1}$, since $(T - \lambda_0 I)^k = O$ for $k \geqslant n$.

We next consider the case that E is the direct sum of E' and E'', where E' is of finite dimension m and E'' is of finite dimension n. Assume that $m \leqslant n$, let $\{g'\} = \{g_1', \ldots, g_m'\}$ be a coordinate system in E', and let the linear transformation T', defined on E', have a matrix in the coordinate system $\{g'\}$ consisting of numbers λ_0 on the principal diagonal, numbers one immediately below it and numbers zero elsewhere. Let, similarly, $\{g''\} = \{g_1'', \ldots, g_n''\}$ be a coordinate system in E'', and let the linear transformation T'', defined on E'', have a matrix in $\{g''\}$ consisting of numbers λ_0 on the principal diagonal, numbers one immediately below it and numbers zero elsewhere. The transformation T on E which we wish to consider is the direct sum of T' and T'', that is, $T = T'$ on E' and $T = T''$ on E''. Since T is completely reduced by (E', E''), the same holds for $T - \lambda I$, and hence also for $(T - \lambda I)^{-1}$, $\lambda \neq \lambda_0$. It follows then that $(T - \lambda I)^{-1}$ is the direct sum of $(T' - \lambda I)^{-1}$

and $(T'' - \lambda I)^{-1}$, so that, on account of $m \leqslant n$ and $(T' - \lambda_0 I)^k = O$ for $k \geqslant m$, formula (1) holds without any change. Evidently, (1) also holds in the case that E is the direct sum of the finite-dimensional subspaces $E^{(1)}, E^{(2)}, \ldots, E^{(d)}$ with maximal dimension n, and the linear transformation T on E is the direct sum of $T^{(1)}, T^{(2)}, \ldots, T^{(d)}$, where $T^{(i)}$ $(i = 1, \ldots, d)$ is defined on $E^{(i)}$ and the matrix of $T^{(i)}$ has, in a suitable coordinate system, the particular form just described for the case $d = 2$.

We are now in a position to describe the form of $(T - \lambda I)^{-1}$ in the general case mentioned at the beginning of the present paragraph. We assume that $\lambda_0 \neq 0$ is a characteristic value of T, and that $\nu = \nu(\lambda_0)$ is the index of λ_0 for T. The diagrams I and II near the end of the preceding paragraph show the structure of the null spaces $M_\nu = N[(T - \lambda_0 I)^\nu]$ and $M_\nu^* = N[(T^* - \lambda_0 I)^\nu]$ respectively. We shall first investigate the behaviour of $(T - \lambda I)^{-1}$ on M_ν. Turning our attention to diagram I, we see that it contains $d = d_1$ columns, so that, denoting by $E^{(i)}$ the subspace determined by the elements in the i-th column, M_ν is the direct sum of $E^{(1)}, \ldots, E^{(d)}$. Evidently T is reduced by each of these subspaces. Denoting by $T^{(i)}$ the linear transformation equal to T on $E^{(i)}$, the matrix of $T^{(i)}$ in the coordinate system of the elements in the i-th column has the particular form which we considered before. Observing now that the maximal dimension of $E^{(1)}, \ldots, E^{(d)}$ is exactly ν, we find, on M_ν,

$$(T - \lambda I)^{-1} = \frac{(T - \lambda_0 I)^{\nu-1}}{-(\lambda - \lambda_0)^\nu} + \frac{(T - \lambda_0 I)^{\nu-2}}{-(\lambda - \lambda_0)^{\nu-1}} + \ldots + \frac{T - \lambda_0 I}{-(\lambda - \lambda_0)^2} + \frac{I}{-(\lambda - \lambda_0)}.$$

Let us look now at $(T - \lambda I)^{-1}$ on the complementary space $L_\nu = W[(T - \lambda_0 I)^\nu]$ (by Theorem 8 of the preceding paragraph E is the direct sum of M_ν and L_ν). Since $L_\nu = L_{\nu+1}$, the space L_ν is transformed by $T - \lambda_0 I$ into all of itself, and this shows that T is reduced by L_ν, and that λ_0 is not a characteristic value of T when T is considered on L_ν only. Then λ_0, and hence also every λ in a sufficiently small neighbourhood of λ_0, belongs to the resolvent set. Hence, on L_ν,

$$(T - \lambda I)^{-1} = R_0 + (\lambda - \lambda_0)R_0^2 + (\lambda - \lambda_0)^2 R_0^3 + \ldots$$

(cf. Ch. 10, § 7, Th. 5), where $R_0 = (T - \lambda_0 I)^{-1}$ on L_ν.

Denote now by P_M the projection on M_ν along L_ν, and by P_L the projection on L_ν along M_ν, hence $P_M + P_L = I$. Then, obviously, on the whole space E,

$$(2)\quad \begin{cases} (T-\lambda I)^{-1} = \dfrac{-(T-\lambda_0 I)^{\nu-1}P_M}{(\lambda-\lambda_0)^\nu} + \dfrac{-(T-\lambda_0 I)^{\nu-2}P_M}{(\lambda-\lambda_0)^{\nu-1}} + \cdots \\ \quad + \dfrac{-(T-\lambda_0 I)P_M}{(\lambda-\lambda_0)^2} + \dfrac{-P_M}{\lambda-\lambda_0} + R_0P_L + (\lambda-\lambda_0)R_0^2P_L + \\ (\lambda-\lambda_0)^2R_0^3P_L + \cdots \end{cases}$$

for $\lambda \neq \lambda_0$ but in a sufficiently small neighbourhood of λ_0. Since $P_M = I - P_L$ we may also write

$$(3)\ (T-\lambda I)^{-1} = \frac{-(T-\lambda_0 I)^{\nu-1}}{(\lambda-\lambda_0)^\nu} + \cdots + \frac{-(T-\lambda_0 I)}{(\lambda-\lambda_0)^2} + \frac{-I}{\lambda-\lambda_0} + \\ + \Sigma_{k=-\nu}^{\infty} (\lambda-\lambda_0)^k (T-\lambda_0 I)^{-(k+1)} P_L.$$

Turning in particular our attention to the highest negative power of $\lambda - \lambda_0$ in (2), we observe that the coefficient $(T-\lambda_0 I)^{\nu-1} P_M$ of $-(\lambda-\lambda_0)^{-\nu}$ is the linear transformation which transforms every element at the top of one of the first d_ν columns in diagram I into the element at the bottom of the same column, whereas it transforms every other element of diagram I, and also every element of L_ν, into the null element. Hence, denoting the elements in the last row of diagram I and diagram II by $e_1, \ldots, e_d$ and $e_1^*, \ldots, e_d^*$ respectively, we may write for any arbitrary element $f \in E$

$$(4)\quad \frac{-(T-\lambda_0 I)^{\nu-1}P_M}{(\lambda-\lambda_0)^\nu} f = \frac{-\Sigma_{i=1}^{d_\nu} e_i^*(f)e_i}{(\lambda-\lambda_0)^\nu}.$$

In the special case that $\nu(\lambda_0) = 1$ (and this is an important case, since for example every characteristic value of a bounded normal transformation in Hilbert space has index one by Theorem 18 of the preceding paragraph), we have

$$(5)\quad (T-\lambda I)^{-1} = -P_M/(\lambda-\lambda_0) + R_0P_L + (\lambda-\lambda_0)R_0^2P_L + \cdots$$

or

$$(6)\quad (T-\lambda I)^{-1}f = -\Sigma_{i=1}^{d} e_i^*(f)e_i/(\lambda-\lambda_0) + R_0P_Lf + (\lambda-\lambda_0)\, R_0^2P_Lf + \cdots.$$

Let now λ run on the circumference of a sufficiently small circle with centre λ_0 and radius r, hence $\lambda - \lambda_0 = re^{i\varphi}$, $0 \leqslant \varphi \leqslant 2\pi$. Then $(T-\lambda I)^{-1} = R_\varphi$ may be considered as depending on φ, and it follows easily from

(2) that

$$\int_0^{2\pi} R_\varphi (\lambda - \lambda_0) d\varphi = - 2\pi P_M,$$

$$\int_0^{2\pi} R_\varphi (\lambda - \lambda_0)^2 d\varphi = - 2\pi (T - \lambda_0 I) P_M,$$

and so on. Generally

$$\int_0^{2\pi} R_\varphi (\lambda - \lambda_0)^{k+1} d\varphi = - 2\pi (T - \lambda_0 I)^k P_M \quad (k = 0, 1, 2, \ldots),$$

hence, if $p_1(\lambda - \lambda_0) = \beta_0 + \beta_1(\lambda - \lambda_0) + \ldots + \beta_k(\lambda - \lambda_0)^k$ is an arbitrary polynomial in $\lambda - \lambda_0$ with complex coefficients,

$$\int_0^{2\pi} R_\varphi p_1(\lambda - \lambda_0) . (\lambda - \lambda_0) d\varphi = - 2\pi p_1(T - \lambda_0 I) P_M.$$

Since every polynomial $p(\lambda) = \alpha_0 + \alpha_1 \lambda + \ldots + \alpha_k \lambda^k$ may be written in the form $p(\lambda) = p_1(\lambda - \lambda_0) = \beta_0 + \beta_1(\lambda - \lambda_0) + \ldots + \beta_k(\lambda - \lambda_0)^k$, we find finally

$$(7) \qquad \int_0^{2\pi} R_\varphi p(\lambda)(\lambda - \lambda_0) d\varphi = - 2\pi p(T) P_M.$$

Extensions of the theory in the present paragraph to the case that the bounded linear transformation T has not necessarily the property that one of its iterates T^p is compact may be found in papers of E. R. LORCH [6] and N. DUNFORD [7].

§ 5. Algebraic Multiplicity of a Characteristic Value for Linear Transformations of Finite Double-Norm in Hilbert Space

Let R be a complete separable Hilbert space, and let T be a linear transformation of finite double-norm on R. Then, by Ch. 9, § 17, Th. 3, the equation $(I - \lambda T)f = g$ has the unique solution $f = [\delta(\lambda)]^{-1} \Delta(\lambda) g$ for every complex λ satisfying $\delta(\lambda) \neq 0$. Here $\delta(\lambda)$ and $\Delta(\lambda)$ are powerseries:

$$\delta(\lambda) = 1 + \Sigma_{n=1}^{\infty} \delta_n \lambda^n,$$

$$\Delta(\lambda) = I + \Sigma_{n=1}^{\infty} \Delta_n \lambda^n,$$

converging for all λ. The coefficients δ_n $(n = 1, 2, \ldots)$ are complex numbers and the coefficients Δ_n $(n = 1, 2, \ldots)$ are bounded linear transformations, defined in Ch. 9, § 16, Th. 4 and 5 respectively. The function $\delta(\lambda)$ is sometimes called the *Fredholm determinant* of T.

In Ch. 9, § 17, Th. 5 it was proved that $\mu_0 \neq 0$ is a characteristic value of T if and only if $\lambda_0 = \mu_0^{-1}$ is a zero of $\delta(\lambda)$. In this case, therefore, $\delta(\lambda)$ contains at least one factor $\lambda - \lambda_0$, when written as a powerseries in

$\lambda - \lambda_0$. We shall prove now that the number of factors $\lambda - \lambda_0$ which $\delta(\lambda)$ contains is exactly the algebraic multiplicity of μ_0. For this purpose we need a preliminary theorem.

Theorem 1. *Let T_1 and T_2 be linear transformations of finite double-norm on R such that $T_1T_2 = T_2T_1 = O$ (the null transformation). Then, if $T = T_1 + T_2$, we have $\delta(\lambda) = \delta_1(\lambda)\delta_2(\lambda)$, where $\delta(\lambda)$, $\delta_1(\lambda)$ and $\delta_2(\lambda)$ are the Fredholm determinants of T, T_1 and T_2 respectively.*

Proof. Denote by σ_n, σ_{n1} and σ_{n2} the traces $\sigma_n = \tau(T^n)$, $\sigma_{n1} = \tau(T_1^n)$ and $\sigma_{n2} = \tau(T_2^n)$ $(n = 2, 3, \ldots)$ respectively. All these traces are finite by Ch. 9, § 10, Th. 6. Since, on account of $T_1T_2 = T_2T_1 = O$, we have $T^n = T_1^n + T_2^n$ $(n = 1, 2, \ldots)$, we have also $\sigma_n = \sigma_{n1} + \sigma_{n2}$ $(n = 2, 3, \ldots)$. Observing next that the coefficients in $\delta(\lambda) = 1 + \Sigma_{n=1}^{\infty} \delta_n\lambda^n$ are defined by the formulas in Ch. 9, § 16, Th. 4, it follows from an inspection of the proof of that theorem that

$$\delta'(\lambda)/\delta(\lambda) = - \Sigma_{n=1}^{\infty} \sigma_{n+1}\lambda^n$$

for $|\lambda|$ sufficiently small. Similar expressions are found for $\delta_1'(\lambda)/\delta_1(\lambda)$ and $\delta_2'(\lambda)/\delta_2(\lambda)$; hence

$$\frac{\delta'(\lambda)}{\delta(\lambda)} = \frac{\delta_1'(\lambda)}{\delta_1(\lambda)} + \frac{\delta_2'(\lambda)}{\delta_2(\lambda)}$$

for λ in a small circle around $\lambda = 0$. Writing now $\delta_1(\lambda)\delta_2(\lambda) = p(\lambda)\delta(\lambda)$ for λ in this circle, we find

$$\delta_1'\delta_2 + \delta_1\delta_2' = p'\delta + p\delta',$$

$$\delta_1\delta_2\left(\frac{\delta_1'}{\delta_1} + \frac{\delta_2'}{\delta_2}\right) = p\delta\left(\frac{p'}{p} + \frac{\delta'}{\delta}\right),$$

hence $p'(\lambda) = 0$ in this circle. Consequently, $p(\lambda)$ is constant in this circle. Since $\delta(0) = \delta_1(0) = \delta_2(0) = 1$, we find $p(\lambda) = 1$, so that $\delta(\lambda) = \delta_1(\lambda)\delta_2(\lambda)$ in the neighbourhood of $\lambda = 0$. Then, however, $\delta(\lambda) = \delta_1(\lambda)\delta_2(\lambda)$ for all λ (cf. Ch. 9, § 17, Lemma α).

Theorem 2. *If $\mu_0 \neq 0$ is a characteristic value with algebraic multiplicity q of the linear transformation T of finite double-norm on R, and if $\lambda_0 = \mu_0^{-1}$, then the Fredholm determinant $\delta(\lambda)$ contains exactly the factor $(\lambda - \lambda_0)^q$ when written as a powerseries in $\lambda - \lambda_0$.*

Proof. Let μ_0 have the index ν for T. Then R is the direct sum of the null space $M_\nu = N[(T - \mu_0 I)^\nu]$ and the range $L_\nu = W[(T - \mu_0 I)^\nu]$. The algebraic multiplicity q of μ_0 is by definition the dimension of M_ν.

By Ch. 9, § 14, Th. 1, $M_\nu^* = N[(T^* - \bar{\mu}_0 I)^\nu]$ is the orthogonal complement of L_ν, and $L_\nu^* = W[(T^* - \bar{\mu}_0 I)^\nu]$ is the orthogonal complement of M_ν. To avoid misunderstandings we observe that T^* is here the Hilbert-adjoint of T, so hat $T^* - \bar{\mu}_0 I$ is the Hilbert-adjoint of $T - \mu_0 I$.

Let now

$$\begin{cases} T_1 = T \text{ on } L_\nu, \\ T_1 = O \text{ on } M_\nu, \end{cases} \qquad \begin{cases} T_2 = O \text{ on } L_\nu, \\ T_2 = T \text{ on } M_\nu. \end{cases}$$

Then, evidently, $T = T_1 + T_2$ and $T_1 T_2 = T_2 T_1 = O$, where we have used that T is reduced both by L_ν and M_ν. Since $T_1 - \mu_0 I$, and therefore also $I - \lambda_0 T_1$, transforms the whole space R one-to-one into all of itself, μ_0 is no characteristic value of T_1. Hence $\delta_1(\lambda_0) \neq 0$.

We prove next that $T_2^* = O$ on L_ν^* and $T_2^* = T^*$ on M_ν^*. If $g \in R$ is arbitrary, we shall write $g = g_1 + g_2$ for the unique decomposition of g into an element $g_1 \in L_\nu$ and an element $g_2 \in M_\nu$. Then, if $f \in L_\nu^*$, we have

$$(T_2^* f, g) = (f, T_2 g_1 + T_2 g_2) = 0,$$

since $T_2 g_1 = 0$ and $T_2 g_2 = T g_2 \in M_\nu = R \ominus L_\nu^*$. Hence $T_2^* = O$ on L_ν^*. If $f \in M_\nu^*$, then

$$(T_2^* f, g) = (f, T_2 g_1 + T_2 g_2) = (f, T g_2) = (f, T g_1 + T g_2) = (T^* f, g),$$

hence $T_2^* = T^*$ on M_ν^*. Now, since $T_2 = O$ on L_ν, it is obviously sufficient in order to find the trace $\sigma_{n2} = \tau(T_2^n)$ to consider an orthonormal system $\varphi_1, \ldots, \varphi_q$ in $M_\nu^* = R \ominus L_\nu$, and to observe that $\sigma_{n2} = \Sigma_{i=1}^q (T_2^n \varphi_i, \varphi_i)$. Then

$$\sigma_{n2} = \Sigma_{i=1}^q (\varphi_i, (T_2^*)^n \varphi_i) = \Sigma_{i=1}^q (\varphi_i, (T^*)^n \varphi_i) = \overline{\sigma_n^*},$$

where $\sigma_n^* = \tau[(T^*)^n]$ under the restriction that T^* is only considered on the q-dimensional space M_ν^*. Hence, upon inspecting the formula for the coefficients δ_{n2} in the powerseries $\delta_2(\lambda) = 1 + \Sigma_{n=1}^\infty \delta_{n2} \lambda^n$ (cf. Ch. 9, § 16, Th. 4), $\delta_2(\lambda) = \overline{\delta^*(\bar{\lambda})}$, where $\delta^*(\lambda)$ is the Fredholm determinant of T^* on M_ν^*. But, denoting by σ_1^* the trace $\tau(T^*)$ on M_ν^*, we have (cf. Ch. 9, § 16)

$$\delta^*(\bar{\lambda}) = e^{\sigma_1^* \bar{\lambda}} d^*(\bar{\lambda}) = e^{\sigma_1^* \bar{\lambda}} \, det\,(I - \bar{\lambda} T^*) =$$

$$e^{\sigma_1^* \bar{\lambda}} (1 - \overline{\mu_0 \lambda})^q = e^{\sigma_1^* \bar{\lambda}} \bar{\mu}_0^q (\bar{\lambda}_0 - \bar{\lambda})^q,$$

since T^* has on M_ν^* only the characteristic value $\bar{\mu}_0$. It follows that $\delta_2(\lambda)$ contains exactly the factor $(\lambda - \lambda_0)^q$. Since $\delta(\lambda) = \delta_1(\lambda)\delta_2(\lambda)$ by Theorem 1, $\delta(\lambda)$ also contains exactly the factor $(\lambda - \lambda_0)^q$.

§ 6. The Characteristic Values of $p(T)$, where $p(T)$ is a Polynomial in T

If E is a Banach space of finite dimension n, and T is a linear transformation on E with characteristic values λ_i $(i = 1, \ldots, n)$, then $p(T) = \alpha_0 I + \alpha_1 T + \ldots + \alpha_k T^k$ (α_i complex) has the characteristic values $p(\lambda_i) = \alpha_0 + \alpha_1 \lambda_i + \ldots + \alpha_k \lambda_i^k$ $(i = 1, \ldots, n)$. This was proved in Ch. 8, § 6. A similar fact holds in case E is an arbitrary Banach space, complete or non-complete, and T has the property that one of its iterates T^p is compact.

We shall use similar notations as before. If therefore $\lambda \neq 0$ is a complex number with index ν for T, we write $M = M(T; \lambda)$ for the null space $N[(T - \lambda I)^\nu]$ and $L = L(T; \lambda)$ for the range $W[(T - \lambda I)^\nu]$. We observe that for $\nu = 0$ the space M contains only the null element, whereas L is then identical with the whole space E.

Theorem 1. *If $\lambda_1, \ldots, \lambda_k$ are different complex numbers, all $\neq 0$, with indices $\nu_1, \ldots, \nu_k$ for T, then the whole space E is the direct sum of $M_1 = M(T; \lambda_1), \ldots, M_k = M(T; \lambda_k)$ and $\Pi_{i=1}^k L_i = \Pi_{i=1}^k L(T; \lambda_i)$.*

Proof. We first prove that $M_i \subset L_j$ for $i \neq j$ $(i, j = 1, \ldots, k)$. If $\nu_i = 0$, the statement is trivial. If $\nu_i > 0$, T is reduced by M_i and has on M_i only the characteristic value λ_i, so that $T - \lambda_j I$ transforms M_i one-to-one into all of itself. The same holds then for $(T - \lambda_j I)^{\nu_j}$, and this show that $M_i \subset L_j$.

Suppose now that $f_i \in M_i$ $(i = 1, \ldots, k)$ and $g = \Sigma_{i=1}^k f_i \in \Pi_{j=1}^k L_j$. Since, by what we have just proved, $f_i \in M_i \subset L_1$ for $i \neq 1$, we have $f_1 = g - (f_2 + \ldots + f_k) \in L_1$. But $f_1 \in M_1$ as well, hence $f_1 = 0$. In the same way $f_2 = \ldots = f_k = 0$. It follows that the linear subspace of all elements $\Sigma_{i=1}^k f_i$, where $f_i \in M_i$, has only the null element in common with the linear subspace $\Pi_{j=1}^k L_j$. Let now n be one of the numbers $1, \ldots, k$. Then, similarly, the linear subspace of all $\Sigma_{i \neq n} f_i$, with $f_i \in M_i$, has only the null element in common with the linear subspace $\Pi_{j \neq n} L_j$. Since $M_n \subset \Pi_{j \neq n} L_j$, we may conclude that M_n has only the null element in common with the subspace of all $\Sigma_{i \neq n} f_i$, $f_i \in M_i$. This shows that the subspace of all $\Sigma_{i=1}^k f_i$, $f_i \in M_i$, is the direct sum of $M_1, \ldots, M_k$. We observe, incidentally, that this fact may also be concluded from Ch. 10, § 9, Th. 3, which asserts that $f_i \in M_i$ $(i = 1, \ldots, k)$ implies the linear independence of $f_1, \ldots, f_k$.

It remains to prove only that every $f \in E$ may be written in the form $f = \Sigma_{i=1}^k f_i + g$, $f_i \in M_i$, $g \in \Pi_{i=1}^k L_i$, since, once the possibility of this decomposition is shown, its uniqueness follows from the already established facts. If $f \in E$ is arbitrary, we have $f = f_i + g_i$, $f_i \in M_i$, $g_i \in L_i$ ($i = 1, \ldots, k$), since E is the direct sum of M_i and L_i. Writing $f - \Sigma_{i=1}^k f_i = g$, we have $g = (f - f_j) - \Sigma_{i \neq j} f_i = g_j - \Sigma_{i \neq j} f_i \in L_j$ for $j = 1, \ldots, k$. Hence $g \in \Pi_{j=1}^k L_j$. This completes the proof.

Let now $p(\lambda) = \alpha_1 \lambda + \ldots + \alpha_n \lambda^n$ be an arbitrary polynomial in λ, satisfying $p(0) = 0$, and let $\mu \neq 0$ be complex. Suppose that $p(\lambda) - \mu = (\lambda - \lambda_1)^{n_1}(\lambda - \lambda_2)^{n_2} \ldots (\lambda - \lambda_k)^{n_k}$, where the numbers $\lambda_1, \ldots, \lambda_k$, all $\neq 0$, are the different solutions of $p(\lambda) = \mu$. The bounded linear transformation $p(T) = \alpha_1 T + \ldots + \alpha_n T^n$ has, as well as T itself, the property that one of its iterates is compact, so that the theory, developed for T, holds for $p(T)$ as well. If $\mu \neq 0$ has the index ν_p for $p(T)$, we write $M[p(T); \mu]$ for the null space $N[\{p(T) - \mu I\}^{\nu_p}]$ and $L[p(T); \mu]$ for the range $W[\{p(T) - \mu I\}^{\nu_p}]$.

Theorem 2. *If $\mu \neq 0$, and $p(\lambda) = \mu$ has the different solutions $\lambda_1, \ldots, \lambda_k$, then $M[p(T); \mu]$ is the direct sum of $M_1, \ldots, M_k$, where $M_i = M(T; \lambda_i)$.*

Proof. If $f \in M_i$, hence $(T - \lambda_i I)^{\nu_i} f = 0$, then $\{(T - \lambda_1 I)^{n_1} \ldots (T - \lambda_k I)^{n_k}\}^{\nu_i} f = 0$ or $\{p(T) - \mu I\}^{\nu_i} f = 0$. Hence, if $f = \Sigma_{i=1}^k f_i$, $f_i \in M_i$, and $\nu = \max(\nu_1, \ldots, \nu_k)$, then $\{p(T) - \mu I\}^{\nu} f = 0$, so that $f \in M[p(T); \mu]$. It follows that the direct sum of $M_1, \ldots, M_k$ is contained in $M[p(T); \mu]$.

By the preceding theorem E is the direct sum of $M_1, \ldots, M_k$ and $S = \Pi_{j=1}^k L_j$, where T, and hence $p(T) - \mu I$ as well, is reduced by each of these subspaces. Since $T - \lambda_1 I, \ldots, T - \lambda_k I$ transform S one-to-one into all of itself, $p(T) - \mu I$ has the same property, and this implies that every $g \in S$ may be written in the form $\{p(T) - \mu I\}^{\nu_p} f$. Hence $S \subset L[p(T); \mu]$.

Observing now that E is the direct sum of $M_1, \ldots, M_k$, S as well as the direct sum of $M[p(T); \mu]$ and $L[p(T); \mu]$, that the direct sum of $M_1, \ldots, M_k$ is contained in $M[p(T); \mu]$, and S is contained in $L[p(T); \mu]$, we may draw the conclusion that $M[p(T); \mu]$ is the direct sum of $M_1, \ldots, M_k$.

The following theorem is now evident.

Theorem 3. *If T has the characteristic values $\lambda_1, \lambda_2, \ldots \neq 0$, where each characteristic value is repeated according to its algebraic multiplicity, and $p(\lambda) = \alpha_1 \lambda + \ldots + \alpha_n \lambda^n$, then $p(\lambda_1), p(\lambda_2), \ldots$, insofar as these numbers are $\neq 0$, are the characteristic values $\neq 0$ of $p(T) = \alpha_1 T + \ldots + \alpha_n T^n$, where the number of repetitions of a given number in this sequence is its algebraic multiplicity.*

§ 7. The Characteristic Values of Linear Transformations of Finite Double-Norm in Hilbert Space

We assume that R is a separable complete Hilbert space. The first theorem we shall prove in the present paragraph asserts that if $T = AB$, where A and B are linear transformations of finite double-norm in R, and $\lambda_1, \lambda_2, \ldots$ is the sequence of characteristic values $\neq 0$ of T, each characteristic value repeated according to its algebraic multiplicity, then $\Sigma |\lambda_i| < \infty$. This theorem was proved by T. Lalesco [8] in a special case, and by R. Gheorghiu [9] and E. Hille and J. D. Tamarkin [10] in the general case we consider here.

Theorem 1 (*Lalesco's Theorem*). *Let $T = AB$, where A and B are linear transformations of finite double-norm in R, and let $\lambda_1, \lambda_2, \ldots$ be the sequence of characteristic values $\neq 0$ of T arranged in some order (e.g. such that $|\lambda_1| \geqslant |\lambda_2| \geqslant \ldots$), each characteristic value repeated according to its algebraic multiplicity. Then $\Sigma |\lambda_i| \leqslant |||A|||.|||B||| < \infty$.*

Proof. Denote by $\mu_1, \mu_2, \ldots$ the different characteristic values $\neq 0$ of T arranged such that $|\mu_1| \geqslant |\mu_2| \geqslant \ldots$. Let μ_i have the index ν_i and the algebraic multiplicity q_i $(i = 1, 2, \ldots)$. The q_i-dimensional null space $N[(T - \mu_i I)^{\nu_i}]$ is denoted by M_i. Since T is reduced by each of the spaces M_i, T is also reduced by S_n, the direct sum of $M_1, \ldots, M_n$. The dimension s_n of S_n is given by $s_n = \Sigma_{i=1}^n q_i$. By Ch. 8, § 6, Th. 2 there exists a coordinate system $\{\varphi\} = \{\varphi_1, \varphi_2, \ldots, \varphi_{s_n}\}$ in S_n such that the matrix of T in this coordinate system has the superdiagonal form. Obviously we may suppose that the system $\{\varphi\}$ is orthonormal (Schmidt's orthogonalization process). The numbers on the principal diagonal of this matrix are the characteristic values of T on S_n, hence μ_1 (q_1 times), $\ldots$, μ_n (q_n times). This implies $\Sigma_{i=1}^{s_n} |(T\varphi_i, \varphi_i)| = \Sigma_{i=1}^n q_i |\mu_i|$. Let now $R_n = R \ominus S_n$ be the orthogonal complement of S_n, and let $\varphi_j (j = s_n + 1, s_n + 2, \ldots)$ be a complete orthonormal system in R_n. Then $\varphi_1, \varphi_2, \ldots$ is complete and orthonormal in the whole space R. Writing now $\alpha_{ij} = (A\varphi_j, \varphi_i)$, $\beta_{ij} = (B\varphi_j, \varphi_i)$, $\tau_{ij} = (T\varphi_j, \varphi_i)$ $(i, j = 1, 2, \ldots)$, we have $\tau_{ii} = \Sigma_j \alpha_{ij}\beta_{ji}$, hence $(\Sigma_i |\tau_{ii}|)^2 \leqslant \Sigma_{ij} |\alpha_{ij}|^2 \Sigma_{ij} |\beta_{ij}|^2 = |||A|||^2.|||B|||^2$. This implies $\Sigma_{i=1}^n q_i |\mu_i| = \Sigma_{i=1}^{s_n} |\tau_{ii}| \leqslant |||A|||.|||B|||$, or, since n is arbitrary,

$$\Sigma_1^\infty |\lambda_i| = \Sigma_1^\infty q_i |\mu_i| \leqslant |||A|||.|||B||| < \infty.$$

Theorem 2 (*Schur's Theorem* [11]). *Let T be of finite double-norm in R, and let $\lambda_1, \lambda_2, \ldots$ be the sequence of characteristic values $\neq 0$ of T arranged in some order (e.g. such that $|\lambda_1| \geqslant |\lambda_2| \geqslant \ldots$), each characteristic value* *repeated according to its algebraic multiplicity. Then* $\Sigma\,|\,\lambda_i\,|^2 \leqslant |||\,T\,|||^2 < \infty$.

Proof. By Theorem 3 of the preceding paragraph T^2 has the characteristic values $\lambda_1^2, \lambda_2^2, \ldots$, where the number of repetitions of a given number in this sequence is its algebraic multiplicity. Hence, by the preceding theorem, $\Sigma\,|\,\lambda_i\,|^2 \leqslant |||\,T\,|||^2 < \infty$.

Remark. Schur's Theorem is the best of its kind in the sense that the exponent 2 in $\Sigma\,|\,\lambda_i\,|^2$ cannot be lowered. Indeed, let $\lambda_1 = 0$, $\lambda_n = n^{-1/2}(\log n)^{-1}$ for $n = 2, 3, \ldots$. Then $\Sigma\,|\,\lambda_n\,|^2 < \infty$ and $\Sigma\,|\,\lambda_n\,|^\rho = \infty$ for $\rho < 2$. Defining now, if φ_n $(n = 1, 2, \ldots)$ is a complete orthonormal system in R, the linear transformation T by $T\varphi_n = \lambda_n\varphi_n$ $(n = 1, 2, \ldots)$, this transformation T is of finite double-norm on account of $|||\,T\,|||^2 = \Sigma\,\|\,T\varphi_i\,\|^2 = \Sigma\,|\,\lambda_i\,|^2 < \infty$, and the numbers $\lambda_1, \lambda_2, \ldots$ are exactly the characteristic values of T. We observe incidentally that T is positive, since for an arbitrary $f = \Sigma\,\alpha_i\varphi_i$ we have $(Tf, f) = (\Sigma\,\lambda_i\alpha_i\varphi_i, \Sigma\,\alpha_i\varphi_i) = \Sigma\,\lambda_i\,|\,\alpha_i\,|^2 \geqslant 0$.

Lemma α. *Let* $\rho > 0$ *and let* T, *of finite double-norm in* R, *have no characteristic values exceeding* $(2\rho)^{-1}$ *in absolute value. In other words, let the Fredholm determinant* $\delta(\lambda)$ *of* T *have no zeros satisfying* $|\,\lambda\,| < 2\rho$. *Then the traces* $\sigma_n = \tau(T^n)$ *satisfy*

$$|\,\sigma_n\,| \leqslant |||\,T\,|||^2/\rho^{n-2} \quad (n = 2, 3, \ldots).$$

Proof. We suppose that the system $\varphi_1, \varphi_2, \ldots$ is complete and orthonormal in R. If p is a positive integer, the subspace determined by $\varphi_1, \ldots, \varphi_p$ is denoted by R_p, and the orthogonal projection P_p and the linear transformation T_p are defined by $P_p\,(\Sigma_1^\infty\,\alpha_i\varphi_i) = \Sigma_1^p\,\alpha_i\varphi_i$ and $T_p = P_pTP_p$ respectively (cf. Ch. 9, § 17). The Fredholm determinants of T and T_p are $\delta(\lambda) = 1 + \Sigma_{n=1}^\infty\,\delta_n\lambda^n$ and $\delta_p(\lambda) = 1 + \Sigma_{n=1}^\infty\,\delta_{np}\lambda^n$ respectively, the traces $\tau(T_p^n)$ are denoted by σ_{np}. In Ch. 9, § 17, Th. 1 and Th. 2 we have seen that $|||\,T_p\,||| \leqslant |||\,T\,|||$,

$$(1) \qquad \left.\begin{matrix} |\,\delta_{np}\,| \\ |\,\delta_n\,| \end{matrix}\right\} \leqslant e^{n/2}\,|||\,T\,|||^n/n^{n/2} \quad (n, p = 1, 2, \ldots),$$

$\lim_{p\to\infty}\delta_{np} = \delta_n$ $(n = 1, 2, \ldots)$ and $\lim_{p\to\infty}\sigma_{np} = \sigma_n$ $(n = 2, 3, \ldots)$. Observing now that $\delta(\lambda) \neq 0$ for $|\,\lambda\,| < 2\rho$, we infer the existence of a positive number $\varepsilon(\rho)$ such that $|\,\delta(\lambda)\,| \geqslant \varepsilon(\rho)$ for $|\,\lambda\,| \leqslant \rho$. Then, on account of (1), there is an index $N(\rho)$ such that $\Sigma_{N+1}^\infty\,|\,\delta_n\lambda^n\,| < \varepsilon/4$ for $|\,\lambda\,| \leqslant \rho$ and $\Sigma_{N+1}^\infty\,|\,\delta_{np}\lambda^n\,| < \varepsilon/4$ for $|\,\lambda\,| \leqslant \rho$ and $p = 1, 2, \ldots$. Finally, since $\lim_{p\to\infty}\delta_{np} = \delta_n$ $(n = 1, 2, \ldots)$, there exists an index $p_0(\rho)$ such that $|\Sigma_1^N \delta_n\lambda^n - \Sigma_1^N \delta_{np}\lambda^n| < \varepsilon/4$ for all $p \geqslant p_0$ and $|\lambda| \leqslant \rho$. Hence, for $p \geqslant p_0$ and $|\lambda| \leqslant \rho$,

$$|\delta(\lambda) - \delta_p(\lambda)| \leqslant |\Sigma_1^N \delta_n\lambda^n - \Sigma_1^N \lambda_{np}\lambda^n| + \varepsilon/2 < 3\varepsilon/4,$$

and this shows that $\delta_p(\lambda) \neq 0$ for $|\lambda| \leqslant \rho$ provided $p \geqslant p_0(\rho)$. It follows that the characteristic values of T_p do not exceed ρ^{-1} in absolute value for $p \geqslant p_0(\rho)$. Denoting the characteristic values of T_p on the subspace R_p by $\lambda_{1p}, \lambda_{2p}, \ldots, \lambda_{pp}$ (the definition of T_p implies that T_p may essentially be considered as a linear transformation on R_p), we have $\sigma_{np} = \Sigma_{i=1}^p \lambda_{ip}^n$ $(n = 2, 3, \ldots)$. Hence

$$|\sigma_{2p}| \leqslant \Sigma_{i=1}^p |\lambda_{ip}|^2 \leqslant |||T_p|||^2 \leqslant |||T|||^2 \quad (p = 1, 2, \ldots),$$

$$|\sigma_{np}| \leqslant \Sigma_{i=1}^p |\lambda_{ip}|^n \leqslant \Sigma_{i=1}^p |\lambda_{ip}|^2/\rho^{n-2} \leqslant |||T|||^2/\rho^{n-2}$$
$$(n = 2, 3, \ldots;\ \ p \geqslant p_0(\rho)).$$

Since $\lim_{p\to\infty} \sigma_{np} = \sigma_n$ $(n = 2, 3, \ldots)$, this implies

$$|\sigma_n| \leqslant |||T|||^2/\rho^{n-2} \ (n = 2, 3, \ldots).$$

Theorem 3. *Let T be of finite double-norm in R, and let $\lambda_1, \lambda_2, \ldots$ be the sequence of characteristic values $\neq 0$ of T, each characteristic value repeated according to its algebraic multiplicity. Then $\sigma_n = \tau(T^n) = \Sigma_i \lambda_i^n$ $(n = 3, 4, \ldots)$.*

Proof. Denote by $\mu_1, \mu_2, \ldots$ the different characteristic values $\neq 0$ of T arranged such that $|\mu_1| \geqslant |\mu_2| \geqslant \ldots$. Let μ_i have the index ν_i and the algebraic multiplicity q_i $(i = 1, 2, \ldots)$. The q_i-dimensional null space $N[(T - \mu_i I)^{\nu_i}]$ is denoted by M_i and the range $W[(T - \mu_i I)^{\nu_i}]$ by L_i. In the same way we write $M_i^* = N[(T^* - \overline{\mu_i}I)^{\nu_i}]$ and $L_i^* = W[(T^* - \overline{\mu_i}I)^{\nu_i}]$. We recall that M_i, L_i^* and M_i^*, L_i are pairs of orthogonal complements. By Theorem 1 of the preceding paragraph the whole space R is the direct sum of S_k and P_k, where S_k is the direct sum of $M_1, \ldots, M_k$ and $P_k = \Pi_{i=1}^k L_i$. In the same way R is the direct sum of S_k^* and P_k^*, where S_k^* is the direct sum of $M_1^*, \ldots, M_k^*$ and $P_k^* = \Pi_{i=1}^k L_i^*$.

We prove first that S_k^* is the orthogonal complement of P_k. Indeed, if $f \in M_i^*$, then $(f, g) = 0$ for all $g \in L_i$; hence, if $f \in S_k^*$, then $(f, g) = 0$ for all $g \in P_k = \Pi_{i=1}^k L_i$. Supposing conversely that f does not belong to S_k^* and that nevertheless $(f, g) = 0$ for all $g \in P_k$, there exists also an element $f_1 \in P_k^*$ such that $f_1 \neq 0$ and $(f_1, g) = 0$ for all $g \in P_k$. But $f_1 \in P_k^*$ implies $(f_1, g) = 0$ for all $g \in S_k$; hence $(f_1, g) = 0$ for all $g \in R$ or $f_1 = 0$. This is a contradiction. The desired result $S_k^* = R \ominus P_k$ follows therefore. In the same way $P_k^* = R \ominus S_k$.

Let now

$$\begin{cases} T_1 = T \text{ on } S_k, \\ T_1 = O \text{ on } P_k, \end{cases} \qquad \begin{cases} T_2 = O \text{ on } S_k, \\ T_2 = T \text{ on } P_k. \end{cases}$$

Then, evidently, $T = T_1 + T_2$ and $T_1T_2 = T_2T_1 = O$, since T is reduced both by S_k and P_k. Hence $\sigma_n = \tau(T^n) = \tau(T_1^n + T_2^n) = \sigma_{n1} + \sigma_{n2}$ $(n = 2, 3, \ldots)$. Furthermore it is easily proved that

$$\begin{cases} T_1^* = T^* \text{ on } S_k^*, \\ T_1^* = O \quad \text{on } P_k^*, \end{cases} \qquad \begin{cases} T_2^* = O \quad \text{on } S_k^*, \\ T_2^* = T^* \text{ on } P_k^*. \end{cases}$$

(compare the proof of § 5, Th. 2). Now, to calculate σ_{n2}, we suppose that $\varphi_1, \ldots, \varphi_s$ $(s = q_1 + \ldots + q_k)$ is a complete orthonormal system in S_k^* and that $\varphi_{s+1}, \varphi_{s+2}, \ldots$ is complete and orthonormal in $P_k = R \ominus S_k^*$. Then

$$\sigma_{n2} = \Sigma_{i=1}^s (T_2^n\varphi_i, \varphi_i) + \Sigma_{i=s+1}^\infty (T_2^n\varphi_i, \varphi_i) =$$

$$\Sigma_1^s (\varphi_i, (T_2^*)^n\varphi_i) + \Sigma_{s+1}^\infty (T^n\varphi_i, \varphi_i) = 0 + \sigma_n',$$

where $\sigma_n' = \tau(T^n)$ under the restriction that T is only considered on P_k. Obviously the double-norm $|||\, T \,|||$ for the restricted T does not exceed the double-norm $|||\, T \,|||$ for T considered in the whole space. Hence, since the restricted T has only characteristic values not exceeding $|\mu_{k+1}|$ in absolute value, we find by the preceding lemma

$$|\sigma_{n2}| = |\sigma_n'| \leqslant |||\, T \,|||^2 (2\,|\mu_{k+1}|)^{n-2} \; (n = 2, 3, \ldots).$$

Next, considering T_1, let $\psi_1, \ldots, \psi_s$ and $\psi_{s+1}, \psi_{s+2}, \ldots$ be complete and orthonormal in S_k and P_k^* respectively. Then

$$\sigma_{n1} = \Sigma_{i=1}^s (T_1^n\psi_i, \psi_i) + \Sigma_{i=s+1}^\infty (T_1^n\psi_i, \psi_i) =$$

$$\Sigma_1^s (T^n\psi_i, \psi_i) + \Sigma_{s+1}^\infty (\psi_i, (T_1^*)^n\psi_i) = \sigma_n'' + 0,$$

where $\sigma_n'' = \tau(T^n)$ under the restriction that T is only considered on S_k. But then $\sigma_{n1} = \sigma_n'' = \Sigma_{i=1}^k q_i\mu_i^n$, hence

$$|\sigma_n - \Sigma_{i=1}^k q_i\mu_i^n| = |\sigma_n - \sigma_{n1}| = |\sigma_{n2}| \leqslant$$

$$|||\, T \,|||^2 (2\,|\mu_{k+1}|)^{n-2} \quad (n = 2, 3, \ldots).$$

On account of $\lim \mu_{k+1} = 0$ we may finally draw the conclusion that

$$\sigma_n = \Sigma\, q_i\mu_i^n = \Sigma\, \lambda_i^n \; (n = 3, 4, \ldots).$$

Remark. If the number of characteristic values $\neq 0$ of T is finite, a small and obvious modification of the proof is necessary.

Theorem 4. *If T is of finite double-norm in R and has no characteristic values $\neq 0$, then $\sigma_n = 0$ $(n = 3, 4, \ldots)$. If conversely, for a positive integer $N \geqslant 2$, $\sigma_n = 0$ for $n > N$, then T has no characteristic values $\neq 0$.*

Proof. If T has no characteristic values $\neq 0$, then $\sigma_n = 0$ $(n = 3, 4, \ldots)$ by the preceding theorem. If conversely $\sigma_n = 0$ for $n > N$, then $\delta'(\lambda)/\delta(\lambda) = -(\sigma_2\lambda + \ldots + \sigma_N\lambda^{N-1})$ for $|\lambda|$ sufficiently small (cf. Ch. 9, § 16, Th. 4), which implies $\delta(\lambda) = e^{p(\lambda)}$ for these values of λ, where $p(\lambda) = -(2^{-1}\sigma_2\lambda^2 + \ldots + N^{-1}\sigma_N\lambda^N)$. But, since both $\delta(\lambda)$ and $e^{p(\lambda)}$ may be written as everywhere converging power series in λ, the equality $\delta(\lambda) = e^{p(\lambda)}$ must hold for all values of λ. This shows that $\delta(\lambda) \neq 0$ for every λ, so that T has no characteristic value $\neq 0$.

§ 8. A Sufficient Condition for Compactness in Hilbert Space, and an Example of a Compact Linear Transformation none of whose Iterates is of Finite Double-Norm

Given the compact normal transformation A in the Hilbert space R, we know already that A has a finite or enumerably infinite number of characteristic values $\lambda_n \neq 0$, and that $\lim \lambda_n = 0$ in the latter case. Ranging them into a sequence $\lambda_1, \lambda_2, \ldots$, where every characteristic value is repeated according to its multiplicity (for a normal transformation geometric and algebraic multiplicity are identical), there exists an orthonormal sequence $\varphi_1, \varphi_2, \ldots$ such that $A\varphi_i = \lambda_i\varphi_i$ $(i = 1, 2, \ldots)$. Indeed, characteristic elements belonging to different characteristic values are orthogonal by Ch. 9, § 15, Th. 1, and for every null space $N(A - \lambda_i I)$ we may determine an orthonormal coordinate system. We shall see later that every $f \in R$ for which $(f, \varphi_i) = 0$ $(i = 1, 2, \ldots)$ satisfies $Af = 0$. It is now interesting that a converse theorem holds under condition that the space R is complete.

Theorem 1. *Let A be a bounded normal transformation in the complete Hilbert space R satisfying:*

1°. Every characteristic value $\neq 0$ of A has finite multiplicity. The number of characteristic values $\lambda \neq 0$ is finite or enumerably infinite, and in the latter case $\lim \lambda = 0$.

2°. Ranging these characteristic values $\neq 0$ into a sequence $\lambda_1, \lambda_2, \ldots$, where every characteristic value $\neq 0$ is repeated according to its multiplicity, and $\varphi_1, \varphi_2, \ldots$ being a corresponding orthonormal sequence of characteristic elements, every element $f \in R$ for which $(f, \varphi_i) = 0$ $(i = 1, 2, \ldots)$ satisfies $Af = 0$.

If A satisfies these conditions, A is compact.

Proof. Since for any bounded normal transformation A the relation $(A - \lambda I)^p f = 0$ for an integer $p \geqslant 1$ implies $(A - \lambda I)f = 0$ by Ch. 9, § 15, Th. 7, we may say that also in the case which we consider here the geometric and algebraic multiplicity of a characteristic value $\neq 0$ are identical. It is therefore allowed to speak simply of multiplicity in our hypotheses.

Evidently we may suppose that $|\lambda_1| \geqslant |\lambda_2| \geqslant \ldots$. If $f \in R$ is arbitrary and $\alpha_i = (f, \varphi_i)$ $(i = 1, 2, \ldots)$, we infer from Bessel's inequality $\Sigma |\alpha_i|^2 \leqslant \|f\|^2$ and from the completeness of the space R that $\Sigma \alpha_i \varphi_i$ exists. The element $h = f - \Sigma \alpha_i \varphi_i$ fulfils then the condition $(h, \varphi_n) = 0$ for $n = 1, 2, \ldots$, so that by hypothesis $Ah = 0$. Furthermore, in the case that the number of characteristic values λ_i is infinite, we have $\lim \lambda_i = 0$ which shows that $\Sigma |\lambda_i \alpha_i|^2 < \infty$. It follows then that $\Sigma \lambda_i \alpha_i \varphi_i$ exists. From $A(\Sigma_1^n \alpha_i \varphi_i + h) = \Sigma_1^n \alpha_i A \varphi_i + Ah = \Sigma_1^n \lambda_i \alpha_i \varphi_i$, holding for every finite value of n (in the case that the total number N of characteristic values λ_i is finite, we suppose of course $n \leqslant N$), we conclude therefore on account of the continuity of A that $Af = \Sigma \lambda_i \alpha_i \varphi_i$.

Denoting by $L[\varphi_1, \ldots, \varphi_n]$ the n-dimensional space determined by $\varphi_1, \ldots, \varphi_n$, we have now for any $f \in R \ominus L[\varphi_1, \ldots, \varphi_n]$ the relation $Af = \Sigma_{n+1} \lambda_i \alpha_i \varphi_i$, hence $\|Af\|^2 = \Sigma_{n+1} |\lambda_i \alpha_i|^2 \leqslant |\lambda_{n+1}|^2 . \|f\|^2$ or $\|Af\| \leqslant |\lambda_{n+1}| . \|f\|$. In the case that the total number N of characteristic values λ_i is finite, the same argument shows that $Af = 0$ for any $f \in R \ominus L[\varphi_1, \ldots, \varphi_N]$.

In order to prove that A is compact, it will be sufficient to show that for any weakly converging sequence f_n the sequence Af_n converges strongly (cf. § 1, Th. 3, also the remark). If the sequence f_n $(n = 1, 2, \ldots)$ is weakly converging, then it is bounded (cf. Ch. 7, § 9, Th. 1); let therefore $\|f_n\| \leqslant C$. Furthermore, if k is a positive integer, every f_n admits the unique decomposition $f_n = g_n + h_n$, $g_n \in L[\varphi_1, \ldots, \varphi_k]$, $h_n \in R \ominus L[\varphi_1, \ldots, \varphi_k]$. Hence, on account of $\|f_n\|^2 = \|g_n\|^2 + \|h_n\|^2$, also $\|h_n\| \leqslant C$ $(n = 1, 2, \ldots)$. By what we have just proved Ah_n $(n = 1, 2, \ldots)$ satisfies then $\|Ah_n\| \leqslant |\lambda_{k+1}| . \|h_n\| \leqslant |\lambda_{k+1}| C$ (in the case that the total number N of characteristic values λ_i is finite, we have $\|Ah_n\| = 0$ for $k = N$). This implies that, given $\varepsilon > 0$, we may take the index k so large that $\|Ah_n\| < \varepsilon/3$ $(n = 1, 2, \ldots)$. We suppose that $k = k(\varepsilon)$ has been chosen such that it fulfils this condition.

As regards the sequence g_n $(n = 1, 2, \ldots)$, it is not difficult to prove that it converges strongly. Indeed, since f_n converges weakly to an element f_0, we have $\lim g_n = \lim \Sigma_{i=1}^k (f_n, \varphi_i)\varphi_i = \Sigma_{i=1}^k (f_0, \varphi_i)\varphi_i$. The sequence Ag_n converges then as well; consequently $\| Ag_m - Ag_n \| \leqslant \varepsilon/3$ for $m, n > n_0(\varepsilon)$.

This shows finally that, for $m, n > n_0(\varepsilon)$,

$$\| Af_m - Af_n \| \leqslant \| Ag_m - Ag_n \| + \| Ah_m \| + \| Ah_n \| < \varepsilon;$$

the sequence Af_n $(n = 1, 2, \ldots)$ converges therefore strongly.

Corollary. *If $\lambda_1, \lambda_2, \ldots$ is a sequence of complex numbers such that $\lim \lambda_n = 0$, and if $\varphi_1, \varphi_2, \ldots$ is a complete orthonormal system in the complete separable Hilbert space R, then the linear transformation A, defined by $A(\Sigma\, \alpha_i \varphi_i) = \Sigma\, \lambda_i \alpha_i \varphi_i$, is normal and compact.*

We are now in a position to give an example of a compact linear transformation in a separable Hilbert space R, none of whose iterates is of finite double-norm. For this purpose we first need a lemma.

Lemma α. *The sequence $\lambda_1, \lambda_2, \ldots$ of positive numbers, defined by*

$$\begin{aligned} \lambda_1 &= 1, \\ \lambda_2 &= 2^{-1/2},\ \lambda_3 = 3^{-1/2},\ \lambda_4 = 4^{-1/2}, \\ \lambda_5 &= 5^{-1/3}, \ldots, \lambda_{27} = 27^{-1/3}, \\ \lambda_{28} &= 28^{-1/4}, \ldots, \lambda_{256} = 256^{-1/4}, \\ &\ldots\ldots, \end{aligned}$$

has the property that $\lim \lambda_n = 0$, but that $\Sigma_n \lambda_n^p = \infty$ for every positive integer p.

Proof. Since the sequence $2^{-1/2}, 5^{-1/3}, 28^{-1/4}, \ldots, (n^n + 1)^{-1/(n+1)}, \ldots$ tends to zero as $n \to \infty$, we have $\lim \lambda_n = 0$. To prove for instance that $\Sigma\, \lambda_n^3 = \infty$, we observe that $\lambda_n^3 = 1/n$ for $n = 5, \ldots, 27$, and $\lambda_n^3 > 1/n$ for $n > 27$. In a similar way it is proved that $\Sigma_n \lambda_n^p = \infty$ for every positive integer p.

Theorem 2. *Let $\varphi_1, \varphi_2, \ldots$ be a complete orthonormal system in the complete separable Hilbert space R, and let $\lambda_1, \lambda_2, \ldots$ be the sequence defined in the preceding Lemma α. Then, if the linear transformation A is defined by $A(\Sigma\, \alpha_i \varphi_i) = \Sigma\, \lambda_i \alpha_i \varphi_i$, the transformation A is compact, but none of its iterates is of finite double-norm.*

Proof. Since $\lim \lambda_n = 0$, A is compact by Theorem 1, Corollary. The transformation A has the characteristic values $\lambda_1, \lambda_2, \ldots$; if p is a positive integer, A^p has therefore the characteristic values $\lambda_1^p, \lambda_2^p, \ldots$ by § 6, Th. 3. Assuming now that A^p were of finite double-norm, we should have $\Sigma_i \lambda_i^{2p} < \infty$ by Schur's Theorem (cf. § 7, Th. 2), and this fails to be true, since $\Sigma_i \lambda_i^{2p} = \infty$ by the preceding lemma.

Remark. A small variation in the definition of A is sufficient to ensure that A is an integral transformation in the separable complete Hilbert space $L_2(\Delta, \mu)$, where Δ is the linear interval $0 \leqslant x \leqslant 1$, and μ is Lebesgue measure. If $\varphi_1(x), \varphi_2(x). \ldots$ is the orthonormal system in $L_2(\Delta, \mu)$ defined in Ch. 9, § 9, Ex. A, if $\lambda_1, \lambda_2, \ldots$ is again the sequence defined in Lemma α, and we write $A(x, y) = \Sigma_{i=1}^{\infty} \lambda_i \varphi_i(x) \varphi_i(y)$, then it is easily seen that for every $(x, y) \in \Delta \times \Delta$ one term at most of this series differs from zero, and that

$$\textstyle\int_0^1 A(x, y) f(y) dy = \Sigma_{i=1}^{\infty} \lambda_i (f, \varphi_i) \varphi_i(x)$$

for every $f(x) \in L_2$. The linear transformation A, defined by $Af = \int_0^1 A(x, y) f(y) dy$, satisfies therefore all desired conditions.

It is perhaps interesting to give a list of the different kinds of bounded linear integral transformations in a Lebesgue space L_2 which we have discussed so far. We observe that the property to be of finite double-norm in L_2 implies compactness and compactness implies boundedness. The list has then the following form:

1°. A bounded integral transformation, none of whose iterates (the transformation itself included) is compact (§ 2, Ex. B).

2°. A bounded integral transformation T with the property that T^q fails to be compact for $1 \leqslant q < p$, where p is a prescribed positive integer, whereas T^q is compact for $q \geqslant p$ (§ 2, Ex. C).

3°. A compact integral transformation, none of whose iterates (the transformation itself included) is of finite double-norm (the example in the present paragraph).

4°. A compact integral transformation T with the property that T^q fails to be of finite double-norm for $1 \leqslant q < p$, where p is a prescribed positive integer, whereas T^q is of finite double-norm for $q \geqslant p$ (§ 2, Ex. F).

5°. Integral transformations of finite double-norm.

§ 9. Ergodic Theorems

There exist in the literature many theorems known as *ergodic theorems* (cf. e.g. the book by E. HOPF [12] for the older results and N. DUNFORD'S paper [7] for some of the newer ideas). We shall state and prove two of these theorems belonging to the so called *mean ergodic theorems*.

We suppose that we have to do with a bounded linear transformation T on a Banach space E, and we shall use the fixed notation $p_n(T)$ for $(I + T + \ldots + T^{n-1})/n$ $(n = 1, 2, \ldots)$.

Theorem 1. *Let one of the iterates T^p of T be compact, and let T^n/n converge uniformly to the null transformation, that is, let $\lim \| T^n \|/n = 0$. Then:*

1°. *The value $\lambda = 1$ has either the index one for T or belongs to the resolvent set of T,*

2°. *$p_n(T)$ converges uniformly to the projection P on the null space $M_1 = N(T - I)$ along the range $L_1 = W(T - I)$.*

Proof. 1°. Assume that the index $\nu(1)$ of $\lambda = 1$ for T satisfies $\nu(1) \geqslant 2$. Then there exists an element $f \in E$ such that $g = (T - I)f \neq 0$ and $(T - I)^2 f = 0$. It follows that $(T - I)g = 0$ or $Tg = g$, so that also $T^n g = g$ $(n = 1, 2, \ldots)$ or $T^n(T - I)f = (T - I)f$. This implies

$$p_n(T)(T - I)f = \frac{I + T + \ldots + T^{n-1}}{n}(T - I)f$$
$$= (T - I)f$$

or, observing that $p_n(T)(T - I) = (T^n - I)/n$,

$$[(T^n - I)/n]f = (T - I)f = g \neq 0.$$

This however is a contradiction, since the expression on the left converges to the null element as $n \to \infty$. Hence either $\nu(1) = 1$ or $\nu(1) = 0$.

2°. By what we have already proved, E is the direct sum of $M_1 = N(T - I)$ and $L_1 = W(T - I)$. Let P be the projection on M_1 along L_1. Since $Tg = g$ for any element $g \in M_1$, we have also $p_n(T)g = g$, hence $p_n(T)P = P$. Furthermore, since T (and therefore also $p_n(T)$) is reduced by M_1 and L_1, we have $Pp_n(T) = p_n(T)P$, hence

$$Pp_n(T) = P. \tag{1}$$

Observing now that

$$(T^n - I)/n = (T - I)p_n(T) = (T - I)Pp_n(T) +$$
$$(T - I)(I - P)p_n(T) = (T - I)(I - P)p_n(T)$$

converges uniformly to the null transformation by hypothesis, and that $T - I$ has on L_1 a bounded inverse, we may draw the conclusion that

$$\lim \| (I - P)p_n(T) \| = 0. \tag{2}$$

Hence, by (1) and (2), $p_n(T) = Pp_n(T) + (I - P)p_n(T)$ converges uniformly to P.

Remarks. 1°. The condition $\lim \| T^n \|/n = 0$ is certainly satisfied if the transformations T^n $(n = 1, 2, \ldots)$ are equibounded, that is, if there exists a constant C such that $\| T^n \| \leqslant C$ $(n = 1, 2, \ldots)$.

2°. The condition on T that one of its iterates should be compact is a rather heavy one. The only use made of it in the proof is where we state that the space E is the direct sum of M_1 and L_1. We may relax the condition and replace it by the hypothesis that E has the property (Ext.), and that $T - I$ transforms bounded closed sets into closed sets. Then the proof of § 3, Th. 2 is applicable and shows that $L_1 = W(T - I)$ is closed. In the same way, by repetition of the argument, $L_n = W(T - I)^n$ $(n = 2, 3, \ldots)$ is closed. The first part of our proof undergoes no modification, hence, writing $M_n = N(T - I)^n$ $(n = 1, 2, \ldots)$, we have $M_1 = M_n$ $(n = 1, 2, \ldots)$. Also, since $\| (T^*)^n \| = \| T^n \|$, in the same way $M_1^* = M_n^*$ $(n = 1, 2, \ldots)$, where $M_n^* = N(T^* - I)^n$. Then, by Ch. 10, § 3, Th. 1, $\overset{\circ}{L_n} = (W(T - I)^n)^\circ = N(T^* - I)^n = M_n^* = M_1^* = N(T^* - I) = (W(T - I))^\circ = \overset{\circ}{L_1}$, so that on account of the property (Ext.) of E we find $L_1 = L_n$ $(n = 1, 2, \ldots)$. The proof of § 3, Th. 8 may now be applied to show that E is the direct sum of M_1 and L_1, and the remaining part of the proof remains as it was.

In our next theorem uniform convergence will be replaced by strong convergence both in hypothesis and statement. This theorem is essentially due to K. Yosida [13].

Theorem 2. *Let the complete Banach space E have the property (Ext.), and let for every element $f \in E$ the sequence $f_n = p_n(T)f$ have the property that every subsequence contains a weakly converging subsequence. Let, furthermore, T^n/n converge strongly to the null transformation, that is, let $\lim T^n f/n = 0$ for every $f \in E$. Then:*

1°. *E is the direct sum of the null space $M_1 = N(T - I)$ and the closure $[L_1]$ of the range $L_1 = W(T - I)$.*

2°. *$p_n(T)$ converges strongly to the projection P on M_1 along $[L_1]$.*

3°. *$M_1 = M_n = N(T - I)^n$ and $[L_1] = [L_n] = [W(T - I)^n]$ $(n = 1, 2, \ldots)$.*

Proof. 1°. For every $f \in E$ the sequence $f_n = p_n(T)f$ has the property that every subsequence contains a weakly converging subsequence. Hence, by Ch. 7, § 9, Th. 1, this sequence f_n is bounded. Then, by the Banach-Steinhaus Theorem (cf. Ch. 7, § 2), the transformations $p_n(T)$ are uniformly bounded, that is, there exists a constant C such that $\| p_n(T) \| \leqslant C (n = 1, 2, \ldots)$.

For a fixed element $f \in E$ the sequence $f_n = p_n(T)f$ contains a subsequence f_k $(k = n_1, n_2, \ldots)$, converging weakly to an element f_0. Then $(T - I)f_k$ converges weakly to $(T - I)f_0$, hence, observing that $(T - I)f_k = (T - I)p_k(T)f = [(T^k - I)/k]f$ converges even strongly to the null element, we find $(T - I)f_0 = 0$. This implies $f_0 \in M_1$.

We prove next that $f - f_0 \in [L_1]$. If this were not so, there would exist an element $f^* \in E^*$ such that $f^*(f - f_0) = 1$ and $f^*(h) = 0$ for all $h \in [L_1]$. Hence, since $(T - I)T^n f \in L_1$ $(n = 0, 1, 2, \ldots)$, we should have $f^*\{(T - I)T^n f\} = 0$ or $f^*(T^n f) = f^*(T^{n+1}f)$, which would imply $f^*\{p_n(T)f\} = f^*(f)$ or $f^*(f_n) = f^*(f)$. The weak convergence of f_k $(k = n_1, n_2, \ldots)$ to f_0 would then involve $f^*(f_0) = f^*(f)$, in contradiction with $f^*(f - f_0) = 1$. It follows that $f = f_0 + (f - f_0)$ is a decomposition of $f \in E$ into an element $f_0 \in M_1$ and an element $f - f_0 \in [L_1]$.

To show finally that E is the direct sum of M_1 and $[L_1]$ it will be sufficient to prove that M_1 and $[L_1]$ have only the null element in common. Since $Tg = g$ for every $g \in M_1$, we have

$$p_n(T)g = g \text{ for every } g \in M_1. \tag{3}$$

If $h \in L_1$, that is, if $h = (T - I)h_1$, we have $p_n(T)h = p_n(T)(T - I)h_1 = [(T^n - I)/n]h_1$, which shows that $\lim p_n(T)h = 0$. Then, on account of $\| p_n(T) \| \leqslant C$ $(n = 1, 2, \ldots)$, also

$$\lim p_n(T)h = 0 \text{ for every } h \in [L_1]. \tag{4}$$

From (3) and (4) it follows that M_1 and $[L_1]$ have only the null element in common.

2°. Denote the projection on M_1 along $[L_1]$ by P. Then, by what we have already proved, $p_n(T)P = P$ and $\lim p_n(T)(I - P)f = 0$ for every $f \in E$. Hence

$$\lim p_n(T)f = \lim \{p_n(T)Pf + p_n(T)(I - P)f\} = Pf.$$

3°. The relation $M_1 = M_n$ $(n = 1, 2, \ldots)$ is proved in the same way as in the preceding theorem. Writing $M_n^* = N(T^* - I)^n$ $(n = 1, 2, \ldots)$, we shall show now that $M_1^* = M_n^*$ $(n = 1, 2, \ldots)$. Assuming that M_{n-1}^* is a proper subspace of M_n^* for some value of $n \geqslant 2$, there exists an element $f^* \in E^*$ such that $g^* = (T^* - I)f^* \neq 0$ and $(T^* - I)^2 f^* = 0$. In the same way as in the proof of the preceding theorem we find now

$$[\{(T^*)^n - I\}/n]f^* = (T^* - I)f^* = g^*,$$

hence, if $g \in E$ is such that $g^*(g) = 1$,

$$\{[\{(T^*)^n - I\}/n]f^*\}(g) = g^*(g) = 1,$$

or

$$f^*\{[(T^n - I)/n]g\} = 1,$$

which leads to a contradiction since the expression on the left tends to zero. Hence $M_1^* = M_n^*$. An application of Ch. 10, § 3, Th. 1 shows then that $[L_n]^\circ = M_n^* = M_1^* = [L_1]^\circ$, hence $[L_1] = [L_n]$ $(n = 1, 2, \ldots)$.

Remarks. 1°. The condition that $\lim T^n f/n = 0$ for every $f \in E$ is certainly satisfied in case the transformations T^n $(n = 1, 2, \ldots)$ are equibounded. The uniform boundedness of the transformations $p_n(T)$ is also an immediate consequence of the equiboundedness of T^n.

2°. Our hypotheses on T may be replaced by the hypotheses that the transformations T^n $(n = 1, 2, \ldots)$ are equibounded and that T is weakly compact, that is, T transforms every bounded infinite set into a set which contains a weakly converging sequence. It was under these latter hypotheses that Yosida originally proved the theorem. The weaker hypotheses are due to Dunford. To prove our statement it is sufficient to observe that $\| T^n \| \leqslant C$ implies $\lim T^n f/n = 0$ for every $f \in E$ and also the boundedness of the sequence $q_n(T)f = [(I + T + \ldots + T^{n-2})/n]f$. Hence every subsequence of $p_n(T)f = [I/n + Tq_n(T)]f$ contains a weakly converging subsequence. It follows that the hypotheses of Theorem 2 are satisfied.

3°. If the space E and its adjoint space E^* both have the property (Ext.) and E is reflexive, then every bounded linear transformation T on E (into E) is weakly compact, since in this case every bounded infinite set contains a weakly converging sequence (cf. Ch. 7, § 9, Th. 2 and Th. 5). In this case, therefore, it is sufficient to suppose that $\| T^n \| \leqslant C$ $(n = 1, 2, \ldots)$. By Ch. 7, § 8, Th. 6, the present remark is applicable in particular if E is of one of the following categories:

(a) E is a complete Hilbert space,

(b) E is an Orlicz space $L_\Phi(\Delta, \mu)$, where $\Phi(u)$ and its complementary function $\Psi(v)$ satisfy $\Phi(2u) \leqslant M\Phi(u)$ and $\Psi(2v) \leqslant M\Psi(v)$ for all u, $v \geqslant 0$, and μ is a separable measure,

(c) E is a Lebesgue space $L_p(\Delta, \mu)$ $(1 < p < \infty)$,

(d) E is a sequence-space $l_p (1 < p < \infty)$.

4°. If we replace the hypothesis that $\lim T^n f/n = 0$ for every $f \in E$ by the hypothesis that $T^n f/n$ converges weakly to the null element for every $f \in E$, then it may be proved in the same way that $p_n(T)f$ converges weakly to Pf for every $f \in E$, where P is again the projection on M_1 along $[L_1]$.

EXAMPLES

1) In § 1, Th. 7 it was proved that if the sequence T_n of compact linear transformations on E_1 (with their ranges in the complete space E_2) converges uniformly to T, then T is compact. If T_n converges strongly to T, then T is not necessarily compact.

(Let R be a separable complete Hilbert space in which $\varphi_1, \varphi_2, \ldots$ is a complete orthonormal system. If $L_n = L[\varphi_1, \ldots, \varphi_n]$ is the n-dimensional subspace determined by $\varphi_1, \ldots, \varphi_n$, and P_n is the projection on L_n along $R \ominus L_n$, we define $T_n = P_n$ $(n = 1, 2, \ldots)$ and $T = I$. Then all T_n are compact by § 1, Th. 5, $\lim T_n f = Tf$ for every $f \in R$, but T fails to be compact).

2) In § 1, Th. 13 it was proved that if A is a bounded normal transformation on the complete Hilbert space R, and A^p is compact for some integer $p > 1$, then A itself is compact. The theorem was first proved for self-adjoint transformations, and to extend it to normal transformations use was made of the factorization theorem for normal transformations. A different proof may be given, using only that $AA^* = A^*A$ if A is normal.

(Let A be normal and let A^p be compact. Then A^q and $(A^*)^q$ are compact for $q \geqslant p$. Hence, using $AA^* = A^*A$, we find that $(A + A^*)^{2p} = \Sigma_{q=0}^{2p} \binom{2p}{q} A^{2p-q}(A^*)^q$ and $(A - A^*)^{2p}$ are compact. Observing that $A + A^*$ and $(A - A^*)/i$ are self-adjoint, we conclude now that $A + A^*$ and $(A - A^*)/i$ are compact, from which the desired result follows).

3) Let A and B be bounded linear transformations on the Banach space E into E. Then, if AB is compact and $\lambda = 0$ is in the resolvent set of B, A is compact.

(The hypothesis that $\lambda = 0$ is in the resolvent set of B is by definition equivalent to the hypothesis that B has a bounded inverse whose domain is the whole space E).

4) Let T be a bounded linear transformation on the Banach space E. Then, if the polynomial $p(\lambda) = \alpha_1\lambda + \ldots + \alpha_n\lambda^n$ satisfies:

(a) $p(\lambda) \neq 0$ for all $\lambda \neq 0$ belonging to the spectrum $\sigma(T)$,

(b) $p(T) = \alpha_1 T + \ldots + \alpha_n T^n$ is compact,

there exists a positive integer p such that T^p is compact.

(It is no restriction of the generality to suppose that $\alpha_n \neq 0$. Let $\alpha_1 = \ldots = \alpha_{p-1} = 0$, $\alpha_p \neq 0$. Then $p(T) = \alpha_n T^p(T - \mu_1 I)(T - \mu_2 I) \ldots (T - \mu_{n-p} I)$ with $\mu_i \neq 0$ $(i = 1, \ldots, n - p)$. Also, by (a), the numbers $\mu_1, \ldots, \mu_{n-p}$ belong to the resolvent set $\rho(T)$, which shows that the transformation $B = (T - \mu_1 I)(T - \mu_2 I) \ldots (T - \mu_{n-p} I)$ has a bounded inverse with domain E. Then, by (b) and the preceding example, T^p is compact).

5) All results on the spectrum and the resolvent of T which were proved in § 3 and § 4 remain valid if the hypothesis that T^p is compact for some positive integer p is replaced by the hypothesis that $p(T) = \alpha_1 T + \ldots + \alpha_n T^n$ is compact and $p(\lambda) \neq 0$ for all $\lambda \neq 0$ belonging to the spectrum $\sigma(T)$.

6) Let R be a separable complete Hilbert space of infinite dimension in which the orthonormal system $\varphi_1, \varphi_2, \ldots$ is complete. In Ch. 10, § 6, Ex. A we have considered the linear transformation T defined by $T\varphi_n = \varphi_{n+1}/(n + 1)$ $(n = 1, 2, \ldots)$ and in Ch. 10, Ex. 3 its adjoint transformation T^* satisfying $T^*\varphi_1 = 0$, $T^*\varphi_n = \varphi_{n-1}/n$ $(n = 2, 3, \ldots)$. Since both T and T^* are of finite

double-norm, the result that every $\lambda \neq 0$ belongs to the resolvent set of both T and T^* is an immediate consequence of the theory in § 3.

(Once having established that the spectrum of T and T^* consists only of the point $\lambda = 0$, it follows from § 3, Th. 9 that every $\lambda \neq 0$ belongs to the resolvent set of T).

7) Let E be an arbitrary Banach space, complete or non-complete, and let the bounded linear transformation T on E (into E) be such that T^p is compact for some positive integer p. Let the complex number $\lambda \neq 0$ have the index ν for T, so that by § 3, Th. 8 the space E is the direct sum of the null space $M_\nu = N(T_\lambda^\nu)$ and the range $L_\nu = W(T_\lambda^\nu)$. We define the linear transformations T_1 and T_2 by

$$\begin{cases} T_1 = T \text{ on } M_\nu, \\ T_1 = O \text{ on } L_\nu, \end{cases} \qquad \begin{cases} T_2 = O \text{ on } M_\nu, \\ T_2 = T \text{ on } L_\nu, \end{cases}$$

hence $T = T_1 + T_2$.

Suppose now that § 3, Th. 1—8 are known but not the further theorems in § 3. Denoting the index of λ for T^* by ν^* (we do not yet know therefore that $\nu = \nu^*$), and writing $M_{\nu^*} = N[(T^* - \lambda I)^{\nu^*}]$, $L_{\nu^*} = W[(T^* - \lambda I)^{\nu^*}]$, we have

$$\begin{cases} T_1^* = T^* \text{ on } M_{\nu^*}, \\ T_1^* = O \text{ on } L_{\nu^*}, \end{cases} \qquad \begin{cases} T_2^* = O \text{ on } M_{\nu^*}, \\ T_2^* = T^* \text{ on } L_{\nu^*}. \end{cases}$$

(Let $\mu = \max(\nu, \nu^*)$ and $f^* \in M_{\nu^*}$, hence $f^*(T_\lambda^n f) = 0$ for every $f \in E$ and $n \geq \mu$. We have to prove first that $T_1^* f^* = T^* f^*$, that is, $f^*(T_1 f) = f^*(Tf)$ for every $f \in E$. For $f \in M_\nu$ this is trivial since then $T_1 f = Tf$. For $f \in L_\nu$ we may write $f = T_\lambda^\mu g$, hence $T_\lambda f = T_\lambda^{\mu+1} g$. Then $Tf = T_\lambda f + \lambda f = T_\lambda^{\mu+1} g + \lambda T_\lambda^\mu g$, so that $f^*(Tf) = f^*(T_\lambda^{\mu+1} g) + \lambda f^*(T_\lambda^\mu g) = 0 + 0 = 0 = f^*(0) = f^*(T_1 f)$. Hence, since $f^*(T_1 f) = f^*(Tf)$ holds for every $f \in M_\nu$ and every $f \in L_\nu$, it holds for every $f \in E$, and this proves that $T_1^* = T^*$ on M_{ν^*}.

Let now $f^* \in L_{\nu^*}$, hence $f^* = (T_\lambda^*)^\mu g^*$. We have to prove that $T_1^* f^* = 0$, that is, $f^*(T_1 f) = 0$ for every $f \in E$. For $f \in L_\nu$ this is trivial, and for $f \in M_\nu$ we have $T_\lambda^\mu T_1 f = T_\lambda^\mu T f = T_\lambda^\mu (T_\lambda f + \lambda f) = T_\lambda^{\mu+1} f + \lambda T_\lambda^\mu f = 0 + 0 = 0$, hence $f^*(T_1 f) = \{(T_\lambda^*)^\mu g^*\}(T_1 f) = g^*(T_\lambda^\mu T_1 f) = 0$.

The result for T_2^* follows immediately by observing that $T^* = T_1^* + T_2^*$).

8) Under the same hypotheses as in the preceding example the equations $(T - \lambda I)f = 0$ and $(T_1 - \lambda I)f = 0$ have the same solutions. The same holds for the equations $(T^* - \lambda I)f^* = 0$ and $(T_1^* - \lambda I)f^* = 0$.

(If $g \in M_\nu$, then also $T_1 g \in M_\nu$, since $T_\lambda^\mu T_1 g = T_\lambda^\mu T g = T_\lambda^\mu (T_\lambda g + \lambda g) = T_\lambda^{\mu+1} g + \lambda T_\lambda^\mu g = 0 + 0 = 0$. But then $T_1 f \in M_\nu$ for every $f \in E$ since the decomposition $f = g + h$, $g \in M_\nu$, $h \in L_\nu$, implies $T_1 f = T_1 g$.

If therefore $T_1 f - \lambda f = 0$, the element f belongs to M_ν, hence $Tf - \lambda f = T_1 f - \lambda f = 0$. If conversely $Tf - \lambda f = 0$, we have $f \in M_1 \subset M_\nu$; hence $T_1 f - \lambda f = Tf - \lambda f = 0$.

The proof for T^* is similar).

9) Under the same hypotheses as in the preceding examples the null spaces $M_1 = N(T_\lambda)$ and $M_1^* = N(T_\lambda^*)$ have the same dimension.

(Proof of J. SCHAUDER [2]. We have to prove that $(T_1 - \lambda I)f = 0$ and $(T_1^* - \lambda I)f^* = 0$ have the same maximal number of linearly independent solutions. Since $T_1 f \in M_\nu$ for every $f \in E$ and M_ν has finite dimension, the range of T_1 has finite dimension. Let it be of dimension n. If $n = 0$, there is nothing left to prove. If $n > 0$, we have $T_1 f = \Sigma_{i=1}^n f_i^*(f) f_i$, where the elements $f_i \in E$ and also the elements $f_i^* \in E^*$ are linearly independent. Indeed, if $f_1^*, \ldots, f_n^*$ were not linearly independent the range of T_1 would be of dimension less than n. Then

$$(T_1^* f^*)(f) = f^*(T_1 f) = \Sigma_{i=1}^n f_i^*(f) f^*(f_i) = (\Sigma_{i=1}^n f^*(f_i) f_i^*)(f),$$

hence $T_1^* f^* = \Sigma_{i=1}^n f^*(f_i) f_i^*$.

Every solution of $(T_1 - \lambda I)f = 0$ has the form $f = \Sigma_{k=1}^n \alpha_k f_k$, and every solution of $(T_1^* - \lambda I)f^* = 0$ has the form $f^* = \Sigma_{k=1}^n \beta_k f_k^*$. These solutions satisfy

$$\Sigma_{k=1}^n \alpha_k \Sigma_{i=1}^n f_i^*(f_k) f_i - \Sigma_{i=1}^n \lambda \alpha_i f_i = 0,$$

$$\Sigma_{k=1}^n \beta_k \Sigma_{i=1}^n f_k^*(f_i) f_i^* - \Sigma_{i=1}^n \lambda \beta_i f_i^* = 0$$

respectively. Hence, taking into account the linear independence of the f_i and the f_i^*,

$$\lambda \alpha_i - \Sigma_{k=1}^n \alpha_k f_i^*(f_k) = 0, \quad \lambda \beta_i - \Sigma_{k=1}^n \beta_k f_k^*(f_i) = 0 \quad (i = 1, \ldots, n).$$

These systems of equations however have the same maximal number of linearly independent solutions by Ch. 8, § 4, Th. 2).

10) An infinite matrix of complex numbers

$$\mathcal{A} = \begin{pmatrix} \alpha_{00} & \alpha_{01} & \ldots & \alpha_{0n} & \ldots \\ \alpha_{10} & \alpha_{11} & \ldots & \alpha_{1n} & \ldots \\ \ldots & \ldots & \ldots & \ldots & \ldots \\ \alpha_{n0} & \alpha_{n1} & \ldots & \alpha_{nn} & \ldots \\ \ldots & \ldots & \ldots & \ldots & \ldots \end{pmatrix}$$

is called a *Toeplitz matrix* or *T-matrix* whenever

(a) $\lim_{i \to \infty} \alpha_{ij} = 0 \ (j = 0, 1, 2, \ldots)$,

(b) $\lim_{i \to \infty} A_i = 1$, where $A_i = \Sigma_{j=0}^\infty \alpha_{ij}$,

(c) $N_i \leqslant C \ (i = 0, 1, 2, \ldots)$, where $N_i = \Sigma_{j=0}^\infty |\alpha_{ij}|$.

Given a sequence f_n of elements of a Banach space E, we consider the sequence $g_n = \alpha_{n0} f_0 + \alpha_{n1} f_1 + \ldots$, provided the series for g_n converges. If $\lim g_n = f$, it is said that the sequence f_n is summable $\mathcal{A}$ to g. Now, if $\mathcal{A}$ is a T-matrix and $\lim f_n = f$, then $\lim g_n = f$.

(If $f_k = f + \varepsilon_k$, $\lim \varepsilon_k = 0$, then $g_n = g_n' + g_n''$, where $g_n' = A_n f$, hence $\lim g_n' = f$ by (b). Given $\varepsilon > 0$, suppose that $\| \varepsilon_k \| < \varepsilon/2C$ for $k > k_0$. Since $\| g_n'' \| \leqslant \Sigma_{j=0}^{k_0} |\alpha_{nj}| \cdot \| \varepsilon_j \| + \Sigma_{j=k_0+1}^\infty |\alpha_{nj}| \cdot \| \varepsilon_j \|$, where the second sum is less than $\varepsilon/2$ and the first sum converges to zero by (a), we have $\| g_n'' \| < \varepsilon$ for n sufficiently large. Hence $\lim g_n = f$).

11) Let $u_n (n = 0, 1, 2, \ldots)$ be a sequence of elements of a Banach space E and let $q_n (n = 0, 1, 2, \ldots)$ be a sequence of positive numbers such that $Q_n = q_0 + \ldots + q_n$ tends to ∞. We write $U_n = u_0 + \ldots + u_n$. Then, if $\lim f_n = \lim u_n/q_n = f$, also $\lim g_n = \lim U_n/Q_n = f$. In particular, if $q_n = 1 (n = 0, 1, 2, \ldots)$, then $\lim u_n = f$ implies $\lim (u_0 + u_1 + \ldots + u_n)/(n+1) = f$.

(We have $g_n = (u_0 + \ldots + u_n)/Q_n = (q_0 f_0 + q_1 f_1 + \ldots + q_n f_n)/Q_n$, which shows that the elements f_n are transformed by a T-matrix with non-negative elements. Hence $\lim g_n = f$ by the preceding example).

12) If $u_n (n = 0, 1, 2, \ldots)$ is a sequence of elements of a Banach space E and the sequence $f_n = (u_0 + \ldots + u_n)/(n+1)$ is bounded, then $\Sigma_{k=0}^\infty u_k \mu^k$ converges for $|\mu| < 1$.

(Let $\| f_n \| \leqslant C$ $(n = 0, 1, 2, \ldots)$. Then $\Sigma \| (k+1) f_k \mu^k \| \leqslant C \, \Sigma \, (k+1) \, | \mu |^k < \infty$ for $| \mu | < 1$. It follows that $\Sigma_{k=0}^{\infty} u_k \mu^k = \Sigma_{k=0}^{\infty} \{(k+1) f_k - k f_{k-1}\} \mu^k$ converges).

13) If $u_n (n = 0, 1, 2, \ldots)$ is a sequence of elements of a Banach space E and the sequence $f_n = (u_0 + \ldots + u_n)/(n+1)$ converges to f, then $(1 - \mu) \Sigma_{k=0}^{\infty} u_k \mu^k$ converges also to f as μ tends to 1 along the real axis from the left.

(We have $(1 - \mu) \Sigma_{k=0}^{\infty} u_k \mu^k = (1 - \mu) \Sigma_{k=0}^{\infty} (k+1)(\mu^k - \mu^{k+1}) f_k$. Hence, considering a sequence of numbers $\mu_i (i = 0, 1, 2, \ldots)$ satisfying $0 < \mu_i < 1$, $\lim \mu_i = 1$, we find

$$(1 - \mu_i) \Sigma_{k=0}^{\infty} u_k \mu_i^k = \Sigma_{k=0}^{\infty} \alpha_{ik} f_k$$

with $\alpha_{ik} = (1 - \mu_i)(k+1)(\mu_i^k - \mu_i^{k+1})$. It is easily verified that the matrix with elements α_{ik} is a T-matrix with positive elements, hence

$$\lim_{i \to \infty} (1 - \mu_i) \Sigma_{k=0}^{\infty} u_k \mu_i^k = \lim f_n = f).$$

14) If T is a bounded linear transformation on the Banach space E into E, and the sequence $p_n(T) = (I + T + \ldots + T^{n-1})/n$ is bounded, then $\Sigma_{k=0}^{\infty} T^k \lambda^{-(k+1)}$ converges for $| \lambda | > 1$ to $- R_\lambda = - (T - \lambda I)^{-1}$.

(The convergence follows from Example 12, and that the sum of the series is $- R_\lambda$ is proved in the same way as in Ch. 10, § 7, Th. 6).

15) If moreover $p_n(T)$ converges uniformly to the bounded linear transformation P, then $(1 - \lambda) R_\lambda$ also converges uniformly to P as λ tends to 1 along the real axis from the right. If $p_n(T)$ converges strongly to the bounded linear transformation P, then $(1 - \lambda) R_\lambda$ also converges strongly to P as λ tends to 1 along the real axis from the right [14].

(Follows from Example 13).

16) If the space E has the property (Ext.), and $p_n(T) = (I + T + \ldots + T^{n-1})/n$ converges strongly to the bounded linear transformation P, then P is the projection on the null space $M_1 = N(T - I)$ along the closure $[L_1]$ of the range $L_1 = W(T - I)$.

(Since $T^n = (n+1) p_{n+1}(T) - n p_n(T)$, we have $T^n/n = (1 + 1/n) p_{n+1}(T) - p_n(T)$, so that T^n/n converges strongly to the null transformation. Hence $(T - I) p_n(T) = (T^n - I)/n$ converges strongly to the null transformation as well, which implies $(T - I)P = O$ or $TP = P$. It follows that $p_n(T)P = P$, $P^2 = P$, and this shows that P is a projection. Writing $Pf = f_0$ for an arbitrary $f \in E$, we have $(T - I) f_0 = (T - I) Pf = TPf - Pf = 0$ on account of $TP = P$, hence $f_0 \in M_1$. The rest of the proof is similar to that of § 9, Th. 2).

REFERENCES

[1] J. Schauder, Über lineare vollstetige Funktionaloperationen, Studia Math. 2 (1930), 183–196. The present proof is due to S. Banach, Théorie des Opérations linéaires, Warsaw (1932), p. 100.

[2] J. Schauder, Über lineare vollstetige Funktionaloperationen, Studia Math. 2 (1930), 183–196.

[3] A. C. Zaanen, On a certain class of Banach spaces, Annals of Math. 47 (1946), 654–666.

[4] E. Hille and J. D. Tamarkin, On the theory of linear integral equations II, Annals of Math. 35 (1934), 445–455.
[5] F. Riesz, Über lineare Funktionalgleichungen, Acta Math. 41 (1918), 71–98.
[6] E. R. Lorch, The spectrum of linear transformations, Transactions Amer. Math. Soc. 52 (1942), 238–248.
[7] N. Dunford, Spectral theory I, Convergence to projections, Transactions Amer. Math. Soc. 54 (1943), 185–217.
[8] T. Lalesco, Un théorème sur les noyaux composés, Bull. Acad. Roumaine 3 (1915), 271—272.
[9] R. Gheorghiu, Sur l'équation de Fredholm, Thesis, Paris (1928).
[10] E. Hille and J. D. Tamarkin, On the characteristic values of linear integral equations, Acta Math. 57 (1931), 1–76.
[11] I. Schur, Über die charakteristische Wurzeln einer linearen Substitution mit einer Anwendung auf die Theorie der Integralgleichungen, Math. Annalen 66 (1909), 488–510.
[12] E. Hopf, Ergodentheorie, Berlin (1937).
[13] K. Yosida, Mean ergodic theorem in Banach spaces, Proc. Imp. Acad. Tokyo 14 (1938), 15–17.
[14] E. Hille, Remarks on ergodic theorems, Transactions Amer. Math. Soc. 57 (1945), 246–269.

CHAPTER 12

COMPACT SYMMETRISABLE, SELF-ADJOINT AND NORMAL TRANSFORMATIONS IN HILBERT SPACE

§ 1. Introduction

In the present chapter we shall investigate the spectral properties of compact linear transformations in Hilbert space, these transformations being either symmetrisable, self-adjoint or normal. It will be proved that under rather weak conditions upon the transformation K in question this transformation K has at least one characteristic value $\neq 0$. Furthermore it will be shown that the characteristic values λ_i $(i = 1, 2, \ldots)$ of K have some interesting extremal properties, and that for elements of the form Kf there exists an expansion theorem, that is, these elements may be approximated according to a certain norm by sums $\Sigma_{i=1}^{n} \lambda_i \alpha_i \varphi_i$, where φ_i $(i = 1, 2, \ldots)$ is a sequence of characteristic elements corresponding with the sequence λ_i. We shall start with the theory of symmetrisable transformations [1] [2] [3] [4], the self-adjoint case will then follow automatically, and most of the results for normal transformations will be shown to be fairly easy consequences of the corresponding results for the self-adjoint case.

The reader who is not interested in symmetrisable, but only in self-adjoint transformations, is referred to § 7, where he may find which of the theorems in the preceding paragraphs are of importance to him.

§ 2. Recapitulation of Former Results on Symmetrisable Transformations

It will perhaps be convenient for the reader to recapitulate shortly the facts about symmetrisable transformations which we have established so far.

Let R be a Hilbert space, separable or not, complete or not. We suppose that $H \neq O$ is a bounded self-adjoint transformation on R, and we denote by $[L]$ the subspace of all $f \in R$ satisfying $Hf = 0$. The orthogonal complement of $[L]$ is denoted by $[M]$ and it is supposed that R is the direct sum of $[L]$ and $[M]$ (this condition is automatically satisfied whenever the space R is complete). Since $H \neq O$, $[L]$ is not identical with R, and this implies that $[M]$ contains other elements besides the null element. Denoting the projection on $[M]$ along $[L]$ by P, P is therefore orthogonal and $P \neq O$. By Ch. 9, § 5, Th. 2 we have $H = HP = PH$. The elements f and g are called H-orthogonal whenever $(Hf, g) = 0$, the system $\{\varphi_n\}$ is called H-orthonormal when $(H\varphi_m, \varphi_n) = 1$ for $m = n$ and $(H\varphi_m, \varphi_n) = 0$ for $m \neq n$, and the elements $\varphi_1, \ldots, \varphi_n$ are said to be H-independent when $H \sum_{i=1}^{n} \alpha_i\varphi_i = 0$ implies $\alpha_1 = \ldots = \alpha_n = 0$. If $\{\varphi_1, \ldots, \varphi_n\}$ is an H-orthonormal system, then $\varphi_1, \ldots, \varphi_n$ are H-independent by Ch. 9, § 5, Th. 3.

The bounded linear transformation K is said to be symmetrisable (relative to H) when $S = HK$ is self-adjoint (Ch. 9, § 12). If K is symmetrisable, we have the following statements:

1°. $T = PK$ is also symmetrisable.

2°. $T = TP$ and $S = SP$ (hence $T = TP = PKP = P^2KP = P(PK)P = PTP$ and $S = SP = HKP = PHKP = PSP$).

3°. $Tf = 0$ if and only if $Sf = 0$.

4°. K^n $(n = 2, 3, \ldots)$ is also symmetrisable.

5°. If $\lambda \neq \bar{\mu}$, $Kf = \lambda f$, $Kg = \mu g$, then $(Hf, g) = (Sf, g) = 0$. Consequently, if $Kf = \lambda f$ and λ is non-real, then $(Hf, f) = (Sf, f) = 0$.

The statements 1°, 2°, 3° were proved in Ch. 9, § 12, Th. 1, the statement 4° in Ch. 9, § 12, Th. 5 and 5° in Ch. 9, § 15, Th. 3. To obtain furthergoing results it was necessary to suppose that K has at least one of two properties, called full and strong symmetrisability respectively. We restate them here:

Full symmetrisability. $Hf \neq 0$ for every $f \in R$ satisfying $Kf = \lambda f \neq 0$.

Strong symmetrisability. $Hf = 0$ implies $Kf = 0$ or, equivalently stated, $K = KP$.

We observe that strong symmetrisability implies full symmetrisability. Furthermore, since $Hf = 0$ implies $Tf = 0$, the transformation T is always strongly symmetrisable even if K is neither fully nor strongly symmetrisable. We have now:

6°. If K is fully symmetrisable and $Kf_i = \lambda f_i \neq 0$ $(i = 1, \ldots, n)$, where $f_1, \ldots, f_n$ are linearly independent, then $K^*Hf_i = \lambda Hf_i$ $(i = 1, \ldots, n)$, where $Hf_1, \ldots, Hf_n$ are linearly independent. It is supposed here, if R is not complete, that H, K, P, T and S are extended onto the complete Hilbert space $\bar{R}$, the closure of R. The adjoint K^* exists on $\bar{R}$ and the relations $K^*Hf_i = \lambda Hf_i$ are to be understood as holding on $\bar{R}$.

7°. If $Tf_i = \lambda f_i \neq 0$ $(i = 1, \ldots, n)$, where $f_1, \ldots, f_n$ are linearly independent, then $K^*Hf_i = T^*Hf_i = \lambda Hf_i$ $(i = 1, \ldots, n)$ where $Hf_1, \ldots, Hf_n$ are linearly independent.

8°. If K is fully symmetrisable, and either H or $S = HK$ is positive, then all characteristic values of K are real. Hence, even if K is not fully symmetrisable but either H or S is positive, all characteristic values of T are real.

9°. If K is fully symmetrisable, and either H or $S = HK$ is positive, then $Kf = \lambda f$, $Kg = \mu g$, $\lambda \neq \mu$ implies $(Hf, g) = (Sf, g) = 0$.

10°. If K is fully symmetrisable, and either H or $S = HK$ is positive, then $(K - \lambda I)^p f = 0$ for a complex number $\lambda \neq 0$ and an integer $p \geqslant 1$ implies $(K - \lambda I)f = 0$.

The statements 6° and 7° were proved in Ch. 9, § 15, Th. 4 and Th. 5 respectively, 8° and 9° in Ch. 9, § 15, Th. 6 and 10° in Ch. 9, § 15, Th. 9.

To conclude this preliminary work, we add the following statements which complete 3° and 4°:

11°. $T^n = PK^n$ $(n = 1, 2, \ldots)$.

12°. $HT^n = HK^n$ $(n = 1, 2, \ldots)$.

13°. *Writing* $S_n = HK^n = HT^n$ $(n = 1, 2, \ldots)$, *and supposing that* H *is positive and* n *is an integer* $\geqslant 1$, *the following four statements are equivalent*: $T = O$, $S = O$, $S_n = O$, $T^n = O$.

Proof. 11°. For $n = 1$ we have $T = PK$ by definition. Supposing that $T^{n-1} = PK^{n-1}$ has already been proved, we find $T^n = TPK^{n-1} = TK^{n-1} = PKK^{n-1} = PK^n$.

12°. Since $T^n = PK^n$ and $H = HP$, we have $HT^n = HPK^n = HK^n$.

13°. $T = O$ and $S = O$ are equivalent by 3°. In the same way $T^n = O$ and $S_n = O$ are equivalent. It remains to prove that $S = O$ is equivalent with $S_n = O$. It is trivial that $S = HK = O$ implies $S_n = HK^n = O$. To prove conversely that $S_n = O$ implies $S = O$ it is obviously sufficient to show that $S_{2m} = O$ implies $S_m = O$ for any positive integer m. Let therefore $HK^{2m} = S_{2m} = O$. Then $(HK^m f, K^m f) = (HK^{2m} f, f) = 0$ for every $f \in R$, and this implies $S_m f = HK^m f = 0$ since H is positive. Hence $S_m = O$.

It will be left to the reader to consider for himself the particular case $H = I$ (the identical transformation), in which case the notions of symmetrisable and self-adjoint transformations become identical.

§ 3. Existence of Characteristic Values for Symmetrisable Transformations in the Case that H is Positive

It will be supposed in the present paragraph that H is positive. Then, extending H onto the closure $\bar{R}$ (if necessary), there exists a bounded positive transformation $H^{1/2}$ on $\bar{R}$, uniquely determined, such that $(H^{1/2})^2 = H$. We shall denote the non-negative number $(Hf, f)^{1/2} = \| H^{1/2}f \|$ by $N(f)$, and we say that $N(f)$ is the H-norm of the element f.

Theorem 1. *If there exists a positive integer p such that $T^p = PK^p$ is compact, then the following two statements are equivalent:*

1°. $S = HK = HT \neq O$.

2°. *T has a characteristic value $\lambda \neq 0$ (then, by § 2, 8°, λ is necessarily real).*

Proof. 2° → 1°. Let $Tf = \lambda f \neq 0$. Then $Sf = HTf = \lambda Hf \neq 0$ since $Hf = 0$ would imply $Tf = 0$. Hence $S \neq O$.

1° → 2°. We suppose first that T itself is compact. Let now $S \neq O$. Then $Sf_0 \neq 0$ for a certain f_0, hence $Hf_0 \neq 0$ by § 2, 2°, or $N(f_0) \neq 0$. We put $\bar{f}_0 = f_0/N(f_0)$ and $f_1 = T\bar{f}_0$. Then $Hf_1 = HT\bar{f}_0 = S\bar{f}_0 \neq 0$, so that $N(f_1) \neq 0$. We define generally

$$\bar{f}_{n-1} = f_{n-1}/N(f_{n-1}),\ f_n = T\bar{f}_{n-1}\ (n = 1, 2, \ldots).$$

In order to justify this definition we have to prove that $N(f_{n+1}) \neq 0$ $(n = 1, 2, \ldots)$. This follows from $N(f_1) \neq 0$ and

$$N(f_n) = (Hf_n, \bar{f}_n) = (HT\bar{f}_{n-1}, \bar{f}_n) = (\bar{f}_{n-1}, HT\bar{f}_n) =$$

$$(H\bar{f}_{n-1}, f_{n+1}) \leqslant N(\bar{f}_{n-1}) . N(f_{n+1}) = N(f_{n+1})\ (n = 1, 2, \ldots),$$

which implies $0 < N(f_1) \leqslant N(f_2) \leqslant N(f_3) \leqslant \ldots$. Furthermore, from $N(f_n) = (H\bar{f}_{n-1}, f_{n+1})$, and observing that the expression $N(f_{n-1})N(f_n)$ is real, we derive

$$(1) \qquad N(f_{n-1})N(f_n) = (Hf_{n-1}, f_{n+1}) = (Hf_{n+1}, f_{n-1}).$$

Up to this point the idea underlying the present proof is the same as in Kellogg's proof [5] for the existence of a characteristic value $\neq 0$ in the case of an integral transformation of finite double-norm with Hermitian kernel. Now however a fundamental difference shows itself due to the fact that we have to do here with two different norms $N(f)$ and $\| f \|$ for the same element $f \in R$. In the self-adjoint case we have $H = I$ (the identical transformation), and then $N(f) = \| f \|$, which makes the situation much simpler. Once having overcome the difficulties in the middle part, the final part of the present proof is again similar to Kellogg's proof.

We want to prove first that $\lim \| \bar{f}_n \| = \infty$ leads to a contradiction. For this purpose we observe that, after extension of H, T and S onto the closure $\bar{R}$, we still have $HT = S$, so that $HT = S = S^* = T^*H$ on $\bar{R}$. This implies

$$\| Hf_n \| = \| HT\bar{f}_{n-1} \| = \| T^*H\bar{f}_{n-1} \| \leqslant \| T^* \|.\| H^{1/2} \|.\| H^{1/2}\bar{f}_{n-1} \|$$
$$= \| T^* \|.\| H^{1/2} \|.N(\bar{f}_{n-1}) = \| T^* \|.\| H^{1/2} \|,$$

so that the sequence Hf_n is bounded. Let us assume now that $\lim \| \bar{f}_n \| = \infty$. Then $\| \bar{f}_{n+2} \| \geqslant \| \bar{f}_n \|$ for an infinity of values of n. Let $\bar{f}_j$ $(j = n_1, n_2, \ldots)$ be a subsequence satisfying $\| \bar{f}_{j+2} \| \geqslant \| \bar{f}_j \|$. Since T is compact, $T\bar{f}_j/\| \bar{f}_j \| = f_{j+1}/\| \bar{f}_j \|$ contains a converging subsequence $f_{k+1}/\| \bar{f}_k \|$, tending to an element g. Then $Hg = \lim Hf_{k+1}/\| \bar{f}_k \| = 0$ on account of $\lim \| \bar{f}_k \| = \infty$ and the boundedness of Hf_{k+1}, whereas $Tg = \lim Tf_{k+1}/\| \bar{f}_k \| = \lim N(f_{k+1})T\bar{f}_{k+1}/\| \bar{f}_k \| = \lim N(f_{k+1})f_{k+2}/\| \bar{f}_k \|$, hence

$$\| Tg \| = \lim N(f_{k+1}) \| f_{k+2} \|/\| \bar{f}_k \| =$$
$$\lim N(f_{k+1})N(f_{k+2}) \| \bar{f}_{k+2} \|/\| \bar{f}_k \| \geqslant N^2(f_1) > 0$$

on account of $N(f_{k+2}) \geqslant N(f_{k+1}) \geqslant N(f_1)$ and $\| \bar{f}_{k+2} \| \geqslant \| \bar{f}_k \|$. But

$$Hg = 0, \; Tg \neq 0$$

is a contradiction by § 2, 2°, so that $\lim \| \bar{f}_n \| = \infty$ is impossible.

The sequence $\bar{f}_n$ contains therefore a bounded subsequence $\bar{f}_i$. Then $f_{i+1} = T\bar{f}_i$ contains a converging subsequence f_q, tending to an element t. From $N(f_q) = \| H^{1/2}f_q \| \leqslant \| H^{1/2} \|.\| f_q \|$ follows that $N(f_q)$ is bounded, so that the whole non-decreasing sequence $N(f_n)$ $(n = 1, 2, \ldots)$ is bounded as well. Hence $\lim N(f_n) = \mu > 0$ exists. Then $\lim \bar{f}_q = t/\mu$ and

$$\left\{ \begin{array}{lll} \lim f_{q+1} = \lim T\bar{f}_q & = Tt/\mu = u, \\ \lim f_{q+2} = \lim T\bar{f}_{q+1} & = Tu/\mu = v, \end{array} \right. \tag{2}$$

hence

$$N^2(t - v) = \lim N^2(f_q - f_{q+2}) =$$
$$\lim [N^2(f_q) - (Hf_q, f_{q+2}) - (Hf_{q+2}, f_q) + N^2(f_{q+2})] =$$
$$\mu^2 - \mu^2 - \mu^2 + \mu^2 = 0$$

on account of (1). Hence $H(t - v) = 0$, so that $T(t - v) = 0$ as well, or $Tt = Tv$.

It follows now from (2) that $\mu u = Tt = Tv$ and $\mu v = Tu$, hence

$$\mu(u + v) = T(u + v), \quad -\mu(u - v) = T(u - v).$$

It is impossible that $u + v = u - v = 0$, since this would imply $u = 0$, whereas we know already that $N(u) = \lim N(f_{q+1}) = \mu > 0$. Hence $Tf = \lambda f \neq 0$ either for $\lambda = \mu$, $f = u + v$, or for $\lambda = -\mu$, $f = u - v$.

It remains to consider the case that $S = HT \neq O$ and T^p is compact for an integer $p > 1$. Since, by § 2, 13°, $S \neq O$ implies $S_p = HT^p \neq O$, and since T^p is also symmetrisable, our argument shows now that T^p has a characteristic value $\neq 0$. Then, by Ch. 11, § 3, Th. 1, 2°, the transformation T has a characteristic value $\neq 0$ as well.

Remark. In connection with the present theorem it is of interest to observe that if K^p is compact for a certain integer $p \geqslant 1$, then of course $T^p = PK^p$ is compact. The converse however is not true. In fact, we shall give an example where K^p fails to be compact for any integer $p \geqslant 1$, whereas $T = PK$ is compact. It is even possible to construct the example such that K is fully symmetrisable. If however K is strongly symmetrisable, the situation is different.

Theorem 2. *There exist bounded linear transformations K, fully symmetrisable relative to a positive transformation H, such that $T = PK$ is compact, whereas neither K itself nor any of its iterates K^p ($p = 2, 3, \ldots$) is compact.*

Proof. Let the Hilbert space R be complete and separable, and let the linear subspaces $[M]$ and $[L]$, both of infinite dimension, be orthogonal complements. We suppose that $\{\varphi_n\}$ and $\{\psi_n\}$ are complete orthonormal systems in $[M]$ and $[L]$ respectively. The bounded linear transformation H is defined by

$$H\varphi_n = \alpha_n \varphi_n, \; \alpha_n > 0, \; \lim \alpha_n = 0; \; H\psi_n = 0.$$

Then, by Ch. 11, § 8, Th. 1, H is compact. Moreover, H is positive and $Hf = 0$ for $f \in [L]$. The bounded linear transformation K is defined by

$$K\varphi_n = H\varphi_n = \alpha_n \varphi_n; \; K\psi_n = \psi_{n+1}.$$

Then $HK\varphi_n = \alpha_n^2 \varphi_n$, $HK\psi_n = 0$, which implies easily that $S = HK = H^2$ is self-adjoint (S is even positive). K is therefore symmetrisable relative to H, and it is evident that this symmetrisability is full. Since $T\varphi_n = PK\varphi_n = PH\varphi_n = H\varphi_n$ and $T\psi_n = PK\psi_n = P\psi_{n+1} = 0$ we have $T = H$, which shows that T is compact. On the other hand, if $p \geqslant 1$ is an integer,

K^p is not compact, since the sequence $K^p\psi_n = \psi_{n+p}$ contains no converging subsequence. This completes the proof.

Theorem 3. *If K is strongly symmetrisable and T^p is compact for an integer $p \geqslant 1$, then K^{p+1} is compact.*

Proof. Observing that $K = KP$, we have $K^{p+1} = KK^p = KPK^p = KT^p$. Hence, if T^p is compact, the same holds for $K^{p+1} = KT^p$.

Remark. If K is strongly symmetrisable, the statement that one of the iterates of K is compact is therefore equivalent to the statement that one of the iterates of T is compact.

Theorem 4. *If there exists an integer $p \geqslant 1$ such that K^p is compact, then $S = HK \neq O$ implies the existence of a (real) characteristic value $\neq 0$ of K. If, moreover, the symmetrisability of K is full, the converse is also true, that is, $Kf = \lambda f \neq 0$ implies $S \neq O$.*

Proof. Suppose that K^p is compact and $S \neq O$. Then T^p is compact, so that Theorem 1 guarantees the existence of a (real) number λ and an element g such that $Tg = \lambda g \neq 0$. Then, by § 2, 7°, $K^*Hg = \lambda Hg \neq 0$; in other words, K^* has the characteristic value $\lambda \neq 0$. But, K^p and $(K^*)^p = (K^p)^*$ being both compact, K has the characteristic value $\lambda = \bar{\lambda}$ as well (cf. Ch. 11, § 3, especially the remarks on the Hilbert adjoint between Th. 17 and Th. 18). Hence, there exists an element $f \neq 0$ satisfying $Kf = \lambda f \neq 0$.

Suppose now moreover that the symmetrisability of K is full. Then $Kf = \lambda f \neq 0$ implies conversely $Sf = HKf = \lambda Hf \neq 0$, for $Kf = \lambda f \neq 0$ and $Hf = 0$ are now incompatible. Hence $S \neq O$.

Corollary. *If K is strongly symmetrisable, and there exists an integer $p \geqslant 1$ such that T^p is compact, then K has a characteristic value $\neq 0$ if and only if $S = HK = HT \neq O$.*

Proof. K^{p+1} is compact under the stated hypotheses by Theorem 3. Hence, if $S \neq O$, K has a characteristic value $\neq 0$. Conversely, if K has a characteristic value $\neq 0$, then $S \neq O$, since K is fully symmetrisable.

Remarks. 1°. Observe the remarkable fact that for compact K^p no additional condition like fullness or strongness of the symmetrisability is necessary to ensure the existence of a characteristic value $\neq 0$ (cf. [6]).

2°. If it is only known that K is compact, then $Kf = \lambda f \neq 0$ need not imply $S \neq O$. Indeed, if φ_n and ψ_n have the same meaning as in

Theorem 2, and H is also defined in the same way, we may define the linear transformation K by $K\varphi_n = 0$, $K\psi_n = \lambda_n\psi_n$ ($\lambda_n > 0$, $\lim \lambda_n = 0$). Then $S = HK = O$, and K is compact.

Theorem 5. *If K is strongly symmetrisable, hence $K = KP$, and if there exists an integer $p \geqslant 1$ such that T^p is compact, the relations $\varphi = P\psi$, $\psi = \lambda^{-1}K\varphi$ define a one-to-one correspondence between all characteristic elements ψ of K, belonging to characteristic values $\lambda \neq 0$, and all characteristic elements φ of T, belonging to characteristic values $\lambda \neq 0$. Corresponding elements have the same characteristic value λ. Every characteristic value $\lambda \neq 0$ has the same multiplicity for K as for T.*

Proof. Let $K\psi = \lambda\psi \neq 0$ and $\varphi = P\psi$. Then $T\varphi = TP\psi = T\psi = PK\psi = \lambda P\psi = \lambda\varphi$ with $\lambda\varphi \neq 0$, for $\varphi = 0$ and $K = KP$ would imply $K\psi = KP\psi = K\varphi = 0$. Different ψ give different φ. Indeed, let us assume that

$$K\psi_1 = \lambda\psi_1 \neq 0,\ K\psi_2 = \mu\psi_2 \neq 0,\ \psi_1 \neq \psi_2,\ \varphi_1 = P\psi_1 = P\psi_2 = \varphi_2.$$

Then $\lambda\varphi_1 = T\varphi_1 = T\varphi_2 = \mu\varphi_2 = \mu\varphi_1$, hence $\lambda = \mu$, so that $K(\psi_1 - \psi_2) = \lambda(\psi_1 - \psi_2) \neq 0$. But $P(\psi_1 - \psi_2) = \varphi_1 - \varphi_2 = 0$ implies $H(\psi_1 - \psi_2) = 0$, so that $K(\psi_1 - \psi_2) = 0$ on account of the strong symmetrisability. This is a contradiction.

We have to show conversely that $T\varphi = \lambda\varphi \neq 0$ implies the existence of an element ψ such that $K\psi = \lambda\psi \neq 0$ and $P\psi = \varphi$. Writing $\psi = \lambda^{-1}K\varphi$, we have $K\psi = \lambda^{-1}KK\varphi = \lambda^{-1}KPK\varphi = \lambda^{-1}KT\varphi = \lambda(\lambda^{-1}K\varphi) = \lambda\psi$ and $P\psi = \lambda^{-1}PK\varphi = \lambda^{-1}T\varphi = \varphi$.

It is evident that every characteristic value $\lambda \neq 0$ has the same geometric multiplicity for K as for T, since a linear relation between some of the ψ implies the same relation between the corresponding φ, and conversely. Finally it follows from § 2, 10° that for every characteristic value $\lambda \neq 0$ the algebraic and the geometric multiplicities are equal, so that we may speak simply of multiplicity.

Theorem 6. *If K is fully symmetrisable, if there exists an integer $p \geqslant 1$ such that K^p is compact, and the linearly independent elements $\psi_1, \ldots, \psi_n$ determine the subspace of all ψ for which $K\psi = \lambda\psi$ ($\lambda \neq 0$), then the elements $\varphi_i = P\psi_i$ ($i = 1, \ldots, n$) are linearly independent and determine the subspace of all φ for which $T\varphi = \lambda\varphi$. Every characteristic value $\neq 0$ has the same multiplicity for K as for T.*

Proof. We observe first that for every characteristic value $\lambda \neq 0$ of K the algebraic and geometric multiplicities are equal by § 2, 10°. The same remark applies to T. Let now $K\psi_i = \lambda\psi_i \neq 0$ and $\varphi_i = P\psi_i$ ($i = 1, \ldots, n$), where $\psi_1, \ldots, \psi_n$ are linearly independent. Then $T\varphi_i = TP\psi_i = T\psi_i = PK\psi_i = \lambda P\psi_i = \lambda\varphi_i$ as in the preceding theorem. Furthermore, if $\Sigma_{i=1}^n \alpha_i\varphi_i = \Sigma_{i=1}^n \alpha_i P\psi_i = 0$ (α_i complex), then $H(\Sigma\, \alpha_i\psi_i) = 0$. But $K(\Sigma\, \alpha_i\psi_i) = \lambda(\Sigma\, \alpha_i\psi_i)$, so that on account of the full symmetrisability we have then $\Sigma\, \alpha_i\psi_i = 0$ or $\alpha_1 = \ldots = \alpha_n = 0$. This shows that $\varphi_1, \ldots, \varphi_n$ are linearly independent. Hence, for the complex number λ,

$$\text{mult. for } T \geqslant \text{mult. for } K.$$

It remains only to prove the inverse inequality. For this purpose we observe that $T^*\chi = \lambda\chi \neq 0$ implies $K^*\chi = \lambda\chi \neq 0$. Indeed, $T = TP$ implies $T^* = PT^*$; hence, if $T^*\chi = \lambda\chi \neq 0$, we have $\lambda P\chi = PT^*\chi = T^*\chi = \lambda\chi \neq 0$ or $\chi = P\chi$. Since $T^* = K^*P$, it follows then that $K^*\chi = K^*P\chi = T^*\chi = \lambda\chi \neq 0$. Hence, for the complex number λ,

$$\text{mult. for } K = \text{mult. for } K^* \geqslant \text{mult. for } T^* = \text{mult. for } T.$$

This completes the proof.

To conclude this paragraph we raise the question whether there actually exist symmetrisable transformations K such that $T^p = PK^p$ is compact for an integer $p > 1$, although T itself is not compact. In the particular case that $H = I$ (the identical transformation), we have also $P = I$, and then $K = T$ is symmetrisable relative to $H = I$ if and only if $K = T$ is self-adjoint. In this case it is impossible that T^p is compact for an integer $p > 1$ without T itself being compact (cf. Ch. 11, § 1, Th. 13). More generally, if H is an orthogonal projection, so that $H = P$, and K is symmetrisable relative to H, then $T = PK = HK = S$ is self-adjoint, so that also in this case the compactness of T^p ($p > 1$) implies the compactness of T itself.

The theorem which follows now will show however that it is possible to construct an example where T^2 is compact although T is not.

Theorem 7. *There exist bounded linear transformations K, strongly symmetrisable relative to a positive transformation H, such that $T^2 = PK^2$ is compact, although $T = PK$ itself fails to be so.*

Proof. Let R be a complete separable Hilbert space of infinite dimension, and let $\{\varphi_n\}$ be a complete orthonormal system in R. The bounded linear transformation H is defined by $H\varphi_n = \varphi_n/n!$ ($n = 1, 2, \ldots$). Evidently H is positive. Since $Hf = 0$ only for $f = 0$, we have $P = I$, hence $K = T$

for the symmetrisable transformation K which will be defined. We write

$$\begin{cases} K\varphi_{2n-1} = \varphi_{2n-1}/(2n-1) + \varphi_{2n}, \\ K\varphi_{2n} \quad = \varphi_{2n-1}/2n \qquad\quad + \varphi_{2n}/2n. \end{cases} \quad (n = 1, 2, \ldots).$$

Since

$$\begin{aligned} HK\varphi_{2n-1} &= \varphi_{2n-1}/[(2n-1)(2n-1)!] + \varphi_{2n}/(2n)!, \\ HK\varphi_{2n} &= \varphi_{2n-1}/(2n)! + \varphi_{2n}/[(2n)(2n)!], \end{aligned} \quad (n = 1, 2, \ldots),$$

the transformation $S = HK$ is self-adjoint, so that K is symmetrisable relative to H. Evidently $K = T$ is strongly symmetrisable. Furthermore $K = T$ is not compact, since the sequence $K\varphi_{2n-1}$ contains no converging subsequence. However,

$$K^2\varphi_{2n-1} = \left\{\frac{1}{(2n-1)^2} + \frac{1}{2n}\right\}\varphi_{2n-1} + \left(\frac{1}{2n-1} + \frac{1}{2n}\right)\varphi_{2n},$$

$$K^2\varphi_{2n} = \left\{\frac{1}{2n(2n-1)} + \frac{1}{4n^2}\right\}\varphi_{2n-1} + \left(\frac{1}{2n} + \frac{1}{4n^2}\right)\varphi_{2n},$$

and from this it may be proved easily, the proof being similar to that of Ch. 11, § 8, Th. 1, that $K^2 = T^2$ is compact.

§ 4. Extremal Properties of the Characteristic Values and Expansion Theorems for Symmetrisable Transformations in the Case that *H* is Positive

We suppose as in the preceding paragraph that H is positive. The transformations P, K, S, T are the same as in the preceding paragraph. We shall distinguish between two cases:

Case A. *There exists an integer $p \geqslant 1$ such that $T^p = PK^p$ is compact.*

Case B. *K is either fully or strongly symmetrisable, and there exists an integer $p \geqslant 1$ such that K^p is compact.*

We observe two facts. In the first place, if K^p is compact for an integer $p \geqslant 1$, but the symmetrisability of K is neither full nor strong, we can say no more than that we are in case A. Secondly, if T^p is compact for an integer $p \geqslant 1$, and K is strongly symmetrisable, we are in case B, since K^{p+1} is compact by § 3, Th. 3.

Case A. *T^p is compact for an integer $p \geqslant 1$.*

By Ch. 11, § 3 the transformation T has an at most enumerable number of characteristic values $\neq 0$ and, in the case that this number is infinite, these values tend to $\lambda = 0$. We may arrange these characteristic values (if any exist, that is, if $S = HT \neq O$) into a sequence λ_n $(n = 1, 2, \ldots)$ such that every one of them is repeated according to its multiplicity, while moreover $|\lambda_1| \geqslant |\lambda_2| \geqslant \ldots$. Choosing now in the finitedimensional space of all characteristic elements, belonging to a certain characteristic value $\lambda \neq 0$, a maximal system of linearly independent elements, it is readily seen that these elements, say $\chi_1, \ldots, \chi_k$, are H-independent. Indeed, $H \Sigma \alpha_i \chi_i = 0$ implying $\lambda \Sigma \alpha_i \chi_i = T \Sigma \alpha_i \chi_i = 0$, it follows from $\lambda \neq 0$ that $\alpha_1 = \ldots = \alpha_k = 0$. Then, by Ch. 9, § 5, Th. 4 (the theorem on H-orthogonalization), we may obtain an H-orthonormal system of k elements that determines the subspace of all φ satisfying $T\varphi = \lambda\varphi$. Doing this for all characteristic values $\neq 0$, the elements of all these H-orthonormal systems may be written into a single sequence $\{\varphi_n\}$ in such a way that φ_n belongs to λ_n for every n. Evidently the whole sequence φ_n is H-orthonormal (cf. § 2, 9°).

Case B. *K is either fully or strongly symmetrisable, and K^p is compact for an integer $p \geqslant 1$.*

We now argue for K as we did in case A for T, and we find in this way the H-orthonormal sequence ψ_n of characteristic elements of K, belonging to the sequence λ_n of characteristic values $\neq 0$. The sequence $\varphi_n = P\psi_n$ $(n = 1, 2, \ldots)$ of characteristic elements of T is also H-orthonormal and satisfies all conditions mentioned in case A. If K is strongly symmetrisable, we have moreover $\psi_n = \lambda_n^{-1} K\varphi_n$ $(n = 1, 2, \ldots)$ by § 3, Th. 5.

Theorem 1. 1°. *$|\lambda_n| = max\, N(Kf)/N(f)$ for all $f \in R$ satisfying $N(f) \neq 0$ and $(Hf, \varphi_1) = \ldots = (Hf, \varphi_{n-1}) = 0$. For $f = \varphi_n$ the maximum is attained.*

2°. *$N(Kf) = 0$ (equivalent to $Sf = HKf = 0$) if and only if $(Hf, \varphi_n) = 0$ for all n.*

3°. *In case B we may replace the elements φ in 1° and 2° by the corresponding elements ψ.*

Proof. 1°. We first consider the case that T itself is compact. Let $N(f) \neq 0$ and $(Hf, \varphi_1) = \ldots = (Hf, \varphi_{n-1}) = 0$. We may suppose without loss of generality that $N(f) = 1$. If $N(Kf) = 0$, we have certainly $N(Kf) \leqslant |\lambda_n|$; if however $N(Kf) \neq 0$, hence $Sf = HTf \neq 0$, we put, as in § 3, Th. 1, $\bar{f}_0 = f$, $\bar{f}_{k-1} = f_{k-1}/N(f_{k-1})$, $f_k = T\bar{f}_{k-1}$ $(k = 1, 2, \ldots)$.

As in § 3, Th. 1 we find then an element φ satisfying $T\varphi = \lambda\varphi \neq 0$. Since $(H\bar{f}_0, \varphi_l) = (Hf, \varphi_l) = 0$ $(l = 1, \ldots, n-1)$, we have $(Hf_1, \varphi_l) = (HT\bar{f}_0, \varphi_l) = (\bar{f}_0, HT\varphi_l) = \lambda_l(H\bar{f}_0, \varphi_l) = 0$, so that, proceeding in this way, we find $(Hf_k, \varphi_l) = 0$ $(k = 1, 2, \ldots;\ l = 1, \ldots, n-1)$. Hence $(H\varphi, \varphi_l) = 0$ $(l = 1, \ldots, n-1)$. It follows that φ is not a linear combination of $\varphi_1, \ldots, \varphi_{n-1}$, so that the characteristic value λ belonging to φ is not identical with one of the values $\lambda_1, \ldots, \lambda_{n-1}$. This implies $|\lambda| \leqslant |\lambda_n|$. Furthermore $\lim N(f_k) = |\lambda|$ for the non-decreasing sequence $N(f_k)$ $(k = 1, 2, \ldots)$, as the proof of § 3, Th. 1 shows. Hence, observing that $N^2(Kf) = (HKf, Kf) = (HTf, Kf) = (Tf, HKf) = (Tf, HTf) = (HTf, Tf) = N^2(Tf)$, we find

$$N(Kf) = N(Tf) = N(f_1) \leqslant |\lambda| \leqslant |\lambda_n|.$$

We next consider the case that T^p is compact for an integer $p > 1$. We first observe that, by the results in Ch. 11, § 3, Th. 1 and Ch. 11, § 6, Th. 3, the sequence $\lambda_1^p, \lambda_2^p, \ldots$ is the sequence of all characteristic values $\neq 0$ of T^p, each characteristic value repeated according to its multiplicity, and $\varphi_1, \varphi_2, \ldots$ is a corresponding sequence of characteristic elements. Let now again $N(f) = 1$ and $(Hf, \varphi_1) = \ldots = (Hf, \varphi_{n-1}) = 0$. If $N(Kf) = 0$, we have certainly $N(Kf) \leqslant |\lambda_n|$; if however $N(Kf) \neq 0$, hence $Sf = HTf \neq 0$, we put again

$$\bar{f}_0 = f,\ \bar{f}_{k-1} = f_{k-1}/N(f_{k-1}),\ f_k = T\bar{f}_{k-1}\ (k = 1, 2, \ldots).$$

We also write

$$\bar{g}_0 = f,\ \bar{g}_{k-1} = g_{k-1}/N(g_{k-1}),\ g_k = T^p\bar{g}_{k-1}\ (k = 1, 2, \ldots).$$

Then, as in § 3, Th. 1, both sequences $N(f_1), N(f_2), \ldots$ and $N(g_1), N(g_2), \ldots$ are non-decreasing, and it is evident that $\bar{g}_k = \bar{f}_{kp}$ $(k = 1, 2, \ldots)$, hence

$$g_{k+1} = T^p\bar{g}_k = T^p\bar{f}_{kp} = T^{p-1}f_{kp+1} =$$

$$N(f_{kp+1})\, T^{p-2}f_{kp+2} = \ldots = \{\Pi_{i=1}^{p-1} N(f_{kp+i})\} f_{(k+1)p}.$$

In the same way as in the first part of our proof we find now that $\lim N(g_k) = |\lambda|^p \leqslant |\lambda_n|^p$, hence also

$$\lim \Pi_{i=1}^{p} N(f_{kp+i}) = |\lambda|^p.$$

Since the sequence $N(f_1), N(f_2), \ldots$ is non-decreasing, this is only possible if $\lim N(f_k) = |\lambda|$. Hence finally

$$N(Kf) = N(Tf) = N(f_1) \leqslant |\lambda| \leqslant |\lambda_n|.$$

For $f = \varphi_n$ the maximum is attained, since $N(K\varphi_n) = N(T\varphi_n) = |\lambda_n| N(\varphi_n) = |\lambda_n|$.

2°. We now suppose immediately that T^p is compact for an integer $p \geqslant 1$. Let first $N(Kf) = 0$, which is equivalent to $Sf = 0$. Then $(Hf, \varphi_n) = \lambda_n^{-1}(Hf, T\varphi_n) = \lambda_n^{-1}(f, S\varphi_n) = \lambda_n^{-1}(Sf, \varphi_n) = 0$ for every n.

Let now conversely $(Hf, \varphi_n) = 0$ for every n. If $N(f) = 0$, then certainly $Sf = 0$ (cf. § 2, 2°); we may suppose therefore that $N(f) = 1$. Hence $N(Kf) \leqslant |\lambda_n|$ for all n by the first part of the present proof. If the number of λ_n is infinite, then $\lim \lambda_n = 0$, hence $N(Kf) = 0$. If the number N of λ_n is finite, and $N(Kf)$ were $\neq 0$, an argument similar to that in the first part of the present proof would lead to the existence of a characteristic element φ satisfying $T^p\varphi = \lambda^p\varphi \neq 0$ and $(H\varphi, \varphi_n) = 0$ for $n=1, \ldots, N$. This however is impossible. Hence $N(Kf)=0$ in any case.

3°. Trivial, since in case B we have $(Hf, \psi_i) = (Hf, \varphi_i)$ for every $f \in R$ and all i, and $N(\psi_n) = N(\varphi_n) = 1$.

Corollary. *If, in case B for example, the element f is H-orthogonal to all ψ_n, then f is H-orthogonal to every element g of the form $g = Kh$. Furthermore, if the element $f = Kg$ is H-orthogonal to all ψ_n, then $Hf = 0$.*

Proof. Suppose first that $(Hf, \psi_n) = 0$ $(n = 1, 2, \ldots)$ and $g = Kh$. The first hypothesis implies $Sf = HKf = 0$, hence $(Hf, g) = (Hf, Kh) = (HKf, h) = 0$.

Let now $f = Kg$ and $(Hf, \psi_n) = 0$ $(n = 1, 2, \ldots)$. Then $\lambda_n (Hg, \psi_n) = (Hg, K\psi_n) = (HKg, \psi_n) = (Hf, \psi_n) = 0$, hence $(Hg, \psi_n) = 0$ $(n = 1, 2, \ldots)$, so that $Hf = HKg = Sg = 0$.

Theorem 2 (*Expansion theorem*). 1°. *If, for arbitrary elements $f, g \in R$, we write $\alpha_n = (Hf, \varphi_n)$, $\beta_n = (Hg, \varphi_n)$ $(n = 1, 2, \ldots)$, then*

$$lim_{k\to\infty} N(Kf - \Sigma_{n=1}^k \lambda_n\alpha_n\varphi_n) = 0.$$

The interpretation in the case that the total number of λ_n is finite is evident. Furthermore

$$(HKf, g) = \Sigma\, \lambda_n\alpha_n\overline{\beta}_n.$$

2°. *In case B we may replace the elements φ_n by the corresponding elements ψ_n.*

Proof. 1°. If the number of λ_n is infinite and $r_{k+1} = f - \Sigma_{n=1}^k \alpha_n\varphi_n$, then $(Hr_{k+1}, \varphi_1) = \ldots = (Hr_{k+1}, \varphi_k) = 0$ and $N^2 (r_{k+1}) = (Hf, f) - \Sigma_1^k (Hf, \alpha_n\varphi_n) - \Sigma_1^k (\alpha_n H\varphi_n, f) + \Sigma_1^k |\alpha_n|^2 = N^2(f) - \Sigma_1^k |\alpha_n|^2 - \Sigma_1^k |\alpha_n|^2 + \Sigma_1^k |\alpha_n|^2 = N^2(f) - \Sigma_1^k |\alpha_n|^2$. Hence, by the preceding theorem,

$$N(Kr_{k+1}) \leqslant |\lambda_{k+1}| N(r_{k+1}) \leqslant |\lambda_{k+1}| N(f),$$

so that $\lim N(Kr_{k+1}) = 0$ on account of $\lim |\lambda_{k+1}| = 0$. But

$$N(Kr_{k+1}) = N(Kf - \Sigma_1^k \alpha_n K\varphi_n) =$$

$$N(Kf - \Sigma_1^k \alpha_n T\varphi_n) = N(Kf - \Sigma_1^k \lambda_n\alpha_n\varphi_n),$$

hence

$$\lim_{k\to\infty} N(Kf - \Sigma_1^k \lambda_n\alpha_n\varphi_n) = 0.$$

If the number N of λ_n is finite, then $N(Kr_{N+1}) = 0$ by the preceding theorem, hence

$$N(Kf - \Sigma_{n=1}^N \lambda_n\alpha_n\varphi_n) = 0.$$

Since

$$\lim_{k\to\infty} |(HKr_{k+1}, g)| = \lim |(H(Kf - \Sigma_1^k \lambda_n\alpha_n\varphi_n), g)|$$

$$\leqslant \lim N(Kf - \Sigma_1^k \lambda_n\alpha_n\varphi_n) . N(g) = 0,$$

we have

$$(HKf, g) = \Sigma\, \lambda_n\alpha_n(H\varphi_n, g) = \Sigma\, \lambda_n\alpha_n\overline{\beta}_n.$$

2°. Trivial.

Remark. If $\lim_{k\to\infty} N(f - \Sigma_1^k \alpha_n\varphi_n) = 0$ holds for every $f \in R$, then any element $g \in R$, satisfying $Sg = HKg = 0$, satisfies also $Hg = 0$. Indeed, under the stated hypothesis we have $(Hf, g) = \Sigma\, \alpha_n\overline{\beta}_n$ for arbitrary f, g, where $\alpha_n = (Hf, \varphi_n)$, $\beta_n = (Hg, \varphi_n)$. If therefore $Sg = 0$, hence $\beta_n = 0$ $(n = 1, 2, \ldots)$ by Th. 1, 2°, then $(f, Hg) = (Hf, g) = \Sigma\, \alpha_n\overline{\beta}_n = 0$ for arbitrary f, which implies $Hg = 0$. A more complete discussion of the conditions under which $\lim_{k\to\infty} N(f - \Sigma_1^k \alpha_n\varphi_n) = 0$ holds will be postponed until § 10, Th. 7.

Theorem 3. *Let λ_{n_i} $(i = 1, 2, \ldots)$ be the subsequence of all positive characteristic values in the sequence λ_n, arranged in non-increasing order, hence $\lambda_{n_1} \geqslant \lambda_{n_2} \geqslant \ldots$. Then $\lambda_{n_i} = \max (HKf, f)/N^2(f)$ for all $f \in R$ satisfying $N(f) \neq 0$ and $(Hf, \varphi_{n_1}) = \ldots = (Hf, \varphi_{n_{i-1}}) = 0$. For $f = \varphi_{n_i}$ the maximum is attained.*

A similar statement holds for the sequence of all negative characteristic values.

In case B the elements φ may be replaced by the corresponding elements ψ.

Proof. Let $N(f) = 1$ and $(Hf, \varphi_{n_1}) = \ldots = (Hf, \varphi_{n_{i-1}}) = 0$. Writing again $\alpha_n = (Hf, \varphi_n)$, we have therefore $\alpha_{n_1} = \ldots = \alpha_{n_{i-1}} = 0$. As in the proof of the preceding theorem we find that $r_{k+1} = f - \Sigma_1^k \alpha_n\varphi_n$

satisfies $N^2(r_{k+1}) = N^2(f) - \Sigma_1^k \mid \alpha_n \mid^2$, hence $\Sigma \mid \alpha_n \mid^2 \leqslant N^2(f) = 1$. Then, by Theorem 2,

$$(HKf, f) = \Sigma \lambda_n \mid \alpha_n \mid^2 \leqslant \lambda_{n_i} \Sigma \mid \alpha_n \mid^2 \leqslant \lambda_{n_i}.$$

For $f = \varphi_{n_i}$ the maximum is attained since then $(HKf, f) = (HT\varphi_{n_i}, \varphi_{n_i}) = \lambda_{n_i}$.

Remark. 1°. If the total number N of positive characteristic values $\neq 0$ is finite, then $0 \geqslant \max (HKf, f)/N^2(f)$ for all $f \in R$ satisfying $N(f) \neq 0$ and $(Hf, \varphi_{n_1}) = \ldots = (Hf, \varphi_{n_N}) = 0$ (cf. § 8, Th. 2).

2°. In the present theorem λ_{n_i} is characterized by a certain maximum property. It may be felt as a disadvantage that for this characterization the elements $\varphi_{n_1}, \ldots, \varphi_{n_{i-1}}$ are supposed to be known beforehand. That this may be avoided will be shown in the next theorem, which for the special case of an integral transformation with Hermitian kernel of finite double-norm was proved by COURANT [7].

Theorem 4. *Let the elements $p_1, \ldots, p_{i-1}$ be arbitrarily given, and let*

$$\mu_i = \textit{upper bound } (HKf, f)/N^2(f)$$

for all $f \in R$ satisfying $N(f) \neq 0$ and $(Hf, p_1) = \ldots = (Hf, p_{i-1}) = 0$. Then μ_i depends evidently on $p_1, \ldots, p_{i-1}$. Letting now these elements run through the whole space R, we have $\lambda_{n_i} = \min \mu_i$.

Proof. We shall prove first that it is possible to find an element $f = \Sigma_{k=1}^i \gamma_k \varphi_{n_k}$ such that $N(f) = 1$ and $(Hf, p_1) = \ldots = (Hf, p_{i-1}) = 0$. These conditions are equivalent to $\Sigma_1^i \mid \gamma_k \mid^2 = 1$ and $\Sigma_{k=1}^i \gamma_k (H\varphi_{n_k}, p_j) = 0$ $(j = 1, \ldots, i-1)$, and it is well-known that these $i - 1$ homogeneous equations have actually a solution $\gamma_1, \ldots, \gamma_i$ for which $\Sigma_1^i \mid \gamma_k \mid^2 = 1$. Observing that $(HK\varphi_{n_k}, \varphi_{n_k}) = (HT\varphi_{n_k}, \varphi_{n_k}) = \lambda_{n_k}$ and $(HK\varphi_{n_k}, \varphi_{n_l}) = (HT\varphi_{n_k}, \varphi_{n_l}) = 0$ for $k \neq l$, we find then that $f = \Sigma_1^i \gamma_k \varphi_{n_k}$ satisfies

$$(HKf, f)/N^2(f) = (HKf, f) = \Sigma_{k,l=1}^i \gamma_k \bar{\gamma}_l (HK\varphi_{n_k}, \varphi_{n_l})$$

$$= \Sigma_1^i \lambda_{n_k} \mid \gamma_k \mid^2 \geqslant \lambda_{n_i} \Sigma_1^i \mid \gamma_k \mid^2 = \lambda_{n_i},$$

which implies

$$\mu_i \geqslant \lambda_{n_i}.$$

On the other hand, if we make the particular choice $p_1 = \varphi_{n_1}, \ldots, p_{i-1} = \varphi_{n_{i-1}}$, and $f \in R$ satisfies $N(f) \neq 0$, $(Hf, p_1) = \ldots = (Hf, p_{i-1}) = 0$, we have $\max (HKf, f)/N^2(f) = \lambda_{n_i}$ by Theorem 3. Hence

$$\lambda_{n_i} = \min \mu_i.$$

Remark. The present theorem is known as a minimax theorem.

Theorem 5. *Necessary and sufficient that* $(Sf, f) = (HKf, f) \geqslant 0$ *should hold for every element* $f \in R$ *is that all characteristic values of* T *(or of* K *in case B) are non-negative.*

Proof. If $T\varphi = \lambda\varphi$, $\varphi \neq 0$, but φ satisfies $N(\varphi) = 0$, then $H\varphi = 0$, so that $T\varphi = 0$ or $\lambda = 0$. If however $T\varphi = \lambda\varphi$ and $N(\varphi) \neq 0$, we may assume without loss of generality that $N(\varphi) = 1$. The inequality $(HKf, f) \geqslant 0$, holding for every $f \in R$, implies then $\lambda = \lambda(H\varphi, \varphi) = (HT\varphi, \varphi) = (HK\varphi, \varphi) \geqslant 0$.

Conversely, if all $\lambda_n \neq 0$ are positive, we have on account of Theorem 2

$$(HKf, f) = \Sigma\, \lambda_n \mid \alpha_n \mid^2 \geqslant 0$$

for every $f \in R$.

§ 5. Extension on the Closure $\bar{R}$

Supposing that the Hilbert space R is not complete, we may consider the complete Hilbert space $\bar{R}$, the closure of R, and extend the bounded linear transformations H, P, K, S and T onto $\bar{R}$ in such a way that their bounds are unchanged. Relations such as $H = PH = HP$, $S = HK = HT$, $T = PK$, holding in R, remain true in $\bar{R}$ after the extension. Although we have already met this situation before we repeat the proof for one of these relations, say $H = HP$. For $f \in \bar{R}$, $f_n \in R$ $(n = 1, 2, \ldots)$, $f = \lim f_n$, we have $Hf = \lim Hf_n = \lim HPf_n$. On the other hand, since $Pf = \lim Pf_n$, we find also $HPf = \lim HPf_n$. Hence $Hf = HPf$. By hypothesis, R is the direct sum of the orthogonal subspaces $[L]$ and $[M]$, where $[L]$ is the set of all $f \in R$ satisfying $Hf = 0$. These subspaces $[L]$ and $[M]$ are not both complete, since in that case R would be complete as well. It is now evident that the closure $\bar{R}$ is the direct sum of $[\bar{L}]$ and $[\bar{M}]$, where $[\bar{L}]$ and $[\bar{M}]$ are the closures of $[L]$ and $[M]$ respectively. Furthermore, since the original transformation P is the projection on $[M]$ along $[L]$, it satisfies $P^2 = P$. Then the extended P also satisfies $P^2 = P$ so that it is again a projection. $Pf = 0$ for all $f \in [L]$ implies $Pf = 0$ for all $f \in [\bar{L}]$, and $Pf = f$ for all $f \in [M]$ implies $Pf = f$ for all $f \in [\bar{M}]$. It follows therefore that the extended P is the projection on $[\bar{M}]$ along $[\bar{L}]$. We may no longer assert that $[\bar{L}]$ is the set of all $f \in \bar{R}$ satisfying $Hf = 0$, since it is not excluded that after the extension $Hf = 0$ also for some elements $f \in [\bar{M}]$. Evidently, since H is positive before the extension, the extended H is still positive. If K is symmetrisable relative to H, so that $S = HK$ is self-adjoint, the extended $S = HK$ is self-adjoint as well, which implies that K remains symmetrisable relative to H. If, before the extension, we are in case A, so that T^p is compact for an integer $p \geqslant 1$, then Ch. 11, § 3, Th. 10 shows that T^p remains compact after the extension, and that no new characteristic values $\neq 0$ are created. The sequences λ_n and φ_n $(n = 1, 2, \ldots)$ of characteristic values $\neq 0$ and corresponding characteristic elements stand therefore in the same relation to T after the extension as before. If, before the extension, we are in case B, so that K^p is compact for an integer $p \geqslant 1$, then K^p remains compact after the extension, and the sequences λ_n and ψ_n $(n = 1, 2, \ldots)$ stand in the same relation to K after the extension as before. If moreover K is fully symmetrisable, that is, if $Hf \neq 0$ for every $f \in R$ satisfying $Kf = \lambda f \neq 0$, then the extended K is also fully symmetrisable, since $Kf = \lambda f \neq 0$ implies that f, as well before as after the extension, is a finite linear combination of some ψ_n. If, finally, K is strongly symmetrisable before the extension, that is, if $Hf = 0$ implies $Kf = 0$, we cannot say that this remains true after the extension. However, we have found that strong symmetrisability may also be formulated as $K = KP$, and this relation remains valid after extension on $\bar{R}$. The one-to-one correspondence $\varphi_n = P\psi_n$, $\psi_n = \lambda_n^{-1}K\varphi_n$, established in § 3, Th. 5, exists of course in $\bar{R}$ as well, since it affects only elements already belonging to R.

We shall prove now that the theorems in the preceding paragraph remain true for all elements $f \in \bar{R}$, so that it is not necessary to restrict ourselves to elements $f \in R$. This may be done by repeating all proofs for this new case and verifying that the arguments remain valid. It is perhaps easier however to show by a short and direct proof that the results for the space $\bar{R}$ follow from the corresponding results for the space R.

Theorem 1. 1°. $|\lambda_n| = \max N(Kf)/N(f)$ *for all* $f \in \bar{R}$ *satisfying* $N(f) \neq 0$ *and* $(Hf, \varphi_1) = \ldots = (Hf, \varphi_{n-1}) = 0$. *For* $f = \varphi_n$ *the maximum is attained.*

2°. $N(Kf) = 0$ (*equivalent to* $Sf = HKf = 0$) *if and only if* $(Hf, \varphi_n) = 0$ *for all* n.

3°. *In case B we may replace the elements* φ *in* 1° *and* 2° *by the corresponding elements* ψ.

Proof. 1°. Let $f \in \bar{R}$, $N(f) \neq 0$ and $(Hf, \varphi_1) = \ldots = (Hf, \varphi_{n-1}) = 0$. Suppose that the sequence $g_i \in R$ $(i = 1, 2, \ldots)$ is such that $\lim g_i = f$, hence also $\lim Hg_i = Hf$. Then the elements $f_i = g_i - \Sigma_{k=1}^{n-1} (Hg_i, \varphi_k)\varphi_k$ belong to the space R, and $(Hf_i, \varphi_1) = \ldots = (Hf_i, \varphi_{n-1}) = 0$ $(i = 1, 2, \ldots)$. It follows on account of § 4, Th. 1 that $N(Kf_i)/N(f_i) \leqslant |\lambda_n|$, provided $N(f_i) \neq 0$. But, since $\lim_{i\to\infty} (Hg_i, \varphi_k) = (Hf, \varphi_k) = 0$ for $k = 1, \ldots, n-1$, we have $\lim f_i = \lim g_i = f$, hence $\lim Kf_i = Kf$, $\lim N(Kf_i) = N(Kf)$ and $\lim N(f_i) = N(f) \neq 0$. The inequality $N(Kf_i)/N(f_i) \leqslant |\lambda_n|$ for i sufficiently large implies therefore that $N(Kf)/N(f) \leqslant |\lambda_n|$. We know already that the maximum is attained for $f = \varphi_n$.

2°. Let first $N(Kf) = 0$, hence $Sf = 0$. Then $(Hf, \varphi_n) = \lambda_n^{-1}(Hf, T\varphi_n) = \lambda_n^{-1}(f, S\varphi_n) = \lambda_n^{-1}(Sf, \varphi_n) = 0$ for every n.

Let now conversely $(Hf, \varphi_n) = 0$ for every n. If $N(f) = 0$, hence $Hf = 0$, then $(Sf, g) = (HKf, g) = (Hf, Kg) = 0$ for every $g \in \bar{R}$, hence $Sf = 0$; we may suppose therefore that $N(f) = 1$. Hence $N(Kf) \leqslant |\lambda_n|$ for all n by the first part of the present proof. If the number of λ_n is infinite, then $\lim \lambda_n = 0$, hence $N(Kf) = 0$. If the number N of λ_n is finite we may assume that $f \in \bar{R}$, $N(f) = 1$ and $(Hf, \varphi_1) = \ldots = (Hf, \varphi_N) = 0$. Then, supposing again the sequence $g_i \in R$ $(i = 1, 2, \ldots)$ to be such that $\lim g_i = f$, the elements $f_i = g_i - \Sigma_{k=1}^{N} (Hg_i, \varphi_k)\varphi_k$ belong to the space R and $(Hf_i, \varphi_1) = \ldots = (Hf_i, \varphi_N) = 0$ $(i = 1, 2, \ldots)$. Hence, by § 4, Th. 1, $N(Kf_i) = 0$. But, since $\lim_{i\to\infty} (Hg_i, \varphi_k) = (Hf, \varphi_k) = 0$ for $k = 1, \ldots, N$, we have $\lim f_i = \lim g_i = f$, so that $N(Kf) = \lim N(Kf_i) = 0$.

3°. Trivial.

Theorem 2. *The Theorems 2, 3, 4, 5 of the preceding paragraph remain true for elements* $f \in \bar{R}$.

Proof. The proofs given in the preceding paragraph may be repeated without any change.

§ 6. Expression of the Solutions of $Tf - \lambda f = g$ and $Kf - \lambda f = g$ in Terms of the Characteristic Elements

We suppose once more that the Hilbert space R is complete or non-complete, and that the bounded linear transformation K is symmetrisable relative to the bounded positive transformation H. Furthermore it is assumed that the conditions of case A are fulfilled. If the additional conditions of case B are supposed to be satisfied as well, it will be expressly stated.

We now recall Ch. 11, § 3, Th. 16, where it was proved that if T is a bounded linear transformation on a Banach space E (complete or not) such that T^p is compact for an integer $p \geqslant 1$, and if $\lambda \neq 0$, then the range $W(T - \lambda I)$ consists of those and only those elements $g \in E$ satisfying $f_i^*(g) = 0$ $(i = 1, \ldots, d)$, where $f_1^*, \ldots, f_d^*$ is a maximal system of linearly independent solutions of $(T_B^* - \lambda I)f^* = 0$. Here T_B^* is the Banach adjoint of T, which operates therefore in the adjoint space E^*. Applying this theorem to our transformation $T = PK$ in Hilbert space R and changing over from the Banach adjoint T_B^* to the Hilbert adjoint T^*, we have to consider besides T the Hilbert adjoint T^*, which has the closure $\bar{R}$ as its domain. We then obtain the following statement: If $\lambda \neq 0$, the range $W(T - \lambda I)$ consists of those and only those elements $g \in R$ satisfying $(\chi_i, g) = 0$ $(i = 1, \ldots, d)$, where $\chi_1, \ldots, \chi_d$ is a maximal system of linearly independent solutions of $(T^* - \bar{\lambda} I)\chi = 0$.

Theorem 1. *If $\lambda \neq 0$ is no characteristic value of T, the equation $T_\lambda f \equiv Tf - \lambda f = g$ has a uniquely determined solution $f \in R$ for every element $g \in R$. If $\lambda \neq 0$ is a characteristic value of T, the equation $T_\lambda f \equiv Tf - \lambda f = g$ has a solution $f \in R$ for those and only those elements $g \in R$ that are H-orthogonal to all characteristic elements of T, belonging to the characteristic value λ. This solution is determined except for a linear combination of these characteristic elements.*

In case B a similar statement holds for the solution $f \in R$ of $K_\lambda f \equiv Kf - \lambda f = g$. The ranges $W(K - \lambda I)$ and $W(T - \lambda I)$ are identical.

Proof. If $\lambda \neq 0$ is no characteristic value of T, it belongs to the resolvent set of T by Ch. 11, § 3, Th. 11, which implies that $Tf - \lambda f = g$ has a uniquely determined solution $f \in R$ for every $g \in R$. If $\lambda \neq 0$ is a characteristic value of T, then λ is identical with one of the numbers λ_n, so that λ is real; $\lambda = \bar{\lambda}$. If $\tilde{\varphi}_1, \ldots, \tilde{\varphi}_d$ is a maximal system of linearly independent solutions of $T\varphi - \lambda\varphi = 0$, then § 2, 6° shows that $\chi_i = H\tilde{\varphi}_i$ $(i = 1, \ldots, d)$ is a maximal system of linearly independent solutions of $(T^* - \bar{\lambda} I)\chi = (T^* - \lambda I)\chi = 0$ (where we have used of course that λ has the same multiplicity for T and T^*). The range $W(T - \lambda I)$ consists therefore of those and only those elements $g \in R$ satisfying $(\chi_i, g) = 0$ $(i = 1, \ldots, d)$. But $(\chi_i, g) = (H\tilde{\varphi}_i, g)$, and this shows that $T_\lambda f \equiv Tf - \lambda f = g$ has a solution $f \in R$ for those and only those elements $g \in R$ that are H-orthogonal to all characteristic elements of T, belonging to the characteristic value λ. This solution is determined except for a linear combination of these characteristic elements, since $T_\lambda f_1 = T_\lambda f_2 = g$ implies $T_\lambda(f_1 - f_2) = 0$, whereas $T_\lambda f = g$ and $T_\lambda \varphi = 0$ imply $T_\lambda(f + \varphi) = g$.

In case B the same argument may be applied to K, using now the maximal system $\tilde{\psi}_1, \ldots, \tilde{\psi}_d$ of linearly independent solutions of $K\varphi - \lambda\varphi = 0$. Since $H\tilde{\psi}_i = H\tilde{\varphi}_i$ $(i = 1, \ldots, d)$ on account of $H\tilde{\varphi}_i = H(P\tilde{\psi}_i) = (HP)\tilde{\psi}_i = H\tilde{\psi}_i$, the conditions $(H\tilde{\psi}_i, g) = 0$ and $(H\tilde{\varphi}_i, g) = 0$ are equivalent, and this shows that the ranges $W(K - \lambda I)$ and $W(T - \lambda I)$ are identical.

Remark. If R is not complete, and H, K, T are extended onto the closure $\bar{R}$, the statements in the present theorem remain true for the extended transformations. This is a consequence of the fact that no new characteristic values $\neq 0$ are created by the extension. Furthermore, if $g \in R$, the equation $Tf - \lambda f = g$ has only solutions f belonging to R; in other words, if $f \in \bar{R} - R$, then $Tf - \lambda f \in \bar{R} - R$ as well (cf. Ch. 11, § 3, Th. 10, Corollary).

Theorem 2. *If we are in case B, and $f \in R$ is a solution of $Kf - \lambda f = g$ ($\lambda \neq 0$), then $f_1 = Pf - \lambda^{-1}(I - P)g$ is a solution of $Tf_1 - \lambda f_1 = g$. If K is strongly symmetrisable (that is, if $K = KP$) and $f_1 \in R$ is a solution of $Tf_1 - \lambda f_1 = g$, then $f = f_1 + \lambda^{-1}(I - P)Kf_1$ is a solution of $Kf - \lambda f = g$.*

Proof. Suppose that $\lambda \neq 0$ and $Kf - \lambda f = g$. Then, on account of $T = TP$ (cf. § 2, 2°), we find

$$TPf - \lambda Pf = Tf - \lambda Pf = PKf - \lambda Pf =$$

$$P(Kf - \lambda f) = Pg = g - (I - P)g,$$

hence $TPf - \lambda(Pf - \lambda^{-1}(I - P)g) = g$ or, on account of $T(I - P)g = 0$,

$$T(Pf - \lambda^{-1}(I - P)g) - \lambda(Pf - \lambda^{-1}(I - P)g) = g.$$

This shows that $f_1 = Pf - \lambda^{-1}(I - P)g$ is a solution of $Tf_1 - \lambda f_1 = g$.

Let now $K = KP$, $\lambda \neq 0$ and $Tf_1 - \lambda f_1 = g$. Then

$$Kf_1 - \lambda f_1 = PKf_1 + (I - P)Kf_1 - \lambda f_1 = g + (I - P)Kf_1,$$

hence $Kf_1 - \lambda(f_1 + \lambda^{-1}(I - P)Kf_1) = g$ or, on account of $K(I - P)Kf_1 = 0$,

$$K(f_1 + \lambda^{-1}(I - P)Kf_1) - \lambda(f_1 + \lambda^{-1}(I - P)Kf_1) = g.$$

This shows that $f = f_1 + \lambda^{-1}(I - P)Kf_1$ is a solution of $Kf - \lambda f = g$.

Remark. If K is strongly symmetrisable and $Kf - \lambda f = g$ ($\lambda \neq 0$), then, writing $f_1 = Pf - \lambda^{-1}(I - P)g$, $f_2 = f_1 + \lambda^{-1}(I - P)Kf_1$, we have $f_2 = f$. The correspondence between f and f_1 is therefore one-to-one. We furthermore observe that it is easily seen that

$$f_1 = \lambda^{-1}(Tf - g), \; f = \lambda^{-1}(Kf_1 - g).$$

Theorem 3. *Let $\lambda \neq 0$ and $g \in R$ belong to the range $W(T - \lambda I)$. Then every solution $f \in R$ of $Tf - \lambda f = g$ satisfies*

$$lim_{k \to \infty} N(f - \sigma_k) = 0,$$

with

$$\sigma_k = -\frac{g}{\lambda} - {}'\Sigma_{n=1}^{k} \frac{\lambda_n}{\lambda(\lambda - \lambda_n)} \alpha_n \varphi_n,$$

where $\alpha_n = (Hg, \varphi_n)$ *for* $\lambda_n \neq \lambda$, *and where the dash in front of the* Σ*-symbol means that for those values of* n *for which* $\lambda_n = \lambda$ *the coefficient of* φ_n *has the value* (Hf, φ_n). *For every set of arbitrarily prescribed values of these latter coefficients there exists a solution of* $Tf - \lambda f = g$.

In case B every solution $f \in R$ *of* $Kf - \lambda f = g$ *satisfies*

$$\lim_{k\to\infty} N(f - s_k) = 0$$

with

$$s_k = -\frac{g}{\lambda} - {}'\Sigma_{n=1}^{k} \frac{\lambda_n}{\lambda(\lambda - \lambda_n)} \alpha_n \psi_n,$$

where $\alpha_n = (Hg, \psi_n)$ *for* $\lambda_n \neq \lambda$, *and where the dash in front of the* Σ*-symbol means that for those values of* n *for which* $\lambda_n = \lambda$ *the coefficient of* ψ_n *has the value* (Hf, ψ_n). *For every set of arbitrarily prescribed values of these latter coefficients, there exists a solution of* $Kf - \lambda f = g$.

Proof. Let $Tf - \lambda f = g$. Writing $\beta_n = (Hf, \varphi_n)$, we have by the expansion theorem

$$\lim_{k\to\infty} N(Tf - \Sigma_1^k \lambda_n\beta_n\varphi_n) = \lim_{k\to\infty} N(Kf - \Sigma_1^k \lambda_n\beta_n\varphi_n) = 0,$$

hence

$$\lim_{k\to\infty} N\left(f + \frac{g}{\lambda} - \Sigma_1^k \frac{\lambda_n}{\lambda} \beta_n\varphi_n\right) = 0. \tag{1}$$

From $(HTf, \varphi_n) = (f, HT\varphi_n) = (Hf, \lambda_n\varphi_n) = \lambda_n\beta_n$ we derive $\lambda_n\beta_n = (HTf, \varphi_n) = (H(g + \lambda f), \varphi_n) = \alpha_n + \lambda\beta_n$, so that for $\lambda_n \neq \lambda$ we find $\beta_n = -\alpha_n/(\lambda - \lambda_n)$. It follows therefore from (1) that

$$\lim_{k\to\infty} N(f - \sigma_k) = 0$$

with

$$\sigma_k = -\frac{g}{\lambda} - {}'\Sigma_{n=1}^{k} \frac{\lambda_n}{\lambda(\lambda - \lambda_n)} \alpha_n \varphi_n.$$

If g is given, f is determined except for an arbitrary linear combination of those φ_n for which $\lambda_n = \lambda$. It follows that there exists a solution f for every set of arbitrarily prescribed values of the coefficients $\beta_n = (Hf, \varphi_n)$ for these values of n. This concludes the proof of the first part of our theorem.

The proof of the second part is similar, substituting everywhere K for T and ψ_n for φ_n.

Remark. The theorem remains valid after extension of H, K, T onto the closure $\bar{R}$.

§ 7. Self-Adjoint Transformations as a Particular Case of Symmetrisable Transformations

In the present paragraph we suppose that R is a Hilbert space, complete or non-complete, and that the bounded linear transformation K is self-adjoint in R. Furthermore we assume that K^p is compact for an integer $p \geqslant 1$. Then, by Ch. 11, § 1, Th. 13, K itself is compact.

The transformation K is symmetrisable relative to the bounded positive transformation $H = I$, the identical transformation. Hence, with the notations of the preceding paragraph, $S = HK = IK = K$, $P = I$, $T = PK = K$. The condition of strong symmetrisability that $Hf = 0$ should imply $Kf = 0$ is automatically satisfied, since $Hf = If = 0$ only for $f = 0$.

We may apply now the theorems in the preceding paragraphs to this particular case. The statements in § 2 show that all characteristic values of K are real, that characteristic elements belonging to different characteristic values are orthogonal, and that the algebraic and geometric multiplicities of any characteristic value $\neq 0$ are equal.

Theorem 1. *K has a characteristic value $\neq 0$ if and only if $K \neq O$.*
Proof. Follows from § 3, Th. 1.

We again write all characteristic values $\neq 0$ of K into a sequence $\lambda_1, \lambda_2, \ldots$, each characteristic value repeated according to its multiplicity, and such that $|\lambda_1| \geqslant |\lambda_2| \geqslant \ldots$. The sequence $\varphi_1, \varphi_2, \ldots$ is a corresponding orthonormal sequence of characteristic elements.

Theorem 2. 1°. *$|\lambda_n| = \max \|Kf\|/\|f\|$ for all $f \in R$ satisfying $\|f\| \neq 0$ and $(f, \varphi_1) = \ldots = (f, \varphi_{n-1}) = 0$. For $f = \varphi_n$ the maximum is attained.*

2°. *$Kf = 0$ if and only if $(f, \varphi_n) = 0$ for all n.*

3°. *If, for arbitrary $f, g \in R$, we write $\alpha_n = (f, \varphi_n)$, $\beta_n = (g, \varphi_n)$ ($n = 1, 2, \ldots$), then $Kf = \Sigma \lambda_n \alpha_n \varphi_n$ and $(Kf, g) = \Sigma \lambda_n \alpha_n \bar{\beta}_n$.*

4°. *If λ_{n_i} ($i = 1, 2, \ldots$) is the subsequence of all positive characteristic values, arranged in non-increasing order, then $\lambda_{n_i} = \max (Kf, f)/\|f\|^2$ for* *all* $f \in R$ *satisfying* $\| f \| \neq 0$ *and* $(f, \varphi_{n_1}) = \ldots = (f, \varphi_{n_{i-1}}) = 0$. *For* $f = \varphi_{n_i}$ *the maximum is attained. A similar statement holds for the subsequence of all negative characteristic values.*

5°. *Let* $p_1, \ldots, p_{i-1} \in R$ *be arbitrarily given, and let* $\mu_i =$ *upper bound* $(Kf, f)/\| f \|^2$ *for all* $f \in R$ *satisfying* $\| f \| \neq 0$ *and* $(f, p_1) = \ldots = (f, p_{i-1}) = 0$. *Then* μ_i *depends on* $p_1, \ldots, p_{i-1}$. *Letting now these elements run through the whole space R, we have* $\lambda_{n_i} = \min \mu_i$.

6°. *Necessary and sufficient that* $(Kf, f) \geqslant 0$ *should hold for all* $f \in R$ *is that all characteristic values of K are non-negative. In other words, K is positive if and only if all* λ_n *are positive.*

7°. *Extending K onto the closure* $\bar{R}$ *of R, the results in 1°–6° remain valid in* $\bar{R}$.

Proof. The statements 1° and 2° follow from § 4, Th. 1; 3° follows from § 4, Th. 2; 4° follows from § 4, Th. 3; 5° follows from § 4, Th. 4 and 6° from § 4, Th. 5. The statement 7° follows from § 5, Th. 1, 2.

The range of the extended transformation K is a linear manifold $W(K)$ in $\bar{R}$. Adding to $W(K)$ all its points of accumulation (in $\bar{R}$), we obtain the linear subspace $[W(K)]$ (compare Ch. 9, § 14). By Ch. 9, § 14, Th. 1, Corollary, we have $N(K) = \bar{R} \ominus [W(K)]$, where $N(K)$ is the null space (in $\bar{R}$) of K.

Theorem 3. *Denoting by* $L(\varphi)$ *the linear subspace of* $\bar{R}$ *determined by* $\varphi_1, \varphi_2, \ldots$, *we have* $L(\varphi) = [W(K)]$.

Proof. It follows from 2° and 7° of the preceding theorem that $N(K) = \bar{R} \ominus L(\varphi)$. Since also $N(K) = \bar{R} \ominus [W(K)]$, we find $L(\varphi) = [W(K)]$.

Theorem 4. *The following four statements are equivalent:*

1°. *The system* $\{\varphi_n\}$ *is complete in* $\bar{R}$.

2°. *The set* $W(K)$ *is dense in* $\bar{R}$.

3°. $Kf = 0$ *only for* $f = 0$ *(in* $\bar{R}$*)*.

4°. *Every* $g \in \bar{R}$ *admits an expansion* $g = \Sigma \beta_n \varphi_n$, *where* $\beta_n = (g, \varphi_n)$ $(n = 1, 2, \ldots)$.

Proof. Statement 1° is equivalent to $[W(K)] = L(\varphi) = \bar{R}$, and this in its turn is equivalent to the statement that $N(K) = \bar{R} \ominus [W(K)]$ contains only the null element. Hence 1° ↔ 2° ↔ 3°.

The equivalence of 1° and 4° has already been proved in Ch. 6, § 11, Th. 4.

Remark. 1°. If K satisfies the conditions of the present theorem, then $g = \Sigma (g, \varphi_n)\varphi_n$ for every $g \in \bar{R}$. For those $g \in \bar{R}$ which may be written in the form $g = Kf$, we find then $Kf = g = \Sigma (Kf, \varphi_n)\varphi_n = \Sigma (f, K\varphi_n)\varphi_n = \Sigma \lambda_n(f, \varphi_n)\varphi_n$ in accordance with Th. 2, 3°.

2°. In the particular case that R is a functionspace $L_2(\Delta, \mu)$, and that K is an integral transformation with a Hermitian kernel of finite double-norm in this space, this kernel is sometimes called general (D. Hilbert) in case the range $W(K)$ is dense in $L_2(\Delta, \mu)$.

Theorem 5. 1°. *If $\lambda \neq 0$ is no characteristic value of K, the equation $K_\lambda f \equiv Kf - \lambda f = g$ has a uniquely determined solution $f \in R$ for every element $g \in R$. If $\lambda \neq 0$ is a characteristic value of K, the equation $K_\lambda f \equiv Kf - \lambda f = g$ has a solution $f \in R$ for those and only those elements $g \in R$ that are orthogonal to all characteristic elements of K, belonging to the characteristic value λ. This solution is determined except for a linear combination of these characteristic elements.*

2°. *If $Kf - \lambda f = g$, then*

$$f = -\frac{g}{\lambda} - {}'\Sigma \frac{\lambda_n}{\lambda(\lambda - \lambda_n)} \alpha_n\varphi_n,$$

where $\alpha_n = (g, \varphi_n)$ for $\lambda_n \neq \lambda$, and where the dash in front of the Σ-symbol means that for those values of n for which $\lambda_n = \lambda$ the coefficient of φ_n has the value (f, φ_n). For every set of arbitrarily prescribed values of these coefficients there exists a solution of $Kf - \lambda f = g$.

3°. *The statements 1°, 2° remain valid after extension of K onto $\bar{R}$.*

Proof. Follows from § 6, Th. 1 and Th. 3.

Remark. The way in which the sequence λ_n is arranged is irrelevant in the expansion theorems (Theorem 2, 3° and Theorem 5, 2°), since any series $\Sigma \gamma_n\varphi_n$ with $\Sigma | \gamma_n |^2 < \infty$ may be arbitrarily rearranged without destroying its convergence or modifying its sum.

§ 8. Self-Adjoint Transformations in a Unitary Space

Let R be an n-dimensional unitary space, that is, an n-dimensional Hilbert space (cf. Ch. 6, § 10), and let $\psi_1, \ldots, \psi_n$ be a complete orthonormal system in R. As an example we mention the n-dimensional Euclidean space $E_{2,n}$ of all elements $f = \{f_1, \ldots, f_n\}$ with $(f, g) = \Sigma_1^n f_i\bar{g}_i$, introduced in Ch. 6, § 6, Ex. C and Ch. 6, § 13, Ex. B. If K is a linear transformation in R with matrix $\{k_{ij}\}$ $(i, j = 1, \ldots, n)$ relative to the coordinate system $\{\psi\}$, then

$$K\psi_i = \Sigma_j \, k_{ji}\psi_j \ (i = 1, \ldots, n).$$

Furthermore, if $f = \Sigma\, \alpha_i\psi_i$, $Kf = \Sigma\, \gamma_i\psi_i$, then

$$\gamma_i = \Sigma_j \, k_{ij}\alpha_j \ (i = 1, \ldots, n)$$

by Ch. 7, § 2, Th. 2. Hence, if $f = \Sigma\, \alpha_i\psi_i$, $g = \Sigma\, \beta_i\psi_i$, then

$$(Kf, g) = \Sigma_j \, (\Sigma_i \, k_{ji}\alpha_i)\bar{\beta}_j = \Sigma_{ij} \, k_{ji}\alpha_i\bar{\beta}_j.$$

By Ch. 7, § 2, Th. 1 we have $K = O$ (the null transformation) if and only if all k_{ij} vanish.

The statement in Ch. 9, § 4, Th. 12 shows that K is self-adjoint if and only if $k_{ij} = \bar{k}_{ji}$ $(i, j = 1, \ldots, n)$, that is, if and only if the matrix $\{k_{ij}\}$ is Hermitian. We shall suppose this to be the case in the present paragraph. K has therefore n characteristic values which are all real. Let $\lambda_1, \ldots, \lambda_N$, arranged in such a way that $|\lambda_1| \geqslant \ldots \geqslant |\lambda_N|$, be the characteristic values $\neq 0$, and let $\lambda_{N+1} = \ldots = \lambda_n = 0$. By § 7, Th. 1 the transformation K has at least one characteristic value $\neq 0$ if and only if one at least of the numbers k_{ij} differs from zero. Determining now the orthonormal sequence $\varphi_1, \ldots, \varphi_N$ such that $K\varphi_i = \lambda_i\varphi_i$ $(i = 1, \ldots, N)$, it follows from § 7, Th. 2, 2° that $Kf = 0$ for those and only those $f \in R$ that are orthogonal to $\varphi_1, \ldots, \varphi_N$. The set of all f satisfying $Kf = 0$ is therefore an $(n - N)$-dimensional unitary space, in which the complete orthonormal system $\varphi_{N+1}, \ldots, \varphi_n$ may be determined. The system $\varphi_1, \ldots, \varphi_n$ is then complete and orthonormal in R, and $K\varphi_i = \lambda_i\varphi_i$ for $i = 1, \ldots, n$.

We shall not repeat all theorems of the preceding paragraph for this particular case, and only pay attention to some of these theorems.

Theorem 1. ([8]). *There exists a unitary transformation $g = Uf$ such that, if $f = \Sigma\, \alpha_i\psi_i$, $g = \Sigma\, \beta_i\psi_i$, the "Hermitian form" $(Kf, f) = \Sigma_{ij}\, k_{ji}\alpha_i\bar{\alpha}_j$ satisfies*

$$\Sigma_{ij} \, k_{ji}\alpha_i\bar{\alpha}_j = \Sigma_{i=1}^{n} \lambda_i \, |\beta_i|^2.$$

Proof. By § 7, Th. 2, 3° we have $(Kf, f) = \Sigma_1^N \lambda_i \, |\beta_i|^2$, where $\beta_i = (f, \varphi_i)$ $(i = 1, \ldots, N)$. Since $\lambda_{N+1} = \ldots = \lambda_n = 0$, we may as well write $(Kf, f) = \Sigma_1^n \lambda_i \, |\beta_i|^2$. The only thing to be proved is therefore that the transformation U, defined by $\Sigma\, \beta_i\psi_i = U(\Sigma\, \alpha_i\psi_i)$, is unitary. U is evidently linear. Suppose now that $f = \varphi_j$. Then $\beta_i = (f, \varphi_i) = 1$ for $i = j$ and $\beta_i = 0$ for $i \neq j$, hence $\Sigma\, \beta_i\psi_i = \psi_j$. This shows that $\psi_j = U\varphi_j$

$(j = 1, \ldots, n)$, and since both systems $\{\varphi\}$ and $\{\psi\}$ are complete and orthonormal, U is unitary by Ch. 9, § 3, Th. 2.

Theorem 2. *Writing the characteristic values* $\lambda_1, \ldots, \lambda_n$ *into a new sequence* $\lambda_{i_1}, \ldots, \lambda_{i_n}$ *such that* $\lambda_{i_1} \geqslant \lambda_{i_2} \geqslant \ldots \geqslant \lambda_{i_n}$, *we have* $\lambda_{i_k} = \max (Kf, f)/\| f \|^2$ *for all* $f \in R$ *satisfying* $\| f \| \neq 0$ *and* $(f, \varphi_{i_1}) = \ldots = (f, \varphi_{i_{k-1}}) = 0$. *The maximum is attained for* $f = \varphi_{i_k}$.

Proof. Follows easily from $(Kf, f) = \Sigma_1^n \lambda_i \,|\, (f, \varphi_i) \,|^2$.

Theorem 3. *Let* $\lambda \neq 0$ *and, in case* λ *is a characteristic value of* K, *let the element* $g \in R$ *be orthogonal to all characteristic elements of* K *belonging to* λ. *Then the solution* f *of* $Kf - \lambda f = g$ *is given by*

$$f = {}'\Sigma_1^n \frac{\alpha_i}{\lambda_i - \lambda} \varphi_i,$$

where $\alpha_i = (g, \varphi_i)$ *for* $\lambda_i \neq \lambda$, *and where the dash in front of the* Σ-*symbol means that for those values of* i *for which* $\lambda_i = \lambda$ *the coefficient of* φ_i *may have any arbitrary value.*

Proof. On account of Th. 5, 2° in the preceding paragraph we have

$$f = -\frac{g}{\lambda} - {}'\Sigma_1^n \frac{\lambda_i}{\lambda(\lambda - \lambda_i)} \alpha_i \varphi_i,$$

hence, since $g = \Sigma_1^n \alpha_i \varphi_i$,

$$f = -\frac{1}{\lambda}\, {}'\Sigma_1^n \left(1 + \frac{\lambda_i}{\lambda - \lambda_i}\right) \alpha_i \varphi_i = {}'\Sigma_1^n \frac{\alpha_i}{\lambda_i - \lambda} \varphi_i.$$

§ 9. The Resolvent. Characterization by their Resolvent of Fully Symmetrisable Transformations

We return to symmetrisable transformations. For simplicity we shall suppose however in the present paragraph that the space R is complete. The bounded linear transformation K is assumed to be symmetrisable relative to the bounded positive transformation H; furthermore we assume that this symmetrisability is full (that is, $Hf \neq 0$ for any $f \in R$ such that $Kf = \lambda f \neq 0$), and that K^p is compact for an integer $p \geqslant 1$. Shortly: we consider ourselves to be in case B (cf. § 4) on a complete space R.

Let $\lambda_0 \neq 0$ be one of the characteristic values $\neq 0$ of K. We know already that for λ_0 the algebraic and geometric multiplicities are equal, hence λ_0 has the index one for K. Denoting the multiplicity of λ_0 by d, there exists an H-orthonormal system $\tilde{\psi}_1, \ldots, \tilde{\psi}_d$ such that every f belonging to the null space $M = N(K - \lambda_0 I)$ has the form $f = \Sigma_1^d \alpha_i \tilde{\psi}_i$. Consequently the diagram I in Ch. 11, § 3 consists of only one row containing the elements $\tilde{\psi}_1, \ldots, \tilde{\psi}_d$. The range $W(K - \lambda_0 I) = R \ominus N(K^* - \lambda_0 I)$ is denoted by L. Since $N(K^* - \lambda_0 I)$ is determined by $\chi_1 = H\tilde{\psi}_1, \ldots, \chi_d = H\tilde{\psi}_d$ (cf. § 2, 6°), the subspace L consists of all elements that are orthogonal to $\chi_1, \ldots, \chi_d$. We observe now that the diagram II in Ch. 11, § 3 consists of one row containing the linear functionals $f_1^*, \ldots, f_d^*$. Since $f_i^*(\tilde{\psi}_j) = 1$ for $i = j$, $f_i^*(\psi_j) = 0$ for $i \neq j$ and $f_i^*(g) = 0$ for $i = 1, \ldots, d$ and all $g \in L$, these functionals $f_1^*, \ldots, f_d^*$ are exactly represented by $\chi_1, \ldots, \chi_d$. The space R is the direct sum of M and L; in the same way as in Ch. 11, § 4 we denote the projection on M along L by P_M and the projection on L along M by P_L.

Lemma α. *The projection P_M is given by*

$$P_M g = \Sigma_1^d (Hg, \tilde{\psi}_i)\tilde{\psi}_i = \Sigma_1^d (g, \chi_i)\tilde{\psi}_i.$$

Proof. If $g \in M$, hence $g = \Sigma_1^d \beta_i \tilde{\psi}_i$, then $(Hg, \tilde{\psi}_j) = \beta_j$ $(j = 1, \ldots, n)$, hence $\Sigma_1^d (Hg, \tilde{\psi}_i)\tilde{\psi}_i = \Sigma_1^d \beta_i \tilde{\psi}_i = g$.

If $g \in L$, hence $g = (K - \lambda_0 I)f$, then $(Hg, \tilde{\psi}_i) = (Kf - \lambda_0 f, H\tilde{\psi}_i) = 0$ $(i = 1, \ldots, d)$. This completes the proof.

Since K is reduced by L, and $Kf - \lambda_0 f = 0$, $f \in L$, implies $f = 0$, the transformation $K - \lambda_0 I$ has a bounded inverse R_0 on L (cf. Ch. 11, § 4).

Theorem 1. *For λ in the neighbourhood of λ_0 we have*

$$(K - \lambda I)^{-1} = -P_M/(\lambda - \lambda_0) + R_0 P_L + (\lambda - \lambda_0) R_0^2 P_L + \ldots$$

or

$$(K - \lambda I)^{-1} f = - \Sigma_1^d (f, \chi_i)\tilde{\psi}_i/(\lambda - \lambda_0) + R_0 P_L f + (\lambda - \lambda_0) R_0^2 P_L f + \ldots$$

Proof. Follows from the preceding lemma and Ch. 11, § 4, (5) and (6).

Remark. If K is self-adjoint, we have the same formula with χ_i replaced by $\tilde{\psi}_i$. The subspaces M and L are now orthogonal complements.

In the terminology of the theory of complex functions we may say that Theorem 1 expresses the fact that the resolvent of a fully symmetrisable transformation K has only real and simple "poles" $\neq 0$. It is interesting that these transformations are completely characterized by this property, that is, a bounded linear transformation K such that K^p is compact for a certain integer $p \geqslant 1$ and such that K has only real characteristic values $\neq 0$ with index one is necessarily fully symmetrisable relative to a bounded positive transformation H. In order to prove this statement, we need a lemma.

Lemma β. *Let the elements of the sequence χ_n $(n = 1, 2, \ldots)$ all differ from the null element, and let the positive numbers μ_n $(n = 1, 2, \ldots)$ be such that $\Sigma\, \mu_n \| \chi_n \|^2 < \infty$. Then the linear transformation H, defined by $Hf = \Sigma\, \mu_n(f, \chi_n)\chi_n$, is bounded and positive.*

Proof. For every $f \in R$ the series $\Sigma\, \mu_n(f, \chi_n)\chi_n$ converges on account of $\Sigma \| \mu_n(f, \chi_n)\chi_n \| \leqslant \| f \| \Sigma\, \mu_n \| \chi_n \|^2$. It follows that H is bounded: $\| H \| \leqslant \Sigma\, \mu_n \| \chi_n \|^2$. Furthermore

$$(Hf, g) = \Sigma\, \mu_n(f, \chi_n)\,(\chi_n, g) = \Sigma\, \mu_n(f, \chi_n)\,\overline{(g, \chi_n)} = (f, \Sigma\, \mu_n(g, \chi_n)\chi_n) = (f, Hg)$$

and

$$(Hf, f) = \Sigma\, \mu_n \,|\, (f, \chi_n) \,|^2 \geqslant 0.$$

Hence H is positive. We observe that $Hf = 0$, that is, $(Hf, f) = 0$, if and only if $(f, \chi_n) = 0$ for all n.

Theorem 2. *Let the bounded linear transformation K be such that K^p is compact for an integer $p \geqslant 1$. Then, if K has one characteristic value $\lambda_0 \neq 0$ at least which is real, K is symmetrisable relative to a bounded positive transformation H.*

Proof. Since K has the real characteristic value $\lambda_0 \neq 0$, K^* has also the characteristic value λ_0. Let $K^*\chi = \lambda_0\chi \neq 0$. Then the linear transformation H, defined by $Hf = (f, \chi)\chi$, is bounded and positive, and $HKf = (Kf, \chi)\chi = (f, K^*\chi)\chi = \lambda_0(f, \chi)\chi$. This shows that HK is self-adjoint, so that K is symmetrisable relative to H.

Remark. The hypotheses of the present theorem show that the conditions on K to ensure that K is symmetrisable are not very heavy. It is when we want K to be moreover fully symmetrisable that the much heavier condition that all characteristic values $\neq 0$ are real and of index one is necessary.

Theorem 3. *Let the bounded linear transformation K be such that K^p is compact for an integer $p \geqslant 1$. Then the following two statements are equivalent:*

1°. *K is fully symmetrisable relative to a bounded positive transformation H, that is, $Hf \neq 0$ for all f such that $Kf = \lambda f \neq 0$.*

2°. *All characteristic values $\neq 0$ of K are real and have the index one.*

Proof. 1° → 2°. Already proved (cf. § 2, 8° and 10°).

2° → 1°. Let $\lambda_1, \lambda_2, \ldots$ be the sequence of all characteristic values $\neq 0$ of K, each repeated according to its multiplicity (since every characteristic value $\neq 0$ has index one we may speak simply of its multiplicity). Since all λ_i $(i = 1, 2, \ldots)$ are real we have $\lambda_i = \bar{\lambda}_i$, so that $\lambda_1, \lambda_2, \ldots$ is also the sequence of all characteristic values $\neq 0$ of K^*, each repeated according to its multiplicity. Let $\varphi_1, \varphi_2, \ldots$ and $\chi_1, \chi_2, \ldots$ be corresponding sequences of characteristic elements of K and K^* respectively. By what we have said about the diagrams I and II in Ch. 11, § 3, the sequences $\{\varphi\}$ and $\{\chi\}$ may be chosen such that $(\varphi_i, \chi_i) = 1$ for $i = 1, 2, \ldots$ and $(\varphi_i, \chi_j) = 0$ if $\lambda_i = \lambda_j$, $i \neq j$. The linear transformation H, defined by

$$Hf = \Sigma\, \mu_n(f, \chi_n)\chi_n, \quad \Sigma\, \mu_n \| \chi_n \|^2 < \infty,$$

is now bounded and positive by Lemma β. Furthermore

$$HKf = \Sigma\, \mu_n(Kf, \chi_n)\chi_n = \Sigma\, \mu_n(f, K^*\chi_n)\chi_n = \Sigma\, \lambda_n\mu_n(f, \chi_n)\chi_n,$$

so that $(HKf, g) = \Sigma\, \lambda_n\mu_n(f, \chi_n)\overline{(g, \chi_n)} = (f, HKg)$. This shows that K is symmetrisable relative to H.

Let now φ be a characteristic element of K, belonging to a characteristic value $\neq 0$. Then φ is a finite linear combination of elements φ_i, hence $\varphi = \Sigma_{i=q}^{r} \alpha_i\varphi_i \neq 0$. It follows that

$$(H\varphi, \varphi) = \Sigma\, \mu_n \mid (\varphi, \chi_n) \mid^2 \geqslant \Sigma_{n=q}^{r} \mu_n \mid (\varphi, \chi_n) \mid^2 = \Sigma_q^r \mu_n \mid \alpha_n \mid^2 > 0,$$

and this shows that the symmetrisability of K is full.

Remark. There remains a wide range of arbitrariness in H on account of the many different possible choices for $\mu_1, \mu_2, \ldots$. Furthermore, although the theorem is also true if K has no characteristic values $\neq 0$ (the transformation H in the second part of the proof is then the null transformation), it is only of interest in case K has at least one characteristic value $\neq 0$.

§ 10. The Relation between Transformations that are Symmetrisable Relative to a Positive Transformation *H* and the Factorspace Relative to *H*

We suppose again that R is a Hilbert space, complete or non-complete, and that H is a bounded positive transformation on R. The subspace of all $f \in R$ satisfying $Hf = 0$ is $[L]$, and its orthogonal complement is $[M]$. As in the preceding paragraphs we suppose that R is the direct sum of $[L]$ and $[M]$, and that P is the projection on $[M]$ along $[L]$. We consider now the factorspace Z of R relative to H which we introduced in Ch. 9, § 5. We shortly recall that every element $[f] \in Z$ is a class of elements $f \in R$. Two elements f and f_1 of R belong to the same class $[f]$ if and only if $H(f - f_1) = 0$, that is, if and only if the H-norm $N(f - f_1)$ vanishes. The element $[f_1] + [f_2]$ is the class of all elements $f_1 + f_2$ where f_1 runs through $[f_1]$ and f_2 through $[f_2]$, and the element $\alpha[f]$ (α complex) is the class of all αf where f runs through $[f]$. Finally the inner product $([f], [g])$ in Z is defined as (Hf, g), where $f \in [f]$, $g \in [g]$. Hence $\| [f] \| = (Hf, f)^{1/2} = N(f)$. It was proved in Ch. 9, § 5 that no contradictions arise from these definitions. The space Z is now a Hilbert space, and it is called the factorspace of R relative to H. The elements $f, g \in R$ are H-orthogonal if and only if the corresponding elements $[f], [g] \in Z$ are orthogonal (Ch. 9, § 5, Th. 5), and the elements $f_1, \ldots, f_n \in R$ are H-independent if and only if the corresponding elements $[f_1], \ldots, [f_n] \in Z$ are linearly independent (Ch. 9, § 5, Th. 6).

For linear transformations T, defined on R, and such that $Hf = 0$ implies $HTf = 0$ (that is, for linear transformations T which are reduced by $[L]$), it is possible to define a corresponding linear transformation $[T]$ on Z by $[T][f] = [Tf]$. With any linear transformation $[T]$ on Z corresponds conversely a class of linear transformations T on R such that $[T][f] = [Tf]$ for all $f \in R$ and for each of these T. We have $[T_1] = [T_2]$ if and only if $HT_1 = HT_2$, that is, if and only if $PT_1 = PT_2$ (Ch. 9, § 5, Th. 7). Furthermore, if T_1 and T_2 are both reduced by $[L]$, then T_1T_2 is reduced by $[L]$ and $[T_1T_2] = [T_1][T_2]$ (Ch. 9, § 5, Th. 8).

Even if the space R is complete, the space Z is not necessarily complete (Ch. 9, § 5, Th. 9). Even if R is complete and T is bounded on R, $[T]$ is not necessarily bounded on Z (Ch. 9, § 5, Th. 10). Even if $[T]$ is bounded on Z, all corresponding T may be unbounded on R (Ch. 9, § 5, Th. 11). See however Example 22 at the end of the present chapter.

We shall suppose now that the bounded linear transformation K on R is symmetrisable relative to H, that $T^p = PK^p$ is compact for an integer $p \geqslant 1$, and that $S = HK = HT \neq O$. Since $Hf = 0$ implies $Sf = HKf = HTf = 0$ (§ 2, 2°), the transformations $[K]$ and $[T]$ on Z exist. Since $S = HK = HT$, we have $[K] = [T]$. On account of § 4, Th. 1 we have

$$\operatorname*{upper\ bound}_{[f] \in Z} \| [K][f] \| / \| [f] \| = \operatorname*{upper\ bound}_{f \in R} N(Kf)/N(f) = | \lambda_1 |,$$

which shows that $[K]$ is bounded and that $\| [K] \| = | \lambda_1 |$. Furthermore

$$([K][f], [g]) = (HKf, g) = (f, HKg) =$$
$$(Hf, Kg) = ([f], [K][g])$$

for all $[f], [g] \in Z$; the transformation $[K]$ is therefore self-adjoint.

Theorem 1. *If $T\varphi = \lambda\varphi \neq 0$, then $[K][\varphi] = \lambda[\varphi] \neq [0]$. Conversely, if $[K][\varphi] = \lambda[\varphi] \neq [0]$, there exists an element $\varphi \in R$ belonging to the class $[\varphi]$ such that $T\varphi = \lambda\varphi \neq 0$. The correspondence between the characteristic elements φ of T and the characteristic elements $[\varphi]$ of $[K]$ is one-to-one.*

Proof. From $T\varphi = \lambda\varphi \neq 0$ follows $[T][\varphi] = \lambda[\varphi]$, hence $[K][\varphi] = \lambda[\varphi]$. We have $[\varphi] \neq [0]$ since $[\varphi] = [0]$ would imply $H\varphi = 0$, hence $T\varphi = 0$, which is not true on account of $T\varphi = \lambda\varphi \neq 0$. Different φ give different $[\varphi]$. Indeed, let us suppose that

$$T\varphi_1 = \lambda\varphi_1 \neq 0,\ T\varphi_2 = \mu\varphi_2 \neq 0,\ \varphi_1 \neq \varphi_2,\ [\varphi_1] = [\varphi_2].$$

Then $\lambda[\varphi_1] = [K][\varphi_1] = [K][\varphi_2] = \mu[\varphi_2] = \mu[\varphi_1]$, hence $\lambda = \mu$ on account of $[\varphi_1] = [\varphi_2] \neq [0]$. Since $\varphi_1 \neq \varphi_2$ and $\lambda = \mu \neq 0$, we have $T(\varphi_1 - \varphi_2) = \lambda(\varphi_1 - \varphi_2) \neq 0$. On the other hand $[\varphi_1] = [\varphi_2]$ implies $H(\varphi_1 - \varphi_2) = 0$, hence $T(\varphi_1 - \varphi_2) = 0$. This is a contradiction.

It remains to show that, if $[K][\varphi] = \lambda[\varphi] \neq [0]$, there exists an element $\varphi \in R$ belonging to the class $[\varphi]$ such that $T\varphi = \lambda\varphi \neq 0$. Let $\psi \in R$ be an arbitrary element belonging to the class $[\varphi]$. Then $\lambda[\psi] = \lambda[\varphi] = [K][\varphi] = [K][\psi] = [T][P\psi]$ implies $\lambda\psi = TP\psi + h$, where $Ph = 0$. Hence $\lambda P\psi = PTP\psi + Ph = TP\psi$, where $P\psi \neq 0$ since $[\psi] = [\varphi] \neq [0]$. The element $\varphi = P\psi$ is therefore the desired element.

Since $S = HK = HT \neq O$ by hypothesis, T has at least one (real) characteristic value $\neq 0$ (§ 3, Th. 1). Our present result shows now that $[K]$ has the same property. But we may assert more. Let $\lambda_1, \lambda_2, \ldots$ be again the sequence of all characteristic values $\neq 0$ of T, each repeated according to its multiplicity, and let $\varphi_1, \varphi_2, \ldots$ be a corresponding H-orthonormal sequence of characteristic elements. Then $\lambda_1, \lambda_2, \ldots$ is also the sequence of all characteristic values $\neq 0$ of $[K]$, and $[\varphi_1], [\varphi_2], \ldots$ is a corresponding orthonormal sequence of characteristic elements.

The results for the symmetrisable transformation T obtained in §§ 4, 5, 6 may now be translated into the terminology of the space Z in order to obtain corresponding results for the self-adjoint transformation $[K]$. We shall see that we get (with appropriate changes in the notation) exactly the statements embodied in the theorems of § 7, where we considered a compact self-adjoint transformation K. There is however one important difference to keep in mind. The results for K in § 7 are a consequence of the hypothesis that K is compact, whereas the properties to be proved for $[K]$ are a consequence of the corresponding properties of the symmetrisable transformation T. Our way of reasoning for $[K]$ will run the other way round as in § 7; the compactness of $[K]$ will not be the starting-point but the final conclusion of our argument.

Theorem 2. 1°. *$|\lambda_n| = \max \|[K][f]\|/\|[f]\|$ for all $[f] \in Z$ satisfying $\|[f]\| \neq 0$ and $([f], [\varphi_1]) = \ldots = ([f], [\varphi_{n-1}]) = 0$. For $[f] = [\varphi_n]$ the maximum is attained.*

2°. *$[K][f] = [0]$ if and only if $([f], [\varphi_n]) = 0$ for all n.*

3°. *If, for arbitrary $[f], [g] \in Z$, we write $\alpha_n = ([f], [\varphi_n])$, $\beta_n = ([g], [\varphi_n])$ $(n = 1, 2, \ldots)$, then $[K][f] = \Sigma \lambda_n \alpha_n [\varphi_n]$ and $([K][f], [g]) = \Sigma \lambda_n \alpha_n \bar{\beta}_n$.*

4°. *If λ_{n_i} $(i = 1, 2, \ldots)$ is the subsequence of all positive characteristic values, arranged in non-increasing order, then $\lambda_{n_i} = \max ([K][f], [f])/\|[f]\|^2$ for all $[f] \in Z$ satisfying $\|[f]\| \neq 0$ and $([f], [\varphi_{n_1}]) = \ldots = ([f], [\varphi_{n_{i-1}}]) = 0$. For $[f] = [\varphi_{n_i}]$ the maximum is attained. A similar statement holds for the subsequence of all negative characteristic values.*

5°. *Let $[p_1], \ldots, [p_{i-1}] \in Z$ be arbitrarily given, and let $\mu_i =$ upper bound $([K][f], [f])/\|[f]\|^2$ for all $[f] \in Z$ satisfying $\|[f]\| \neq 0$ and $([f], [p_1]) = \ldots = ([f], [p_{i-1}]) = 0$. Then μ_i depends on $[p_1], \ldots, [p_{i-1}]$. Letting now these elements run through the whole space Z, we have $\lambda_{n_i} = \min \mu_i$.*

6°. *Necessary and sufficient that $([K][f], [f]) \geqslant 0$ should hold for all $[f] \in Z$ is that all characteristic values of $[K]$ are non-negative. In other words, $[K]$ is positive if and only if all λ_n are positive.*

Proof. Follows from the corresponding statements for T in § 4.

In the same way as we have obtained the complete Hilbert space $\bar{R}$, the closure of R, by adjunction of ideal elements, we may obtain the complete Hilbert space $\bar{Z}$, the closure of Z. The bounded self-adjoint transformation $[K]$ on Z may then be extended onto $\bar{Z}$ in such a way that its bound $\|[K]\| = |\lambda_1|$ remains unchanged, and that $[K]$ remains self-adjoint.

Theorem 3. *The statements in Theorem 2 remain true for the extended transformation $[K]$ on $\bar{Z}$.*

Proof. This theorem is proved in the same way as the corresponding theorem (§ 5, Th. 1, 2) for the symmetrisable transformation T.

Remark. Before proving the theorem for T in § 5 we observed that we might follow two ways. In the first place it was possible to repeat all former proofs, using the fact that the compactness of T on R implies the compactness of the extended T on $\bar{R}$. We preferred however the shorter way of showing by a direct method that the results in $\bar{R}$ follow from the corresponding results in R. The latter method did not use the compactness of T. It will be evident that in the present situation only the second method is available, since we do not yet know whether $[K]$ is compact or not.

We see readily now that by the process of extension of $[K]$ onto $\bar{Z}$ no new characteristic values $\neq 0$ are created, and that the multiplicity of every characteristic value $\neq 0$ remains the same. Indeed, in the opposite case there would exist a new characteristic element $[\varphi] \in \bar{Z}$, satisfying $[K][\varphi] = \lambda[\varphi] \neq [0]$ and $([\varphi], [\varphi_n]) = 0$ for every value of n (if $\lambda \neq \lambda_n$ for all n, then $([\varphi], [\varphi_n]) = 0$ is well-known; if $\lambda = \lambda_n$ for a certain n, then orthogonalization gives the desired $[\varphi]$). The relations $([\varphi], [\varphi_n]) = 0$ $(n = 1, 2, \ldots)$ however would imply, by Theorem 2, 2° and Theorem 3, that $[K][\varphi] = [0]$, in contradiction with $[K][\varphi] = \lambda[\varphi] \neq [0]$.

Theorem 4. *The bounded self-adjoint transformation $[K]$ on $\bar{Z}$ is compact.*

Proof. The bounded self-adjoint transformation $[K]$ on the complete space $\bar{Z}$ satisfies the following conditions:

1°. Every characteristic value $\neq 0$ of $[K]$ has finite multiplicity. The number of characteristic values $\lambda \neq 0$ is finite or enumerably infinite, and in the latter case $\lim \lambda = 0$.

2°. Ranging these characteristic values $\neq 0$ into a sequence $\lambda_1, \lambda_2, \ldots$, every characteristic value $\neq 0$ being repeated according to its multiplicity, and $[\varphi_1], [\varphi_2], \ldots$ being a corresponding orthonormal sequence of characteristic elements, every $[f] \in \bar{Z}$ for which $([f], [\varphi_i]) = 0$ $(i = 1, 2, \ldots)$ satisfies $[K][f] = [0]$.

All conditions mentioned in Ch. 11, § 8, Th. 1 are therefore satisfied, so that $[K]$ is compact on account of this theorem.

Theorem 5. 1°. *If $\lambda \neq 0$ is no characteristic value of $[K]$, the equation $[K][f] - \lambda[f] = [g]$ has a uniquely determined solution $[f] \in Z$ for every element $[g] \in Z$. If $\lambda \neq 0$ is a characteristic value of $[K]$, the equation $[K][f] - \lambda[f] = [g]$ has a solution $[f] \in Z$ for those and only those elements $[g] \in Z$ that are orthogonal to all characteristic elements of $[K]$, belonging* *to the characteristic value* λ. *This solution is determined except for a linear combination of these characteristic elements.*

2°. *If* $[K][f] - \lambda[f] = [g]$, *then*

$$[f] = -\frac{[g]}{\lambda} - {}'\Sigma \frac{\lambda_n}{\lambda(\lambda - \lambda_n)} \alpha_n[\varphi_n],$$

where $\alpha_n = ([g], [\varphi_n])$ *for* $\lambda_n \neq \lambda$, *and where the dash in front of the* Σ-*symbol means that for those values of* n *for which* $\lambda_n = \lambda$ *the coefficient of* $[\varphi_n]$ *has the value* $([f], [\varphi_n])$. *For every set of arbitrarily prescribed values of these coefficients there exists a solution* $[f]$ *of* $[K][f] - \lambda[f] = [g]$.

3°. *The statements* 1°, 2° *remain valid after extension of* $[K]$ *onto* $\bar{Z}$.

Proof. The statements 1° and 2° follow from § 6, Th. 1 and Th. 3. Taking into account that $[K]$ is compact on $\bar{Z}$, the statement 3° is identical with § 7, Th. 5.

Remark. Since the arrangement of the sequence λ_n is irrelevant in the expansion theorems for $[K]$, the same holds in the expansion theorems for K (§ 4, Th. 2; § 5, Th. 2 and § 6, Th. 3).

Theorem 6. *The following four statements are equivalent:*

1°. *The system* $[\varphi_n]$ *is complete in* $\bar{Z}$.

2°. *The range* $W[K]$ *is dense in* $\bar{Z}$.

3°. $[K][f] = [0]$ *only for* $[f] = [0]$ (*in* $\bar{Z}$).

4°. *Every* $[g] \in \bar{Z}$ *admits an expansion* $[g] = \Sigma\, \beta_n[\varphi_n]$, *where* $\beta_n = ([g], [\varphi_n])$ $(n = 1, 2, \ldots)$.

Proof. As in § 7, Th. 4.

We are now in a position to give a more detailed discussion of the problem considered already in § 4, Th. 2, Remark.

Theorem 7. *Necessary and sufficient that*

$$\lim_{k\to\infty} N(f - \Sigma_1^k \alpha_n\varphi_n) = 0$$

should hold for every $f \in R$ (*where* $\alpha_n = (Hf, \varphi_n)$ *for every* n) *is that any sequence* $f_n \in R$, *satisfying lim* $N(f_n - f_m) = 0$ *as* $m, n \to \infty$ *and lim* $(HKf_n, Kf_n) = 0$, *also satisfies lim* $(Hf_n, f_n) = 0$.

Proof. Each of the following statements is equivalent to the one next to it:

1°. $\lim_{k\to\infty} N(f - \Sigma_1^k (Hf, \varphi_n)\varphi_n) = 0$ for every $f \in R$.

2°. $[f] = \Sigma\, ([f], [\varphi_n])\, [\varphi_n]$ for every $[f] \in Z$.

3°. The system $[\varphi_n]$ is complete in Z.

4°. The system $[\varphi_n]$ is complete in $\bar{Z}$.

5°. There exists no element $[f] \neq [0]$ in $\bar{Z}$ such that $[K][f] = [0]$.

6°. There exists no fundamental sequence $[f_n]$ in Z such that $\lim \| [f_n] \| \neq 0$ and $\lim \| [Kf_n] \| = 0$.

7°. Every fundamental sequence $[f_n]$ in Z for which $\lim \| [Kf_n] \| = 0$ satisfies $\lim \| [f_n] \| = 0$.

8°. Every sequence $f_n \in R$ for which $\lim N(f_n - f_m) = 0$ as $m, n \to \infty$ and $\lim (HKf_n, Kf_n) = 0$ satisfies $\lim (Hf_n, f_n) = 0$.

We shall conclude this paragraph by considering the transformation $[K]$, corresponding to the symmetrisable transformation K which served as an example in the proof of § 3, Th. 7. The system $\{\varphi_n\}$ is complete and orthonormal in the complete separable Hilbert space R of infinite dimension, and the bounded positive transformation H is defined by $H\varphi_n = \varphi_n/n!$ $(n = 1, 2, \ldots)$. The system $\{\varphi_n\}$ is therefore H-orthogonal although not H-orthonormal. Writing $\Phi_n = (n!)^{1/2}\varphi_n$, the system $\{\Phi_n\}$ is H-orthonormal, so that the system $[\Phi_n]$ is orthonormal in the factor-space Z of R relative to H. The symmetrisable transformation $K = T$ is defined by

$$\begin{aligned} K\varphi_{2n-1} &= \varphi_{2n-1}/(2n-1) + \varphi_{2n}, \\ K\varphi_{2n} &= \varphi_{2n-1}/2n \qquad\quad + \varphi_{2n}/2n. \end{aligned} \qquad (n = 1, 2, \ldots).$$

Hence

$$\begin{aligned} [K][\Phi_{2n-1}] &= [\Phi_{2n-1}]/(2n-1) + [\Phi_{2n}]/(2n)^{1/2}, \\ [K][\Phi_{2n}] &= [\Phi_{2n-1}]/(2n)^{1/2} \quad + [\Phi_{2n}]/2n, \end{aligned}$$

from which it follows easily that $[K]$ is actually self-adjoint and compact on $\bar{Z}$.

§ 11. Symmetrisable Transformations in a Unitary Space

Let R be an n-dimensional unitary space, and let $\psi_1, \ldots, \psi_n$ be a complete orthonormal system in R. We suppose that H is a positive transformation in R. If therefore $\{h_{ij}\}$ is the matrix of H relative to the coordinate system $\{\psi\}$, we have $H\psi_i = \Sigma_j h_{ji}\psi_j$ $(i = 1, \ldots, n)$, $h_{ij} = \bar{h}_{ji}$ and $(Hf, f) = \Sigma_{ij} h_{ji}\alpha_i\bar{\alpha}_j \geqslant 0$ for any $f = \Sigma \alpha_i\psi_i$.

We shall suppose for simplicity in the present paragraph that $Hf = 0$ implies $f = 0$. Since $Hf = 0$ if and only if $(Hf, f) = 0$, this is equivalent to supposing that $(Hf, f) = \Sigma_{ij} h_{ji}\alpha_i\bar{\alpha}_j > 0$ for $\| f \|^2 = \Sigma |\alpha_i|^2 > 0$. In other words, we assume that $\Sigma_{ij} h_{ji}\alpha_i\bar{\alpha}_j$ is a positive definite Hermitian form. In this case the subspace $[L]$ of all elements f satisfying $Hf = 0$ contains only the null element, so that the orthogonal complement $[M]$ is identical with the whole space R. The projection P on $[M]$ along $[L]$ is the identical transformation, and there is a one-to-one correspondence between the elements f of R and the elements $[f]$ of the factorspace Z. The space Z contains the same elements as R with only a different inner product $([f], [g]) = (Hf, g) = \Sigma h_{ji}\alpha_i\bar{\beta}_j$ introduced instead of $(f, g) = \Sigma \alpha_i\bar{\beta}_i$. Furthermore, since $H \Sigma \alpha_i f_i = 0$ if and only if $\Sigma \alpha_i f_i = 0$, the notions of linear independence and H-independence in R are now equivalent; the same is therefore true of the notions of linear independence in the spaces R and Z. It follows that these spaces have the same dimension n. If $[u_1], \ldots, [u_n]$ is a complete orthonormal system in Z, the system $u_1, \ldots, u_n$ is complete and H-orthonormal in R. If $[f] = \Sigma_1^n \alpha_i[u_i]$, then $\alpha_i = ([f], [u_i]) = (Hf, u_i)$ and $(Hf, f) = ([f], [f]) = \Sigma_1^n |\alpha_i|^2$.

Theorem 1. *Under the stated hypothesis that $Hf = 0$ only for $f = 0$, the inverse transformation H^{-1} exists. This inverse H^{-1} is also positive.*

Proof. The existence of H^{-1} follows from Ch. 8, § 1. Writing $g_1 = H^{-1}g$ for an arbitrary $g \in R$, we have $(H^{-1}f, g) = (H^{-1}f, Hg_1) = (HH^{-1}f, g_1) = (f, H^{-1}g)$ for every $f \in R$. This shows that H^{-1} is self-adjoint. Finally, writing $f_1 = H^{-1}f$, we find $(H^{-1}f, f) = (f_1, Hf_1) = (Hf_1, f_1) \geqslant 0$ for every $f \in R$, so that H^{-1} is positive.

Theorem 2. *Under the same hypotheses on H every self-adjoint transformation S is expressible in the form $S = HAH$, where A is self-adjoint. The class of all symmetrisable transformations K is identical with the class of all transformations AH, where A is self-adjoint (compare Ch. 9, § 12, Th. 4).*

Proof. Given the self-adjoint transformation S, the transformation $A = H^{-1}SH^{-1}$ is also self-adjoint. Furthermore $S = HH^{-1}SH^{-1}H = HAH$.

To prove the second statement we observe first that every transformation $K = AH$ is symmetrisable whenever A is self-adjoint, since in this case $HK = HAH$ is self-adjoint. Conversely, if K is symmetrisable, $S = HK$ must be self-adjoint; hence, since S is expressible in the form HAH with a self-adjoint A, we have $HK = HAH$ or $K = H^{-1}HK = H^{-1}HAH = AH$. This completes the proof.

Let now K be symmetrisable relative to H, hence $K = AH$, where A

is self-adjoint. If $\{a_{ij}\}$ and $\{k_{ij}\}$ are the matrices of A and K respectively (in the coordinate system $\{\psi\}$), we have therefore $a_{ij} = \overline{a_{ji}}$ and $k_{ij} = \Sigma_q a_{iq} h_{qj}$ $(i, j = 1, \ldots, n)$. On account of $S = HAH$ and $A = H^{-1}SH^{-1}$ we have $S = HK \neq O$ if and only if $A \neq O$, that is, if and only if one at least of the matrixelements a_{ij} does not vanish.

Theorem 3. *K has a characteristic value $\neq 0$ if and only if one at least of the matrixelements a_{ij} does not vanish.*

Proof. Follows from § 3, Th. 1.

The transformation K has n characteristic values which are all real. Let $\lambda_1, \ldots, \lambda_N$, arranged in such a way that $|\lambda_1| \geqslant \ldots \geqslant |\lambda_N|$, be the characteristic values $\neq 0$, and let $\lambda_{N+1} = \ldots = \lambda_n = 0$. Determining now the H-orthonormal sequence $\varphi_1, \ldots, \varphi_N$ such that $K\varphi_i = \lambda_i\varphi_i$ $(i = 1, \ldots, N)$, it follows from § 4, Th. 1, 2° that $Sf = HKf = 0$, hence also $Kf = 0$, for those and only those $f \in R$ that are H-orthogonal to $\varphi_1, \ldots, \varphi_N$. Adding therefore to the orthonormal system $[\varphi_1], \ldots, [\varphi_N]$ in the space Z the elements $[\varphi_{N+1}], \ldots, [\varphi_n]$ in such a way that the system $[\varphi_1], \ldots, [\varphi_n]$ is complete and orthonormal in Z, the system $\varphi_1, \ldots, \varphi_n$ is complete and H-orthonormal in R, and $K\varphi_i = \lambda_i\varphi_i$ for $i = 1, \ldots, n$.

We shall not repeat all theorems on symmetrisable transformations for this particular case and only pay attention to some of these theorems.

Theorem 4. *For any element $f \in R$ we have $g = Kf = \Sigma_1^n \lambda_i\alpha_i\varphi_i$, where $\alpha_i = (Hf, \varphi_i)$ for $i = 1, \ldots, n$.*

Proof. From § 4, Th. 2 follows $N(Kf - \Sigma_1^n \lambda_i\alpha_i\varphi_i) = 0$, which is equivalent to $H(Kf - \Sigma_1^n \lambda_i\alpha_i\varphi_i) = 0$. Since however $Hh = 0$ implies $h = 0$ for any $h \in R$, we find $Kf = \Sigma_1^n \lambda_i\alpha_i\varphi_i$. A direct proof runs as follows: Since the system $\varphi_1, \ldots, \varphi_n$ is complete and H-orthonormal in R, we have $f = \Sigma_1^n \alpha_i\varphi_i$, hence $g = Kf = \Sigma_1^n \alpha_i K\varphi_i = \Sigma_1^n \lambda_i\alpha_i\varphi_i$.

Theorem 5. ([9]). *There exists a non-singular linear transformation $g = Uf$ such that, if $f = \Sigma\, \alpha_i\psi_i$, $g = \Sigma\, \beta_i\psi_i$, the Hermitian forms $(Hf, f) = \Sigma\, h_{ji}\alpha_i\bar{\alpha}_j$ and $(Sf, f) = (HKf, f) = \Sigma\, s_{ji}\alpha_i\bar{\alpha}_j$ satisfy*

$$\Sigma\, h_{ji}\alpha_i\bar{\alpha}_j = \Sigma_1^n |\beta_i|^2 \text{ and } \Sigma\, s_{ji}\alpha_i\bar{\alpha}_j = \Sigma_1^n \lambda_i |\beta_i|^2.$$

Proof. By § 4, Th. 2 we have $(Sf, f) = (HKf, f) = \Sigma_1^N \lambda_i |\beta_i|^2 = \Sigma_1^n \lambda_i |\beta_i|^2$, where $\beta_i = (Hf, \varphi_i)$ $(i = 1, \ldots, n)$. Furthermore, since $[\varphi_1], \ldots, [\varphi_n]$ is a complete orthonormal system in Z, we have $(Hf, f) =$

$([f], [f]) = \Sigma_1^n |([f], [\varphi_i])|^2 = \Sigma_1^n |(Hf, \varphi_i)|^2 = \Sigma_1^n |\beta_i|^2$. The only thing to be proved is therefore that the transformation U, defined by $Uf = \Sigma (Hf, \varphi_i)\psi_i$, is non-singular. U is evidently linear. Suppose now that $f = \varphi_j$. Then $\beta_i = (Hf, \varphi_i) = 1$ for $i = j$ and $\beta_i = 0$ for $i \neq j$, hence $\Sigma \beta_i \psi_i = \psi_j$. This shows that $\psi_j = U\varphi_j$ $(j = 1, \ldots, n)$, so that U is non-singular, since both systems $\{\varphi\}$ and $\{\psi\}$ are complete in R.

Theorem 6. *Writing the characteristic values $\lambda_1, \ldots, \lambda_n$ into a new sequence $\lambda_{i_1}, \ldots, \lambda_{i_n}$ such that $\lambda_{i_1} \geqslant \lambda_{i_2} \geqslant \ldots \geqslant \lambda_{i_n}$, we have $\lambda_{i_k} =$ max $(Sf, f)/(Hf, f)$ for all $f \in R$ satisfying $f \neq 0$ and $(Hf, \varphi_{i_1}) = \ldots = (Hf, \varphi_{i_{k-1}}) = 0$. The maximum is attained for $f = \varphi_{i_k}$.*

Proof. Follows easily from $(Sf, f) = \Sigma_1^n \lambda_i |(Hf, \varphi_i)|^2$.

Theorem 7. *Let $\lambda \neq 0$ and, in case λ is a characteristic value of K, let the element $g \in R$ be H-orthogonal to all characteristic elements of K belonging to λ. Then the solution f of $Kf - \lambda f = g$ is given by*

$$f = {}'\Sigma_1^n \frac{\alpha_i}{\lambda_i - \lambda} \varphi_i,$$

where $\alpha_i = (Hg, \varphi_i)$ for $\lambda_i \neq \lambda$, and where the dash in front of the Σ-symbol means that for those values of i for which $\lambda_i = \lambda$ the coefficient of φ_i may have any arbitrary value.

Proof. On account of § 6, Th. 3 we have

$$N\left(f + \frac{g}{\lambda} + {}'\Sigma_1^n \frac{\lambda_i}{\lambda(\lambda - \lambda_i)} \alpha_i\varphi_i\right) = 0,$$

hence

$$f = -\frac{g}{\lambda} - {}'\Sigma_1^n \frac{\lambda_i}{\lambda(\lambda - \lambda_i)} \alpha_i\varphi_i.$$

Observing that $g = \Sigma_1^n \alpha_i\varphi_i$, we find therefore

$$f = -\frac{1}{\lambda} {}'\Sigma_1^n \left(1 + \frac{\lambda_i}{\lambda - \lambda_i}\right)\alpha_i\psi_i = {}'\Sigma_1^n \frac{\alpha_i}{\lambda_i - \lambda} \varphi_i.$$

§ 12. Symmetrisable Transformations of the Form $K = AH$

We suppose in the present paragraph that the space R is complete, that H is a bounded positive transformation on R and that A is a bounded linear transformation such that $K = AH$ is symmetrisable relative to

H. Hence $S = HK$ is self-adjoint, that is, $HAH = S = S^* = HA^*H$.

The condition that $K = AH$ is symmetrisable is in particular satisfied whenever A is self-adjoint. On the other hand we know by Ch. 9, § 12, Th. 4 that if the range $W(H)$ of H is identical with the whole space R, then any symmetrisable transformation K is necessarily of the form $K = AH$ with A bounded and self-adjoint. It is possible to weaken slightly the hypothesis that $W(H) = R$, but in exchange we have then to assume more about K. This is shown in the following theorem:

Theorem 1. *If $Hf = 0$ only for $f = 0$, A is bounded and $K = AH$ is symmetrisable, then A is self-adjoint.*

Proof. By hypothesis the null space $N(H)$ of H contains only the null element. Then, since $[W(H)] = R \ominus N(H)$, the range $W(H)$ is dense in R. Hence, since HAH is self-adjoint, A is self-adjoint by Ch. 9, § 4, Th. 6, 2°.

We return to the general case that $K = AH$ is symmetrisable, where A is bounded.

Theorem 2. *If M is a self-adjoint transformation such that $M^2 = H$, then MAM is self-adjoint.*

Proof. Since $HAH = HA^*H$, we have $H(AH - A^*H) = O$. Hence, since $Hf = 0$ if and only if $Mf = 0$ for any $f \in R$ ($Hf = 0$ implies $(Mf, Mf) = (M^2f, f) = (Hf, f) = 0$), we find $M(AH - A^*H) = O$. Then the adjoint transformation $HA^*M - HAM$ is also identical with the null transformation, so that $H(A^*M - AM) = O$. This implies finally $M(A^*M - AM) = O$ or $MA^*M = MAM$, which shows that MAM is self-adjoint.

Corollary. *The transformation $H^{1/2}AH^{1/2}$ is self-adjoint.*

We shall suppose now that $K = AH$ itself or one of its iterates is compact. Furthermore, it is trivial that if $Hf = 0$ for an element $f \in R$, then $Kf = AHf = 0$. We are therefore in case B of § 4, and denoting again by λ_i ($i = 1, 2, \ldots$) the sequence of characteristic values $\neq 0$ of K, and by ψ_i the corresponding H-orthonormal sequence of characteristic elements of K, all properties of these sequences proved in §§ 4, 6, 9, 10 are valid. We may prove more however. We observe first that if the self-adjoint transformation M satisfies $M^2 = H$ and $K^p = (AH)^p$ is compact, then $(MAM)^{p+1} = M(AH)^pAM$ is compact as well, so that on account of the self-adjointness of MAM, the transformation MAM itself is compact.

Theorem 3. *If M is a self-adjoint transformation such that $M^2 = H$, then the self-adjoint transformation MAM has the same sequence λ_i ($i = 1, 2, \ldots$) of characteristic values $\neq 0$ as $K = AH$ (each characteristic value repeated according to its multiplicity) with the corresponding orthonormal sequence $\Psi_i = M\psi_i$ of characteristic elements.*

Furthermore, if the transformations B_n ($n = 1, 2, \ldots$) are defined by $B_1 = A$, $B_2 = AHA$, $\ldots$, generally $B_n = AHB_{n-1} = KB_{n-1}$, then $K^n = B_nH$ and $(MAM)^n = MB_nM$.

Proof. Let $K\psi = AH\psi = \lambda\psi \neq 0$. Then $\Psi = M\psi$ satisfies $MAM\Psi = MAH\psi = \lambda M\psi = \lambda\Psi$, where $\lambda\Psi \neq 0$ since $\lambda \neq 0$ and $AM\Psi = AH\psi = \lambda\psi \neq 0$.

Conversely, if $MAM\Psi = \lambda\Psi \neq 0$, then, writing $\psi = \lambda^{-1}AM\Psi$, we find $M\psi = \lambda^{-1}MAM\Psi = \Psi$ and $K\psi = AMM\psi = AM\Psi = \lambda\psi$, where $\lambda\psi \neq 0$ since $M\lambda\psi = \lambda M\psi = \lambda\Psi \neq 0$. This shows that the relations $\Psi = M\psi$, $\psi = \lambda^{-1}AM\Psi$ establish a linear one-to-one correspondence between the characteristic elements of K and MAM such that corresponding elements belong to the same characteristic value $\neq 0$. Since the sequence ψ_i is H-orthonormal, the corresponding sequence $\Psi_i = M\psi_i$ is orthonormal.

The relations $K^n = B_nH$, $(MAM)^n = MB_nM$ are true for $n = 1$; for $n > 1$ they follow immediately by induction.

Theorem 4 (*Expansion theorem*). *If M is a self-adjoint transformation such that $M^2 = H$, and the element g is of the form AMf, then*

$$g = AMf = \Sigma_i (Hg, \psi_i)\psi_i + p,$$

where $Hp = 0$.

Proof. We observe first that

$$(1) \quad \begin{cases} (Hg, \psi_i) = (HAMf, \psi_i) = (MMAMf, \psi_i) = (MAMf, M\psi_i) = \\ (f, MAMM\psi_i) = (f, MAH\psi_i) = (f, MK\psi_i) = \lambda_i (f, M\psi_i) \end{cases}$$

for $i = 1, 2, \ldots$. Furthermore, since the system $\Psi_i = M\psi_i$ ($i = 1, 2, \ldots$) is orthonormal, every element $f \in R$ may be written as

$$f = \Sigma_i (f, M\psi_i)M\psi_i + h,$$

where h belongs to the orthogonal complement of the subspace determined by the system $M\psi_i$ ($i = 1, 2, \ldots$), hence $(h, M\psi_i) = 0$ ($i = 1, 2, \ldots$). Then, by (1),

$$g = AMf = \Sigma_i (f, M\psi_i)AMM\psi_i + AMh = \Sigma_i (f, M\psi_i)K\psi_i + AMh$$
$$= \Sigma \lambda_i (f, M\psi_i)\psi_i + AMh = \Sigma_i (Hg, \psi_i)\psi_i + AMh.$$

This shows that only $HAMh = 0$ remains to be proved. Since h is orthogonal to all $\Psi_i = M\psi_i$, and since the sequence Ψ_i is exactly the sequence of characteristic elements of the self-adjoint transformation MAM, we have $MAMh = 0$ (cf. § 7, Th. 2, 2°). Hence $HAMh = MMAMh = 0$.

Theorem 5 (*Expansion theorem*). *If $f \in R$ is arbitrary and $\alpha_i = (Hf, \psi_i)$ for $i = 1, 2, \ldots$, then*

$$Kf = \Sigma\, \lambda_i \alpha_i \psi_i + p,\ Hp = 0.$$

For $n \geqslant 2$ we have

$$K^n f = \Sigma\, \lambda_i^n \alpha_i \psi_i.$$

Proof. By the preceding theorem we have

$$Kf = AHf = AM(Mf) = \Sigma_i\, (HKf, \psi_i)\psi_i + p =$$

$$\Sigma\, (Hf, K\psi_i)\psi_i + p = \Sigma\, \lambda_i(Hf, \psi_i)\psi_i + p = \Sigma\, \lambda_i \alpha_i \psi_i + p$$

with $Hp = 0$.

From this we derive

$$K^2 f = \Sigma\, \lambda_i \alpha_i K\psi_i + Kp = \Sigma\, \lambda_i^2 \alpha_i \psi_i + Kp,$$

but, since $Hp = 0$, we have $Kp = AHp = 0$; hence

$$K^2 f = \Sigma\, \lambda_i^2 \alpha_i \psi_i.$$

The relation

$$K^n f = \Sigma\, \lambda_i^n \alpha_i \psi_i \ (n > 2)$$

follows now by induction.

Remark. Although in the general case of a symmetrisable transformation K we have only proved that the expansion $\Sigma\, \lambda_i \alpha_i \psi_i$ converges relative to the H-norm (cf. § 4, Th. 2), the present theorem shows that in the case $K = AH$ which we consider here the expansion converges also relative to the ordinary norm. In the next paragraph we shall show by an example that in the general case the expansion may diverge relative to the ordinary norm. It may be asked now whether the element p, satisfying $Kf = \Sigma\, \lambda_i \alpha_i \psi_i + p$, $Hp = 0$, is not always identical with the null element. The answer is negative.

Theorem 6. *The element p in Theorem 5 is not always identical with the null element.*

Proof. Let R be a complete separable Hilbert space in which φ_n ($n = 1, 2, \ldots$) is a complete orthonormal system, and let $\mu_3, \mu_4, \ldots$ and $\nu_3, \nu_4, \ldots$ be sequences of positive numbers for which $\lim \mu_n = \lim \nu_n = 0$, $\mu_3 > \mu_4 > \ldots$ and $\nu_3 > \nu_4 > \ldots$. Defining the positive transformation H and the self-adjoint transformation A by

$$H\varphi_1 = \varphi_1, \quad H\varphi_2 = 0, \quad H\varphi_i = \mu_i\varphi_i \quad (i = 3, 4, \ldots),$$

$$A\varphi_1 = \varphi_2, \quad A\varphi_2 = \varphi_1, \quad A\varphi_i = \nu_i\varphi_i \quad (i = 3, 4, \ldots),$$

it is not difficult to see that both H and A are compact (cf. Ch. 11, § 8, Th. 1). We have

$$AH\varphi_1 = \varphi_2, \; AH\varphi_2 = 0, \; AH\varphi_i = \nu_i\mu_i\varphi_i \; (i = 3, 4, \ldots).$$

In order to find the characteristic elements of AH, belonging to characteristic values $\neq 0$, we write $AHf = \lambda f$ for $f = \Sigma\, \alpha_i\varphi_i$ and $\lambda \neq 0$. From this we derive

$$\alpha_1\varphi_2 + \Sigma_3\, \nu_i\mu_i\alpha_i\varphi_i = \Sigma_1\, \lambda\alpha_i\varphi_i;$$

hence $\alpha_1 = \alpha_2 = 0$ and $\nu_i\mu_i\alpha_i = \lambda\alpha_i$ ($i = 3, 4, \ldots$). Since $\nu_i\mu_i \neq \nu_k\mu_k$ for $i \neq k$, we have therefore $\lambda = \nu_k\mu_k$ for a certain value of $k (\geqslant 3)$ and $\alpha_i = 0$ for $i \neq k$, which shows that the elements $\alpha_k\varphi_k$ ($k \geqslant 3$) are the only characteristic elements with characteristic values $\neq 0$. Making them H-normal we find the elements $\mu_k^{-1/2}\varphi_k$ with characteristic values $\lambda_k = \nu_k\mu_k$, hence, by Theorem 4,

$$AHf = \Sigma_3\, \nu_i(Hf, \varphi_i)\varphi_i + p$$

for every $f \in R$. Now take $f = \varphi_1$. Then $(Hf, \varphi_i) = (H\varphi_1, \varphi_i) = (\varphi_1, \varphi_i) = 0$ for $i \geqslant 3$, so that the whole series vanishes. Hence

$$0 \neq \varphi_2 = AH\varphi_1 = p.$$

Theorem 7. *Let $\lambda \neq 0$ and, in case λ is a characteristic value of $K = AH$, let the element $g \in R$ be H-orthogonal to all characteristic elements of K belonging to λ. Then the solution f of $Kf - \lambda f = g$ is given by*

$$f = -\frac{g}{\lambda} - {}'\Sigma \frac{\lambda_i}{\lambda(\lambda - \lambda_i)} \alpha_i\psi_i + q,$$

where $\alpha_i = (Hg, \psi_i)$ for $\lambda_i \neq \lambda$, $Hq = 0$, and where the dash in front of the Σ-symbol means that for those values of i for which $\lambda_i = \lambda$ the coefficient of ψ_i may have any arbitrary value.

Proof. Let $Kf - \lambda f = g$. By Theorem 5 we have

$$Kf = AHf = \Sigma\, \lambda_i\beta_i\psi_i + p,$$

where $\beta_i = (Hf, \psi_i)$ and $Hp = 0$. Since $\lambda_i\beta_i = (Hf, K\psi_i) = (HKf, \psi_i) = (H(g + \lambda f), \psi_i) = \alpha_i + \lambda\beta_i$, we find $\beta_i = -\alpha_i/(\lambda - \lambda_i)$ for $\lambda_i \neq \lambda$, hence

$$\lambda f + g = Kf = -{}'\Sigma\, \lambda_i(\lambda - \lambda_i)^{-1}\alpha_i\psi_i + p,$$

or

$$f = -\frac{g}{\lambda} - {}'\Sigma \frac{\lambda_i}{\lambda(\lambda - \lambda_i)}\alpha_i\psi_i + q,$$

where we have written $q = p/\lambda$. Since $Hp = 0$, we have also $Hq = 0$.

Remark. The arrangement of the sequence λ_i is irrelevant in the expansion theorems.

§ 13. An Example where the Expansion $\Sigma\, \lambda_i(Hf, \psi_i)\psi_i$ diverges Relative to the Ordinary Norm

In the preceding paragraph we have seen that if the Hilbert space R is complete, H is bounded and positive on R, A is bounded on R, and the compact transformation $K = AH$ is symmetrisable relative to H, then the expansion $\Sigma\, \lambda_i(Hf, \psi_i)\psi_i$ converges for every $f \in R$, and represents Kf except for an element p satisfying $Hp = 0$. In the more general case where we only know that the compact transformation K is symmetrisable, and that moreover $Kf = 0$ whenever $Hf = 0$, we have only proved that the expansion $\Sigma\, \lambda_i(Hf, \psi_i)\psi_i$ converges relative to the H-norm (cf. § 4, Th. 2). It might be asked now whether this expansion does not always converge relative to the ordinary norm as well. The answer to this question is negative as we shall show by an example. In fact, we shall prove that $\Sigma\, \lambda_i^k(Hf, \psi_i)\psi_i$ may diverge for all exponents k, even although the transformation K which possesses this curious property is a transformation of finite double-norm on a complete separable Hilbert space. The question whether there exist symmetrisable transformations K, satisfying the condition that $Kf = 0$ whenever $Hf = 0$ but not of the form $K = AH$ with a bounded A, will then be answered at the same time, since the divergence of the expansion implies that K is not of the form $K = AH$. The example is essentially due to Toeplitz ([6]; p. 1571 —1573).

We suppose that the system $\{\varphi_n\}$ $(n = 1, 2, \ldots)$ is complete and orthonormal in the complete separable Hilbert space R of infinite dimension. The numbers λ_n, ρ_n, μ_n $(n = 1, 2, \ldots)$ are all assumed positive;

$\Sigma (\lambda_n^2 + \rho_n^2 + \mu_n^2) < \infty$; $\lambda_1, \mu_1, \lambda_2, \mu_2, \ldots$ are all different, and $\mu_n > \lambda_n$ $(n = 1, 2, \ldots)$. The bounded linear transformation K is now defined by

$$K\varphi_{2n-1} = \lambda_n \varphi_{2n-1} + \rho_n \varphi_{2n},$$
$$K\varphi_{2n} = \mu_n \varphi_{2n}$$

for $n = 1, 2, \ldots$. Since $\Sigma_{ij} \mid (K\varphi_i, \varphi_j) \mid^2 = \Sigma (\lambda_n^2 + \rho_n^2 + \mu_n^2) < \infty$, the transformation K is of finite double-norm and therefore compact. Obviously K is reduced by every subspace $L[\varphi_{2n-1}, \varphi_{2n}]$. We shall now define a bounded positive transformation H which has this same property. We put

$$H\varphi_{2n-1} = \alpha_n \varphi_{2n-1} + \beta_n \varphi_{2n},$$
$$H\varphi_{2n} = \beta_n \varphi_{2n-1} + \gamma_n \varphi_{2n}$$

for $n = 1, 2, \ldots$, where $\alpha_n, \beta_n, \gamma_n$ are bounded, $\alpha_n > 0$, $\beta_n > 0$, $\gamma_n > 0$ and $\alpha_n \gamma_n - \beta_n^2 > 0$. It is easily seen that this implies $(Hf, f) > 0$ for every $f \neq 0$, so that H is positive and $Hf = 0$ only for $f = 0$. We find now

$$HK\varphi_{2n-1} = (\lambda_n \alpha_n + \rho_n \beta_n) \varphi_{2n-1} + (\lambda_n \beta_n + \rho_n \gamma_n) \varphi_{2n},$$
$$HK\varphi_{2n} = \mu_n \beta_n \varphi_{2n-1} + \mu_n \gamma_n \varphi_{2n}.$$

In order that K be symmetrisable relative to H, that is, in order that $S = HK$ be self-adjoint, it is necessary and sufficient that $\mu_n \beta_n = \lambda_n \beta_n + \rho_n \gamma_n$, hence $\beta_n(\mu_n - \lambda_n) = \rho_n \gamma_n$ or $\rho_n/(\mu_n - \lambda_n) = \beta_n/\gamma_n$. Furthermore, on account of $\beta_n^2 < \alpha_n \gamma_n$, we must have $\beta_n/\gamma_n < \alpha_n/\beta_n$. Choosing now

$$\beta_n = \rho_n \pi_n, \quad \gamma_n = (\mu_n - \lambda_n)\pi_n, \quad \alpha_n = 2\rho_n^2 \pi_n/(\mu_n - \lambda_n),$$

where π_n is a factor of proportionality, all these conditions are satisfied. Taking π_n sufficiently small for large n, we can, if we want, make H of finite double-norm.

We consider now the transformations K and H on one of the subspaces $L[\varphi_{2n-1}, \varphi_{2n}]$. Since the discussion for all these subspaces is identical (except for the index n), we take $n = 1$ and drop the index in $\lambda_1, \rho_1, \mu_1, \alpha_1, \beta_1, \gamma_1$. Hence

$$K\varphi_1 = \lambda\varphi_1 + \rho\varphi_2, \qquad H\varphi_1 = \alpha\varphi_1 + \beta\varphi_2,$$
$$K\varphi_2 = \mu\varphi_2, \qquad H\varphi_2 = \beta\varphi_1 + \gamma\varphi_2.$$

It is easily verified that K has the characteristic values λ and μ;

$$K\tilde{\psi}_1 = \lambda\tilde{\psi}_1, \qquad K\tilde{\psi}_2 = \mu\tilde{\psi}_2,$$

where the characteristic elements $\tilde{\psi}_1$ and $\tilde{\psi}_2$ are given by

$$\tilde{\psi}_1 = (\mu - \lambda)\varphi_1 - \rho\varphi_2,$$
$$\tilde{\psi}_2 = \varphi_2.$$

Hence, observing that $(\mu - \lambda)\beta - \rho\gamma = 0$, we find

$$H\tilde{\psi}_1 = (\mu - \lambda)(\alpha\varphi_1 + \beta\varphi_2) - \rho(\beta\varphi_1 + \gamma\varphi_2) =$$
$$\{(\mu - \lambda)\alpha - \rho\beta\}\varphi_1 + \{(\mu - \lambda)\beta - \rho\gamma\}\varphi_2 =$$
$$\{(\mu - \lambda)\alpha - \rho\beta\}\varphi_1 = (2\rho^2\pi - \rho^2\pi)\varphi_1 = \rho^2\pi\varphi_1;$$
$$H\tilde{\psi}_2 = H\varphi_2 = \beta\varphi_1 + \gamma\varphi_2 = \rho\pi\varphi_1 + (\mu - \lambda)\pi\varphi_2,$$

so that

$$(H\tilde{\psi}_1, \tilde{\psi}_1) = (\mu - \lambda)\rho^2\pi = P^2, \ (H\tilde{\psi}_2, \tilde{\psi}_2) = (\mu - \lambda)\pi = Q^2.$$

Then, writing $\psi_1 = \tilde{\psi}_1/P$ and $\psi_2 = \tilde{\psi}_2/Q$, the system $\{\psi_1, \psi_2\}$ is H-orthonormal. We obtain therefore

$$\psi_1 = \frac{\sqrt{\mu - \lambda}}{\rho\sqrt{\pi}}\varphi_1 - \frac{1}{\sqrt{\mu - \lambda}\sqrt{\pi}}\varphi_2, \quad H\psi_1 = \frac{\rho\sqrt{\pi}}{\sqrt{\mu - \lambda}}\varphi_1,$$

$$\psi_2 = \frac{1}{\sqrt{\mu - \lambda}\sqrt{\pi}}\varphi_2, \quad H\psi_2 = \frac{\rho\sqrt{\pi}}{\sqrt{\mu - \lambda}}\varphi_1 + \sqrt{\mu - \lambda}\sqrt{\pi}\varphi_2,$$

or, writing $\sqrt{\mu - \lambda}/\rho\sqrt{\pi} = A$ and $1/\sqrt{(\mu - \lambda)\pi} = B$,

$$\psi_1 = A\varphi_1 - B\varphi_2, \quad H\psi_1 = A^{-1}\varphi_1,$$
$$\psi_2 = B\varphi_2, \quad H\psi_2 = A^{-1}\varphi_1 + B^{-1}\varphi_2.$$

We next consider the expansion of an element $f \in R$. The subspace $L[\varphi_1, \varphi_2]$ gives the two terms $\lambda(Hf, \psi_1)\psi_1 + \mu(Hf, \psi_2)\psi_2$. For the first term we find

$$\lambda(Hf, \psi_1)\psi_1 = \lambda(f, H\psi_1)\psi_1 = \lambda(f, A^{-1}\varphi_1)(A\varphi_1 - B\varphi_2) =$$
$$\lambda(f, \varphi_1)\varphi_1 - \lambda BA^{-1}(f, \varphi_1)\varphi_2 = \lambda(f, \varphi_1)\varphi_1 - \frac{\lambda\rho}{\mu - \lambda}(f, \varphi_1)\varphi_2.$$

In the same way, if we consider the subspace $L[\varphi_{2n-1}, \varphi_{2n}]$, we obtain

$$\lambda_n(Hf, \psi_{2n-1})\psi_{2n-1} = \lambda_n(f, \varphi_{2n-1})\varphi_{2n-1} - \frac{\lambda_n\rho_n}{\mu_n - \lambda_n}(f, \varphi_{2n-1})\varphi_{2n}.$$

Let us make now a more definite choice for λ_n, ρ_n and μ_n. We take $\lambda_n = n^{-1}$, $\rho_n = n^{-1}$, $\mu_n = n^{-1} + e^{-n}$. Then $\lambda_n\rho_n/(\mu_n - \lambda_n) = e^n/n^2$ tends to infinity with n. For the element $f = \Sigma\,(n^{-1}\varphi_{2n-1} + n^{-1}\varphi_{2n})$ we have $(f, \varphi_{2n-1}) = (f, \varphi_{2n}) = n^{-1}$, and therefore

$$\lim \| \lambda_n(f, \varphi_{2n-1})\varphi_{2n-1} \| = 0,$$

$$\lim \| \lambda_n\rho_n(\mu_n - \lambda_n)^{-1}(f, \varphi_{2n-1})\varphi_{2n} \| = \lim e^n/n^3 = \infty,$$

hence

$$\lim \| \lambda_n(Hf, \psi_{2n-1})\psi_{2n-1} \| = \infty.$$

This shows that the expansion with terms $\lambda_n(Hf, \psi_{2n-1})\psi_{2n-1}$ and $\mu_n(Hf, \psi_{2n})\psi_{2n}$ diverges. In the same way, if we consider the expansion with terms $\lambda_n^k(Hf, \psi_{2n-1})\psi_{2n-1}$ and $\mu_n^k(Hf, \psi_{2n})\psi_{2n}$ for an arbitrary integer k, we also find divergence since $\lim e^n/n^{2+k} = \infty$ for $n \to \infty$.

It is interesting to observe that if we take the terms together in groups of two, hence $\Sigma\,[\lambda_n(Hf, \psi_{2n-1})\psi_{2n-1} + \mu_n(Hf, \psi_{2n})\psi_{2n}]$, this series converges to Kf for every $f \in R$. Indeed, dropping indices again, we find

$$\lambda(Hf, \psi_1)\psi_1 + \mu(Hf, \psi_2)\psi_2 = \lambda(f, H\psi_1)\psi_1 + \mu(f, H\psi_2)\psi_2 =$$

$$\lambda(f, A^{-1}\varphi_1)(A\varphi_1 - B\varphi_2) + \mu(f, A^{-1}\varphi_1 + B^{-1}\varphi_2)B\varphi_2 =$$

$$\lambda(f, \varphi_1)\varphi_1 - \lambda BA^{-1}(f, \varphi_1)\varphi_2 + \mu BA^{-1}(f, \varphi_1)\varphi_2 + \mu(f, \varphi_2)\varphi_2 =$$

$$\lambda(f, \varphi_1)\varphi_1 + (\mu - \lambda)BA^{-1}(f, \varphi_1)\varphi_2 + \mu(f, \varphi_2)\varphi_2 =$$

$$\lambda(f, \varphi_1)\varphi_1 + \rho(f, \varphi_1)\varphi_2 + \mu(f, \varphi_2)\varphi_2 =$$

$$(f, \varphi_1)K\varphi_1 + (f, \varphi_2)K\varphi_2 = K\{(f, \varphi_1)\varphi_1 + (f, \varphi_2)\varphi_2\},$$

so that

$$\Sigma\,[\lambda_n(Hf, \psi_{2n-1})\psi_{2n-1} + \mu_n(Hf, \psi_{2n})\psi_{2n}] =$$

$$\Sigma\, K\{(f, \varphi_{2n-1})\varphi_{2n-1} + (f, \varphi_{2n})\varphi_{2n}\} = K\,\Sigma_{i=1}^{\infty}\,(f, \varphi_i)\varphi_i = Kf.$$

§ 14. Expansions for H

We suppose that the space R is complete, and that the bounded linear transformation K has the property that K^p is compact for an integer $p \geqslant 1$. Then, if all characteristic values $\neq 0$ of K are real and of index one, there exists a bounded positive transformation $\tilde{H}$ such that K is fully symmetrisable relative to $\tilde{H}$ (cf. § 9, Th. 3). We shortly repeat how to construct such a transformation $\tilde{H}$. If $\lambda_1, \lambda_2, \ldots$ is the sequence of characteristic values $\neq 0$ of K (and therefore also of K^*), each characteristic value repeated according to its multiplicity, there exist sequences $\psi_1, \psi_2, \ldots$ and $\chi_1, \chi_2, \ldots$ of characteristic elements of K and K^* respectively such that $K\psi_i = \lambda_i\psi_i$, $K^*\chi_i = \lambda_i\chi_i$, $(\psi_i, \chi_j) = 1$ for $i = j$ and $(\psi_i, \chi_j) = 0$ for $i \neq j$ $(i, j = 1, 2, \ldots)$. Then $\tilde{H}$ is defined by

$$\tilde{H}f = \Sigma\ \mu_n(f, \chi_n)\chi_n,$$

where the positive numbers μ_n $(n = 1, 2, \ldots)$ are chosen such that the series for $\tilde{H}f$ converges. Since $\tilde{H}\psi_i = \Sigma\ \mu_n(\psi_i, \chi_n)\chi_n = \mu_i\chi_i$, we have $(\tilde{H}\psi_i, \psi_j) = 0$ for $i \neq j$; the system $\{\psi_i\}$ is therefore $\tilde{H}$-orthogonal. Furthermore $(\tilde{H}\psi_i, \psi_i) = \mu_i$; hence, writing $\tilde{\psi}_i = \psi_i/\mu_i^{1/2}$, $\tilde{\chi}_i = \mu_i^{1/2}\chi_i$, the system $\{\tilde{\psi}_i\}$ is $\tilde{H}$-orthonormal, and the relations $(\tilde{\psi}_i, \tilde{\chi}_j) = 1$ for $i = j$ and $(\tilde{\psi}_i, \tilde{\chi}_j) = 0$ for $i \neq j$ hold. We have now

$$\tilde{H}f = \Sigma\ (f, \tilde{\chi}_n)\tilde{\chi}_n,$$

hence

$$\tilde{H}\tilde{\psi}_i = \tilde{\chi}_i\ (i = 1, 2, \ldots).$$

Let us consider now, after this preliminary discussion, a bounded positive transformation H on the space R. Furthermore, let the bounded linear transformation K have the property that K^p is compact for an integer $p \geqslant 1$, and let K be fully symmetrisable relative to H. Then all characteristic values $\neq 0$ of K are real and of index one. If $\lambda_1, \lambda_2, \ldots$ is again the sequence of characteristic values $\neq 0$ of K, $\psi_1, \psi_2, \ldots$ is a corresponding H-orthonormal sequence of characteristic elements, and $\chi_i = H\psi_i$ $(i = 1, 2, \ldots)$, we have therefore $(\psi_i, \chi_j) = 1$ for $i = j$ and $(\psi_i, \chi_j) = 0$ for $i \neq j$. It is now easy to prove that $\Sigma\ (f, \chi_n)\chi_n$ converges for every $f \in R$. Indeed, since the system $\Psi_i = H^{1/2}\psi_i$ $(i = 1, 2, \ldots)$ is orthogonal, the series $\Sigma\ (g, \Psi_n)\Psi_n$ converges for every $g \in R$, so that, taking $g = H^{1/2}f$ for an arbitrary $f \in R$, the series $\Sigma\ (H^{1/2}f, \Psi_n)\Psi_n = \Sigma\ (f, \chi_n)\Psi_n$ converges for every $f \in R$. Then $\Sigma\ (f, \chi_n)\chi_n = H^{1/2}\{\Sigma\ (f, \chi_n)\Psi_n\}$ converges as well. We write

$$\tilde{H}f = \Sigma\ (f, \chi_n)\chi_n,$$

hence

$$\tilde{H}\psi_i = \chi_i\ (i = 1, 2, \ldots).$$

By what we have already seen in the first part of the present paragraph, K is now fully symmetrisable relative to $\tilde{H}$. Furthermore the system $\{\psi_i\}$ is $\tilde{H}$-orthonormal. By hypothesis however, the same statements hold with $\tilde{H}$ replaced by H. It is therefore natural to ask what is the connection between the given transformation H and the new transformation $\tilde{H}$. The answer is contained in the following theorem:

Theorem 1. *We have $H = \tilde{H} + Q$, where Q is positive and satisfies $QK = O$, that is, $H = \tilde{H}$ on the range of K. The transformation $\tilde{H}$ may be described in more detail by stating that if P_1 is the orthogonal projection on the subspace determined by the system $\Psi_i = H^{1/2}\psi_i$ $(i = 1, 2, \ldots)$, then $\tilde{H} = H^{1/2}P_1H^{1/2}$.*

Proof. We have $P_1 f = \Sigma (f, \Psi_n)\Psi_n$ for every $f \in R$, since the system $\{\Psi_i\}$ is orthonormal. Hence $P_1 H^{1/2} f = \Sigma (H^{1/2}f, \Psi_n)\Psi_n = \Sigma (f, \chi_n)\Psi_n$, or

$$H^{1/2}P_1H^{1/2}f = \Sigma (f, \chi_n)\chi_n = \tilde{H}f.$$

Defining now Q by $Q = H - \tilde{H}$, this transformation Q is evidently self-adjoint. Since

$$(Qf, f) = (Hf, f) - \Sigma (f, \chi_n)(\chi_n, f) = (Hf, f) - \Sigma \,|\, (f, \chi_n) \,|^2 =$$

$$\| H^{1/2}f \|^2 - \Sigma \,|\, (H^{1/2}f, \Psi_n) \,|^2 \geqslant 0$$

by Bessel's inequality, Q is positive. Furthermore

$$(\tilde{H}Kf, g) = \Sigma (Kf, \chi_n)(\chi_n, g) = \Sigma (HKf, \psi_n)(H\psi_n, g) =$$

$$\Sigma (Hf, K\psi_n)(\psi_n, Hg) = \Sigma \lambda_n (Hf, \psi_n)\overline{(Hg, \psi_n)} = (HKf, g)$$

for arbitrary $f, g \in R$ by § 4, Th. 2, hence $HKf = \tilde{H}Kf$, or $QKf = 0$ for every $f \in R$. This shows that $QK = O$.

Theorem 2. *If moreover H is compact, then (provided $Q \neq O$)*

$$Hf = \Sigma (f, \chi_n)\chi_n + \Sigma \rho_n (f, \eta_n)\eta_n,$$

where

(α) *the system $\{\eta_n\}$ is orthonormal,*
(β) *all $\rho_n > 0$,*
(γ) $K^*\eta_n = 0$ $(n = 1, 2, \ldots)$.

Proof. If H is compact, then $H^{1/2}$ is also compact, since H is self-adjoint. Hence $Q = H^{1/2}(I - P_1)H^{1/2}$ is compact. It follows that Q has at most an enumerable number of characteristic values $\rho_n \neq 0$, and, since Q is positive, we have $\rho_n > 0$ $(n = 1, 2, \ldots)$. If η_n $(n = 1, 2, \ldots)$ is a corresponding orthonormal system of characteristic elements of Q, then $Qf = \Sigma \rho_n (f, \eta_n)\eta_n$ by § 7, Th. 2, 3°. Finally, since $QK = O$, we have also $K^*Q = (QK)^* = O$, hence $K^*\eta_n = K^*(\rho_n^{-1}Q\eta_n) = \rho_n^{-1}K^*Q\eta_n = 0$ $(n = 1, 2, \ldots)$.

Remark. The present theorem is the abstract analogue of one of Mercer's main results on symmetrisable kernels [10] (cf. also [6]; p. 1542—1543).

§ 15. Existence of Characteristic Values and Expansion Theorems in the Case that not H but $S = HK$ is Positive

Let R be a Hilbert space, complete or not, and let $H \neq O$ be bounded and self-adjoint but not necessarily positive. Denoting by $[L]$ the null space of H and by $[M]$ its orthogonal complement, we suppose again that R is the direct sum of $[L]$ and $[M]$, and we denote by P the projection on $[M]$ along $[L]$.

In the present paragraph we shall consider bounded linear transformations K, symmetrisable relative to H, and having the property that $S = HK$ is positive. Transformations of this kind were introduced in a particular case by ZIMMERBERG [4]. Since the whole theory is similar to that for positive H we shall only mention the main points.

We first observe that K, supposed symmetrisable relative to H, is symmetrisable relative to S as well, in other words, SK is self-adjoint. Indeed, $SK = HK^2$, hence $(SKf, g) = (HK^2f, g) = (Kf, HKg) = (HKf, Kg) = (f, HK^2g) = (f, SKg)$. Furthermore $SK = (SP)K = S(PK) = ST$, so that $T = PK$ is also symmetrisable relative to S. Also, by § 2, 8°, 9° and 10°, if K is fully symmetrisable, then all characteristic values of K are real; $Kf = \lambda f$, $Kg = \mu g$, $\lambda \neq \mu$ implies $(Hf, g) = (Sf, g) = 0$, and $(K - \lambda I)^p f = 0$ for an integer $p \geqslant 1$ implies $(K - \lambda I)f = 0$.

The S-norm $(Sf, f)^{1/2} = \| S^{1/2}f \|$ of an element $f \in R$ will be denoted by $N_S(f)$.

Theorem 1. *If there exists a positive integer p such that $T^p = PK^p$ is compact, then the following two statements are equivalent:*

1°. $SK = ST \neq O$.

2°. *T has a characteristic value $\lambda \neq 0$ (then λ is necessarily real).*

Proof. 2° → 1°. Let $Tf = \lambda f \neq 0$. Then $STf = \lambda Sf = \lambda HTf = \lambda^2 Hf \neq 0$, since $Hf = 0$ would imply $Tf = 0$. Hence $SK = ST \neq O$.

1° → 2°. We suppose first that T itself is compact. Let now $ST \neq O$. Then $STf_0 \neq 0$ for a certain f_0, hence $Sf_0 \neq 0$, since $Sf_0 = 0$ would imply $Tf_0 = 0$ by § 2, 3°. Then also $N_S(f_0) \neq 0$. We put $\bar{f}_0 = f_0/N_S(f_0)$ and $f_1 = T\bar{f}_0$. Then $Sf_1 = ST\bar{f}_0 \neq 0$, so that $N_S(f_1) \neq 0$. Now defining generally

$$\bar{f}_{n-1} = f_{n-1}/N_S(f_{n-1}),\ f_n = T\bar{f}_{n-1}\ (n = 1, 2, \ldots),$$

the remaining part of the proof is similar to that of § 3, Th. 1, replacing everywhere H by S, observing that T^p is symmetrisable relative to S, and using that $ST \neq O$ is equivalent to $ST^p \neq O$.

Theorem 2. *If there exists an integer $p \geqslant 1$ such that K^p is compact, then $SK \neq O$ implies the existence of a (real) characteristic value $\neq 0$ of K. If moreover K is fully symmetrisable, the converse is also true, that is, $Kf = \lambda f \neq 0$ implies $SK \neq O$.*
Proof. As in § 3, Th. 4.

Corollary. *If K is strongly symmetrisable, and there exists an integer $p \geqslant 1$ such that T^p is compact, then K has a characteristic value $\neq 0$ if and only if $SK = ST \neq O$.*
Proof. Since $K = KP$ under the stated hypothesis, we have $K^{p+1} = KK^p = KPK^p = KT^p$, which shows that K^{p+1} is compact. Hence, if $SK \neq O$, K has a characteristic value $\neq 0$. Conversely, if K has a characteristic value $\neq 0$, then $SK \neq O$, since K is fully symmetrisable.

Theorem 3. *If K is strongly symmetrisable, hence $K = KP$, and if there exists an integer $p \geqslant 1$ such that T^p is compact, the relations $\varphi = P\psi$, $\psi = \lambda^{-1}K\varphi$ define a one-to-one correspondence between all characteristic elements ψ of K, belonging to characteristic values $\lambda \neq 0$, and all characteristic elements φ of T, belonging to characteristic values $\lambda \neq 0$. Corresponding elements have the same characteristic value λ. Every characteristic value $\lambda \neq 0$ has the same multiplicity for K as for T.*
Proof. As in § 3, Th. 5.

Theorem 4. *If K is fully symmetrisable, if there exists an integer $p \geqslant 1$ such that K^p is compact, and the linearly independent elements $\psi_1, \ldots, \psi_n$ determine the subspace of all ψ for which $K\psi = \lambda\psi$ ($\lambda \neq 0$), then the elements $\varphi_i = P\psi_i$ ($i = 1, \ldots, n$) are linearly independent, and determine the subspace of all φ for which $T\varphi = \lambda\varphi$. Every characteristic value $\neq 0$ has the same multiplicity for K as for T.*
Proof. As in § 3, Th. 6.

As in § 4, we again distinguish between two cases:

Case A. *There exists an integer $p \geqslant 1$ such that $T^p = PK^p$ is compact.*

Case B. *K is either fully or strongly symmetrisable, and there exists an integer $p \geqslant 1$ such that K^p is compact.*

In case A we find in the same way as in § 4 the sequence λ_n of characteristic values $\neq 0$ of T ($|\lambda_1| \geqslant |\lambda_2| \geqslant \ldots$) and a corresponding sequence φ_n of characteristic elements which is H-orthogonal as well as S-orthogonal, and which is normalized such that $(S\varphi_n, \varphi_n) = |\lambda_n|$, hence $\lambda_n (H\varphi_n, \varphi_n) = |\lambda_n|$, or $(H\varphi_n, \varphi_n) = \text{sgn}\,\lambda_n$. In case B we find the sequence λ_n of characteristic values $\neq 0$ of K ($|\lambda_1| \geqslant |\lambda_2| \geqslant \ldots$) and a corresponding sequence ψ_n of characteristic elements which is H-orthogonal as well as S-orthogonal. It is again normalized such that $(H\psi_n, \psi_n) = \text{sgn}\,\lambda_n$. The sequence $\varphi_n = P\psi_n$ ($n = 1, 2, \ldots$) of characteristic elements of T is now also H-orthogonal as well as S-orthogonal and $(H\varphi_n, \varphi_n) = \text{sgn}\,\lambda_n$. If K is strongly symmetrisable, we have moreover $\psi_n = \lambda_n^{-1} K\varphi_n$ by Theorem 3.

Theorem 5. 1°. *$|\lambda_n| = \max N_S(Kf)/N_S(f)$ for all $f \in R$ satisfying $N_S(f) \neq 0$ and $(Hf, \varphi_1) = \ldots = (Hf, \varphi_{n-1}) = 0$. For $f = \varphi_n$ the maximum is attained.*

2°. *$N_S(Kf) = 0$ (equivalent to $SKf = 0$) if and only if $(Hf, \varphi_n) = 0$ for all n.*

3°. *In case B we may replace the elements φ in 1° and 2° by the corresponding elements ψ.*

Proof. As in § 4, Th. 1.

Theorem 6 (*Expansion theorem*). *If, for arbitrary elements $f, g \in R$, we write $\alpha_n = \text{sgn}\,\lambda_n (Hf, \varphi_n)$, $\beta_n = \text{sgn}\,\lambda_n (Hg, \varphi_n)$ ($n = 1, 2, \ldots$), then*

$$\lim_{k\to\infty} N_S\,(Kf - \Sigma_{n=1}^{k} \lambda_n \alpha_n \varphi_n) = 0.$$

Furthermore

$$(SKf, g) = (HKf, Kg) = \Sigma\, \lambda_n^2\, \text{sgn}\,\lambda_n . \alpha_n \bar{\beta}_n.$$

In case B we may replace the elements φ_n by the corresponding elements ψ_n.

Proof. As in § 4, Th. 2.

Theorem 7. *Let λ_{n_i} ($i = 1, 2, \ldots$) be the subsequence of all positive characteristic values in the sequence λ_n, arranged in non-increasing order, hence $\lambda_{n_1} \geqslant \lambda_{n_2} \geqslant \ldots$. Then $\lambda_{n_i} = \max (SKf, f)/N_S^2(f)$ for all $f \in R$ satisfying $N_S(f) \neq 0$ and $(Hf, \varphi_{n_1}) = \ldots = (Hf, \varphi_{n_{i-1}}) = 0$. For $f = \varphi_{n_i}$ the maximum is attained.*

A similar statement holds for the sequence of all negative characteristic values.

In case B the elements φ may be replaced by the corresponding elements ψ.

Proof. As in § 4, Th. 3.

Theorem 8. *Let the elements* $p_1, \ldots, p_{i-1} \in R$ *be arbitrarily given and let*

$$\mu_i = \text{upper bound } (SKf, f)/N_S^2(f)$$

for all $f \in R$ *satisfying* $N_S(f) \neq 0$ *and* $(Sf, p_1) = \ldots = (Sf, p_{i-1}) = 0$. *Then* μ_i *depends evidently on* $p_1, \ldots, p_{i-1}$. *Letting now these elements run through the whole space* R, *we have* $\lambda_{n_i} = \min \mu_i$.

Proof. As in § 4, Th. 4.

In case the space R is not complete we may again extend the transformations H, P, K, S and T onto $\bar{R}$, the closure of R, and the results stated in the Theorems 5, 6, 7, 8 remain valid on $\bar{R}$. This is proved as in § 5. In the same way the discussion of the solutions f and f_1 of $Kf - \lambda f = g$ and $Tf_1 - \lambda f_1 = g$ offers no new aspects and is similar to that in § 6.

We conclude this paragraph by considering the case that the space R is complete and that $K = AH$, where A is bounded and K^p is compact for an integer $p \geqslant 1$. Then $K^2 = AHAH = AS$, hence $SAS = SK^2 = HK^3$ is self-adjoint. It follows that $K^2 = AS$ is symmetrisable relative to the positive transformation S. Then $S^{1/2}AS^{1/2}$ is self-adjoint (cf. § 12, Th. 2) and, since $K^2 = AS$ has the sequence $\lambda_1^2, \lambda_2^2, \ldots$ of characteristic values $\neq 0$ with the corresponding sequence $\psi_1, \psi_2, \ldots$ of characteristic elements, the transformation $S^{1/2}AS^{1/2}$ has the same sequence $\lambda_1^2, \lambda_2^2, \ldots$ of characteristic values $\neq 0$ with the orthonormal sequence $S^{1/2}\psi_n/|\lambda_n|^{1/2}$ of characteristic elements (cf. § 12, Th. 3).

Theorem 9. *If* $g \in R$ *is of the form* $g = AS^{1/2}f$, *and* $\beta_i = \operatorname{sgn} \lambda_i . (Hg, \psi_i)$ *for* $i = 1, 2, \ldots$, *then*

$$g = AS^{1/2}f = \Sigma\, \beta_i \psi_i + p,$$

where $Sp = 0$.

Proof. We observe first that

$$(1)\quad \begin{cases} (Hg, \psi_i) = \lambda_i^{-1}(HAS^{1/2}f, K\psi_i) = \lambda_i^{-1}(HKAS^{1/2}f, \psi_i) = \\ \lambda_i^{-1}(SAS^{1/2}f, \psi_i) = \lambda_i^{-1}(S^{1/2}AS^{1/2}f, S^{1/2}\psi_i) = \lambda_i^{-1}(f, S^{1/2}AS\psi_i) = \\ \lambda_i^{-1}(f, S^{1/2}K^2\psi_i) = \lambda_i(f, S^{1/2}\psi_i) \end{cases}$$

for $i = 1, 2, \ldots$. Furthermore, since the system $\Psi_i = S^{1/2}\psi_i/|\lambda_i|^{1/2}$ $(i = 1, 2, \ldots)$ is orthonormal, every element $f \in R$ may be written as

$$f = \Sigma_i\, |\lambda_i|^{-1}(f, S^{1/2}\psi_i)S^{1/2}\psi_i + h,$$

where h belongs to the orthogonal complement of the subspace determined by the system $\{\Psi_i\}$, hence $(h, S^{1/2}\psi_i) = 0$ $(i = 1, 2, \ldots)$. Then, by (1),

$$g = AS^{1/2}f = \Sigma_i \mid \lambda_i \mid^{-1}(f, S^{1/2}\psi_i)AS\psi_i + AS^{1/2}h =$$

$$\Sigma_i \mid \lambda_i \mid^{-1}(f, S^{1/2}\psi_i)K^2\psi_i + AS^{1/2}h = \Sigma_i \lambda_i \operatorname{sgn} \lambda_i(f, S^{1/2}\psi_i)\psi_i + AS^{1/2}h =$$

$$\Sigma_i \operatorname{sgn} \lambda_i(Hg, \psi_i)\psi_i + AS^{1/2}h = \Sigma \beta_i\psi_i + AS^{1/2}h.$$

This shows that only $SAS^{1/2}h = 0$ remains to be proved. Since h is orthogonal to all Ψ_i, and since the sequence Ψ_i is exactly the sequence of characteristic elements of the self-adjoint transformation $S^{1/2}AS^{1/2}$, we have $S^{1/2}AS^{1/2}h = 0$ (cf. § 7, Th. 2, 2°). Hence $SAS^{1/2}h = 0$.

Theorem 10 (*Expansion theorem*). *If* $f \in R$ *is arbitrary, and* $\alpha_i =$ *sgn* λ_i (Hf, ψ_i) *for* $i = 1, 2, \ldots,$ *then*

$$K^2f = \Sigma \lambda_i^2\alpha_i\psi_i + p, \; Hp = 0.$$

For $n \geqslant 3$ *we have*

$$K^nf = \Sigma \lambda_i^n\alpha_i\psi_i.$$

Proof. By the preceding theorem we have

$$K^2f = ASf = AS^{1/2}(S^{1/2}f) = \Sigma_i \operatorname{sgn} \lambda_i(HK^2f, \psi_i)\psi_i + p =$$

$$\Sigma_i \operatorname{sgn} \lambda_i \, (Hf, K^2\psi_i)\psi_i + p = \Sigma \lambda_i^2\alpha_i\psi_i + p,$$

where $Sp = 0$. We have to prove however that $Hp = 0$. Observing that $\lim_{k\to\infty} N_S(Kf - \Sigma_{i=1}^k \lambda_i\alpha_i\psi_i) = 0$ by Theorem 6, we have

$$(Hp, g) = \lim_{k\to\infty} (H(K^2f - \Sigma_{i=1}^k \lambda_i^2\alpha_i\psi_i), g) =$$

$$\lim_{k\to\infty} (S(Kf - \Sigma_{i=1}^k \lambda_i\alpha_i\psi_i), g) = 0$$

for arbitrary g, hence $Hp = 0$.

The result for $n \geqslant 3$ follows now by induction.

§ 16. Functions of Self-Adjoint Transformations

Let the Hilbert space R be complete, and let K be a bounded self-adjoint transformation, having the property that there exists a real number λ_0 such that $K_1 = K - \lambda_0 I$ is compact. We observe that K_1 is self-adjoint as well. Denoting the characteristic values $\neq 0$ of K_1 by $\lambda_1 - \lambda_0, \lambda_2 - \lambda_0, \ldots,$ and supposing that $\varphi_1, \varphi_2, \ldots$ is a corresponding orthonormal sequence of characteristic elements, the numbers $\lambda_1, \lambda_2, \ldots$ are therefore real, and

$$K_1f = \Sigma (\lambda_i - \lambda_0)(f, \varphi_i)\varphi_i$$

for every $f \in R$. We have $K_1 f = 0$ if and only if f is orthogonal to $L[\varphi_1, \varphi_2, \ldots]$, the linear subspace determined by $\varphi_1, \varphi_2, \ldots$. Denoting by P_0 the orthogonal projection on $R_0 = R \ominus L[\varphi_1, \varphi_2, \ldots]$, we may write therefore $\lambda_0 f = \lambda_0 \Sigma (f, \varphi_i)\varphi_i + \lambda_0 P_0 f$, hence

$$Kf = K_1 f + \lambda_0 f = \Sigma \lambda_i (f, \varphi_i)\varphi_i + \lambda_0 P_0 f.$$

Since $K\varphi_i = \lambda_i \varphi_i$ and $KP_0 f = \lambda_0 P_0 f$ for any $f \in R$, we find by induction

(1) $$K^n f = \Sigma_i \lambda_i^n (f, \varphi_i)\varphi_i + \lambda_0^n P_0 f \quad (n = 1, 2, \ldots).$$

Let now $F(\lambda)$ be a complex-valued bounded function defined on the λ-interval $-\| K \| \leqslant \lambda \leqslant \| K \|$. This interval contains all λ_i ($i = 0, 1, 2, \ldots$), since $| \lambda_i | = \| \lambda_i \varphi_i \| = \| K\varphi_i \| \leqslant \| K \|$ for $i = 1, 2, \ldots$ and $| \lambda_0 | \, \| P_0 f \| = \| \lambda_0 P_0 f \| = \| KP_0 f \| \leqslant \| K \| . \| P_0 f \|$ for all $f \in R$. The values $F(\lambda_i)$ are therefore determined. The series $\Sigma F(\lambda_i)(f, \varphi_i)\varphi_i + F(\lambda_0)P_0 f$ converges for every $f \in R$, since $\Sigma | F(\lambda_i) |^2 | (f, \varphi_i) |^2 < \infty$. Writing

$$F(K)f = \Sigma F(\lambda_i)(f, \varphi_i)\varphi_i + F(\lambda_0)P_0 f,$$

the transformation $F(K)$ is then evidently linear on R. It is bounded since

$$\| F(K)f \|^2 = \Sigma | F(\lambda_i) |^2 | (f, \varphi_i) |^2 + | F(\lambda_0) |^2 \| P_0 f \|^2 \leqslant$$
$$\{\text{upper bound } | F(\lambda) |^2\} \{\Sigma | (f, \varphi_i) |^2 + \| P_0 f \|^2\} =$$
$$\{\text{upper bound } | F(\lambda) |^2\} \| f \|^2,$$

hence

$$\| F(K) \| \leqslant \text{upper bound } | F(\lambda) |.$$

Furthermore, if $F(\lambda) = \alpha_1 \lambda + \alpha_2 \lambda^2 + \ldots + \alpha_n \lambda^n$, then $F(K) = \alpha_1 K + \alpha_2 K^2 + \ldots + \alpha_n K^n$ by (1). Also if $F(\lambda) = \alpha_0$ (constant), then $F(K)f = \alpha_0 \{\Sigma (f, \varphi_i)\varphi_i + P_0 f\} = \alpha_0 f$, hence $F(K) = \alpha_0 I$.

It is said that the transformation $F(K)$ is a function of K, corresponding with the complex-valued function $F(\lambda)$ of λ.

Theorem 1. *If* $F(\lambda) = \alpha_1 F_1(\lambda) + \alpha_2 F_2(\lambda)$, *then* $F(K) = \alpha_1 F_1(K) + \alpha_2 F_2(K)$. *If* $F(\lambda) = F_1(\lambda)F_2(\lambda)$, *then* $F(K) = F_1(K)F_2(K)$.

Proof. The first statement is evident. Let now $F(\lambda) = F_1(\lambda)F_2(\lambda)$. Since $F_1(K)\varphi_i = F_1(\lambda_i)\varphi_i$, $F_1(K)P_0 f = F_1(\lambda_0)P_0 f$ and

$$F_2(K)f = \Sigma F_2(\lambda_i)(f, \varphi_i)\varphi_i + F_2(\lambda_0)P_0 f,$$

we find

$$F_1(K)F_2(K)f = \Sigma F_1(\lambda_i)F_2(\lambda_i)(f, \varphi_i)\varphi_i + F_1(\lambda_0)F_2(\lambda_0)P_0 f.$$

Theorem 2. *$F(K)$ is normal and $(F(K))^* = \overline{F}(K)$, where $\overline{F}(\lambda)$ and $F(\lambda)$ are conjugate complex for every λ. If $F(\lambda)$ is real, then $F(K)$ is self-adjoint. If $F(\lambda) \geqslant 0$, then $F(K)$ is positive.*

Proof. We have

$$(f, (F(K))^*g) = (F(K)f, g) =$$

$$(\Sigma F(\lambda_i)(f, \varphi_i)\varphi_i + F(\lambda_0)P_0 f, \Sigma (g, \varphi_i)\varphi_i + P_0 g) =$$

$$\Sigma F(\lambda_i)(f, \varphi_i)\overline{(g, \varphi_i)} + (F(\lambda_0)P_0 f, P_0 g) =$$

$$(\Sigma (f, \varphi_i)\varphi_i + P_0 f, \Sigma \overline{F}(\lambda_i)(g, \varphi_i)\varphi_i + \overline{F}(\lambda_0)P_0 g) = (f, \overline{F}(K)g),$$

hence $(F(K))^* = \overline{F}(K)$. It follows that $F(K)(F(K))^*$ and $(F(K))^*F(K)$ both correspond with $F(\lambda)\overline{F}(\lambda) = | F(\lambda) |^2$, which shows that $F(K)$ is normal. The other statements are now trivial.

Theorem 3. *Let the functions $F_0(\lambda)$, $F_1(\lambda)$, $F_2(\lambda)$, ... be uniformly bounded on $-\| K \| \leqslant \lambda \leqslant \| K \|$, and let $\lim F_n(\lambda) = F_0(\lambda)$ on this interval. Then $\lim F_n(K)f = F_0(K)f$ for all $f \in R$. If moreover $\lim F_n(\lambda) = F_0(\lambda)$ uniformly, then $\lim \| F_0(K) - F_n(K) \| = 0$.*

Proof. Let $| F_n(\lambda) | \leqslant M$ for $n = 0, 1, 2, \ldots$ and all λ. Since

$$F_0(K)f - F_n(K)f = \Sigma_i \{F_0(\lambda_i) - F_n(\lambda_i)\}(f, \varphi_i)\varphi_i + \{F_0(\lambda_0) - F_n(\lambda_0)\}P_0 f$$

and $\Sigma_{N+1}^{\infty} | (f, \varphi_i) |^2 < \varepsilon$ for $N = N(\varepsilon)$, we find

$$\| F_0(K)f - F_n(K)f \|^2 \leqslant$$

$$\Sigma_{i=1}^{N} | F_0(\lambda_i) - F_n(\lambda_i) |^2 | (f, \varphi_i) |^2 + | F_0(\lambda_0) - F_n(\lambda_0) |^2 \| P_0 f \|^2 + 4M^2\varepsilon,$$

which is smaller than $5M^2\varepsilon$ for n sufficiently large. If $\lim F_n(\lambda) = F_0(\lambda)$ uniformly in λ, let $| F_0(\lambda) - F_n(\lambda) | < \varepsilon$ for $n \geqslant n_0(\varepsilon)$ and all λ. Then

$$\| F_0(K)f - F_n(K)f \|^2 \leqslant \varepsilon^2\{ \Sigma | (f, \varphi_i) |^2 + \| P_0 f \|^2\} = \varepsilon^2 \| f \|^2$$

for $n \geqslant n_0(\varepsilon)$.

We proceed with an example. Let the number a lie in the interval $-\| K \| \leqslant \lambda \leqslant \| K \|$. The function $F(\lambda)$ is now defined by

$$F(\lambda) = \begin{cases} 1 \text{ for } \lambda \leqslant a, \\ 0 \text{ for } \lambda > a. \end{cases}$$

Since $\{F(\lambda)\}^2 = F(\lambda)$ and $F(\lambda)$ is real for all λ, hence $\{F(K)\}^2 = F(K)$ and $F(K)$ self-adjoint, the transformation $F(K)$ is an orthogonal projection (cf. Ch. 9, § 11, Th. 1). We shall denote this projection by E_a. It is easy to see on and along which subspaces E_a is a projection. Consider those

λ_i which satisfy $\lambda_i \leqslant a$ (if $\lambda_0 \leqslant a$, then λ_0 is therefore included) and let $[L]_a$ be the linear subspace determined by the corresponding characteristic elements (if $\lambda_0 \leqslant a$, the whole subspace R_0 is therefore contained in $[L]_a$). In the same way we construct the linear subspace $[M]_a$ from all $\lambda_i > a$. Then E_a is the projection on $[L]_a$ along $[M]_a$. If a and b both lie in the interval $-\| K \| \leqslant \lambda \leqslant \| K \|$, and $a < b$, then $[L]_a \subset [L]_b$, hence $E_a E_b = E_b E_a = E_a$ by Ch. 9, § 11, Th. 7. Furthermore, since $E_b - E_a$ corresponds with the function $F(\lambda)$, which satisfies $F(\lambda) = 1$ for $a < \lambda \leqslant b$ and vanishes elsewhere, $E_b - E_a$ is also an orthogonal projection, evidently on the subspace constructed in the way indicated from those λ_i which satisfy $a < \lambda_i \leqslant b$. The set of projections E_a, where a runs through $-\| K \| \leqslant \lambda \leqslant \| K \|$, is called the family of projections associated with K.

As a second application we mention that $F_1(K) = F_2(K)$ if and only if $F_1(\lambda) = F_2(\lambda)$ for $\lambda = \lambda_0, \lambda_1, \lambda_2, \ldots$. Hence, if α is a complex number not identical with any of the numbers $\lambda_0, \lambda_1, \lambda_2, \ldots$, and we define the bounded function $F(\lambda)$ such that $F(\lambda_i) = (\lambda_i - \alpha)^{-1}$ $(i = 0, 1, 2, \ldots)$ and that $F_1(\lambda) = 1/F(\lambda)$ is also bounded, then $F_1(\lambda_i) = \lambda_i - \alpha$ $(i = 0, 1, 2, \ldots)$, so that $F_1(K) = K - \alpha I$. It follows that $F(K) = R_\alpha = (K - \alpha I)^{-1}$. Hence

$$(K - \alpha I)^{-1} f = \Sigma\, (\lambda_i - \alpha)^{-1} (f, \varphi_i) \varphi_i + (\lambda_0 - \alpha)^{-1} P_0 f.$$

§ 17. Dependence of Characteristic Values and Characteristic Elements on the Transformation

In the present paragraph we shall suppose that the space R is complete. Let H be a bounded positive transformation on R, and let the compact transformation K be fully symmetrisable relative to H. Then K has an at most enumerable number of characteristic values $\neq 0$, which are all real. We shall denote the positive characteristic values, arranged in non-ascending order, by $\lambda_1^+, \lambda_2^+, \ldots$. Let now $\tilde{K}$ have the same properties as K and $\| K - \tilde{K} \| < \varepsilon$. Then, denoting the positive characteristic values of $\tilde{K}$, also arranged in non-ascending order, by $\tilde{\lambda}_1^+, \tilde{\lambda}_2^+, \ldots$, we shall prove that $| \lambda_i^+ - \tilde{\lambda}_i^+ | \leqslant \varepsilon$ for those λ_i^+ which satisfy $\lambda_i^+ > \varepsilon$. A similar statement holds for the negative characteristic values.

Before announcing the exact statement we first introduce the following notation:

$$\mu_1 = \max\, (HKf, f)/(Hf, f) \text{ for all } f \in R \text{ with } (Hf, f) \neq 0,$$

$$\mu_n(p_1, \ldots, p_{n-1}) = \text{upper bound } (HKf, f)/(Hf, f) \; (n = 2, 3, \ldots)$$

for all $f \in R$ satisfying $(Hf, f) \neq 0$ and $(Hf, p_1) = \ldots = (Hf, p_{n-1}) = 0$, where $p_1, \ldots, p_{n-1}$ are $n - 1$ arbitrary elements of R. Then, denoting by $\psi_1^+, \psi_2^+, \ldots$ an H-orthonormal sequence of characteristic elements of K, corresponding with $\lambda_1^+, \lambda_2^+, \ldots$, we have by § 4, Th. 4

$$\lambda_1^+ = \mu_1,$$
$$\lambda_n^+ = \mu_n(\psi_1^+, \ldots, \psi_{n-1}^+) = \min_{p_i \in R} \mu_n(p_1, \ldots, p_{n-1}) \; (n = 2, 3, \ldots),$$

as far as λ_n^+ exists.

In the case that there exists only a finite number N of positive characteristic values it is evident that, for $n > N$, we nevertheless may consider the expression $\mu_n (p_1, \ldots, p_{n-1})$. Then (cf. the remark in § 4, Th. 3)

$$\text{lower bound}_{p_i \in R} \mu_n (p_1, \ldots, p_{n-1}) \leqslant 0.$$

If therefore, for a certain positive δ and a certain positive integer n,

$$\mu_n (p_1, \ldots, p_{n-1}) \geqslant \delta$$

for all possible choices of $p_1, \ldots, p_{n-1}$, we may draw the conclusion that λ_n^+ exists and that $\lambda_n^+ \geqslant \delta$.

Theorem 1. *Given the compact fully symmetrisable transformation K with the non-ascending sequence $\lambda_1^+, \lambda_2^+, \ldots$ of positive characteristic values, and the positive number ε such that $\lambda_n^+ > \varepsilon$ $(n = 1, \ldots, N)$, then, if the symmetrisable transformation $\tilde{K}$ satisfies the same conditions as K and $\| K - \tilde{K} \| < \varepsilon$, this transformation $\tilde{K}$ has at least N positive characteristic values $\tilde{\lambda}_1^+, \ldots, \tilde{\lambda}_N^+$, and*

$$| \lambda_n^+ - \tilde{\lambda}_n^+ | \leqslant \varepsilon \; (n = 1, \ldots, N).$$

A similar statement holds for the negative characteristic values.

Proof. Denote for a moment by l_1 the characteristic value of $T - \tilde{T}$ with largest absolute value, where $T = PK$, $\tilde{T} = P\tilde{K}$ in the notation of § 4. Since $(T - \tilde{T})f = l_1 f$ $(f \neq 0)$ implies

$$| l_1 | . \| f \| = \| (T - \tilde{T})f \| = \| P(K - \tilde{K})f \| \leqslant \| P \| . \| K - \tilde{K} \| . \| f \| \leqslant \varepsilon \| f \|,$$

we have $| l_1 | \leqslant \varepsilon$. But

$$| l_1 | = \max_{f \in R} | (HKf, f) - (H\tilde{K}f, f) | / (Hf, f),$$

hence

$$| (HKf, f) - (H\tilde{K}f, f) | / (Hf, f) \leqslant \varepsilon$$

for every $f \in R$ satisfying $(Hf, f) \neq 0$. This shows immediately that, for arbitrary $p_1, \ldots, p_{n-1} \in R$, we have

(1) $\mu_n(p_1, \ldots, p_{n-1}) - \varepsilon \leqslant \tilde{\mu}_n(p_1, \ldots, p_{n-1}) \leqslant \mu_n(p_1, \ldots, p_{n-1}) + \varepsilon$

so that, assuming that $n \leqslant N$,

$$\tilde{\mu}_n(p_1, \ldots, p_{n-1}) \geqslant \mu_n(p_1, \ldots, p_{n-1}) - \varepsilon \geqslant \lambda_n^+ - \varepsilon > 0$$

for all $p_1, \ldots, p_{n-1} \in R$. By what we have observed earlier we may derive from this inequality that $\tilde{\lambda}_n^+$ exists, and

$$\tilde{\lambda}_n^+ \geqslant \lambda_n^+ - \varepsilon.$$

Furthermore, since by (1)

$$\tilde{\lambda}_n^+ \leqslant \tilde{\mu}_n(p_1, \ldots, p_{n-1}) \leqslant \mu_n(p_1, \ldots, p_{n-1}) + \varepsilon,$$

we find, taking $p_i = \psi_i^+$ $(i = 1, \ldots, n-1)$, that

$$\tilde{\lambda}_n^+ \leqslant \mu_n(\psi_1^+, \ldots, \psi_{n-1}^+) + \varepsilon = \lambda_n^+ + \varepsilon.$$

Hence, on account of $\lambda_n^+ - \varepsilon \leqslant \tilde{\lambda}_n^+ \leqslant \lambda_n^+ + \varepsilon$, we have finally

$$|\lambda_n^+ - \tilde{\lambda}_n^+| \leqslant \varepsilon \; (n = 1, \ldots, N).$$

The proof for the negative characteristic values may be given in a similar way.

Remark. It follows from the present theorem that if the compact transformations $K, K_1, K_2, \ldots$ are all fully symmetrisable relative to H, and if moreover $\lim \| K - K_i \| = 0$, then $\lim_{i\to\infty} \lambda_n^{(i)} = \lambda_n$, where λ_n and $\lambda_n^{(i)}$ are corresponding characteristic values $\neq 0$ of K and K_i respectively. The present theorem gives no information however as to what happens with the corresponding characteristic elements. For the particular case that K and all K_i $(i = 1, 2, \ldots)$ are self-adjoint, we shall consider this problem in the next two theorems.

Theorem 2. *Let $A, A_1, A_2, \ldots$ all be self-adjoint and compact, and let $\lim \| A - A_n \| = 0$. Then, if E_λ and $E_\lambda^{(n)}$ are the families of projections associated with A and A_n respectively (cf. the preceding paragraph), we have $\lim \| E_\lambda - E_\lambda^{(n)} \| = 0$ for any real λ in the resolvent set of A.*

Proof. Let the real number λ_0 be in the resolvent set of A, that is, $\lambda_0 \neq 0$ and λ_0 not identical with a characteristic value of A. We define

$$K = A - \lambda_0 I, \; K_n = A_n - \lambda_0 I \; (n = 1, 2, \ldots),$$

and we shall denote the families of projections associated with K and K_n by D_λ and $D_\lambda^{(n)}$ respectively. Evidently we have to prove that $\lim \| D_0 - D_0^{(n)} \| = 0$.

Since $\lim \| A - A_n \| = 0$, we have also $\lim \| K - K_n \| = 0$, hence $\lim \| p(K) - p(K_n) \| = 0$ for any polynomial $p(\lambda) = \alpha_0 + \alpha_1\lambda + \ldots + \alpha_n\lambda^n$. Suppose now that $\| K \| \leqslant M$ and $\| K_n \| \leqslant M$ $(n = 1, 2, \ldots)$, and that $F(\lambda)$ is a continuous real-valued function on $-M \leqslant \lambda \leqslant M$. Since, for any $\varepsilon > 0$, there exists a polynomial $p(\lambda)$ such that $| F(\lambda) - p(\lambda) | \leqslant \varepsilon$ for all λ in $-M \leqslant \lambda \leqslant M$, we have

$$\| F(K) - p(K) \| \leqslant \varepsilon, \ \| F(K_n) - p(K_n) \| \leqslant \varepsilon \ (n = 1, 2, \ldots)$$

by Theorem 3 of the preceding paragraph. Hence

$$\lim \| F(K) - F(K_n) \| = 0.$$

Now take $F(\lambda) = e_0(\lambda)\lambda$, where

$$e_0(\lambda) = \begin{cases} 1 \text{ for } \lambda \leqslant 0, \\ 0 \text{ for } \lambda > 0. \end{cases}$$

Then $F(K) = D_0K$ and $F(K_n) = D_0^{(n)}K_n$. We have therefore $\lim \| D_0K - D_0^{(n)}K_n \| = 0$. Since $\| D_0K - D_0^{(n)}K \| \leqslant \| D_0K - D_0^{(n)}K_n \| + \| D_0^{(n)}(K_n - K) \| \leqslant \| D_0K - D_0^{(n)}K_n \| + \| K - K_n \|$, this implies $\lim \| (D_0 - D_0^{(n)})K \| = 0$. But $\lambda = 0$ is in the resolvent set of K, so that the inverse K^{-1} exists and is bounded. Hence, on account of

$$\| D_0 - D_0^{(n)} \| = \| (D_0 - D_0^{(n)})KK^{-1} \| \leqslant \| (D_0 - D_0^{(n)})K \| . \| K^{-1} \|,$$

we find finally

$$\lim \| D_0 - D_0^{(n)} \| = 0.$$

Lemma α. *If P and Q are orthogonal projections on the linear subspaces $[M]$ and $[N]$ respectively, and $\| P - Q \| < 1$, then $[M]$ and $[N]$ have the same dimension.*

Proof. We prove first that the set $Q[M]$ (the set of all Qg with $g \in [M]$) is dense in $[N]$. Evidently $Qg \in [N]$ for every $g \in [M]$. Suppose now that $Q[M]$ is not dense in $[N]$. Then, by Ch. 6, § 12, Th. 3, there exists an element $f \in [N]$, $f \neq 0$, and f orthogonal to $Q[M]$. Hence, if $g \in [M]$ is arbitrary, $(f, g) = (Qf, g) = (f, Qg) = 0$, that is, f is orthogonal to $[M]$. But then $Pf = 0$, and this, together with $Qf = f$ and $\| P - Q \| < 1$, implies

$$\| f \| = \| (P - Q)f \| < \| f \|,$$

which is a contradiction. Hence $Q[M]$ is dense in $[N]$. If now $\{S\}$ is a complete set of elements in $[M]$ (cf. Ch. 6, § 3), then $Q\{S\}$ is therefore a complete set in $[N]$, and this shows that $\dim [N] \leqslant \dim [M]$. In the same way it is proved that $\dim [M] \leqslant \dim [N]$; hence $\dim [M] = \dim [N]$.

Theorem 3. *Let $A, A_1, A_2, \ldots$ all be self-adjoint and compact, and let $\lim \| A - A_n \| = 0$. Let $\lambda_0 \neq 0$ be a characteristic value of A with multiplicity $m > 0$, and let the projection P be defined by $Pf = \Sigma_1^m (f, \varphi_i)\varphi_i$, where $\varphi_1, \ldots, \varphi_m$ is an orthonormal system of characteristic elements of A belonging to the characteristic value λ_0. Then, if $\lambda_0 - \varepsilon \leqslant \lambda \leqslant \lambda_0 + \varepsilon$ contains no other points of the spectrum of A, the transformation A_n has for n sufficiently large exactly m characteristic values $\lambda_1^{(n)}, \ldots, \lambda_m^{(n)}$ in this interval. Denoting by $\varphi_1^{(n)}, \ldots, \varphi_m^{(n)}$ a corresponding orthonormal system of characteristic elements of A_n, and defining the projection P_n by $P_n f = \Sigma_1^m (f, \varphi_i^{(n)})\varphi_i^{(n)}$, we have $\lim \| P - P_n \| = 0$.*

Proof. By Theorem 2 we have

$$\lim_{n\to\infty} \| (E_{\lambda_0+\varepsilon} - E_{\lambda_0-\varepsilon}) - (E^{(n)}_{\lambda_0+\varepsilon} - E^{(n)}_{\lambda_0-\varepsilon}) \| = 0,$$

and by hypothesis $E_{\lambda_0+\varepsilon} - E_{\lambda_0-\varepsilon} = P$, where the subspace on which P is the orthogonal projection has the dimension m. Hence, by Lemma α, $E^{(n)}_{\lambda_0+\varepsilon} - E^{(n)}_{\lambda_0-\varepsilon}$ is also the orthogonal projection on a subspace of dimension m. It follows that A_n has m characteristic values $\lambda_1^{(n)}, \ldots, \lambda_m^{(n)}$ in $\lambda_0 - \varepsilon \leqslant \lambda \leqslant \lambda_0 + \varepsilon$ for n sufficiently large. Hence, with the introduced notation, $E^{(n)}_{\lambda_0+\varepsilon} - E^{(n)}_{\lambda_0-\varepsilon} = P_n$ and $\lim \| P - P_n \| = 0$.

Remark. The statement about the characteristic values might also be deduced from Theorem 1. Using the simple Lemma α however, the present proof does not depend on Theorem 1, but only on Theorem 2.

In the Theorems 1, 2 and 3 we have investigated what happens when a sequence of transformations K_n converges uniformly to a transformation K, that is, when $\| K - K_n \|$ becomes small. In the theorems which will follow now we shall compare in several cases the characteristic values of two transformations A and $\tilde{A}$, but it will not be necessary that $\| A - \tilde{A} \|$ is small. This condition is replaced by suitable other conditions.

Theorem 4. *Let A and $\tilde{A}$ be self-adjoint and compact, and let $\tilde{A} - A$ be positive. Then, if $\lambda_1^+ \geqslant \lambda_2^+ \geqslant \ldots$ and $\tilde{\lambda}_1^+ \geqslant \tilde{\lambda}_2^+ \geqslant \ldots$ are the sequences of positive characteristic values of A and $\tilde{A}$ respectively, we have*

$$\tilde{}^{+}_{n} \geqslant \lambda^{+}_{n}.$$

In the same way, if $\lambda_1^- \leqslant \lambda_2^- \leqslant \ldots$ and $\tilde{\lambda}_1^- \leqslant \tilde{\lambda}_2^- \leqslant \ldots$ are the sequences of negative characteristic values of A and $\tilde{A}$, we have $\tilde{\lambda}_n^- \geqslant \lambda_n^-$, or $| \tilde{\lambda}_n^- | \leqslant | \lambda_n^- |$.

Proof. Using once more the notations

$$\mu_1 = \max (Af, f)/(f, f) \text{ for all } f \neq 0,$$

$$\mu_n(p_1, \ldots, p_{n-1}) = \text{upper bound } (Af, f)/(f, f) \; (n = 2, 3, \ldots)$$

for all $f \neq 0$ satisfying $(f, p_1) = \ldots = (f, p_{n-1}) = 0$, we have evidently

$$\tilde{\mu}_n (p_1, \ldots, p_{n-1}) \geqslant \mu_n (p_1, \ldots, p_{n-1})$$

for arbitrary $p_1, \ldots, p_{n-1}$. Hence $\tilde{\lambda}_n^+ \geqslant \lambda_n^+$. The proof for the negative characteristic values follows immediately by observing that $-A - (-\tilde{A}) = \tilde{A} - A$ is positive.

Theorem 5. *Let H be positive and compact, and let A be bounded and self-adjoint, so that $K = AH$ is compact. Furthermore, let $(Af, f) \leqslant (f, f)$ for all $f \in R$. Then, if $\lambda_1^+ \geqslant \lambda_2^+ \geqslant \ldots$ and $\nu_1 \geqslant \nu_2 \geqslant \ldots$ are the positive characteristic values of K and H respectively, we have $\lambda_n^+ \leqslant \nu_n$.*

Proof. By § 12, Th. 3 the transformations $K = AH$ and $\tilde{K} = H^{1/2}AH^{1/2}$ have the same characteristic values. Furthermore, since

$$(H^{1/2}AH^{1/2}f, f) = (AH^{1/2}f, H^{1/2}f) \leqslant (H^{1/2}f, H^{1/2}f) = (Hf, f)$$

for all $f \in R$, the transformation $H - \tilde{K}$ is positive. It follows then from the preceding theorem that $\lambda_n^+ \leqslant \nu_n$.

Corollary. *If $-(f, f) \leqslant (Af, f) \leqslant (f, f)$, and $\lambda_1^- \leqslant \lambda_2^- \leqslant \ldots$ are the negative characteristic values of $K = AH$, then $\lambda_n^+ \leqslant \nu_n$ and $|\lambda_n^-| \leqslant \nu_n$. This holds in particular if $A^2 = I$.*

Proof. We have only to show that $A^2 = I$ implies $-(f, f) \leqslant (Af, f) \leqslant (f, f)$. Since $2(I - A) = I - 2A + I = I - 2A + A^2 = (I - A)^2$, the transformation $I - A$ is positive. In the same way, since $2(I + A) = (I + A)^2$, the transformation $I + A$ is positive.

Let T be a bounded linear transformation on the Hilbert space R, and let R be the direct sum of the orthogonal subspaces $[L]$ and $[M]$. We denote the projection on $[L]$ along $[M]$ by P, and we consider the linear transformation $\tilde{T} = PTP$. Since $(\tilde{T}f, g) = (PTPf, g) = (TPf, Pg)$, we see that $(\tilde{T}f, g) = (Tf, g)$ whenever $f, g \in [L]$. On the other hand $\tilde{T}f = 0$ whenever $f \in [M]$. Also $(\tilde{T}f, g) = (TPf, Pg) = 0$ whenever $g \in [M]$. In the particular case that R is separable and that $[L]$ is of finite dimension n, we may construct an orthonormal coordinate system $\{\varphi_1, \varphi_2, \ldots\}$ in R such that $\{\varphi_1, \ldots, \varphi_n\}$ is a coordinate system in $[L]$. Then, if the matrix of T in the system $\{\varphi\}$ has the elements $\tau_{ij} = (T\varphi_j, \varphi_i)$, the matrix $\{\tilde{\tau}_{ij}\}$ of $\tilde{T}$ satisfies $\tilde{\tau}_{ij} = \tau_{ij}$ $(i, j = 1, \ldots, n)$ and $\tilde{\tau}_{ij} = 0$ for all other matrixelements.

After this introduction we now state the following theorem:

Theorem 6. *Let R be the direct sum of the orthogonal subspaces $[L]$ and $[M]$, and let P be the projection on $[L]$ along $[M]$. The transformation A is assumed to be self-adjoint and compact, and $\tilde{A} = PAP$. If $\lambda_1^+ \geqslant \lambda_2^+ \geqslant \ldots$ and $\tilde{\lambda}_1^+ \geqslant \tilde{\lambda}_2^+ \geqslant \ldots$ are the positive characteristic values of A and $\tilde{A}$, then $\tilde{\lambda}_n^+ \leqslant \lambda_n^+$.*

In the same way, if $\lambda_1^- \leqslant \lambda_2^- \leqslant \ldots$ and $\tilde{\lambda}_1^- \leqslant \tilde{\lambda}_2^- \leqslant \ldots$ are the negative characteristic values of A and $\tilde{A}$, then $\tilde{\lambda}_n^- \geqslant \lambda_n^-$, or $|\tilde{\lambda}_n^-| \leqslant |\lambda_n^-|$.

Proof. Let $p_1, \ldots, p_{n-1}$ be arbitrary elements of R. Then

$$\mu_n(p_1, \ldots, p_{n-1}) = \text{upper bound } (Af, f)$$

for all $f \in R$ satisfying $\|f\| = 1$ and $(f, p_1) = \ldots = (f, p_{n-1}) = 0$. Also, using that $\tilde{A}$ is essentially a transformation on $[L]$,

$$\tilde{\mu}_n(Pp_1, \ldots, Pp_{n-1}) = \text{upper bound } (\tilde{A}f, f)$$

for all $f \in [L]$ satisfying $\|f\| = 1$ and $(f, Pp_1) = \ldots = (f, Pp_{n-1}) = 0$. Hence, since $f \in [L]$ implies $(f, Pp_i) = (Pf, p_i) = (f, p_i)$, and since $(\tilde{A}f, f) = (Af, f)$ for $f \in [L]$, we find

$$\tilde{\mu}_n(Pp_1, \ldots, Pp_{n-1}) = \text{upper bound } (Af, f)$$

for all $f \in [L]$ satisfying $\|f\| = 1$ and $(f, p_1) = \ldots = (f, p_{n-1}) = 0$. It follows that

$$\tilde{\mu}_n(Pp_1, \ldots, Pp_{n-1}) \leqslant \mu_n(p_1, \ldots, p_{n-1}).$$

Varying $p_1, \ldots, p_{n-1}$ in R, and therefore automatically varying $Pp_1, \ldots, Pp_{n-1}$ in $[L]$, we obtain finally

$$\tilde{\lambda}_n^+ \leqslant \lambda_n^+.$$

Observing that $-\tilde{A} = P(-A)P$, we find $|\tilde{\lambda}_n^-| \leqslant |\lambda_n^-|$.

Corollary. *Let H be positive and compact with the sequence $\lambda_1 \geqslant \lambda_2 \geqslant \ldots$ of characteristic values (if H has only q positive characteristic values, then $\lambda_{q+1} = \lambda_{q+2} = \ldots = 0$). Let $\psi_1, \ldots, \psi_n$ be an arbitrary orthonormal system of n elements. Then, denoting the value of the determinant formed by the elements $h_{ij} = (H\psi_j, \psi_i)$ $(i, j = 1, \ldots, n)$ by D, we have $D \leqslant \Pi_1^n \lambda_i$ (the left side or even both sides of this inequality may vanish).*

Proof. Denote by P the orthogonal projection on the subspace $[L]$ determined by $\psi_1, \ldots, \psi_n$, and let $\tilde{H} = PHP$. The transformation $\tilde{H}$

is also positive, and it has on $[L]$ the n characteristic values $\tilde{\lambda}_1 \geqslant \tilde{\lambda}_2 \geqslant \ldots \geqslant \tilde{\lambda}_n \geqslant 0$. Since

$$\det \begin{vmatrix} h_{11} - \lambda & h_{12} & \ldots & h_{1n} \\ h_{21} & h_{22} - \lambda & \ldots & h_{2n} \\ \vdots & \vdots & & \vdots \\ h_{n1} & h_{n2} & \ldots & h_{nn} - \lambda \end{vmatrix} = \Pi_1^n (\tilde{\lambda}_i - \lambda),$$

we have $D = \Pi_1^n \tilde{\lambda}_i$, so that, since $\tilde{\lambda}_i \leqslant \lambda_i (i = 1, \ldots, n)$ by what we have just proved, $D \leqslant \Pi_1^n \lambda_i$.

§ 18. Singular Values and Singular Elements of a Bounded Linear Transformation

We suppose that the space R is complete, and that T is a bounded linear transformation on R. Since R is complete, the adjoint T^* exists, and $\| T^* \| = \| T \|$.

Theorem 1. *If T^*T or one of its iterates is compact, then T is compact.*
Proof. The transformation T^*T is positive, so that $(T^*T)^{1/2}$ exists. Hence, if $(T^*T)^p = \{(T^*T)^{1/2}\}^{2p}$ is compact, then $(T^*T)^{1/2}$ is compact (cf. Ch. 11, § 1, Th. 13). But $T = U(T^*T)^{1/2}$, where U is an isometric transformation, defined on the range $W\{(T^*T)^{1/2}\}$ (cf. Ch. 9, § 14, Th. 4), and this shows that T is compact.

Corollary. 1°. *If TT^* or one of its iterates is compact, then T is compact.*
2°. *If T is not compact, then neither T^*T nor any of its iterates is compact.*
Proof. 1°. If $TT^* = (T^*)^*T^*$ or one of its iterates is compact, then T^* is compact, so that also T is compact.
2°. Evident.

We shall suppose, in what follows, that T is compact. Then T^*, T^*T and TT^* are also compact. The transformations T^*T and TT^* are positive.

Theorem 2. *T^*T and TT^* have the same characteristic values $\neq 0$ with the same multiplicities.*
Proof. Since T^*T and TT^* are positive, their characteristic values are $\geqslant 0$. Let now $T^*T\varphi = \lambda^2\varphi \neq 0$. Then $TT^*(T\varphi) = \lambda^2 T\varphi$ with $T\varphi \neq 0$,

since $T^*T\varphi \neq 0$. Conversely, if $TT^*\psi = \lambda^2\psi \neq 0$, then $T^*T(T^*\psi) = \lambda^2 T^*\psi$ with $T^*\psi \neq 0$, since $TT^*\psi \neq 0$. The relations $\psi = \lambda^{-1}T\varphi$, $\varphi = \lambda^{-1}T^*\psi$ define therefore a one-to-one correspondence between all φ for which $T^*T\varphi = \lambda^2\varphi \neq 0$ and all ψ for which $TT^*\psi = \lambda^2\psi \neq 0$.

Let $\lambda_1^2 \geqslant \lambda_2^2 \geqslant \ldots$ be the sequence of characteristic values $\neq 0$ of T^*T and TT^*. If $\varphi_1, \varphi_2, \ldots$ is a corresponding orthonormal system of characteristic elements of T^*T, hence $T^*T\varphi_i = \lambda_i^2\varphi_i$, and we write $\psi_i = \lambda_i^{-1}T\varphi_i$ $(i = 1, 2, \ldots)$, we have therefore $TT^*\psi_i = \lambda_i^2\psi_i$ and $\varphi_i = \lambda_i^{-1}T^*\psi_i$ $(i = 1, 2, \ldots)$. Moreover, the system $\{\psi_i\}$ is also orthonormal, since $(\psi_i, \psi_j) = (\lambda_i\lambda_j)^{-1}(T\varphi_i, T\varphi_j) = (\lambda_i\lambda_j)^{-1}(T^*T\varphi_i, \varphi_j) = \lambda_i\lambda_j^{-1}(\varphi_i, \varphi_j)$.

Theorem 3. *We have* $T\varphi_i = \lambda_i\psi_i$, $T^*\psi_i = \lambda_i\varphi_i$ $(i = 1, 2, \ldots)$. *Conversely, if* $T\varphi = \lambda\psi$, $T^*\psi = \lambda\varphi \neq 0$, *then* λ^2 *is identical with one of the values* λ_i^2, *and* φ *is a linear combination of those* φ_j *for which* $\lambda_j^2 = \lambda^2$.
Proof. We have $T\varphi_i = \lambda_i^{-1}TT^*\psi_i = \lambda_i\psi_i$ and $T^*\psi_i = \lambda_i^{-1}T^*T\varphi_i = \lambda_i\varphi_i$. Let now conversely $T\varphi = \lambda\psi$, $T^*\psi = \lambda\varphi \neq 0$. Then $T^*T\varphi = \lambda T^*\psi = \lambda^2\varphi \neq 0$, and this shows that $\lambda^2 = \lambda_i^2$ for a certain value of i, and that φ is a linear combination of those φ_j for which $\lambda_j^2 = \lambda_i^2 = \lambda^2$.

The positive numbers $\lambda_1, \lambda_2, \ldots$ are called the *singular values* of T and T^*, and the sequences $\varphi_1, \varphi_2, \ldots$ and $\psi_1, \psi_2, \ldots$ are called sequences of *singular elements* of T and T^*. The theory of singular values and elements was developed by Schmidt [11] in the particular case that T is of finite double-norm.

Theorem 4. $\lambda_n = max \| Tf \|/\| f \|$ *for all* $f \in R$ *satisfying* $f \neq 0$ *and* $(f, \varphi_1) = \ldots = (f, \varphi_{n-1}) = 0$. *The maximum is attained for* $f = \varphi_n$.
$\lambda_n = max \|T^*f \|/\| f \|$ *for all* $f \in R$ *satisfying* $f \neq 0$ *and* $(f, \psi_1) = \ldots = (f, \psi_{n-1}) = 0$. *The maximum is attained for* $f = \psi_n$.
Proof. Observing that T^*T has the sequence $\lambda_1^2, \lambda_2^2, \ldots$ of characteristic values $\neq 0$ with the corresponding orthonormal sequence $\varphi_1, \varphi_2, \ldots$ of characteristic elements, we have

$$\lambda_n^2 = \max (T^*Tf, f)/\| f \|^2 = \max \| Tf \|^2/\| f \|^2$$

for all $f \in R$ with $f \neq 0$ and $(f, \varphi_1) = \ldots = (f, \varphi_{n-1}) = 0$. Hence

$$\lambda_n = \max \| Tf \|/\| f \|$$

for all $f \in R$ with $f \neq 0$ and $(f, \varphi_1) = \ldots = (f, \varphi_{n-1}) = 0$.

The second statement is proved in the same way by considering TT^*.

Theorem 5. *$Tf = 0$ if and only if $(f, \varphi_n) = 0$ for all n. $T^*f = 0$ if and only if $(f, \psi_n) = 0$ for all n.*

Proof. If $Tf = 0$, then $(f, \varphi_n) = \lambda_n^{-1}(f, T^*\psi_n) = \lambda_n^{-1}(Tf, \psi_n) = 0$ for all n. Conversely, if $(f, \varphi_n) = 0$ for all n, then $T^*Tf = 0$ by § 7, Th. 2, 2°, hence $\| Tf \|^2 = (T^*Tf, f) = 0$, or $Tf = 0$. The proof of the second statement is similar.

Theorem 6. *We have*

$$Tf = \Sigma\, \lambda_i(f, \varphi_i)\psi_i, \qquad (Tf, g) = \Sigma\, \lambda_i(f, \varphi_i)\overline{(g, \psi_i)},$$

$$T^*f = \Sigma\, \lambda_i(f, \psi_i)\varphi_i, \qquad (T^*f, g) = \Sigma\, \lambda_i(f, \psi_i)\overline{(g, \varphi_i)}$$

for all $f, g \in R$.

Proof. Consider, for an arbitrary $f \in R$ and an arbitrary integer $n \geqslant 1$, the expression $r_n = f - \Sigma_{i=1}^{n-1} (f, \varphi_i)\varphi_i$. Since, by Theorem 4, $\| Tg \| \leqslant \lambda_n \| g \|$ for all g satisfying $(g, \varphi_1) = \ldots = (g, \varphi_{n-1}) = 0$ (for $g = 0$ this is trivial), and since $r_n = g$ satisfies these conditions, we have $\| Tr_n \| \leqslant \lambda_n \| r_n \| \leqslant \lambda_n \| f \|$. Hence, observing that $Tr_n = Tf - \Sigma_1^{n-1} \lambda_i(f, \varphi_i)\psi_i$, we find $\| Tf - \Sigma_1^{n-1} \lambda_i(f, \varphi_i)\psi_i \| \leqslant \lambda_n \| f \|$. If therefore the number of singular values λ_n is infinite, so that $\lim \lambda_n = 0$, we obtain finally

$$Tf = \Sigma\, \lambda_i(f, \varphi_i)\psi_i.$$

If the total number N of λ_n is finite, then $Tr_{N+1} = 0$, hence $Tf - \Sigma_1^N \lambda_i(f, \varphi_i)\psi_i = 0$ by Theorem 5.

The relation $(Tf, g) = \Sigma\, \lambda_i(f, \varphi_i)\overline{(g, \psi_i)}$ is now evident. Finally, the proof for T^*f and (T^*f, g) is similar.

Remark. The expansions of Tf and T^*f may be arbitrarily rearranged without destroying their convergence or modifying their sums.

Theorem 7. *Let T have the sequence $\xi_1, \xi_2, \ldots$ of characteristic values $\neq 0$, each characteristic value repeated according to its algebraic multiplicity, and arranged such that $| \xi_1 | \geqslant | \xi_2 | \geqslant \ldots$. Let furthermore $\lambda_1 \geqslant \lambda_2 \geqslant \ldots$ be the sequence of singular values of T and T^*. Then $\Pi_1^n | \xi_i | \leqslant \Pi_1^n \lambda_i$* [12].

Proof. There exist n linearly independent elements $f_1, \ldots, f_n$ such that either $Tf_i = \xi_i f_i$ or $Tf_i = \xi_i f_i + f_j$ $(i = 1, \ldots, n; j < i)$. (Indeed, if e.g. $\xi_1 = \ldots = \xi_{20} = \xi$, the characteristic value ξ has the algebraic multiplicity 20. Consider now the diagram I in Ch. 11, § 3 for this particular characteristic value ξ, and suppose that it consists e.g. of three rows containing 4, 6 and 10 elements respectively. If $n = 8$, we take for

$f_1, \ldots, f_8$ the first eight elements of the third row. Then $Tf_i = \xi_i f_i$ $(i = 1, \ldots, 8)$. If $n = 12$, we take for $f_1, \ldots, f_{10}$ the elements of the third row and for f_{11}, f_{12} the first two elements of the second row. Then $Tf_i = \xi_i f_i$ $(i = 1, \ldots, 10)$ and $Tf_i = \xi_i f_i + f_{i-10}$ $(i = 11, 12)$. If $n = 18$ we take all elements of the third and second rows and the first two elements of the first row). The orthogonalization process of Schmidt is applied to the system $f_1, \ldots, f_n$, by which we obtain the orthonormal system $\psi_1, \ldots, \psi_n$. Since $\psi_i = \alpha_{i1} f_1 + \ldots + \alpha_{ii} f_i$ $(i = 1, \ldots, n)$, we have $T\psi_i = \alpha_{ii}\xi_i f_i + \Sigma_{j=1}^{i-1} \beta_{ij} f_j$. Hence, observing that every f_j is a linear combination of $\psi_1, \ldots, \psi_j$, so that $\alpha_{ii} f_i = \psi_i - \alpha_{i1} f_1 - \ldots - \alpha_{i,i-1} f_{i-1}$ $= \psi_i + \Sigma_{j=1}^{i-1} \gamma_{ij}\psi_j$, we find $T\psi_i = \xi_i \psi_i + \Sigma_{j=1}^{i-1} \delta_{ij}\psi_j$. It follows that $(T\psi_i, \psi_i) = \xi_i$ and $(T\psi_i, \psi_j) = 0$ for $j > i$.

Denoting now by $[L]$ the subspace determined by $\psi_1, \ldots, \psi_n$, the transformation T is evidently reduced by $[L]$. We shall write T_r for this reduced transformation. The matrix of T_r in the coordinate system $\{\psi_1, \ldots, \psi_n\}$ has only zeros below the main diagonal and the numbers $\xi_1, \ldots, \xi_n$ on the main diagonal. It follows that the determinantvalue of this matrix is $\Pi_1^n \xi_i$. Since the matrix of $T_r^* = (T_r)^*$ has only zeros above the main diagonal and the numbers $\bar{\xi}_1, \ldots, \bar{\xi}_n$ on the main diagonal, the determinantvalue of this matrix is $\Pi_1^n \bar{\xi}_i$. The matrix of $T_r^* T_r$ is the matrixproduct of mat (T_r^*) and mat (T_r), so that its determinantvalue is $\Pi_1^n \bar{\xi}_i \, \Pi_1^n \xi_i = \Pi_1^n \mid \xi_i \mid^2$. Hence, the determinant with elements $(T_r^* T_r \psi_j, \psi_i) = (T_r \psi_j, T_r \psi_i) = (T\psi_j, T\psi_i) = (T^*T\psi_j, \psi_i)$ $(i, j = 1, \ldots, n)$ has the value $\Pi_1^n \mid \xi_i \mid^2$.

By § 17, Th. 6, Corollary, this same determinant with elements $(T^*T\psi_j, \psi_i)$ $(i, j = 1, \ldots, n)$ does not exceed $\Pi_1^n \lambda_i^2$ in value, since $\lambda_1^2 \geqslant \lambda_2^2 \geqslant \ldots$ is the sequence of characteristic values $\neq 0$ of T^*T. Hence $\Pi_1^n \mid \xi_i \mid^2$ $\leqslant \Pi_1^n \lambda_i^2$ or $\Pi_1^n \mid \xi_i \mid \leqslant \Pi_1^n \lambda_i$.

For furthergoing results on the numbers ξ_i and λ_i we need some definitions and lemmas. We shall prove somewhat more than we strictly need for our purposes.

Let $a_1, \ldots, a_n$ and $a_1', \ldots, a_n'$ be two sequences of real numbers. We shall write $(a') \prec (a)$ whenever

(1) $$a_1' + \ldots + a_n' = a_1 + \ldots + a_n,$$

(2) $$a_1' \geqslant \ldots \geqslant a_n' \, ; \quad a_1 \geqslant \ldots \geqslant a_n,$$

(3) $$a_1' + \ldots + a_\nu' \leqslant a_1 + \ldots + a_\nu \; (1 \leqslant \nu < n).$$

Evidently $(a) \prec (a)$. Furthermore, if $a_i \geqslant 0$ $(i = 1, \ldots, n)$, we write $(0) \prec (a)$.

Let now $(0) \prec (a)$, and suppose that $a_k > a_l$. Then, if $\rho = (a_k + a_l)/2$ and $\tau = (a_k - a_l)/2$, we have $a_k = \rho + \tau$, $a_l = \rho - \tau$ $(0 < \tau \leqslant \rho)$. Taking an arbitrary number σ such that $0 \leqslant \sigma \leqslant \tau \leqslant \rho$, the *smoothing transformation* $(a') = T(a)$ is defined by

$$(4) \quad \begin{cases} a_k' = \rho + \sigma = \dfrac{\tau + \sigma}{2\tau} a_k + \dfrac{\tau - \sigma}{2\tau} a_l, \\[2ex] a_l' = \rho - \sigma = \dfrac{\tau - \sigma}{2\tau} a_k + \dfrac{\tau + \sigma}{2\tau} a_l, \\[2ex] a_\nu' = a_\nu \ (\nu \neq k, \ \nu \neq l). \end{cases}$$

Lemma α. *If* $(0) \prec (a)$, $(0) \prec (a')$ *and* $(a') \prec (a)$, *then* (a') *may be obtained from* (a) *by successive application of a finite number of smoothing transformations* T.

Proof. The number of differences $a_\nu - a_\nu' \neq 0$ is called the discrepancy of (a) and (a'). If the discrepancy is zero, (a) and (a') are identical and then our lemma is true. Suppose that the discrepancy is $r > 0$, and that the proof has already been given in the case that the discrepancy is smaller than r. Since $\Sigma_1^n (a_\nu - a_\nu') = 0$ and not all terms vanish, there must be positive and negative differences $a_\nu - a_\nu'$. The first difference $\neq 0$ in $\Sigma_1^n (a_\nu - a_\nu')$ is positive by (3). There exists also a first negative difference $a_l - a_l'$, so that we have indices k and l such that

$$a_k' < a_k, \ a_{k+1}' = a_{k+1}, \ldots, a_{l-1}' = a_{l-1}, \ a_l' > a_l.$$

Write $a_k = \rho + \tau$, $a_l = \rho - \tau$ and $\sigma = \max(|a_k' - \rho|, \ |a_l' - \rho|)$. Since $a_k > a_l \geqslant 0$, we have $0 < \tau \leqslant \rho$. Since $a_k > a_k' \geqslant a_l' > a_l$ and $\rho = (a_k + a_l)/2$, we have either $a_k' - \rho = \sigma$ or $a_l' - \rho = -\sigma$ or both. Furthermore $\sigma < \tau$.

It follows from this all that $0 \leqslant \sigma < \tau \leqslant \rho$, so that the smoothing transformation $(a'') = T(a)$ may be defined by

$$a_k'' = \rho + \sigma, \ a_l'' = \rho - \sigma, \ a_\nu'' = a_\nu \ (\nu \neq k, \ \nu \neq l).$$

Since either $a_k' - \rho = \sigma$ or $a_l' - \rho = -\sigma$ or both, we have either $a_k'' = a_k'$ or $a_l'' = a_l'$ or both, so that the discrepancy between (a'') and (a') is $r - 1$ or $r - 2$.

We shall prove now that $(a') \prec (a'')$. On account of $a_k'' + a_l'' = 2\rho = a_k + a_l$ we find $\Sigma_1^n a_\nu' = \Sigma_1^n a_\nu = \Sigma_1^n a_\nu''$, hence (1) for (a') and $(a''$.)

Furthermore

$$\begin{cases} a'_k \leqslant \rho + |a'_k - \rho| \leqslant \rho + \sigma = a''_k, \\ a'_l \geqslant \rho - |a'_l - \rho| \geqslant \rho - \sigma = a''_l, \end{cases}$$

so that

$$\begin{cases} a''_{k-1} = a_{k-1} \geqslant a_k = \rho + \tau > \rho + \sigma = a''_k \geqslant a'_k \geqslant a'_{k+1} = a_{k+1} = a''_{k+1}, \\ a''_{l-1} = a_{l-1} = a'_{l-1} \geqslant a'_l \geqslant a''_l = \rho - \sigma > \rho - \tau = a_l \geqslant a_{l+1} = a''_{l+1}, \end{cases}$$

hence (2) for (a''). Finally $a'_1 + \ldots + a'_\nu \leqslant a''_1 + \ldots + a''_\nu$ holds certainly for $\nu < k$ or $\nu \geqslant l$. It holds for $\nu = k$, since it holds for $\nu = k - 1$ and $a'_k \leqslant a''_k$. It holds for $k < \nu < l$, since it holds for $\nu = k$ and $a'_i = a_i = a''_i$ for $k < i < l$. Hence $(a') \prec (a'')$ with a discrepancy $< r$ between (a') and (a''). By our induction hypothesis (a') may now be obtained from (a'') by successive application of a finite number of smoothing transformations. Since $(a'') = T(a)$, this completes the proof.

Definition. *The sequence (a') is called an average of (a) whenever there exist n^2 numbers p_{ij} $(i, j = 1, \ldots, n)$ such that*

(5) $$p_{ij} \geqslant 0,\ \Sigma_{i=1}^n p_{ij} = 1,\ \Sigma_{j=1}^n p_{ij} = 1,\ a'_i = \Sigma_{j=1}^n p_{ij} a_j.$$

We observe that $\Sigma_{i=1}^n p_{ij} = \Sigma_{j=1}^n p_{ij} = 1$ implies and is implied by the conditions that $\Sigma_1^n a'_i = \Sigma_1^n a_i$ and that $a'_i = 1$ for all i if only $a_i = 1$ for all i. It follows that if (a') is an average of (a) and (a'') is an average of (a'), then (a'') is an average of (a). Of course the numbers p_{ij} may be different for different averages. Finally, if $(0) \prec (a)$ and $(a') = T(a)$, where T is a smoothing transformation, we see from (4) that (a') is an average of (a).

Lemma β. *If $(0) \prec (a)$ and $(0) \prec (a')$, then $(a') \prec (a)$ if and only if (a') is an average of (a).*

Proof. Let $(a') \prec (a)$. Then (a') may be obtained from (a') by successive application of a finite number of smoothing transformations. Hence, by what we have just observed, (a') is an average of (a).

Let now conversely (a') be an average of (a). Then, by (5), we have $\Sigma_1^n a'_i = \Sigma_1^n a_i$. We may suppose without loss of generality that $a'_1 \geqslant \ldots \geqslant a'_n$ and $a_1 \geqslant \ldots \geqslant a_n$. Write $p_{1j} + p_{2j} + \ldots + p_{mj} = k_j$. Then $k_j \leqslant 1$ and $\Sigma_{j=1}^n k_j = m$, so that

$$a'_1 + \ldots + a'_m = k_1 a_1 + \ldots + k_{m-1} a_{m-1} + k_m a_m \leqslant$$
$$k_1 a_1 + \ldots + k_{m-1} a_{m-1} + (m - k_1 - \ldots - k_{m-1}) a_m \leqslant$$
$$(a_1 - a_m) + \ldots + (a_{m-1} - a_m) + m a_m = a_1 + \ldots + a_m \ (1 \leqslant m \leqslant n).$$

Hence $(a') \prec (a)$.

Lemma γ. *The conditions* $(0) \prec (a)$ *and* $(0) \prec (a')$ *in Lemma* β *are superfluous.*

Proof. We have $(a') \prec (a)$ if and only if $(a' + b) \prec (a + b)$ for any fixed real number b. This follows immediately from (1), (2) and (3). Furthermore (a') is an average of (a) if and only if $(a' + b)$ is the same average of $(a + b)$. This follows from the definition of an average.

Definition. *The continuous real function* $\Phi(x)$, *defined on the real interval* $\Delta\,[a \leqslant x \leqslant b]$, *is called convex whenever*

$$\Phi(p_1x_1 + p_2x_2) \leqslant p_1\Phi(x_1) + p_2\Phi(x_2)$$

for arbitrary $x_1, x_2 \in \Delta$ *and arbitrary numbers* p_1, p_2, *satisfying* $p_1 \geqslant 0$, $p_2 \geqslant 0$, $p_1 + p_2 = 1$.

Lemma δ. *If* $\Phi(x)$ *is convex on* Δ, *if* $x_1, \ldots, x_n \in \Delta$ *and* $p_i \geqslant 0$ $(i = 1, \ldots, n)$, $p_1 + \ldots + p_n = 1$, *then* $\Phi(p_1x_1 + \ldots + p_nx_n) \leqslant p_1\Phi(x_1) + \ldots + p_n\Phi(x_n)$.

Proof. The statement is true for $n = 2$. Suppose that it is true for $n - 1$, and write $q_n = p_1 + \ldots + p_{n-1}$, hence $q_n + p_n = 1$. Then $p_1x_1 + \ldots + p_nx_n = q_n\{(p_1x_1 + \ldots + p_{n-1}x_{n-1})/q_n\} + p_nx_n$, so that

$$\Phi(p_1x_1 + \ldots + p_nx_n) \leqslant q_n\Phi\{(p_1x_1 + \ldots + p_{n-1}x_{n-1})/q_n\} + p_n\Phi(x_n)$$
$$\leqslant q_n\{p_1q_n^{-1}\Phi(x_1) + \ldots + p_{n-1}q_n^{-1}\Phi(x_{n-1})\} + p_n\Phi(x_n) =$$
$$p_1\Phi(x_1) + \ldots + p_n\Phi(x_n).$$

Lemma ϵ. *If* $a_1 \geqslant \ldots \geqslant a_n$ *and* $a_1' \geqslant \ldots \geqslant a_n'$, *then* $(a') \prec (a)$ *if and only if* $\Phi(a_1') + \ldots + \Phi(a_n') \leqslant \Phi(a_1) + \ldots + \Phi(a_n)$ *for all continuous convex functions* $\Phi(x)$, *where it is supposed of course that all* a_i *and all* a_i' *are contained in the interval on which* $\Phi(x)$ *is defined* ([13]; *p.* 89).

Proof. Let $(a') \prec (a)$. Then (a') is an average of (a) by Lemma γ. Hence

$$a_i' = \Sigma_{j=1}^n p_{ij}a_j,\ p_{ij} \geqslant 0,\ \Sigma_{i=1}^n p_{ij} = 1,\ \Sigma_{j=1}^n p_{ij} = 1.$$

Then, if $\Phi(x)$ is continuous and convex, we have

$$\Phi(a_i') \leqslant p_{i1}\Phi(a_1) + \ldots + p_{in}\Phi(a_n),$$

so that, by summation, we find

$$\Phi(a_1') + \ldots + \Phi(a_n') \leqslant \Phi(a_1) + \ldots + \Phi(a_n). \tag{6}$$

Suppose now conversely that (6) holds for every continuous convex $\Phi(x)$. Since the functions x and $-x$ are both continuous and convex, this implies $\Sigma_1^n a_i' \leqslant \Sigma_1^n a_i$ and $\Sigma_1^n (-a_i') \leqslant \Sigma_1^n (-a_i)$, hence $\Sigma_1^n a_i' = \Sigma_1^n a_i$. Let now $\Phi(x)$ be defined by

$$\Phi(x) = \begin{cases} 0 & \text{for } x \leqslant a_\nu, \\ x - a_\nu & \text{for } x > a_\nu. \end{cases}$$

Then $\Phi(x)$ is continuous and convex, and $\Phi(x) \geqslant 0$, $\Phi(x) \geqslant x - a_\nu$. Hence

$$a_1' + \ldots + a_\nu' - \nu a_\nu = (a_1' - a_\nu) + \ldots + (a_\nu' - a_\nu) \leqslant$$

$$\Sigma_{i=1}^{\nu} \Phi(a_i') = \Sigma_{i=1}^{\nu} \Phi(a_i') + \Sigma_{\nu+1}^{n} 0 \leqslant$$

$$\Sigma_{i=1}^{n} \Phi(a_i') \leqslant \Sigma_{i=1}^{n} \Phi(a_i) = a_1 + \ldots + a_\nu - \nu a_\nu,$$

or

$$a_1' + \ldots + a_\nu' \leqslant a_1 + \ldots + a_\nu \; (1 \leqslant \nu < n).$$

Lemma χ. *If* $a_1' \geqslant \ldots \geqslant a_n'$ *and* $a_1' + \ldots + a_\nu' \leqslant a_1 + \ldots + a_\nu$ $(1 \leqslant \nu \leqslant n)$, *then* $\Phi(a_1') + \ldots + \Phi(a_n') \leqslant \Phi(a_1) + \ldots + \Phi(a_n)$ *for any continuous, convex and non-decreasing function* $\Phi(x)$ [14].

Proof. We have $d = (a_1 + \ldots + a_n) - (a_1' + \ldots + a_n') \geqslant 0$. Take an arbitrary $a_{n+1}' \leqslant a_n'$, and write $a_{n+1} = a_{n+1}' - d$. Then $a_1' + \ldots + a_{n+1}' = a_1 + \ldots + a_{n+1}$. Now we arrange $a_1, \ldots, a_{n+1}$ in non-increasing order, by which we obtain the sequence $a_1'' \geqslant a_2'' \geqslant \ldots \geqslant a_{n+1}''$. Then certainly $a_1' + \ldots + a_\nu' \leqslant a_1'' + \ldots + a_\nu''$ $(1 \leqslant \nu \leqslant n)$, hence, by Lemma ε,

$$\Phi(a_1') + \ldots + \Phi(a_{n+1}') \leqslant \Phi(a_1'') + \ldots + \Phi(a_{n+1}'') = \Phi(a_1) + \ldots + \Phi(a_{n+1}). \tag{7}$$

But $a_{n+1} \leqslant a_{n+1}'$ and $\Phi(x)$ is non-decreasing. This implies $\Phi(a_{n+1}) \leqslant \Phi(a_{n+1}')$, or

$$-\Phi(a_{n+1}') \leqslant -\Phi(a_{n+1}). \tag{8}$$

Addition of (7) and (8) gives the desired result.

Lemma η. *If* $\Phi(x)$ *is defined on the linear interval* Δ, *and it has a second derivative which is non-negative, then* $\Phi(x)$ *is convex.*

Proof. Let $x_1 < x_2$ be points of Δ, and let $x_1 < x_3 < x_2$, hence $x_3 = p_1x_1 + p_2x_2$ with $p_1 = (x_2 - x_3)/(x_2 - x_1)$ and $p_2 = (x_3 - x_1)/(x_2 - x_1)$.

Since generally $\Phi(x + h) = \Phi(x) + h\Phi'(x) + \frac{1}{2}h^2\Phi''(x + \theta h)$ with $0 < \theta < 1$, we find $\Phi(x + h) - \Phi(x) \geqslant h\Phi'(x)$, hence

$$\{\Phi(x + h) - \Phi(x)\}/h \geqslant \Phi'(x) \text{ for positive } h,$$

$$\{\Phi(x) - \Phi(x + h)\}/|\, h \,| \leqslant \Phi'(x) \text{ for negative } h.$$

This implies

$$\frac{\Phi(x_2) - \Phi(x_3)}{x_2 - x_3} \geqslant \Phi'(x_3) \geqslant \frac{\Phi(x_3) - \Phi(x_1)}{x_3 - x_1},$$

hence $(x_3 - x_1)\{\Phi(x_2) - \Phi(x_3)\} \geqslant (x_2 - x_3)\{\Phi(x_3) - \Phi(x_1)\}$ or $(x_2 - x_1)\Phi(x_3) \leqslant (x_2 - x_3)\Phi(x_1) + (x_3 - x_1)\Phi(x_2)$. This gives finally

$$\Phi(p_1x_1 + p_2x_2) = \Phi(x_3) \leqslant p_1\Phi(x_1) + p_2\Phi(x_2).$$

Theorem 8. *Let the bounded linear transformation T have the sequence $\xi_1, \xi_2, \ldots$ of characteristic values $\neq 0$, each characteristic value repeated according to its algebraic multiplicity, and arranged such that $|\,\xi_1\,| \geqslant |\,\xi_2\,| \geqslant \ldots$. Let furthermore $\lambda_1 \geqslant \lambda_2 \geqslant \ldots$ be the sequence of singular values of T and T^*. Then, if $\omega(x)$, defined for $x \geqslant 0$, is continuous and non-decreasing and such that $\Phi(x) = \omega(e^x)$ is a convex function of x, we have*

$$\Sigma_1^n\, \omega(|\,\xi_i\,|) \leqslant \Sigma_1^n\, \omega(\lambda_i).$$

In particular, if $s > 0$ is arbitrary,

$$\Sigma_1^n\, |\,\xi_i\,|^s \leqslant \Sigma_1^n\, \lambda_i^s,$$

so that, if the number of characteristic values ξ_i is infinite, the series $\Sigma_1^\infty |\,\xi_i\,|^s$ converges if $\Sigma_1^\infty \lambda_i^s$ converges [12] [15].

Proof. Let $\omega(x)$ be defined for $x \geqslant 0$ as a continuous and non-decreasing function such that $\omega(e^x)$ is convex in x. Then $\Phi(x) = \omega(e^x)$ is defined for all real x as a continuous convex function which is non-decreasing. By Theorem 7 we have $\Pi_1^n\, |\,\xi_i\,| \leqslant \Pi_1^n\, \lambda_i$; hence, writing $a_i' = \log |\,\xi_i\,|$, $a_i = \log \lambda_i$,

$$\Sigma_1^n\, a_i' \leqslant \Sigma_1^n\, a_i.$$

Then, on account of Lemma χ,

$$\Sigma_1^n\, \Phi(a_i') \leqslant \Sigma_1^n\, \Phi(a_i),$$

or, since $\Phi(x) = \omega(e^x)$,

$$\Sigma_1^n\, \omega(|\,\xi_i\,|) \leqslant \Sigma_1^n\, \omega(\lambda_i).$$

Taking $\omega(x) = x^s$, where $s > 0$, $x \geqslant 0$, the corresponding function

$\Phi(x) = \omega(e^x) = e^{sx}$ has a second derivative which is non-negative, so that $\Phi(x)$ is convex by Lemma η. Hence

$$\Sigma_1^n \mid \xi_i \mid^s \leqslant \Sigma_1^n \lambda_i^s.$$

§ 19. Compact Normal Transformations

We suppose in the present paragraph that the space R is complete, and that N is a compact normal transformation on R. Then the positive transformation $N^*N = NN^*$ is also compact. By Ch. 9, § 15, Th. 7 the geometric and the algebraic multiplicity of every characteristic value $\neq 0$ of N are the same, that is, if $(N - \lambda I)^p f = 0$ for a complex number λ and an integer $p \geqslant 1$, then $(N - \lambda I)f = 0$.

Theorem 1. *If $N\varphi = \lambda\varphi \neq 0$ (hence $N^*\varphi = \bar{\lambda}\varphi \neq 0$ by Ch. 9, § 15, Th. 1), then $N^*N\varphi = \mid \lambda \mid^2 \varphi \neq 0$.*
Proof. $N^*N\varphi = \lambda N^*\varphi = \lambda\bar{\lambda}\varphi = \mid \lambda \mid^2 \varphi$.

Remark. We see from the present theorem that if $\lambda \neq 0$ is a characteristic value of N, then $\mid \lambda \mid^2$ is a characteristic value of $N^*N = NN^*$. It may be asked now whether, if $a^2 > 0$ is a characteristic value of N^*N, there also exists a characteristic value λ of N such that $\mid \lambda \mid^2 = a^2$. A detailed answer will be given in the next theorem.

Theorem 2. *Let $a > 0$ be given, and let $\mu_1, \ldots, \mu_q$ be all the different characteristic values of N satisfying $\mid \mu_1 \mid^2 = \ldots = \mid \mu_q \mid^2 = a^2$. Then, if $\mu_1, \ldots, \mu_q$ have the multiplicities $m_1, \ldots, m_q$ respectively, the number a^2 is a characteristic value of N^*N with multiplicity $m = \Sigma_1^q m_i$. Conversely, if $a^2 > 0$ is a characteristic value of N^*N, there exists at least one characteristic value μ of N such that $\mid \mu \mid^2 = a^2$.*
Proof. Let $a > 0$ be given, and let $\mu_1, \ldots, \mu_q$ be all the different characteristic values of N satisfying $\mid \mu_1 \mid^2 = \ldots = \mid \mu_q \mid^2 = a^2$. Let $\mu_1, \ldots, \mu_q$ have the multiplicities $m_1, \ldots, m_q$ respectively. Then, by the preceding theorem, the number a^2 is a characteristic value of N^*N, and its multiplicity m satisfies $m \geqslant \Sigma_1^q m_i$. Suppose now that the orthonormal system $\tilde{\varphi}_1, \ldots, \tilde{\varphi}_m$ determines the space R_m of all φ for which $NN^*\varphi = N^*N\varphi = a^2\varphi$, and let us apply the transformation $U = a^{-1}N$ on an arbitrary element φ of R_m. The thus obtained element $U\varphi = a^{-1}N\varphi$ satisfies

$$NN^*(U\varphi) = a^{-1}NN^*N\varphi = a^{-1}N(a^2\varphi) = a^2(a^{-1}N\varphi) = a^2U\varphi,$$

hence $U\varphi \in R_m$ for every $\varphi \in R_m$. Furthermore

$$(U\tilde{\varphi}_i, U\tilde{\varphi}_j) = a^{-2}(N\tilde{\varphi}_i, N\tilde{\varphi}_j) = a^{-2}(N^*N\tilde{\varphi}_i, \tilde{\varphi}_j) =$$
$$(\tilde{\varphi}_i, \tilde{\varphi}_j) \quad (i, j = 1, \ldots, m),$$

so that the system $U\tilde{\varphi}_1, \ldots, U\tilde{\varphi}_m$ is orthonormal. But then (cf. Ch. 9, § 3, Th. 2) the transformation U is unitary on R_m. It follows that U (on R_m) has m characteristic values $\varepsilon_1, \ldots, \varepsilon_m$ with $|\varepsilon_i| = 1$ $(i = 1, \ldots, m)$. Hence, there exists an orthonormal system $\psi_1, \ldots, \psi_m$ in R_m such that $U\psi_i = \varepsilon_i\psi_i$ $(i = 1, \ldots, m)$. This implies $N\psi_i = aU\psi_i = a\varepsilon_i\psi_i$ with $|a\varepsilon_i| = a$, or

$$N\psi_i = \nu_i\psi_i, \quad |\nu_i| = a \quad (i = 1, \ldots, m).$$

We see therefore that the original multiplicities $m_1, \ldots, m_q$ must satisfy $\Sigma_1^q m_i \geqslant m$. Hence $m = \Sigma_1^q m_i$.

The same proof shows that if $a^2 > 0$ is a characteristic value of N^*N, there exists at least one characteristic value μ of N such that $|\mu|^2 = a^2$.

Observing now that characteristic elements of N belonging to different characteristic values are orthogonal, we immediately obtain the following theorem:

Theorem 3. *If $\lambda_1, \lambda_2, \ldots$ is the sequence of all characteristic values $\neq 0$ of N, arranged such that $|\lambda_1| \geqslant |\lambda_2| \geqslant \ldots$, and $\varphi_1, \varphi_2, \ldots$ is a corresponding orthonormal sequence of characteristic elements, then $|\lambda_1|^2 \geqslant |\lambda_2|^2 \geqslant \ldots$ is the sequence of all characteristic values $\neq 0$ of $N^*N = NN^*$, and $\varphi_1, \varphi_2, \ldots$ is a corresponding sequence of characteristic elements.*

Remark. In the preceding paragraph we considered an arbitrary compact linear transformation T, and we have seen that if $|\lambda_1|^2 \geqslant |\lambda_2|^2 \geqslant \ldots$ is the sequence of all characteristic values $\neq 0$ of T^*T with a corresponding orthonormal sequence $\varphi_1, \varphi_2, \ldots$ of characteristic elements, then $|\lambda_1|^2 \geqslant |\lambda_2|^2 \geqslant \ldots$ is also the sequence of all characteristic values $\neq 0$ of TT^*, and $\psi_1, \psi_2, \ldots$, where $\psi_i = |\lambda_i|^{-1}T\varphi_i$, is a corresponding orthonormal sequence of characteristic elements. In the present case where $T = N$ is normal, N^*N and NN^* are identical and it might be thought therefore that the corresponding sequences $\{\varphi_n\}$ and $\{\psi_n\}$ are also identical. This is not true however, since $\psi_i = |\lambda_i|^{-1}N\varphi_i = \{\lambda_i/|\lambda_i|\}\varphi_i$ $(i = 1, 2, \ldots)$.

Theorem 4. *$|\lambda_n| = \max \|Nf\|/\|f\| = \max \|N^*f\|/\|f\|$ for all $f \in R$ satisfying $f \neq 0$ and $(f, \varphi_1) = \ldots = (f, \varphi_{n-1}) = 0$. The maximum is attained for $f = \varphi_n$.*
Proof. Follows from § 18, Th. 4.

Theorem 5. *$Nf = 0$ if and only if $(f, \varphi_n) = 0$ for all n. Also $N^*f = 0$ if and only if $(f, \varphi_n) = 0$ for all n.*
Proof. Follows from § 18, Th. 5.

Theorem 6. *We have*

$$Nf = \Sigma\, \lambda_i(f, \varphi_i)\varphi_i, \qquad (Nf, g) = \Sigma\, \lambda_i(f, \varphi_i)\overline{(g, \varphi_i)},$$

$$N^*f = \Sigma\, \bar{\lambda}_i(f, \varphi_i)\varphi_i, \qquad (N^*f, g) = \Sigma\, \bar{\lambda}_i(f, \varphi_i)\overline{(g, \varphi_i)}$$

for arbitrary $f, g \in R$.
Proof. By § 18, Th. 6 we have

$$Nf = \Sigma\, |\lambda_i|\, (f, \varphi_i)\psi_i = \Sigma\, |\lambda_i|\, (f, \varphi_i)\{\lambda_i/|\lambda_i|\}\varphi_i = \Sigma\, \lambda_i(f, \varphi_i)\varphi_i,$$

$$N^*f = \Sigma\, |\lambda_i|\, (f, \psi_i)\varphi_i = \Sigma\, |\lambda_i|\, \{\bar{\lambda}_i/|\lambda_i|\}(f, \varphi_i)\varphi_i = \Sigma\, \bar{\lambda}_i(f, \varphi_i)\varphi_i.$$

Theorem 7. *The following four statements are equivalent:*
1°. *The system $\{\varphi_n\}$ is complete in R.*
2°. *The range of N is dense in R.*
3°. *$Nf = 0$ only for $f = 0$.*
4°. *Every $g \in R$ admits an expansion $g = \Sigma\, \beta_n\varphi_n$, where $\beta_n = (g, \varphi_n)$ $(n = 1, 2, \ldots)$.*
Proof. As in § 7, Th. 4.

Theorem 8. *If $\lambda \neq 0$ is no characteristic value of N, the equation $N_\lambda f \equiv Nf - \lambda f = g$ has a uniquely determined solution $f \in R$ for every $g \in R$. If $\lambda \neq 0$ is a characteristic value of N, the equation $N_\lambda f \equiv Nf - \lambda f = g$ has a solution $f \in R$ for those and only those $g \in R$ that are orthogonal to all characteristic elements of N belonging to the characteristic value λ. This solution is determined except for a linear combination of these characteristic elements.*

2°. *If $Nf - \lambda f = g$, then*

$$f = -\frac{g}{\lambda} - {}'\Sigma\, \frac{\lambda_n}{\lambda(\lambda - \lambda_n)}\, \alpha_n\varphi_n,$$

where $\alpha_n = (g, \varphi_n)$ for $\lambda_n \neq \lambda$, and where the dash in front of the Σ-symbol means that for those values of n for which $\lambda_n = \lambda$ the coefficient of φ_n has *the value* (f, φ_n). *For every set of arbitrarily prescribed values of these coefficients there exists a solution of* $Nf - \lambda f = g$.

Proof. 1°. If $\lambda \neq 0$ is a characteristic value of N, then $\bar{\lambda}$ is a characteristic value of N^*, and $Nf - \lambda f = 0$ if and only if $N^*f - \bar{\lambda}f = 0$. The null spaces of $N - \lambda I$ and $N^* - \bar{\lambda}I$ are therefore identical. Observing now that the range $W(N - \lambda I)$ is the orthogonal complement of the null space of $N^* - \bar{\lambda}I$, our statement follows.

2°. As in § 6, Th. 3.

Remark. The arrangement of the sequence λ_n is irrelevant in the expansion theorems (Theorem 6 and Theorem 8, 2°).

We now consider a somewhat more extensive class of normal transformations than only those that are compact. Let N be bounded and normal, and let there exist a complex number λ_0 such that $N_1 = N - \lambda_0 I$ is compact. Denoting the characteristic values $\neq 0$ of N_1 by $\lambda_1 - \lambda_0$, $\lambda_2 - \lambda_0, \ldots$, and supposing that $\varphi_1, \varphi_2, \ldots$ is a corresponding orthonormal sequence of characteristic elements, we have

$$N_1 f = \Sigma\, (\lambda_i - \lambda_0)(f, \varphi_i)\varphi_i$$

for every $f \in R$. Hence, denoting by P_0 the orthogonal projection on $R_0 = R \ominus L[\varphi_1, \varphi_2, \ldots]$, also

$$N f = N_1 f + \lambda_0 f = \Sigma\, \lambda_i (f, \varphi_i)\varphi_i + \lambda_0 P_0 f,$$
$$N^* f = N_1^* f + \bar{\lambda}_0 f = \Sigma\, \bar{\lambda}_i (f, \varphi_i)\varphi_i + \bar{\lambda}_0 P_0 f.$$

By induction we find then

$$\left.\begin{aligned} N^n f &= \Sigma_i\, \lambda_i^n (f, \varphi_i)\varphi_i + \lambda_0^n P_0 f, \\ (N^*)^n f &= \Sigma_i\, \bar{\lambda}_i^n (f, \varphi_i)\varphi_i + \bar{\lambda}_0^n P_0 f. \end{aligned}\right. \quad (n = 1, 2, \ldots).$$

Let now $F(\lambda)$ be a complex-valued bounded function, defined for all complex λ satisfying $|\lambda| \leqslant \|N\|$. Since all λ_i $(i = 0, 1, 2, \ldots)$ are contained in $|\lambda| \leqslant \|N\|$, all values $F(\lambda_i)$ are therefore determined. The transformation $F(N)$ is defined by

$$F(N) f = \Sigma\, F(\lambda_i)(f, \varphi_i)\varphi_i + F(\lambda_0) P_0 f.$$

Evidently $F(N)$ is linear. It is also bounded with $\|F(N)\| \leqslant$ upper bound $|F(\lambda)|$. If $F(\lambda) = \alpha_0 + \alpha_1\lambda + \alpha_2\lambda^2 + \ldots + \alpha_n\lambda^n$, then $F(N) = \alpha_0 I + \alpha_1 N + \alpha_2 N^2 + \ldots + \alpha_n N^n$. Furthermore, if $F(\lambda) = \bar{\lambda}$, then $F(N) = N^*$. The following properties are easily proved as in § 16:

1°. If $F(\lambda) = \alpha_1 F_1(\lambda) + \alpha_2 F_2(\lambda)$, then $F(N) = \alpha_1 F_1(N) + \alpha_2 F_2(N)$.

2°. If $F(\lambda) = F_1(\lambda)F_2(\lambda)$, then $F(N) = F_1(N)F_2(N)$. In particular, taking $F_1(\lambda) = \bar{\lambda}$, $F_2(\lambda) = \lambda$, we find $N^*Nf = \Sigma \mid \lambda_i \mid^2 (f, \varphi_i)\varphi_i + \mid \lambda_0 \mid^2 P_0 f$.

3°. $F(N)$ is normal, and $(F(N))^* = \bar{F}(N)$. If $F(\lambda)$ is real, then $F(N)$ is self-adjoint. If $F(\lambda) \geqslant 0$, then $F(N)$ is positive.

4°. If $F_0(\lambda), F_1(\lambda), F_2(\lambda), \ldots$ are uniformly bounded in $\mid \lambda \mid \leqslant \| N \|$, and $\lim F_n(\lambda) = F_0(\lambda)$ in this circle, then $\lim F_n(N)f = F_0(N)f$ for all $f \in R$. If moreover $\lim F_n(\lambda) = F_0(\lambda)$ uniformly, then $\lim \| F_0(N) - F_n(N) \| = 0$.

Let the number μ lie in $\mid \lambda \mid \leqslant \| N \|$. Defining $F(\lambda)$ by

$$F(\lambda) = \begin{cases} 1 \text{ for } \mid \lambda - \mu \mid \leqslant r, \\ 0 \text{ elsewhere,} \end{cases}$$

$F(\lambda)$ is real and $\{F(\lambda)\}^2 = F(\lambda)$. The corresponding transformation $F(N)$ is therefore an orthogonal projection $E(\mu, r)$. It is easy to see on and along which subspaces $E(\mu, r)$ is a projection. Consider those λ_i which satisfy $\mid \lambda_i - \mu \mid \leqslant r$, and let $[L]_{\mu,r}$ be the linear subspace determined by the corresponding characteristic elements. In the same way we construct the linear subspace $[M]_{\mu,r}$ from all λ_i satisfying $\mid \lambda_i - \mu \mid > r$. Then $E(\mu, r)$ is the projection on $[L]_{\mu,r}$ along $[M]_{\mu,r}$.

As an application we mention that $F_1(N) = F_2(N)$ if and only if $F_1(\lambda) = F_2(\lambda)$ for $\lambda = \lambda_0, \lambda_1, \lambda_2, \ldots$. Hence, if α is a complex number, not identical with one of the numbers $\lambda_0, \lambda_1, \lambda_2, \ldots$ and we define the bounded function $F(\lambda)$ such that $F(\lambda_i) = (\lambda_i - \alpha)^{-1}$ $(i = 0, 1, 2, \ldots)$ and that $F_1(\lambda) = 1/F(\lambda)$ is also bounded, then $F_1(\lambda_i) = \lambda_i - \alpha$ $(i = 0, 1, 2, \ldots)$, so that $F_1(N) = N - \alpha I$. It follows that $F(N) = R_\alpha = (N - \alpha I)^{-1}$. Hence

$$(N - \alpha I)^{-1}f = \Sigma\, (\lambda_i - \alpha)^{-1}(f, \varphi_i)\varphi_i + (\lambda_0 - \alpha)^{-1}P_0 f.$$

Theorem 9. *Let $N, N_1, N_2, \ldots$ all be normal and compact, and let $\lim \| N - N_n \| = 0$. Let $\lambda_0 \neq 0$ be a characteristic value of N with multiplicity $m > 0$, and let the projection P be defined by $Pf = \Sigma_1^m (f, \varphi_i)\varphi_i$, where $\varphi_1, \ldots, \varphi_m$ is an orthonormal system of characteristic elements of N belonging to the characteristic value λ_0. Then, if $\mid \lambda - \lambda_0 \mid \leqslant \varepsilon$ contains no other points of the spectrum of N, the transformation N_n has, for n sufficiently large, exactly m characteristic values $\lambda_1^{(n)}, \ldots, \lambda_m^{(n)}$ in this circle. Denoting by $\varphi_1^{(n)}, \ldots, \varphi_m^{(n)}$ a corresponding orthonormal system of characteristic elements of N_n, and defining the projection P_n by $P_n f = \Sigma_1^m (f, \varphi_i^{(n)})\varphi_i^{(n)}$, we have $\lim \| P - P_n \| = 0$.*

Proof. Let $\tilde{N} = N - \lambda_0 I$, $\tilde{N}_n = N_n - \lambda_0 I$. Then $\lim \| \tilde{N} - \tilde{N}_n \| = 0$, and $\lambda = 0$ is an isolated characteristic value of $\tilde{N}$ of multiplicity m, and with $\varphi_1, \ldots, \varphi_m$ as corresponding characteristic elements. Furthermore $\lim \| \tilde{N}^* - \tilde{N}_n^* \| = 0$, hence $\lim \| \tilde{N}^*\tilde{N} - \tilde{N}_n^*\tilde{N}_n \| = 0$. Since $\tilde{N}^*\tilde{N}$ is self-adjoint (even positive), and has $\lambda = 0$ as an isolated characteristic value of multiplicity m with $\varphi_1, \ldots, \varphi_m$ as corresponding characteristic elements, we may apply § 17, Th. 3. This gives the result that $\tilde{N}_n^*\tilde{N}_n$, for n sufficiently large, has exactly m characteristic values $| \mu_1^{(n)} |^2, \ldots, | \mu_m^{(n)} |^2$ in $| \lambda |^2 \leqslant \varepsilon^2$. But then $\tilde{N}_n$ has exactly m characteristic values $\mu_1^{(n)}, \ldots, \mu_m^{(n)}$ in $| \lambda | \leqslant \varepsilon$. Furthermore, if $\varphi_1^{(n)}, \ldots, \varphi_m^{(n)}$ is a corresponding orthonormal system of characteristic elements of $\tilde{N}_n$, these same elements are characteristic elements of $\tilde{N}_n^*\tilde{N}_n$ belonging to $| \mu_1^{(n)} |^2, \ldots, | \mu_m^{(n)} |^2$ respectively. Denoting by P_n the projection defined by $P_n f = \Sigma_1^m (f, \varphi_i^{(n)})\varphi_i^{(n)}$, we have therefore $\lim \| P - P_n \| = 0$, again by § 17, Th. 3. Observing now that N_n has exactly the characteristic values $\lambda_i^{(n)} = \mu_i^{(n)} + \lambda_0$ $(i = 1, \ldots, m)$ in $| \lambda - \lambda_0 | \leqslant \varepsilon$, and that $\varphi_1^{(n)}, \ldots, \varphi_m^{(n)}$ are corresponding characteristic elements, the result follows.

EXAMPLES

1) If the Hilbert space R is separable, and $K \neq O$ is a self-adjoint transformation of finite double-norm on R, there exists a very short proof that K has at least one characteristic value $\neq 0$, provided it is already known that the traces $\sigma_n = \tau(K^n)$ satisfy $\sigma_n = \Sigma_i \lambda_i^n$ for $n \geqslant 3$ (cf. Ch. 11, § 7, Th. 3).

(Let K, if necessary, be extended onto the closure $\bar{R}$, and let $\{\varphi_n\}$ be orthonormal and complete in $\bar{R}$. Supposing that K has no characteristic value $\neq 0$, we have $0 = \Sigma \lambda_i^4 = \tau(K^4) = \Sigma (K^4\varphi_i, \varphi_i) = \Sigma (K^2\varphi_i, K^2\varphi_i) = \Sigma \| K^2\varphi_i \|^2$, hence $K^2\varphi_i = 0$ for all φ_i. This implies $K^2 = O$, so that $(Kf, Kf) = (K^2f, f) = 0$ for all f, or $K = O$, in contradiction with $K \neq O$).

2) In § 3, Th. 2 it was proved that there exist bounded linear transformations K, fully symmetrisable relative to a positive H, such that $T = PK$ is compact, whereas K itself and all its iterates $K^p (p = 2, 3, \ldots)$ are not compact. In the particular case that the Hilbert space R is a Lebesgue space $L_2(\Delta, \mu)$, where Δ is a finite interval and μ is Lebesgue measure, K and H may be chosen such that they are integral transformations.

(Let Δ be the interval $0 \leqslant x \leqslant 1$, and let $\{\varphi_n(x)\}$ be the orthonormal system in $L_2(\Delta)$, defined in Ch. 9, § 9, Ex. A. If $L[\varphi]$ is the subspace determined by $\{\varphi_n(x)\}$ and $L[\psi]$ is its orthogonal complement, we suppose that $\{\psi_n(x)\}$ is orthonormal and complete in $L[\psi]$. Let now H be defined by $H\psi_n = \alpha_n\psi_n$, $H\varphi_n = 0$, where the positive numbers α_n converge to zero sufficiently rapidly to ensure that H is of finite double-norm. Then H is an integral transformation with kernel $H(x, y)$. The kernel $K(x, y)$ is defined by

$$K(x, y) = H(x, y) + \Sigma_1^\infty \varphi_{n+1}(x)\varphi_n(y).$$

The transformation K with kernel $K(x, y)$ satisfies the desired conditions).

3) Under the hypotheses of § 4, Th. 3 we have $\Sigma_{i=1}^q \lambda_{ni} = \max \Sigma_{i=1}^q (HKf_i, f_i)$ for all possible H-orthonormal systems $f_1, \ldots, f_q$ [16].

(If $\lambda_j (j = 1, 2, \ldots)$ is the sequence of all characteristic values $\neq 0$ of $T = PK$, and φ_j is a corresponding H-orthonormal sequence of characteristic elements, then § 4, Th. 2 shows that

$$(HKf_i, f_i) = \Sigma_j \lambda_j \mid (Hf_i, \varphi_j) \mid^2 =$$
$$\lambda_{n_q} \Sigma_j \mid (Hf_i, \varphi_j) \mid^2 + \Sigma_j (\lambda_j - \lambda_{n_q}) \mid (Hf_i, \varphi_j) \mid^2,$$

hence, observing that $\Sigma_j \mid (Hf_i, \varphi_j) \mid^2 \leqslant (Hf_i, f_i) = 1$,

$$(HKf_i, f_i) \leqslant \lambda_{n_q} + \Sigma_{j=1}^q (\lambda_{nj} - \lambda_{n_q}) \mid (Hf_i, \varphi_j) \mid^2,$$

so that

$$\lambda_{ni} - (HKf_i, f_i) \geqslant \lambda_{ni} - \lambda_{n_q} - \Sigma_{j=1}^q (\lambda_{nj} - \lambda_{n_q}) \mid (Hf_i, \varphi_j) \mid^2$$

or

$$\Sigma_{i=1}^q \lambda_{ni} - \Sigma_{i=1}^q (HKf_i, f_i) \geqslant \Sigma_{j=1}^q (\lambda_{nj} - \lambda_{n_q}) \{1 - \Sigma_{i=1}^q \mid (Hf_i, \varphi_j) \mid^2\}.$$

Observing now that $f_1, \ldots, f_q$ is H-orthonormal, we find $\Sigma_{i=1}^q \mid (Hf_i, \varphi_j) \mid^2 \leqslant (H\varphi_j, \varphi_j) = 1$, from which the result soon follows).

4) Let K be self-adjoint and compact on the Hilbert space R. Then, if $\lambda \neq 0$ and $Kf - \lambda f = g$, we have found in § 7, Th. 5 that

$$f = -\frac{g}{\lambda} - {}'\Sigma \frac{\lambda_n}{\lambda(\lambda - \lambda_n)} \alpha_n \varphi_n$$

with $\alpha_n = (g, \varphi_n)$ for $\lambda_n \neq \lambda$. If the space R is complete and separable, and $\{\psi_n\}$ is a complete orthonormal system in $R \ominus [W(K)]$ (hence $K\psi_n = 0$ for all ψ_n), then $Kf - \lambda f = g$ implies

$$f = {}'\Sigma \frac{\alpha_n}{\lambda_n - \lambda} \varphi_n + \Sigma \frac{\beta_n}{-\lambda} \psi_n$$

with $\beta_n = (g, \psi_n)$. Compare this formula with the last formula in § 16.

(Proof as in § 8, Th. 3).

5) Under the hypotheses of § 12, Th. 5 we have found for $K = AH$ the expansion

$$Kf = AHf = \Sigma \lambda_i \alpha_i \psi_i + p, \quad Hp = 0, \quad \alpha_i = (Hf, \psi_i),$$

hence, writing $H\psi_i = \chi_i$, so that $\lambda_i \alpha_i = (HKf, \psi_i) = (Kf, \chi_i)$, we have

$$Kf = \Sigma (Kf, \chi_i)\psi_i + Qf, \; HQ = O.$$

We have also

$$K^*f = \Sigma (K^*f, \psi_i)\chi_i + Q^*f, \; Q^*H = O.$$

(We have

$$(K^*f, g) = (f, Kg) = \Sigma (f, \psi_i)\overline{(Kg, \chi_i)} + (f, Qg) = \Sigma (f, \psi_i)(K^*\chi_i, g)$$
$$+ (Q^*f, g) = \Sigma \lambda_i (f, \psi_i)(\chi_i, g) + (Q^*f, g) = \Sigma (K^*f, \psi_i)(\chi_i, g) + (Q^*f, g),$$

from which the result follows).

6) Under the hypotheses of § 14, Th. 1 we have found that $Hf = \Sigma (f, \chi_n)\chi_n + Qf$, where the positive transformation $Q = H^{1/2}(I - P_1)H^{1/2}$ satisfies $QK = O$.

In the particular case that $K = AH$ with A bounded, the expansion for Kf is a consequence of this result.

($Hf = \Sigma\,(f, \chi_n)\,\chi_n + Qf$ implies $Kf = AHf = \Sigma\,(f, \chi_n)\,AH\psi_n + AQf = \Sigma\,\lambda_n\,(Hf, \psi_n)\psi_n + AQf$. It remains to prove that $HAQ = O$. But $HAQ = H^{1/2}.H^{1/2}AH^{1/2}.(I-P_1)H^{1/2} = H^{1/2}.H^{1/2}A^*H^{1/2}.(I-P_1)H^{1/2} = HA^*Q$; hence $QAH = QK = O$ implies $HAQ = HA^*Q = (QAH)^* = O$).

7) In § 13 we have proved that for positive H the expansion $\Sigma\,\lambda_i(Hf, \psi_i)\psi_i$ does not always converge relative to the ordinary norm. In § 15 we considered the case that H is not necessarily positive, but $S = HK$ is positive. The expansion has then the form $\Sigma\,\lambda_i \operatorname{sgn} \lambda_i(Hf, \psi_i)\psi_i$. In this case as well, the expansion does not always converge relative to the ordinary norm. The same holds if λ_i is replaced by λ_i^k, where k is a fixed positive integer.

(Let the separable space R be the direct sum of the orthogonal subspaces $L[\varphi]$ and $L[\chi]$, both of infinite dimension, where $\{\varphi_n\}$ and $\{\chi_n\}$ are complete orthonormal systems in $L[\varphi]$ and $L[\chi]$ respectively. In $L[\varphi]$ the transformations H and K are defined as in § 13; in $L[\chi]$ we define

$$K\chi_{2n-1} = l_n\chi_{2n-1} + r_n\chi_{2n},$$

$$K\chi_{2n} = m_n\chi_{2n},$$

where $m_n > 0,\quad r_n > 0,\quad l_n < 0,\quad \Sigma\,(l_n^2 + m_n^2 + r_n^2) < \infty$, and

$$H\chi_{2n-1} = a_n\chi_{2n-1} + b_n\chi_{2n},$$

$$H\chi_{2n} = b_n\chi_{2n-1} + c_n\chi_{2n}$$

with

$$a_n = -\,r_n^2p_n/(m_n - l_n),\quad b_n = r_np_n,\quad c_n = (m_n - l_n)p_n,$$

where p_n is a positive factor of proportionality. Then it is easily seen that on $L[\chi]$ the transformation H is not positive, but $S = HK$ is positive. The same is then true on the whole space R. The divergence of the expansion on $L[\varphi]$ leads now to the desired result).

8) Let the compact linear transformation T have the sequence $\xi_1, \xi_2, \ldots$ of characteristic values $\neq 0$, and let $\lambda_1 \geqslant \lambda_2 \geqslant \ldots$ be the sequence of singular values of T and T^*. Then we have seen in § 18, Th. 8 that $\Sigma\,|\,\xi_n\,|$ converges if $\Sigma\,\lambda_n$ converges. The converse is not true [15].

(Suppose that the space R is the direct sum of two orthogonal subspaces of infinite dimension, in which the systems $\{\varphi_n\}$ and $\{\psi_n\}$ are complete and orthonormal. Let now

$$T\varphi_{2n-1} = 0,\qquad T\psi_{2n-1} = \varphi_{2n-1}/(2n-1),$$

$$T\varphi_{2n} = \varphi_{2n}/4n^2,\qquad T\psi_{2n} = 0$$

for $n = 1, 2, \ldots$. Then it is easily seen that T is of finite double-norm, and has only the characteristic values $\xi_n = (4n^2)^{-1}$. Hence $\Sigma\,|\,\xi_n\,| < \infty$. Since

$$T^*\varphi_{2n-1} = \psi_{2n-1}/(2n-1),\qquad T^*\psi_{2n-1} = 0,$$

$$T^*\varphi_{2n} = \varphi_{2n}/4n^2,\qquad T^*\psi_{2n} = 0,$$

hence

$$T^*T\varphi_{2n-1} = 0, \qquad T^*T\psi_{2n-1} = \psi_{2n-1}/(2n-1)^2,$$

$$T^*T\varphi_{2n} = \varphi_{2n}/(4n^2)^2, \qquad T^*T\psi_{2n} = 0,$$

we see that the sequence $\lambda_n (n = 1, 2, \ldots)$ consists of the numbers $1, 2^{-2}, 3^{-1}, 5^{-1}, \ldots, 15^{-1}, 4^{-2}, 17^{-1}, \ldots, 35^{-1}, 6^{-2}, 37^{-1}, \ldots$. This shows that $\Sigma \lambda_n = \infty$.

In the case that R is the functionspace $L_2[0, 2\pi]$ and $T(x, y)$ is the kernel corresponding with T, we may take for example

$$T(x, y) \sim \Sigma \frac{\cos 2nx \cos 2ny}{4n^2} + \Sigma \frac{\cos (2n-1)x \sin (2n-1)y}{2n-1}).$$

9) Let the compact linear transformation T on the complete Hilbert space R have the sequence $\{\lambda_n\}$ of singular values and the corresponding orthonormal sequences $\{\varphi_n\}$ and $\{\psi_n\}$ of singular elements, hence $T\varphi_n = \lambda_n\psi_n$ and $T^*\psi_n = \lambda_n\varphi_n$ $(n = 1, 2, \ldots)$. Then, if $g = \Sigma \beta_n\psi_n$, the equation $Tf = g$ has a solution f if and only if $\Sigma \lambda_n^{-2} \mid \beta_n \mid^2 < \infty$.

(Suppose first that $Tf = g$. Since $Tf = \Sigma \lambda_n(f, \varphi_n)\psi_n$ by § 18, Th. 6, we have $\beta_n = \lambda_n(f, \varphi_n)$, hence $\Sigma \lambda_n^{-2} \mid \beta_n \mid^2 < \infty$. Let now conversely $g = \Sigma \beta_n\psi_n$ with $\Sigma \lambda_n^{-2} \mid \beta_n \mid^2 < \infty$. Put $\alpha_n = \lambda_n^{-1}\beta_n$. Then, since $\Sigma \mid \alpha_n \mid^2 < \infty$, the element $f = \Sigma \alpha_n\varphi_n$ exists. It follows that $Tf = \Sigma \alpha_n T\varphi_n = \Sigma \lambda_n\alpha_n\psi_n = \Sigma \beta_n\psi_n = g$).

10) Let the Hilbert space R be complete, and let R^2 be the productspace of R by itself (cf. Ch. 6, § 15) with $(\{f_1, f_2\}, \{g_1, g_2\}) = (f_1, g_1) + (f_2, g_2)$. If T is a bounded linear transformation on R, then the set B_T of all elements $\{f, Tf\}$ is a linear subspace of R^2.

(Let $\{f_0, g_0\} = \lim \{f_n, Tf_n\}$. Then $f_0 = \lim f_n$, $g_0 = \lim Tf_n$. But $Tf_0 = \lim Tf_n$ as well, hence $g_0 = Tf_0$).

11) The orthogonal complement $R^2 \ominus B_T$ is identical with the set of all $\{T^*g, -g\}$, where g runs through R.

(The element $\{h, -g\}$ is orthogonal to all $\{f, Tf\}$ if and only if $(h, f) - (g, Tf) = 0$ for all $f \in R$, that is, if and only if $(h, f) = (g, Tf)$ for all $f \in R$. Hence $\{h, -g\} \in R^2 \ominus B_T$ if and only if $h = T^*g$).

12) If $h \in R$ is arbitrary, the element $\{h, 0\} \in R^2$ may be written by the preceding example as the sum of an element belonging to B_T and an element belonging to $R^2 \ominus B_T$, hence $\{h, 0\} = \{f, Tf\} + \{T^*g, -g\}$. Then $f = (T^*T + I)^{-1}h$ and $g = T(T^*T + I)^{-1}h$, where the linear transformation $B = (T^*T + I)^{-1}$ is bounded and positive, and the linear transformation $C = T(T^*T + I)^{-1}$ is bounded.

(We have $\{h, 0\} = \{f, Tf\} + \{T^*g, -g\}$, hence $h = f + T^*g$, $0 = Tf - g$. Since f and g are uniquely determined by h, we may define $Bh = f$, $Ch = g$. It follows that $I = B + T^*C$, $O = TB - C$, hence

$$C = TB, \; I = B + T^*TB = (I + T^*T)B.$$

Furthermore, since $\{f, Tf\}$ and $\{T^*g, -g\}$ are orthogonal,

$$\| h \|^2 = \| \{h, 0\} \|^2 = \| \{f, Tf\} \|^2 + \| \{T^*g, -g\} \|^2$$

$$= \| f \|^2 + \| Tf \|^2 + \| T^*g \|^2 + \| g \|^2,$$

hence $\| Bh \|^2 + \| Ch \|^2 = \| f \|^2 + \| g \|^2 \leqslant \| h \|^2$, which implies $\| B \| \leqslant 1$ and $\| C \| \leqslant 1$.

Since $((T^*T + I)f, f) = (T^*Tf, f) + (f, f) = \| Tf \|^2 + \| f \|^2$, we see that $(T^*T + I)f = 0$ implies $f = 0$. It follows that $(T^*T + I)^{-1}$ exists. On account of $I = (T^*T + I)B$ we find then $B = (T^*T + I)^{-1}$. Hence $C = TB = T(T^*T + I)^{-1}$.

Finally, from $((T^*T + I)f, f) = \| Tf \|^2 + \| f \|^2$ we derive $(h, Bh) = \| TBh \|^2 + \| Bh \|^2 \geqslant 0$, which shows (observing that (Bh, h) is real for all h) that B is self-adjoint and positive. We observe that $(Bh, h) = 0$ if and only if $Bh = 0$, that is, if and only if $h = (T^*T + I)Bh = 0$).

13) Let the linear transformations $T, T_1, T_2, \dots$ all be bounded, and let $\lim \| T - T_n \| = 0$. Let Q be the orthogonal projection (in the productspace R^2) on B_T and Q_n the orthogonal projection on B_{T_n}. Then $\lim \| Q - Q_n \| = 0$.

(Since $\| T - T_n \| = \| T^* - T_n^* \|$, we have $\lim \| T^* - T_n^* \| = 0$. Hence, if $\eta > 0$ is given, there exists an index $n_0(\eta)$ such that $\| Tf - T_nf \| \leqslant \frac{1}{2}\eta(\| f \|^2 + \| Tf \|^2)^{1/2}$ and $\| T^*f - T_n^*f \| \leqslant \frac{1}{2}\eta(\| f \|^2 + \| T^*f \|^2)^{1/2}$ for $n \geqslant n_0(\eta)$.

Let now $\varphi = \{f, Tf\}$ and $\varphi_n = \{f, T_nf\}$. Then, if $\varepsilon > 0$ is given,

$$\| \varphi - \varphi_n \| = \| \{0, Tf - T_nf\} \| = \| Tf - T_nf \|$$
$$\leqslant \tfrac{1}{2}\varepsilon(\| f \|^2 + \| Tf \|^2)^{1/2} = \tfrac{1}{2}\varepsilon \| \varphi \|$$

for $n \geqslant n_0(\varepsilon)$, hence also $\| Q_n\varphi - \varphi_n \| = \| Q(\varphi - \varphi_n) \| \leqslant \| \varphi - \varphi_n \| \leqslant \frac{1}{2}\varepsilon \| \varphi \|$. It follows by addition that $\| Q_n\varphi - \varphi \| \leqslant \varepsilon \| \varphi \|$. This implies that for every $\chi \in R^2$ we have $\| Q_nQ\chi - Q\chi \| \leqslant \varepsilon \| Q\chi \| \leqslant \varepsilon \| \chi \|$, hence $\lim \| Q_nQ - Q \| = 0$.

Let now $\psi = \{T^*g, -g\}$ and $\psi_n = \{T_n^*g, -g\}$, hence $Q_n\psi_n = 0$, since $\psi_n \in R^2 \ominus B_{T_n}$. Then $\| \psi - \psi_n \| = \| T^*g - T_n^*g \| \leqslant \frac{1}{2}\varepsilon(\| g \|^2 + \| T^*g \|^2)^{1/2} = \frac{1}{2}\varepsilon \| \psi \|$ for $n \geqslant n_0(\varepsilon)$, hence also $\| Q_n\psi \| = \| Q_n(\psi - \psi_n) \| \leqslant \| \psi - \psi_n \| \leqslant \frac{1}{2}\varepsilon \| \psi \|$. This implies that for every $\chi \in R^2$ we have $\| Q_n(I - Q)\chi \| \leqslant \frac{1}{2}\varepsilon \| (I - Q)\chi \| \leqslant \frac{1}{2}\varepsilon \| \chi \|$, hence $\lim \| Q_n(I - Q) \| = 0$.

It follows, since $\| Q_n - Q \| \leqslant \| Q_n(I - Q) \| + \| Q_nQ - Q \|$, that $\lim \| Q - Q_n \| = 0$).

14) If, in the same situation as in the preceding example, we introduce the notations $B = (T^*T + I)^{-1}$, $C = TB$ and $B_n = (T_n^*T_n + I)^{-1}$, $C_n = T_nB_n$, then $\lim \| B - B_n \| = 0$ and $\lim \| C - C_n \| = 0$.

(We have $Q\{h, 0\} = \{Bh, Ch\}$ and $Q_n\{h, 0\} = \{B_nh, C_nh\}$, hence $\| (Q - Q_n)\{h, 0\} \|^2 = \| (B - B_n)h \|^2 + \|(C - C_n)h \|^2$).

15) Let the conditions of § 4, Th. 2, Case B be satisfied, so that $\lim_{k\to\infty} N(Kf - \Sigma_{n=1}^k \lambda_n(Hf, \psi_n)\psi_n) = 0$. Then, if there exists a constant C such that $\| Kg \| \leqslant C \| H^{1/2}g \|$ for every polynomial g in the elements ψ_n, we have $Kf = \Sigma\, \lambda_n(Hf, \psi_n)\psi_n + p$, $Hp = 0$. This holds in particular whenever $K = AH$ with A bounded, so that § 12, Th. 5 is a consequence of the present result. For the transformation K in § 13 there does not even exist a constant C satisfying $\| K\psi_n \| \leqslant C \| H^{1/2}\psi_n \|$ for all ψ_n.

(Let $\| Kg \| \leqslant C \| H^{1/2}g \|$ for every polynomial g in the elements ψ_n. Writing $H^{1/2}\psi_n = \Psi_n$, the system $\{\Psi_n\}$ is orthonormal. Then $\Sigma_p^q\, \lambda_n(Hf, \psi_n)\psi_n = K(\Sigma_p^q\,(Hf, \psi_n)\psi_n)$, hence

$$\| \Sigma_p^q\, \lambda_n(Hf, \psi_n)\psi_n \|^2 \leqslant C^2 \| \Sigma_p^q\,(Hf, \psi_n)\Psi_n \|^2$$
$$= C^2\, \Sigma_p^q\, | (Hf, \psi_n) |^2 = C^2\, \Sigma_p^q\, | (H^{1/2}f, \Psi_n) |^2,$$

which tends to zero for $p, q \to \infty$. Hence $\Sigma\, \lambda_n(Hf, \psi_n)\psi_n$ converges. The desired result follows now from § 4, Th. 2).

16) Let R be a complete separable Hilbert space on which the bounded positive transformation H is defined. Suppose that both the null space $[L]$ of H and its orthogonal complement $[M]$ are of infinite dimension, and that $\{\chi_n\}$ and $\{\varphi_n\}$ are complete orthonormal systems in $[L]$ and $[M]$ respectively. Let the linear transformation K be defined by

$$K\varphi_n = \lambda_n\varphi_n + \chi_n,\ K\chi_n = \tau_n\chi_{n+1}\ (n = 1, 2, \ldots),$$

where $\lambda_n > 0$, $\lambda_n > \lambda_{n+1}$, $\lim \lambda_n = 0$, $\tau_n > 0$, $\lim \tau_n = 0$, while H satisfies e.g. $H\varphi_n = \alpha_n\varphi_n$, $H\chi_n = 0$, $0 < \alpha_n < 1$. Then K is symmetrisable relative to H, K^2 is compact, and K is fully but not strongly symmetrisable. Determine the characteristic values $\neq 0$ of K and the corresponding characteristic elements.

(A straightforward computation shows that K has the characteristic values λ_n, and that the corresponding characteristic elements are $\psi_n = \varphi_n + \Sigma_{i=n}^{\infty} \tau_n\tau_{n+1} \ldots \tau_{i-1}\lambda_n^{-i+n-1}\chi_i$. The transformation $T = PK$ has also the characteristic values $\lambda_n \neq 0$ with the elements φ_n as corresponding characteristic elements. Observe that $\varphi_n = P\psi_n$, but not $\psi_n = \lambda_n^{-1}K\varphi_n$).

17) Let E be an arbitrary complete Banach space and E^* its adjoint space. If $f \in E$ and $f^* \in E^*$, we shall write (f, f^*) for the complex number $f^*(f)$. The bounded transformation A, on E into E^*, will be called *pseudo-self-adjoint* whenever $(f, Ag) = \overline{(g, Af)}$ for all $f, g \in E$. Except in the trivial case that A is the null transformation, the pseudo-self-adjoint transformation A is not linear. Furthermore (f, Af) is real for all $f \in E$.

(If A is pseudo-self-adjoint and α is complex, then $(g, A(\alpha f)) = \overline{(\alpha f, Ag)} = \bar{\alpha}\overline{(f, Ag)} = \bar{\alpha}(g, Af) = (g, \bar{\alpha}Af)$, hence $A(\alpha f) = \bar{\alpha}Af$. From $(f, Af) = \overline{(f, Af)}$ follows that (f, Af) is real).

18) We use the same notations as in the preceding example. If A is pseudo-self-adjoint, and if moreover $(f, Af) \geqslant 0$ for all $f \in E$, the transformation A will be called *pseudo-positive*. If $\chi_1, \chi_2, \ldots \in E^*$, and $\mu_1, \mu_2, \ldots$ are positive numbers such that $\Sigma\, \mu_n \| \chi_n \|^2 < \infty$, the transformation A, defined by $Af = \Sigma\, \mu_n\overline{(f, \chi_n)}\chi_n$, is pseudo-positive (cf. § 14).

19) With the same notations as in the preceding examples we define:

Class A. The linear transformation T (on E into E) is said to belong to class A whenever T itself or one of its iterates is compact.

Class B. The subclass B is the class of all transformations K belonging to class A and satisfying moreover:

(B_1). K has at least one characteristic value $\neq 0$.

(B_2). All characteristic values $\neq 0$ of K are real and of index one.

Class C. The subclass C is the class of all transformations K belonging to class A and satisfying moreover:

(C_1). There exists a bounded pseudo-positive transformation H (on E into E^* therefore) such that $S = HK$ is pseudo-self-adjoint.

(C_2). If $Kf = \lambda f \neq 0$, then $(f, Hf) \neq 0$.

(C_3). $S = HK \neq O$ (the null transformation).

Prove that the class B is included in class C.

(Let $K \in$ class B, and denote by $\lambda_n (n = 1, 2, \ldots)$ the sequence of all characteristic values $\neq 0$ of K, each characteristic value repeated according to its multiplicity. Let φ_n be a corresponding sequence of linearly independent characteristic elements. Then λ_n is also the sequence of all characteristic values $\neq 0$ of K^*, and a corresponding sequence χ_n of characteristic elements may be chosen such that $(\varphi_i, \chi_j) = 1$ for $i = j$ and $(\varphi_i, \chi_j) = 0$ for $i \neq j$. This is possible by (B_2). Let now the positive numbers μ_n be such that $\Sigma\, \mu_n \| \chi_n \|^2 < \infty$, and define H by $Hf = \Sigma\, \mu_n \overline{(f, \chi_n)} \chi_n$. Then H satisfies (C_1). The rest of the proof is similar to that in § 9, Th. 3).

20) With the same notations as in the preceding examples, prove that the classes B and C are identical (cf. § 9, Th. 3).

(We have only to show that the class C is included in class B. Let $K \in$ class C, and suppose that $Kf = \lambda f \neq 0$, hence $(f, Hf) > 0$ by (C_2). Then $\bar{\lambda}(f, Hf) = (f, \bar{\lambda} Hf) = (f, H\lambda f) = (f, HKf)$, and this is real by ($C_1$). It follows that λ is real. The proof that λ has the index one is similar to that in Ch. 9, § 15, Th. 9. To show now that K has at least one characteristic value $\neq 0$, we observe:

(I). $S = HK = K^*H$. Indeed, $(g, HKf) = \overline{(f, HKg)} = (Kg, Hf) = (g, K^*Hf)$ for all $f, g \in E$.

(II). If $Hf = 0$, then $Sf = 0$. This follows immediately from (I).

(III). Writing $N(f)$ for the non-negative number $(f, Hf)^{1/2}$, we have $| (f, Hg) | \leqslant N(f) . N(g)$. The proof is similar to that in Ch. 9, § 4, Th. 11, Remark.

(IV). We have $\| Hf \| \leqslant \| H \|^{1/2} N(f)$. To prove this inequality, we observe that for $\| g \| \leqslant 1$ we have $N^2(g) = (g, Hg) \leqslant \| g \| . \| Hg \| \leqslant \| H \| . \| g \|^2 \leqslant \| H \|$, so that $| (g, Hf) | \leqslant N(g) . N(f) \leqslant \| H \|^{1/2} N(f)$ for arbitrary f and $\| g \| \leqslant 1$. Since $\| Hf \| =$ upper bound $| (g, Hf) |$ for $\| g \| \leqslant 1$, the desired result follows.

(V). The set $[L]$ of all elements $f \in E$ satisfying $Hf = 0$ is a linear subspace of E. We consider now the factorspace $F = E/[L]$ (cf. Ch. 6, § 5). The elements of F will be denoted by $\tilde{f}$. Observing that $H(f_1 - f_2) = 0$ implies $HK(f_1 - f_2) = 0$ by (II), we may define the linear transformation $\tilde{K}$ on F into F by $\tilde{K}\tilde{f} = (\widetilde{Kf})$, where $f \in \tilde{f}$. If K is compact, then $\tilde{K}$ is compact.

(VI). The transformation $\tilde{H}$ on F into E^* is defined by $\tilde{H}\tilde{f} = Hf$, where $f \in \tilde{f}$. Evidently $\tilde{H}\tilde{f} = 0$ only for $\tilde{f} = \tilde{o}$. We write $N(\tilde{f}) = (f, Hf)^{1/2}$, where $f \in \tilde{f}$. The symbol $(\tilde{g}, \tilde{H}\tilde{f})$ is defined to be (g, Hf) where $g \in \tilde{g}$ and $f \in \tilde{f}$. All these definitions are without contradiction. Then $(\tilde{g}, \tilde{H}\tilde{K}\tilde{f}) = \overline{(\tilde{f}, \tilde{H}\tilde{K}\tilde{g})}$, and $\tilde{H}\tilde{K} \neq O$ by (C_3).

(VII). Supposing that K itself is compact, we may prove now that $\tilde{K}$ has a real characteristic value $\neq 0$. The proof is similar to that in § 3, Th. 1. If now $\tilde{K}\tilde{f} = \lambda \tilde{f} \neq \tilde{o}$, and f is an arbitrary element of $\tilde{f}$, then $Kf = \lambda f + p$ with $Hf \neq 0$, $Hp = 0$. Hence, using (I) and observing that λ is real, $K^*Hf = HKf = H\lambda f + Hp = \lambda Hf \neq 0$. This shows that K^* has the characteristic value $\lambda \neq 0$. But then K has the characteristic value $\lambda \neq 0$ as well.

(VIII). If not K itself but K^p is compact for an integer $p > 1$, we observe that HK^p is also pseudo-self-adjoint, and that $HK \neq O$ implies $HK^p \neq O$. Hence K^p has a characteristic value $\neq 0$ by (VII). But then K itself has a characteristic value $\neq 0$ as well).

21) If R is a Hilbert space, complete or not, and H and K are bounded linear

transformations on R such that H is positive and K is symmetrisable relative to H, then

$$|(HKf, f)| \leqslant \|K\| (Hf, f)$$

for all $f \in R$ [2; (1951)].

(Observing that $(ab)^{1/2} \leqslant (a + b)/2$ for $a \geqslant 0$, $b \geqslant 0$, we find $|(Hf, g)| \leqslant (Hf, f)^{1/2}(Hg, g)^{1/2} \leqslant [(Hf, f) + (Hg, g)]/2$, hence $|(HK^nf, f)| \leqslant [(HK^nf, K^nf) + (Hf, f)]/2 = [(HK^{2n}f, f) + (Hf, f)]/2$ for $n = 1, 2, \ldots$, and by induction

$$|(HKf, f)| \leqslant (2^{-1} + 2^{-2} + \ldots + 2^{-n}) (Hf, f) + 2^{-n}(HK^{2^n}f, f).$$

Now, if $\|K\| \leqslant 1$, we have $|(HK^pf, f)| \leqslant \|H\| . \|f\|^2$ for $p = 1, 2, \ldots$, and hence the second term on the right in the above inequality tends to zero as $n \to \infty$. It follows that $|(HKf, f)| \leqslant (Hf, f)$ in case $\|K\| \leqslant 1$, which is equivalent to what was to be proved).

22) Let H be a bounded positive transformation on the complete or non-complete Hilbert space R, and suppose that R is the direct sum of the null space $[L]$ of H and the orthogonal complement $[M]$ of $[L]$. The factorspace of R relative to H is denoted by Z (cf. Ch. 9, § 5 for its definition). With every linear transformation T on R which is reduced by $[L]$ corresponds a linear transformation $[T]$ on Z in such a way that $[T][f] = [Tf]$. We know that, even if R is complete and T is bounded on R, $[T]$ is not necessarily bounded on Z (Ch. 9, § 5, Th. 10). If however T is bounded and symmetrisable relative to H, then $[T]$ exists and is bounded.

(We have $(HTf, Tf) = (HT^2f, f) \leqslant \|T^2\| (Hf, f)$ by the preceding example, hence $Hf = 0$ implies $HTf = 0$, which shows that T is reduced by $[L]$. Consequently $[T]$ exists. Then $\|[Tf]\|^2 = (HTf, Tf) \leqslant \|T^2\| . (Hf, f) = \|T^2\| . \|[f]\|^2$, so that $[T]$ is bounded).

23) In Ch. 9, § 4, Th. 8 we have seen that if G and H are bounded, positive and permutable, then $HG = GH$ is also positive. A different proof follows immediately from Example 21 above [2; (1951)].

(Without loss of generality we may assume that $I \geqslant I - G \geqslant O$. Then, since $H(I - G)$ is self-adjoint, $I - G$ is symmetrisable relative to H, and $\|I - G\| \leqslant 1$, hence $(H(I - G)f, f) \leqslant (Hf, f)$, so that $H \geqslant H(I - G)$ or $HG \geqslant O$).

24) If the Hilbert space R is complete or not, if K is symmetrisable relative to the positive transformation H, and if there exists an integer $p \geqslant 1$ such that K^p is compact, then we have proved in § 3, Th. 4 that $S = HK \neq O$ implies the existence of a real characteristic value $\neq 0$ of K. There is a different proof which uses the fact that if $\lambda_1 \neq 0$ belongs to the resolvent set of K, then $\lambda_1 I - K$ has a bounded inverse [2; (1951)].

(If $S = HK \neq O$, there exists an element f satisfying $(Sf, f) \neq 0$; without loss of generality we may suppose that $(Sf, f) > 0$. Then $(Hf, f) > 0$ by Example 21. Let λ_1 be the upper bound of (Sf, f) for all f with $(Hf, f) = 1$. By Example 21 we have $0 < \lambda_1 < \infty$. There exists a sequence f_n such that $(Hf_n, f_n) = 1$ and $\lim(Sf_n, f_n) = \lambda_1$. Furthermore $H(\lambda_1 I - K) \geqslant O$. Supposing that λ_1 is not a characteristic value of K, the transformation $\lambda_1 I - K$ has a bounded inverse $R(\lambda_1)$ by Ch. 11, § 3, Th. 11; moreover, the self-adjointness of $H(\lambda_1 I - K)$ implies immediately that of $HR(\lambda_1)$. Let now $g_n = R(\lambda_1)f_n$, hence $f_n = (\lambda_1 I - K)g_n$ ($n = 1, 2, \ldots$). Then

$$1 = (Hf_n, f_n) = (H(\lambda_1 I - K)g_n, f_n) = (H(\lambda_1 I - K)f_n, g_n)$$

and

$$0 \leqslant (H(\lambda_1 I - K)g_n, g_n) = (Hf_n, R(\lambda_1)f_n) = (HR(\lambda_1)f_n, f_n) \leqslant \| R(\lambda_1) \|$$

by Example 21.

In view of these relations $h_n = f_n - g_n/\| R(\lambda_1) \|$ satisfies

$$(H(\lambda_1 I - K)h_n, h_n) = (H(\lambda_1 I - K)f_n, f_n) - 2/\| R(\lambda_1) \|$$
$$+ (H(\lambda_1 I - K)g_n, g_n)/\| R(\lambda_1) \|^2 \leqslant (H(\lambda_1 I - K)f_n, f_n) - 1/\| R(\lambda_1) \|.$$

But $\lim (HKf_n, f_n) = \lambda_1 = \lambda_1(Hf_n, f_n)$, hence $\lim (H(\lambda_1 I - K)f_n, f_n) = 0$, so that $(H(\lambda_1 I - K)h_n, h_n) < 0$ for large n, in contradiction with $H(\lambda_1 I - K) \geqslant O$. Hence λ_1 is a real characteristic value of K).

25) Let $\{\varphi_1, \varphi_2\}$ be an orthonormal system in a two-dimensional Hilbert space, and let the linear transformations H and K be defined by $H\varphi_1 = \varphi_1$, $H\varphi_2 = 0$; $K\varphi_1 = \varphi_1 + \varphi_2$, $K\varphi_2 = \varphi_2$. Then H is positive, K is symmetrisable relative to H, and K has only the characteristic value $\lambda = 1$ with characteristic element φ_2. Hence K is not fully symmetrisable [2; (1951)].

26) Suppose, under the hypotheses of Example 24, that the symmetrisability of K is full (so that all characteristic values of K are real), and that $\lambda_1 \geqslant \ldots \geqslant \lambda_{n-1} > 0$ are characteristic values of K with corresponding H-orthonormal characteristic elements $\psi_1, \ldots, \psi_{n-1}$. Assume furthermore that for $k = 1, \ldots, n-1$ we know already that $\lambda_k = \max (HKf, f)$ for all $f \in E_k$ satisfying $(Hf, f) = 1$, where E_k is the set of all f which are H-orthogonal to $\psi_1, \ldots, \psi_{k-1}$. Then, if there exists an element $f \in E_n$ such that $(HKf, f) > 0$, the upper bound λ_n of (HKf, f) for all $f \in E_n$ satisfying $(Hf, f) = 1$ is a characteristic value of K possessing a corresponding characteristic element $\psi_n \in E_n$ satisfying $(H\psi_n, \psi_n) = 1$, and hence $(HK\psi_n, \psi_n) = \lambda_n$ [2; (1951)]. This result, essentially § 4, Th. 3, may be derived directly from Example 24.

(Consider $K_n f = Kf - \Sigma_1^{n-1} (HKf, \psi_i)\psi_i = Kf - \Sigma_1^{n-1} (Hf, \psi_i)K\psi_i$. Obviously K_n is symmetrisable relative to H, and $K_n\psi_i = 0$ $(i = 1, \ldots, n-1)$. Furthermore $K_n f \in E_n$ for arbitrary f, so that $K_n f = \lambda f \neq 0$ implies $f \in E_n$ and hence $K_n f = Kf$; in particular, K_n is fully symmetrisable relative to H.

Observe now that for an arbitrary f we have $(HK_n f, f) \leqslant (HKf, f)$ with equality if and only if $f \in E_n$, and that for $f = g + \Sigma_1^{n-1} (Hf, \psi_i)\psi_i$ we have $(Hg, g) \leqslant (Hf, f)$. Hence $(HK_n f, f) = (HK_n g, g) = (HKg, g) \leqslant \lambda_n(Hg, g) \leqslant \lambda_n(Hf, f)$ for arbitrary f, so that λ_n is also the upper bound of $(HK_n f, f)$ for all f satisfying $(Hf, f) = 1$. Then, by Example 24, λ_n is a characteristic value of K_n, and therefore also of K, possessing a characteristic element $\psi_n \in E_n$ such that $(H\psi_n, \psi_n) = 1$).

27) If K_1 and K_2 are both symmetrisable relative to the positive H, and $HK_1 = HK_2$, then we have:

1°. If K_1 is fully symmetrisable, and $K_1\psi_i = \lambda\psi_i \neq 0$ $(i = 1, \ldots, n)$ with $\psi_1, \ldots, \psi_n$ linearly independent, then $\chi_i = H\psi_i$ $(i = 1, \ldots, n)$ are linearly independent characteristic elements of K_2^* for λ; in particular, the geometric multiplicity of K_1 does not exceed that of K_2, if K_2 or one of its iterates is compact.

2°. If K_1 and K_2 are both fully symmetrisable and both have a compact iterate, then every characteristic value $\neq 0$ of K_1 is a characteristic value of K_2 with the same multiplicity, and conversely.

3°. If K_1 is fully and K_2 is strongly symmetrisable, and $\psi_i (i = 1, \ldots, n)$ are linearly independent characteristic elements of K_1 for $\lambda \neq 0$, then $\varphi_i = \lambda^{-1}K_2\psi_i$ are linearly independent characteristic elements of K_2 for λ, and $(H\psi_i, \psi_j) = (H\varphi_i, \varphi_j)$, $(H\psi_i, f) = (H\varphi_i, f)$ for arbitrary f [2; (1951)].

(For 1° we observe that λ is real, and then we argue as in the proofs of § 2, 6° and § 2, 7°. Statement 2° is an immediate consequence. To prove 3°, we observe that $0 = H(K_1\psi_i - \lambda\psi_i) = H(K_2\psi_i - \lambda\psi_i)$ implies the linear independence of the elements $K_2\psi_i$ in view of the linear independence of the elements $H\psi_i$. Furthermore $0 = H(K_2\psi_i - \lambda\psi_i)$ implies $0 = K_2(K_2\psi_i - \lambda\psi_i) = \lambda(K_2\varphi_i - \lambda\varphi_i)$, hence $K_2\varphi_i = \lambda\varphi_i$. The remaining relations follow now).

REFERENCES

[1] A. C. Zaanen, Über vollstetige symmetrische und symmetrisierbare Operatoren, Nieuw Archief v. Wiskunde (2) 22 (1943), 57–80.
A. C. Zaanen, On the theory of linear integral equations I, Proc. Akad. Amsterdam 49 (1946), 194–204 (Indagationes Math. 8, 91–101).

[2] W. T. Reid, Expansion problems associated with a system of linear integral equations, Transactions Amer. Math. Soc. 33 (1931), 475–485.
W. T. Reid, Symmetrizable completely continuous linear transformations in Hilbert space, Duke Math. Journal 18 (1951), 41–56.

[3] J. Ernest Wilkins, Definitely self-conjugate adjoint integral equations, Duke Math. Journal 11 (1944), 155–166.

[4] H. J. Zimmerberg, Definite integral systems, Duke Math. Journal 15 (1948), 371-388.

[5] O. D. Kellogg, On the existence and closure of sets of characteristic functions, Math. Annalen 86 (1922), 14–17.

[6] E. Hellinger and O. Toeplitz, Integralgleichungen und Gleichungen mit unendlichvielen Unbekannten, Encyklopädie der Math. Wissenschaften, Band II. 3, Heft 9 (1927), Leipzig, in particular p. 1541–1543.

[7] R. Courant, Zur Theorie der linearen Integralgleichungen, Math. Annalen 89 (1923), 161–178.

[8] R. Courant and D. Hilbert, Methoden der mathematischen Physik I, second ed., Berlin (1931), Ch. I, § 3,3.

[9] R. Courant and D. Hilbert, Methoden der mathematischen Physik I, second ed., Berlin (1931), Ch. I, § 5,3.

[10] J. Mercer, Symmetrisable functions and their expansion in terms of biorthogonal functions, Proc. Royal Soc. (A) 97 (1920), 401–413.

[11] E. Schmidt, Entwicklung willkürlicher Funktionen nach Systemen vorgeschriebener, Math. Annalen 63 (1907), 433–476.

[12] H. Weyl, Inequalities between the two kinds of eigenvalues of a linear transformation, Proc. Nat. Acad. of Sciences 35 (1949), 408–411.

[13] G. H. Hardy, J. E. Littlewood and G. Pólya, Inequalities, Cambridge (1934, 1952).

[14] G. Pólya, Remark on Weyl's note "Inequalities between the two kinds of eigenvalues of a linear transformation", Proc. Nat. Acad. of Sciences 36 (1950), 49–51.

[15] S. H. Chang, On the distribution of characteristic values and singular values of linear integral equations, Transactions Amer. Math. Soc. 67 (1949), 351–367.

[16] Ky Fan, On a theorem of Weyl concerning eigenvalues of linear transformations I, Proc. Nat. Acad. of Sciences 35 (1949), 652–655.

PART III

NON-SINGULAR LINEAR INTEGRAL EQUATIONS

Chapter 13

GENERAL THEORY OF NON-SINGULAR LINEAR INTEGRAL EQUATIONS

§ 1. Introduction and Definitions

We suppose in the present chapter that Δ is an arbitrary μ-measurable set, and that $\Phi(u)$ and $\Psi(v)$ are complementary functions in the sense of Young, where $\Phi(u)$ satisfies $\Phi(2u) \leqslant M\Phi(u)$ for a fixed constant M and all $u \geqslant 0$. We shall not suppose that the analogous inequality for $\Psi(v)$ necessarily holds, so that e.g. $\Phi(u) = u$ is permitted.

Let now the function $T(x, y)$, measurable on $\Delta \times \Delta$, have the property (P) relative to the Orlicz space $L_\Phi(\Delta, \mu)$; hence, by the definition of the property (P) in Ch. 9, § 7, $\int_\Delta | T(x, y)f(y) | d\mu \in L_\Phi$ whenever $f \in L_\Phi$. Then, if the linear transformation T is defined by

$$Tf = \int_\Delta T(x, y)f(y)d\mu,$$

we have:

(a) T is a bounded transformation on L_Φ into L_Φ (cf. Ch. 9, § 7, Th. 2).

(b) $T = O$ (the null transformation) if and only if $T(x, y) = 0$ almost everywhere on $\Delta \times \Delta$ (cf. Ch. 9, § 7, Th. 1).

(c) $T^n (n = 2, 3, \ldots)$ has the kernel $T_n(x, y) = \int_\Delta T_{n-1}(x, z)T(z, y)d\mu$, and $T_n(x, y)$ has the property (P) (cf. Ch. 9, § 7, Th. 1).

(d) If $g^* \in (L_\Phi)^*$ is represented by $g^*(x) \in L_\Psi$, that is, if $g^*(f) = \int_\Delta f(x)g^*(x)d\mu$ for all $f \in L_\Phi$, and T^* is the Banach adjoint of T, then $f^* = T^*g^*$ is represented by $f^*(x) = \int_\Delta T(y, x)g^*(y)d\mu$, where the kernel $T^*(x, y) = T(y, x)$ has the property (P) relative to L_Ψ. In the same way the iterates $(T^*)^n = (T^n)^*$ correspond with the kernels $T_n(y, x)$, where $T_n(x, y)$ is defined as in (c) (cf. Ch. 9, § 7, Th. 3).

The properties (a), (b) and (c) are independent of the hypothesis that $\Phi(2u) \leqslant M\Phi(u)$ for all $u \geqslant 0$.

Definition. *If the linear integral transformation T (on L_Φ into L_Φ), whose kernel $T(x, y)$ has the property (P) relative to L_Φ, has the additional* *property that T itself or one of its iterates T^n is compact, then T is called a non-singular linear integral transformation.*

Supposing that $g(x) \in L_\Phi$ is given, the equations $Tf = g$ and $(T-\lambda I)f=g$ take the form

$$\int_\Delta T(x, y)f(y)d\mu = g(x), \tag{1}$$

$$\int_\Delta T(x, y)f(y)d\mu - \lambda f(x) = g(x), \tag{2}$$

where the sign of equality means equality almost everywhere on Δ.

Definition. *Whenever T is non-singular, the equations* (1) *and* (2) *are called non-singular linear integral equations of the first kind and second kind respectively.*

Since the compactness of T^n for an integer $n \geqslant 1$ implies the compactness of $(T^n)^* = (T^*)^n$, the transformation on L_{Ψ} into L_{Ψ} with kernel $T^*(x, y) = T(y, x)$ is also a non-singular integral transformation. This follows from the proof at the end of Example D in Ch. 11, § 2 because, although we have supposed for more general purposes in this example that $\Psi(2v) \leqslant M\Psi(v)$ for all $v \geqslant 0$, this is not necessary for the compactness proof in question. In fact, we only use that every bounded linear functional $g^*(f)$ in L_Φ is of the form $g^*(f) = \int_\Delta f(x)g^*(x)d\mu$, where the uniquely determined function $g^*(x) \in L_{\Psi}$ satisfies $\| g^*(x) \|_{\Psi}/2 \leqslant \| g^* \| \leqslant \| g^*(x) \|_{\Psi}$. We may therefore carry over our conclusions about T^* on the integral transformation with kernel $T(y, x)$.

The equations

$$\int_\Delta T(y, x)f^*(y)d\mu = g^*(x), \tag{3}$$

$$\int_\Delta T(y, x)f^*(y)d\mu - \lambda f^*(x) = g^*(x) \tag{4}$$

in the Orlicz space L_{Ψ} are called the adjoint equations of (1) and (2) respectively.

We insert some remarks on the question under what conditions T is non-singular. If μ is separable, and $\Psi(2v) \leqslant M\Psi(v)$ for a fixed constant M and all $v \geqslant 0$, it is sufficient for the compactness of T^n that the kernel $T_n(x, y)$ of T^n is of finite double-norm, that is, $T_n(x, y) \in L_{\Psi}$ as a function of y for almost every $x \in \Delta$, and $t_n(x) = \| T_n(x, y) \|_{\Psi} \in L_\Phi$. In particular, if L_Φ is the space $L_p (1 < p < \infty)$, so that L_{Ψ} is the space L_q with

$1/p + 1/q = 1$, it is sufficient that $\int_\Delta (\int_\Delta | T_n(x, y) |^q d\mu)^{p/q} d\mu < \infty$ (cf. Ch. 11, § 2, Ex. D.). For $\Phi(u) = u$ the spaces L_Φ and L_Ψ are identical with L and L_∞ respectively, so that $\Psi(2v) \leqslant M\Psi(v)$ is not satisfied for any M. Nevertheless, if $T_n(x, y)$ is of finite double-norm, that is, if $\int_\Delta \| T_n(x, y) \|_\infty d\mu < \infty$, then T^{2n} is compact (cf. Ch. 11, § 2, Ex. E), so that T is non-singular. As an example we mention the case that Δ is the linear interval $[0, 1]$, μ is Lebesgue measure, and $T(x, y) = B(x, y) | x - y |^{-\alpha}$, where $B(x, y)$ is measurable and bounded, and $0 < \alpha < 1$. Then, since $T_n(x, y)$ is bounded for $n > 1/(1 - \alpha)$ by Ch. 9, § 9, Ex. C, Lemma 11, the integral equation with kernel $T(x, y)$ is non-singular in $L_p(\Delta, \mu)$ for $1 \leqslant p < \infty$. The Example F in Ch. 11, § 2 gives the more precise information that for $1 < p < \infty$ the transformation T with kernel $T(x, y) = B(x, y) | x - y |^{-\alpha}$ is itself compact.

Definition. *If* $g(x) = 0$ (*almost everywhere*) *in* (1) *and* (2), *these equations are called homogeneous. In the case that* $g(x) \neq 0$ (*that is,* $g(x) \neq 0$ *on a set of positive measure*) *the equations are said to be inhomogeneous. A similar definition applies to the equations* (3) *and* (4).

Those values of λ for which the homogeneous equation

$$\int_\Delta T(x, y) f(y) d\mu - \lambda f(x) = 0 \tag{5}$$

has a solution $f(x) \neq 0$ (that is, $f(x) \neq 0$ on a set of positive measure) are exactly the characteristic values of T. The solution $f(x)$ is called a *characteristic function* of the equation (5), belonging to the characteristic value λ. One may also state that $f(x)$ is a characteristic function of the transformation T, or of the kernel $T(x, y)$. The set of all solutions $f(x)$ of (5) (with $f(x) = 0$ included therefore) is the null space of $T - \lambda I$; this set is therefore a linear subspace of $L_\Phi(\Delta, \mu)$.

If n is an integer > 1, we consider the productspace L_Φ^n, where the norm in L_Φ^n is chosen such that L_Φ^n may be considered as the direct sum of n separate spaces L_Φ (cf. Ch. 6, § 15). We suppose that the n^2 kernels $T_{ij}(x, y)$ $(i, j = 1, \ldots, n)$ all have the property (P) relative to L_Φ, and we define the linear transformation T on L_Φ^n into L_Φ^n by $\{g\} = T\{f\}$, where $g^i(x) = \sum_{j=1}^n \int_\Delta T_{ij}(x, y) f^j(y) d\mu$ $(i = 1, \ldots, n)$.

Then, by Ch. 9, § 7, Th. 4,

(e) T is a bounded transformation on L_Φ^n into L_Φ^n.

(f) $T = O$ if and only if all $T_{ij}(x, y) = 0$ almost everywhere on $\Delta \times \Delta$.

(g) If $\{g^*\} \in (L^n_\Phi)^*$ is represented by $\{g^{*1}(x), \ldots, g^{*n}(x)\} \in L^n_\Psi$, and $\{f^*\} = T^*\{g^*\}$ is represented by $\{f^{*1}(x), \ldots, f^{*n}(x)\} \in L^n_\Psi$, then

$$f^{*i}(x) = \Sigma_{j=1}^n \int_\Delta T_{ji}(y, x) g^{*j}(y) d\mu \quad (i = 1, \ldots, n).$$

(h) If S and T have matrixkernels $\{S_{ij}(x, y)\}$ and $\{T_{ij}(x, y)\}$ with the property (P), then $V = ST$ has the matrixkernel $\{V_{ij}(x, y)\}$ with the property (P), where $V_{ij}(x, y) = \Sigma_{k=1}^n \int_\Delta S_{ik}(x, z) T_{kj}(z, y) d\mu$.

Assuming now that T or one of its iterates is compact, T is again called a non-singular linear integral transformation, this time on L^n_Φ into L^n_Φ. The equation $(T - \lambda I)\{f\} = \{g\}$ takes the form

$$\text{(6)} \qquad \Sigma_{j=1}^n \int_\Delta T_{ij}(x, y) f^j(y) d\mu - \lambda f^i(x) = g^i(x) \quad (i = 1, \ldots, n),$$

and this system (6) is called a non-singular linear system of integral equations (of the second kind). The adjoint equation $(T^* - \lambda I)\{f^*\} = \{g^*\}$ corresponds with the system

$$\text{(7)} \qquad \Sigma_{j=1}^n \int_\Delta T_{ji}(y, x) f^{*j}(y) d\mu - \lambda f^{*i}(x) = g^{*i}(x) \quad (i = 1, \ldots, n)$$

in L_Ψ. Instead of speaking about characteristic values and the corresponding characteristic functions as in the case of one equation it is necessary here to speak about characteristic values and the corresponding characteristic functionsets.

In the same way as in the case of one equation we make some remarks on the question what conditions are sufficient in order that T be non-singular. If μ is separable, and $\Psi(2v) \leqslant M\Psi(v)$ for a fixed constant M and all $v \geqslant 0$, it is certainly sufficient for the compactness of T that all $T_{ij}(x, y)$ are of finite double-norm (cf. Ch. 11, § 2, Ex. D). For $\Phi(u) = u$ (hence $L_\Phi = L$ and $L_\Psi = L_\infty$) the condition $\Psi(2v) \leqslant M\Psi(v)$ is not satisfied for any M. Nevertheless, if all $T_{ij}(x, y)$ are of finite double-norm, then T^2 is compact. Indeed, the elements $T^{(2)}_{ij}(x, y)$ of the matrixkernel of T^2 are given by $T^{(2)}_{ij}(x, y) = \Sigma_{k=1}^n \int_\Delta T_{ik}(x, z) T_{kj}(z, y) d\mu$, and, $T_{ik}(x, z)$ and $T_{kj}(z, y)$ being both of finite double-norm, it follows from Ch. 11, § 2, Ex. E, Remark that $\int_\Delta T_{ik}(x, z) T_{kj}(z, y) d\mu$ is the kernel of a compact transformation in L. Then $T^{(2)}_{ij}(x, y)$ is also the kernel of a compact transformation in L, and this shows that T^2 is compact in L^n.

§ 2. Spectral Properties

As in the preceding paragraph we consider the Orlicz space $L_\Phi(\Delta, \mu)$, where $\Phi(2u) \leqslant M\Phi(u)$ for all $u \geqslant 0$, and we assume that

$$\text{(1)} \qquad \int_\Delta T(x, y) f(y) d\mu - \lambda f(x) = g(x)$$

is a non-singular linear integral equation on L_Φ. The corresponding linear transformation T (on L_Φ into L_Φ) is therefore non-singular. The adjoint equation in L_Ψ is

$$\int_\Delta T(y, x)f^*(y)d\mu - \lambda f^*(x) = g^*(x). \tag{2}$$

It is our purpose to reformulate in terms of the present situation the main results obtained in Ch. 11, § 3 for abstract linear transformations T, one of whose iterates is compact. A similar reformulation is possible for a non-singular linear system of equations, like (6) in the preceding paragraph. Since however this would offer no new aspects we shall restrict ourselves to the case of one equation (but we shall use in the sequel, whenever it is necessary, the corresponding results for a system).

As we know, the complex number λ is a characteristic value of the equation (1) whenever $(T - \lambda I)f = 0$ for a function $f(x) \in L_\Phi$ which does not vanish identically. For any complex number λ the geometric multiplicity of λ is the dimension m_1 of the null space of $T - \lambda I$, that is, m_1 is the maximal number of linearly independent characteristic functions belonging to λ. Hence $m_1 > 0$ or $m_1 = 0$, according as λ is or is not a characteristic value. Evidently, the dimensions m_k of the null spaces of $(T - \lambda I)^k$ $(k = 0, 1, 2, \ldots)$ form a non-decreasing sequence with $m_0 = 0$, but, provided $\lambda \neq 0$, this sequence does not tend to infinity. By Ch. 11, § 3, Th. 6 all m_k are finite, and there exists an index $\nu = \nu(\lambda)$ such that $m_k = m_\nu$ for $k \geqslant \nu$, whereas $m_k < m_{k+1}$ for $k < \nu$. The number m_ν is the algebraic multiplicity of λ, and the index ν is the index of λ for the transformation T.

Using these notions, we have:

Theorem 1. *Every complex number $\lambda \neq 0$ belongs either to the resolvent set of T and T^*, or it is a characteristic value of T and T^*. In the first case the equations* (1) *and* (2) *have therefore uniquely determined solutions $f(x) \in L_\Phi$ and $f^*(x) \in L_\Psi$ for every $g(x) \in L_\Phi$ and $g^*(x) \in L_\Psi$. Furthermore the transitions from $g(x)$ to $f(x)$ and from $g^*(x)$ to $f^*(x)$ are then performed by bounded linear transformations.*

Proof. Follows from Ch. 11, § 3, Th. 13 and Th. 11.

Theorem 2. 1°. *The number of different characteristic values of* (1) *and* (2) *is zero, finite or enumerably infinite, and in the latter case they tend to zero.*

2°. *Every characteristic value $\lambda \neq 0$ has the same finite geometric multiplicity for the equation* (1) *as for the adjoint equation* (2).

3°. *Every characteristic value* $\lambda \neq 0$ *has the same finite algebraic multiplicity for* (1) *as for* (2).

4°. *Every characteristic value* $\lambda \neq 0$ *has the same index for* (1) *as for* (2).

Proof. Follows from Ch. 11, § 3, Th. 5 and Th. 14.

Theorem 3. *If* $\lambda \neq 0$, *the inhomogeneous equation* (1) *has a solution* $f(x) \in L_\Phi$ *for those and only those* $g(x) \in L_\Phi$ *which satisfy* $\int_\Delta g(x)f^*(x)d\mu = 0$ *for all solutions* $f^*(x) \in L_{\Psi'}$ *of the homogeneous adjoint equation* (2) (*that is, equation* (2) *with* $g^*(x) = 0$).

If $\lambda \neq 0$, *the inhomogeneous adjoint equation* (2) *has a solution* $f^*(x) \in L_{\Psi'}$ *for those and only those* $g^*(x) \in L_{\Psi'}$ *which satisfy* $\int_\Delta f(x)g^*(x)d\mu = 0$ *for all solutions* $f(x) \in L_\Phi$ *of the homogeneous equation* (1) (*that is, equation* (1) *with* $g(x) = 0$).

Proof. Follows from Ch. 11, § 3, Th. 16 and Th. 17.

Theorem 4. *If* $\lambda \neq 0$ *is a characteristic value with index* ν, *there exist integers* $d_1 \geqslant d_2 \geqslant \dots \geqslant d_\nu > 0$ *and functions* $f_1(x), \dots, f_{d_1}(x) \in L_\Phi$ *such that the functions in the following diagram I*

diagram I

$f_1 \dots f_{d_\nu}$				
$T_\lambda f_1 \dots T_\lambda f_{d_\nu}$	$f_{d_\nu+1} \dots f_{d_{\nu-1}}$			
$T_\lambda^{\nu-1} f_1 \dots T_\lambda^{\nu-1} f_{d_\nu}$	$T_\lambda^{\nu-2} f_{d_\nu+1} \dots T_\lambda^{\nu-2} f_{d_{\nu-1}}$			$f_{d_2+1} \dots f_{d_1}$

(*where* $T_\lambda^k f$ *means* $(T - \lambda I)^k f$) *form a maximal set of linearly independent functions in the null space of* $(T - \lambda I)^\nu$, *and such that the functions in the last* n *rows* ($n = 1, 2, \dots, \nu$) *form a maximal set of linearly independent functions in the null space of* $(T - \lambda I)^n$. *The number of functions in the last row is therefore the geometric multiplicity of* λ, *and the total number of functions in the diagram is the algebraic multiplicity of* λ.

In the same way there exist functions $g_1^*(x), \dots, g_{d_1}^*(x) \in L_{\Psi'}$ *with the property that the functions in the following diagram II* (*where* $T_\lambda^* g^*$ *means* $\int_\Delta T(y, x)g^*(y)d\mu - \lambda g^*(x)$, *so that the meaning of* $(T_\lambda^*)^k g^*$ *is evident*) *have corresponding properties for the adjoint integral equation.*

$g_1^* \dots g_{d_\nu}^*$				
$T_\lambda^* g_1^* \dots T_\lambda^* g_{d_\nu}^*$	$g_{d_\nu+1}^* \dots g_{d_{\nu-1}}^*$			
$(T_\lambda^*)^{\nu-1} g_1^* \dots (T_\lambda^*)^{\nu-1} g_{d_\nu}^*$	$(T_\lambda^*)^{\nu-2} g_{d_\nu+1}^* \dots (T_\lambda^*)^{\nu-2} g_{d_{\nu-1}}^*$			$g_{d_2+1}^* \dots g_{d_1}^*$

diagram II

In addition, once the functions $f_1(x), \dots, f_{d_1}(x)$ are determined, the functions $g_1^*(x), \dots, g_{d_1}^*(x)$ may be chosen such that if $\varphi^*(x)$ is the i-th function (from top) in the j-th column of diagram II and $\varphi(x)$ is the i-th function (from below) in the j-th column of diagram I, then

$$\int_\Delta \varphi(x)\varphi^*(x)d\mu = 1,$$

whereas

$$\int_\Delta \chi(x)\varphi^*(x)d\mu = 0$$

for all other functions $\chi(x)$ in diagram I.

Proof. Follows from Ch. 11, § 3, Th. 13 and Th. 19.

Definition. *Every linear combination of the functions in diagram I is called a fundamental function or a principal function of the kernel $T(x, y)$. In the same way, every linear combination of the functions in diagram II is said to be a fundamental function or principal function of the adjoint kernel $T(y, x)$.*

The functions in diagram I form therefore a maximal set of linearly independent fundamental functions of $T(x, y)$.

Theorem 5. *If $\lambda \neq 0$ is a characteristic value, every $f(x) \in L_\Phi$ admits the unique decomposition $f(x) = g(x) + k(x)$, where $g(x)$ is such that $Th - \lambda h = g$ has a solution $h(x)$, and $k(x)$ is a linear combination of $f_1(x), \dots, f_{d_1}(x)$. A similar decomposition is possible for all $f^*(x) \in L_\Psi$.*

Proof. In the proof of Ch. 11, § 3, Th. 13 it was shown that the whole space is the direct sum of L_1 and P, where L_1 is the range of $T - \lambda I$ and P is the subspace determined by $f_1, \dots, f_{d_1}$.

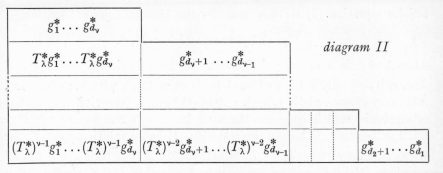

In the case that $L_\Phi(\Delta, \mu)$ is the Hilbert space $L_2(\Delta, \mu)$, the Hilbert adjoint of T corresponds with the kernel $\overline{T(y, x)}$. Instead of the Banach adjoint equation (2) we now consider the Hilbert adjoint equation

$$\int_\Delta \overline{T(y, x)} f^*(y) d\mu - \bar{\lambda} f^*(x) = g^*(x). \tag{3}$$

Then $\lambda \neq 0$ is a characteristic value of the equation (1) with kernel $T(x, y)$ if and only if $\bar{\lambda}$ is a characteristic value of (3) with kernel $\overline{T(y, x)}$, and every characteristic value $\lambda \neq 0$ of (1) has the same finite (geometric or algebraic) multiplicity and the same index as $\bar{\lambda}$ has for the equation (3). Furthermore, if $\lambda \neq 0$, the equation (1) has a solution $f(x) \in L_2$ for those and only those $g(x) \in L_2$ which satisfy $\int_\Delta g(x)\overline{f^*(x)} d\mu = 0$ for all solutions $f^*(x) \in L_2$ of the homogeneous equation (3). A similar small modification has to be made in the statement of Theorem 4.

We conclude this paragraph by a theorem which is essentially Theorem 2 in Ch. 11, § 6.

Theorem 6. *If $T(x, y)$ has the characteristic values $\lambda_1, \lambda_2, \ldots \neq 0$, where each characteristic value is repeated according to its algebraic multiplicity, and $p(\lambda) = \alpha_1\lambda + \alpha_2\lambda^2 + \ldots + \alpha_n\lambda^n$, then $p(\lambda_1)$, $p(\lambda_2)$, ..., insofar as these numbers are $\neq 0$, are the characteristic values $\neq 0$ of the kernel $\alpha_1 T(x, y) + \alpha_2 T_2(x, y) + \ldots + \alpha_n T_n(x, y)$, where the number of repetitions of a given number in this sequence is its algebraic multiplicity.*

§ 3. The Banach Space of all Kernels $T(x, y)$ Satisfying only the Condition (P) relative to L_Φ

In the present paragraph we first add some results on the resolvent of a bounded linear transformation T to those collected already in Ch. 10, § 7. We next assume that the transformation T is an integral transformation on L_Φ into L_Φ, whose kernel $T(x, y)$ has the property (P) relative to L_Φ. Unless expressly stated, we shall not assume the existence of a constant M, satisfying $\Phi(2u) \leqslant M\Phi(u)$ for all $u \geqslant 0$. This will lead to some special properties of the resolvent. We finally investigate to what extent the theorems in the preceding paragraph remain true in the case which we consider here.

Let E be a complete Banach space, and let T be a bounded linear transformation on E into E. Then, if the complex number λ satisfies $|\lambda| > \|T\|$, the number λ belongs to the resolvent set of T, and the resolvent $R_\lambda = (T - \lambda I)^{-1}$ admits the expansion

$$R_\lambda = (T - \lambda I)^{-1} = -\lambda^{-1}I - \lambda^{-2}T - \lambda^{-3}T^2 - \ldots,$$

where this series converges uniformly (cf. Ch. 10, § 7, Th. 6). Furthermore, if λ_0 (either $|\lambda_0| > \|T\|$ or $|\lambda_0| \leqslant \|T\|$) belongs to the resolvent set of T, all λ in a sufficiently small neighbourhood of λ_0 also belong to the resolvent set of T, and, writing $R_0 = (T - \lambda_0 I)^{-1}$, $R_\lambda = (T - \lambda I)^{-1}$, we have

$$R_\lambda = R_0 + (\lambda - \lambda_0)R_0^2 + (\lambda - \lambda_0)^2 R_0^3 + \ldots,$$

where this series converges uniformly (cf. Ch. 10, § 7, Th. 5).

Theorem 1. *Let $\lambda \neq 0$ belong to the resolvent set of T. Then, writing $(T - \lambda I)^{-1} = -\lambda^{-1}I - \lambda^{-2}H_\lambda$, the bounded linear transformation H_λ satisfies*

$$(T - \lambda I)H_\lambda = H_\lambda(T - \lambda I) = -\lambda T,$$

or

$$H_\lambda = -\lambda T R_\lambda = -\lambda R_\lambda T.$$

If T^n is compact for an integer $n \geqslant 1$, the same holds for $(H_\lambda)^n$.

If $\lambda_0 \neq 0$ belongs to the resolvent set of T, and we write $H_0 = H_{\lambda_0}$, $\mu_0 = \lambda_0^{-1}$, $\mu = \lambda^{-1}$, then

$$H_\lambda = H_0 + (\mu - \mu_0)H_0^2 + (\mu - \mu_0)^2 H_0^3 + \ldots$$

for all λ in a sufficiently small neighbourhood of λ_0, where this series converges uniformly.

Proof. By the definition of H_λ we have $H_\lambda = -\lambda I - \lambda^2 (T - \lambda I)^{-1}$, hence

$$(T - \lambda I)H_\lambda = (T - \lambda I)\{-\lambda I - \lambda^2(T - \lambda I)^{-1}\} =$$

$$-\lambda(T - \lambda I) - \lambda^2 I = -\lambda T.$$

In the same way $H_\lambda(T - \lambda I) = -\lambda T$. Observing that T and R_λ commute, we see that the compactness of T^n implies the compactness of $(H_\lambda)^n$.

If now $\lambda_0 \neq 0$ belongs to the resolvent set of T, and $|\mu - \mu_0| < \|H_0\|^{-1}$, the series $X_\lambda = H_0 + (\mu - \mu_0)H_0^2 + (\mu - \mu_0)^2 H_0^3 + \ldots$ obviously converges uniformly. Furthermore, observing that for $\mu = \lambda^{-1}$ the relation $(T - \lambda I)H_\lambda = -\lambda T$ is equivalent to $(\mu T - I)H_\lambda = -T$, we find

$$(\mu T - I)X_\lambda = (\mu_0 T - I)\,\Sigma_{k=0}^\infty\,(\mu - \mu_0)^k H_0^{k+1} + (\mu - \mu_0)T\,\Sigma_{k=0}^\infty\,(\mu - \mu_0)^k H_0^{k+1}$$

$$= -T\,\Sigma_{k=0}^\infty(\mu - \mu_0)^k H_0^k + T\,\Sigma_{k=1}^\infty(\mu - \mu_0)^k H_0^k = -T,$$

hence $X_\lambda = H_\lambda$. This completes the proof.

Let $\Phi(u)$ and $\Psi(v)$ be complementary in the sense of Young, and let $T(x, y)$, measurable on $\Delta \times \Delta$, have the property (P) relative to L_Φ, hence $\int_\Delta |T(x, y)f(y)| d\mu \in L_\Phi$ for every $f \in L_\Phi$. Then, obviously,

$$(1) \qquad \int_{\Delta\times\Delta} |T(x, y)f(y)g^*(x)| \, d(\mu \times \mu) < \infty$$

for all $f \in L_\Phi$, $g^* \in L_\Psi$. Conversely, if (1) holds, then $T(x, y)$ has the property (P) relative to L_Φ. In § 1 we have already seen that the linear transformation T with kernel $T(x, y)$ is bounded. Evidently the linear transformation T_a with kernel $|T(x, y)|$ also has the property (P). We define

$$\| T \|_{\Phi\Psi} = \text{upper bound} \int_{\Delta\times\Delta} |T(x, y)f(y)g^*(x)| \, d(\mu \times \mu)$$

for all $f(y)$ and $g^*(x)$ satisfying $\int_\Delta \Phi |f| \, d\mu \leqslant 1$ and $\int_\Delta \Psi |g^*| \, d\mu \leqslant 1$ respectively.

Theorem 2. *We have* $\| T \| \leqslant \| T_a \|$ *and* $\| (T_1T_2)_a \| \leqslant \| T_{1a} \| . \| T_{2a} \|$. *In particular* $\| (T^n)_a \| \leqslant \| T_a \|^n$.

Proof. If $\varepsilon > 0$ is given, there exists a function $f \in L_\Phi$ such that $\| f \|_\Phi = 1$ and $\| T \| - \varepsilon/2 < \| Tf \|_\Phi$. Hence there also exists a function $g^* \in L_\Psi$ such that $\int_\Delta \Psi |g^*| \, d\mu \leqslant 1$ and

$$\left| \int_{\Delta\times\Delta} T(x, y)f(y)g^*(x) d(\mu \times \mu) \right| > \| Tf \|_\Phi - \varepsilon/2 > \| T \| - \varepsilon.$$

Then $\| T \| - \varepsilon < \int_{\Delta\times\Delta} |T(x, y)f(y)g^*(x)| \, d(\mu \times \mu) \leqslant \| \int_\Delta |T(x, y)f(y)| d\mu \|_\Phi \leqslant \| T_a \|$, since the L_Φ-norms of f and $|f|$ are both 1. It follows that $\| T \| \leqslant \| T_a \|$.

The same kind of proof shows that if $T_3(x, y)$ and $T_4(x, y)$ are kernels with the property (P) such that $|T_3(x, y)| \leqslant |T_4(x, y)|$ almost everywhere on $\Delta \times \Delta$, then $\| T_{3a} \| \leqslant \| T_{4a} \|$.

Let now $T_1(x, y)$ and $T_2(x, y)$ both have the property (P). Then $(T_1T_2)_a$ has the kernel $T_3(x, y) = \left| \int_\Delta T_1(x, z)T_2(z, y) d\mu \right| \leqslant \int_\Delta |T_1(x, z)T_2(z, y)| \, d\mu = T_4(x, y)$, which is the kernel of $T_{1a}T_{2a}$. Hence $\| (T_1T_2)_a \| \leqslant \| T_{1a}T_{2a} \| \leqslant \| T_{1a} \| . \| T_{2a} \|$. In particular $\| (T^n)_a \| \leqslant \| (T_a)^n \| \leqslant \| T_a \|^n$.

Theorem 3. *We have*

$$\| \alpha T \|_{\Phi\Psi} = |\alpha| . \| T \|_{\Phi\Psi} \text{ for all complex } \alpha,$$

$$\| T_1 + T_2 \|_{\Phi\Psi} \leqslant \| T_1 \|_{\Phi\Psi} + \| T_2 \|_{\Phi\Psi},$$

$$\| T_a \| \leqslant \| T \|_{\Phi\Psi} \leqslant 2 \| T_a \|,$$

$\| T \|_{\Phi\Psi} = 0$ *if and only if* $T(x, y) = 0$ *almost everywhere on* $\Delta \times \Delta$.

Proof. The first two statements are evident. The last statement is a consequence of the third statement, since $\| T \|_{\Phi\Psi} = 0$ if and only if $\| T_a \| = 0$. To prove the third statement we observe that there exist, if $\varepsilon > 0$ is given, two functions $f(y) \in L_\Phi$ and $g^*(x) \in L_\Psi$, satisfying $\| f \|_\Phi = 1$ and $\int_\Delta \Psi \mid g^* \mid d\mu \leqslant 1$, such that

$$\| T_a \| - \varepsilon < \mid \int_{\Delta \times \Delta} \mid T(x, y) \mid f(y) g^*(x) d(\mu \times \mu) \mid .$$

But $\| f \|_\Phi = 1$ implies $\int_\Delta \Phi \mid f \mid d\mu \leqslant 1$ (cf. Ch. 5, § 5, Th. 2), hence

$$\| T_a \| - \varepsilon < \int_{\Delta \times \Delta} \mid T(x, y) f(y) g^*(x) \mid d(\mu \times \mu) \leqslant \| T \|_{\Phi\Psi}.$$

On the other hand, if $\varepsilon > 0$ is given, there exists a function $f(y)$, satisfying $\int_\Delta \Phi \mid f \mid d\mu \leqslant 1$, for which $\| T \|_{\Phi\Psi} - \varepsilon < \| \int_\Delta \mid T(x, y) f(y) \mid d\mu \|_\Phi$. Hence, observing that $\| f \|_\Phi \leqslant \int_\Delta \Phi \mid f \mid d\mu + 1 \leqslant 2$, we find

$$\| T \|_{\Phi\Psi} - \varepsilon < \| T_a \| . \| f \|_\Phi \leqslant 2 \| T_a \|.$$

It follows that $\| T_a \| \leqslant \| T \|_{\Phi\Psi} \leqslant 2 \| T_a \|$.

Theorem 4. *The space of all kernels $T(x, y)$ having the property (P) relative to $L_\Phi(\Delta, \mu)$ is a complete Banach space $L_{\Phi\Psi}(\Delta \times \Delta, \mu)$, provided the norm of $T(x, y)$ is taken to be $\| T \|_{\Phi\Psi}$.*

Proof. We have only to prove that the space is complete. Let therefore the sequence $T_n(x, y)$ $(n = 1, 2, \ldots)$ be given, and let $\| T_n \|_{\Phi\Psi} < \infty$, $\lim \| T_n - T_m \|_{\Phi\Psi} = 0$ as $m, n \to \infty$. We suppose first that Δ is of finite measure. Then there exist positive numbers p and q such that $\mu(\Delta)\Phi(p) \leqslant 1$ and $\mu(\Delta)\Psi(q) \leqslant 1$, so that, taking $f(y) = p$ and $g^*(x) = q$, we have $\int_\Delta \Phi \mid f \mid d\mu \leqslant 1$ and $\int_\Delta \Psi \mid g^* \mid d\mu \leqslant 1$. It follows that

$$\lim \int_{\Delta \times \Delta} \mid T_n(x, y) - T_m(x, y) \mid d(\mu \times \mu) = 0$$

for $m, n \to \infty$, from which we conclude by a well-known argument (cf. Ch. 5, § 6, Th. 1) that a subsequence $T_k(x, y)$ $(k = n_1, n_2, \ldots)$ converges pointwise to a measurable function $T(x, y)$. Letting now in

$$\int_{\Delta \times \Delta} \mid (T_n - T_m) f(y) g^*(x) \mid d(\mu \times \mu) \leqslant \varepsilon,$$

holding for $m, n \geqslant N(\varepsilon)$, the index m run through the subsequence $k = n_1, n_2, \ldots$, Fatou's Theorem yields

$$\int_{\Delta \times \Delta} \mid (T_n - T) f(y) g^*(x) \mid d(\mu \times \mu) \leqslant \varepsilon$$

for $n \geqslant N(\varepsilon)$. Hence $\lim \| T_n - T \|_{\Phi\Psi} = 0$. The extension to a set Δ of infinite measure is proved as in Ch. 5, § 6, Th. 1.

Remark. If $T(x, y) \in L_{\Phi\Psi}$, the kernels $T_1(x, y) = T(y, x)$ and $| T_1(x, y) |$ correspond to linear integral transformations T_1 and T_{1a} which are bounded on L_{Ψ} into L_{Ψ}, and for which $\| T_1 \| \leqslant \| T_{1a} \| \leqslant \| T \|_{\Phi\Psi} \leqslant 2 \| T_{1a} \|$.

Theorem 5. *If T has the kernel $T(x, y) \in L_{\Phi\Psi}$, and $| \lambda | > \| T_a \|$, so that λ belongs to the resolvent set of T, then the transformation H_λ, defined as in Theorem 1 by $(T - \lambda I)^{-1} = - \lambda^{-1} I - \lambda^{-2} H_\lambda$, is an integral transformation with kernel $H_\lambda(x, y) \in L_{\Phi\Psi}$.*

Proof. Since $| \lambda | > \| T_a \| \geqslant \| T \|$, we have

$$(T - \lambda I)^{-1} = - \lambda^{-1} I - \lambda^{-2} T - \lambda^{-3} T^2 - \ldots,$$

hence $H_\lambda = \Sigma_{n=0}^{\infty} \lambda^{-n} T^{n+1}$, where this series converges uniformly, and its partial sums are integral transformations with kernels belonging to $L_{\Phi\Psi}$. The series $\Sigma | \lambda |^{-n} \| T_a \|^{n+1}$ also converges. From

$$\| \Sigma_p^q \lambda^{-n} T^{n+1} \|_{\Phi\Psi} \leqslant \Sigma_p^q | \lambda |^{-n} \| T^{n+1} \|_{\Phi\Psi} \leqslant$$

$$2 \, \Sigma_p^q | \lambda |^{-n} \| (T^{n+1})_a \| \leqslant 2 \, \Sigma_p^q | \lambda |^{-n} \| T_a \|^{n+1}$$

(cf. Theorem 2) we derive then that the series for H_λ converges in $L_{\Phi\Psi}$. The completeness of $L_{\Phi\Psi}$ guarantees now that H_λ has a kernel $H_\lambda(x, y) \in L_{\Phi\Psi}$.

Remark. If there exists a number M such that $\Phi(2u) \leqslant M \Phi(u)$ for all $u \geqslant 0$, so that T^* corresponds with the kernel $T(y, x)$, the transformation H_λ^*, defined by $(T^* - \lambda I)^{-1} = - \lambda^{-1} I - \lambda^{-2} H_\lambda^*$, corresponds with the kernel $H_\lambda(y, x)$.

Theorem 6. *If T has the kernel $T(x, y) \in L_{\Phi\Psi}$ and if $\lambda_0 \neq 0$, belonging to the resolvent set of T, has the property that $H_0 = H_{\lambda_0}$ is an integral transformation with kernel $H_0(x, y) \in L_{\Phi\Psi}$, then, for all λ in a sufficiently small neighbourhood of λ_0, the transformation H_λ is an integral transformation with kernel $H_\lambda(x, y) \in L_{\Phi\Psi}$.*

Proof. For $| \lambda^{-1} - \lambda_0^{-1} | < \| (H_0)_a \|^{-1}$ the series $\Sigma | \lambda^{-1} - \lambda_0^{-1} |^k \| (H_0)_a \|^{k+1}$ converges, and furthermore $H_\lambda = \Sigma_{k=0}^{\infty} (\lambda^{-1} - \lambda_0^{-1})^k H_0^{k+1}$ by Theorem 1, where the latter series converges uniformly. A proof along the same lines as the proof of Theorem 5 may therefore be given.

It seems difficult to say more about the character of the transformation H_λ without making additional hypotheses.

Theorem 7. *Let the following hypotheses be satisfied:*

(*a*) $\Phi(2u) \leqslant M\Phi(u)$ *for a fixed constant* M *and all* $u \geqslant 0$.

(*b*) $T(x, y)$ *satisfies the condition* (P) *relative to* $L_\Phi(\Delta)$.

(*c*) $T(x, y) \in L_\Psi$ *as a function of* y *for almost every* $x \in \Delta$.

Then, if $\lambda \neq 0$ *belongs to the resolvent set of* T, *there exists a function* $H_\lambda(x, y)$, *belonging to* L_Ψ *as a function of* y *for almost every* $x \in \Delta$, *such that* $g = H_\lambda f$ *is given by* $g(x) = \int_\Delta H_\lambda(x, y)f(y)d\mu$.

Proof. Before giving the proof we observe that (b) does not imply (c). Indeed, if L_Φ is the space $L_2(\Delta, \mu)$, where $\Delta = [0, 1]$ and μ is Lebesgue measure, and $T(x, y) = |x - y|^{-\alpha}$ with $1 > \alpha \geqslant 1/2$, then (b) is satisfied (cf. Ch. 9, § 9, Ex. C), but (c) is not. In the second place we stress the fact that it will not follow from our proof that $H_\lambda(x, y)$, as a function on $\Delta \times \Delta$, is measurable.

Since (a) is satisfied, there exists a one-to-one correspondence between all elements $g^* \in (L_\Phi)^*$ and all $g^*(x) \in L_\Psi$. Considering $T(x, y)$ as a function of y, we have $T(x, y) \in L_\Psi$ for all $x \in \Delta - E_0$, where E_0 is of measure zero by (c). We may therefore apply the transformation $-\lambda R_\lambda^*$ to $T(x, y)$, and we obtain a function $H_\lambda(x, y)$, belonging to L_Ψ for $x \in \Delta - E_0$. Hence $(-\lambda R_\lambda^*)T(x, y) = H_\lambda(x, y)$. Then, if $f(y) \in L_\Phi$ is arbitrary and $x \in \Delta - E_0$, we have

$$\int_\Delta H_\lambda(x, y)f(y)d\mu = \{(-\lambda R_\lambda^*)T(x, y)\}f =$$
$$\{T(x, y)\}(-\lambda R_\lambda f) = \int_\Delta T(x, y)h(y)d\mu,$$

where we have written $h = -\lambda R_\lambda f$. But evidently $h(y) \in L_\Phi$, so that $g(x) = \int_\Delta T(x, y)h(y)d\mu \in L_\Phi$ as well. Since $\int_\Delta H_\lambda(x, y)f(y)d\mu$ and $g(x)$ are identical for $x \in \Delta - E_0$, we are permitted to say that

$$\int_\Delta H_\lambda(x, y)f(y)dy = g(x) = Th = T(-\lambda R_\lambda f) = -\lambda TR_\lambda f = H_\lambda f.$$

This completes the proof.

Remark. If in particular $|\lambda| > \| T_a \|$, it is to be expected that the function $H_\lambda(x, y)$ of the present theorem is identical almost everywhere with the function $H_\lambda(x, y)$ found in Theorem 5. This is indeed the case provided μ is separable, and the proof is similar to the final part of the proof of Ch. 9, § 10, Th. 11.

The equation $Tf - \lambda f = g$ may also be written as $f - \lambda^{-1}Tf = -\lambda^{-1}g$ or, writing $\lambda^{-1} = \mu$ and $-\lambda^{-1}g = -\mu g = g_1$, as $f - \mu Tf = g_1$. The solution $f = -\lambda^{-1}g - \lambda^{-2}H_\lambda g$ may then be written as $f = g_1 + \mu H_\lambda g_1$. Hence

$$f - \mu Tf = g_1, \; f = g_1 + \mu H_\lambda g_1.$$

This way of writing both equation and solution may be found in most of the classical treatises on linear integral equations (cf. also Ch. 9, § 16 and § 17), and $H_\lambda(x, y)$, the kernel of H_λ, is then called the *resolvent kernel*. We shall, however, make no use of this name in order to avoid confusion with the resolvent $R_\lambda = (T - \lambda I)^{-1}$.

Theorem 8. *Let μ be separable, and let the hypotheses (a) and (b) of the preceding theorem be satisfied, so that T^* corresponds with the kernel $T(y, x)$. Let furthermore the equations*

$$\int_\Delta T(x, y)f(y)d\mu - \lambda f(x) = g(x), \tag{2}$$

$$\int_\Delta T(y, x)f^*(y)d\mu - \lambda f^*(x) = g^*(x) \tag{3}$$

be given. Then, for any complex λ ($\lambda = 0$ is therefore permitted), the solutions of the homogeneous equation (3) (that is, (3) with $g^*(x) = 0$) are those and only those $f^*(x) \in L_{\Psi}$, satisfying $\int_\Delta g(x)f^*(x)d\mu = 0$ for every $g(x) \in L_\Phi$ for which the equation (2) has a solution.

If L_Φ is reflexive, in particular if $\Psi(2v) \leqslant M\Psi(v)$ for a fixed constant M and all $v \geqslant 0$, the solutions of the homogeneous equation (2) are those and only those $f(x) \in L_\Phi$, satisfying $\int_\Delta f(x)g^*(x)d\mu = 0$ for every $g^*(x) \in L_{\Psi}$ for which the equation (3) has a solution.

If L_Φ is not reflexive, and $f(x) \in L_\Phi$ is a solution of the homogeneous equation (2), then $\int_\Delta f(x)g^*(x)d\mu = 0$ for every $g^*(x) \in L_{\Psi}$ for which the equation (3) has a solution. There may exist, however, a function $f_1(x) \in L_\Phi$ which is no solution of the homogeneous equation (2), and which nevertheless satisfies $\int_\Delta f_1(x)g^*(x)d\mu = 0$ for every $g^*(x) \in L_{\Psi}$ for which (3) has a solution.

Proof. The three statements follow from Ch. 10, § 3, Th. 1, 2 and 3 respectively by observing that L_Φ is separable under the present hypotheses.

Remark. It is not permitted to state that (2) has a solution for those and only those $g(x)$ satisfying $\int_\Delta g(x)f^*(x)d\mu = 0$ for every solution $f^*(x)$ of the homogeneous equation (3), since the set of all $g(x)$ for which (2) has a solution is not identical with, but only lying dense in the subspace of all $h(x)$ satisfying $\int_\Delta h(x)f^*(x)d\mu = 0$ for every solution $f^*(x)$ of the homogeneous equation (3).

Theorem 9. *If μ is separable, and the same hypotheses (a) and (b) are satisfied, we have:*

1°. *The complex number λ belongs to the resolvent set of T if and only if λ belongs to the resolvent set of T^*.*

2°. *If λ belongs to the residual spectrum of T, then λ is a characteristic value of T^*.*

3°. *If λ is a characteristic value of T, then λ is either a characteristic value of T^* or it belongs to the residual spectrum of T^*.*

4°. *If λ belongs to the continuous spectrum of T^*, then λ belongs to the continuous spectrum of T. If L_Φ is reflexive the inverse statement is also true.*

Proof. Statement 1° follows from Ch. 10, § 9, Th. 4 and Ch. 10, Ex. 2. The statements 2° and 3° follow from Ch. 10, § 9, Th. 5 and 6 respectively. Statement 4° follows from Ch. 10, Ex. 1.

§ 4. The Resolvent of a Non-Singular Kernel

We return to the case that the integral transformation T with kernel $T(x, y)$ is non-singular. One of the most important examples will be the case that μ is separable, and $T(x, y)$ or one of its iterates is of finite double-norm $|||\, T\, |||$. We repeat the definition. The kernel $T(x, y)$, measurable on $\Delta \times \Delta$, is of finite double-norm $|||\, T\, |||$ relative to L_Φ whenever $T(x, y) \in L_\Psi$ as a function of y for almost every $x \in \Delta$, and $t(x) = \|\, T(x, y)\, \|_\Psi \in L_\Phi$. The double-norm is then defined by $|||\, T\, ||| = \|\, t(x)\, \|_\Phi$. It has advantages to generalize this definition somewhat. For any measurable $T(x, y)$ we may define $t(x)$ by $t(x) = \|\, T(x, y)\, \|_\Psi$, provided we permit that perhaps $t(x) = \infty$ on a set of positive measure. It is, however, not à priori evident that this function $t(x)$ is now a measurable function of x. Whenever it is measurable, we may consider $\|\, t(x)\, \|_\Phi$, where it is of course possible that $\|\, t(x)\, \|_\Phi = \infty$, even if $t(x)$ itself should be finite for all $x \in \Delta$. For $t(x)$ measurable, $|||\, T\, |||$ may be defined therefore by

$$|||\, T\, ||| = \|\, t(x)\|_\Phi,\ t(x) = \|\, T(x, y)\, \|_\Psi.$$

In case $t(x)$ is not measurable, we denote by $t_{maj}(x)$ an arbitrary measurable majorant of $t(x)$, hence $t_{maj}(x) \geqslant t(x)$ almost everywhere on Δ. Such a majorant always exist; $t_{maj}(x) = \infty$ for all $x \in \Delta$ is an example. The double-norm $|||\, T\, |||$ is now defined by

$$|||\, T\, ||| = \text{lower bound } \|\, t_{maj}(x)\, \|_\Phi,\ t_{maj}(x) \geqslant t(x) = \|\, T(x, y)\, \|_\Psi,$$

where the lower bound is taken over all possible majorants of $t(x)$.

What we do, actually, is to replace the possibly non-existing measure of an ordinate set by exterior measure (cf. Ch. 2 and Ch.3). Evidently, if $t(x)$ itself is measurable, the present definition gives the same value for $|||\, T\, |||$ as the definition above. From now on we shall say that $T(x, y)$ is of finite double-norm whenever $|||\, T\, ||| < \infty$, where $|||\, T\, |||$ is to be understood in the new sense. It is immediately seen that in this case the proof in Ch. 7, § 15, Ex. B for the boundedness of T and the proof in Ch.11, § 2, Ex. D for the compactness of T need only minor modifications.

For the sake of completeness we shall prove now that in the most important cases $t(x) = \| T(x, y) \|_{\Psi}$ is always measurable.

Lemma α. *If Δ is a set of finite or infinite measure, and Δ is the limit of the ascending sequence of sets Δ_r of finite measure, such that $\mu(\Delta_r) \leqslant r$, then, for any measurable $f(y)$ on Δ,*

$$\| f \|_{\infty} = lim_{r \to \infty} (\{\mu(\Delta_r)\}^{-1} \textstyle\int_{\Delta_r} | f |^r \, d\mu)^{1/r},$$

where both sides may be $+ \infty$.

Proof. Let first $M' < \| f \|_{\infty}$, and let E be a set of finite positive measure on which $| f(y) | > M'$, chosen such that $E \subset \Delta_r$ for r sufficiently large. Hence

$$A_r = (\{\mu(\Delta_r)\}^{-1} \textstyle\int_{\Delta_r} | f |^r d\mu)^{\,1/r} \geqslant$$

$$\{\mu(\Delta_r)\}^{-1/r} \{\mu(E)\}^{1/r} M' \geqslant (r)^{-1/r} \{\mu(E)\}^{1/r} M',$$

which implies $\liminf A_r \geqslant M'$ or $\liminf A_r \geqslant \| f \|_{\infty}$. On the other hand $A_r \leqslant \| f \|_{\infty}$, so that $\limsup A_r \leqslant \| f \|_{\infty}$. It follows that $\| f \|_{\infty} = \lim A_r$.

Theorem 1. *If L_{Φ} is one of the spaces $L_p \,(1 \leqslant p \leqslant \infty)$ and $T(x, y)$ is measurable on $\Delta \times \Delta$, then $t(x) = \| T(x, y) \|_{\Psi}$ is a measurable function of x on Δ.*

Proof. If $1 < p < \infty$, we have $\Phi(u) = u^p/p$, hence $\Psi(v) = v^q/q$ with $1/p + 1/q = 1$. Then $\| f \|_{\Phi} = q^{1/q} \| f \|_p$ and $\| f \|_{\Psi} = p^{1/p} \| f \|_q$ (cf. Ch. 5, § 5). Similarly, for $p = \infty$, we have $\Psi(v) = v$ and $\| f \|_{\Psi} = \| f \|_1$. It follows that

$$\| T(x, y) \|_{\Psi} = \begin{cases} p^{1/p} (\int_{\Delta} | T(x, y) |^q d\mu)^{1/q}, & 1 < p < \infty, \\ \int_{\Delta} | T(x, y) | \, d\mu, & p = \infty. \end{cases}$$

Hence, since $| T(x, y) |^q \,(1 \leqslant q < \infty)$ is measurable on $\Delta \times \Delta$, $\| T(x,y) \|_{\Psi}$ is a measurable function of x by Fubini's Theorem. This completes the proof for $1 < p \leqslant \infty$. Let now $p = 1$, $\Phi(u) = u$. Then (cf. Ch. 5, § 5) $\| f \|_\Phi = \| f \|_1$ and $\| f \|_\Psi = \| f \|_\infty$. Hence, by Lemma α,

$$\| T(x, y) \|_\Psi = \lim_{r\to\infty} (\{\mu(\Delta_r)\}^{-1} \int_{\Delta_r} | T(x, y) |^r \, d\mu)^{1/r},$$

which shows that $t(x) = \| T(x, y) \|_\Psi$ is measurable.

Theorem 2. *If $T(x, y)$ is measurable, then $\| T \|_{\Phi\Psi} \leqslant ||| T |||$. Hence, if $T(x, y)$ is of finite double-norm, then $T(x, y) \in L_{\Phi\Psi}$.*
Proof. For $\int_\Delta \Phi | f | \, d\mu \leqslant 1$ we have

$$\int_\Delta | T(x, y)f(y) | \, d\mu \leqslant \| T(x, y) \|_\Psi \leqslant t_{maj}(x),$$

where $t_{maj}(x)$ is an arbitrary measurable majorant of $t(x) = \| T(x, y) \|_\Psi$. Hence, provided also $\int_\Delta \Psi | g^* | \, d\mu \leqslant 1$,

$$\int_{\Delta\times\Delta} | T(x, y)f(y)g^*(x) | \, d(\mu \times \mu) \leqslant \int_\Delta | t_{maj}(x)g^*(x) | \, d\mu \leqslant \| t_{maj} \|_\Phi.$$

Since this holds for all $t_{maj}(x)$, we find $\| T \|_{\Phi\Psi} \leqslant ||| T |||$.

Definition. *The class D_Φ is the class of all measurable $T(x, y)$ satisfying $||| T ||| < \infty$.*

Theorem 3. *For elements T, T_1, T_2 of D_Φ we have*

$$||| \alpha T ||| = | \alpha | . ||| T ||| \text{ for all complex } \alpha,$$

$$||| T_1 + T_2 ||| \leqslant ||| T_1 ||| + ||| T_2 |||,$$

$||| T ||| = 0$ *if and only if* $T(x, y) = 0$ *almost everywhere on* $\Delta \times \Delta$.
Proof. Trivial.

Theorem 4. *The class D_Φ is a complete Banach space with norm $||| T |||$.*
Proof. We have only to prove that D_Φ is complete. Let for this purpose the sequence $T_n(x, y) \in D_\Phi$ $(n = 1, 2, \ldots)$, satisfying $\lim ||| T_n - T_m ||| = 0$, be given. Since this implies $T_n(x, y) \in L_{\Phi\Psi}$ and $\lim \| T_n - T_m \|_{\Phi\Psi} = 0$, there exists a subsequence $T_k(x, y)$ $(k = n_1, n_2, \ldots)$, converging almost everywhere on $\Delta \times \Delta$ to a measurable $T(x, y)$ (cf. the proof of § 3, Th. 4). Hence, for n fixed, by Fatou's Theorem,

$$\int_\Delta | T(x, y) - T_n(x, y) | . | f(y) | \, d\mu \leqslant$$
$$\liminf \int_\Delta | T_k(x, y) - T_n(x, y) | . | f(y) | \, d\mu$$

for almost every $x \in \Delta$, where k runs through $n_1, n_2, \ldots$ and $f \in L_\Phi$. If in particular $\int_\Delta \Phi \mid f \mid d\mu \leqslant 1$, the integral on the right does not exceed $\| T_k(x, y) - T_n(x, y) \|_\Psi$, hence

$$d(x) = \| T(x, y) - T_n(x, y) \|_\Psi \leqslant \liminf \| T_k(x, y) - T_n(x, y) \|_\Psi = \liminf d_k(x).$$

Let now $m_k(x)$ be a measurable majorant of $d_k(x)$ $(k = n_1, n_2, \ldots)$. Then $m(x) = \liminf m_k(x)$ is a measurable majorant of $d(x)$. The majorants $m_k(x)$ may be chosen such that $\| m_k(x) \|_\Phi \leqslant 2 ||| T_k - T_n |||$. For $\int_\Delta \Psi \mid g^* \mid d\mu \leqslant 1$ we have therefore

$$\int_\Delta m(x) \mid g^*(x) \mid d\mu = \int_\Delta \liminf m_k(x) \mid g^*(x) \mid d\mu \leqslant$$

$$\liminf \int_\Delta m_k(x) \mid g^*(x) \mid d\mu \leqslant \liminf \| m_k \|_\Phi \leqslant \liminf 2 ||| T_k - T_n |||,$$

hence $\| m \|_\Phi \leqslant \liminf 2 ||| T_k - T_n |||$, so that certainly

$$||| T - T_n ||| \leqslant \liminf 2 ||| T_k - T_n |||.$$

This shows that $||| T - T_n |||$ tends to zero as $n \to \infty$.

Theorem 5. *If* $T(x, y) \in D_\Phi$, $S(x, y) \in L_{\Phi\Psi}$ and $V = TS$, *then* $V(x, y) \in D_\Phi$ *and*

$$||| V ||| \leqslant ||| T ||| . \| S \|_{\Phi\Psi}.$$

In particular, if T_1 *and* $T_2 \in D_\Phi$, *then* $T_1T_2 \in D_\Phi$ *and* $||| T_1T_2 ||| \leqslant ||| T_1 ||| . ||| T_2 |||$. *If* $T \in D_\Phi$, *then* $||| T^n ||| \leqslant ||| T |||^n$ $(n = 1, 2, \ldots)$.

Proof. We observe first that the transformation with kernel $S_1(x, y) = S(y, x)$ is bounded on L_Ψ into L_Ψ by § 3, Th. 4, Remark, and that its bound does not exceed $\| S \|_{\Phi\Psi}$. Since both $T(x, y)$ and $S(x, y)$ belong to $L_{\Phi\Psi}$, the transformation $V = TS$ is an integral transformation with kernel $V(x, y) = \int_\Delta T(x, z)S(z, y)d\mu \in L_{\Phi\Psi}$. Then $V_x(y) = V(x, y) = \int_\Delta S(z, y)T_x(z)d\mu$ for almost every $x \in \Delta$. Hence, by what we have observed, $\| V_x(y) \|_\Psi \leqslant \| S \|_{\Phi\Psi} . \| T_x(y) \|_\Psi$ for these values of x. This implies $||| V ||| \leqslant ||| T ||| . \| S \|_{\Phi\Psi}$.

Definition. *The inverse double-norm* $||| T |||^{inv}$ *of* $T(x, y)$ *relative to* L_Φ *is defined as the double-norm of* $T_1(x, y) = T(y, x)$ *relative to* L_Ψ. *Whenever* $||| T |||^{inv} < \infty$, *we shall say that* $T(x, y)$ *is inversely of finite double-norm.*

We observe that $||| T |||^{inv} < \infty$ implies $T_1(x, y) \in L_{\Psi\Phi}$, hence $T(x, y) \in L_{\Phi\Psi}$.

Theorem 6. *Assume that* $T_1(x, y) \in D_\Phi$, *and that* $T_2(x, y)$ *is inversely of finite double-norm. Then, defining the trace* $\tau(T_1T_2)$ *of* T_1T_2 *by*

$$\tau(T_1T_2) = \int_{\Delta\times\Delta} T_1(x, y)T_2(y, x)d(\mu \times \mu),$$

we have

$$| \tau(T_1T_2) | \leqslant ||| T_1 |||.||| T_2 |||^{inv}.$$

Proof. We have

$$\int_\Delta | T_1(x, y)T_2(y, x) | d\mu \leqslant \| T_1(x, y) \|_\Psi . \| T_2(y, x) \|_\Phi \leqslant m_1(x)m_2(x),$$

where $m_1(x)$ and $m_2(x)$ are measurable majorants. Hence

$$| \tau(T_1T_2) | \leqslant \int_\Delta m_1(x)m_2(x)d\mu \leqslant \| m_1 \|_\Phi \| m_2 \|_\Psi$$

for all m_1, m_2, which implies $| \tau(T_1T_2) | \leqslant ||| T_1 |||.||| T_2 |||^{inv}$.

Corollary. *If* $S \in D_\Phi$, *and* T *is inversely of finite double-norm, then* $V = ST \in D_\Phi$ *(cf. Theorem 5),* V *has a finite trace* $\tau(V)$, *and the kernel* $V(x, z) = \int_\Delta S(x, y)T(y, z)d\mu$ *satisfies*

$$| \tau(V) | = | \int_\Delta V(x, x)d\mu | \leqslant ||| S |||.||| T |||^{inv}.$$

If moreover $S = \Sigma_1^\infty S_i$, *where all* S_i *belong to* D_Φ, *and if the series converges in double-norm (that is,* $\lim ||| S - \Sigma_1^n S_i ||| = 0$ *for* $n \to \infty$*), then* $\tau(ST) = \Sigma_1^\infty \tau(S_iT)$.

Theorem 7. *Let* $\Phi(u)$ *and* $\Psi(v)$ *be complementary in the sense of Young, and let the following hypotheses be satisfied:*

(*a*) *There exists a constant* M *such that* $\Phi(2u) \leqslant M\Phi(u)$ *for all* $u \geqslant 0$.

(*b*) $T(x, y) \in L_{\Phi\Psi}$ *and* $||| T^n ||| < \infty$ *for an integer* $n \geqslant 1$.

(*c*) *The linear transformation* T *on* L_Φ *into* L_Φ, *having* $T(x, y)$ *as its kernel, is non-singular.*

Then, if $\lambda \neq 0$ *is not a characteristic value of* T, *its corresponding transformation* H_λ, *defined by* $(T - \lambda I)^{-1} = - \lambda^{-1}I - \lambda^{-2}H_\lambda$, *is an integral transformation with kernel* $H_\lambda(x, y) \in L_{\Phi\Psi}$, *and*

$$H_\lambda(x, y) = T(x, y) + \lambda^{-1}T_2(x, y) + \dots$$
$$+ \lambda^{-(n-2)}T_{n-1}(x, y) + \lambda^{-(n-1)}K_\lambda(x, y),$$

where $||| K_\lambda ||| < \infty$. *The functions* $T_p(x, y)$ $(p = 2, 3, \dots)$ *are here the kernels of* T^p. *In particular,* $||| T ||| < \infty$ *implies* $||| H_\lambda ||| < \infty$.

Proof. Note first that hypothesis (c) is a consequence of (a) and (b) in case μ is separable and $\Psi(2v) \leqslant M_1\Psi(v)$ for all $v \geqslant 0$, since then T^n is compact by Ch. 11, § 2, Ex. D. This covers $\Phi(u) = u^p/p$ $(1 < p < \infty)$. If μ is separable and $\Phi(u) = u$, hypothesis (b) implies the compactness of T^{2n} by Ch. 11, § 2, Ex. E, so that in this case (c) is also satisfied. There remains a gap to bridge between these two cases, e.g. for those $\Phi(u)$ which behave like $u \log u$ for large u. It may be proved (cf. Ex. 4—7 at the end of the present chapter) that (a), (b) and the separability of μ always imply (c).

The proof itself will be divided into three parts.

1°. Write $H_\lambda = T + \lambda^{-1}T^2 + \ldots + \lambda^{-(n-2)}T^{n-1} + \lambda^{-(n-1)}K_\lambda$. Then, by direct computation,

$$(T - \lambda I)K_\lambda = K_\lambda(T - \lambda I) = -\lambda T^n.$$

Suppose now that we know already that H_λ is an integral transformation with kernel $H_\lambda(x, y) \in L_{\Phi\Psi}$. Then, since $T(x, y)$ and all iterates $T_j(x, y)$ belong to $L_{\Phi\Psi}$, the transformation K_λ has also a kernel $K_\lambda(x, y) \in L_{\Phi\Psi}$. The relation $K_\lambda(T - \lambda I) = -\lambda T^n$ implies therefore

$$\int_\Delta T(y, x)K_\lambda(z, y)d\mu - \lambda K_\lambda(z, x) = -\lambda T_n(z, x)$$

almost everywhere on $\Delta \times \Delta$. But this shows that, for almost every $z \in \Delta$, the function $f^*(x) = K_\lambda(z, x)$ is a solution of

$$\int_\Delta T(y, x)f^*(y)d\mu - \lambda f^*(x) = -\lambda T_n(z, x) = g^*(x).$$

Observing that the adjoint transformation T^* in $(L_\Phi)^*$ corresponds (due to (a)) with the kernel $T(y, x)$, and that $-\lambda T_n(z, x) = g^*(x) \in L_\Psi$, so that $g^*(x)$ corresponds with an element $g^* \in (L_\Phi)^*$, our last equation is seen to be equivalent to the equation $(T^* - \lambda I)f^* = g^*$ in $(L_\Phi)^*$. Hence, λ being in the resolvent set of T^*, we have $\| f^* \| \leqslant \| R_\lambda^* \| . \| g^* \| \leqslant \| R_\lambda \| . \| g^* \|$. This implies

$$\| f^*(x) \|_\Psi \leqslant 2 \| f^* \| \leqslant 2 \| R_\lambda \| . \| g^* \| \leqslant 2 \| R_\lambda \| . \| g^*(x) \|_\Psi$$

or

$$\| K_\lambda(z, x) \|_\Psi \leqslant 2 \| R_\lambda \| . \| \lambda T_n(z, x) \|_\Psi = 2 \| \lambda R_\lambda \| . \| T_n(z, x) \|_\Psi.$$

It follows that

$$||| K_\lambda ||| \leqslant 2 \| \lambda R_\lambda \| . ||| T^n ||| < \infty.$$

2°. Since $\| K_\lambda \|_{\Phi\Psi} \leqslant ||| K_\lambda |||$, we find under the same extra hypothesis as in 1° that

$$\| H_\lambda \|_{\Phi\Psi} \leqslant \| T \|_{\Phi\Psi} + | \lambda |^{-1} \| T^2 \|_{\Phi\Psi} + \ldots$$
$$\ldots + | \lambda |^{-(n-2)} \| T^{n-1} \|_{\Phi\Psi} + 2 | \lambda |^{-(n-1)} \| \lambda R_\lambda \| . ||| T^n ||| = F(\lambda).$$

We furthermore recall that $\| (H_\lambda)_a \| \leqslant \| H_\lambda \|_{\Phi\Psi}$ by § 3, Th. 3, where $(H_\lambda)_a$ is the transformation with kernel $| H_\lambda(x, y) |$.

3°. Suppose that $\lambda_1 \neq 0$ is an arbitrary point in the resolvent set of T. In view of the first part of the present proof we have only to show that

H_{λ_1} is an integral transformation with kernel $H_1(x, y) \in L_{\Phi\Psi}$. By § 3, Th. 5 we know already that for $|\lambda^*| > \|T_a\|$ the transformation H_{λ^*} has a kernel $H_{\lambda^*}(x, y) \in L_{\Phi\Psi}$. Since there are at most a finite number of points λ in the point spectrum of T for which $|\lambda| \geqslant |\lambda_1|$, we may join λ_1 by a straight linesegment with a point λ^* in $|\lambda^*| > \|T_a\|$ in such a way that every point on this linesegment is in the resolvent set of T. The expression $F(\lambda)$ in the second part of the present proof is continuous on the segment; it has therefore a finite non-negative maximum B on it. If λ_0 is an arbitrary point on the segment, we consider the open set $|\lambda^{-1} - \lambda_0^{-1}| < B^{-1}$ in the λ-plane. Obviously we may cover the closed segment from λ^* to λ_1 by a finite number of these sets in such a way that λ^* is the "centre" of the first set, and that each centre is in the interior of the preceding set. Assume now that λ_0 is the centre of one of these sets, and that we know already that $H_0 = H_{\lambda_0}$ is an integral transformation with kernel $H_0(x, y) \in L_{\Phi\Psi}$. Then $\|(H_0)_a\| \leqslant \|H_0\|_{\Phi\Psi} \leqslant B$ by the second part of the present proof and the definition of B. It follows therefore from the proof of § 3, Th. 6 that H_λ is an integral transformation with kernel $H_\lambda(x, y) \in L_{\Phi\Psi}$ for all λ satisfying $|\lambda^{-1} - \lambda_0^{-1}| < \|(H_0)_a\|^{-1}$; hence, since $B^{-1} \leqslant \|(H_0)_a\|^{-1}$, certainly for all λ satisfying $|\lambda^{-1} - \lambda_0^{-1}| < B^{-1}$, that is, for all λ in the particular set around λ_0 which we consider. Since we know that $H_{\lambda^*}(x, y) \in L_{\Phi\Psi}$, a successive application of this argument shows that H_{λ_1} is an integral transformation with kernel $H_1(x, y) \in L_{\Phi\Psi}$.

Let us assume that the non-singular integral transformation T has the kernel $T(x, y)$, where $T(x, y) \in L_{\Phi\Psi}$ and $\Phi(2u) \leqslant M\Phi(u)$ for all $u \geqslant 0$ (the same hypotheses therefore as in § 2). Let $\lambda_0 \neq 0$ be a characteristic value of T with index $\nu = \nu(\lambda_0)$. Then the diagrams I and II in § 2, Th. 4 show the structure of the null spaces $M_\nu = N[(T - \lambda_0 I)^\nu]$ and $M_\nu^* = N[(T^* - \lambda_0 I)^\nu]$ respectively. As we know, the space L_Φ is the direct sum of M_ν and the range $L_\nu = W[(T - \lambda_0 I)^\nu]$ (cf. Ch. 11, § 3, Th. 8), so that the projection P_M on M_ν along L_ν and the projection P_L on L_ν along M_ν exist. Since $T - \lambda_0 I$ transforms L_ν one-to-one into itself, it has a bounded inverse R_0 on L_ν. For $\lambda \neq \lambda_0$, but in a sufficiently small neighbourhood of λ_0, we have by Ch. 11, § 4, (2),

$$(1) \quad \begin{cases} R_\lambda = (T - \lambda I)^{-1} = \dfrac{-B_{\nu-1}}{(\lambda - \lambda_0)^\nu} + \dfrac{-B_{\nu-2}}{(\lambda - \lambda_0)^{\nu-1}} + \dots \\ \qquad + \dfrac{-B_0}{\lambda - \lambda_0} + R_\lambda P_L, \end{cases}$$

where

$$B_k = (T - \lambda_0 I)^k P_M \quad (k = 0, 1, \ldots, \nu - 1),$$

$$R_\lambda P_L = R_0 P_L + (\lambda - \lambda_0) R_0^2 P_L + (\lambda - \lambda_0)^2 R_0^3 P_L + \cdots.$$

Let us consider the negative powers of $\lambda - \lambda_0$. We first observe that diagram I contains m_ν functions $f_i(x) \in L_\Phi$ $(i = 1, \ldots, m_\nu)$, where m_ν is the dimension of M_ν. The functions in diagram II will be called $g_i^*(x)$ $(i = 1, \ldots, m_\nu)$, where the $g_i^*(x)$ are ordered such that

$$g_i^*(f_j) = \int_\Delta g_i^*(y) f_j(y) d\mu = \begin{cases} 0 \text{ for } i \neq j, \\ 1 \text{ for } i = j. \end{cases} \tag{2}$$

This is possible by § 2, Th. 4, and the mutual positions of $f_i(x)$ and $g_i^*(x)$ are indicated in the same theorem. They are in the same column, and $f_i(x)$ is as far from the top as $g_i^*(x)$ from the bottom. It will be convenient to complete each column of diagram I by an infinite sequence of zeros below. The thus obtained diagram will be called diagram III.

Theorem 8. *The coefficients* $B_k = (T - \lambda_0 I)^k P_M$ $(k = 0, 1, \ldots, \nu - 1)$ *in* (1) *are integral transformations with kernels*

$$B_k(x, y) = \Sigma_{i=1}^{m_\nu} g_i^*(y) h_i(x),$$

where $h_i(x)$ *is the function in diagram III in the same column as* $f_i(x)$ *but* k *rows below. In particular* $B_0 = P_M$ *has the kernel* $B_0(x, y) = \Sigma_{i=1}^{m_\nu} g_i^*(y) f_i(x)$ *and* $B_{\nu-1} = (T - \lambda_0 I)^{\nu-1} P_M$ *has the kernel* $B_{\nu-1}(x, y) = \Sigma_{i=1}^{d_\nu} e_i^*(y) e_i(x)$, *where* $e_i(x)$ *and* $e_i^*(x)$ *are the functions in the last rows of the diagrams I and II respectively, ordered from left to right.*

We have $\int_\Delta B_0(x, x) d\mu = m_\nu$, $\int_\Delta B_k(x, x) d\mu = 0$ $(k = 1, \ldots, \nu - 1)$.

Proof. It is easily seen that $B_0 f = P_M f = \Sigma_1^{m_\nu} g_i^*(f) f_i$ in the notation of Banach space. Indeed, since this is true for any $f \in L_\nu$ on account of $g_i^*(P_L f) = 0$ (cf. Ch. 11, § 3, Th. 19), and also for every $f = f_i$ $(i = 1, \ldots, m_\nu)$, it holds for any $f \in L_\Phi$. This shows that $B_0 = P_M$ has the kernel $B_0(x, y) = \Sigma_1^{m_\nu} g_i^*(y) f_i(x)$.

Consider now $B_k = (T - \lambda_0 I)^k P_M$. Observing that $(T - \lambda_0 I)^k$ transforms every $f_i(x)$ in diagram III into the function $h_i(x)$ in the same column but k rows below, we obtain the desired result. In particular, for $k = \nu - 1$, only the functions in the first row of diagram III have the property that k rows below there are still the functions $e_1(x), \ldots, e_{d_\nu}(x)$, which do not vanish identically. It follows that $B_{\nu-1}$ has the kernel $B_{\nu-1}(x, y) = \Sigma_1^{d_\nu} e_i^*(y) e_i(x)$.

The last statements follow immediately from (2).

We shall consider more closely the formula (1) for $R_\lambda = (T - \lambda I)^{-1}$. For brevity we denote by B_λ the sum of all negative powers of $\lambda - \lambda_0$ in (1). The transformation H_λ is defined as before by $R_\lambda = -\lambda^{-1}I - \lambda^{-2}H_\lambda$, and S_λ is defined by $S_\lambda = T - H_\lambda$. Observe that $S_\lambda = -\lambda^{-1}H_\lambda T$ by § 3, Th. 1.

Theorem 9. *For $\lambda \neq \lambda_0$, but $|\lambda - \lambda_0|$ sufficiently small, we have*

$$S_\lambda = T - H_\lambda = T - H_\lambda P_L + \lambda P_M + \lambda^2 B_\lambda,$$

where $T - H_\lambda P_L$ may be expanded in terms of non-negative powers of $\mu - \mu_0$, $\mu = \lambda^{-1}$, $\mu_0 = \lambda_0^{-1}$.

Proof. Observing that $P_L P_M = O$, we conclude from (1) that $H_\lambda P_M = (-\lambda I - \lambda^2 R_\lambda)P_M = -\lambda P_M - \lambda^2 B_\lambda$, hence

$$S_\lambda = T - H_\lambda = T - H_\lambda P_L - H_\lambda P_M = T - H_\lambda P_L + \lambda P_M + \lambda^2 B_\lambda.$$

In order to find the expansion for $T - H_\lambda P_L$, we introduce the transformation $T_L = TP_L$. We have

$$T_L - \lambda I = \begin{cases} -\lambda I \text{ on } M_\nu, \\ T - \lambda I \text{ on } L_\nu. \end{cases}$$

For $|\lambda - \lambda_0|$ sufficiently small ($\lambda = \lambda_0$ included), $T - \lambda I$ has a bounded inverse on L_ν. For $\lambda \neq \lambda_0$ this inverse is R_λ, and for $\lambda = \lambda_0$ it is the transformation R_0 in (1). Hence

$$(R_L)_\lambda = (T_L - \lambda I)^{-1} = \begin{cases} -\lambda^{-1}P_M + R_\lambda P_L, \ \lambda \neq \lambda_0, \\ -\lambda^{-1}P_M + R_0 P_L, \ \lambda = \lambda_0, \end{cases}$$

which for $\lambda \neq \lambda_0$ implies

$$(H_L)_\lambda = -\lambda I - \lambda^2 (R_L)_\lambda = -\lambda I + \lambda P_M - \lambda^2 R_\lambda P_L =$$

$$-\lambda P_L - \lambda^2 R_\lambda P_L = H_\lambda P_L.$$

Furthermore, since λ_0 is in the resolvent set of T_L, the transformation $(H_L)_\lambda$ may be expanded in terms of non-negative powers of $\mu - \mu_0$ by § 3, Th. 1. Denoting $(H_L)_\lambda$ for $\lambda = \lambda_0$ by $(H_L)_0$, we find then

$$T - H_\lambda P_L = T - (H_L)_\lambda =$$

$$T - (H_L)_0 - (\mu - \mu_0)(H_L)_0^2 - (\mu - \mu_0)^2 (H_L)_0^3 - \ldots .$$

This is the desired result. We shall however write the obtained series in a slightly different form. From $H_\lambda = -\lambda R_\lambda T$ (cf. § 3, Th. 1) we conclude

$$H_\lambda = -\lambda(-\lambda^{-1}I - \lambda^{-2}H_\lambda)T = (I + \lambda^{-1}H_\lambda)T,$$

hence, with T replaced by T_L, $n \geqslant 2$, $\lambda = \lambda_0$,

$$(H_L)_0^n = (H_L)_0^{n-1}\{I + \lambda_0^{-1}(H_L)_0\}T_L = \{(H_L)_0^{n-1} + \mu_0(H_L)_0^n\}T_L.$$

Furthermore, in view of the general relation $S_\lambda = T - H_\lambda = -\lambda^{-1}H_\lambda T$, we find

$$T - (H_L)_0 = TP_M + T_L - (H_L)_0 = TP_M - \mu_0(H_L)_0 T_L.$$

The final result is therefore that

$$(3)\quad \begin{cases} T - H_\lambda P_L = TP_M - [(\mu-\mu_0)(H_L)_0 + (\mu-\mu_0)^2(H_L)_0^2 + \ldots]T_L \\ \qquad - \mu_0[(H_L)_0 + (\mu-\mu_0)(H_L)_0^2 + (\mu-\mu_0)^2(H_L)_0^3 + \ldots]T_L. \end{cases}$$

Definition. *The measurable function $T(x, y)$ on $\Delta \times \Delta$ will be said to be completely of finite double-norm relative to L_Φ whenever $|||\, T \,||| < \infty$ and $|||\, T \,|||^{inv} < \infty$.*

Remark. Note that for $L_\Phi = L_2$ we have $|||\, T \,||| = |||\, T \,|||^{inv}$, so that in this case $T(x, y)$ is completely of finite double-norm whenever it is of finite double-norm.

Theorem 10. *Let $\Phi(u)$ and $\Psi(v)$ be complementary in the sense of Young, and let the following hypotheses be satisfied (cf. Theorem 7):*

(*a*) *There exists a constant M such that $\Phi(2u) \leqslant M\Phi(u)$ for all $u \geqslant 0$.*

(*b*) *$T(x, y)$ is completely of finite double-norm.*

(*c*) *The linear transformation T on L_Φ into L_Φ, having $T(x, y)$ as its kernel, is non-singular.*

Then, if $\lambda_0 \neq 0$ is a characteristic value of T with algebraic multiplicity m_ν, $\lambda \neq \lambda_0$ and $|\lambda - \lambda_0|$ sufficiently small, the transformation $S_\lambda = T - H_\lambda$ has a finite trace $\tau(S_\lambda)$, which satisfies

$$\tau(S_\lambda) = m_\nu(\mu - \mu_0)^{-1} + \Sigma_{k=0}^{\infty}\, \alpha_k(\mu - \mu_0)^k,\ \mu = \lambda^{-1},\ \mu_0 = \lambda_0^{-1}.$$

If $\lambda_0 \neq 0$ is in the resolvent set of T, the first term in this expansion vanishes.

Proof. Let us assume first that $\lambda_0 \neq 0$ is a characteristic value of T with index ν and algebraic multiplicity m_ν. Observing that $P_M = B_0$ has the kernel $B_0(x, y) = \Sigma_1^{m_\nu} g_i^*(y)f_i(x)$, we see that $T_L = TP_L = T - TP_M$ has the kernel $T(x, y) - \Sigma_1^{m_\nu} g_i^*(y)Tf_i(x)$, so that T_L is completely of finite double-norm. We derive therefore from Theorem 7 that $(H_L)_\lambda$ is of finite double-norm for all λ in the resolvent set of T_L, in particular for $\lambda = \lambda_0$ and all λ in a sufficiently small neighbourhood of λ_0. Hence $|||\, (H_L)_0 \,||| < \infty$ and, by Theorem 5, $|||\, (H_L)_0^n \,||| \leqslant |||\, (H_L)_0 \,|||^n$

($n = 2, 3, \ldots$). It follows that for $| \mu - \mu_0 | < ||| (H_L)_0 |||^{-1}$ the series $\Sigma_1^\infty (\mu - \mu_0)^k (H_L)_0^k$ and $\Sigma_0^\infty (\mu - \mu_0)^k (H_L)_0^{k+1}$ converge in double-norm. These series are exactly those between the square brackets in (3). Noting that TP_M has a finite trace, we find therefore by Theorem 6, Corollary, that

$$\tau(T - H_\lambda P_L) = \Sigma_0^\infty \alpha_k (\mu - \mu_0)^k.$$

By Theorem 9 we have $S_\lambda = \lambda^2 B_\lambda + \lambda P_M + (T - H_\lambda P_L)$, and we know already that $\lambda^2 B_\lambda + \lambda P_M$ is an integral transformation with kernel

$$\lambda^2 \left\{ \frac{-B_{\nu-1}(x, y)}{(\lambda - \lambda_0)^\nu} + \ldots + \frac{-B_0(x, y)}{\lambda - \lambda_0} \right\} + \lambda B_0(x, y);$$

hence, on account of Theorem 8,

$$\tau(\lambda^2 B_\lambda + \lambda P_M) = -\lambda^2 m_\nu (\lambda - \lambda_0)^{-1} + \lambda m_\nu =$$
$$-\lambda\lambda_0 (\lambda - \lambda_0)^{-1} m_\nu = m_\nu (\mu - \mu_0)^{-1}.$$

This leads to the final result that

$$\tau(S_\lambda) = m_\nu (\mu - \mu_0)^{-1} + \Sigma_0^\infty \alpha_k (\mu - \mu_0)^k.$$

If $\lambda_0 \neq 0$ is no characteristic value of T, a similar but easier argument (it is not necessary to introduce T_L now) shows that in this case the term with $(\mu - \mu_0)^{-1}$ vanishes.

Theorem 11. *Under the same conditions for $\Phi(u)$ and $T(x, y)$ we have, for $| \lambda |$ sufficiently large,*

$$\tau(S_\lambda) = -(\mu\sigma_2 + \mu^2\sigma_3 + \ldots),$$

where $\sigma_n = \tau(T^n)$ ($n = 2, 3, \ldots$) and $\mu = \lambda^{-1}$.

Proof. For small $| \mu |$ we have $H_\lambda = T + \mu T^2 + \mu^2 T^3 + \ldots$ (cf. the proof of § 3, Th. 5). This series converges in double-norm for $| \mu | < ||| T |||^{-1}$. Hence, since $S_\lambda = -\mu H_\lambda T$,

$$\tau(S_\lambda) = -(\mu\sigma_2 + \mu^2\sigma_3 + \ldots).$$

The reader who is acquainted with the theory of complex functions will see that from the facts established in the Theorems 10 and 11 we may draw the conclusion that there exists a power series $\delta(\mu) = 1 + \Sigma_1^\infty \delta_n \mu^n$, converging for all complex μ, and having the property that its logarithmic derivative $\delta'(\mu)/\delta(\mu)$ satisfies

$$\delta'(\mu)/\delta(\mu) = \tau(S_\lambda)$$

for all $\mu = \lambda^{-1}$ for which λ is in the resolvent set of T (cf. e.g. TITCHMARSH, The Theory of Functions, second ed., Oxford (1939), 8.11, or KNOPP, Theory of Functions, Dover Publ. (1947), Part II, Ch. 1, or HURWITZ–COURANT, Funktionentheorie, third ed., Berlin (1929), Part I, Ch. 6, § 9). The sum $\delta(\mu)$ of this power series, the Fredholm determinant of T (cf. Ch. 11, § 5), has then a zero of multiplicity m_ν in $\mu_0 = \lambda_0^{-1}$ if and only if λ_0 is a characteristic value of T with algebraic multiplicity m_ν.

Theorem 12. *The coefficients* δ_n $(n = 1, 2, \ldots)$ *in* $\delta(\mu) = 1 + \Sigma_1^\infty \delta_n \mu^n$ *satisfy*

$$\delta_n = \frac{(-1)^n}{n!} \det \begin{vmatrix} 0 & n-1 & 0 & - & - & - & 0 & 0 \\ \sigma_2 & 0 & n-2 & - & - & - & 0 & 0 \\ - - & - - & - - & - & - & - & - & - \\ \sigma_{n-1} & \sigma_{n-2} & \sigma_{n-3} & - & - & - & 0 & 1 \\ \sigma_n & \sigma_{n-1} & \sigma_{n-2} & - & - & - & \sigma_2 & 0 \end{vmatrix}.$$

Proof. Write $\delta_0 = 1$. For small $|\mu|$ we have, by Theorem 11,

$$\delta'(\mu)/\delta(\mu) = \tau(S_\lambda) = -\Sigma_1^\infty \sigma_{n+1}\mu^n,$$

hence

$$\Sigma_0^\infty (n+1)\delta_{n+1}\mu^n = (-\Sigma_1^\infty \sigma_{n+1}\mu^n)(\Sigma_0^\infty \delta_n \mu^n),$$

or

$$\delta_1 = 0,\ (n+1)\delta_{n+1} = -\Sigma_{m=0}^{n-1} \delta_m \sigma_{n+1-m}\ (n = 1, 2, \ldots).$$

The remaining part of the proof is similar to that of Ch. 9, § 16, Th. 2.

Everything which precedes leads up to the following main theorem:

Theorem 13. *Let* $\Phi(2u) \leqslant M\Phi(u)$ *for all* $u \geqslant 0$, *and let the kernel* $T(x, y)$ *of the non-singular transformation* T *be completely of finite double-norm. Then, if* $\lambda \neq 0$ *is not in the point spectrum of* T, *and* $\lambda = \mu^{-1}$, *we have* $H_\lambda(x, y) = H'_\lambda(x, y)/\delta(\mu)$, *where*

$$H'_\lambda(x, y) = \Sigma_0^\infty H_n(x, y)\mu^n,$$

$$\delta(\mu) = 1 + \Sigma_1^\infty \delta_n \mu^n.$$

The coefficients δ_n *and* $H_n(x, y)$ *are the Fredholm–Carleman expressions of Ch. 9, § 17, Th. 7. Both series converge for all* μ, *the series for* $H'_\lambda(x, y)$ *almost everywhere on* $\Delta \times \Delta$. *This series even converges in double-norm.*

Proof. Let $\lambda = \mu^{-1} \neq 0$ run through the resolvent set of T, and let $\delta(\mu) = 1 + \Sigma_1^\infty \delta_n \mu^n$ be the power series introduced above. Consider now the transformation H'_λ, defined by $H'_\lambda = \delta(\mu) H_\lambda$. If $|\mu|$ is small,

$$H'_\lambda = (\Sigma_0^\infty \delta_n \mu^n)(T + \mu T^2 + \mu^2 T^3 + \ldots) = \Sigma_0^\infty H_n \mu^n.$$

Since $\delta_0 = 1$, $\delta_1 = 0$, we find $H_0 = T$, $H_1 = T^2$. Generally, for $n \geqslant 1$,

$$H_n = \delta_n T + \delta_{n-1} T^2 + \ldots + \delta_0 T^{n+1} = \delta_n T + T H_{n-1}.$$

It follows that all H_n are integral transformations with kernels $H_n(x, y)$ of finite double-norm. Furthermore, from $H_n - \delta_n T = \delta_{n-1} T^2 + \ldots + \delta_0 T^{n+1}$ for $n \geqslant 1$, we derive

$$\tau(H_n - \delta_n T) = \delta_{n-1}\sigma_2 + \ldots + \delta_0 \sigma_{n+1} = -(n+1)\delta_{n+1}.$$

This formula also holds for $n = 0$, hence for all n.

One may prove now exactly as in Ch. 9, § 17, Th. 7, that the recurrence formulas

$$\left.\begin{aligned} H_n &= \delta_n T + T H_{n-1}, \\ -n\delta_n &= \tau(H_{n-1} - \delta_{n-1} T), \end{aligned}\right. \quad (n = 1, 2, \ldots),$$

imply that $H_n(x, y)$ and δ_n are the Fredholm-Carleman expressions.

It remains only to prove the statements concerning the convergence of $\Sigma_0^\infty H_n \mu^n$. Evidently all partial sums are of finite double-norm. Let $\lambda_0 = \mu_0^{-1}$ be a characteristic value of T with index ν and algebraic multiplicity m_ν. Then it follows easily from what we have proved in Theorem 9 that H_λ has for small $|\lambda - \lambda_0|$ an expansion in terms of powers of $\mu - \mu_0$ with exponents $\geqslant -\nu$, the expansion converging in double-norm. Hence, since $\delta(\mu)$ has a zero of multiplicity $m_\nu \geqslant \nu$ in $\mu = \mu_0$, the transformation $H'_\lambda = \delta(\mu) H_\lambda$ has an expansion in terms of non-negative powers of $\mu - \mu_0$. The same is trivially true whenever $\lambda_0 \neq 0$ is in the resolvent set of T. These facts imply that the radius of convergence of $\Sigma_0^\infty H_n \mu^n$ (which represents H'_λ for small $|\mu|$) is infinite, since the theorem that the sum of a power series with a finite radius of convergence has a singularity on the circle of convergence remains true in the case that the coefficients are elements of a Banach space (here the space D_Φ of all kernels of finite double-norm). The elementary proof of this theorem as it is reproduced e.g. in HURWITZ-COURANT, Funktionentheorie, third ed., Berlin (1929), Part 1, Ch. 3, § 5, may be taken over practically without modifications. Hence $H'_\lambda = \Sigma_0^\infty H_n \mu^n$ in double-norm for all μ. But then also $\Sigma \, |||H_n||| . |\mu|^n < \infty$, just as the convergence of an ordinary power series implies its absolute convergence. It follows that

$\Sigma \| H_n \mu^n \|_{\Phi\Psi} < \infty$ as well, so that by the same argument as in § 3, Theorem 4 we have

$$\Sigma_n \int_{\Delta_1 \times \Delta_1} | H_n(x, y)\mu^n | \, d(\mu \times \mu) < \infty$$

for every set $\Delta_1 \subset \Delta$ of finite measure. Hence $\Sigma | H_n(x, y)\mu^n | < \infty$ almost everywhere on $\Delta_1 \times \Delta_1$ by Ch. 3, § 3, Th. 9. This shows that $\Sigma H_n(x, y)\mu^n$ converges almost everywhere on $\Delta \times \Delta$. That its sum is $H'_\lambda(x, y)$ may be concluded by applying Fatou's Theorem as in Theorem 4.

Remark. It hardly needs observing that, for any $\lambda = \mu^{-1}$ in the resolvent set of T, the equation

$$f - \mu T f = g, \; g \in L_\Phi,$$

has the solution

$$f(x) = g(x) + \mu H_\lambda g(x) =$$

$$g(x) + \frac{\mu}{\delta(\mu)} \Sigma_0^\infty \mu^n \int_\Delta H_n(x, y) g(y) dy,$$

where this series converges according to the L_Φ-norm, and also pointwise almost everywhere on Δ.

Our final result is therefore that we have extended the main theorems of Carleman and Smithies for kernels of finite double-norm in the space $L_2(\Delta, \mu)$ (cf. Ch. 9, § 17) to kernels which are completely of finite double-norm in the space $L_\Phi(\Delta, \mu)$. It has been necessary however to use nearly the whole spectral theory of non-singular transformations and, besides that, some facts from the theory of complex functions, all of which may be avoided in Smithies' method of discussing the L_2-case.

The L_p-case ($1 < p < \infty$) was considered by Ickovič [1], the L_Φ-case by the present author [9].

§ 5. Uniform Convergence of the Resolvent Expansions. Boundedness or Continuity of the Solutions of the Integral Equation

In the case that Δ is a set in Euclidean space, and μ is Lebesgue measure in this space, we may prove under somewhat stronger hypotheses that the expansions for $H_\lambda(x, y)$ in the preceding paragraphs converge uniformly. For this purpose we define:

Class B. *The kernel* $T(x, y) \in L_{\Phi\Psi}$ *belongs to the class B whenever there exists a constant c such that, for all* $x \in \Delta$ *and all* $y \in \Delta$,

$$t(x) = \| T(x, y) \|_{\Psi} \leqslant c, \quad s(y) = \| T(x, y) \|_{\Phi} \leqslant c.$$

Class Cm. *In case the set* Δ *is bounded and closed, the measurable kernel* $T(x, y)$ *belongs to the class Cm whenever, for all* $x_1, x_2 \in \Delta$ *and all* $y_1, y_2 \in \Delta$,

$$\lim_{x_2 \to x_1} \| T(x_2, y) - T(x_1, y) \|_{\Psi} = 0,$$

$$\lim_{y_2 \to y_1} \| T(x, y_2) - T(x, y_1) \|_{\Phi} = 0.$$

Whenever $T(x, y) \in Cm$, *we shall also say that* $T(x, y)$ *is continuous in mean (relative to* L_{Φ}*).*

Obviously, if Δ is bounded and $T(x, y) \in B$, then $||| T ||| < \infty$ and $||| T |||^{inv} < \infty$. Furthermore, if $T(x, y) \in Cm$, the mean continuity is uniform on Δ, since Δ is supposed to be bounded and closed in this case (apply the Heine-Borel-Lebesgue Covering Theorem). It follows that $t(x) = \| T(x, y) \|_{\Psi}$ and $s(y) = \| T(x, y) \|_{\Phi}$ are continuous on Δ, and therefore bounded. Then $T(x, y) \in B$, so that, by what we already observed, T is completely of finite double-norm.

Theorem 1. *If T has the kernel* $T(x, y) \in B$, *and* $| \lambda | > \| T_a \|$ *(so that* λ *belongs to the resolvent set of T on account of* $\| T_a \| \geqslant \| T \|$*), then the Neumann series*

$$T(x, y) + \lambda^{-1} T_2(x, y) + \lambda^{-2} T_3(x, y) + \dots$$

converges uniformly on $\Delta \times \Delta$ *to* $H_{\lambda}(x, y)$. *We have* $H_{\lambda}(x, y) \in B$, *and* $S_{\lambda}(x, y) = T(x, y) - H_{\lambda}(x, y)$ *is bounded on* $\Delta \times \Delta$.

If $T(x, y) \in Cm$, *then* $H_{\lambda}(x, y) \in Cm$, *and all iterated kernels* $T_p(x, y)$ $(p = 2, 3, \dots)$ *are continuous on* $\Delta \times \Delta$, *so that* $S_{\lambda}(x, y)$ *is continuous as well.*

Proof. Since $T_2(x, y)$ may be defined now by

$$T_2(x, y) = \int_{\Delta} T(z, y) T(x, z) dz$$

for all $(x, y) \in \Delta \times \Delta$ (not, as before, only for almost all $(x, y) \in \Delta \times \Delta$), we have, as in the proof of § 4, Th. 5,

$$t_2(x) = \| T_2(x, y) \|_{\Psi} \leqslant \| T \|_{\Phi\Psi} \| T(x, y) \|_{\Psi} \leqslant c \| T \|_{\Phi\Psi}.$$

Generally

$$t_n(x) = \| T_n(x, y) \|_{\Psi} \leqslant c \| T^{n-1} \|_{\Phi\Psi} \; (n \geqslant 2).$$

In the same way

$$s_n(y) = \| T_n(x, y) \|_\Phi \leqslant c \, \| T^{n-1} \|_{\Phi\Psi} \ (n \geqslant 2).$$

It follows that

$$| T_2(x, y) | \leqslant t(x)s(y) \leqslant c^2,$$

$$| T_n(x, y) | = | \textstyle\int_\Delta T_{n-1}(x, z)T(z, y)dz | \leqslant$$

$$t_{n-1}(x)s(y) \leqslant c^2 \, \| T^{n-2} \|_{\Phi\Psi} \ (n > 2).$$

The uniform convergence of the Neumann series for $|\lambda| > \| T_a \|$ is proved now by a similar argument as in § 3, Th. 5. In the same way it is seen that $\Sigma_0^\infty |\lambda|^{-n} \| T_{n+1}(x, y) \|_\Psi$ and $\Sigma_0^\infty |\lambda|^{-n} \| T_{n+1}(x, y) \|_\Phi$ converge uniformly on Δ. Hence $H_\lambda(x, y) \in B$, and $S_\lambda(x, y)$ is bounded.

If $T(x, y) \in Cm$, then $T_2(x, y)$ is a continuous function of x uniformly in y and a continuous function of y uniformly in x. This shows that $T_2(x, y)$ is continuous on $\Delta \times \Delta$. The same holds for $T_p(x, y)$ ($p = 3, 4, \ldots$). It follows then from the uniform convergence of the Neumann series that $S_\lambda(x, y)$ is continuous on $\Delta \times \Delta$ for $|\lambda| > \| T_a \|$, so that $H_\lambda(x, y) \in Cm$.

Remark. If λ_0 is in the resolvent set of $T(x, y) \in B$, and we know that $H_0(x, y) = H_{\lambda_0}(x, y) \in B$ and that $T(x, y) - H_0(x, y)$ is bounded, then it may be proved similarly that for $|\lambda^{-1} - \lambda_0^{-1}| < \| (H_0)_a \|^{-1}$ the series $H_\lambda(x, y) = H_0(x, y) + (\lambda^{-1} - \lambda_0^{-1})H_{0,2}(x, y) + (\lambda^{-1} - \lambda_0^{-1})^2 H_{0,3}(x, y) + \ldots$ converges uniformly on $\Delta \times \Delta$, and that all $H_{0,p}(x, y)$ ($p = 2, 3, \ldots$) are bounded. Hence $H_\lambda(x, y) \in B$, and $T(x, y) - H_\lambda(x, y)$ is bounded for these values of λ.

In the same way, if $T(x, y) \in Cm$, $H_0(x, y) \in Cm$, and $T(x, y) - H_0(x, y)$ is continuous, then $H_\lambda(x, y) \in Cm$, and $T(x, y) - H_\lambda(x, y)$ is continuous for $|\lambda^{-1} - \lambda_0^{-1}| < \| (H_0)_a \|^{-1}$.

Theorem 2. *If $\Phi(2u) \leqslant M\Phi(u)$ for all $u \geqslant 0$, $T(x, y) \in B$ is non-singular and $||| T ||| < \infty$, then $H_\lambda(x, y) \in B$, and $T(x, y) - H_\lambda(x, y)$ is bounded for all $\lambda \neq 0$ in the resolvent set of T. If $T(x, y) \in Cm$, then $H_\lambda(x, y) \in Cm$ and $T(x, y) - H_\lambda(x, y)$ is continuous for all $\lambda \neq 0$ in the resolvent set of T.*

Proof. Follows from the preceding theorem by observing that, starting from a point λ^* in $|\lambda^*| > \| T_a \|$, any $\lambda_1 \neq 0$ in the resolvent set of T may be reached in a finite number of steps of the kind described in the remark above (cf. the proof of § 4, Th. 7).

Theorem 3. *Let $\Phi(2u) \leqslant M\Phi(u)$ for all $u \geqslant 0$, and let the kernel $T(x, y)$ of the non-singular transformation T be completely of finite double-norm. Let moreover $T(x, y) \in B$. Then, if $\lambda \neq 0$ is in the resolvent set of T and $\lambda = \mu^{-1}$, we have, with the notations of § 4, Th. 13,*

$$H_\lambda(x, y) = \{\delta(\mu)\}^{-1} \Sigma_0^\infty H_n(x, y)\mu^n$$

uniformly on $\Delta \times \Delta$. Furthermore $H_n(x, y) - \delta_n T(x, y)$ is bounded for $n = 0, 1, 2, \ldots$. If $T(x, y) \in Cm$, then $H_n(x, y) - \delta_n T(x, y)$ is continuous for $n = 0, 1, 2, \ldots$.

Proof. In view of $H_0 = T$, $H_n = \delta_n T + \delta_{n-1} T^2 + \ldots + \delta_0 T^{n+1} = \delta_n T + H_{n-1} T$ $(n \geqslant 1)$, we find

$$h_n(x) = \| H_n(x, y) \|_\Psi \leqslant | \delta_n | . \| T(x, y) \|_\Psi + \| H_{n-1} \|_{\Phi\Psi} \| T(x, y) \|_\Psi$$
$$\leqslant (| \delta_n | + ||| H_{n-1} |||)c \quad (n \geqslant 1),$$

hence

$$| H_0(x, y) - \delta_0 T(x, y) | = 0,$$
$$| H_1(x, y) - \delta_1 T(x, y) | = | T_2(x, y) | \leqslant c^2,$$
$$| H_{n+1}(x, y) - \delta_{n+1} T(x, y) | \leqslant \| H_n(x, y) \|_\Psi \| T(x, y) \|_\Phi$$
$$\leqslant (| \delta_n | + ||| H_{n-1} |||)c^2 \quad (n \geqslant 1).$$

Since $\Sigma | \delta_n \mu^n | < \infty$ and $\Sigma ||| H_n |||.| \mu |^n < \infty$ by the proof of § 4, Th. 13, it follows that $\Sigma_0^\infty | H_n(x, y) - \delta_n T(x, y) |.| \mu |^n$ converges uniformly on $\Delta \times \Delta$. The same holds then for

$$H_\lambda(x, y) - T(x, y) = \{\delta(\mu)\}^{-1} \Sigma_0^\infty [H_n(x, y) - \delta_n T(x, y)]\mu^n.$$

The remaining statements are now evident.

Theorem 4. *If $\Phi(2u) \leqslant M\Phi(u)$ for all $u \geqslant 0$ and $T(x, y) \in B$ is non-singular, then the characteristic functions of $T(x, y)$, belonging to characteristic values $\neq 0$, are bounded on the whole set Δ. If $\lambda \neq 0$, and the bounded function $g(x)$ is such that the integral equation $Tf - \lambda f = g$ admits a solution $f(x)$, this solution is bounded on the whole set Δ. In particular, if λ is in the resolvent set of T, the equation has a uniquely determined bounded solution $f(x)$ for every bounded $g(x)$.*

If $T(x, y) \in Cm$, the characteristic functions of $T(x, y)$, belonging to characteristic values $\neq 0$, are continuous on the whole set Δ. If $\lambda \neq 0$, and the continuous function $g(x)$ is such that $Tf - \lambda f = g$ admits a solution $f(x)$, this solution is continuous on the whole set Δ. In particular, if λ is *in the resolvent set of T, the equation has a uniquely determined continuous solution $f(x)$ for every continuous $g(x)$.*

Proof. Let $T(x, y) \in B$. Then, writing $h = Tf$ for an arbitrary $f \in L_\Phi$, we have

$$| h(x) | = | \int_\Delta T(x, y)f(y)dy | \leqslant \| T(x, y) \|_\Psi \| f \|_\Phi \leqslant c \| f \|_\Phi$$

for all x, hence $h(x)$ is bounded on Δ. If therefore $\lambda \neq 0$, and $g(x)$ is bounded, every solution $f \in L_\Phi$ of $Tf - \lambda f = g$ is bounded on Δ. In particular, taking $g(x) = 0$ for every x, every characteristic function is seen to be bounded on Δ.

Let $T(x, y) \in Cm$. Then, writing $h = Tf$ for an arbitrary $f \in L_\Phi$, we have

$$| h(x_2) - h(x_1) | = | \int_\Delta \{T(x_2, y) - T(x_1, y)\}f(y)dy |$$

$$\leqslant \| T(x_2, y) - T(x_1, y) \|_\Psi \| f \|_\Phi,$$

which shows that $h(x)$ is continuous on Δ. If therefore $\lambda \neq 0$, and $g(x)$ is continuous, every solution $f \in L_\Phi$ of $Tf - \lambda f = g$ is continuous on Δ. In particular, taking $g(x) = 0$ for every x, every characteristic function is seen to be continuous.

Example. Let Δ be the linear interval $[0, 1]$, and consider the linear integral transformation T in $L_p(\Delta)$ $(1 \leqslant p < \infty)$ whose kernel is $T(x, y) = B(x, y) | x - y |^{-\alpha}$ $(0 \leqslant \alpha < 1)$, where $B(x, y)$ is bounded on $\Delta \times \Delta$. We shall prove that every characteristic function $f(x)$ of T, belonging to a characteristic value $\lambda \neq 0$, is bounded on Δ.

In Ch. 9, § 9, Ex. C we have seen that T is bounded, and that for $n > 1/(1 - \alpha)$ the iterated kernel $T_n(x, y)$ is bounded on $\Delta \times \Delta$. Hence $T_n(x, y) \in B$ for these values of n. Also $||| T^n ||| < \infty$, so that T is non-singular. Let now $\lambda \neq 0$, and

$$\int_\Delta T(x, y)f(y)dy = \lambda f(x)$$

for all $x \in \Delta$. Then

$$\int_\Delta T_n(x, y)f(y)dy = \lambda^n f(x)$$

for almost every $x \in \Delta$, hence $f(x)$ is bounded almost everywhere on Δ. This shows that $| B(x, y)f(y) | \leqslant C$ for almost every y. The boundedness of $f(x)$ for every $x \in \Delta$ follows therefore from

$$| f(x) | \leqslant | \lambda |^{-1} C \int_0^1 | x - y |^{-\alpha}dy \leqslant 2 | \lambda |^{-1}C \int_0^1 y^{-\alpha}dy.$$

§ 6. Singular Values and Singular Functions of a Kernel of Finite Double-Norm on $L_2(\Delta)$

In Ch. 12, § 18 we have considered a compact linear transformation T on a complete Hilbert space R, and we have found several properties of the singular values and singular elements of T. If $\lambda_1^2 \geqslant \lambda_2^2 \geqslant \ldots > 0$ is the sequence of characteristic values $\neq 0$ of T^*T and TT^*, then $\lambda_1 \geqslant \lambda_2 \geqslant \ldots > 0$ is the sequence of singular values $\neq 0$ of T and T^*. Denoting by φ_i $(i = 1, 2, \ldots)$ a corresponding orthonormal system of characteristic elements of T^*T, hence $T^*T\varphi_i = \lambda_i^2\varphi_i$, the system $\psi_i = \lambda_i^{-1}T\varphi_i$ $(i = 1, 2, \ldots)$ is an orthonormal system of characteristic elements of TT^*, hence $TT^*\psi_i = \lambda_i^2\psi_i$. We have $T\varphi_i = \lambda_i\psi_i$, $T^*\psi_i = \lambda_i\varphi_i$ $(i = 1, 2, \ldots)$ by Ch. 12, § 18, Th. 3; $Tf = 0$ if and only if $(f, \varphi_i) = 0$ for all i, and $T^*f = 0$ if and only if $(f, \psi_i) = 0$ for all i by Ch. 12, § 18, Th. 5. The sequences φ_i and ψ_i are called sequences of singular elements of T and T^*.

Let now the Hilbert space R be the space $L_2(\Delta, \mu)$, where μ is a separable measure and Δ is a μ-measurable set, and let T be of finite double-norm, hence $||| T ||| < \infty$. Then (cf. Ch. 9, § 10) T is an integral transformation with kernel $T(x, y)$ satisfying $||| T |||^2 = \int_{\Delta\times\Delta} | T(x, y) |^2 d(\mu \times \mu) < \infty$. We recall that $||| T |||^2 = \Sigma_i \| T\chi_i \|^2$ if $\{\chi_i\}$ is a complete orthonormal system in $L_2(\Delta, \mu)$ (cf. the proof of Ch. 9, § 10, Th. 7).

Theorem 1. *If $\lambda_1 \geqslant \lambda_2 \geqslant \ldots > 0$ is the sequence of singular values of T, then*

$$||| T |||^2 = \int_{\Delta\times\Delta} | T(x, y) |^2 d(\mu \times \mu) = \Sigma \lambda_i^2.$$

Proof. Observing that $Tf = 0$ if f is orthogonal to all φ_i, we find

$$||| T |||^2 = \Sigma \| T\varphi_i \|^2 = \Sigma \| \lambda_i\psi_i \|^2 = \Sigma \lambda_i^2.$$

Remark. If T has the sequence ξ_i $(i = 1, 2, \ldots)$ of characteristic values $\neq 0$, each characteristic value repeated according to its algebraic multiplicity, then $\Sigma_i | \xi_i |^s \leqslant \Sigma_i \lambda_i^s$ for all $s > 0$ by Ch. 12, § 18, Th. 8. Hence, for $s = 2$,

$$\Sigma | \xi_i |^2 \leqslant \Sigma \lambda_i^2 = ||| T |||^2.$$

We thus have reestablished Schur's Theorem, proved differently in Ch. 11, § 7, Th. 2.

Theorem 2. *If $T = AB$, where A and B are of finite double-norm, and if T has the singular values $\lambda_1 \geqslant \lambda_2 \geqslant \ldots > 0$, then*

$$\Sigma \lambda_i \leqslant ||| A ||| . ||| B ||| \ [2].$$

Proof. We have

$$\lambda_i = (\lambda_i\psi_i, \psi_i) = (T\varphi_i, \psi_i) = (B\varphi_i, A^*\psi_i) \leqslant \| B\varphi_i \| . \| A^*\psi_i \|,$$

hence

$$\Sigma\, \lambda_i \leqslant (\Sigma \| B\varphi_i \|^2)^{1/2} (\Sigma \| A^*\psi_i \|^2)^{1/2} \leqslant$$
$$||| B |||.||| A^* ||| = ||| A |||.||| B |||,$$

where we have used that $||| A ||| = ||| A^* |||$ by Ch. 9, § 10, Th. 1.

Remark. If T has the sequence ξ_i $(i = 1, 2, \ldots)$ of characteristic values $\neq 0$, each characteristic value repeated according to its algebraic multiplicity, then

$$\Sigma \mid \xi_i \mid \leqslant \Sigma\, \lambda_i \leqslant ||| A |||.||| B |||.$$

We thus have reestablished Lalesco's Theorem, proved differently in Ch. 11, § 7, Th. 1.

Theorem 3 (*Expansion theorem*). *If* $f(x) \in L_2$, *then*

$$\int_\Delta T(x, y) f(y) d\mu \sim \Sigma\, \lambda_i (f, \varphi_i) \psi_i(x),$$
$$\int_\Delta \overline{T(y, x)} f(y) d\mu \sim \Sigma\, \lambda_i (f, \psi_i) \varphi_i(x),$$

where the symbol $\sim$ *denotes convergence in mean with index* 2 *on the set* Δ (*cf. Ch.* 6, § 13, *Ex. A*).

Proof. Follows immediately from Ch. 12, § 18, Th. 6.

Theorem 4 (*Expansion theorem for the kernel*). *We have*

$$T(x, y) \sim \Sigma\, \lambda_i \psi_i(x) \overline{\varphi_i(y)}, \tag{1}$$

where $\sim$ *denotes convergence in mean with index* 2 *on* $\Delta \times \Delta$. *Furthermore*

$$\int_\Delta \mid T(x, y) \mid^2 d\mu_y = \Sigma\, \lambda_i^2 \mid \psi_i(x) \mid^2, \tag{2}$$

$$\int_\Delta \mid T(x, y) \mid^2 d\mu_x = \Sigma\, \lambda_i^2 \mid \varphi_i(y) \mid^2, \tag{3}$$

where (2) *holds for almost every* $x \in \Delta$, *and* (3) *holds for almost every* $y \in \Delta$.

Proof. Consider $T(x, y) = T_y(x)$ as a function $t(x)$ of x. Then $t(x) \in L_2$ for almost every $y \in \Delta$. Hence, also for almost every $y \in \Delta$,

$$(t, \psi_i) = \int_\Delta T(x, y) \overline{\psi_i(x)} d\mu = \lambda_i \overline{\varphi_i(y)} \quad (i = 1, 2, \ldots),$$

and, if f is orthogonal to all ψ_i,

$$(t, f) = \int_\Delta T(x, y) \overline{f(x)} d\mu = 0.$$

It follows that $t = \Sigma\,(t, \psi_i)\psi_i$, hence

$$\| t - \Sigma_1^n (t, \psi_i)\psi_i \|^2 = \Sigma_{n+1} | (t, \psi_i) |^2,$$

or

$$\int_\Delta | T(x, y) - \Sigma_1^n \lambda_i\psi_i(x)\overline{\varphi_i(y)} |^2 d\mu = \Sigma_{n+1} \lambda_i^2 \, | \varphi_i(y) |^2 \tag{4}$$

for almost every $y \in \Delta$. Taking $n = 0$ we obtain (3), and integrating (4) over y, we find

$$\int_{\Delta\times\Delta} | T(x, y) - \Sigma_1^n \lambda_i\psi_i(x)\overline{\varphi_i(y)} |^2 d(\mu \times \mu) = \Sigma_{n+1}\lambda_i^2.$$

For $n = 0$ we find again Theorem 1, and, making $n \to \infty$, we get (1).

Considering $T(x, y) = T_x(y)$ as a function of y, we find (2) in a similar way.

Remark. The expansion (1) may also be found by observing that $R_n(x, y) = T(x, y) - \Sigma_1^n \lambda_i\psi_i(x)\overline{\varphi_i(y)}$ satisfies $|||\, R_n \,|||^2 = \Sigma_{n+1}^\infty \lambda_i^2$, hence $\lim |||\, R_n \,||| = 0$.

Theorem 5. *The convergence in mean in Theorem 3 may be replaced by ordinary pointwise convergence for almost every $x \in \Delta$. Both series even converge absolutely for these x.*

Proof. We have $\int_\Delta | T(x, y) |^2 d\mu = \Sigma \lambda_i^2 \, | \psi_i(x) |^2$ for almost every $x \in \Delta$, that is, for $x \in \Delta - E$ where E has measure zero. Then, if $x \in \Delta - E$,

$$\Sigma_1^n | \lambda_i(f, \varphi_i)\psi_i(x) | \leqslant (\Sigma_1^n | (f, \varphi_i) |^2)^{1/2}(\Sigma_1^n\lambda_i^2 \, | \psi_i(x) |^2)^{1/2}$$
$$\leqslant \| f \| (\int_\Delta | T(x, y) |^2 d\mu)^{1/2},$$

which shows that $\Sigma\,\lambda_i(f, \varphi_i)\psi_i(x)$ converges absolutely. It follows already from Theorem 3 that a subsequence of partial sums converges pointwise to $\int_\Delta T(x, y)f(y)d\mu$ almost everywhere on Δ, so that, since now the series itself converges, its sum is almost everywhere on Δ equal to $\int_\Delta T(x, y)f(y)d\mu$. The proof for $\Sigma\,\lambda_i(f, \psi_i)\varphi_i(x)$ is similar.

Theorem 6. *If $T = AB$, where A and B are of finite double-norm, then*

$$T(x, y) = \Sigma\,\lambda_i\psi_i(x)\overline{\varphi_i(y)}$$

almost everywhere on $\Delta \times \Delta$. The series even converges absolutely almost everywhere on $\Delta \times \Delta$.

Proof. Since

$$\Sigma\,\lambda_i \int_\Delta | \psi_i(x) |^2 \, d\mu = \Sigma\,\lambda_i < \infty$$

by Theorem 2, we have $\Sigma \lambda_i \mid \psi_i(x) \mid^2 < \infty$ almost everywhere on Δ (cf. Ch. 3, § 3, Th. 9). In the same way $\Sigma \lambda_i \mid \varphi_i(y) \mid^2 < \infty$ almost everywhere on Δ. Hence

$$\Sigma \mid \lambda_i \psi_i(x) \overline{\varphi_i(y)} \mid \leqslant (\Sigma \lambda_i \mid \psi_i(x) \mid^2)^{1/2} (\Sigma \lambda_i \mid \varphi_i(y) \mid^2)^{1/2} < \infty$$

almost everywhere on $\Delta \times \Delta$. That the sum of $\Sigma \lambda_i \psi_i(x) \overline{\varphi_i(y)}$ is $T(x, y)$ follows by a similar argument as in the preceding theorem.

If Δ is a set in Euclidean space, and μ is Lebesgue measure, the kernel $T(x, y)$ of finite double-norm belongs to class B (cf. § 5) whenever there exists a constant c such that

$$t(x) = (\textstyle\int_\Delta \mid T(x, y) \mid^2 dy)^{1/2} \leqslant c, \quad s(y) = (\textstyle\int_\Delta \mid T(x, y) \mid^2 dx)^{1/2} \leqslant c.$$

The kernel $T(x, y)$ belongs to the class Cm whenever Δ is bounded and closed, and

$$\lim_{x_2 \to x_1} \textstyle\int_\Delta \mid T(x_2, y) - T(x_1, y) \mid^2 dy = 0,$$

$$\lim_{y_2 \to y_1} \textstyle\int_\Delta \mid T(x, y_2) - T(x, y_1) \mid^2 dx = 0.$$

Theorem 7. *If $T(x, y) \in B$, the series $\Sigma \lambda_i(f, \varphi_i)\psi_i(x)$ converges uniformly and its sum is $\int_\Delta T(x, y)f(y)dy$ almost everywhere on Δ. A similar statement holds for $\Sigma \lambda_i(f, \psi_i)\varphi_i(x)$.*

If $T(x, y) \in Cm$, then all terms in $\Sigma \lambda_i(f, \varphi_i)\psi_i(x)$ are continuous, and the series converges uniformly on the whole set Δ to the continuous sum $\int_\Delta T(x, y)f(y)dy$.

Proof. Let $T(x, y) \in B$. We have only to prove that $\Sigma \lambda_i(f, \varphi_i)\psi_i(x)$ converges uniformly. This follows from

$$\mid \Sigma_p^q \lambda_i(f, \varphi_i)\psi_i(x) \mid = \mid \textstyle\int_\Delta T(x, y) \, \Sigma_p^q (f, \varphi_i)\varphi_i(y)dy \mid$$

$$\leqslant (\textstyle\int_\Delta \mid T(x, y) \mid^2 dy)^{1/2} \parallel \Sigma_p^q (f, \varphi_i)\varphi_i \parallel \leqslant c \, \Sigma_p^q \mid (f, \varphi_i) \mid^2,$$

holding for all $x \in \Delta$.

Let now $T(x, y) \in Cm$. Then every function of the form $\int_\Delta T(x, y)f(y)dy$ is continuous on Δ if $f \in L_2$, and the same holds for every function $\int_\Delta \overline{T(x, y)}f(x)dx$. It follows that all terms in $\Sigma \lambda_i(f, \varphi_i)\psi_i(x)$ are continuous, so that, since this series converges uniformly on Δ by the above argument, its sum is also continuous. But, this sum being equal to $\int_\Delta T(x, y)f(y)dy$ almost everywhere on Δ, and $\int_\Delta T(x, y)f(y)dy$ being continuous as well, the series converges to $\int_\Delta T(x, y)f(y)dy$ for every $x \in \Delta$.

For our further purposes we need a theorem about uniform convergence.

Theorem 8 (*Dini's Theorem*). *If Δ is a bounded closed set, and the series $\Sigma f_n(x)$ of non-negative continuous functions converges to the continuous function $f(x)$ for all $x \in \Delta$, then the convergence is uniform.*

Proof. Writing $g_n(x) = f(x) - \Sigma_1^n f_i(x)$, the functions $g_n(x)$ are continuous, $g_n(x) \geqslant g_{n+1}(x)$ $(n = 1, 2, \ldots)$, and $\lim g_n(x) = 0$ for every $x \in \Delta$. We have to prove that $\lim g_n(x) = 0$ uniformly on Δ.

Given $\varepsilon > 0$ and an arbitrary point $x_0 \in \Delta$, there exists an index N, depending on ε and x_0, such that $g_N(x_0) < \varepsilon$. Then, since $g_N(x)$ is continuous, $g_N(x) < \varepsilon$ holds in the common part of Δ and an open interval I_{x_0} around x_0. Hence $g_n(x) \leqslant g_N(x) < \varepsilon$ for $n \geqslant N(\varepsilon, x_0)$, $x \in I_{x_0} . \Delta$. On account of the Heine-Borel-Lebesgue Theorem we may cover Δ by a finite number $I_{x_1}, \ldots, I_{x_k}$ of these open intervals, so that, writing

$$N_0 = \max [N(\varepsilon, x_1), \ldots, N(\varepsilon, x_k)],$$

we find

$$g_n(x) \leqslant g_{N_0}(x) < \varepsilon \text{ for } n \geqslant N_0, \ x \in \Delta.$$

This completes the proof.

Theorem 9. *If* $T(x, y) \in Cm$, *then*

(2) $$\int_\Delta | T(x, y) |^2 \, dy = \Sigma \lambda_i^2 \, | \psi_i(x) |^2,$$

(3) $$\int_\Delta | T(x, y) |^2 \, dx = \Sigma \lambda_i^2 \, | \varphi_i(y) |^2,$$

uniformly on Δ.

Proof. Upon inspection of the proof of Theorem 4 it is easily seen that (3) holds for all $y \in \Delta$ in the present case. The uniform convergence of $\Sigma \lambda_i^2 \, | \varphi_i(y) |^2$ follows then by Dini's Theorem. The proof for (2) is similar.

Remark. The arrangement of the sequence λ_i is irrelevant in all expansion theorems.

§ 7. Positive Kernels

We shall consider a linear transformation of finite double-norm on $L_2(\Delta, \mu)$ where the measure μ is separable, and the kernel $T(x, y)$ satisfies $T(x, y) > 0$ on $\Delta \times \Delta$, or at least almost everywhere on $\Delta \times \Delta$. Kernels of this kind, under the extra hypothesis that Δ is a bounded set in Euclidean space, and $T(x, y)$ is continuous or at least continuous in mean, were considered by R. Jentzsch [3] and E. Hopf [4]. We prove (essentially by Jentzsch's method):

Theorem 1. *Let* $T(x, y) > 0$ *almost everywhere on* $\Delta \times \Delta$ *and* $\int_{\Delta\times\Delta} | T |^2 d(\mu \times \mu) < \infty$. *Then the corresponding transformation* T *has at least one positive characteristic value. There exists a positive characteristic value* λ_0 *such that* $| \lambda_i | < \lambda_0$ *for all other characteristic values* λ_i. *The algebraic multiplicity of* λ_0 *is one, and every characteristic function belonging to* λ_0 *is a constant multiple of an almost everywhere positive function.*

Proof. We divide the proof into several parts.

1°. It follows from our hypothesis that the iterated kernel $T_2(x, y)$ satisfies $T_2(x, y) > 0$ almost everywhere on $\Delta \times \Delta$. Generally $T_n(x,y) > 0$ $(n = 2, 3, \ldots)$ almost everywhere on $\Delta \times \Delta$. This implies

$$\sigma_n = \tau(T^n) = \int_{\Delta\times\Delta} T(x, y)T_{n-1}(y, x)d(\mu \times \mu) > 0 \quad (n = 2, 3, \ldots),$$

which shows that T has at least one characteristic value $\neq 0$ (cf. Ch. 11, § 7, Th. 4).

Let λ_1 be a characteristic value of T such that all λ satisfying $| \lambda | > | \lambda_1 |$ belong to the resolvent set of T. Write $\lambda_1^{-1} = \mu_1$, $| \lambda_1 | = \lambda_0$ and $\lambda_0^{-1} = \mu_0$. Then, with the notations of § 4, Th. 11, the power series

$$\tau(S_\lambda) = -\ (\mu\sigma_2 + \mu^2\sigma_3 + \ldots)$$

has μ_0 as its radius of convergence. Furthermore, by § 11, Th. 10, we have

$$\tau(S_\lambda) = m_\nu(\mu - \mu_1)^{-1} + \Sigma_{k=0}^{\infty}\alpha_k(\mu - \mu_1)^k$$

in a neighbourhood of μ_1. This shows that $\mu\sigma_2 + \mu^2\sigma_3 + \ldots$ is unbounded as $\lim \mu = \mu_1$, $| \mu | < | \mu_1 | = \mu_0$. But then

$$| \mu | \sigma_2 + | \mu |^2 \sigma_3 + \ldots$$

is certainly unbounded, so that $\mu = \mu_0$ is also a singularity of $\tau(S_\lambda)$. Hence $\lambda_0 = \mu_0^{-1}$ is a characteristic value of $T(x, y)$, and, as we know, also of $T(y, x)$.

2°. By § 3, Th. 5 we have

$$H_\lambda = T + \mu T^2 + \mu^2 T^3 + \ldots,$$

where the series converges for small $| \mu |$ according to the L_{22}-norm. But then the proof of § 3, Th. 4 shows the existence of a subsequence of partial sums converging pointwise to $H_\lambda(x, y)$. Since all partial sums $T(x, y) + \ldots + \mu^{n-1}T_n(x, y)$ are positive for positive μ, we see therefore that for small positive μ the sequence of all partial sums (and not only a subsequence) converges, and that the sumfunction $H_\lambda(x, y)$ is positive almost everywhere on $\Delta \times \Delta$. The radius of convergence of

$$H_\lambda(x, y) = T(x, y) + \mu T_2(x, y) + \mu^2 T_3(x, y) + \ldots$$

is again μ_0, hence

$$\lim (\lambda - \lambda_0)^k H_\lambda(x, y) \geqslant 0 \tag{1}$$

as $\lim \lambda = \lambda_0$, $\lambda > \lambda_0$, $k \geqslant 0$.

3°. With the notation of § 4, Th. 9 we have

$$H_\lambda = - \lambda^2 B_\lambda - \lambda P_M + H_\lambda P_L,$$

where $H_\lambda P_L$ is a series which converges in double-norm for small $| \lambda - \lambda_0 |$; hence, if λ_0 has the index ν,

$$\lim (\lambda - \lambda_0)^\nu H_\lambda = \lambda_0^2 B_{\nu-1} \tag{2}$$

in double-norm, where $B_{\nu-1}$ is by § 4, Th. 8 an integral transformation whose kernel $B_{\nu-1}(x, y)$ is a finite sum $\Sigma\, e_i(x) e_i^*(y)$. Every $e_i(x)$ is here a characteristic function of $T(x, y)$ belonging to λ_0, and every $e_i^*(y)$ is a characteristic function of $T(y, x)$, also belonging to λ_0. An inspection of (1) and (2) shows that $B_{\nu-1}(x, y) \geqslant 0$ almost everywhere on $\Delta \times \Delta$. Observing moreover that $B_{\nu-1}(x, y)$ does not vanish identically, we may conclude that there exist functions $\varphi_0(x) \geqslant 0$ and $\psi_0(y) \geqslant 0$ (take $\varphi_0(x) = B_{\nu-1}(x, y)$ for a suitable y), not vanishing identically and such that

$$\textstyle\int_\Delta T(x, y)\varphi_0(y) d\mu = \lambda_0 \varphi_0(x), \quad \int_\Delta T(z, x)\psi_0(z) d\mu = \lambda_0 \psi_0(x).$$

But then $\varphi_0(x) > 0$, $\psi_0(x) > 0$ almost everywhere on Δ.

4°. Let us assume now that $\varphi(x)$ is a characteristic function of $T(x, y)$, belonging to a characteristic value λ such that $| \lambda | = \lambda_0$. We shall prove that in this case $\lambda = \lambda_0$, and that $\varphi(x)$ is a constant multiple of $\varphi_0(x)$. From $T\varphi = \lambda\varphi$ we infer

$$\lambda_0 \, | \varphi(x) | \leqslant \textstyle\int_\Delta T(x, y) \, | \varphi(y) | \, d\mu,$$

hence

$$\lambda_0 \textstyle\int_\Delta | \varphi(x) | \, \psi_0(x) d\mu \leqslant \int_{\Delta \times \Delta} T(x, y) \psi_0(x) \, | \varphi(y) | \, d(\mu \times \mu)$$
$$= \lambda_0 \textstyle\int_\Delta | \varphi(y) | \, \psi_0(y) d\mu,$$

which shows that

$$\textstyle\int_\Delta \left(\int_\Delta T(x, y) \, | \varphi(y) | \, d\mu - \lambda_0 \, | \varphi(x) | \right) \psi_0(x) d\mu = 0.$$

In view of $\psi_0(x) > 0$ almost everywhere, this implies

$$\textstyle\int_\Delta T(x, y) \, | \varphi(y) | \, d\mu = \lambda_0 \, | \varphi(x) |.$$

5°. Choose a value $x \in \Delta$ such that $T(x, y) > 0$ for almost all $y \in \Delta$, and

$$\left| \textstyle\int_\Delta T(x, y) \varphi(y) d\mu \right| = \lambda_0 \, | \varphi(x) | = \int_\Delta T(x, y) \, | \varphi(y) | \, d\mu < \infty.$$

Write $\int_\Delta T(x, y)\varphi(y)d\mu = re^{i\chi}$ ($r > 0$, χ real) and $\varphi(y)e^{-i\chi} = \varphi_1(y)$. Then

$$r = \int_\Delta T(x, y)\varphi_1(y)d\mu = \int_\Delta T(x, y) \mid \varphi_1(y) \mid d\mu,$$

hence $\varphi_1(y) = \mid \varphi_1(y) \mid$ almost everywhere on Δ. It follows that

$$\varphi(y) = e^{i\chi}\varphi_1(y) = e^{i\chi} \mid \varphi_1(y) \mid = e^{i\chi} \mid \varphi(y) \mid = C \mid \varphi(y) \mid$$

(C constant with $\mid C \mid = 1$) almost everywhere. Substituting this in $T\varphi = \lambda\varphi$ and observing that $T \mid \varphi \mid = \lambda_0 \mid \varphi \mid$, we find already $\lambda = \lambda_0$.

6°. The function $f_{\alpha\beta}(x) = \alpha \mid \varphi(x) \mid + \beta\varphi_0(x)$ (α, β real constants) is a characteristic function of $T(x, y)$ belonging to λ_0. Applying the arguments which were used in 4° and 5° for $\varphi(x)$ now to $f_{\alpha\beta}(x)$, we find $f_{\alpha\beta}(x) = C_1 \mid f_{\alpha\beta}(x) \mid$ (C_1 constant with $\mid C_1 \mid = 1$) almost everywhere on Δ. Choose in particular $\alpha = (\varphi_0, \varphi_0)$, $\beta = -(\mid \varphi \mid, \varphi_0)$, hence

$$f(x) = f_{\alpha\beta}(x) = (\varphi_0, \varphi_0) \mid \varphi(x) \mid - (\mid \varphi \mid, \varphi_0)\varphi_0(x).$$

Then $(f, \varphi_0) = 0$ trivially; hence, in view of $f(x) = C_1 \mid f(x) \mid$ with $\mid C_1 \mid = 1$, also $(\mid f \mid, \varphi_0) = \int_\Delta \mid f(x) \mid \varphi_0(x)d\mu = 0$. Since $\varphi_0(x) > 0$ almost everywhere, we find $f(x) = 0$ or $\mid \varphi(x) \mid = C_2\varphi_0(x)$. Together with $\varphi(x) = C \mid \varphi(x) \mid$ this yields

$$\varphi(x) = CC_2\varphi_0(x) = C_3\varphi_0(x),$$

which is the desired result for $\varphi(x)$. It shows already that λ_0 has the geometric multiplicity one. The diagrams I and II in § 2, Th. 4 consist therefore of one column and at the bottom of these columns are written constant multiples of $\varphi_0(x)$ and $\psi_0(x)$ respectively. Should the height of the columns exceed one, then $\int_\Delta \varphi_0(x)\psi_0(x)d\mu = 0$ by § 2, Th. 4. This however is impossible, since $\varphi_0(x)$ and $\psi_0(x)$ are positive almost everywhere on Δ. It follows that λ_0 has the algebraic multiplicity one.

Remarks. 1°. Let $\varphi_1(x)$ be a characteristic function of $T(x, y)$, belonging to a characteristic value $\lambda_1 \neq \lambda_0$. Then $(\varphi_1, \psi_0) = 0$, which shows that it is excluded that $\varphi_1(x)$ is non-negative almost everywhere on Δ.

2°. Let $\varphi_n(x)$ ($n = 1, 2, \ldots$) be an orthonormal system of real functions on $L_2(\Delta)$ and λ_n ($n = 1, 2, \ldots$) a sequence of real numbers such that $\mid \lambda_1 \mid \geqslant \mid \lambda_2 \mid \geqslant \ldots$ and $\Sigma \lambda_n^2 < \infty$. Then $\Sigma \lambda_n\varphi_n(x)\varphi_n(y)$ converges on $\Delta \times \Delta$ in mean with index 2 to a real function $T(x, y) \in L_2(\Delta \times \Delta)$. This kernel $T(x, y)$ has exactly the sequence λ_n as its sequence of characteristic values $\neq 0$ with $\varphi_n(x)$ as a corresponding sequence of characteristic functions. If now $T(x, y) > 0$ almost everywhere on

$\Delta \times \Delta$, it is necessary that $\lambda_1 > 0$, $\lambda_1 > |\lambda_i|$ $(i = 2, 3, \ldots)$, and that $\varphi_1(x)$ is a constant (real) multiple of an almost everywhere positive function.

§ 8. A Necessary and Sufficient Condition for an Integral Transformation in $L_2(\Delta)$ to be Compact

In Ch. 7, § 6 we have proved that a complete Hilbert space R has the property (Ext.), that is, every bounded linear functional, defined on a linear subspace of R, may be extended onto the whole space R in such a way that its bound does not increase. It follows from the one-to-one correspondence between the elements of R and those of the adjoint space R^* (cf. Ch. 7, § 7, Th. 3) that R^* has also the property (Ext.). Furthermore, by Ch. 7, § 8, Th. 6, the complete Hilbert space R is reflexive, that is, $R^{**} = R$. Hence, by Ch. 11, § 1, Th. 3, Remark, the linear transformation T on R into R is compact if and only if it has the property that for every sequence f_n in R, converging weakly to f_0, the sequence Tf_n converges strongly to Tf_0.

Theorem 1. *Let T be a bounded linear transformation on R into R. Then T is compact if and only if it has the property that for every sequence f_n in R, converging weakly to the null element, the sequence (Tf_n, f_n) converges to zero.*

Proof. Assume first that T is compact and that the sequence f_n converges weakly to the null element. Then $\lim Tf_n = 0$ and, by Ch. 7, § 9, Th. 1, the sequence f_n is bounded, hence $\| f_n \| \leqslant M$ $(n = 1, 2, \ldots)$. It follows that $|(Tf_n, f_n)| \leqslant \| Tf_n \| . M$, so that $\lim (Tf_n, f_n) = 0$.

Let now conversely $\lim (Tf_n, f_n) = 0$ for every sequence f_n converging weakly to the null element. Then, if the sequences f_n and g_n both converge weakly to the null element, and if α is arbitrarily complex, we have

$$\lim (Tf_n, f_n) = \lim (Tg_n, g_n) = \lim (Tf_n + \alpha Tg_n, f_n + \alpha g_n) = 0,$$

hence

$$\lim [\bar{\alpha}(Tf_n, g_n) + \alpha(Tg_n, f_n)] = 0.$$

Take first $\alpha = 1$ and then $\alpha = -i$. Subtraction yields now $\lim (Tf_n, g_n) = 0$. Since $\lim (Tf_n, h) = \lim (f_n, T^*h) = 0$ for every $h \in R$, the sequence Tf_n also converges weakly to the null element, so that, taking $g_n = Tf_n$, we find $\lim (Tf_n, Tf_n) = 0$ or $\lim Tf_n = 0$. Hence, if f_n converges weakly to f_0, we have $\lim T(f_n - f_0) = 0$, or $\lim Tf_n = Tf_0$. This shows that T is compact.

Theorem 2. *If the kernel $T(x, y)$, defined on $\Delta \times \Delta$, has the property that*

$$g(x) = \int_\Delta T(x, y)f(y)d\mu$$

defines a bounded linear transformation T on $L_2(\Delta, \mu)$ into $L_2(\Delta, \mu)$, then T is compact if and only if

$$\lim \int_\Delta \left(\int_\Delta T(x, y)f_n(y)d\mu\right)\overline{f_n(x)}d\mu = 0$$

for every sequence $f_n(x)$ converging weakly to zero, that is, for every sequence $f_n(x)$ such that

$$\lim \int_\Delta f_n(x)h(x)d\mu = 0$$

for every $h(x) \in L_2$.

Proof. Follows immediately from Theorem 1.

Theorem 3. *If the kernel $T(x, y)$ belongs to $L_{22}(\Delta \times \Delta)$, that is, if $\int_\Delta | T(x, y)f(y) | d\mu \in L_2(\Delta)$ for every $f \in L_2(\Delta)$, then the linear transformation T with kernel $T(x, y)$ is compact if and only if*

$$\lim \int_{\Delta\times\Delta} T(x, y)\overline{f_n(x)}f_n(y)d(\mu \times \mu) = 0$$

for every sequence $f_n(x)$ converging weakly to zero.

Proof. The linear transformation T is bounded by Ch. 9, § 7, Th. 2, so that the present theorem is a consequence of the preceding one.

§ 9. Volterra Kernels

Let Δ be the interval $[0, 1; \ldots; 0, 1]$ in real m-dimensional Euclidean space R_m, and let the kernel $T(x, y)$, measurable on $\Delta \times \Delta$, have the property that there exists an index k $(1 \leqslant k \leqslant m)$ such that $T(x, y) = 0$ at those points $(x, y) = (x_1, \ldots, x_m; y_1, \ldots, y_m)$ for which $y_k > x_k$. A kernel having this property is called a *Volterra kernel*. Without loss of generality we may assume that $k = m$. For $m = 1$ it is immediately seen that $T(x, y)$ is a Volterra kernel if and only if $T(x, y) = 0$ above the diagonal $y = x$ in the square $[0, 1; 0, 1]$.

Assume now that $1 \leqslant p < \infty$, and that the Volterra kernel $T(x, y)$ is of finite double-norm relative to $L_p(\Delta, \mu)$, where μ is Lebesgue measure. The non-singular linear integral transformation T in the space $L_p(\Delta)$, defined by

$$Tf = \int_\Delta T(x, y)f(y)dy,$$

may then be written in the form

$$Tf = \int_0^1 \ldots \int_0^1 \int_0^{x_m} T(x_1, \ldots, x_m; y_1, \ldots, y_m) f(y_1, \ldots, y_m) dy_1 \ldots dy_m,$$

or, introducing the abbreviation

$$\int_0^x dy = \int_0^1 \ldots \int_0^1 \int_0^{x_m} dy_1 \ldots dy_m,$$

in the form

$$Tf = \int_0^x T(x, y) f(y) dy.$$

The linear integral equation

$$\int_0^x T(x, y) f(y) dy - \lambda f(x) = g(x)$$

is now called a *Volterra equation*. The theory of Volterra equations with bounded kernels was developed somewhat earlier than that of the general equation (VOLTERRA, 1896, [5]).

We first prove some lemmas.

Lemma α. *Let $f(x)$ be summable over the linear interval $0 \leqslant x \leqslant 1$. Then, if $0 \leqslant x \leqslant 1$ and $n \geqslant 1$ is an integer,*

$$n \int_0^x f(y) \left(\int_0^y f(t) dt \right)^{n-1} dy = \left(\int_0^x f(t) dt \right)^n. \tag{1}$$

Proof. For $n = 1$ the lemma is true. Suppose that $n \geqslant 2$, and that the lemma has already been proved for $n - 1$, hence

$$(n-1) \int_0^x f(y) \left(\int_0^y f(t) dt \right)^{n-2} dy = \left(\int_0^x f(t) dt \right)^{n-1}.$$

Write $g(y) = nf(y) \left(\int_0^y f(t) dt \right)^{n-2}$, $F(y) = \int_0^y f(t) dt$ and $G(y) = \int_0^y g(t) dt$. Hence, by our induction hypothesis,

$$G(y) = n \left(\int_0^y f(t) dt \right)^{n-1} / (n-1).$$

Observing now that the integral on the left in (1) may be written as $\int_0^x F(y) g(y) dy$, integration by parts yields the desired result.

Lemma β. *Let $f(x)$ be summable over the linear interval $0 \leqslant x \leqslant 1$. Then, if $0 \leqslant x \leqslant 1$ and $n \geqslant 1$ is an integer,*

$$n! \int_0^x dt_1 f(t_1) \int_0^{t_1} dt_2 f(t_2) \ldots \int_0^{t_{n-1}} dt_n f(t_n) = \left(\int_0^x f(t) dt \right)^n. \tag{2}$$

Proof. For $n = 1$ the lemma is true. Suppose that $n \geqslant 2$, and that the lemma has already been proved for $n - 1$, hence

$$(n-1)! \int_0^{t_1} dt_2 f(t_2) \ldots \int_0^{t_{n-1}} dt_n f(t_n) = \left(\int_0^{t_1} f(t) dt \right)^{n-1}.$$

It remains to prove that $n\int_0^x f(t_1)(\int_0^{t_1} f(t)dt)^{n-1}dt_1 = (\int_0^x f(t)dt)^n$. But this is exactly Lemma α.

Lemma γ. *Let $f(x) = f(x_1, \ldots, x_m)$ be summable over Δ. Then, with $\int_0^x dy$ shortly for $\int_0^1 \ldots \int_0^1 \int_0^x dy_1 \ldots dy_m$, the formula* (2) *remains true.*

Proof. Write $f_1(x) = \int_0^1 \ldots \int_0^1 f(x_1, \ldots, x_{m-1}, x)dx_1 \ldots dx_{m-1}$, and apply Lemma β to $f_1(x)$.

Theorem 1. *Let $1 \leqslant p < \infty$, and let the Volterra kernel $T(x, y)$ be of finite double-norm relative to $L_p(\Delta)$. Then every $\lambda \neq 0$ belongs to the resolvent set of the corresponding transformation T, and $R_\lambda = (T - \lambda I)^{-1}$ is given by*

$$R_\lambda = -(\lambda^{-1}I + \lambda^{-2}T + \lambda^{-3}T^2 + \ldots), \tag{3}$$

where this series converges uniformly [6]. *For $p = \infty$ this statement is no longer true.*

Proof. Let $1 \leqslant p < \infty$ and $g(x) \in L_p(\Delta)$. Write $g_n = T^n g$ $(n = 1, 2, \ldots)$ and

$$\alpha(x) = \begin{cases} (\int_0^x |T(x, y)|^q dy)^{1/q}, & p > 1,\ 1/p + 1/q = 1, \\ \| T(x, y) \|_\infty, & p = 1. \end{cases}$$

Then $|g_1(x)| \leqslant \alpha(x) \| g \|$ for almost every $x \in \Delta$, hence

$$|g_2(x)| \leqslant \| g \| \int_0^x |T(x, y)| \alpha(y)dy \leqslant \| g \| \alpha(x)(\int_0^x \alpha^p(y)dy)^{1/p},$$

$$|g_3(x)| \leqslant \| g \| \int_0^x |T(x, y)| \alpha(y)(\int_0^y \alpha^p(t)dt)^{1/p}dy$$

$$\leqslant \| g \| \alpha(x)[\int_0^x dy\, \alpha^p(y) \int_0^y dt\, \alpha^p(t)]^{1/p},$$

generally

$$|g_n(x)| \leqslant \| g \| \alpha(x)[\int_0^x dt_1\, \alpha^p(t_1) \int_0^{t_1} dt_2\, \alpha^p(t_2) \ldots \int_0^{t_{n-2}} dt_{n-1}\, \alpha^p(t_{n-1})]^{1/p}$$

$$= \| g \| \alpha(x) \left[\frac{(\int_0^x \alpha^p(t)dt)^{n-1}}{(n-1)!} \right]^{1/p},$$

where we have used Lemma γ. It follows that

$$|g_n(x)|^p \leqslant \| g \|^p \alpha^p(x) (\int_0^1 \alpha^p(t)dt)^{n-1}/(n-1)!,$$

hence, for $n \geqslant 1$ (with $0! = 1$),

$$\| T^n g \| = \| g_n \| \leqslant \| g \| . ||| T |||^n/[(n-1)!]^{1/p}$$

or

$$\| T^n \| \leqslant ||| T |||^n/[(n-1)!]^{1/p}.$$

This shows that $\Sigma_0^\infty \| \lambda^{-(n+1)} T^n \|$ converges for every complex $\lambda \neq 0$, so that $R_\lambda = \Sigma_0^\infty - \lambda^{-(n+1)} T^n$ converges uniformly. Since $(T - \lambda I)R_\lambda = R_\lambda(T - \lambda I) = I$, our proof for $1 \leqslant p < \infty$ is complete. We observe that, as a consequence of what we have proved, the unique solution f of $Tf - \lambda f = g$ is given by the Neumann series

$$f = R_\lambda g = -(\lambda^{-1}g + \lambda^{-2}Tg + \lambda^{-3}T^2 g + \ldots),$$

where this series converges according to the L_p-norm. We have even $\Sigma \| \lambda^{-(n+1)} T^n g \| < \infty$.

The falseness of the corresponding statement for $p = \infty$ is shown by the example

$$T(x, y) = \begin{cases} x^{-1}, & 0 \leqslant y \leqslant x, \\ 0, & x < y \leqslant 1, \end{cases}$$

considered already in Ch. 11, § 2, Ex. D. Here $\int_0^1 | T(x, y) | \, dy = 1$ for all x, hence $||| T ||| = 1$. It follows that $\| T \| \leqslant 1$. Since on the other hand all λ in $0 < \lambda \leqslant 1$ are characteristic values of T, we have $\| T \| \geqslant 1$. Hence $\| T \| = 1$. The relation (3) holds therefore only for $| \lambda | > 1$ in this case.

Remark. If $1 \leqslant p < \infty$, $1/p + 1/q = 1$, and $T(x, y)$ is a Volterra kernel belonging to L_{pq}, then it is easily seen that all iterated kernels $T_n(x, y)$ $(n = 2, 3, \ldots)$ are also Volterra kernels; $T_n(x, y) = \int_y^x T(x, z) T_{n-1}(z, y) dz$ for $y \leqslant x$ and $T_n(x, y) = 0$ for $y > x$ in our short notation. If now, instead of $T(x, y)$ itself, one of these iterated Volterra kernels $T_r(x, y)$ is of finite double-norm relative to $L_p(\Delta)$, the statement in Theorem 1 remains true. Indeed, since $I + \lambda^{-r} T^r + \lambda^{-2r} T^{2r} + \ldots$ converges uniformly by what we have already proved, and since $T \in L_{pq}$ is bounded, the $r - 1$ series $\lambda^{-k} T^k + \lambda^{-(r+k)} T^{r+k} + \lambda^{-(2r+k)} T^{2r+k} + \ldots$ $(k = 1, \ldots, r - 1)$ also converge uniformly. Addition yields the desired result.

Theorem 2. *If, under the same conditions as in the preceding theorem, H_λ is defined by $R_\lambda = -\lambda^{-1} I - \lambda^{-2} H_\lambda$ for every $\lambda \neq 0$, then $T + \lambda^{-1} T^2 + \lambda^{-2} T^3 + \ldots$ converges in double-norm to H_λ.*

Proof. If S is an integral transformation with kernel $S(x, y)$, we denote by S_a the transformation with kernel $| S(x, y) |$. It is easily seen that $| T_n(x, y) |$, the kernel of $(T^n)_a$, does not exceed the kernel of $(T_a)^n$, hence $\| (T^n)_a \| \leqslant \| (T_a)^n \|$ (cf. § 3, Th. 2). Observing now that $||| T ||| < \infty$

and $T^n \in L_{pq}$, we find by § 4, Th. 5 and § 3, Th. 3 that

$$||| T^{n+1} ||| \leqslant ||| T |||.\| T^n \|_{pq} \leqslant 2 ||| T |||.\| (T^n)_a \|$$
$$\leqslant 2 ||| T |||.\| (T_a)^n \|.$$

But $\| (T_a)^n \| \leqslant ||| T |||^n/[(n-1)!]^{1/p}$ by the proof of the preceding theorem, hence

$$||| T^{n+1} ||| \leqslant 2 ||| T |||^{n+1}/[(n-1)!]^{1/p} \quad (n \geqslant 2).$$

It follows that $||| T ||| + ||| \lambda^{-1}T^2 ||| + ||| \lambda^{-2}T^3 ||| + \ldots < \infty$ for every $\lambda \neq 0$, so that $T + \lambda^{-1}T^2 + \lambda^{-2}T^3 + \ldots$ converges in double-norm. Taking into account that we know already that its uniform sum is H_λ, we see therefore that its double-norm sum is H_λ as well.

Corollary. *If moreover $T(x, y)$ belongs to the class B (that is, if $t(x) = \| T(x, y) \|_q \leqslant c$ and $s(y) = \| T(x, y) \|_p \leqslant c$), the Neumann series $T(x, y) + \lambda^{-1}T_2(x, y) + \lambda^{-2}T_3(x, y) + \ldots$ converges uniformly to $H_\lambda(x, y)$ for all $\lambda \neq 0$.*

Proof. As in § 5, Th. 1, but using now that $\| T^n \|_{pq} \leqslant 2 ||| T |||^n/[(n-1)!]^{1/p}$.

If we have to do with a system of Volterra equations

$$\Sigma_{j=1}^n \int_0^x T_{ij}(x, y) f^j(y)dy - \lambda f^i(x) = g^i(x) \quad (i = 1, \ldots, n),$$

similar theorems hold. The principles upon which the corresponding proofs rest are the same, although the computations are slightly more complicated.

§ 10. Examples

We shall give some examples of Volterra equations.

Example A. Let Δ be the linear interval $0 \leqslant x \leqslant 1$, and let

$$T(x, y) = \begin{cases} 1, & 0 \leqslant y \leqslant x, \\ 0, & x < y \leqslant 1. \end{cases}$$

We examine the transformation T with kernel $T(x, y)$ in the space $L_p(\Delta, \mu)$, where $1 \leqslant p < \infty$ and μ is Lebesgue measure (compare Ch. 10, § 9, Th. 2, Remark, where we had the same kernel in $L_2(\Delta, \mu)$). Hence, if $f \in L_p$, then $Tf = \int_0^x f(y)dy$. Obviously T is of finite double-norm relative to L_p; it even belongs to the class B. Direct computation gives

$$T_n(x, y) = \begin{cases} (x-y)^{n-1}/(n-1)!, & 0 \leqslant y \leqslant x, \\ 0 & , x < y \leqslant 1 \end{cases}$$

for $n = 2, 3, \ldots$. For $\lambda \neq 0$ the Neumann series becomes therefore

$$H_\lambda(x, y) = 1 + \lambda^{-1}(x-y) + \lambda^{-2}(x-y)^2/2! + \ldots = e^{(x-y)/\lambda}$$

for $0 \leqslant y \leqslant x$, and $H_\lambda(x, y) = 0$ for $x < y \leqslant 1$. It follows that the Volterra equation

$$\textstyle\int_0^x f(y)dy - \lambda f(x) = g(x), \ \lambda \neq 0,$$

has the unique solution

$$f(x) = R_\lambda g = -\lambda^{-1}g(x) - \lambda^{-2} \textstyle\int_0^x e^{(x-y)/\lambda} g(y)dy.$$

Since $Tf = 0$ (that is, $\int_0^x f(y)dy = 0$ for all $x \in \Delta$) implies $f = 0$, the inverse T^{-1} exists. This shows that $\lambda = 0$ does not belong to the point spectrum of T. We now observe that the system $\{\sin n\pi x\}$ $(n = 1, 2, \ldots)$ is complete in $L_p(\Delta)$. Indeed, by Ch. 7, § 6, Th. 8, the system $\{1, \cos \pi x, \sin \pi x, \cos 2\pi x, \sin 2\pi x, \ldots\}$ is complete in $L_p[-1, 1]$, so that, if $f(x) \in L_p(\Delta)$ is extended onto $[-1, 0)$ by $f(-x) = -f(x)$, and $\varepsilon > 0$ is given, there exists a polynomial $p_1(x) + p_2(x)$ such that $p_1(x) = \Sigma_0\, \alpha_n \cos n\pi x$, $p_2(x) = \Sigma\, \beta_n \sin n\pi x$ and $(\int_{-1}^1 |f - (p_1 + p_2)|^p dx)^{1/p} < \varepsilon$. Then $(\int_0^1)^{1/p} < \varepsilon$ and $(\int_{-1}^0)^{1/p} < \varepsilon$, hence $\| (f - p_2) - p_1 \| < \varepsilon$, and also $\| (-f + p_2) - p_1 \| < \varepsilon$ or $\| (f - p_2) + p_1 \| < \varepsilon$. It follows by addition that $\| f - p_2 \| = \| f - \Sigma\, \beta_n \sin n\pi x \| < \varepsilon$. Since $T(n\pi \cos n\pi x) = n\pi \int_0^x \cos n\pi y dy = \sin n\pi x$, the range of T is therefore dense in $L_p(\Delta)$. Finally, since $\| \sin n\pi x \| = \| \cos n\pi x \|$ $(n = 1, 2, \ldots)$, so that $\| T (\cos n\pi x) \| = (n\pi)^{-1} \| \sin n\pi x \| = (n\pi)^{-1} \| \cos n\pi x \|$, we find that T^{-1} is not bounded. The value $\lambda = 0$ forms therefore the continuous spectrum of T, whereas its point spectrum and its residual spectrum are empty.

Example B. Let Δ once again be the linear interval $0 \leqslant x \leqslant 1$, let $\beta > 0$, and

$$T(x, y) = \begin{cases} \{\Gamma(\beta)\}^{-1}(x-y)^{\beta-1}, & 0 \leqslant y \leqslant x, \\ 0 & , x < y \leqslant 1. \end{cases}$$

If T is the transformation with kernel $T(x, y)$ in the space $L_p(\Delta)(1 \leqslant p < \infty)$, then

$$Tf = \frac{1}{\Gamma(\beta)} \int_0^x (x-y)^{\beta-1} f(y)dy,$$

so that Tf is the fractional integral of $f(x)$ of order β(cf. Ch. 3, § 9, and Ch. 11, § 2, Ex. F, Remarks). For $\beta = 1$ we get the preceding example. Since

$$T_n(x, y) = \begin{cases} \{\Gamma(n\beta)\}^{-1}(x-y)^{n\beta-1}, & 0 \leqslant y \leqslant x, \\ 0 & , x < y \leqslant 1, \end{cases}$$

the kernels $T_n(x, y)$ with $n\beta \geqslant 1$ are bounded, and therefore of finite double-norm. For $\lambda \neq 0$ the solution of $Tf - \lambda f = g$ becomes (cf. Theorem 1, Remark)

$$f(x) = -\lambda^{-1}g(x) - \lambda^{-2}\{\Gamma(\beta)\}^{-1}\int_0^x (x-y)^{\beta-1}g(y)dy$$
$$-\lambda^{-3}\{\Gamma(2\beta)\}^{-1}\int_0^x (x-y)^{2\beta-1}g(y)dy - \ldots,$$

where this series converges according to the L_p-norm. To mention a particular example, let us take $p = 1$, $\beta = 1/2$, $g(x) = x^{-1/2} \in L(\Delta)$, so that our integral equation becomes

$$\frac{1}{\sqrt{\pi}}\int_0^x \frac{f(y)}{\sqrt{x-y}}\,dy - \lambda f(x) = \frac{1}{\sqrt{x}}.$$

Writing $\lambda^{-1} = \mu$, and taking into account the result of Ch. 3, § 9, Th. 3, we find

$$\mu^{n+1}\{\Gamma(n\beta)\}^{-1}\int_0^x (x-y)^{n\beta-1}g(y)dy = \mu^{n+1}\{\Gamma(n/2)\}^{-1}\int_0^x (x-y)^{n/2-1}y^{1/2-1}\,dy$$
$$= \mu^{n+1}\{\Gamma(n/2)\}^{-1}x^{(n-1)/2}\Gamma(n/2)\Gamma(1/2)/\Gamma\{(n+1)/2\} =$$
$$\mu^{n+1}\pi^{1/2}x^{(n-1)/2}/\Gamma\{(n+1)/2\} = \mu(\pi/x)^{1/2}(\mu\sqrt{x})^n/\Gamma\{(n+1)/2\},$$

so that

$$f(x) = -\mu/\sqrt{x} - \mu(\pi/x)^{1/2}\,\Sigma_1^\infty\,(\mu\sqrt{x})^n/\Gamma\{(n+1)/2\}. \tag{1}$$

This series converges pointwise, uniformly on Δ, so that its ordinary sum is certainly identical with its sum according to the L-norm. To determine this sumfunction we first consider the function

$$h(x) = \frac{x}{\frac{1}{2}} + \frac{x^3}{\frac{1}{2}\cdot\frac{3}{2}} + \frac{x^5}{\frac{1}{2}\cdot\frac{3}{2}\cdot\frac{5}{2}} + \ldots.$$

Since the derivative $h'(x)$ satisfies $h'(x) = 2 + 2xh(x)$, we easily find $h(x) = 2e^{x^2}\int_0^x e^{-y^2}dy$. Now split up the series in (1) into its terms with odd and its terms with even indices. Those with odd indices give

$$\mu\sqrt{x}/1 + (\mu\sqrt{x})^3/1! + (\mu\sqrt{x})^5/2! + \ldots = \mu\sqrt{x}\,e^{\mu^2 x}.$$

On account of $\Gamma(p+1) = p\Gamma(p)$ (cf. Ch. 3, § 9, Th. 2), those with even indices give

$$\frac{(\mu\sqrt{x})^2}{\frac{1}{2}\Gamma(\frac{1}{2})} + \frac{(\mu\sqrt{x})^4}{\frac{1}{2}\cdot\frac{3}{2}\Gamma(\frac{1}{2})} + \frac{(\mu\sqrt{x})^6}{\frac{1}{2}\cdot\frac{3}{2}\cdot\frac{5}{2}\Gamma(\frac{1}{2})} + \ldots =$$

$$\pi^{-1/2}\mu\sqrt{x}\, h(\mu\sqrt{x}) = 2\pi^{-1/2}\mu\sqrt{x}\, e^{\mu^2 x} \int_0^{\mu\sqrt{x}} e^{-y^2} dy.$$

Hence

$$\Sigma_1^\infty (\mu\sqrt{x})^n/\Gamma\{(n+1)/2\} = \pi^{-1/2}\mu\sqrt{x}\, e^{\mu^2 x}(\pi^{1/2} + 2\int_0^{\mu\sqrt{x}} e^{-y^2} dy).$$

The solution $f(x)$ thus becomes

$$f(x) = -\mu/\sqrt{x} - \mu^2 e^{\mu^2 x}(\pi^{1/2} + 2\int_0^{\mu\sqrt{x}} e^{-y^2} dy).$$

We return to the general case ($1 \leqslant p < \infty$, $\beta > 0$), and, as in the preceding example, we want to determine the spectral character of the value $\lambda = 0$. For this purpose we denote our transformation T by T_β. For $\beta_1, \beta_2 > 0$ we have $T_{\beta_1}T_{\beta_2} = T_{\beta_1+\beta_2}$. Since $T_1 f = 0$ implies $f = 0$ by the preceding example, it follows therefore that $T_n f = 0$ (n a positive integer) implies $f = 0$ as well. Hence, if $\beta > 0$ is arbitrary and $T_\beta f = 0$, then $f = 0$. This shows that T_β^{-1} exists. We next observe that if S_1 and S_2 are bounded linear transformations in $L_p(\Delta)$ whose ranges are dense in $L_p(\Delta)$, then the range of S_1S_2 is also dense in $L_p(\Delta)$. To prove this statement we have to show that, given $f \in L_p$ and $\varepsilon > 0$, there exists an element $g \in L_p$ such that $\| f - S_1S_2g \| < \varepsilon$. By hypothesis there exists an element $h \in L_p$ such that $\| f - S_1h \| < \varepsilon/2$ and an element $g \in L_p$ such that $\| h - S_2g \| < \varepsilon/2 \| S_1 \|$. Hence $\| S_1h - S_1S_2g \| < \varepsilon/2$, and by addition $\| f - S_1S_2g \| < \varepsilon$. Since the range of T_1 is dense in L_p by the preceding example, we find now by induction that the range of T_n, where n is a positive integer, is dense in L_p as well. Furthermore, if $\beta > 0$, and if the integer n satisfies $n \geqslant \beta$, the range of T_n is a subset of the range of T_β. This shows that the range of T_β is dense in L_p. By Ch. 11, § 3, Th. 12 the value $\lambda = 0$ cannot belong to the resolvent set of T. Combining these results we find that $\lambda = 0$ forms the continuous spectrum of T.

Example C. Let Δ be the linear interval $0 \leqslant x \leqslant 1$, and

$$T(x, y) = \begin{cases} 1, & 0 \leqslant y \leqslant x/2, \\ -1, & x/2 < y \leqslant x, \\ 0, & x < y \leqslant 1, \end{cases}$$

hence $Tf = \int_0^{x/2} f(y)dy - \int_{x/2}^{x} f(y)dy$ for $f \in L_p(\Delta)$, $1 \leqslant p < \infty$. In this case $\lambda = 0$ forms the point spectrum of T, since the function $f(x) = 1$ obviously satisfies $Tf = 0$.

Example D. We shall also consider some Volterra equations of the first kind. Let Δ, $\beta > 0$ and $T(x, y)$ be defined as in Example B, so that, if T_β is the transformation with kernel $T(x, y)$ in the space $L(\Delta)$, and $g(x) \in L(\Delta)$, the equation $T_\beta f = g$ may be written as

$$\frac{1}{\Gamma(\beta)} \int_0^x (x - y)^{\beta-1} f(y) dy = g(x).$$

This equation has a solution $f(x) \in L(\Delta)$ if and only if $g(x)$ is the fractional integral of order β of some function $F(x) \in L(\Delta)$, and in this case the unique solution is given by $f(x) = F(x)$. Indeed, if $g(x)$ is the fractional integral of order β of $F(x)$, then $g = T_\beta F$, so that $f = F$ is a solution of $T_\beta f = g$. This solution is uniquely determined since $T_\beta f_1 = T_\beta f_2 = g$ implies $f_1 = f_2$ by what we have proved in Example B. If conversely $T_\beta f = g$ has a solution $f(x) \in L(\Delta)$, then $g(x)$ is evidently the fractional integral of order β of this function $f(x)$.

If $0 < \beta < 1$, we observe that $T_\beta f = g$ implies $T_1 f = T_{1-\beta} T_\beta f = T_{1-\beta} g$, hence

$$\int_0^x f(y) dy = \{\Gamma(1 - \beta)\}^{-1} \int_0^x (x - y)^{-\beta} g(y) dy,$$

which in some practical cases may be used to compute $f(x)$.

Let $p > -1$, so that $x^p \in L(\Delta)$. Then, if $\beta > 0$, we have

$$T_\beta x^p = \{\Gamma(\beta)\}^{-1} \int_0^x (x - y)^{\beta-1} y^p dy = x^{p+\beta} \{\Gamma(\beta)\}^{-1} \int_0^1 t^p (1 - t)^{\beta-1} dt$$

$$= x^{p+\beta} \Gamma(p + 1)/\Gamma(p + 1 + \beta),$$

hence

$$x^{p+\beta} = T_\beta \{x^p \Gamma(p + 1 + \beta)/\Gamma(p + 1)\},$$

which shows that the equation

$$\{\Gamma(\beta)\}^{-1} \int_0^x (x - y)^{\beta-1} f(y) dy = x^q$$

with $q > \beta - 1$ has the solution

$$f(x) = x^{q-\beta} \Gamma(q + 1)/\Gamma(q + 1 - \beta).$$

A special case (equation of Abel) is obtained by taking $\beta = 1/2$, $q = 0$, hence $T_{1/2}f = 1$, or

$$\int_0^x \frac{f(y)}{\sqrt{x-y}}\,dy = \sqrt{\pi}.$$

Its solution is $f(x) = x^{-1/2}\Gamma(1)/\Gamma(1/2) = 1/\sqrt{\pi x}$.

We finally consider the case that $0 < \beta < 1$ and $g(x) = e^x$, hence

$$\{\Gamma(\beta)\}^{-1} \int_0^x (x-y)^{\beta-1} f(y)dy = e^x.$$

Then $T_1 f = T_{1-\beta} e^x = T_{1-\beta}[\Sigma_0^\infty x^n/\Gamma(n+1)] = \Sigma_0^\infty x^{n+1-\beta}/\Gamma(n+2-\beta)$, so that

$$f(x) = \Sigma_0^\infty x^{n-\beta}/\Gamma(n+1-\beta).$$

In particular, for $\beta = 1/2$, we find

$$f(x) = \Sigma_0^\infty x^{n-1/2}/\Gamma(n+1/2) =$$

$$\frac{1}{\sqrt{\pi x}} + \frac{1}{\sqrt{\pi}}\left(\frac{\sqrt{x}}{\frac{1}{2}} + \frac{(\sqrt{x})^3}{\frac{1}{2}\cdot\frac{3}{2}} + \ldots\right) = \frac{1}{\sqrt{\pi x}} + \frac{2}{\sqrt{\pi}} e^x \int_0^{\sqrt{x}} e^{-y^2}dy.$$

EXAMPLES

1) Suppose that E is a complete Banach space, and that T is a bounded linear transformation on E into E one of whose iterates is compact. Let $\alpha \neq 0$ be in the resolvent set of T, let $R_\alpha = (T - \alpha I)^{-1}$ and $R_\alpha = -\alpha^{-1}I - \alpha^{-2}H_\alpha$, hence $H_\alpha = -\alpha I - \alpha^2(T - \alpha I)^{-1}$. Then, if T has the non-null characteristic values λ_i, H_α has the non-null characteristic values $\mu_i = \alpha\lambda_i/(\alpha - \lambda_i) = -\alpha - \alpha^2(\lambda_i - \alpha)^{-1}$, and the element f is a characteristic element of H_α belonging to μ_i if and only if it is a characteristic element of T belonging to λ_i.

(Write $\beta = \alpha^{-1}$, and let λ be one of the λ_i. Then $1 - \lambda\beta \neq 0$. Writing now $\mu = \alpha\lambda/(\alpha - \lambda) = \lambda/(1 - \lambda\beta)$, we have $\lambda = \mu/(1 + \mu\beta)$, hence $Tf = \lambda f$ implies $(1 + \mu\beta)Tf = \mu f$, which is equivalent to $\beta(1 + \mu\beta)Tf = \mu\beta f = (1 + \mu\beta)f - f$, or $(I - \beta T)(1 + \mu\beta)f = f$, or $(T - \alpha I)(-\beta - \beta^2\mu)f = f$, or $(-\beta - \beta^2\mu)f = R_\alpha f$. But also $R_\alpha f = -\beta f - \beta^2 H_\alpha f$, hence $H_\alpha f = \mu f$.

Conversely, if $H_\alpha f = \mu f \neq 0$, then $R_\alpha f = -\beta f - \beta^2 H_\alpha f = (-\beta - \beta^2\mu)f$, which is equivalent to $(1 + \mu\beta)Tf = \mu f$ by what we have just seen. It is impossible that $1 + \mu\beta = 0$, for this would imply $\mu = 0$ and $\mu = -\alpha \neq 0$ at the same time. Hence $Tf = \lambda f$ with $\lambda = \mu/(1 + \mu\beta)$, or $\mu = \alpha\lambda/(\alpha - \lambda)$).

2) Suppose that E is a complete Banach space, and that T is a bounded linear transformation on E into E. Let λ^n be in the resolvent set of T^n (n is a positive integer), and $P_\lambda = (T^n - \lambda^n I)^{-1}$. Then λ is in the resolvent set of T, and $R_\lambda = (T - \lambda I)^{-1} = P_\lambda(\lambda^{n-1}I + \lambda^{n-2}T + \ldots + T^{n-1}) = (\lambda^{n-1}I + \lambda^{n-2}T + \ldots + T^{n-1})P_\lambda$.

(Write $X_\lambda = P_\lambda(\lambda^{n-1}I + \ldots + T^{n-1})$ and $Y_\lambda = (\lambda^{n-1}I + \ldots + T^{n-1})P_\lambda$. Then $X_\lambda(T^n - \lambda^n I) = P_\lambda(T^n - \lambda^n I)(\lambda^{n-1}I + \ldots + T^{n-1}) = \lambda^{n-1}I + \ldots + T^{n-1} = Y_\lambda(T^n - \lambda^n I)$, hence $(X_\lambda - Y_\lambda)(T^n - \lambda^n I) = O$ or $X_\lambda = Y_\lambda$. Also $X_\lambda(T - \lambda I) = I$ and $(T - \lambda I)Y_\lambda = I$, hence $X_\lambda = Y_\lambda = (T - \lambda I)^{-1}$).

3) With the notations and under the hypotheses of § 3, Th. 5 the Neumann series $\Sigma_0^\infty \lambda^{-n} T_{n+1}(x, y)$ converges almost everywhere on $\Delta \times \Delta$ pointwise to $H_\lambda(x, y)$. With the notations and under the hypotheses of § 3, Th. 6 the series $\Sigma_0^\infty (\lambda^{-1} - \lambda_0^{-1})^k H_{0,k+1}(x, y)$ converges almost everywhere on $\Delta \times \Delta$ to $H_\lambda(x, y)$.

(The convergence of $\Sigma_0^\infty \| \lambda^{-n} T^{n+1} \|_{\Phi\Psi}$ implies that $\Sigma \int_{\Delta_1 \times \Delta_1} | T_{n+1}(x, y)\lambda^{-n} | d(\mu \times \mu) < \infty$ for every set $\Delta_1 \subset \Delta$ of finite measure. Hence $\Sigma | T_{n+1}(x, y)\lambda^{-n} | < \infty$ almost everywhere on $\Delta_1 \times \Delta_1$ by Ch. 3, § 3, Th. 9. It follows that $\Sigma_0^\infty \lambda^{-n} T_{n+1}(x, y)$ converges almost everywhere on $\Delta \times \Delta$. That its sum is $H_\lambda(x, y)$ may be seen by applying Fatou's Theorem as in § 3, Th. 4).

4) Let $\Phi(u)$ and $\Psi(v)$ be complementary, and let $L_\Phi(\Delta, \mu)$ and $L_\Psi(\Delta, \mu)$ be the corresponding Orlicz spaces. The measure of the measurable set X is denoted by $\mu(X)$. If $f(x)$ is defined on Δ and $X \subset \Delta$, then the function $f_X = f(x)_X$ is defined by

$$f_X = \begin{cases} f(x), & x \in X, \\ 0 & \text{elsewhere on } \Delta. \end{cases}$$

If now $p > 0$ is such that $\Psi(p) \leqslant 1$, and X is a measurable subset of Δ of finite measure, then

$$\int_X | f | \, d\mu \leqslant p^{-1}(\mu(X) + 1) \, \| f_X \|_\Phi .$$

(We have

$$\int_X | f | \, d\mu = \int_X | p^{-1} f | \, p \, d\mu \leqslant \| p^{-1} f_X \|_\Phi \, \| (p)_X \|_\Psi$$
$$\leqslant p^{-1} \| f_X \|_\Phi \left(\int_X \Psi(p) d\mu + 1\right) \leqslant p^{-1}(\mu(X) + 1) \, \| f_X \|_\Phi).$$

5) Let $\Phi(2u) \leqslant M\Phi(u)$ for all $u \geqslant 0$, and let all $f(x)$ of the set $\{f\}$ belong to $L_\Phi(\Delta, \mu)$, and hence to $L_\Phi^*(\Delta, \mu)$ by Ch. 5, § 5, Th. 2, Corollary. We furthermore suppose that for each $\eta > 0$ there exists a number $\tau(\eta) > 0$ such that for all $f \in \{f\}$ we have $\int_X \Phi \, | f | \, d\mu < \eta$ as soon as $\mu(X) < \tau$. Moreover, in the case that Δ is of infinite measure, we assume that for each $\eta > 0$ there exists a subset $E_\eta \subset \Delta$ of finite measure such that $\int_{\Delta - E_\eta} \Phi \, | f | \, d\mu < \eta$ for all $f \in \{f\}$. The functions of a set $\int_X \Phi \, | f | \, d\mu$ are therefore uniformly absolutely continuous.

Then, if $\varepsilon > 0$ is given, there exists a number $\delta(\varepsilon)$ and (if Δ is of infinite measure) there also exists a subset $\Delta_\varepsilon \subset \Delta$ of finite measure such that for all $f \in \{f\}$ we have $\| f_X \|_\Phi < \varepsilon$ as soon as $\mu(X) < \delta$, and also $\| f_{\Delta - \Delta_\varepsilon} \|_\Phi < \varepsilon$. Futhermore, if μ is non-atomic, there exists a constant A such that $\| f \|_\Phi \leqslant A$ for all $f \in \{f\}$.

(If $\varepsilon > 0$ is given, we choose the positive integer l such that $2/2^l < \varepsilon$. Then we take $\eta = M^{-l}$ and determine $\tau(\eta)$. This $\tau(\eta)$ may be chosen as $\delta(\varepsilon)$ since, if $\mu(X) < \delta(\varepsilon) = \tau(\eta)$, then $\int_X \Phi \, | f | \, d\mu < \eta = M^{-l}$, hence $\| f_X \|_\Phi \leqslant 2/2^l < \varepsilon$ by Ch. 5, § 7, Lemma α. Similarly the interval E_η may be taken as Δ_ε.

Now take $\eta = 1$ in the hypothesis. Then there exists a set $E_1 \subset \Delta$ of finite measure such that $\int_{\Delta - E_1} \Phi \, | f | \, d\mu < 1$ for all $f \in \{f\}$. Now determine N such that E_1 may be covered by N sets of measure smaller than $\tau(1)$, which is possible since μ is non-atomic. Then $\int_{E_1} \Phi \mid f \mid d\mu < N$ for all $f \in \{f\}$. This yields $\int_\Delta \Phi \mid f \mid d\mu < N + 1$; hence $\| f \|_\Phi < N + 2 = A$ for all $f \in \{f\}$ by Ch. 5, § 5, Th. 1).

6) Let $\Phi(2u) \leqslant M\Phi(u)$ for all $u \geqslant 0$, and let the set $\{f\}$ of functions $f(x) \in L_\Phi(\Delta, \mu)$ have the property that the functions of a set $\int_X \Phi \mid f \mid d\mu$ are uniformly absolutely continuous as defined in the preceding example. Then, if μ is separable and non-atomic, this set $\{f\}$ contains a sequence f_n converging weakly to a function $f_0 \in L_\Phi$. In other words,

$$\lim \int_\Delta f_n g \, d\mu = \int_\Delta f_0 g \, d\mu$$

for every $g \in L_\Psi$. If the hypothesis that μ is non-atomic is dropped, the same is true if the hypothesis that $\| f \|_\Phi \leqslant A$ for all $f \in \{f\}$ is added.

(Let A, $\delta(\varepsilon)$ and Δ_ε have the same meaning as in the preceding example, and consider the set of all bounded linear functionals $f^*(g) = \int_\Delta fg \, d\mu$ in L_Ψ, where f runs through $\{f\}$. Obviously $\mid f^*(g) \mid \leqslant A \| g \|_\Psi$ for all f^* in this set. We now restrict $g(x)$ to the characteristic functions of sets $F . \Delta$, where F runs through the sets of the enumerable collection Z, introduced in Ch. 5, § 3, and we may find by the diagonal process a sequence $f_n \in \{f\}$ such that $\int_\Delta f_n g \, d\mu = \int_{F.\Delta} f_n \, d\mu$ converges for all $F \in Z$. If therefore X is a set of finite measure, contained in Δ, and $F \in Z$ is chosen such that $\mu(X - F.\Delta) < \delta(\varepsilon)$ and $\mu(F.\Delta - X) < \delta(\varepsilon)$, we have, by Example 4,

$$\begin{aligned}
&\mid \int_X (f_n - f_m) d\mu \mid = \mid \int_{F.\Delta} + \int_{X-F.\Delta} - \int_{F.\Delta-X} \mid \leqslant \\
&\mid \int_{F.\Delta} \mid + \int_{X-F.\Delta} \mid f_n - f_m \mid d\mu + \int_{F.\Delta-X} \mid f_n - f_m \mid d\mu \leqslant \\
&\mid \int_{F.\Delta} \mid + p^{-1}(\delta(\varepsilon)+1) \| (f_n - f_m)_{X-F.\Delta} \|_\Phi + p^{-1}(\delta(\varepsilon)+1) \| (f_n - f_m)_{F.\Delta-X} \|_\Phi \leqslant \\
&\mid \int_{F.\Delta} \mid + 4p^{-1}(\delta(\varepsilon) + 1)\varepsilon.
\end{aligned}$$

This implies that $\int_X f_n \, d\mu$ converges for any measurable set $X \subset \Delta$ of finite measure.

Assume now that $A_1 \subset \Delta$ is of finite measure, and define $F(X) = \lim \int_X f_n \, d\mu$ for $X \subset A_1$. Since $\mu(X) < \delta(\varepsilon)$ implies $\mid \int_X f_n \, d\mu \mid \leqslant p^{-1}(\delta + 1) \| (f_n)_X \|_\Phi < p^{-1}(\delta + 1)\varepsilon$, we have $\lim F(X) = 0$ for $\lim \mu(X) = 0$. It follows that $F(X)$ is additive and absolutely continuous on A_1, so that, by the Radon-Nikodym Theorem (cf. Ch. 4, § 3, Th. 3 and Ch. 4, § 4),

$$\lim \int_X f_n \, d\mu = F(X) = \int_X f_0 \, d\mu,$$

where f_0 is summable over A_1. We may extend $f_0(x)$ onto the whole set Δ in such a way that $\lim \int_X f_n \, d\mu = \int_X f_0 \, d\mu$ for every set $X \subset \Delta$ of finite measure. Then also $\lim \int_\Delta (f_n - f_0) g \, d\mu = 0$ for every simple function $g(x)$, assuming only finite values, and vanishing outside a set of finite measure.

Next, let $g(x)$ be measurable, vanishing outside a set $\Delta_1 \subset \Delta$ of finite measure, and such that $\| g \|_\infty < \infty$. We may assume that $g(x) \geqslant 0$. Then there exists a sequence of simple functions $g_n(x)$ such that $g_n(x) \geqslant 0$, $g(x) = \lim g_n(x)$, and all $g_n(x)$ vanish outside Δ_1. Furthermore, if $\varepsilon > 0$ is given, there exists a positive $\delta'(\varepsilon)$ such that $\int_X \mid f_0 \mid d\mu < \varepsilon$ as soon as $\mu(X) < \delta'(\varepsilon)$, $X \subset \Delta_1$. Take $\delta'' = \min [\delta(\varepsilon), \delta'(\varepsilon)]$. Then Egoroff's Theorem guarantees the existence of an index $N(\varepsilon)$ and a set $Q \subset \Delta_1$ such that $\mu(Q) < \delta''$ and $\mid g_n(x) - g(x) \mid < \varepsilon$ for $n \geqslant N$,

$x \in \Delta_1 - Q$. Hence

$$|\int_\Delta (f_i - f_0)(g - g_N)\, d\mu| = |\int_{\Delta_1}| \leqslant$$
$$2 \| g \|_\infty \int_Q | f_i - f_0 | \, d\mu + \varepsilon \int_{\Delta_1 - Q} | f_i - f_0 | \, d\mu \leqslant$$
$$2 \| g \|_\infty \{\varepsilon + \int_Q | f_i | \, d\mu\} + \varepsilon\{\int_{\Delta_1} | f_0 | \, d\mu + \int_{\Delta_1} | f_i | \, d\mu\} \leqslant$$
$$2 \| g \|_\infty \{\varepsilon + p^{-1}(\delta'' + 1)\varepsilon\} + \varepsilon\{\int_{\Delta_1} | f_0 | \, d\mu + p^{-1}(\mu(\Delta_1) + 1)A\},$$

and this shows that $\lim \int_\Delta f_i g \, d\mu = \int_\Delta f_0 g \, d\mu$.

We next write $\Delta = \lim \Delta_n$, where Δ_n is an ascending sequence of sets of finite measure. Supposing that $g(x) \in L_\Psi$, we define $g_n(x)$ $(n = 1, 2, \ldots)$ by

$$g_n(x) = \begin{cases} | g(x) | / \operatorname{sgn} f_0(x), \ | g(x) | \leqslant n, \ x \in \Delta_n, \\ 0 \qquad \text{elsewhere on } \Delta. \end{cases}$$

Then $g_n(x) f_0(x) = | g_n(x) f_0(x) |$, $\lim | g_n(x) | = | g(x) |$, and $\| g_n \|_\Psi \leqslant \| g \|_\Psi$ on account of $| g_n(x) | \leqslant | g(x) |$. Furthermore, since $g_n(x)$ is bounded and vanishing outside Δ_n, $\int_\Delta g_n f_0 \, d\mu = \lim_i \int_\Delta g_n f_i \, d\mu$ with $| \int_\Delta g_n f_i \, d\mu | \leqslant \| f_i \|_\Phi \| g_n \|_\Psi \leqslant A \| g \|_\Psi$, hence $\int_\Delta g_n f_0 \, d\mu \leqslant A \| g \|_\Psi$ for all n. It follows by Fatou's Theorem that

$$\int_\Delta | g f_0 | \, d\mu \leqslant \liminf \int_\Delta | g_n f_0 | \, d\mu = \liminf \int_\Delta g_n f_0 \, d\mu \leqslant A \| g \|_\Psi,$$

which shows that $f_0 \in L_\Phi$.

It remains to prove that $\lim \int_\Delta (f_i - f_0) g \, d\mu = 0$ for every $g \in L_\Psi$. Let first $g(x) = 0$ outside a set Δ_1 of finite measure, and define $g_n(x)$ $(n = 1, 2, \ldots)$ by

$$g_n(x) = \begin{cases} g(x), \ | g(x) | \leqslant n, \ x \in \Delta_1, \\ 0 \quad \text{elsewhere on } \Delta. \end{cases}$$

Then $| g_n(x) | \leqslant | g(x) |$, $g(x) = \lim g_n(x)$ and $\| g_n \|_\Psi \leqslant \| g \|_\Psi$. If $\varepsilon > 0$ is given, there exists a positive $\delta_1(\varepsilon)$ such that $\| (f_0)_X \|_\Phi < \varepsilon$ as soon as $\mu(X) < \delta_1(\varepsilon)$, $X \subset \Delta_1$. Take $\delta_2 = \min [\delta(\varepsilon), \delta_1(\varepsilon)]$. Then Egoroff's Theorem guarantees the existence of a set $Q \subset \Delta_1$ and an index $N(\varepsilon)$ such that $\mu(Q) < \delta_2$ and $| g_n(x) - g(x) | < \varepsilon$ for $n \geqslant N$, $x \in \Delta_1 - Q$. Hence

$$| \int_\Delta (f_i - f_0)(g - g_N) d\mu | \leqslant 2 \| g \|_\Psi \| (f_i - f_0)_Q \|_\Phi + \varepsilon \int_{\Delta_1 - Q} | f_i - f_0 | \, d\mu \leqslant$$
$$2 \| g \|_\Psi \{\varepsilon + \varepsilon\} + \varepsilon\{\int_{\Delta_1} | f_0 | \, d\mu + p^{-1} (\mu(\Delta_1) + 1)A\},$$

which shows that $\lim \int_\Delta (f_i - f_0) g \, d\mu = 0$ for this $g(x)$. Let finally $g \in L_\Psi$ without any restriction. If $\varepsilon > 0$ is given, there exists a set $\Delta^*(\varepsilon)$ of finite measure such that $\| (f_0)_{\Delta - \Delta^*} \|_\Phi < \varepsilon$. Let Q be a set of finite measure which contains Δ_ε and Δ^*. Then $\| (f_i - f_0)_{\Delta - Q} \|_\Phi < 2\varepsilon$ for all f_i, hence $| \int_{\Delta - Q} (f_i - f_0) g \, d\mu | < 2\varepsilon \| g \|_\Psi$. Since $\lim \int_Q (f_i - f_0) g \, d\mu = 0$, we find therefore

$$\lim \int_\Delta f_i g \, d\mu = \int_\Delta f_0 g \, d\mu).$$

7) If $\Phi(2u) \leqslant M\Phi(u)$ for all $u \geqslant 0$, and if the linear integral transformation T with kernel $T(x, y)$ is of finite double-norm relative to $L_\Phi(\Delta, \mu)$, where μ is separable, then T^2 is compact on L_Φ into L_Φ.

(For any $f \in L_\Phi$ and for almost every $x \in \Delta$ we have $| \int_\Delta T(x, y) f(y) d\mu | \leqslant \| T_x(y) \|_\Psi \| f \|_\Phi$, hence $\| Tf \|_\Phi \leqslant ||| T ||| . \| f \|_\Phi$. This shows already that T is bounded. Let now $\{f\}$ be a bounded set of functions $f(x) \in L_\Phi$; $\| f \|_\Phi \leqslant B$ for all

$f \in \{f\}$. Then $\| Tf \|_\Phi \leqslant B \, ||| T |||$ for all $f \in \{f\}$. If $t_{maj}(x)$ is a measurable majorant of $\| T_x(y) \|_\Psi$ such that $\| t_{maj} \|_\Phi < \infty$, then also $\int_\Delta \Phi \mid B . t_{maj}(x) \mid d\mu < \infty$. It follows that to each $\eta > 0$ may be assigned a number $\tau(\eta) > 0$ and a set $E(\eta) \subset \Delta$ of finite measure such that $\int_X \Phi \mid B . t_{maj} \mid d\mu < \eta$ as soon as $\mu(X) < \tau$ and such that $\int_{\Delta - E} \Phi \mid B . t_{maj} \mid d\mu < \eta$. But, since for any $h = Tf$, $f \in \{f\}$, we have $| h(x) | \leqslant \| f \|_\Phi t_{maj}(x) \leqslant B . t_{maj}(x)$, this implies $\int_{\Delta - E} \Phi \mid h \mid d\mu < \eta$ and $\int_X \Phi \mid h \mid d\mu < \eta$ for $\mu(X) < \tau$. Hence, by the preceding example, there exists a sequence $h_n(x) = Tf_n(x)$, and there exists a function $h_0(x) \in L_\Phi$ such that

$$\lim \int_\Delta h_n(y) g(y) d\mu = \int_\Delta h_0(y) g(y) d\mu$$

for every $g \in L_\Psi$. The remaining part of the proof is similar to that in Ch. 11, § 2, Ex. D).

8) Let R be a complete Hilbert space, separable or not, and let H be positive and compact with the sequence $\lambda_1 \geqslant \lambda_2 \geqslant \ldots$ of characteristic values (if H has only q positive characteristic values, then $\lambda_{q+1} = \lambda_{q+2} = \ldots = 0$). Let $f_1, \ldots, f_n$ be an arbitrary system of n elements. Then, denoting the value of the determinant with elements (Hf_j, f_i) $(i, j = 1, \ldots, n)$ by $\det \| (Hf_j, f_i) \|$, we have ([10])

$$\det \| (Hf_j, f_i) \| \leqslant \Pi_1^n \lambda_i . \det \| (f_j, f_i) \|.$$

(If $f_1, \ldots, f_n$ are not linearly independent, both sides of the inequality vanish. Suppose therefore that $f_1, \ldots, f_n$ are linearly independent. Then the orthogonal system $\varphi_1, \ldots, \varphi_n$ may be determined such that $\varphi_1 = f_1$, $\varphi_2 = f_2 + \alpha\varphi_1$, $\varphi_3 = f_3 + \beta\varphi_2 + \gamma\varphi_1$, and so on. Normalizing $\varphi_1, \ldots, \varphi_n$, we obtain $\psi_1, \ldots, \psi_n$. Since $\det \| (H\psi_j, \psi_i) \| \leqslant \Pi_1^n \lambda_i = \Pi_1^n \lambda_i . \det \| (\psi_j, \psi_i) \|$ by Ch. 12, § 17, Th. 6, Corollary, we find $\det \| (H\varphi_j, \varphi_i) \| \leqslant \Pi_1^n \lambda_i . \det \| (\varphi_j, \varphi_i) \|$. Observing now that by elementary determinant rules $\det \| (f_j, f_i) \| = \det \| (\varphi_j, \varphi_i) \|$ and $\det \| (Hf_j, f_i) \| = \det \| (H\varphi_j, \varphi_i) \|$, we obtain the desired result).

9) Let R be a complete Hilbert space, separable or not, and let T_1 and T_2 be compact linear transformations with singular values $\lambda_1 \geqslant \lambda_2 \geqslant \ldots$ and $\mu_1 \geqslant \mu_2 \geqslant \ldots$ respectively. Then, if $T = T_1 T_2$ has the singular values $\xi_1 \geqslant \xi_2 \geqslant \ldots$, we have $\Pi_1^n \xi_i \leqslant \Pi_1^n \lambda_i \mu_i$ for every positive integer n [10].

(Let $\varphi_1, \ldots, \varphi_n$ be an orthonormal system of characteristic elements of TT^*, corresponding with the characteristic values $\xi_1^2, \ldots, \xi_n^2$. Then, by the preceding example,

$$\Pi_1^n \xi_i^2 = \det \| (TT^* \varphi_j, \varphi_i) \| = \det \| (T_1 T_2 T_2^* T_1^* \varphi_j, \varphi_i) \| =$$

$$\det \| (T_2 T_2^* T_1^* \varphi_j, T_1^* \varphi_i) \| \leqslant \Pi_1^n \mu_i^2 . \det \| (T_1^* \varphi_j, T_1^* \varphi_i) \| =$$

$$\Pi_1^n \mu_i^2 . \det \| (T_1 T_1^* \varphi_j, \varphi_i) \| \leqslant \Pi_1^n \lambda_i^2 \mu_i^2 . \det \| (\varphi_j, \varphi_i) \| = \Pi_1^n \lambda_i^2 \mu_i^2).$$

10) Let R be a complete Hilbert space, separable or not, and let $T_1, \ldots, T_p$ be compact linear transformations. The singular values of T_k are $\lambda_1^{(k)} \geqslant \lambda_2^{(k)} \geqslant \ldots$. Then, if $T = T_1 T_2 \ldots T_p$ has the singular values $\xi_1 \geqslant \xi_2 \geqslant \ldots$, we have $\Pi_1^n \xi_i \leqslant \Pi_1^n \lambda_i^{(1)} \lambda_i^{(2)} \ldots \lambda_i^{(p)}$ for every positive integer n.

(Follows from the preceding example by induction).

11) Under the same hypotheses as in the preceding example we have $\Sigma_1^n \xi_i^s \leqslant \Sigma_1^n (\lambda_i^{(1)} \ldots \lambda_i^{(p)})^s$, where s is arbitrarily positive. More generally, if $\omega(x)$, defined

for $x \geqslant 0$, is continuous and non-decreasing and such that $\Phi(t) = \omega(e^t)$ is a convex function of t, we have $\Sigma_1^n \omega(\xi_i) \leqslant \Sigma_1^n \omega(\lambda_i^{(1)} \ldots \lambda_i^{(p)})$.

(Proof as in Ch. 12, § 18, Th. 8).

12) If, under the same hypotheses as in the preceding example, $\Sigma_{i=1}^\infty (\lambda_i^{(k)})^2 < \infty$ for $k = 1, \ldots, p$, then $\Sigma\, \xi_i^{2/p} < \infty$. This holds in particular if R is the space $L_2(\Delta, \mu)$, where μ is a separable measure, and $T_1, T_2, \ldots, T_p$ are transformations of finite double-norm on $L_2(\Delta, \mu)$ [7].

(We have $\Sigma\, \xi_i^{2/p} \leqslant \Sigma\, (\lambda_i^{(1)} \ldots \lambda_i^{(p)})^{2/p} \leqslant \{\Sigma\, (\lambda_i^{(1)})^2\}^{1/p} \{\Sigma\, (\lambda_i^{(2)} \ldots \lambda_i^{(p)})^{2/(p-1)}\}^{1-1/p}$ by Hölder's inequality).

13) If T is of finite double-norm on $L_2(\Delta, \mu)$, where μ is a separable measure, $p > 1$ is an integer and $\Sigma\, \xi_i^{2/p} < \infty$, where $\xi_1 \geqslant \xi_2 \geqslant \ldots$ are the singular values of T, then we have $T = T_1 T_2 \ldots T_p$ with all $T_k (k = 1, \ldots, p)$ of finite double-norm [2].

(By § 6, Th. 4 we have $T(x, y) \sim \Sigma\, \xi_i \psi_i(x) \overline{\varphi_i(y)}$. Take $\lambda_i^{(k)} = \xi_i^{1/p} (k = 1, \ldots, p)$, and choose orthonormal systems $\psi_i^{(k)}$, $\varphi_i^{(k)} (k = 1, \ldots, p)$ such that $\psi_i^{(1)} = \psi_i$, $\varphi_i^{(p)} = \varphi_i$ and $\psi_i^{(k+1)} = \varphi_i^{(k)}$. Then take $T_k(x, y) \sim \Sigma\, \lambda_i^{(k)} \psi_i^{(k)}(x) \overline{\varphi_i^{(k)}(y)}$).

14) Suppose that R is a complete Hilbert space, separable or not, that T_1 is a bounded linear transformation satisfying $\| T_1 \| = m_1$, and T_2 is compact with singular values $\lambda_1 \geqslant \lambda_2 \geqslant \ldots$. Then, if $T = T_1 T_2$ has the singular values $\xi_1 \geqslant \xi_2 \geqslant \ldots$, we have $\xi_i \leqslant m_1 \lambda_i$ $(i = 1, 2, \ldots)$.

(The positive transformations $T_2^* T_2$ and $T_2^* T_1^* T_1 T_2$ have the characteristic values λ_i^2 and ξ_i^2 respectively. Since $(T_2^* T_1^* T_1 T_2 f, f) = (T_1^* T_1 T_2 f, T_2 f) \leqslant \| T_1^* T_1 \| . \| T_2 f \|^2 = m_1^2 (T_2^* T_2 f, f)$ for all f, we find $O \leqslant T_2^* T_1^* T_1 T_2 \leqslant m_1^2 T_2^* T_2$, hence $\xi_i^2 \leqslant m_1^2 \lambda_i^2$ for $i = 1, 2, \ldots$ by Ch. 12, § 17, Th. 4).

15) Suppose that R is a complete Hilbert space, separable or not, and that the bounded linear transformation T is the product (in some order) of p factors $A_1, \ldots, A_p$ and q factors $B_1, \ldots, B_q$, where all A_i are compact with singular values $\lambda_1^{(i)} \geqslant \lambda_2^{(i)} \geqslant \ldots$ and all B_i are bounded with $\| B_i \| = m_i$. Then, if T has the singular values $\xi_1 \geqslant \xi_2 \geqslant \ldots$, we have $\Pi_1^n \xi_i \leqslant (m_1 m_2 \ldots m_q)^n \Pi_{i=1}^n \lambda_i^{(1)} \lambda_i^{(2)} \ldots \lambda_i^{(p)} = \Pi_{i=1}^n m_1 m_2 \ldots m_q \lambda_i^{(1)} \lambda_i^{(2)} \ldots \lambda_i^{(p)}$ for every positive integer n. Hence $\Sigma_1^n \xi_i^s \leqslant (m_1 m_2 \ldots m_q)^s\, \Sigma_{i=1}^n (\lambda_i^{(1)} \lambda_i^{(2)} \ldots \lambda_i^{(p)})^s$ for every $s > 0$.

(Follows from the preceding example, together with Example 10 and Example 11).

16) Suppose that R is a complete Hilbert space, separable or not, that T is bounded with $\| T \| \leqslant 1$, and that H is positive and compact with characteristic values $\lambda_1 \geqslant \lambda_2 \geqslant \ldots \geqslant 0$. Then, if $K = TH$ has the characteristic values μ_i with $| \mu_1 | \geqslant | \mu_2 | \geqslant \ldots$ and the singular values $\xi_1 \geqslant \xi_2 \geqslant \ldots$, we have $\Pi_1^n | \mu_i | \leqslant \Pi_1^n \xi_i \leqslant \Pi_1^n \lambda_i$ for every positive integer n. Hence $\Sigma_1^n | \mu_i |^s \leqslant \Sigma_1^n \xi_i^s \leqslant \Sigma_1^n \lambda_i^s$ for every $s > 0$.

(Follows from Ch. 12, § 18, Th. 8, together with Example 14).

17) Let R be a complete Hilbert space, separable or not, let H be positive and compact with characteristic values $\lambda_1 \geqslant \lambda_2 \geqslant \ldots \geqslant 0$, and let A be self-adjoint with $\| A \| \leqslant 1$. Then, if $K = AH$ has the positive characteristic values $\mu_1^+ \geqslant \mu_2^+ \geqslant \ldots$ and the negative characteristic values $\mu_1^- \leqslant \mu_2^- \leqslant \ldots$, we have proved in Ch. 12, § 17, Th. 5 that $\mu_i^+ \leqslant \lambda_i$ and $| \mu_i^- | \leqslant \lambda_i$. Furthermore, ranging these characteristic values of K into a single sequence μ_i such that $| \mu_1 | \geqslant | \mu_2 | \geqslant \ldots$, we have $\Sigma_1^n | \mu_i | \leqslant \Sigma_1^n \lambda_i$ by the preceding example. In view of these

statements one might think now that perhaps $|\mu_i| \leqslant \lambda_i$ for all values of i. This, however, is not necessarily true.

(Let $\{\varphi_1, \varphi_2\}$ be orthonormal in a two-dimensional Hilbert space, and define H and A by $H\varphi_1 = \varphi_1$, $H\varphi_2 = \alpha\varphi_2$ $(0 < \alpha < 1)$; $A\varphi_1 = \varphi_2$, $A\varphi_2 = \varphi_1$. Then $AH\varphi_1 = \varphi_2$, $AH\varphi_2 = \alpha\varphi_1$, and it is easily seen that $K = AH$ has the characteristic values $\mu_1 = \alpha^{1/2}$, $\mu_2 = -\alpha^{1/2}$, whereas those of H are $\lambda_1 = 1$, $\lambda_2 = \alpha$. Hence $|\mu_2| > \lambda_2$. Observe that $\Pi_1^2 |\mu_i| = \Pi_1^2 \lambda_i$, and that $\Sigma_1^2 |\mu_i| < \Sigma_1^2 \lambda_i$).

18) Let R be a complete Hilbert space, separable or not, let H be positive and compact with characteristic values $\lambda_1 \geqslant \lambda_2 \geqslant \ldots \geqslant 0$, and let A be bounded such that $\|A\| \leqslant 1$ and $HAH = HA^*H$. Hence $K = AH$ is strongly symmetrisable relative to H. If K has the characteristic values μ_i with $|\mu_1| \geqslant |\mu_2| \geqslant \ldots$, then $\Pi_1^n |\mu_i| \leqslant \Pi_1^n \lambda_i$ by Example 16. In this particular case the same result may be obtained without using Weyl's Theorem (Ch. 12, § 18, Th. 8).

($K = AH$ and the self-adjoint transformation $H^{1/2}AH^{1/2}$ have the same characteristic values $\neq 0$ by Ch. 12, § 12, Th. 3, hence $H^{1/2}AH^{1/2}$ has the singular values $|\mu_i|$. Denoting the singular values of $AH^{1/2}$ by p_i, we have $p_i \leqslant \lambda_i^{1/2}$ by Example 14. Furthermore $\Pi_1^n |\mu_i| \leqslant \Pi_1^n \lambda_i^{1/2} p_i$ by Example 9. Hence $\Pi_1^n |\mu_i| \leqslant \Pi_1^n \lambda_i$).

19) Let K be an integral transformation on $L_2(\Delta)$ with a Garbe kernel $K(x, y) = A(x)H(x, y)$, where $A(x)$ is real, measurable and bounded, $H(x, y)$ is of positive type (that is, the corresponding transformation H is positive) and compact with characteristic values $\lambda_1 \geqslant \lambda_2 \geqslant \ldots \geqslant 0$ (cf. Ch. 9, § 12, Ex. B). Then, if $-1 \leqslant A(x) \leqslant 1$ and $K(x, y)$ has the characteristic values μ_i with $|\mu_1| \geqslant |\mu_2| \geqslant \ldots$, the inequality $\Pi_1^n |\mu_i| \leqslant \Pi_1^n \lambda_i$ is an immediate consequence of the preceding example, hence also $\Sigma_1^n |\mu_i|^s \leqslant \Sigma_1^n \lambda_i^s$ for $s > 0$. In the particular case that $A(x)$ assumes only the values ± 1 (kernel $K(x, y)$ of *polar type*), the inequality $\Sigma |\mu_i| \leqslant \Sigma \lambda_i$ was proved already by GARBE [8].

20) Let R be a complete Hilbert space, separable or not, let H be positive with $\|H\| \leqslant 1$, and let A be self-adjoint and compact with characteristic values λ_i such that $|\lambda_1| \geqslant |\lambda_2| \geqslant \ldots$. Then, if $K = AH$ has the characteristic values μ_i with $|\mu_1| \geqslant |\mu_2| \geqslant \ldots$, we have $|\mu_i| \leqslant |\lambda_i|$. This holds in particular if K is an integral transformation on $L_2(\Delta)$ with kernel $K(x, y) = A(x, y)h(y)$, where $A(x, y)$ is Hermitian and compact, and the measurable function $h(y)$ satisfies $0 \leqslant h(y) \leqslant 1$ on Δ (compare Ch. 9, § 12, Ex. A).

(Observe once more that $H^{1/2}AH^{1/2}$ has the singular values $|\mu_i|$).

REFERENCES

[1] I. A. Ickovič, On the Fredholm series, Doklady Akad. Nauk SSSR (N.S.) 59 (1948), 423–425 (Russian).

[2] S. H. Chang, A generalization of a theorem of Lalesco, Journal London Math. Soc. 22 (1947), 185–189.

[3] R. Jentzsch, Über Integralgleichungen mit positivem Kern, Journal für Math. 141 (1912), 235–244.

[4] E. Hopf, Über lineare Integralgleichungen mit positivem Kern, Sitzungsberichte Akad. Berlin (1928), 233–245.

[5] V. VOLTERRA, Sulla inversione degli integrali definiti, Rom Acc. Linc. Rend. (5) 5 (1896), 177–185.

[6] F. SMITHIES, On the theory of linear integral equations, Proc. Cambridge Philos. Soc. 31 (1935), 76–84.

[7] S. H. CHANG, On the distribution of characteristic values and singular values of linear integral equations, Transactions Amer. Math. Soc. 67 (1949), 351–367.

[8] E. GARBE, Zur Theorie der Integralgleichung dritter Art, Math. Annalen 76 (1915), 527–547.

[9] A. C. ZAANEN, Integral transformations and their resolvents in Orlicz and Lebesgue spaces, Compositio Math. 10 (1952), 56–94.

[10] A. HORN, On the singular values of a product of completely continuous operators, Proc. Nat. Acad. of Sciences 36 (1950), 374–375.

Chapter 14

INTEGRAL EQUATION WITH NORMAL KERNEL

§ 1. Introduction

In the present chapter we assume again that Δ is a μ-measurable set of finite or infinite measure, and we consider the linear integral equation

$$\int_\Delta N(x, y)f(y)d\mu - \lambda f(x) = g(x)$$

in the Lebesgue space $L_2(\Delta, \mu)$, where the kernel $N(x, y)$ of the equation satisfies the following conditions:

1°. $N(x, y)$ has the property (P) relative to $L_2(\Delta)$. Stated alternatively, $N(x, y) \in L_{22}(\Delta \times \Delta)$. Hence the linear transformation N, corresponding with $N(x, y)$, is bounded.

2°. The linear transformation N is normal, that is, $NN^* = N^*N$ or, since N^* has the kernel $\overline{N(y, x)}$,

$$\int_\Delta N(x, z)\overline{N(y, z)}d\mu = \int_\Delta \overline{N(z, x)}N(z, y)d\mu$$

for almost every point (x, y) on $\Delta \times \Delta$. This condition is satisfied in particular whenever $N(x, y)$ is Hermitian, that is, whenever $N(x, y) = \overline{N(y, x)}$ almost everywhere on $\Delta \times \Delta$, since $N^* = N$ (hence N self-adjoint) in this case.

If $n > 1$ is an integer, the productspace $L_2^n = [L_2(\Delta)]^n$ with inner product $(\{f\}, \{g\}) = \Sigma_{i=1}^n (f^i, g^i) = \Sigma_{i=1}^n \int_\Delta f^i(x)\overline{g^i(x)}d\mu$ is the direct sum of n separate spaces $L_2(\Delta)$. We shall consider the linear equation $N\{f\} - \lambda\{f\} = \{g\}$ with matrixkernel $\{N_{ij}(x, y)\}$ in L_2^n, that is to say, we shall consider the set of equations

$$\Sigma_{j=1}^n \int_\Delta N_{ij}(x, y)f^j(y)d\mu - \lambda f^i(x) = g^i(x) \quad (i = 1, \ldots, n)$$

in L_2, where $\{N_{ij}(x, y)\}$ satisfies the following conditions:

1°. All $N_{ij}(x, y)$ $(i, j = 1, \ldots, n)$ have the property (P) relative to L_2. Hence N is bounded in L_2^n.

2°. The linear transformation N is normal; in other words, since N^* has the matrixkernel $\overline{\{N_{ji}(y, x)\}}$,

$$\Sigma_{k=1}^n \int_\Delta N_{ik}(x, z)\overline{N_{jk}(y, z)}d\mu = \Sigma_{k=1}^n \int_\Delta \overline{N_{ki}(z, x)}N_{kj}(z, y)d\mu$$

for almost every point (x, y) on $\Delta \times \Delta$ and for $i, j = 1, \ldots, n$. This condition is satisfied in particular whenever $\{N_{ij}(x, y)\}$ is Hermitian, that is, whenever $N_{ij}(x, y) = \overline{N_{ji}(y, x)}$ almost everywhere on $\Delta \times \Delta$, since $N^* = N$ (hence N self-adjoint) in this case.

In the greater part of what follows we shall suppose that the kernel $N(x, y)$ or the matrixkernel $\{N_{ij}(x, y)\}$ is non-singular, that is, according to the definition of a non-singular kernel, we shall suppose that the transformation N or one of its iterates $N^p (p = 2, 3, \ldots)$ is compact. Since however for a normal transformation N the compactness of N^p for an integer $p > 1$ implies the compactness of N itself by Ch. 11, § 1, Th. 13, it is no loss of generality to suppose immediately that N itself is compact in this case. This will be so in particular whenever μ is separable, and $N(x, y)$ or $\{N_{ij}(x, y)\}$ is of finite double-norm $|||\, N \,|||$, hence, whenever $|||\, N \,|||^2 = \int_{\Delta\times\Delta} |\, N(x, y) \,|^2 \, d(\mu \times \mu) < \infty$ or $|||\, N \,|||^2 = \Sigma_{ij=1}^n \int_{\Delta\times\Delta} |\, N_{ij}(x, y) \,|^2 \, d(\mu \times \mu) < \infty$ respectively (cf. Ch. 9, § 10, Th. 13).

§ 2. Normal Kernels Satisfying only the Condition (*P*) relative to $L_2(\Delta, \mu)$

We consider the integral equation

$$(1) \qquad \int_\Delta N(x, y)f(y)d\mu - \lambda f(x) = g(x) \leftrightarrow (N - \lambda I)f = g$$

and its adjoint equation

$$(2) \qquad \int_\Delta \overline{N(y, x)}f(y)d\mu - \bar{\lambda} f(x) = g(x) \leftrightarrow (N^* - \bar{\lambda} I)f = g$$

in L_2, where the kernel $N(x, y)$ is normal and satisfies the condition (P) relative to L_2.

Theorem 1. *For any complex* λ ($\lambda = 0$ *is therefore permitted*) *the solutions of the homogeneous equation* (1) (*that is, all* $f(x)$ *satisfying* $(N - \lambda I)f = 0$) *are those and only those functions* $f(x)$ *satisfying* $(f, g) = \int_\Delta f(x)\, \overline{g(x)}\, d\mu = 0$ *for every* $g(x)$ *for which* (1) *has a solution. A similar statement holds for the equation* (2).

The homogeneous equations (1) *and* (2), *that is, the equations* $Nf = \lambda f$ *and* $N^*f = \bar{\lambda}f$, *have the same set of solutions.*

Proof. Observe that $N - \lambda I$ and $N^* - \bar{\lambda}I$ are each other's adjoints, so that $N - \lambda I$ is normal. The null space of $N - \lambda I$ and the closure of the range of $N - \lambda I$ are therefore orthogonal complements by Ch. 9, § 14, Th. 1, Corollary. Noting finally that $\| (N - \lambda I)f \| = \| (N^* - \bar{\lambda}I)f \|$ for every $f \in L_2$ by Ch. 9, § 13, Th. 1, we see that $(N - \lambda I)f = 0$ if and only if $(N^* - \bar{\lambda}I)f = 0$ (cf. also Ch. 9, § 15, Th. 1).

Theorem 2. 1°. *The residual spectrum of* N *is empty.*

2°. *Characteristic functions, belonging to different values in the point spectrum of* N, *are orthogonal.*

3°. *If, in particular,* N *is self-adjoint, every non-real number belongs to the resolvent set of* N.

4°. *If, in particular,* N *is unitary* ($NN^* = N^*N = I$), *every complex* λ *such that* $|\lambda| \neq 1$ *belongs to the resolvent set of* N.

Proof. Statement 1° follows from Ch. 10, § 9, Th. 7, and 2° from Ch. 9, § 15, Th. 1. The statements 3° and 4° were proved in Ch. 10, § 9, Th. 8 and Th. 9 respectively.

Theorem 3. *If* $p > 1$ *is an integer, the null spaces of* $N - \lambda I$ *and* $(N - \lambda I)^p$ *are identical. Hence, if the dimension of this null space is finite but positive, the algebraic multiplicity of the characteristic value* λ *is equal to its geometric multiplicity.*

Proof. Follows from Ch. 9, § 15, Th. 7.

Similar statements hold for a system with a matrixkernel $\{N_{ij}(x, y)\}$ which is normal and satisfies the condition (P).

The existence of an integral transformation N of the kind considered here, and which fails to be compact, is shown by the example in Ch. 11, § 2, Ex. B. In this example $N(x, y)$ is of the form $N(x, y) = \Sigma_1^\infty \varphi_n(x)\varphi_n(y)$, where $\{\varphi_n(x)\}$ is a certain orthonormal system of non-negative functions in $L_2[0, 1]$. Hence N is self-adjoint (and even positive) in this case. An example where N is normal, but not self-adjoint, is found by taking a sequence $\{\lambda_n\}$ of non-real numbers with e.g. $1 < |\lambda_n| < 2$, and defining $N(x, y) = \Sigma_1^\infty \lambda_n \varphi_n(x)\varphi_n(y)$.

§ 3. Non-Singular Normal Kernel

Once more we consider the integral equation

$$(1) \qquad \int_\Delta N(x, y)f(y)d\mu - \lambda f(x) = g(x)$$

in $L_2(\Delta, \mu)$, and we now assume about the kernel $N(x, y)$ that the corresponding transformation N is normal and compact. Then every number $\lambda \neq 0$ is either a characteristic value, or it belongs to the resolvent set of N, and every characteristic value $\neq 0$ has finite multiplicity. The total number of characteristic values is finite or enumerable, and in the latter case the characteristic values tend to zero. If $N(x, y)$ is Hermitian, all characteristic values are real (cf. Th. 2, 3° in the preceding paragraph). We shall assume that $\lambda_1, \lambda_2, \ldots$ is the sequence of all characteristic values $\neq 0$ of N, each characteristic value repeated according to its multiplicity and arranged such that $|\lambda_1| \geqslant |\lambda_2| \geqslant \ldots$, and that $\varphi_1(x), \varphi_2(x), \ldots$ is a corresponding orthonormal sequence of characteristic functions. Then $\bar{\lambda}_1, \bar{\lambda}_2, \ldots$ and $\varphi_1(x), \varphi_2(x), \ldots$ are the corresponding sequences for N^*.

Theorem 1. *The sequence $|\lambda_1|^2, |\lambda_2|^2, \ldots$ is the sequence of all characteristic values $\neq 0$ of $NN^* = N^*N$, each characteristic value repeated according to its multiplicity, and $\varphi_1(x), \varphi_2(x), \ldots$ is a corresponding sequence of characteristic functions.*

Proof. Follows from Ch. 12, § 19, Th. 3.

Theorem 2. *If $k(x) = \int_\Delta N(x, y)f(y)d\mu$ and $k^*(x) = \int_\Delta \overline{N(y, x)}\, f(y)d\mu$, then*

$$|\lambda_n|^2 = \max \frac{\int_\Delta |k|^2 \, d\mu}{\int_\Delta |f|^2 \, d\mu} = \max \frac{\int_\Delta |k^*|^2 \, d\mu}{\int_\Delta |f|^2 \, d\mu}$$

for all $f(x) \in L_2$ satisfying $\int_\Delta |f|^2 \, d\mu \neq 0$ and $\int_\Delta f\overline{\varphi_1}\, d\mu = \ldots = \int_\Delta f\overline{\varphi_{n-1}}\, d\mu = 0$. The maximum is attained for $f(x) = \varphi_n(x)$.

Proof. Follows from Ch. 12, § 19, Th. 4.

Theorem 3. *Suppose that $N(x, y)$ is Hermitian, and that $\lambda_1^+ \geqslant \lambda_2^+ \geqslant \ldots$ is the sequence of all its positive characteristic values with the corresponding sequence $\varphi_1^+(x), \varphi_2^+(x), \ldots$ of characteristic functions. Then*

$$\lambda_n^+ = \max \int_{\Delta\times\Delta} N(x, y)\overline{f(x)}f(y)d(\mu \times \mu) / \int_\Delta |f|^2 \, d\mu$$

for all $f(x) \in L_2$ satisfying $\int_\Delta |f|^2 \, d\mu \neq 0$ and $\int_\Delta f\overline{\varphi_1^+}\, d\mu = \ldots = \int_\Delta f\,\overline{\varphi_{n-1}^+}\, d\mu = 0$. A similar statement holds for the sequence of all negative characteristic values.

Proof. Follows from Ch. 12, § 7, Th. 2, 4°.

Theorem 4 *(Courant's Theorem). Let* $p_1(x), \ldots, p_{n-1}(x)$ *be arbitrary functions belonging to* L_2*, let* $N(x, y)$ *be Hermitian, and write*

$$\mu_n = \textit{upper bound} \int_{\Delta\times\Delta} N(x, y)\,\overline{f(x)}\,f(y)\,d(\mu \times \mu) \,/\, \int_\Delta |f|^2\,d\mu$$

for all $f(x) \in L_2$ *satisfying* $\int_\Delta |f|^2\,d\mu \neq 0$ *and* $\int_\Delta f\bar{p}_1\,d\mu = \ldots = \int_\Delta f\overline{p_{n-1}}\,d\mu = 0$*. Then* μ_n *depends on* $p_1(x), \ldots, p_{n-1}(x)$*. Letting now these functions run through the whole space* L_2*, we have*

$$\lambda_n^+ = \min \mu_n.$$

A similar statement holds for the negative characteristic values.

Proof. Follows from Ch. 12, § 7, Th. 2, 5°.

Remark. As we already observed earlier (cf. Ch. 12, § 4, Th. 3 and Th. 4), the present theorem was proved by Courant for the special case of a Hermitian kernel of finite double-norm.

Theorem 5. *We have* $\int_\Delta N(x, y)f(y)d\mu = 0$ *(for almost every* x*) and also* $\int_\Delta \overline{N(y, x)}f(y)\,d\mu = 0$ *(for almost every* x*) if and only if* $\int_\Delta f\overline{\varphi_n}\,d\mu = 0$ $(n = 1, 2, \ldots)$*. The value* $\lambda = 0$ *belongs therefore either to the point spectrum or to the continuous spectrum of* N*.*

Proof. Follows from Ch. 12, § 19, Th. 5. We observe that $\lambda = 0$ is in the point spectrum of N if the system $\{\varphi_n(x)\}$ is not complete in L_2, and in the continuous spectrum of N if $\{\varphi_n(x)\}$ is complete in L_2.

Theorem 6. *If* $N(x, y)$ *is Hermitian, the transformation* N *is positive if and only if all* λ_n *are positive.*

Proof. Follows from Ch. 12, § 7, Th. 2, 6°.

Theorem 7 *(Expansion theorem). If* $f(x) \in L_2$*, then*

$$\int_\Delta N(x, y)f(y)d\mu \sim \Sigma\, \lambda_i(f, \varphi_i)\varphi_i(x),$$

$$\int_\Delta \overline{N(y, x)}f(y)d\mu \sim \Sigma\, \bar{\lambda}_i(f, \varphi_i)\varphi_i(x),$$

where the symbol $\sim$ *denotes convergence in mean with index 2 on the set* Δ*. Furthermore*

$$\int_{\Delta\times\Delta} N(x, y)\overline{g(x)}f(y)\,d(\mu \times \mu) = \Sigma\, \lambda_i(f, \varphi_i)\overline{(g, \varphi_i)},$$

$$\int_{\Delta\times\Delta} \overline{N(y, x)}g(x)f(y)d(\mu \times \mu) = \Sigma\, \bar{\lambda}_i(f, \varphi_i)\overline{(g, \varphi_i)}.$$

Proof. Follows from Ch. 12, § 19, Th. 6.

Theorem 8. *The following four statements are equivalent:*

1°. *The system* $\{\varphi_n(x)\}$ *is complete in* L_2.

2°. *The range of* N *is dense in* L_2. *In other words, given* $g(x) \in L_2$ *and* $\varepsilon > 0$, *there exists a function* $f(x) \in L_2$ *such that*

$$\int_\Delta | g(x) - \int_\Delta N(x, y)f(y)d\mu |^2 d\mu < \varepsilon.$$

3°. $\int_\Delta N(x, y)f(y)d\mu = 0$ *(almost everywhere) if and only if* $f(x) = 0$ *(almost everywhere).*

4°. *Every* $g(x) \in L_2$ *has an expansion* $g(x) \sim \Sigma\, \beta_n\varphi_n(x)$, *where* $\beta_n = (g, \varphi_n)$ *for* $n = 1, 2, \ldots.$

Proof. Follows from Ch. 12, § 19, Th. 7.

Remark. As we already observed earlier (cf. Ch. 12, § 7, Th. 4), a kernel having the properties mentioned in the present theorem is sometimes called a general kernel.

Theorem 9. *If* $\lambda \neq 0$ *is no characteristic value of* N, *the equation* (1) *has a uniquely determined solution* $f(x) \in L_2$ *for every* $g(x) \in L_2$. *If* $\lambda \neq 0$ *is a characteristic value of* N, *the equation* (1) *has a solution* $f(x) \in L_2$ *for those and only those* $g(x) \in L_2$ *which are orthogonal to all characteristic functions of* N *belonging to the characteristic value* λ. *This solution* $f(x)$ *is determined except for a linear combination of these characteristic functions.*

More precisely, if $\int_\Delta N(x, y)f(y)d\mu - \lambda f(x) = g(x)$, *then*

$$f(x) \sim -\frac{g(x)}{\lambda} - {}'\Sigma \frac{\lambda_n}{\lambda(\lambda - \lambda_n)} \alpha_n\varphi_n(x),$$

where $\alpha_n = (g, \varphi_n)$ *for* $\lambda_n \neq \lambda$, *and where the dash in front of the* Σ*-symbol means that for those values of* n *for which* $\lambda_n = \lambda$ *the coefficient of* $\varphi_n(x)$ *has the value* (f, φ_n). *For every set of arbitrarily prescribed values of these coefficients there exists a solution* $f(x)$.

Proof. Follows from Ch. 12, § 19, Th. 8.

Remark. The arrangement of the sequence λ_n is irrelevant in the expansion theorems.

Similar statements hold for a system with a matrixkernel $\{N_{ij}(x, y)\}$ which is normal and non-singular. To quote one example:

If $\{\varphi_k(x)\} = \{\varphi_k^1(x), \ldots, \varphi_k^n(x)\}$ is the k-th characteristic functionset, and $f(x) \in L_2$, then, writing

$$\alpha_k^j = (f, \varphi_k^j) = \int_\Delta f(x)\overline{\varphi_k^j(x)}d\mu \ (j = 1, \ldots, n;\ k = 1, 2, \ldots),$$

we have

$$\int_\Delta N_{ij}(x, y)f(y)d\mu \sim \Sigma_k \lambda_k \alpha_k^j \varphi_k^i(x).$$

To prove this statement, we consider the element $\{f\}$ in L_2^n with j-th component $f(x)$ and all other components zero. Then $(\{f\}, \{\varphi_k\}) = (f, \varphi_k^j) = \alpha_k^j$ for $k = 1, 2, \ldots$, so that the i-th component of $\Sigma \lambda_k(\{f\}, \{\varphi_k\})\{\varphi_k\}$ is $\Sigma_k \lambda_k \alpha_k^j \varphi_k^i(x)$. On the other hand the i-th component of $N\{f\}$ consists only of the single term $\int_\Delta N_{ij}(x, y)f(y)d\mu$.

The existence of an integral transformation N of the kind considered here, and which has the property that neither N itself nor any of its iterates is of finite double-norm, is shown by the example in Ch. 11, § 8, Th. 2, Remark. In this example $N(x, y)$ is of the form $N(x, y) = \Sigma \lambda_n \varphi_n(x)\varphi_n(y)$, where $\{\varphi_n(x)\}$ is a certain orthonormal system of non-negative functions in $L_2[0, 1]$, and $\{\lambda_n\}$ is a sequence of positive numbers, tending sufficiently slowly to zero. Hence N is self-adjoint (and even positive) in this case. An example where N is normal, but not self-adjoint, is found by replacing the sequence $\{\lambda_n\}$ by the sequence $\{\mu_n\}$, where for example $\mu_n = \lambda_n e^{i\pi n\alpha}$ (α irrational).

§ 4. Normal Kernel of Finite Double-Norm

We now assume that the measure μ is separable, and that the kernel $N(x, y)$ of our integral equation is normal and of finite double-norm, hence $||| N |||^2 = \int_{\Delta\times\Delta} | N(x, y) |^2 d(\mu \times \mu) < \infty$. Then the linear transformation N is compact, so that all theorems in the preceding paragraph hold. We may prove somewhat more in the present case however. Besides the expansion theorem for functions of the form $\int_\Delta N(x, y)f(y)d\mu$, there is now also an expansion theorem for the kernel $N(x, y)$ itself. Moreover, we shall establish some results on the pointwise convergence of these expansions. The theorems in the present paragraph, and also the expansion theorems in the preceding paragraph (Theorem 7 and Theorem 9) were proved in a somewhat different way, following the method of SCHMIDT [1] for continuous kernels, by SMITHIES [2].

Theorem 1 (*Expansion theorem for the kernel*). *We have*

$$(1)\qquad \begin{cases} N(x, y) \sim \Sigma \lambda_i \varphi_i(x)\overline{\varphi_i(y)}, \\ \overline{N(y, x)} \sim \Sigma \bar{\lambda}_i \varphi_i(x)\overline{\varphi_i(y)}, \end{cases}$$

where $\sim$ *denotes convergence in mean with index* 2 *on* $\Delta \times \Delta$. *Furthermore*

$$(2)\qquad \begin{cases} \int_\Delta |N(x,y)|^2\,d\mu = \Sigma\,|\lambda_i|^2\,|\varphi_i(x)|^2 \text{ (integration over } y), \\ \int_\Delta |N(x,y)|^2\,d\mu = \Sigma\,|\lambda_i|^2\,|\varphi_i(y)|^2 \text{ (integration over } x) \end{cases}$$

for almost every $x \in \Delta$ *and almost every* $y \in \Delta$ *respectively.*

Proof. Consider $N(x, y) = N_y(x)$ as a function $n(x)$ of x. Then $n(x) \in L_2$ for almost every $y \in \Delta$. Hence, also for almost every $y \in \Delta$,

$$(n, \varphi_i) = \int_\Delta N(x,y)\overline{\varphi_i(x)}d\mu = \int_\Delta \overline{\overline{N(x,y)}\varphi_i(x)}d\mu =$$

$$\lambda_i\overline{\varphi_i(y)} \quad (i = 1, 2, \ldots),$$

and, if $f(x)$ is orthogonal to all $\varphi_i(x)$,

$$(n, f) = \int_\Delta N(x,y)\overline{f(x)}d\mu = \int_\Delta \overline{\overline{N(x,y)}f(x)}d\mu = 0.$$

It follows that $n = \Sigma\,(n, \varphi_i)\varphi_i$, hence

$$\|\, n - \Sigma_{i=1}^k (n, \varphi_i)\varphi_i \,\|^2 = \Sigma_{k+1}\,|(n, \varphi_i)|^2,$$

or

$$(3)\qquad \int_\Delta |\, N(x,y) - \Sigma_1^k \lambda_i\varphi_i(x)\overline{\varphi_i(y)}\,|^2\,d\mu = \Sigma_{k+1}\,|\lambda_i|^2\,|\varphi_i(y)|^2$$

for almost every $y \in \Delta$. Taking $k = 0$, we obtain the second part of (2), and integrating (3) over y, we find

$$(4)\qquad \int_{\Delta\times\Delta} |\, N(x,y) - \Sigma_1^k \lambda_i\varphi_i(x)\overline{\varphi_i(y)}\,|^2\,d(\mu\times\mu) = \Sigma_{k+1}\,|\lambda_i|^2.$$

Taking $k = 0$ we see that $\Sigma_1^\infty |\lambda_i|^2 < \infty$, hence, upon making $k \to \infty$, we get the first part of (1).

Considering $N(x, y) = N_x(y)$ as a function of y, we find in a similar way the first part of (2).

Theorem 2. *We have*

$$|||\, N \,|||^2 = \int_{\Delta\times\Delta} |N(x,y)|^2\,d(\mu\times\mu) = \Sigma_1^\infty\,|\lambda_i|^2.$$

Consequently, there exists at least one characteristic value $\neq 0$ *if and only if* $|||\, N \,||| \neq 0$.

Proof. Follows by taking $k = 0$ in (4) above. A different proof may be obtained by observing that $Nf = 0$ if f is orthogonal to all φ_i, hence $|||\, N \,|||^2 = \Sigma\,\|N\varphi_i\|^2 = \Sigma\,\|\lambda_i\varphi_i\|^2 = \Sigma\,|\lambda_i|^2$.

Theorem 3. *If* $f(x) \in L_2$, *then*

$$\int_\Delta N(x, y)f(y)d\mu = \Sigma\, \lambda_i(f, \varphi_i)\varphi_i(x),$$
$$\int_\Delta \overline{N(y, x)}f(y)d\mu = \Sigma\, \bar{\lambda}_i(f, \varphi_i)\varphi_i(x),$$

where the sign of equality stands for pointwise convergence for almost every $x \in \Delta$. *The series even converge absolutely for these values of* x.

Proof. By Theorem 1 we have $\Sigma \mid \lambda_i \mid^2 \mid \varphi_i(x) \mid^2 = \int_\Delta \mid N(x, y) \mid^2 d\mu$ for $x \in \Delta - E$, where E has measure zero. Hence, if $x \in \Delta - E$,

$$\Sigma_1^n \mid \lambda_i(f, \varphi_i)\varphi_i(x) \mid \leqslant (\Sigma_1^n \mid (f, \varphi_i) \mid^2)^{1/2} (\Sigma_1^n \mid \lambda_i \mid^2 \mid \varphi_i(x) \mid^2)^{1/2}$$
$$\leqslant \| f \| (\int_\Delta \mid N(x, y) \mid^2 d\mu)^{1/2},$$

which shows that $\Sigma\, \lambda_i(f, \varphi_i)\varphi_i(x)$ converges absolutely. It follows already from the convergence in mean to $\int_\Delta N(x, y)f(y)d\mu$ that there exists a subsequence of partial sums which converges pointwise to the same sum almost everywhere on Δ. Since in the present case the whole series converges, its sum is therefore $\int_\Delta N(x, y)f(y)d\mu$ for almost every $x \in \Delta$. The proof for $\Sigma\, \bar{\lambda}_i(f, \varphi_i)\varphi_i(x)$ is similar.

Remark. In the same way, the series in Theorem 9 of the preceding paragraph converges now pointwise for almost every $x \in \Delta$. This is an immediate consequence of the fact that the series in question is the expansion of $\lambda^{-1} \int_\Delta N(x, y)f(y)d\mu$.

Theorem 4. *If* $N(x, y) = \int_\Delta A(x, z)B(z, y)d\mu$, *where* $A(x, y)$ *and* $B(x, y)$ *are of finite double-norm, then*

$$N(x, y) = \Sigma\, \lambda_i\varphi_i(x)\overline{\varphi_i(y)}$$

almost everywhere on $\Delta \times \Delta$. *The series even converges absolutely almost everywhere on* $\Delta \times \Delta$.

Proof. The transformations N, A and B, corresponding with $N(x, y)$, $A(x, y)$ and $B(x, y)$ respectively, satisfy $N = AB$. Hence, observing that N has the singular values $\mid \lambda_1 \mid, \mid \lambda_2 \mid, \ldots$, we see that $\Sigma \mid \lambda_i \mid < \infty$ by Ch. 13, § 6, Th. 2, so that also $\Sigma \mid \lambda_i \mid \int_\Delta \mid \varphi_i(x) \mid^2 d\mu = \Sigma \mid \lambda_i \mid < \infty$. But then $\Sigma \mid \lambda_i \mid . \mid \varphi_i(x) \mid^2 < \infty$ almost everywhere on Δ (cf. Ch. 3, § 3, Th. 9), which implies

$$\Sigma \mid \lambda_i\varphi_i(x)\overline{\varphi_i(y)} \mid \leqslant (\Sigma \mid \lambda_i \mid . \mid \varphi_i(x) \mid^2)^{1/2}(\Sigma \mid \lambda_i \mid . \mid \varphi_i(y) \mid^2)^{1/2} < \infty$$

almost everywhere on $\Delta \times \Delta$. That the sum of $\Sigma\, \lambda_i\varphi_i(x)\overline{\varphi_i(y)}$ is $N(x, y)$ follows by a similar argument as in the preceding theorem.

Remark. The arrangement of the sequence λ_i in these expansion theorems is irrelevant.

Similar statements hold for a system with matrixkernel $\{N_{ij}(x, y)\}$ which is normal and of finite double-norm. To quote one example:

Theorem 5. *If* $\{\varphi_k(x)\} = \{\varphi_k^1(x), \ldots, \varphi_k^n(x)\}$ *is the k-th characteristic functionset, then*

$$(5) \qquad N_{ij}(x, y) \sim \Sigma_k \lambda_k \varphi_k^i(x)\overline{\varphi_k^j(y)} \quad (i, j = 1, \ldots, n),$$

$$(6) \quad \Sigma_{i=1}^n \int_\Delta | N_{ij}(x, y) |^2 d\mu = \Sigma_k | \lambda_k |^2 | \varphi_k^j(y) |^2 \ (\textit{integration over } x)$$

for $j = 1, \ldots, n$ *and for almost every* $y \in \Delta$,

$$(7) \qquad ||| N |||^2 = \Sigma_{ij=1}^n \int_{\Delta\times\Delta} | N_{ij}(x, y) |^2 d(\mu \times \mu) = \Sigma | \lambda_k |^2.$$

Proof. It follows from $N_{ij}(x, y) \in L_2(\Delta \times \Delta)$ that the element $\{h\} = \{h^1(x), \ldots, h^n(x)\}$, where $h^i(x) = N_{ij}(x, y)$ and j is fixed, belongs to L_2^n for almost every $y \in \Delta$. Then

$$(\{h\}, \{\varphi_k\}) = \Sigma_{i=1}^n \int_\Delta N_{ij}(x, y)\overline{\varphi_k^i(x)}d\mu =$$

$$\Sigma_{i=1}^n \int_\Delta \overline{\overline{N_{ij}(x, y)}\varphi_k^i(x)}d\mu = \lambda_k\overline{\varphi_k^j(y)}$$

for almost every $y \in \Delta$, and, if $(\{f\}, \{\varphi_k\}) = 0$ for all values of k, so that $N\{f\} = N^*\{f\} = \{0\}$, we have

$$(\{h\},\{f\}) = \Sigma_{i=1}^n \int_\Delta N_{ij}(x, y)\overline{f^i(x)}d\mu = \Sigma_{i=1}^n \int_\Delta \overline{\overline{N_{ij}(x, y)}f^i(x)}d\mu = 0$$

for almost every $y \in \Delta$. It follows that $\{h\} = \Sigma\,(\{h\}, \{\varphi_k\})\{\varphi_k\}$, hence

$$\| \{h\} - \Sigma_{k=1}^p (\{h\}, \{\varphi_k\})\{\varphi_k\} \|^2 = \Sigma_{k=p+1} | (\{h\}, \{\varphi_k\}) |^2$$

or

$$\Sigma_{i=1}^n \int_\Delta | N_{ij}(x, y) - \Sigma_{k=1}^p \lambda_k\overline{\varphi_k^j(y)}\varphi_k^i(x) |^2 d\mu = \Sigma_{k=p+1} | \lambda_k |^2 | \varphi_k^j(y) |^2$$

for almost every $y \in \Delta$. Taking $p = 0$ we obtain (6), and summing from $j = 1$ to $j = n$ and integrating over y, we see that

$$\Sigma_{ij=1}^n \int_{\Delta\times\Delta} | N_{ij}(x, y) - \Sigma_{k=1}^p \lambda_k\varphi_k^i(x)\overline{\varphi_k^j(y)} |^2 d(\mu \times \mu) = \Sigma_{k=p+1} | \lambda_k |^2.$$

For $p = 0$ we have (7), and, making $p \to \infty$, we find (5).

§ 5. The Iterated Kernels and the Traces

Introducing the iterated kernels $N_p(x, y) = \int_\Delta N(x, z)N_{p-1}(z, y)d\mu$ ($p = 2, 3, \ldots$) of our normal kernel $N(x, y)$, it is seen immediately that they are normal as well. Indeed, $N_p(x, y)$ corresponds with N^p and $N^p(N^p)^* = N^p(N^*)^p = (N^*)^p N^p = (N^p)^* N^p$ on account of $NN^* = N^*N$. If $N(x, y)$ is Hermitian, hence $N = N^*$, then all $N_p(x, y)$ are Hermitian, since $N^p = (N^*)^p = (N^p)^*$. Furthermore, in those cases where the normal kernel $N(x, y)$ has the sequences $\{\lambda_n\}$ and $\{\varphi_n(x)\}$ of non-null characteristic values and characteristic functions respectively, $N_p(x, y)$ has the corresponding sequences $\{\lambda_n^p\}$ and $\{\varphi_n(x)\}$. In fact, $Nf = \lambda f$ implies $N^p f = \lambda^p f$, and $N^p f = \lambda f \neq 0$ for a function f which is not a finite linear combination of the φ_n would imply the existence of a function g such that $N^p g = \lambda g \neq 0$, $(g, \varphi_n) = 0$ for all n. This however contradicts § 3, Th. 5.

It follows that all theorems in the preceding paragraphs remain true upon replacing $N(x, y)$ and λ_n by $N_p(x, y)$ and λ_n^p respectively. We observe in particular:

Theorem 1. *If $N(x, y)$ is non-singular and Hermitian, then all kernels $N_{2p}(x, y)$ $(p = 1, 2, \ldots)$ are of positive type.*
Proof. Follows from § 3, Th. 6, since the characteristic values λ_1^{2p}, $\lambda_2^{2p}, \ldots$ are positive.

Theorem 2. *If $N(x, y)$ is of finite double-norm, then*

$$N_p(x, y) = \Sigma\, \lambda_i^p \varphi_i(x)\overline{\varphi_i(y)} \quad (p = 2, 3, \ldots)$$

almost everywhere on $\Delta \times \Delta$ (pointwise absolute convergence).
Proof. Follows from § 4, Th. 4.

If $N(x, y)$ is of finite double-norm, the numbers

$$\tau_p = \tau(N^p) = \int_{\Delta\times\Delta} N(x, y)N_{p-1}(y, x)\, d(\mu \times \mu) = \int_\Delta N_p(x, x)\, d\mu$$
$$(p = 2, 3, \ldots)$$

are the traces of $N_p(x, y)$ (cf. Ch. 9, § 10, Th. 10 and Ch. 13, § 4, Th. 6). By Ch. 11, § 7, Th. 3 we have $\tau_p = \Sigma_i \lambda_i^p$ for $p = 3, 4, \ldots$. We shall prove, however, that in the present case this relation is also true for $p = 2$. Our proof, for $p = 2, 3, \ldots$, will be independent of the earlier result in Ch. 11, § 7, Th. 3.

Theorem 3. *We have*

$$\tau_p = \Sigma_i \lambda_i^p \quad (p = 2, 3, \ldots).$$

Proof. Let $f_k(y, x)$ $(k = 1, 2, \ldots)$ be a sequence of functions on $\Delta \times \Delta$ such that $\int_{\Delta\times\Delta} | f_k(y, x) |^2 \, d(\mu \times \mu)$ tends to zero as $k \to \infty$. Then, by Schwarz's inequality, $\int_{\Delta\times\Delta} g(x, y) f_k(y, x) \, d(\mu \times \mu)$ also tends to zero for every $g(x, y) \in L_2(\Delta \times \Delta)$. Now take $f_k(y, x) = N_{p-1}(y, x) - \Sigma_{i=1}^k \lambda_i^{p-1} \varphi_i(y)\overline{\varphi_i(x)}$, where $p \geqslant 2$ is an integer, and $g(x, y) = N(x, y)$. Then

$$\int_{\Delta\times\Delta} g(x, y) f_k(y, x) \, d(\mu \times \mu) =$$

$$\int_{\Delta\times\Delta} N(x, y) N_{p-1}(y, x) \, d(\mu\times\mu) - \Sigma_{i=1}^k \lambda_i^{p-1} \int_\Delta \overline{\varphi_i(x)} [\int_\Delta N(x, y)\varphi_i(y) d\mu] d\mu =$$

$$\tau_p - \Sigma_{i=1}^k \lambda_i^p \int_\Delta | \varphi_i(x) |^2 \, d\mu = \tau_p - \Sigma_{i=1}^k \lambda_i^p;$$

hence, making $k \to \infty$,

$$\tau_p = \Sigma_i \lambda_i^p \quad (p = 2, 3, \ldots).$$

The extension to the case that we have to do with a matrixkernel $\{N_{ij}(x, y)\}$ offers no difficulties.

§ 6. Normal Kernels Belonging to the Class *B*

As we have defined before (cf. Ch. 13, § 5 or Ch. 13, § 6, Th. 7), the kernel $T(x, y)$ of finite double-norm, defined on the set $\Delta \times \Delta$ in Euclidean space, belongs to the class B whenever there exists a constant c such that

$$\int_\Delta | T(x, y) |^2 \, dy \leqslant c^2, \quad \int_\Delta | T(x, y) |^2 \, dx \leqslant c^2$$

for all $x \in \Delta$ and all $y \in \Delta$ respectively.

We shall suppose now that $N(x, y)$ is normal and $N(x, y) \in B$.

Theorem 1. *If $f(x) \in L_2$, the series $\Sigma \lambda_i(f, \varphi_i)\varphi_i(x)$ converges uniformly, and its sum is $\int_\Delta N(x, y) f(y) dy$ almost everywhere on Δ. A similar statement holds for $\Sigma \bar{\lambda}_i(f, \varphi_i)\varphi_i(x)$.*

Proof. On account of § 4, Th. 3 we have only to prove that the series converges uniformly. This uniform convergence follows from

$$| \Sigma_p^q \lambda_i(f, \varphi_i)\varphi_i(x) | = | \int_\Delta N(x, y) \, \Sigma_p^q (f, \varphi_i)\varphi_i(y) dy | \leqslant$$

$$(\int_\Delta | N(x, y) |^2 \, dy)^{1/2} \, \| \Sigma_p^q (f, \varphi_i)\varphi_i \| \leqslant c \, \Sigma_p^q | (f, \varphi_i) |^2,$$

holding for all $x \in \Delta$.

Theorem 2. *If $\lambda \neq 0$ and $\int_\Delta N(x, y) f(y) dy - \lambda f(x) = g(x)$, we have, for almost every $x \in \Delta$,*

$$f(x) = -\frac{g(x)}{\lambda} - {}'\Sigma \frac{\lambda_n}{\lambda(\lambda - \lambda_n)} \alpha_n \varphi_n(x)$$

with the notations of § 3, Th. 9, where the series on the right converges uniformly on Δ.

Proof. The series in question is the expansion of $\lambda^{-1}\int_\Delta N(x, y)f(y)dy$. A second way to obtain the desired result is by observing that $'\Sigma\, \lambda_n\alpha_n\varphi_n(x)$ converges uniformly by the preceding theorem and that $|\, 1/\lambda(\lambda - \lambda_n)\,| < 2/|\,\lambda\,|^2$ for sufficiently large n.

Theorem 3. *We have*

$$\Sigma\,|\,\lambda_i\,|^2\,|\,\varphi_i(y)\,|^2 \leqslant \int_\Delta |\,N(x, y)\,|^2\,dx \leqslant c^2,$$

$$\Sigma\,|\,\lambda_i\,|^2\,|\,\varphi_i(x)\,|^2 \leqslant \int_\Delta |\,N(x, y)\,|^2\,dy \leqslant c^2$$

for all $y \in \Delta$ *and all* $x \in \Delta$ *respectively.*

Proof. Since $N(x, y) = N_y(x) = n(x) \in L_2(\Delta)$ for all $y \in \Delta$, we have $(n, \varphi_i) = \int_\Delta N(x, y)\overline{\varphi_i(x)}dx = \lambda_i\overline{\varphi_i(y)}$ $(i = 1, 2, \ldots)$ for all $y \in \Delta$. Hence $\|\,n\,\|^2 \geqslant \Sigma\,|\,(n, \varphi_i)\,|^2$, or $\Sigma\,|\,\lambda_i\,|^2\,|\,\varphi_i(y)\,|^2 \leqslant \int_\Delta |\,N(x, y)\,|^2\,dx \leqslant c^2$ for all $y \in \Delta$.

Remark. By § 4, Th. 1 we have $\Sigma\,|\,\lambda_i\,|^2\,|\,\varphi_i(y)\,|^2 = \int_\Delta |\,N(x, y)\,|^2\,dx$ for almost every $y \in \Delta$. If we want a result which holds for all $y \in \Delta$, however, we merely find that the sum of the series does not exceed the integral. This is a consequence of the fact that $(f, \varphi_i) = 0$ for all $\varphi_i(x)$ implies $(n, f) = \int_\Delta N(x, y)\overline{f(x)}dx = 0$ for almost every $y \in \Delta$, but not necessarily for all $y \in \Delta$ (cf. the proof of § 4, Th. 1).

Theorem 4. *For* $p = 3, 4, \ldots$ *the series* $\Sigma_i\,\lambda_i^p\varphi_i(x)\overline{\varphi_i(y)}$ *converges uniformly on* $\Delta \times \Delta$, *and its sum is* $N_p(x, y)$ *for almost every point* $(x, y) \in \Delta \times \Delta$.

Proof. On account of § 5, Th. 2 we have only to prove that the series converges uniformly. We observe first that, given a sequence $\{\alpha_i\}$ of complex numbers tending to zero, the series $\Sigma\,\alpha_i\,|\,\lambda_i\,|^2\,|\,\varphi_i(x)\,|^2$ converges uniformly. In fact, if $|\,\alpha_i\,| < \varepsilon/c^2$ for $i \geqslant N$, we have

$$|\,\Sigma_N^\infty\,\alpha_i\,|\,\lambda_i\,|^2\,|\,\varphi_i(x)\,|^2\,| \leqslant \frac{\varepsilon}{c^2}\,\Sigma_N^\infty\,|\,\lambda_i\,|^2\,|\,\varphi_i(x)\,|^2 \leqslant \varepsilon$$

by the preceding theorem. Hence, in particular, $\Sigma\,|\,\lambda_i\,|^p\,|\,\varphi_i(x)\,|^2$ converges uniformly for $p = 3, 4, \ldots$. From

$$\Sigma_i\,|\,\lambda_i^p\varphi_i(x)\overline{\varphi_i(y)}\,| \leqslant (\Sigma_i\,|\,\lambda_i\,|^p\,|\,\varphi_i(x)\,|^2)^{1/2}(\Sigma_i\,|\,\lambda_i\,|^p\,|\,\varphi_i(y)\,|^2)^{1/2}$$

follows then the uniform convergence of $\Sigma\,\lambda_i^p\varphi_i(x)\overline{\varphi_i(y)}$ for $p = 3, 4, \ldots$.

Theorem 5. *The series* $\Sigma\, \lambda_i^2 \varphi_i(x)\overline{\varphi_i(y)}$ *converges for every point* $(x, y) \in \Delta \times \Delta$, *and for a fixed point* $y \in \Delta$ *the convergence is uniform in* x. *The sum is* $N_2(x, y)$ *for almost every* $(x, y) \in \Delta \times \Delta$.

Proof. Considering a fixed value of y and a number $\varepsilon > 0$, there exists an index N such that $(\Sigma_N \mid \lambda_i \mid^2 \mid \varphi_i(y) \mid^2)^{1/2} < \varepsilon/c$. Hence, since $\Sigma \mid \lambda_i \mid^2 \mid \varphi_i(x) \mid^2 \leqslant c^2$ for every $x \in \Delta$, we have

$$\Sigma_N \mid \lambda_i^2 \varphi_i(x)\overline{\varphi_i(y)} \mid \leqslant (\Sigma_N \mid \lambda_i \mid^2 \mid \varphi_i(x) \mid^2)^{1/2} (\Sigma_N \mid \lambda_i \mid^2 \mid \varphi_i(y) \mid^2)^{1/2} \leqslant \varepsilon$$

for all $x \in \Delta$.

Remark. In all these theorems the arrangement of the sequence λ_i is irrelevant.

Similar theorems hold for the case of a normal matrixkernel $\{N_{ij}(x, y)\}$ $(i, j = 1, \ldots, n)$ satisfying

$$\Sigma_{j=1}^n \textstyle\int_\Delta \mid N_{ij}(x, y) \mid^2 dy \leqslant c^2, \quad \Sigma_{i=1}^n \int_\Delta \mid N_{ij}(x, y) \mid^2 dx \leqslant c^2,$$

for all $x \in \Delta$ and all $y \in \Delta$ respectively. Obviously, this condition is equivalent to the condition that all $N_{ij}(x, y)$ $(i, j = 1, \ldots, n)$ belong to the class B.

§ 7. Normal Kernels which are Continuous in Mean

As we have defined before (cf. Ch. 13, § 5 or Ch. 13, § 6, Th. 7) the kernel $T(x, y)$ on $\Delta \times \Delta$ (in Euclidean space) is continuous in mean or, equivalently, $T(x, y) \in Cm$ whenever Δ is bounded and closed, and

$$\lim_{x_2 \to x_1} \textstyle\int_\Delta \mid T(x_2, y) - T(x_1, y) \mid^2 dy = 0,$$

$$\lim_{y_2 \to y_1} \textstyle\int_\Delta \mid T(x, y_2) - T(x, y_1) \mid^2 dx = 0.$$

Then, by Ch. 13, § 5, the functions $\int_\Delta \mid T(x, y) \mid^2 dx$ and $\int_\Delta \mid T(x, y) \mid^2 dy$ are continuous on Δ, and therefore bounded. It follows that $T(x, y)$ is of finite double-norm, and that $T(x, y)$ belongs to the class B discussed in the preceding paragraph. By Ch. 13, § 5, Th. 1 all iterated kernels $T_p(x, y)$ $(p = 2, 3, \ldots)$ are continuous on $\Delta \times \Delta$. Finally, any function $g(x) = \int_\Delta T(x, y) f(y) dy$, where $f(x) \in L_2(\Delta)$, is obviously continuous on Δ. In particular, all characteristic functions of $T(x, y)$ are continuous.

We shall suppose now that $N(x, y)$ is normal and continuous in mean.

Theorem 1. *If $f(x) \in L_2$, the series $\Sigma\, \lambda_i(f, \varphi_i)\varphi_i(x)$ converges uniformly to the continuous function $\int_\Delta N(x, y)f(y)dy$ on the whole interval Δ. A similar statement holds for $\Sigma\, \bar{\lambda}_i(f, \varphi_i)\varphi_i(x)$.*

Proof. Every term in $\Sigma\, \lambda_i(f, \varphi_i)\varphi_i(x)$ is continuous, and the series converges uniformly by the same argument as in Theorem 1 of the preceding paragraph. Its sum is therefore continuous. We know already that this sum is equal to $g(x) = \int_\Delta N(x, y)f(y)dy$ for almost every $x \in \Delta$. Hence, since $g(x)$ is also continuous, there is equality for every $x \in \Delta$.

Theorem 2. *If $\lambda \neq 0$ and $\int_\Delta N(x, y)f(y)dy - \lambda f(x) = g(x)$, we have, for every $x \in \Delta$,*

$$f(x) = -\frac{g(x)}{\lambda} - {}'\Sigma \frac{\lambda_n}{\lambda(\lambda - \lambda_n)} \alpha_n \varphi_n(x)$$

with the notations of § 3, Th. 9, where the series on the right converges uniformly on the whole interval Δ.

Proof. The series in question is the expansion of $\lambda^{-1} \int_\Delta N(x, y)f(y)dy = f(x) + g(x)/\lambda$.

Theorem 3. *We have*

$$\Sigma\, |\, \lambda_i\, |^2\, |\, \varphi_i(y)\, |^2 = \int_\Delta |\, N(x, y)\, |^2\, dx,$$

$$\Sigma\, |\, \lambda_i\, |^2\, |\, \varphi_i(x)\, |^2 = \int_\Delta |\, N(x, y)\, |^2\, dy$$

for all $y \in \Delta$ and all $x \in \Delta$ respectively, and both series converge uniformly on Δ.

Proof. Since $N(x, y) = N_y(x) = n(x) \in L_2(\Delta)$ for all $y \in \Delta$, we have $(n, \varphi_i) = \int_\Delta N(x, y)\overline{\varphi_i(x)}dx = \lambda_i\overline{\varphi_i(y)}$ $(i = 1, 2, \ldots)$ for all $y \in \Delta$. Furthermore, if $(f, \varphi_i) = 0$ for all $\varphi_i(x)$, we have $(n, f) = \int_\Delta N(x, y)\overline{f(x)}dx = 0$ for almost every $y \in \Delta$. On account of the continuity of (n, f) as a function of y, this last statement holds actually for all $y \in \Delta$. Hence $\|\, n\, \|^2 = \Sigma\, |\, (n, \varphi_i)\, |^2$, or $\Sigma\, |\, \lambda_i\, |^2\, |\, \varphi_i(y)\, |^2 = \int_\Delta |\, N(x, y)\, |^2\, dx$ for all $y \in \Delta$. Since the functions $|\, \lambda_i\, |^2\, |\, \varphi_i(y)\, |^2$ are continuous and non-negative, and since the sum $\int_\Delta |\, N(x, y)\, |^2\, dx$ is continuous, the convergence is uniform by Dini's Theorem (cf. Ch. 13, § 6, Th. 8). The proof for the other series is similar.

Theorem 4. *We have*

$$N_p(x, y) = \Sigma_i\, \lambda_i^p \varphi_i(x)\overline{\varphi_i(y)} \quad (p = 2, 3, \ldots),$$

uniformly on $\Delta \times \Delta$.

Proof. We first consider the case $p = 2$. From

$$\Sigma \mid \lambda_i^2 \varphi_i(x)\overline{\varphi_i(y)} \mid \leqslant (\Sigma \mid \lambda_i \mid^2 \mid \varphi_i(x) \mid^2)^{1/2} (\Sigma \mid \lambda_i \mid^2 \mid \varphi_i(y) \mid^2)^{1/2},$$

together with the preceding theorem, follows the uniform convergence of $\Sigma \lambda_i^2 \varphi_i(x)\overline{\varphi_i(y)}$; its sum is therefore continuous. By Th. 5 of the preceding paragraph this sum is equal to $N_2(x, y)$ for almost every $(x, y) \in \Delta \times \Delta$. Hence, since $N_2(x, y)$ is also continuous, there exists equality for every point $(x, y) \in \Delta \times \Delta$.

The uniform convergence of $\Sigma_i \lambda_i^p \varphi_i(x)\overline{\varphi_i(y)}$ for $p = 3, 4, \ldots$ was already proved in Theorem 4 of the preceding paragraph; its continuous sum is therefore equal to the continuous function $N_p(x, y)$ in the whole interval $\Delta \times \Delta$.

The extension to the case of a normal matrixkernel $\{N_{ij}(x, y)\}$ which is continuous in mean (that is, all $N_{ij}(x, y)$ are continuous in mean) presents no difficulties.

§ 8. Interlude

Before proceeding with the theory of Hermitian kernels of positive type, we prove some simple theorems in an abstract Hilbert space R.

Theorem 1. *Given the compact normal transformation N in the Hilbert space R with the sequences $\{\lambda_n\}$ and $\{\varphi_n\}$ of non-null characteristic values and orthonormal characteristic elements, the transformation $\tilde{N}$, defined by*

$$\tilde{N}f = Nf - \Sigma_{i=1}^n \lambda_i(f, \varphi_i)\varphi_i,$$

is compact, normal, and has the sequence $\lambda_{n+1}, \lambda_{n+2}, \ldots$ of characteristic values $\neq 0$ with the sequence $\varphi_{n+1}, \varphi_{n+2}, \ldots$ of corresponding characteristic elements. If N is self-adjoint, then $\tilde{N}$ is self-adjoint. If N is positive, then $\tilde{N}$ is positive.

In particular, if N is determined in $L_2(\Delta)$ by the normal (or Hermitian) kernel $N(x, y)$, then $\tilde{N}$ is determined by the normal (or Hermitian) kernel $\tilde{N}(x, y) = N(x, y) - \Sigma_{i=1}^n \lambda_i \varphi_i(x)\overline{\varphi_i(y)}$.

Proof. The transformation N', defined by $N'f = \Sigma_{i=1}^n \lambda_i(f, \varphi_i)\varphi_i$, transforms every $f \in R$ into an element of the finite dimensional subspace determined by $\varphi_1, \ldots, \varphi_n$. It follows that N', and therefore also $\tilde{N} = N - N'$, is compact. Since $(\tilde{N})^* f = N^* f - \Sigma_{i=1}^n \bar{\lambda}_i(f, \varphi_i)\varphi_i$, direct computation shows that $\tilde{N}(\tilde{N})^* = (\tilde{N})^*\tilde{N}$, so that $\tilde{N}$ is normal. If N is self-adjoint, all λ_i are real; hence $\tilde{N} = (\tilde{N})^*$, which shows that $\tilde{N}$ is self-adjoint.

Finally, from $\tilde{N}\varphi_k = N\varphi_k - \Sigma_{i=1}^n \lambda_i(\varphi_k, \varphi_i)\varphi_i$, we derive $\tilde{N}\varphi_k = \lambda_k\varphi_k$ for $k > n$ and $\tilde{N}\varphi_k = 0$ for $k \leqslant n$, while for an element g, orthogonal to all φ_i, we have $Ng = 0$ and $(g, \varphi_i) = 0$, hence $\tilde{N}g = 0$. This shows that $\lambda_{n+1}, \lambda_{n+2}, \ldots$ and $\varphi_{n+1}, \varphi_{n+2}, \ldots$ have the stated properties. If N is positive, all λ_i are positive. Hence $\tilde{N}$ is positive (cf. Ch. 12, § 7, Th. 2, 6°).

Theorem 2. *Given the compact positive transformation H in the complete Hilbert space R with the sequences $\{\lambda_n\}$ and $\{\varphi_n\}$ of non-null characteristic values and orthonormal characteristic elements, the positive transformation $H^{1/2}$ is compact, and has the sequence $\{\lambda_n^{1/2}\}$ of non-null characteristic values with $\{\varphi_n\}$ as a corresponding sequence of characteristic elements.*

Proof. Since $(H^{1/2})^2 = H$ is compact, the same is true of $H^{1/2}$ itself by Ch. 11, § 1, Th. 13. Let now $H\varphi = \lambda\varphi \neq 0$ (hence $\lambda > 0$), and write $H^{1/2}\varphi - \lambda^{1/2}\varphi = \tilde{\varphi}$. Then $H^{1/2}\tilde{\varphi} + \lambda^{1/2}\tilde{\varphi} = H\varphi - \lambda\varphi = 0$, so that, assuming $\tilde{\varphi} \neq 0$, the negative number $-\lambda^{1/2}$ would be a characteristic value of the positive transformation $H^{1/2}$. This is impossible. Hence $\tilde{\varphi} = 0$ or $H^{1/2}\varphi = \lambda^{1/2}\varphi$, which shows already that $H^{1/2}\varphi_n = \lambda_n^{1/2}\varphi_n$ $(n = 1, 2, \ldots)$. Any further characteristic element g of $H^{1/2}$, not a finite linear combination of the φ_n, may be assumed to be orthogonal to all φ_n. Then however $Hg = 0$, hence also $\| H^{1/2}g \|^2 = (Hg, g) = 0$, or $H^{1/2}g = 0$. It follows that $\{\lambda_n\}$ and $\{\varphi_n\}$ have the stated properties.

§ 9. Kernels of Positive Type

We assume now that the kernel $H(x, y)$, defined on $\Delta \times \Delta$ (in Euclidean space), is of finite double-norm and of positive type (that is, the corresponding transformation H is positive). Hence $H(x, y)$ is Hermitian and

$$\int_{\Delta\times\Delta} H(x, y)\overline{f(x)}f(y)dx\,dy \geqslant 0$$

for every $f(x) \in L_2$. If Δ_1 is a subset of Δ of finite measure, and we take $f(x) = 1$ on Δ_1 and $f(x) = 0$ elsewhere on Δ, then $f(x) \in L_2$, hence $\int_{\Delta_1\times\Delta_1} H(x, y)\,dx\,dy \geqslant 0$. Furthermore, if $H(x, y)$ is continuous at every point $(x, x) \in \Delta \times \Delta$, we have $H(x, x) \geqslant 0$ for every $x \in \Delta$ (cf. Ch. 9, § 8, Th. 1).

In § 7 we have proved, under the hypothesis that the normal kernel

$N(x, y)$ is continuous in mean, the relation

$$N_p(x, y) = \Sigma_i \lambda_i^p \varphi_i(x)\overline{\varphi_i(y)} \quad (p = 2, 3, \ldots),$$

holding uniformly on $\Delta \times \Delta$ for every arrangement of the sequence λ_i. It may be asked under what additional conditions this relation is also valid for $p = 1$. Evidently, since the partial sums of the series $\Sigma \lambda_i \varphi_i(x)\overline{\varphi_i(y)}$ are continuous on $\Delta \times \Delta$, the continuity of $N(x, y)$ is a necessary condition. It may be shown however that this alone is not sufficient, and a further condition must be added. We shall prove now that the property to be of positive type is such an additional condition. This however is such a severe restriction that the hypothesis of continuity may be partially dropped again. It is sufficient to assume that the kernel is continuous in mean, of positive type, and continuous at all points (x, x). The continuity on the whole interval $\Delta \times \Delta$ is then a consequence of these hypotheses. The theorem which follows now was proved by MERCER [3] for the case of a continuous kernel of positive type.

Theorem 1 (*Mercer's Theorem*). *If the kernel $H(x, y)$ is continuous in mean on $\Delta \times \Delta$ (hence Δ bounded and closed), of positive type, and continuous at every point $(x, x) \in \Delta \times \Delta$, then $H(x, y)$ is almost everywhere on $\Delta \times \Delta$ equal to a continuous function $H_c(x, y)$, and*

$$H_c(x, y) = \Sigma \lambda_i \varphi_i(x)\overline{\varphi_i(y)},$$

uniformly on $\Delta \times \Delta$ for every arrangement of the sequence λ_i.

Proof. Writing $H^{(n)}(x, y) = H(x, y) - \Sigma_{i=1}^n \lambda_i \varphi_i(x)\overline{\varphi_i(y)}$ for an arbitrary positive integer n, the kernel $H^{(n)}(x, y)$ is by Theorem 1 of the preceding paragraph also of positive type. Furthermore, since all $\varphi_i(x)$ are continuous, $H^{(n)}(x, y)$ is continuous at every point $(x, x) \in \Delta \times \Delta$. Hence $H^{(n)}(x, x) \geqslant 0$, or

$$\Sigma_1^n \lambda_i \mid \varphi_i(x) \mid^2 \leqslant H(x, x),$$

which proves that $\Sigma \lambda_i \mid \varphi_i(x) \mid^2$ converges for every $x \in \Delta$, and that its sum is bounded. Indeed, $H(x, x)$ is a continuous function of x in the bounded and closed set Δ. Let $\Sigma \lambda_i \mid \varphi_i(x) \mid^2 \leqslant M$ for all $x \in \Delta$.

Choose now a fixed point $y_0 \in \Delta$. Given $\varepsilon > 0$, there exists an index N such that $\Sigma_N \lambda_i \mid \varphi_i(y_0) \mid^2 < \varepsilon^2/M$. Then

$$\Sigma_N \mid \lambda_i \varphi_i(x)\overline{\varphi_i(y_0)} \mid \leqslant (\Sigma_N \lambda_i \mid \varphi_i(x) \mid^2)^{1/2} (\Sigma_N \lambda_i \mid \varphi_i(y_0) \mid^2)^{1/2} < \varepsilon,$$

which shows that $\Sigma \lambda_i \varphi_i(x)\overline{\varphi_i(y_0)}$ converges uniformly in x, so that its sum is continuous in x. Now consider

$$H^*(x, y_0) = H(x, y_0) - \Sigma \lambda_i \varphi_i(x)\overline{\varphi_i(y_0)},$$

hence

$$\overline{H^*(x, y_0)} = \overline{H(x, y_0)} - \Sigma \lambda_i \overline{\varphi_i(x)}\varphi_i(y_0).$$

Since term by term integration over x is allowed on account of the uniform convergence, we find

$$\int_\Delta | H^*(x, y_0) |^2 dx = \int_\Delta | H(x, y_0) |^2 dx - \Sigma \lambda_i^2 | \varphi_i(y_0) |^2 - \Sigma \lambda_i^2 | \varphi_i(y_0) |^2$$
$$+ \Sigma \lambda_i^2 | \varphi_i(y_0) |^2 = \int_\Delta | H(x, y_0) |^2 dx - \Sigma \lambda_i^2 | \varphi_i(y_0) |^2 = 0$$

by § 7, Th. 3, hence $H^*(x, y_0) = 0$, or

$$H(x, y_0) = \Sigma \lambda_i \varphi_i(x)\overline{\varphi_i(y_0)} \tag{1}$$

for almost every $x \in \Delta$. At $x = y_0$ both $H(x, y_0)$ and $\Sigma \lambda_i \varphi_i(x)\overline{\varphi_i(y_0)}$ are continuous, so that in particular $H(y_0, y_0) = \Sigma \lambda_i | \varphi_i(y_0) |^2$. This holds for every $y_0 \in \Delta$; applying Dini's Theorem we find therefore that $\Sigma \lambda_i | \varphi_i(y) |^2$ converges uniformly on Δ. But then

$$| \Sigma \lambda_i \varphi_i(x)\overline{\varphi_i(y)} | \leqslant (\Sigma \lambda_i | \varphi_i(x) |^2)^{1/2} (\Sigma \lambda_i | \varphi_i(y) |^2)^{1/2}$$

shows that $\Sigma \lambda_i \varphi_i(x)\overline{\varphi_i(y)}$ converges uniformly on $\Delta \times \Delta$; its sum $H_c(x, y)$ is therefore continuous.

Finally, (1) shows that $H(x, y) = H_c(x, y)$ almost everywhere on $\Delta \times \Delta$.

Theorem 2. *If the normal kernel $K(x, y)$ is continuous in mean on $\Delta \times \Delta$ and continuous for every point $(x, x) \in \Delta \times \Delta$, and if all characteristic values of $K(x, y)$, except a finite number, are non-negative, then $K(x, y)$ is almost everywhere on $\Delta \times \Delta$ equal to a continuous function $K_c(x, y)$, and*

$$K_c(x, y) = \Sigma \lambda_i \varphi_i(x)\overline{\varphi_i(y)}$$

uniformly on $\Delta \times \Delta$.

Proof. If the sequence $\{\lambda_n\}$ is ordered such that $\lambda_1, \ldots, \lambda_k$ are all the exceptional characteristic values, the kernel $H(x, y) = K(x, y) - \Sigma_{i=1}^k \lambda_i \varphi_i(x)\overline{\varphi_i(y)}$ satisfies all hypotheses of Mercer's Theorem.

Theorem 3. *If the Hermitian kernel $K(x, y)$ is continuous in mean on $\Delta \times \Delta$ and continuous for every point $(x, x) \in \Delta \times \Delta$, without being essentially equal (that is, equal almost everywhere on $\Delta \times \Delta$) to a continuous* *function, then $K(x, y)$ possesses an infinite number of positive and an infinite number of negative characteristic values.*

Proof. Follows by applying the preceding theorem to $K(x, y)$ and to $-K(x, y)$.

Definition. *Any Hermitian kernel $K(x, y)$ satisfying the hypotheses of Theorem 2 above will be called a Mercer kernel.*

Theorem 4. *If $K(x, y)$ is a Mercer kernel, then*

$$\int_\Delta K(x, x)\, dx = \Sigma \lambda_i.$$

Proof. Follows from Theorem 2 by observing that $K(x, x) = K_c(x, x)$.

Theorem 5. *If the positive transformation H has the Mercer kernel $H(x, y)$ of positive type, then $H^{1/2}$ is determined by a kernel $H_{1/2}(x, y)$ of positive type which is essentially continuous in mean. More precisely, there exists a set $E \subset \Delta$ of measure zero such that if x_1 and x_2 belong to $\Delta - E$, then*

(2) $$lim_{x_2 \to x_1} \int_\Delta | H_{1/2}(x_2, y) - H_{1/2}(x_1, y) |^2 dy = 0,$$

and there exists a set $E' \subset \Delta$ of measure zero such that if y_1 and y_2 belong to $\Delta - E'$, then

(3) $$lim_{y_2 \to y_1} \int_\Delta | H_{1/2}(x, y_2) - H_{1/2}(x, y_1) |^2 dx = 0.$$

Proof. Since $H^{1/2}$ has the sequence $\{\lambda_n^{1/2}\}$ of non-null characteristic values, and $\Sigma (\lambda_i^{1/2})^2 = \Sigma \lambda_i = \int_\Delta H(x, x) dx < \infty$, the transformation $H^{1/2}$ is of finite double-norm. It is determined therefore by a kernel $H_{1/2}(x, y) \in L_2(\Delta \times \Delta)$ of positive type. Now, by the same argument as in the proof of § 4, Th. 1, there exists a set $E' \subset \Delta$ of measure zero such that for $y \in \Delta - E'$ the function $H_{1/2}(x, y) = h_y(x)$ belongs to $L_2(\Delta)$ and $(h, \varphi_i) = \lambda_i^{1/2}\overline{\varphi_i(y)}$ $(i = 1, 2, \ldots)$, while $(h, f) = 0$ for any $f(x)$ which is orthogonal to all $\varphi_i(x)$. Then, provided y_1 and y_2 both belong to $\Delta - E'$, and writing $d(x) = H_{1/2}(x, y_2) - H_{1/2}(x, y_1)$, we have $(d, \varphi_i) = \lambda_i^{1/2}[\overline{\varphi_i(y_2)} - \overline{\varphi_i(y_1)}]$ $(i = 1, 2, \ldots)$ and $(d, f) = 0$ for any $f(x)$ orthogonal to all $\varphi_i(x)$. Hence $\| d \|^2 = \Sigma | (d, \varphi_i) |^2 = \Sigma (d, \varphi_i)\overline{(d, \varphi_i)}$, or

$$\int_\Delta | H_{1/2}(x, y_2) - H_{1/2}(x, y_1) |^2 dx = \Sigma \lambda_i[\varphi_i(y_2) - \varphi_i(y_1)]\,[\overline{\varphi_i(y_2)} - \overline{\varphi_i(y_1)}] =$$

$$\Sigma \lambda_i | \varphi_i(y_2) |^2 - \Sigma \lambda_i \varphi_i(y_2)\overline{\varphi_i(y_1)} - \Sigma \lambda_i \varphi_i(y_1)\overline{\varphi_i(y_2)} + \Sigma \lambda_i | \varphi_i(y_1) |^2 =$$

$$H(y_2, y_2) - H(y_2, y_1) - H(y_1, y_2) + H(y_1, y_1),$$

and this last expression tends to zero as y_2 tends to y_1. Thus (3) is proved. The proof of (2) is similar.

The extension of these theorems to the case of a matrixkernel offers no difficulties.

§ 10. Dependence of the Characteristic Values and Functions upon the Kernel and the Interval

Theorem 1. *Let $N(x, y), N_1(x, y), N_2(x, y), \ldots$ be normal kernels of finite double-norm, and let*

$$lim_{n\to\infty} \int_{\Delta\times\Delta} | N(x, y) - N_n(x, y) |^2 \, d(\mu \times \mu) = 0.$$

Let $\lambda_0 \neq 0$ be a characteristic value of $N(x, y)$ of multiplicity $p > 0$, and let the projection P be defined by $Pf = g(x) = \Sigma_1^p(f, \varphi_i)\varphi_i(x)$, where $\varphi_1(x), \ldots, \varphi_p(x)$ is an orthonormal system of characteristic functions of $N(x, y)$ belonging to λ_0. Then, if $| \lambda - \lambda_0 | \leqslant \varepsilon$ contains no other characteristic values of $N(x, y)$, the kernel $N_n(x, y)$ has for sufficiently large n exactly p non-null characteristic values $\lambda_1^{(n)}, \ldots, \lambda_p^{(n)}$ in this circle. Denoting by $\varphi_1^{(n)}(x), \ldots, \varphi_p^{(n)}(x)$ a corresponding orthonormal system of characteristic functions of $N_n(x, y)$, and defining the projection P_n by $P_nf = g_n(x) = \Sigma_1^p (f, \varphi_i^{(n)})\varphi_i^{(n)}(x)$, we have

$$\int_\Delta | g(x) - g_n(x) |^2 \, d\mu \leqslant \delta_n \int_\Delta | f |^2 \, d\mu, \quad lim\ \delta_n = 0.$$

Proof. Follows from Ch. 12, § 19, Th. 9.

Theorem 2. *If $K(x, y)$ and $\tilde{K}(x, y)$ are non-singular Hermitian kernels such that $\tilde{K}(x, y) - K(x, y)$ is of positive type, and $\lambda_1^+ \geqslant \lambda_2^+ \geqslant \ldots$ and $\tilde{\lambda}_1^+ \geqslant \tilde{\lambda}_2^+ \geqslant \ldots$ are the positive characteristic values of $K(x, y)$ and $\tilde{K}(x, y)$ respectively, then*

$$\tilde{\lambda}_n^+ \geqslant \lambda_n^+.$$

In the same way, if $\lambda_1^- \leqslant \lambda_2^- \leqslant \ldots$ and $\tilde{\lambda}_1^- \leqslant \tilde{\lambda}_2^- \leqslant \ldots$ are the corresponding negative characteristic values, then

$$\tilde{\lambda}_n^- \geqslant \lambda_n^-.$$

Proof. Follows from Ch. 12, § 17, Th. 4.

Theorem 3. *If $K(x, y)$ is a non-singular Hermitian kernel on $\Delta \times \Delta$, if Δ_1 is an arbitrary measurable subset of Δ, and $\tilde{K}(x, y)$ is defined by*

$$\tilde{K}(x, y) = K(x, y), \ (x, y) \in \Delta_1 \times \Delta_1,$$
$$\tilde{K}(x, y) = 0 \text{ elsewhere on } \Delta \times \Delta,$$

while $\lambda_1^+ \geqslant \lambda_2^+ \geqslant \ldots$ *and* $\tilde{\lambda}_1^+ \geqslant \tilde{\lambda}_2^+ \geqslant \ldots$ *are the positive characteristic values of* $K(x, y)$ *and* $\tilde{K}(x, y)$ *respectively, then*

$$\tilde{\lambda}_n^+ \leqslant \lambda_n^+.$$

In the same way, if $\lambda_1^- \leqslant \lambda_2^- \leqslant \ldots$ *and* $\tilde{\lambda}_1^- \leqslant \tilde{\lambda}_2^- \leqslant \ldots$ *are the corresponding negative characteristic values, then*

$$| \tilde{\lambda}_n^- | \leqslant | \lambda_n^- |.$$

Proof. Let $[L]$ be the subspace of $L_2(\Delta)$, consisting of all functions $f(x) \in L_2$ which vanish outside Δ_1, and $[M]$ the orthogonal subspace. The projection on $[L]$ along $[M]$ is denoted by P. Then, if $f_1 = Pf$, we have $f_1(x) = f(x)$ for $x \in \Delta_1$ and $f_1(x) = 0$ outside Δ_1. Obviously, if K and $\tilde{K}$ are the self-adjoint transformations corresponding with $K(x, y)$ and $\tilde{K}(x, y)$, we have $\tilde{K} = PKP$. The desired result follows therefore from Ch. 12, § 17, Th. 6.

Theorem 4. *If* $N(x, y)$ *is a non-singular normal kernel on* $\Delta \times \Delta$, *having the sequence* $\{\lambda_n\}$ *of non-null characteristic values ordered such that* $| \lambda_1 | \geqslant | \lambda_2 | \geqslant \ldots$, *if* Δ_1 *is an arbitrary measurable subset of* Δ, *and* $\tilde{N}(x, y)$ *is defined by*

$$\tilde{N}(x, y) = N(x, y), \quad (x, y) \in \Delta_1 \times \Delta_1,$$

$$\tilde{N}(x, y) = 0 \quad \textit{elsewhere on } \Delta \times \Delta,$$

while $\mu_1 \geqslant \mu_2 \geqslant \ldots$ *are the singular values of* $\tilde{N}(x, y)$, *then*

$$\mu_n \leqslant | \lambda_n |.$$

Proof. We observe first that, with the same notations as in the preceding theorem, we have $\tilde{N} = PNP$, but $\tilde{N}$ is not necessarily normal. This is the reason for introducing the singular values of $\tilde{N}$. We consider NN^* and $\tilde{N}(\tilde{N})^* = PNP^2N^*P$. They have the sequences $| \lambda_1 |^2 \geqslant |\lambda_2 |^2 \geqslant \ldots$ and $\mu_1^2 \geqslant \mu_2^2 \geqslant \ldots$ of characteristic values. Since $(NP^2N^*f, f) = (PN^*f, PN^*f) \leqslant (N^*f, N^*f) = (NN^*f, f)$, so that $NN^* - NP^2N^*$ is positive, the characteristic values of the positive transformation NP^2N^* do not exceed those of NN^* by Th. 2. Furthermore, by the preceding theorem the characteristic values of the positive transformation PNP^2N^*P do not exceed those of NP^2N^*. Hence $\mu_n^2 \leqslant | \lambda_n |^2$ or $\mu_n \leqslant | \lambda_n |$.

§ 11. A Non-Singular Normal Integral Transformation in $L_2\,[0,2\pi]$. The Fourier Series of a Function

We assume that $g(x)$ is a measurable function, defined on $-\infty <$

$x < \infty$, having the period 2π (hence $g(x + 2\pi) = g(x)$ for all x), and Lebesgue summable over $\Delta = [0, 2\pi]$. Then $g(x)$ is obviously summable over any interval of length 2π, and $\int_0^{2\pi} | g(x + t) | dt = \int_x^{x+2\pi} | g(t) | dt = \int_0^{2\pi} | g(t) | dt = \| g \|$ for any x. We now define the integral transformation G in the Lebesgue space $L_2(\Delta)$ by its kernel $G(x, y)$, where

$$G(x, y) = (2\pi)^{-1/2} g(x - y), \quad (x, y) \in \Delta \times \Delta.$$

By Ch. 9, § 9, Ex. C (Lemma 4) the function $\int_\Delta | G(x, y)f(y) | dy = (2\pi)^{-1/2} \int_\Delta | g(x - y) | . | f(y) | dy$ belongs to $L_2(\Delta)$ for every $f \in L_2(\Delta)$; the kernel $G(x, y)$ satisfies therefore the condition (P) relative to $L_2(\Delta)$. Hence G is bounded (by the already mentioned lemma we have $\| G \| \leqslant (2\pi)^{-1/2} \|g\|$). The adjoint transformation G^* has the kernel $G^*(x, y) = (2\pi)^{-1/2} \overline{g(y - x)}$, hence

$$(GG^*)(x, y) = (2\pi)^{-1} \int_\Delta g(x - z)\overline{g(y - z)}dz = (2\pi)^{-1} \int_\Delta g(x - y + t)\overline{g(t)}dt,$$

$$(G^*G)(x, y) = (2\pi)^{-1} \int_\Delta \overline{g(z - x)}g(z - y)dz = (2\pi)^{-1} \int_\Delta g(x - y + t)\overline{g(t)}dt.$$

This shows that $GG^* = G^*G$; the transformation G is therefore normal.

Theorem 1. *The normal transformation G is non-singular; its characteristic functions are the orthonormal functions $\varphi_n(x) = (2\pi)^{-1/2} e^{inx}$ $(n = 0, \pm 1, \pm 2, \ldots)$, belonging to the characteristic values $\lambda_n = \int_\Delta g(x)\overline{\varphi_n(x)}dx$ (where some of the λ_n may be zero).*

Proof. We have

$$G\varphi_n = (2\pi)^{-1} \int_\Delta g(x - y)e^{iny}dy = (2\pi)^{-1}e^{inx} \int_\Delta g(x - y)\overline{e^{in(x-y)}}dy =$$

$$= (2\pi)^{-1/2}e^{inx} \int_\Delta g(t)\overline{\varphi_n(t)}dt = \lambda_n\varphi_n(x),$$

and, since the system $\{\varphi_n(x)\}$ $(n = 0, \pm 1, \pm 2, \ldots)$ is complete in $L_2(\Delta)$, there exist no further characteristic functions. To prove that G is compact, it will be sufficient therefore to show that $\lim \lambda_n = 0$ as $n \to \pm \infty$. We first observe that $\int_\Delta | g(x + h) - g(x) | dx$ tends to zero with h. Indeed, if $\varepsilon > 0$ is given, there exists a simple function $g_1(x)$ such that $\| g - g_1 \| < \varepsilon/2$; consequently, there exists a continuous $g_2(x)$ of period 2π such that $\| g - g_2 \| < \varepsilon$. It follows, since $\int_\Delta | g_2(x + h) - g_2(x) | dx$ tends to zero with h, that the same is true for the corresponding integral with g instead of g_2. Let now $I_n = \int_0^{2\pi} g(x)e^{inx}dx$. Writing $x = y - \pi/n$, we have $e^{inx} = - e^{iny}$, hence $I_n = - \int_{\pi/n}^{2\pi+\pi/n} g(y - \pi/n)e^{iny}dy$ or

$$2I_n = \int_0^{\pi/n} g(x)e^{inx}dx - \int_{2\pi}^{2\pi+\pi/n} g(x - \pi/n)e^{inx}dx +$$

$$\int_{\pi/n}^{2\pi} \{g(x) - g(x - \pi/n)\}e^{inx}dx,$$

from which $\lim I_n = 0$ follows now immediately. Hence also $\lim \lambda_n = 0$.

Definition. *The expansion* $f(x) \sim \Sigma_{-\infty}^{\infty}(f, \varphi_n)\varphi_n(x)$, *which by the completeness of the system* $\{\varphi_n(x)\}$ *holds for every* $f(x) \in L_2(\Delta)$, *is called the Fourier expansion of* $f(x)$. *The series* $\Sigma\,(f, \varphi_n)\varphi_n(x)$ *is also said to be the Fourier series of* $f(x)$.

Theorem 2. *With* $g(x) \in L(\Delta)$ *and* $\{\varphi_n(x)\}$ *defined as above, with* $g_n = \int_\Delta g(x)\overline{\varphi_n(x)}dx$ *and* $f_n = (f, \varphi_n)$ *for an arbitrary* $f(x) \in L_2(\Delta)$, *the following Fourier expansions are valid*:

$$(1) \qquad \begin{cases} (2\pi)^{-1/2} \int_\Delta g(x-y)f(y)dy \sim \Sigma\, g_n f_n \varphi_n(x), \\ (2\pi)^{-1/2} \int_\Delta \overline{g(y-x)}f(y)dy \sim \Sigma\, \bar{g}_n f_n \varphi_n(x). \end{cases}$$

Proof. Observing that $g_n = \lambda_n$, and that the functions on the left are Gf and G^*f respectively, we see that the desired result is a consequence of § 3, Th. 7.

Theorem 3. *If* $g(x) \in L_2$, *the kernel* $G(x, y)$ *is continuous in mean, so that in this case the expansions in the preceding theorem converge uniformly. The series* $\Sigma \mid f_n g_n \mid$ *of the absolute values of the coefficients is even convergent.*

Proof. If $g(x) \in L_2$, we have

$$||| G |||^2 = (2\pi)^{-1} \int_{\Delta\times\Delta} | g(x-y) |^2 dx\, dy =$$
$$(2\pi)^{-1} \int_\Delta dy \int_\Delta | g |^2 dx = \| g \|^2,$$

hence $G(x, y)$ is of finite double-norm. Furthermore

$$\lim_{h\to 0} \int_0^{2\pi} | g(x+h-y) - g(x-y) |^2 dy = 0$$

for every $x \in \Delta$ by a similar argument as in the proof of Th. 1. The convergence of $\Sigma \mid f_n g_n \mid$ follows from

$$\Sigma \mid f_n g_n \mid \leqslant (\Sigma \mid f_n \mid^2)^{1/2}(\Sigma \mid g_n \mid^2)^{1/2} \leqslant \| f \|_2 \cdot \| g \|_2.$$

Remark. Taking $x = 0$ in the second formula (1), and observing that $\varphi_n(0) = (2\pi)^{-1/2}$ for $n = 0, \pm 1, \pm 2, \ldots$, we find

$$\int_0^{2\pi} f(y)\overline{g(y)}dy = \Sigma\, f_n \bar{g}_n = \Sigma\, (f, \varphi_n)\overline{(g, \varphi_n)}$$

for $f(x)$, $g(x) \in L_2$. It is evident, therefore, that for functions belonging to $L_2(\Delta)$ the relation (1), holding uniformly on Δ, is a generalisation of Parseval's relation (cf. Ch. 6, § 13, Ex. A).

Theorem 4. *If* $g(x) \in L_2[0, 2\pi]$, *having the period* 2π, *is continuous at* $x = 0$, *and*

$$g_n = (g, \varphi_n) = (2\pi)^{-1/2} \int_0^{2\pi} g(x)e^{-inx}dx \geqslant 0 \ (n = 0, \pm 1, \pm 2, \ldots),$$

then $g(x)$ *is equal almost everywhere on* Δ *to a continuous function* $g_c(x)$, *and the Fourier series of* $g(x)$ *converges uniformly to* $g_c(x)$ *on the whole interval* Δ.

Proof. Since all characteristic values $\lambda_n = g_n$ of the kernel $G(x, y) = (2\pi)^{-1/2}g(x - y)$ are non-negative, $G(x, y)$ is of positive type. In fact, $(Gf, h) = \Sigma \lambda_n(f, \varphi_n)\overline{(h, \varphi_n)} = (f, Gh)$ and $(Gf, f) = \Sigma \lambda_n \mid (f, \varphi_n) \mid^2 \geqslant 0$ for all $f(x)$, $h(x) \in L_2(\Delta)$. Furthermore, since $g(x)$ is continuous at $x = 0$, the function $G(x, y)$ is continuous at all points $(x, x) \in \Delta \times \Delta$. Hence, by Mercer's Theorem, $G(x, y)$ is almost everywhere on $\Delta \times \Delta$ equal to a continuous function $G_c(x, y)$, and $G_c(x, y) = \Sigma \lambda_n\varphi_n(x)\overline{\varphi_n(y)}$ uniformly on $\Delta \times \Delta$. But $\Sigma \lambda_n\varphi_n(x)\overline{\varphi_n(y)} = (2\pi)^{-1/2} \Sigma (g, \varphi_n)\varphi_n(x - y)$, which shows that $g(x)$ is almost everywhere on Δ equal to the sum $g_c(x)$ of the uniformly converging Fourier series $\Sigma (g, \varphi_n)\varphi_n(x)$.

Remark. By § 9, Th. 2 our theorem remains true whenever $g_n = (g, \varphi_n) \geqslant 0$ holds with a finite number of exceptions.

The system of functions $c_n(x) = (2/\pi)^{1/2} \cos nx \ (n = 1, 2, \ldots)$ is orthonormal in the interval $[0, \pi]$, and the same holds for the system $s_n(x) = (2/\pi)^{1/2} \sin nx \ (n = 1, 2, \ldots)$. These systems play a part in the theorem and the examples which follow next.

Theorem 5. *Let* $g(x)$ *have the period* 2π, $g(x) \in L_2[0,2\pi]$ *and* $g(x)$ *even, hence* $g(x) = g(-x)$ *for all* x. *Then the kernel* $(2\pi)^{-1/2}[g(x - y) - g(x + y)]$ *has in* $0 \leqslant x, y \leqslant \pi$ *the characteristic values* $\lambda_n = g_n = \int_0^{\pi} g(x)c_n(x)dx$ $(n = 1, 2, \ldots)$ *with the corresponding set* $s_n(x)$ *of characteristic functions. The kernel* $(2\pi)^{-1/2}[g(x - y) + g(x + y)] - g_0/\pi$, *where* $g_0 = (2/\pi)^{1/2} \int_0^{\pi} g(x)dx$, *has the same characteristic values, but with the corresponding set* $c_n(x)$ *of characteristic functions. Hence*

$$(2\pi)^{-1/2}[g(x - y) - g(x + y)] \sim \Sigma_1^{\infty} \left(\int_0^{\pi} g(x)c_n(x)dx\right)s_n(x)s_n(y),$$

$$(2\pi)^{-1/2}[g(x - y) + g(x + y)] - g_0/\pi \sim \Sigma_1^{\infty} \left(\int_0^{\pi} g(x)c_n(x)dx\right)c_n(x)c_n(y)$$

on $0 \leqslant x, y \leqslant \pi$.

Proof. The kernel $G(x, y) = (2\pi)^{-1/2}g(x-y)$ satisfies

$$G(x, y) = (2\pi)^{-1/2}g(x-y) \sim \Sigma_{-\infty}^{\infty} \lambda_n\varphi_n(x)\overline{\varphi_n(y)} =$$

$$(2\pi)^{-1}\Sigma_{-\infty}^{\infty} g_n e^{in(x-y)},$$

where $\lambda_n = g_n = (g, \varphi_n) = (2\pi)^{-1/2}\int_0^{2\pi} g(x)e^{-inx}dx$, and where the symbol $\sim$ denotes convergence in mean over $0 \leqslant x, y \leqslant 2\pi$. On account of the periodicity we may as well take convergence in mean over $-\pi \leqslant x, y \leqslant \pi$. Furthermore, since $g(x)$ is even, we have $\int_0^{2\pi} g(x) \sin nx\, dx = \int_{-\pi}^{\pi} g(x) \sin nx\, dx = 0$, hence

$$g_n = g_{-n} = (2\pi)^{-1/2}\int_0^{2\pi} g(x) \cos nx\, dx =$$

$$(2/\pi)^{1/2}\int_0^{\pi} g(x) \cos nx\, dx = \int_0^{\pi} g(x)c_n(x)dx$$

for $n = 1, 2, \ldots$, whereas $g_0 = (2/\pi)^{1/2}\int_0^{\pi} g(x)dx$. It follows that

$$(2\pi)^{-1/2}g(x-y) \sim g_0/2\pi + (2\pi)^{-1}\Sigma_1^{\infty} g_n\{e^{in(x-y)} + e^{-in(x-y)}\} =$$

$$g_0/2\pi + \pi^{-1}\Sigma_1^{\infty} g_n \cos n(x-y)$$

over $-\pi \leqslant x, y \leqslant \pi$. But then also

$$(2\pi)^{-1/2}g(x+y) \sim g_0/2\pi + \pi^{-1}\Sigma_1^{\infty} g_n \cos n(x+y)$$

over $-\pi \leqslant x, y \leqslant \pi$. Hence, by subtraction,

$$(2\pi)^{-1/2}[g(x-y) - g(x+y)] \sim (2/\pi)\,\Sigma_1^{\infty} g_n \sin nx \sin ny$$

$$= \Sigma_1^{\infty} g_n s_n(x)s_n(y),$$

and, by addition,

$$(2\pi)^{-1/2}[g(x-y) + g(x+y)] - g_0/\pi \sim (2/\pi)\,\Sigma_1^{\infty} g_n \cos nx \cos ny$$

$$= \Sigma_1^{\infty} g_n c_n(x)c_n(y).$$

This holds over $-\pi \leqslant x, y \leqslant \pi$, and therefore certainly over $0 \leqslant x, y \leqslant \pi$.

Lemma α. *We have* $-(2/\pi)^{1/2}\log 2 \sin (x/2) \sim \Sigma_1^{\infty} n^{-1}c_n(x)$ *on* $0 \leqslant x \leqslant \pi$.

Proof. On account of the completeness of the system $\{\cos nx\}$ ($n = 0, 1, 2, \ldots$) in $[0, \pi]$ (cf. Ch. 10, § 9, Th. 2, Remark) we have only to prove that $\int_0^{\pi} \log 2 \sin (x/2)dx = 0$ and $-(2/\pi)^{1/2}\int_0^{\pi} \log 2 \sin (x/2)c_n(x)dx = n^{-1}$.

Write $A = \int_0^{\pi/2} \log 2 \sin x \, dx$. Then also $\int_0^{\pi/2} \log 2 \cos x \, dx = A$, hence by addition

$$2A = \int_0^{\pi/2} \log 2 \sin 2x \, dx = \tfrac{1}{2} \int_0^{\pi} \log 2 \sin y \, dy = \tfrac{1}{2}.2A = A,$$

which implies $A = 0$, so that $\int_0^{\pi} \log 2 \sin (x/2)dx = 0$ as well.

For $n = 1, 2, \ldots$ we have

$$B_n = -(2/\pi)^{1/2} \int_0^{\pi} \log 2 \sin (x/2) . c_n(x)dx =$$

$$-(2/\pi) \int_0^{\pi} \log 2 \sin (x/2) \cos nx \, dx = -(2/\pi) \int_0^{\pi} \log \sin (x/2) \cos nx \, dx$$

$$= (-1)^{n+1} (2/\pi) \int_0^{\pi} \log \cos (x/2) \cos nx \, dx = (-1)^{n+1} (2/\pi) \int_0^{\pi} F(x)g(x) \, dx,$$

where $F(x) = \log \cos (x/2) = \int_0^x (-1/2)\, tg\, (y/2)dy = \int_0^x f(y)dy$ and $g(x) = \cos nx$. Hence, writing $G(x) = \int_0^x g(y)dy = n^{-1} \sin nx$, we find by partial integration

$$B_n = (-1)^{n+1}(2/\pi) \{F(\pi)G(\pi) - \int_0^{\pi} f(x)G(x)dx\} =$$

$$(-1)^{n+1}(2/\pi)(2n)^{-1} \int_0^{\pi} \text{tg } (x/2) \sin nx \, dx =$$

$$(\pi n)^{-1} \int_0^{\pi} \text{cotg } (x/2) \sin nx \, dx,$$

so that we have to prove that $\int_0^{\pi} \text{cotg } (x/2) \sin nx \, dx = \pi$, or $\int_0^{\pi/2} \text{cot g } x \sin 2nx \, dx = \pi/2$ for $n = 1, 2, \ldots$. For $n = 1$ this is trivial, and supposing that it has already been proved for a certain integer $n \geqslant 1$, we have

$$\int_0^{\pi/2} \sin (2n + 2)x \text{ cotg } x \, dx =$$

$$\int_0^{\pi/2} \sin 2nx \cos 2x \text{ cotg } x \, dx + \int_0^{\pi/2} \cos 2nx \sin 2x \text{ cotg } x \, dx =$$

$$\int_0^{\pi/2} \sin 2nx \text{ cotg } x \, dx - 2 \int_0^{\pi/2} \sin 2nx \sin x \cos x \, dx +$$

$$2 \int_0^{\pi/2} \cos 2nx \cos^2 x \, dx =$$

$$\pi/2 + 2 \int_0^{\pi/2} \cos (2n + 1)x \cos x \, dx =$$

$$\pi/2 + \int_0^{\pi/2} \cos (2n + 2)x \, dx + \int_0^{\pi/2} \cos 2nx \, dx = \pi/2.$$

Example A. *On* $0 \leqslant x, y \leqslant \pi$ *we have*

$$\frac{1}{\pi} \log \left| \frac{\sin (x + y)/2}{\sin (x - y)/2} \right| \sim \Sigma_1^{\infty} \frac{s_n(x)s_n(y)}{n}$$

and

$$-\frac{1}{\pi} \log | 2 \cos x - 2 \cos y | \sim \Sigma_1^{\infty} \frac{c_n(x)c_n(y)}{n}.$$

Proof. Define $g(x)$ in $-\infty < x < \infty$ by $g(x) = -(2/\pi)^{1/2} \log | 2 \sin (x/2) |$. Then $g(x)$ satisfies all conditions of Theorem 5, and by Lemma α we have $g_0 = (2/\pi)^{1/2} \int_0^\pi g(x)dx = 0$ and $g_n = \int_0^\pi g(x)c_n(x)dx = n^{-1}$ for $n = 1, 2, \ldots$. Since

$$(2\pi)^{-1/2}[g(x-y) - g(x+y)] =$$

$$-\frac{1}{\pi}\log\left|\frac{\sin (x-y)/2}{\sin (x+y)/2}\right| = \frac{1}{\pi}\log\left|\frac{\sin (x+y)/2}{\sin (x-y)/2}\right|$$

and

$$(2\pi)^{-1/2}[g(x-y) + g(x+y)] =$$

$$-\frac{1}{\pi} \log | 4 \sin \tfrac{1}{2}(x+y) \sin \tfrac{1}{2}(x-y) | = -\frac{1}{\pi} \log | 2 \cos x - 2 \cos y |,$$

the desired result is an immediate consequence of Theorem 5.

Lemma β. *We have* $(2/\pi)^{1/2}(x^2/4 - \pi x/2 + \pi^2/6) \sim \Sigma_1^\infty n^{-2}c_n(x)$ *on* $0 \leqslant x \leqslant \pi$.

Proof. Similar to the proof of Lemma α, but with much simpler computations.

Example B. *On* $0 \leqslant x, y \leqslant \pi$ *we have*

$$\tfrac{1}{2}(x+y) - \tfrac{1}{2}|x-y| - \frac{1}{\pi}xy \sim \Sigma_1^\infty \frac{s_n(x)s_n(y)}{n^2}$$

and

$$\frac{x^2+y^2}{2\pi} - \tfrac{1}{2}(x+y) - \tfrac{1}{2}|x-y| + \frac{\pi}{3} \sim \Sigma_1^\infty \frac{c_n(x)c_n(y)}{n^2}.$$

Proof. Define $g(x)$ in $0 \leqslant x \leqslant \pi$ by $g(x) = (2/\pi)^{1/2}(x^2/4 - \pi x/2 + \pi^2/6)$, and extend this function on $-\infty < x < \infty$ in such a way that it is even and has the period 2π. Then $g(x)$ satisfies all conditions of Theorem 5, and by Lemma β we have $g_0 = (2/\pi)^{1/2} \int_0^\pi g(x)dx = 0$ and $g_n = \int_0^\pi g(x)c_n(x)dx = n^{-2}$ $(n = 1, 2, \ldots)$. Furthermore, since $g(x) = (2/\pi)^{1/2}(x^2/4 - \pi |x|/2 + \pi^2/6)$ on $-\pi \leqslant x \leqslant \pi$, we have

$$g(x-y) = (2/\pi)^{1/2}[(x-y)^2/4 - \pi |x-y|/2 + \pi^2/6]$$

on $0 \leqslant x, y \leqslant \pi$. Observing now that $x^2/4 - \pi x/2 + \pi^2/6$ may also be written in the form $(\pi - x)^2/4 - \pi^2/12$, we see that the original expression for $g(x)$ on $0 \leqslant x \leqslant \pi$ is also valid on $\pi \leqslant x \leqslant 2\pi$, so that

$$g(x+y) = (2/\pi)^{1/2}[(x+y)^2/4 - \pi(x+y)/2 + \pi^2/6]$$

on $0 \leqslant x,\ y \leqslant \pi$. Hence

$$(2\pi)^{-1/2}[g(x-y) - g(x+y)] =$$
$$\pi^{-1}\{(x-y)^2/4 - (x+y)^2/4 - \pi \mid x-y \mid /2 + \pi(x+y)/2\} =$$
$$\tfrac{1}{2}(x+y) - \tfrac{1}{2} \mid x-y \mid - \frac{1}{\pi} xy$$

and

$$(2\pi)^{-1/2}[g(x-y) + g(x+y)] =$$
$$\pi^{-1}\{x^2/2 + y^2/2 - \pi(x+y)/2 - \pi \mid x-y \mid /2 + \pi^2/3\} =$$
$$\frac{x^2+y^2}{2\pi} - \tfrac{1}{2}(x+y) - \tfrac{1}{2} \mid x-y \mid + \frac{\pi}{3}.$$

The desired result is now again an immediate consequence of Theorem 5.

EXAMPLES

1) There exists a normal integral transformation N on $L_2[0, 1]$ which is non-singular, but such that neither N itself nor any of its iterates is of finite double-norm, and which has the additional property that its kernel $N(x, y)$ is general (that is, the range of N is dense in $L_2[0, 1]$).

(Consider the example mentioned at the end of § 3, and denote by $[L]$ the subspace determined by all $\varphi_n(x)$. Denoting the orthogonal subspace by $[M]$, we assume that $\{\psi_n(x)\}$ is a complete orthonormal system in $[M]$. Now define N_1 by $N_1\varphi_n = 0$, $N_1\psi_n = \mu_n\psi_n$, where all $\mu_n \neq 0$ and $\Sigma \mid \mu_n \mid^2 < \infty$. Hence N_1 is normal and of finite double-norm. Adding the kernel $N_1(x, y)$ of N_1 to the kernel of the already mentioned example, we obtain a kernel with the desired properties).

2) Let Δ be a bounded closed set in Euclidean space, and suppose that:

1°. $f_1(x, y)$ is continuous at all points $(x, x) \in \Delta \times \Delta$.

2°. $f_2(x, y)$ is continuous in x for all $y \in \Delta$ and continuous in y for all $x \in \Delta$.

3°. $f_1(x, y) = f_2(x, y)$ almost everywhere on $\Delta \times \Delta$.

Then $f_1(x, x) = f_2(x, x)$ at all $x \in \Delta$.

(Suppose that $A = f_1(x_0, x_0) \neq f_2(x_0, x_0)$. Then there exists a positive ε such that $\mid f_2(x_0, x_0) - A \mid > 3\varepsilon$ and a neighbourhood $\Delta_1 \times \Delta_1$ of (x_0, x_0) on which $\mid f_1(x, y) - A \mid < \varepsilon$. It follows that there exists a neighbourhood $\Delta_2 \subset \Delta_1$ of x_0 on which

$$\mid f_2(x, x_0) - A \mid > 2\varepsilon. \tag{1}$$

Furthermore we have for almost every $x \in \Delta_2$ the inequality

$$\mid f_2(x, y) - A \mid = \mid f_1(x, y) - A \mid < \varepsilon$$

for almost every $y \in \Delta_1$. Let $x = x_1$ be an x-value of this kind, hence $| f_2(x_1, y) - A | < \varepsilon$ for almost every $y \in \Delta_1$. But $f_2(x_1, y)$ is continuous in y, hence $| f_2(x_1, x_0) - A | < \varepsilon$, in contradiction with (1)).

3) Mercer's Theorem in § 9, Th. 1 may be strengthened as follows: If the set Δ is bounded and closed, and the kernel $H(x, y)$ on $\Delta \times \Delta$ has the property (P) relative to $L_2(\Delta)$ and is non-singular; if furthermore all characteristic functions $\varphi_n(x)$, belonging to characteristic values $\lambda_n \neq 0$, are continuous on Δ; if $H(x, y)$ is of positive type and continuous at every point $(x, x) \in \Delta \times \Delta$, then $H(x, y)$ is almost everywhere on $\Delta \times \Delta$ equal to a continuous function $H_c(x, y)$, and

$$H_c(x, y) = \Sigma\, \lambda_i \varphi_i(x)\overline{\varphi_i(y)}$$

uniformly on $\Delta \times \Delta$.

(The proof runs as in § 9, Th. 1 until we come to $H^*(x, y) = H(x, y) - \Sigma\, \lambda_i \varphi_i(x)\overline{\varphi_i(y)}$, uniformly in x for every $y \in \Delta$, and of course also uniformly in y for every $x \in \Delta$. Hence, for an arbitrary $f(y) \in L_2$,

$$\int_\Delta H^*(x, y)f(y)dy = \int_\Delta H(x, y)f(y)dy - \Sigma\, \lambda_i(f, \varphi_i)\varphi_i(x)$$

for every $x \in \Delta$, which implies on account of the expansion theorem in § 3, Th. 7 that

$$\int_{\Delta\times\Delta} H^*(x, y)\overline{g(x)}f(y)dx\, dy =$$

$$\int_{\Delta\times\Delta} H(x, y)\overline{g(x)}f(y)dx\, dy - \Sigma\, \lambda_i(f, \varphi_i)\overline{(g, \varphi_i)} = 0$$

for arbitrary $f, g \in L_2(\Delta)$. It follows in a well-known way that $H^*(x, y) = 0$ almost everywhere on $\Delta \times \Delta$, so that

$$H(x, y) = \Sigma\, \lambda_i \varphi_i(x)\overline{\varphi_i(y)}$$

almost everywhere on $\Delta \times \Delta$. Hence, with $f_1(x, y) = H(x, y)$ and $f_2(x, y) = \Sigma\, \lambda_i \varphi_i(x)\overline{\varphi_i(y)}$, we have exactly the situation of the preceding example. So $H(x, x) = \Sigma\, \lambda_i\, | \varphi_i(x) |^2$ for all $x \in \Delta$, so that by Dini's Theorem the series $\Sigma\, \lambda_i\, | \varphi_i(x) |^2$ converges uniformly. The remaining part of the proof is as in § 9, Th. 1).

4) We may strengthen Theorem 4 in § 11 as follows: If $g(x) \in L\ [0, 2\pi]$, having the period 2π, is continuous at $x = 0$, and $g_n = (g, \varphi_n) = (2\pi)^{-1/2} \int_0^{2\pi} g(x)e^{-inx}dx \geqslant 0$ $(n = 0, \pm 1, \pm 2, \ldots)$, then $g(x)$ is equal almost everywhere to a continuous function $g_c(x)$, and the Fourier series of $g(x)$ converges uniformly to $g_c(x)$ on the whole interval $[0, 2\pi]$.

(The kernel $G(x, y) = (2\pi)^{-1/2} g(x - y)$ satisfies all conditions of the preceding example).

5) There exists, of course, a short and direct proof of the theorem in the preceding example.

(Write $s_n(x) = (2\pi)^{-1/2}\, \Sigma_{-n}^{n}\, g_n e^{inx}$. Then $s_n(0) \geqslant 0$ for all n, hence $\sigma_n(0) = [s_0(0) + s_1(0) + \ldots + s_n(0)]/(n + 1) \geqslant 0$ for all n. Since $g(x)$ is continuous at $x = 0$, we have $\lim \sigma_n(0) = g(0)$ by a well-known theorem on Fourier series, and this shows that $g(0) \geqslant 0$. Considering now the function $g_n(x) = g(x) - s_n(x)$, this function satisfies all hypotheses of the theorem, hence $g_n(0) \geqslant 0$ or $(2\pi)^{-1/2}\, \Sigma_{-n}^{n}\, g_n \leqslant g(0)$. It follows that $\Sigma_{-\infty}^{\infty}\, g_n < \infty$, which implies the uniform convergence of $(2\pi)^{-1/2}\,\Sigma_{-\infty}^{\infty}\, g_n e^{inx}$ to a continuous $g_c(x)$. From

$$\int_0^{2\pi} [g(x) - g_c(x)]e^{inx}dx = 0 \ (n = 0, \pm 1, \pm 2, \ldots)$$

follows then that $g(x) = g_c(x)$ almost everywhere).

6) If $g(x) \in L[0, 2\pi]$, having the period 2π and satisfying $g(x) = \overline{g(-x)}$, is continuous at $x = 0$ without being essentially equal (that is, equal almost everywhere on $[0, 2\pi]$) to a continuous function, then $g(x)$ possesses an infinite number of positive and an infinite number of negative Fourier coefficients g_n. (Compare § 9, Th. 3, and observe that $G(x, y) = (2\pi)^{-1/2}g(x - y)$ is Hermitian).

7) Solve the equation

$$f(x) = x + \frac{1}{8}\int_0^{\pi}\left(x + y - |\, x - y \,| - \frac{2xy}{\pi}\right) f(y)dy.$$

(The equation may be written in the form $\int_0^{\pi} K(x, y)f(y)dy - 4f(x) = -4x$ with $K(x, y) = (x + y)/2 - |\, x - y \,|/2 - xy/\pi \sim \Sigma\, n^{-2}s_n(x)s_n(y)$. Hence

$$f(x) \sim -\frac{-4x}{4} - \Sigma_1^{\infty} \frac{n^{-2}}{4(4 - n^{-2})}\, \alpha_n s_n(x) = x - \Sigma_1^{\infty} \frac{1}{4(4n^2 - 1)}\, \alpha_n s_n(x)$$

with $\alpha_n = \int_0^{\pi} -4xs_n(x)dx = -4\beta_n$. Then

$$f(x) \sim \Sigma\, \beta_n s_n(x) + \Sigma \frac{4\beta_n}{4(4n^2 - 1)}\, s_n(x) = \Sigma \frac{4n^2}{4n^2 - 1}\, \beta_n s_n(x) =$$

$$\Sigma\, (-1)^{n+1}\sqrt{2\pi}\,\{4n/(4n^2 - 1)\}s_n(x).$$

An easy computation shows that $\int_0^{\pi} \sin(x/2)s_n(x)dx = (-1)^{n+1}\sqrt{2/\pi}$ $\{4n/(4n^2 - 1)\}$, hence $f(x) = \pi \sin x/2$ for $0 \leqslant x \leqslant \pi$).

8) Solve the equation

$$1 = f(x) - \frac{1}{2\pi}\int_0^{\pi} \log \left| \frac{\sin (x + y)/2}{\sin (x - y)/2} \right| f(y)dy.$$

(The equation may be written in the form $\int_0^{\pi} K(x, y)f(y)dy - 2f(x) = -2$ with $K(x, y) = \pi^{-1} \log |\, \{\sin (x + y)/2\}/\{\sin (x - y)/2\}\, | \sim \Sigma\, n^{-1}s_n(x)s_n(y)$. Hence

$$f(x) \sim -\frac{-2}{2} - \Sigma_1^{\infty} \frac{n^{-1}}{2(2 - n^{-1})}\, \alpha_n s_n(x) = 1 - \Sigma_1^{\infty} \frac{\alpha_n}{4n - 2}\, s_n(x)$$

with $\alpha_n = \int_0^{\pi} -2s_n(x)dx = 0$ for n even and $= -4n^{-1}\sqrt{2/\pi}$ for n odd. So

$$f(x) \sim 1 + \Sigma_1^{\infty} \frac{4\sqrt{2/\pi}}{(2n - 1)(8n - 6)}\, s_{2n-1}(x) =$$

$$2\sqrt{\frac{2}{\pi}}\,\Sigma_1^{\infty} \frac{s_{2n-1}(x)}{2n - 1} + 2\sqrt{\frac{2}{\pi}}\,\Sigma_1^{\infty} \frac{s_{2n-1}(x)}{(2n - 1)(4n - 3)} = 4\sqrt{\frac{2}{\pi}}\,\Sigma_1^{\infty} \frac{s_{2n-1}(x)}{4n - 3}$$

on $0 \leqslant x \leqslant \pi$).

9) Let N be normal and compact in the Hilbert space R; its characteristic values $\neq 0$ and a corresponding orthonormal set of characteristic elements will be denoted by $\lambda_1, \lambda_2, \ldots$ and $\varphi_1, \varphi_2, \ldots$. Let $f \neq 0$ be an element of the form $f = \Sigma\, (f, \varphi_i)\varphi_i = \Sigma\, f_i\varphi_i$, and let $p(\lambda) = \alpha + \beta\lambda + \gamma\bar{\lambda} + \delta\lambda\bar{\lambda}$ be a "*bipolynomial*"

(α, β, γ, δ arbitrary complex coefficients). By the *moment* of $p(\lambda)$ (relative to f) we mean the complex number $\langle p(\lambda) \rangle = \alpha(f, f) + \beta(Nf, f) + \gamma(f, Nf) + \delta(Nf, Nf)$. Then, if $0 \leqslant Re \langle p \rangle$ (by $Re \langle p \rangle$ is meant the real part of $\langle p \rangle$), we have $Re\, p(\lambda_n) \geqslant 0$ for at least one λ_n, that is, there exists at least one λ_n lying in the closed circular region or closed halfplane determined by $Re\, p(\lambda) \geqslant 0$ [4].

(Since $(f, f) = \Sigma \mid f_i \mid^2$, $(Nf, f) = \Sigma \lambda_i \mid f_i \mid^2$, $(f, Nf) = \Sigma \bar{\lambda}_i \mid f_i \mid^2$ and $(Nf, Nf) = \Sigma \lambda_i \bar{\lambda}_i \mid f_i \mid^2$, we have

$$0 \leqslant Re \langle p \rangle = Re\, \Sigma\, (\alpha + \beta\lambda_i + \gamma\bar{\lambda}_i + \delta\lambda_i\bar{\lambda}_i) \mid f_i \mid^2 = \Sigma \mid f_i \mid^2 Re\, p(\lambda_i).$$

Hence there is at least one λ_n satisfying $Re\, p(\lambda_n) \geqslant 0$).

10) Under the hypotheses of the preceding example every closed halfplane which is bounded by a straight line through the point $\rho = (Nf, f)/(f, f)$ contains at least one λ_n.

(Each of the halfplanes in question may be written in the form $Re\, p(\lambda) \geqslant 0$ with $p(\lambda) = \beta(\lambda - \rho)$, where β is suitably chosen. This $p(\lambda)$ satisfies $\langle p \rangle = \beta[(Nf, f) - \rho(f, f)] = 0$).

11) Under the hypotheses of the preceding examples we write $(Nf, Nf)/(f, f) - \rho\bar{\rho} = (Nf, Nf)/(f, f) - \mid (Nf, f) \mid^2/(f, f)^2 = \delta^2$. Then each of the two closed regions bounded by the circle $\mid \lambda - \rho \mid = \delta$ contains at least one λ_n. If $\delta = 0$, then ρ itself is one of the λ_n, and f is a corresponding characteristic element.

(Taking $p(\lambda) = (\lambda - \rho)(\bar{\lambda} - \bar{\rho}) - \delta^2$, we find $\langle p \rangle = (Nf, Nf) - \rho(f, Nf) - \bar{\rho}(Nf, f) + \rho\bar{\rho}(f, f) - \delta^2(f, f) = (Nf, Nf) - 2 \mid (Nf, f) \mid^2/(f, f) + \mid (Nf, f) \mid^2/(f, f) - \delta^2(f, f) = 0$. Observing that $Re\, p(\lambda) = p(\lambda) = \mid \lambda - \rho \mid^2 - \delta^2$, we find therefore that both $\mid \lambda - \rho \mid \geqslant \delta$ and $\mid \lambda - \rho \mid \leqslant \delta$ contain at least one λ_n. If $\delta = 0$, then $\mid (Nf, f) \mid^2 = (Nf, Nf) \cdot (f, f)$, and it is easily seen from the derivation of Schwarz's inequality (cf. Ch. 6, § 8, Th. 1) that in this case f and Nf are proportional, hence $Nf - \lambda f = 0$. But $(Nf, f) - \rho(f, f) = 0$ by the definition of ρ, so that $\lambda = \rho$ or, finally, $Nf = \rho f$).

12) If, under the hypotheses of the preceding examples, the orthonormal system $\{\psi_n\}$ is complete in the range of N, and $0 \neq f = \Sigma\, \sigma_i \psi_i$, $Nf = \Sigma\, \tau_i \psi_i$, then every closed circular region or halfplane, which contains all quotients τ_n/σ_n for which $\mid \tau_n \mid^2 + \mid \sigma_n \mid^2 \neq 0$, contains at least one λ_n.

(The circular region or halfplane may be written in the form $Re\, p(\lambda) \geqslant 0$ for a suitable $p(\lambda) = \alpha + \beta\lambda + \gamma\bar{\lambda} + \delta\lambda\bar{\lambda}$. Then

$$Re \langle p \rangle = \Sigma\, Re(\alpha\bar{\sigma}_i\sigma_i + \beta\bar{\sigma}_i\tau_i + \gamma\bar{\tau}_i\sigma_i + \delta\bar{\tau}_i\tau_i)$$
$$= \Sigma' \mid \sigma_i \mid^2 Re\, p(\tau_i/\sigma_i) + \Sigma'' \mid \tau_i \mid^2 Re\, \delta,$$

where Σ' is over all $\sigma_i \neq 0$ and Σ'' over all $\sigma_i = 0$. Both sums are non-negative, the first since all τ_i/σ_i belong to the region, the second since for $\sigma_i = 0$ either $\tau_i = 0$ or the region contains the point at infinity which implies $Re\, \delta \geqslant 0$).

13) Let $A(x, y) = B(x, y) \mid x - y \mid^{-\alpha}$ on $0 \leqslant x, y \leqslant 1$, where $B(x, y)$ is measurable, bounded and Hermitian, and where $0 < \alpha < 1$. Then, if there exists a subinterval $\Delta_1 \subset [0, 1]$ such that the real part of $B(x, y)$ exceeds a constant $M > 0$ on $\Delta_1 \times \Delta_1$, the kernel $A(x, y)$ has an infinity of positive characteristic values.

(Assume that $A(x, y)$ has only the positive characteristic values $\lambda_1^+, \ldots, \lambda_n^+$

with the corresponding orthonormal system of characteristic functions $\varphi_1^+(x), \ldots, \varphi_n^+(x)$. Write

$$A_1(x, y) = A(x, y) - \Sigma_1^n \lambda_i^+ \varphi_i^+(x)\overline{\varphi_i^+(y)} =$$

$$= [B(x, y) - | x - y |^\alpha \Sigma_1^n \lambda_i^+ \varphi_i^+(x)\overline{\varphi_i^+(y)}] . | x - y |^{-\alpha} = B_1(x, y) | x - y |^{-\alpha}.$$

Then, observing that the functions $\varphi_1^+(x), \ldots, \varphi_n^+(x)$ are bounded by Ch. 13, § 5, Example, we see that there exists an interval $\Delta_2 \subset \Delta_1$ such that the real part of $B_1(x, y)$ exceeds $M/2$ on $\Delta_2 \times \Delta_2$. Obviously, since $A_1(x, y)$ has only non-positive characteristic values, $(A_1 f, f) \leqslant 0$ for all $f(x) \in L_2[0, 1]$. On the other hand, taking $f(x) = 1$ on Δ_2 and $f(x) = 0$ elsewhere, we have $(A_1 f, f)$ $\int_{\Delta_2 \times \Delta_2} B_1(x, y) | x - y |^{-\alpha} dx\, dy > 0$. This is a contradiction).

14) Let $A(x, y) = B(x, y) | x - y |^{-\alpha}$ on $0 \leqslant x, y \leqslant 1$, where $B(x, y)$ is measurable, bounded and Hermitian, and where $0 < \alpha < 1$. Then, if there exists a closed subinterval $\Delta_1 \subset [0, 1]$ such that $B(x, y)$ is continuous on $\Delta_1 \times \Delta_1$ and $B(x, x) > 0$ on Δ_1, and if $\{\lambda_n^+\}$ is the non-increasing sequence of positive characteristic values of $A(x, y)$, the series $\Sigma_1^\infty (\lambda_n^+)^{1/(1-\alpha)}$ diverges [5].

(We have $(Af, f) \leqslant \Sigma \lambda_n^+ | (f, \varphi_n^+) |^2 \leqslant \Sigma_1^m \lambda_n^+ | (f, \varphi_n^+) |^2 + \lambda_{m+1}^+$ for every f satisfying $\| f \| = 1$. Hence, if $\psi_1(x), \ldots, \psi_m(x)$ is an orthonormal system, $(A\psi_k, \psi_k) \leqslant \Sigma_{n=1}^m \lambda_n^+ | (\psi_k, \varphi_n^+) |^2 + \lambda_{m+1}^+$. Consequently

$$\Sigma_{k=1}^m (A\psi_k, \psi_k) \leqslant \Sigma_{n=1}^m \lambda_n^+ \Sigma_{k=1}^m | (\psi_k, \varphi_n^+) |^2 + m\lambda_{m+1}^+$$
$$\leqslant \lambda_1^+ + \ldots + \lambda_m^+ + m\lambda_{m+1}^+.$$

Now divide the interval Δ_1 of length d into m equal parts $E_1, \ldots, E_m$, and define $\psi_k(x)$ $(k = 1, \ldots, m)$ as $(m/d)^{1/2}$ on E_k and zero elsewhere. Then $(A\psi_k, \psi_k)$ $= (m/d) \int_{E_k \times E_k} A(x, y) dx\, dy = (m/d) B(\xi_k, \eta_k) \int_{E_k \times E_k} | x - y |^{-\alpha} dx\, dy$, where (ξ_k, η_k) is a point in $E_k \times E_k$. But

$$\int_{E_k \times E_k} | x - y |^{-\alpha}\, dx\, dy = \int_0^{d/m} \int_0^{d/m} | x - y |^{-\alpha}\, dx\, dy =$$
$$\frac{2}{(1 - \alpha)(2 - \alpha)} \left(\frac{d}{m}\right)^{2-\alpha}.$$

Hence $(A\psi_k, \psi_k) = 2(1 - \alpha)^{-1}(2 - \alpha)^{-1} (m/d)^\alpha B(\xi_k, \eta_k)\, (d/m)$, so that, if $\delta > 0$ is prescribed,

$$\Sigma_{k=1}^m (A\psi_k, \psi_k) > 2(1 - \alpha)^{-1}(2 - \alpha)^{-1}(m/d)^\alpha \left[\int_{\Delta_1} B(x, x) dx - \delta\right]$$

for m sufficiently large. Now, since $B(x, x) > 0$ on Δ_1, there exists a number M satisfying

$$0 < M < 2(1 - \alpha)^{-1}(2 - \alpha)^{-1}(1/d)^\alpha \int_{\Delta_1} B(x, x) dx.$$

Hence $Mm^\alpha < \Sigma_1^m (A\psi_k, \psi_k) \leqslant \lambda_1^+ + \ldots + \lambda_m^+ + m\lambda_{m+1}^+$ for $m \geqslant m_0$.

Assume now that $\Sigma (\lambda_n^+)^{1/(1-\alpha)} < \infty$. Then $\lim m(\lambda_m^+)^{1/(1-\alpha)} = 0$, so that $m(\lambda_m^+)^{1/(1-\alpha)}$ $< \varepsilon$ for $m \geqslant m_1(\varepsilon)$, or $\lambda_m^+ < (\varepsilon/m)^{1-\alpha}$. Consequently, for $m \geqslant \max [m_0, m_1]$,

$$Mm^\alpha < \Sigma_{i=1}^{m_1} \lambda_i^+ + \Sigma_{\nu=1}^m \left(\frac{\varepsilon}{\nu}\right)^{1-\alpha} + \frac{m\varepsilon^{1-\alpha}}{(m + 1)^{1-\alpha}}$$

$$< \Sigma_1^{m_1} \lambda_i^+ + \varepsilon^{1-\alpha} \int_0^m \frac{dx}{x^{1-\alpha}} + \varepsilon^{1-\alpha} m^\alpha = \Sigma_1^{m_1} \lambda_i^+ + \varepsilon^{1-\alpha} m^\alpha \left(1 + \frac{1}{\alpha}\right).$$

Hence, dividing by m^{α} and making $m \to \infty$, we find $M \leqslant \varepsilon^{1-\alpha}(1 + \alpha^{-1})$, which implies $M = 0$ since $\varepsilon > 0$ is arbitrary. This is in contradiction with $M > 0$).

REFERENCES

[1] E. SCHMIDT, Entwicklung willkürlicher Funktionen nach Systemen vorgeschriebener, Math. Annalen 63 (1907), 433–476.

[2] F. SMITHIES, The eigenvalues and singular values of integral equations, Proc. London Math. Soc. (2) 43 (1937), 255–279.

[3] J. MERCER, Functions of positive and negative type and their connection with the theory of integral equations, Transactions London Phil. Soc. (A) 209 (1909), 415–446.

[4] H. WIELANDT, Ein Einschlieszungssatz für characteristische Wurzeln normaler Matrizen, Archiv der Math. 1 (1948–49), 348–352.

[5] T. CARLEMAN, Sur la distribution des valeurs singulières d'une classe des noyaux infinis, Arkiv för Mat., Astr. och Fysik (13) 1918, No. 6, 1–7.

CHAPTER 15

INTEGRAL EQUATION WITH A SYMMETRISABLE KERNEL, EXPRESSIBLE AS THE PRODUCT OF A KERNEL OF FINITE DOUBLE-NORM AND A BOUNDED NON-NEGATIVE FUNCTION

§ 1. Introduction

Assuming once more that Δ is a μ-measurable set of finite or infinite measure, and that μ is separable, we shall consider the linear integral equation

$$\int_\Delta K(x, y)f(y)d\mu - \lambda f(x) = g(x)$$

in the Lebesgue space $L_2(\Delta, \mu)$, where $K(x, y) = A(x, y)h(y)$, these functions $A(x, y)$ and $h(y)$ satisfying the following conditions:

1°. $h(y)$ is measurable, bounded and non-negative on Δ.

2°. $A(x, y)$ is of finite double-norm (relative to $L_2(\Delta, \mu)$).

3°. The kernel $S(x, y) = h(x)K(x, y) = h(x)A(x, y)h(y)$ is Hermitian. Then, by 1°, the linear transformation H in L_2, defined by $Hf = h(x)f(x)$, is bounded and positive (cf. Ch. 9, § 6, Th. 1), while by 2° the linear transformation A in L_2, defined by $Af = \int_\Delta A(x, y)f(y)d\mu$, is compact. Finally, by 3°, the compact transformation $K = AH$ with kernel $K(x, y) = A(x, y)h(y)$ is strongly symmetrisable relative to H. Indeed, the condition 3° expresses that $S = HK = HAH$ is self-adjoint, hence $HAH = HA^*H$. We observe that 3° is automatically satisfied whenever $A(x, y)$ is Hermitian.

In many of the classical textbooks on integral equations kernels of the form $K(x, y) = A(x, y)h(y)$ are considered, where $A(x, y)$ is Hermitian and the positive function $h(y)$ is bounded. It is proved then that for every theorem on integral equations with Hermitian kernels there exists an analogous theorem on equations with a kernel of this kind. This is done by writing

$$K(x, y) = \frac{h^{1/2}(y)}{h^{1/2}(x)} h^{1/2}(x)A(x, y)h^{1/2}(y) = \frac{h^{1/2}(y)}{h^{1/2}(x)} \tilde{K}(x, y),$$

where $\tilde{K}(x, y)$ is evidently Hermitian, and proving then in the first place that $K(x, y)$ and $\tilde{K}(x, y)$ have the same sequence of characteristic values $\neq 0$. The hypothesis that $h(x) \neq 0$ on Δ is however essential in the arguments used. The theory of symmetrisable transformations, as developed in Chapter 12, will enable us to show that this restriction is unnecessary [1].

We shall also consider the linear equation $K\{f\} - \lambda\{f\} = \{g\}$ with matrixkernel $\{K_{ij}(x, y)\}$ in the productspace $[L_2(\Delta, \mu)]^n$, that is to say, we shall consider the set of equations

$$\Sigma_{j=1}^{n} \int_\Delta K_{ij}(x, y) f^j(y) d\mu - \lambda f^i(x) = g^i(x) \quad (i = 1, \ldots, n)$$

in $L_2(\Delta, \mu)$, where $\{K_{ij}(x, y)\}$ is the matrixproduct of the matrixkernel $\{A_{ij}(x, y)\}$ and the matrix $\{h_{ij}(y)\}$, the following conditions being satisfied:

1°. All $h_{ij}(y)$ $(i, j = 1, \ldots, n)$ are measurable and bounded on Δ. Furthermore $h_{ij}(y) = \overline{h_{ji}(y)}$ $(i, j = 1, \ldots, n)$ and $\Sigma_{ij=1}^{n} h_{ij}(y)\bar{\alpha}_i\alpha_j \geqslant 0$ for every system $\alpha_1, \ldots, \alpha_n$ of complex numbers; the matrix $\{h_{ij}(y)\}$ is therefore Hermitian and of positive type.

2°. All $A_{ij}(x, y)$ $(i, j = 1, \ldots, n)$ are of finite double-norm (relative to L_2).

3°. The matrixproduct $\{S_{ij}(x, y)\} = \{h_{ij}(x)\}.\{K_{ij}(x, y)\} = \{h_{ij}(x)\}.\{A_{ij}(x, y)\}.\{h_{ij}(y)\}$ is Hermitian.

Then, by 1°, the linear transformation $\{g\} = H\{f\}$ in L_2^n, defined by $g^i(x) = \Sigma_{j=1}^{n} h_{ij}(x) f^j(x)$ $(i = 1, \ldots, n)$, is bounded and positive (cf. Ch. 9, § 6, Th. 1), while by 2° the linear transformation $\{g\} = A\{f\}$ in L_2^n, defined by $g^i(x) = \Sigma_{j=1}^{n} \int_\Delta A_{ij}(x, y) f^j(y) d\mu$, is compact (cf. Ch. 11, § 1, Th. 12). Finally, by 3°, the compact transformation $K = AH$ with matrixkernel $\{K_{ij}(x, y)\} = \{A_{ij}(x, y)\}.\{h_{ij}(y)\}$ is strongly symmetrisable relative to H. The condition 3° is automatically satisfied whenever $\{A_{ij}(x, y)\}$ is Hermitian.

Equations of this kind were considered by WILKINS [2] who generalized earlier results of REID [3]. He however supposed all $h_{ij}(y)$ to be continuous on Δ, and all $A_{ij}(x, y)$ to be bounded on $\Delta \times \Delta$ with only discontinuities of a very special kind; restrictions which may be removed [4].

We shall use the fact that, provided $\{h_{ij}(y)\}$ is defined as above, there exists a uniquely determined Hermitian matrix $\{h_{ij}^{(1/2)}(y)\}$ of positive type consisting of measurable and bounded functions such that the matrixproduct of $\{h_{ij}^{(1/2)}(y)\}$ by itself is the matrix $\{h_{ij}(y)\}$ (cf. Ch. 9, § 6, Th. 3). It follows (cf. Ch. 9, § 6, Th. 4) that the positive transformation

$\{g\} = H^{1/2}\{f\}$ in L_2^n is given by

$$g^i(x) = \Sigma_{j=1}^n h_{ij}^{(1/2)}(y)f^j(y) \quad (i = 1, \ldots, n).$$

We recall that if Δ is a set in Euclidean space, and all $h_{ij}(y)$ are continuous on Δ, the same holds for all $h_{ij}^{(1/2)}(y)$. For $n = 1$, when $Hf = h(x)f(x)$, we have obviously $H^{1/2}f = h^{1/2}(x)f(x)$.

As in the preceding chapter we shall state most theorems only for the case of one equation. Only at a few places (e.g. the expansion theorem for the kernel) we shall also consider the case that we have to do with a matrixkernel.

§ 2. Kernels of the Form $k_1(x)A(x, y)k_2(y)$

Theorem 1. *Let the Hermitian kernel $A(x, y)$ be of finite double-norm, while the product of the bounded measurable functions $k_1(x)$ and $k_2(x)$ is non-negative or non-positive throughout Δ. Let furthermore $k_1^{-1}(x)$ exist and be bounded. Then the kernel $K(x, y) = k_1(x)A(x, y)k_2(y)$ is expressible in the form $K(x, y) = \tilde{A}(x, y)h(y)$, where $\tilde{A}(x, y)$ is Hermitian and of finite double-norm and the function $h(y)$ is bounded and non-negative.*

Proof. We may assume without loss of generality that $k_1(x)k_2(x) \geqslant 0$ on Δ, since in the case that $k_1(x)k_2(x) \leqslant 0$ we may replace $k_1(x)$ and $A(x, y)$ by $-k_1(x)$ and $-A(x, y)$. Hence $k_1(x)k_2(x)/|k_1(x)|^2 \geqslant 0$, or $k_2(x)\overline{k_1^{-1}(x)} \geqslant 0$. Writing $h(y) = k_2(y)\overline{k_1^{-1}(y)}$, the function $h(y)$ is therefore bounded and non-negative. Finally

$$K(x, y) = k_1(x)A(x, y)\overline{k_1(y)}k_2(y)\overline{k_1^{-1}(y)} = \tilde{A}(x, y)h(y),$$

where $\tilde{A}(x, y)$ is Hermitian and of finite double-norm.

The present theorem shows that integral equations with kernels $K(x, y)$ of the indicated kind are of the type introduced in § 1.

§ 3. Symmetrisable Kernels $K(x, y) = A(x, y)h(y)$

We consider the equation

$$(1) \qquad \int_\Delta K(x, y)f(y)d\mu - \lambda f(x) = g(x), \quad K(x, y) = A(x, y)h(y),$$

introduced in § 1. The corresponding linear transformation $K = AH$ is compact and strongly symmetrisable relative to the bounded positive transformation H. The results obtained in Ch. 12 (in particular § 3, 4, 6, 13) may therefore be applied. Every non-real number λ is in the resolvent set of K, and every real $\lambda \neq 0$ is either a characteristic value or it belongs to the resolvent set of K. Every characteristic value $\neq 0$ has finite multiplicity (algebraic and geometric multiplicity are the same here by Ch. 12, § 2, 10°). The total number of characteristic values is finite or enumerable, and in the latter case the characteristic values tend to zero. We shall assume that $\lambda_1, \lambda_2, \ldots$ is the sequence of all characteristic values $\neq 0$ of K, each of them repeated according to its multiplicity and arranged such that $|\lambda_1| \geqslant |\lambda_2| \geqslant \ldots$, and that $\psi_1(x), \psi_2(x), \ldots$ is a corresponding H-orthonormal sequence of characteristic functions. Hence

$$\int_\Delta h(x)\psi_i(x)\overline{\psi_j(x)}\, d\mu = \begin{cases} 1 \text{ for } i = j, \\ 0 \text{ for } i \neq j. \end{cases}$$

Writing $h(x)\psi_i(x) = \chi_i(x)$ $(i = 1, 2, \ldots)$, we have therefore

$$\int_\Delta \psi_i(x)\overline{\chi_j(x)}\, d\mu = \begin{cases} 1 \text{ for } i = j, \\ 0 \text{ for } i \neq j. \end{cases}$$

In the case of a matrixkernel $\{K_{ij}(x, y)\}$ we use the notations $\lambda_1, \lambda_2, \ldots$ and $\psi_1^i(x), \psi_2^i(x), \ldots$ $(i = 1, \ldots, n)$ for the characteristic values and corresponding H-orthonormal characteristic functionsets. Hence, writing $\chi_k^i(x) = \sum_{j=1}^n h_{ij}(x)\psi_k^j(x)$ (so that $H\{\psi_k\} = \{\chi_k\}$), we have

$$\sum_{i=1}^n \int_\Delta \psi_k^i(x)\overline{\chi_l^i(x)} d\mu = \begin{cases} 1 \text{ for } k = l, \\ 0 \text{ for } k \neq l. \end{cases}$$

Theorem 1. *In order that, for $f(x) \in L_2$, the relation $h(x) \int_\Delta K(x, y)f(y)d\mu = 0$ should hold for almost every $x \in \Delta$, it is necessary and sufficient that $\int_\Delta f(x)\overline{\chi_k(x)}d\mu = 0$ for $k = 1, 2, \ldots$.*

Proof. $HKf = 0$ if and only if $(f, \chi_k) = (Hf, \psi_k) = 0$ for $k = 1, 2, \ldots$ by Ch. 12, § 4, Th. 1.

Theorem 2. *Suppose that $\lambda_1^+ \geqslant \lambda_2^+ \geqslant \ldots$ is the subsequence of all positive characteristic values and that $\psi_1^+(x), \psi_2^+(x), \ldots$ is a corresponding H-orthonormal sequence of characteristic functions. Write $\chi_k^+(x) = h(x)\psi_k^+(x)$ $(k = 1, 2, \ldots)$. Then*

$$\lambda_n^+ = \max \int_{\Delta\times\Delta} h(x)K(x, y)\overline{f(x)}f(y)d(\mu \times \mu) / \int_\Delta h(x) \, |f(x)|^2 \, d\mu$$

for all $f(x) \in L_2$ *satisfying* $\int_\Delta h(x) \mid f(x) \mid^2 d\mu \neq 0$ *and* $\int_\Delta f\overline{\chi_1^+} d\mu = \ldots = \int_\Delta f\overline{\chi_{n-1}^+} d\mu = 0$. *For* $f(x) = \psi_n^+(x)$ *the maximum is attained. A similar statement holds for the negative characteristic values.*

Proof. Follows from Ch. 12, § 4, Th. 3.

Theorem 3. *Let* $p_1(x), \ldots, p_{n-1}(x)$ *be arbitrary functions belonging to* L_2, *and write*

$$\mu_n = \text{upper bound} \int_{\Delta\times\Delta} h(x)K(x, y)\overline{f(x)}f(y)d(\mu \times \mu) / \int_\Delta h(x) \mid f(x) \mid^2 d\mu$$

for all $f(x) \in L_2$ *satisfying* $\int_\Delta h(x) \mid f(x) \mid^2 d\mu \neq 0$ *and* $\int_\Delta hf\overline{p_1}\, d\mu = \ldots = \int_\Delta hf\overline{p_{n-1}}\, d\mu = 0$. *Then* μ_n *depends on* $p_1(x), \ldots, p_{n-1}(x)$. *Letting now these functions run through the whole space* L_2, *we have*

$$\lambda_n^+ = \min \mu_n.$$

A similar statement holds for the negative characteristic values.

Proof. Follows from Ch. 12, § 4, Th. 4.

Theorem 4 (*Expansion theorem*). *If* $f(x) \in L_2$, *then*

$$\int_\Delta K(x, y)f(y)d\mu \sim \Sigma\, \lambda_k(f, \chi_k)\psi_k(x) + p(x),$$

where $h(x)p(x) = 0$ *(almost everywhere), and where the symbol* $\sim$ *denotes convergence in mean with index 2 on* Δ. *Furthermore*

$$\int_{\Delta\times\Delta} h(x)K(x, y)\overline{g(x)}f(y)d(\mu \times \mu) = \Sigma\, \lambda_i(f, \chi_i)\overline{(g, \chi_i)}.$$

Proof. Follows from Ch. 12, § 12, Th. 5 and Ch. 12, § 4, Th. 2.

Remark. The corresponding expansion theorem for the case of a matrixkernel runs as follows:

If $\{f\} = \{f^1(x), \ldots, f^n(x)\} \in L_2^n$, then

$$\Sigma_{j=1}^n \int_\Delta K_{ij}(x, y)f^j(y)d\mu \sim \Sigma_k\, \lambda_k(\{f\}, \{\chi_k\})\psi_k^i(x) + p^i(x) \;(i = 1, \ldots, n),$$

where $\{p\} = \{p^1(x), \ldots, p^n(x)\}$ satisfies $H\{p\} = \{0\}$, that is,

$$\Sigma_{j=1}^n h_{ij}(x)p^j(x) = 0 \;(i = 1, \ldots, n).$$

Theorem 5. *If* $\lambda \neq 0$ *is no characteristic value of* K, *the equation* (1) *has a uniquely determined solution* $f(x) \in L_2$ *for every* $g(x) \in L_2$. *If* $\lambda \neq 0$ *is a characteristic value of* K, *the equation* (1) *has a solution* $f(x) \in L_2$ *for those and only those* $g(x) \in L_2$ *which are H-orthogonal to all characteristic* *functions of K belonging to the characteristic value λ. This solution is determined except for a linear combination of these characteristic functions.*

More precisely, if $\int_\Delta K(x, y)f(y)d\mu - \lambda f(x) = g(x)$, then

$$f(x) \sim -\frac{g(x)}{\lambda} - {}'\Sigma \frac{\lambda_n}{\lambda(\lambda - \lambda_n)} \alpha_n \psi_n(x) + q(x),$$

where $\alpha_n = \int_\Delta g\bar{\chi}_n d\mu$ for $\lambda_n \neq \lambda$, $h(x)q(x) = 0$ (almost everywhere), and where the dash in front of the Σ-symbol means that for those values of n for which $\lambda_n = \lambda$ the coefficient of $\psi_n(x)$ has the value $\int_\Delta f\bar{\chi}_n d\mu$. For every set of arbitrarily prescribed values of these coefficients there exists a solution $f(x)$.

Proof. Follows from Ch. 12, § 6, Th. 1 and Ch. 12, § 12, Th. 7.

Theorem 6 (*Expansion theorem for the kernel*). *We have*

$$K(x, y) \sim \Sigma\, \lambda_k \psi_k(x)\overline{\chi_k(y)} + p(x, y),$$

where $p(x, y)$ is of finite double-norm and satisfies $h(x)p(x, y) = 0$ (almost everywhere on $\Delta \times \Delta$), and where $\sim$ denotes convergence in mean with index 2 on $\Delta \times \Delta$.

Proof. We observe first that by Ch. 12, § 12, Th. 3 the self-adjoint transformation $\tilde{K} = H^{1/2}AH^{1/2}$ has the same sequence λ_k ($k = 1, 2, \ldots$) of characteristic values $\neq 0$ as $K = AH$, and that $\Psi_k(x) = h^{1/2}(x)\psi_k(x)$ is a corresponding orthonormal sequence of characteristic elements. Hence, by Ch. 14, § 4, Th. 1,

$$h^{1/2}(x)A(x, y)h^{1/2}(y) \sim \Sigma\, \lambda_k \Psi_k(x)\overline{\Psi_k(y)},$$

so that, multiplying by $h^{1/2}(y)$,

$$h^{1/2}(x)K(x, y) \sim \Sigma\, \lambda_k \Psi_k(x)\overline{\chi_k(y)}. \tag{2}$$

It is evidently not permitted to multiply now by $h^{-1/2}(x)$, since $h^{-1/2}(x)$ may be infinite on a set of positive measure. We proceed, therefore, in a different way. Consider the kernel $D(x, y) = A(x, y)h^{1/2}(y)$ of finite double-norm, belonging to the transformation $D = AH^{1/2}$. For almost every $x \in \Delta$ the function $d_x(y) = D(x, y)$ belongs to $L_2(\Delta)$. Hence, by Bessel's inequality (the system $\overline{\Psi_k(x)}$ is orthonormal),

$$\Sigma \mid (d_x, \overline{\Psi}_k) \mid^2 \leqslant \| d_x \|^2,$$

or, since $(d_x, \overline{\Psi}_k) = \int_\Delta A(x, y)h(y)\psi_k(y)d\mu = \lambda_k\psi_k(x)$ almost everywhere,

$$\Sigma\, \lambda_k^2 \mid \psi_k(x) \mid^2 \leqslant \int_\Delta \mid D(x, y) \mid^2 d\mu \tag{3}$$

for almost every $x \in \Delta$.

We next observe that the functions $f_k(x, y) = \lambda_k \psi_k(x)\overline{\Psi_k(y)}$ are orthogonal in the space $L_2(\Delta \times \Delta)$ on account of the orthogonality of the system $\overline{\Psi_k(y)}$ in $L_2(\Delta)$. Furthermore, by (3),

$$\Sigma \| f_k(x, y) \|^2 = \Sigma \lambda_k^2 \int_{\Delta \times \Delta} | \psi_k(x) |^2 | \Psi_k(y) |^2 d(\mu \times \mu) =$$

$$\Sigma \lambda_k^2 \int_\Delta | \psi_k(x) |^2 d\mu \leqslant \int_{\Delta \times \Delta} | D(x, y) |^2 d(\mu \times \mu) < \infty,$$

which shows, since $\| \Sigma_p^q f_k(x, y) \|^2 = \Sigma_p^q \| f_k(x, y) \|^2$ by the orthogonality, that $\Sigma f_k(x, y)$ converges in mean on $\Delta \times \Delta$. Denoting the sum by $f(x, y)$, we have therefore

$$f(x, y) \sim \Sigma \lambda_k \psi_k(x)\overline{\Psi_k(y)},$$

so that, writing $f(x, y)h^{1/2}(y) = K(x, y) - p(x, y)$, we find

$$K(x, y) - p(x, y) \sim \Sigma \lambda_k \psi_k(x)\overline{\chi_k(y)}. \tag{4}$$

The only thing that remains to be proved is $h(x)p(x, y) = 0$. From (4) we deduce

$$h^{1/2}(x)K(x, y) - h^{1/2}(x)p(x, y) \sim \Sigma \lambda_k \Psi_k(x)\overline{\chi_k(y)},$$

hence, comparing this with (2), $h^{1/2}(x)p(x, y) = 0$, or $h(x)p(x, y) = 0$ almost everywhere on $\Delta \times \Delta$.

Theorem 7 (*Expansion theorem for the matrixkernel*). *We have*

$$K_{ij}(x, y) \sim \Sigma_k \lambda_k \psi_k^i(x)\overline{\chi_k^j(y)} + p_{ij}(x, y) \quad (i, j = 1, \ldots, n),$$

where all $p_{ij}(x, y)$ are of finite double-norm, and where (almost everywhere on $\Delta \times \Delta$)

$$\Sigma_{q=1}^n h_{iq}(x)p_{qj}(x, y) = 0.$$

Proof. The kernel $\{\tilde{K}_{ij}(x, y)\}$ of $\tilde{K} = H^{1/2}AH^{1/2}$ satisfies

$$\tilde{K}_{iq}(x, y) \sim \Sigma_k \lambda_k \Psi_k^i(x)\overline{\Psi_k^q(y)} \quad (i, q = 1, \ldots, n)$$

with $\Psi_k^i(x) = \Sigma_{j=1}^n h_{ij}^{(1/2)}(x)\psi_k^j(x)$, so that

$$\Sigma_{r=1}^n h_{ir}^{(1/2)}(x)K_{rj}(x, y) = \Sigma_{rs=1}^n h_{ir}^{(1/2)}(x)A_{rs}(x, y)h_{sj}(y) =$$

$$\Sigma_{q=1}^n \tilde{K}_{iq}(x, y)h_{qj}^{(1/2)}(y) \sim \Sigma_k \lambda_k \Psi_k^i(x) \, (\overline{\Sigma_{q=1}^n \Psi_k^q(y)h_{jq}^{(1/2)}(y)}),$$

or

$$\Sigma_{r=1}^n h_{ir}^{(1/2)}(x)K_{rj}(x, y) \sim \Sigma_k \lambda_k \Psi_k^i(x)\overline{\chi_k^j(y)}. \tag{5}$$

Consider now the matrixkernel $\{D_{ij}(x, y)\}$ of $D = AH^{1/2}$. For every

i $(i = 1, \ldots, n)$ and for almost every $x \in \Delta$, the functionset $\{d_i\} = \{d_i^1(y), \ldots, d_i^n(y)\}$, where $d_i^j(y) = D_{ij}(x, y)$, belongs to L_2^n. Hence, by Bessel's inequality (the system of functionsets $\overline{\Psi_k^i(x)}$ is orthonormal),

$$\Sigma_k \mid (\{d_i\}, \{\overline{\Psi}_k\}) \mid^2 \leqslant \| d_i \|^2,$$

or, since

$$(\{d_i\}, \{\overline{\Psi}_k\}) = \Sigma_{j=1}^n \int_\Delta d_i^j(y) \Psi_k^j(y) d\mu = \Sigma_{j=1}^n \int_\Delta D_{ij}(x, y) \Psi_k^j(y) d\mu =$$
$$\Sigma_{j=1}^n \int_\Delta \Sigma_{qr=1}^n A_{iq}(x, y) h_{qj}^{(1/2)}(y) h_{jr}^{(1/2)}(y) \psi_k^r(y) d\mu =$$
$$\Sigma_{r=1}^n \int_\Delta K_{ir}(x, y) \psi_k^r(y) d\mu = \lambda_k \psi_k^i(x)$$

almost everywhere,

$$\Sigma_k \lambda_k^2 \mid \psi_k^i(x) \mid^2 \leqslant \Sigma_{j=1}^n \int_\Delta \mid D_{ij}(x, y) \mid^2 d\mu \tag{6}$$

for almost every $x \in \Delta$.

We next observe that in the space $[L_2(\Delta \times \Delta)]^{n^2}$ the elements

$$\{f_k\} = \{f_k^{ij}(x, y) = \lambda_k \psi_k^i(x) \overline{\Psi_k^j(y)}\} \quad (i, j = 1, \ldots, n)$$

are orthogonal on account of the orthogonality of the system $\{\overline{\Psi}_k\}$ in $[L_2(\Delta)]^n$. Furthermore, by (6),

$$\Sigma \| \{f_k\} \|^2 = \Sigma_k \lambda_k^2 (\Sigma_{ij=1}^n \int_{\Delta \times \Delta} \mid \psi_k^i(x) \mid^2 \mid \Psi_k^j(y) \mid^2 d(\mu \times \mu) =$$
$$\Sigma \lambda_k^2 (\Sigma_{i=1}^n \int_\Delta \mid \psi_k^i(x) \mid^2 d\mu) \leqslant \Sigma_{ij=1}^n \int_{\Delta \times \Delta} \mid D_{ij}(x, y) \mid^2 d(\mu \times \mu) < \infty,$$

which shows, since $\| \Sigma_p^q \{f_k\} \|^2 = \Sigma_p^q \| \{f_k\} \|^2$ by the orthogonality, that $\Sigma \{f_k\}$ converges in $[L_2(\Delta \times \Delta)]^{n^2}$. This implies that, for $i, j = 1, \ldots, n$, the series $\Sigma_k \lambda_k \psi_k^i(x) \overline{\Psi_k^j(y)}$ converges in mean on $\Delta \times \Delta$. Hence

$$f_{ij}(x, y) \sim \Sigma_k \lambda_k \psi_k^i(x) \overline{\Psi_k^j(y)},$$

so that, writing

$$\Sigma_{q=1}^n f_{iq}(x, y) h_{qj}^{(1/2)}(y) = K_{ij}(x, y) - p_{ij}(x, y),$$

we find

$$K_{ij}(x, y) - p_{ij}(x, y) \sim \Sigma_k \lambda_k \psi_k^i(x) \overline{\chi_k^j(y)} \quad (i, j = 1, \ldots, n). \tag{7}$$

It remains to be proved that $\Sigma_{q=1}^n h_{iq}(x) p_{qj}(x, y) = 0$. From (7) we deduce

$$\Sigma_{r=1}^n h_{ir}^{(1/2)}(x) K_{rj}(x, y) - \Sigma_{r=1}^n h_{ir}^{(1/2)}(x) p_{rj}(x, y) \sim \Sigma_k \lambda_k \Psi_k^i(x) \overline{\chi_k^j(y)},$$

hence, comparing this with (5), $\Sigma_{r=1}^n h_{ir}^{(1/2)}(x) p_{rj}(x, y) = 0$, or $\Sigma_{r=1}^n h_{ir}(x) p_{rj}(x, y) = 0$. This completes the proof.

Theorem 8. *We have, for almost every* $x \in \Delta$,

$$K_2(x, x) = \int_\Delta K(x, y)K(y, x)d\mu = \Sigma \lambda_k^2 \mid \Psi_k(x) \mid^2 = \Sigma \lambda_k^2 h(x) \mid \psi_k(x) \mid^2.$$

Proof. On account of $HAH = HA^*H$ we have

$$K_2(x, x) = \int_\Delta K(x, y)K(y, x)d\mu = \int_\Delta A(x, y)h(y)A(y, x)h(x)d\mu =$$

$$\int_\Delta A(x, y)h(y)\overline{A(x, y)}h(x)d\mu = \int_\Delta \mid h^{1/2}(x)A(x, y)h^{1/2}(y) \mid^2 d\mu$$

for almost every $x \in \Delta$, and by Ch. 14, § 4, Th. 1 the Hermitian kernel $\tilde{K}(x, y) = h^{1/2}(x)A(x, y)h^{1/2}(y)$ of $\tilde{K} = H^{1/2}AH^{1/2}$ satisfies, for almost every $x \in \Delta$,

$$\int_\Delta \mid h^{1/2}(x)A(x, y)h^{1/2}(y) \mid^2 d\mu = \Sigma \lambda_k^2 \mid \Psi_k(x) \mid^2.$$

Theorem 9. *If* $f(x) \in L_2(\Delta)$, *then*

$$\int_\Delta K(x, y)f(y)d\mu = \Sigma \lambda_k(f, \chi_k)\psi_k(x) + p(x),$$

where the sign of equality stands for pointwise convergence almost everywhere on Δ, *and where* $p(x)$ *is the same function as in Theorem* 4 (*hence* $h(x)p(x)=0$).

Proof. Since $(f, \chi_k) = (f, H^{1/2}\Psi_k) = (H^{1/2}f, \Psi_k)$ and the system Ψ_k is orthonormal, the series $\Sigma \mid (f, \chi_k) \mid^2$ converges. Furthermore, by (3) in the proof of Theorem 6, the series $\Sigma \lambda_k^2 \mid \psi_k(x) \mid^2$ converges for almost every $x \in \Delta$. Hence, in virtue of

$$\Sigma \mid \lambda_k(f, \chi_k)\psi_k(x) \mid \leqslant (\Sigma \mid (f, \chi_k) \mid^2)^{1/2}(\Sigma \lambda_k^2 \mid \psi_k(x) \mid^2)^{1/2},$$

the series $\Sigma \lambda_k(f, \chi_k)\psi_k(x)$ converges absolutely at almost every $x \in \Delta$. The statement on the sum is proved as in the corresponding theorem for normal kernels (cf. Ch. 14, § 4, Th. 3).

§ 4. The Iterated Kernels and the Traces

Introducing the iterated kernels $K_p(x, y) = \int_\Delta K(x, z)K_{p-1}(z, y)d\mu$ ($p = 2, 3, \ldots$) of our kernel $K(x, y)$, it is easily seen that they may be written in the form $K_p(x, y) = B_p(x, y)h(y)$, where $B_p(x, y)$ has similar properties as $A(x, y)$. More precisely, if we define the transformations $B_p (p = 1, 2, \ldots)$ of finite double-norm by $B_1 = A$, $B_2 = AHB_1, \ldots$, generally by $B_p = AHB_{p-1}$, then $K^p = B_pH$ and $\tilde{K}^p = (H^{1/2}AH^{1/2})^p = H^{1/2}B_pH^{1/2}$ (cf. Ch. 12, § 12, Th. 3). The transformations $K^p = B_pH$ and $\tilde{K}^p = H^{1/2}B_pH^{1/2}$ stand therefore in a similar relation to each other as the original transformations K and $\tilde{K}$. But $\tilde{K}^p$ has the sequence $\lambda_1^p, \lambda_2^p, \ldots$ of characteristic values $\neq 0$ with the corresponding orthonormal sequence $\Psi_1(x), \Psi_2(x), \ldots$ of characteristic functions (cf. Ch. 14, § 5). Hence, by the one-to-one correspondence between the characteristic values and functions of K^p and $\tilde{K}^p$ (cf. Ch. 12, § 12, Th. 3), K^p has the sequence $\lambda_1^p, \lambda_2^p, \ldots$ of characteristic values $\neq 0$ with $\psi_1(x), \psi_2(x), \ldots$ as a corresponding H-orthonormal sequence of characteristic functions.

It follows that all theorems in the preceding paragraph remain true upon replacing $K(x, y)$ and λ_k by $K_p(x, y)$ and λ_k^p respectively. As we shall prove now, the functions which would be the analogues of $p(x)$ in Theorem 4 (and Theorem 9) and of $p(x, y)$ in Theorem 6 vanish for $p \geqslant 2$.

Theorem 1. *If $f(x) \in L_2$ and $p \geqslant 2$, then*

$$\int_\Delta K_p(x, y) f(y) d\mu \sim \Sigma_k \lambda_k^p (f, \chi_k) \psi_k(x)$$

with pointwise convergence almost everywhere on Δ. Furthermore

$$K_p(x, y) \sim \Sigma_k \lambda_k^p \psi_k(x) \overline{\chi_k(y)}.$$

Proof. The first part of the theorem follows from Ch. 12, § 12, Th. 5. In order to prove the second part we observe that

$$K(z, y) - p(z, y) \sim \Sigma \lambda_k \psi_k(z) \overline{\chi_k(y)}$$

implies by Schwarz's inequality

$$\int_\Delta K(x, z) K(z, y) d\mu - \int_\Delta K(x, z)\, p(z, y)\, d\mu \sim \Sigma \lambda_k \overline{\chi_k(y)} \int_\Delta K(x, z) \psi_k(z) d\mu$$

(cf. the similar argument in Ch. 14, § 5, Th. 3). Hence, since $K(x, z) p(z, y) = A(x, z) h(z) p(z, y) = 0$, we find

$$K_2(x, y) \sim \Sigma \lambda_k^2 \psi_k(x) \overline{\chi_k(y)}.$$

The proof for $p > 2$ follows easily by induction.

Theorem 2. *We have*

$$K_p(x, y) = \Sigma_k \lambda_k^p \psi_k(x) \overline{\chi_k(y)} \quad (p = 2, 3, \ldots)$$

almost everywhere on $\Delta \times \Delta$ (pointwise absolute convergence).

Proof. Since $\Sigma \lambda_k^2 \mid \psi_k(x) \mid^2$ converges for almost every $x \in \Delta$, the same is true of $\Sigma_k \lambda_k^p \mid \psi_k(x) \mid^2$ for $p > 2$. The inequality

$$\Sigma \mid \lambda_k^p \psi_k(x) \overline{\psi_k(y)} \mid \leqslant (\Sigma \lambda_k^2 \mid \psi_k(x) \mid^2)^{1/2} (\Sigma \lambda_k^{2p-2} \mid \psi_k(y) \mid^2)^{1/2}$$

shows then that, for $p \geqslant 2$, the series $\Sigma \lambda_k^p \psi_k(x) \overline{\psi_k(y)}$ converges absolutely almost everywhere on $\Delta \times \Delta$. Hence the same holds for $\Sigma \lambda_k^p \psi_k(x) \overline{\chi_k(y)}$.

The numbers

$$\tau_p = \tau(K^p) = \int_{\Delta\times\Delta} K(x, y)K_{p-1}(y, x)d(\mu \times \mu) = \int_\Delta K_p(x, x)d\mu$$
$$(p = 2, 3, \ldots)$$

are the traces of $K_p(x, y)$. By Ch. 11, § 7, Th. 3 we have $\tau_p = \Sigma_k \lambda_k^p$ for $p = 3, 4, \ldots$. We shall prove that in the present case this relation is also true for $p = 2$. Our proof for $p = 2, 3, \ldots$ will be independent of the earlier result in Ch. 11, § 7, Th. 3.

Theorem 3. *We have*

$$\tau_p = \Sigma_k \lambda_k^p \; (p = 2, 3, \ldots).$$

Proof. The relation $K(y, x) \sim p(y, x) + \Sigma \lambda_k \psi_k(y)\overline{\chi_k(x)}$ implies

$$\tau_p = \int_{\Delta\times\Delta} K_{p-1}(x, y)K(y, x)d(\mu \times \mu) =$$
$$\int_{\Delta\times\Delta} K_{p-1}(x, y)p(y, x)\, d(\mu \times \mu) + \Sigma \lambda_k^p \int_\Delta \psi_k(x)\overline{\chi_k(x)}d\mu = \Sigma \lambda_k^p.$$

§ 5. The Case that $A(x, y)$ is Continuous in Mean and $h(y)$ is Continuous

We now assume that $A(x, y)$ is continuous in mean on $\Delta \times \Delta$, that is, we suppose that Δ is a bounded and closed set in Euclidean space, and that

$$\lim_{x_2\to x_1} \int_\Delta | A(x_2, y) - A(x_1, y) |^2 dy = 0,$$
$$\lim_{y_2\to y_1} \int_\Delta | A(x, y_2) - A(x, y_1) |^2 dx = 0.$$

We furthermore assume that $h(y)$ is continuous on Δ. It is not difficult to see that, under these conditions, both $K(x, y) = A(x, y)h(y)$ and $\tilde{K}(x, y) = h^{1/2}(x)A(x, y)h^{1/2}(y)$ are also continuous in mean. Hence (cf. Ch. 13, § 5, Th. 1) all iterated kernels $K_p(x, y)$ $(p = 2, 3, \ldots)$ are continuous on $\Delta \times \Delta$. Furthermore, any function $g(x) = Kf(x)$, where $f(x) \in L_2(\Delta)$, is obviously continuous on Δ. In particular, all characteristic functions $\psi_k(x)$ are continuous.

In the case of a matrixkernel we suppose that all $A_{ij}(x, y)$ are continuous in mean and all $h_{ij}(y)$ are continuous. Then, using the fact that all $h_{ij}^{(1/2)}(y)$ are continuous as well (cf. Ch. 9, § 6, Th. 3), similar conclusions may be drawn.

Theorem 1 *(Expansion theorem). If $f(x) \in L_2$, the series $\Sigma \lambda_k(f, \chi_k)\psi_k(x)$ converges uniformly to the continuous function $\int_\Delta K(x, y)f(y)dy - \tilde{p}(x)$*

on the whole interval Δ, *where the continuous function* $\tilde{p}(x)$ *satisfies* $h(x)\tilde{p}(x) = 0$ *for every* $x \in \Delta$.

Proof. We know already that $\Sigma \mid (f, \chi_k) \mid^2$ converges (cf. the proof of § 3, Th. 9). Furthermore the kernel $D(x, y) = A(x, y)h^{1/2}(y)$ of $D = AH^{1/2}$ is continuous in mean, so that $\int_\Delta \mid D(x, y) \mid^2 dy$ is a continuous function of x, satisfying therefore $\int_\Delta \mid D(x, y) \mid^2 dy \leqslant M$ with M not depending on x. Hence $d_x(y) = D(x, y) \in L_2$ for every $x \in \Delta$. Then, by Bessel's inequality, $\Sigma \mid (d_x, \overline{\Psi}_k) \mid^2 \leqslant \| d_x \|^2$, or, since $(d_x, \overline{\Psi}_k) = \int_\Delta A(x, y)h(y)\psi_k(y)dy = \lambda_k\psi_k(x)$ for every x,

$$\Sigma\, \lambda_k^2 \mid \psi_k(x) \mid^2 \leqslant \int_\Delta \mid D(x, y) \mid^2 dy \leqslant M. \tag{1}$$

Consequently, if $\varepsilon > 0$ is given, and p and q are sufficiently large, we have

$$\Sigma_p^q \mid \lambda_k(f, \chi_k)\psi_k(x) \mid \leqslant M^{1/2}(\Sigma_p^q \mid (f, \chi_k) \mid^2)^{1/2} < \varepsilon$$

for every $x \in \Delta$. The series $\Sigma\, \lambda_k(f, \chi_k)\psi_k(x)$ of continuous functions converges therefore uniformly on Δ to a continuous sum. Since $\int_\Delta K(x, y)f(y)dy$ is also continuous, the same holds for the difference $\tilde{p}(x)$. By § 3, Th. 4 we have $h(x)\tilde{p}(x) = 0$ almost everywhere on Δ. Since however $h(x)\tilde{p}(x)$ is continuous, we find $h(x)\tilde{p}(x) = 0$ for every $x \in \Delta$.

Theorem 2 (*Expansion theorem for the iterated kernels*). *We have*

$$K_p(x, y) = \Sigma_k\, \lambda_k^p \psi_k(x)\overline{\chi_k(y)} \quad (p = 2, 3, \ldots)$$

uniformly on $\Delta \times \Delta$.

Proof. In view of § 4, Th. 2, where we have already proved that $K_p(x, y) \sim \Sigma_k \lambda_k^p \psi_k(x)\overline{\chi_k(y)}$ $(p = 2, 3, \ldots)$, and taking into account the continuity of $K_p(x, y)$ $(p = 2, 3, \ldots)$, we have only to show that the series converges uniformly. We first consider the case $p = 2$. By Ch. 14, § 7, Th. 2 we have

$$\tilde{K}_2(x, y) = \Sigma\, \lambda_k^2 \Psi_k(x)\overline{\Psi_k(y)}$$

uniformly on $\Delta \times \Delta$. Hence, multiplying by $h^{1/2}(x)h^{1/2}(y)$, we see that $\Sigma\, \lambda_k^2 \chi_k(x)\overline{\chi_k(y)}$ converges uniformly on $\Delta \times \Delta$. In particular, $\Sigma\, \lambda_k^2 \mid \chi_k(x) \mid^2$ converges uniformly on Δ. Since, by (1) in the proof of the preceding theorem, $\Sigma\, \lambda_k^2 \mid \psi_k(x) \mid^2 \leqslant M$ for all $x \in \Delta$, we find now

$$\Sigma \mid \lambda_k^2 \psi_k(x)\overline{\chi_k(y)} \mid \leqslant M^{1/2}\, (\Sigma\, \lambda_k^2 \mid \chi_k(y) \mid^2)^{1/2}.$$

This shows that $\Sigma\, \lambda_k^2 \psi_k(x)\overline{\chi_k(y)}$ converges uniformly on $\Delta \times \Delta$. The proof for $p > 2$ follows immediately.

The extension of these theorems to the case of a matrixkernel offers no difficulties.

§ 6. An Example

We shall illustrate the theorems, proved in the preceding paragraphs, by an example showing that the functions $p(x)$ and $p(x, y)$ in § 3, Th. 4 (the expansion theorem for functions of the form $Kf(x)$) and § 3, Th. 6 (the expansion theorem for the kernel) need not vanish identically. The principle upon which the construction of this example is based is the same as that which was used in Ch. 12, § 12, Th. 6.

Let Δ be the linear interval $[0, 3]$ and Δ_1, Δ_2, Δ_3 the subintervals $[0, 1]$, $(1, 2)$, $[2, 3]$. The orthonormal system of functions $\varphi_1(x)$, $\varphi_2(x)$, $\varphi_3(x)$ is defined by

$$\varphi_i(x) = \begin{cases} 1 \text{ on } \Delta_i, \\ 0 \text{ on } \Delta - \Delta_i. \end{cases} \qquad (i = 1, 2, 3).$$

Denoting by $[L]$ the threedimensional subspace of $L_2(\Delta)$ determined by φ_1, φ_2 and φ_3, we shall suppose that the system $\varepsilon_n(x)$ $(n = 1, 2, \ldots)$ is orthonormal and complete in the orthogonal complement of $[L]$.

Let now $h(x) = 1$ in Δ_1 and Δ_3, $h(x) = 0$ in Δ_2. The bounded linear transformation H in L_2, defined by $Hf = h(x)f(x)$, is then positive. We observe that

$$H\varphi_1 = \varphi_1, \quad H\varphi_2 = 0, \quad H\varphi_3 = \varphi_3.$$

The bounded self-adjoint linear transformation A is now defined by

$$A\varphi_1 = \varphi_2, \quad A\varphi_2 = \varphi_1, \quad A\varphi_3 = \varphi_3, \quad A\varepsilon_n = 0.$$

Evidently A has only two characteristic values $\neq 0$; it has $\lambda = 1$ with the orthonormal characteristic functions $2^{-1/2}[\varphi_1(x) + \varphi_2(x)]$ and $\varphi_3(x)$, and $\lambda = -1$ with the normal characteristic function $2^{-1/2}[\varphi_1(x) - \varphi_2(x)]$. This transformation A has therefore the Hermitian kernel

$$\begin{aligned} \mathrm{A}(x, y) &= 2^{-1}[\varphi_1(x) + \varphi_2(x)][\varphi_1(y) + \varphi_2(y)] + \varphi_3(x)\varphi_3(y) \\ &\quad - 2^{-1}[\varphi_1(x) - \varphi_2(x)][\varphi_1(y) - \varphi_2(y)] \\ &= \varphi_1(x)\varphi_2(y) + \varphi_2(x)\varphi_1(y) + \varphi_3(x)\varphi_3(y). \end{aligned}$$

The symmetrisable kernel $K(x, y) = A(x, y)h(y)$ and the Hermitian kernel $\tilde{K}(x, y) = h^{1/2}(x)A(x, y)h^{1/2}(y)$ are given by

$$K(x, y) = \varphi_2(x)\varphi_1(y) + \varphi_3(x)\varphi_3(y),$$

$$\tilde{K}(x, y) = \varphi_3(x)\varphi_3(y).$$

0	0	1
1	0	0
0	1	0

$A(x, y)$

0	0	1
0	0	0
0	1	0

$K(x, y)$

0	0	1
0	0	0
0	0	0

$\tilde{K}(x, y)$

As we know, $K(x, y)$ and $\tilde{K}(x, y)$ have the same characteristic values $\neq 0$; hence, since $\tilde{K}(x, y)$ has evidently only the characteristic value $\lambda = 1$, different from zero, with the characteristic function $\varphi_3(x)$, the kernel $K(x, y)$ has also $\lambda_1 = 1$ as the only characteristic value $\neq 0$ with the H-normal characteristic function $\psi_1(x) = \varphi_3(x)$. Observing that $\overline{\chi_1(y)} = \overline{h(y)\psi_1(y)} = h(y)\varphi_3(y) = \varphi_3(y)$, so that $\lambda_1\psi_1(x)\overline{\chi_1(y)} = \varphi_3(x)\varphi_3(y)$, we find therefore

$$K(x, y) - p(x, y) = \lambda_1\psi_1(x)\overline{\chi_1(y)} = \varphi_3(x)\varphi_3(y),$$

hence $p(x, y) = \varphi_2(x)\varphi_1(y) \neq 0$ for $(x, y) \in \Delta_2 \times \Delta_1$. Evidently $h(x)p(x, y) = 0$ as required by § 3, Th. 6.

Furthermore

$$\int_\Delta K(x, y)f(y)dy = \lambda_1(f, \chi_1)\psi_1(x) + p(x) = (f, \varphi_3)\varphi_3(x) + p(x).$$

Taking $f(x) = \varphi_1(x)$, we have $Kf = K\varphi_1 = AH\varphi_1 = \varphi_2(x)$ and $(f, \varphi_3) = (\varphi_1, \varphi_3) = 0$, hence

$$\varphi_2(x) = p(x).$$

This shows that $p(x) \neq 0$ for $x \in \Delta_2$. Evidently $h(x)p(x) = 0$ as required by § 3, Th. 4.

EXAMPLES

1) Assume that $A(x, y)$ belongs to the class B; hence $\int_\Delta | A(x, y) |^2 dy \leqslant c^2$, $\int_\Delta | A(x, y) |^2 dx \leqslant c^2$ for all $x \in \Delta$ and all $y \in \Delta$ respectively. Then (with the notations of §§ 3, 4, 5), if $f(x) \in L_2$, the series $\Sigma\, \lambda_k(f, \chi_k)\psi_k(x)$ converges uniformly, and its sum is $K.f(x) - p(x)$ for almost every $x \in \Delta$, where $p(x)$ is the same function as in § 3, Th. 4.

(The uniform convergence may be proved as in § 5, Th. 1).

2) Under the same hypotheses as in the preceding example the following statement holds: For $p = 3, 4, \ldots$ the series $\Sigma_k\, \lambda_k^p\psi_k(x)\overline{\chi_k(y)}$ converges uniformly on $\Delta \times \Delta$, and its sum is $K_p(x, y)$ for almost every point $(x, y) \in \Delta \times \Delta$.

(Since (1) in the proof of § 5, Th. 1 is now true for every $x \in \Delta$, we see immediately that $\Sigma\, | \lambda_k |^p \, | \psi_k(x) |^2$ converges uniformly on Δ for $p = 3, 4, \ldots$. It follows that $\Sigma\, | \lambda_k^p\psi_k(x)\overline{\psi_k(y)} |$ converges uniformly on $\Delta \times \Delta$, so that the same is true of $\Sigma\, | \lambda_k^p\psi_k(x)\overline{\chi_k(y)} |$).

3) Under the same hypotheses as in the preceding examples the series $\Sigma \lambda_k^2 \psi_k(x)\overline{\chi_k(y)}$ converges for every point $(x, y) \in \Delta \times \Delta$, and for a fixed point $y \in \Delta$ the convergence is uniform in x, while for a fixed $x \in \Delta$ it is uniform in y. The sum is $K_2(x, y)$ for almost every $(x, y) \in \Delta \times \Delta$.

(Considering a fixed $y \in \Delta$ and a number $\varepsilon > 0$, there exists an index N such that $\Sigma_N \mid \lambda_k \mid^2 \mid \chi_k(y) \mid^2 < \varepsilon^2/M$, where M is such that $\Sigma \lambda_k^2 \mid \psi_k(x) \mid^2 \leqslant M$ for all $x \in \Delta$. Then $\Sigma_N \mid \lambda_k^2 \psi_k(x)\overline{\chi_k(y)} \mid \leqslant M^{1/2}.\varepsilon/M^{1/2} = \varepsilon$ for all $x \in \Delta$).

4) Assume that $K(x, y) = A(x, y)h(y)$ as in § 3, but that $h(y)$, although real, is not necessarily non-negative on Δ. Assume instead that $S(x, y) = h(x)K(x, y) = h(x)A(x, y)h(y)$ is of positive type. Similarly, in the case of a matrixkernel $\{K_{ij}(x, y)\}$, assume that $\{S_{ij}(x, y)\} = \{h_{ij}(x)\}\{K_{ij}(x, y)\}$ is of positive type [5]. Denoting the characteristic values $\neq 0$ of $K(x, y)$ by $\lambda_n(\mid \lambda_1 \mid \geqslant \mid \lambda_2 \mid \geqslant \dots)$, there exists a corresponding sequence of characteristic functions $\psi_n(x)$ which is H-orthogonal as well as S-orthogonal, and which may be normalized such that $\int_\Delta h(x) \mid \psi_n(x) \mid^2 d\mu = \operatorname{sgn} \lambda_n$, hence $\int_\Delta \psi_n(x)\overline{\chi_n(x)} d\mu = \operatorname{sgn} \lambda_n$. In order that, for $f(x) \in L_2(\Delta, \mu)$, the relation

$$\int_{\Delta\times\Delta} S(x, z)K(z, y)f(y)d(\mu \times \mu) = 0$$

should hold for almost every $x \in \Delta$, it is necessary and sufficient that $\int_\Delta f\overline{\chi}_n d\mu = 0$ for $n = 1, 2, \dots$.

(Follows from Ch. 12, § 15, in particular Th. 5).

5) Under the same hypotheses as in the preceding example we have

$$\lambda_n^+ = \max \int_{\Delta\times\Delta\times\Delta} S(x, z)K(z, y)\overline{f(x)}f(y)d(\mu \times \mu \times \mu) / \int_{\Delta\times\Delta} S(x, y)\overline{f(x)}f(y)d(\mu \times \mu)$$

for all $f(x) \in L_2$, satisfying $\int_{\Delta\times\Delta} S(x, y)\overline{f(x)}f(y)d(\mu \times \mu) \neq 0$ and $\int_\Delta f\overline{\chi_1^+} d\mu = \dots = \int_\Delta f\overline{\chi_{n-1}^+} d\mu = 0$.

(Follows from Ch. 12, § 15, Th. 7).

6) Under the same hypotheses as in the preceding example we have, for $f(x) \in L_2$,

$$\int_\Delta K_2(x, y)f(y)d\mu \sim \Sigma \lambda_k^2(f, \chi_k)\psi_k(x) + p(x),$$

where $h(x)p(x) = 0$ almost everywhere on Δ. Furthermore

$$\int_\Delta K_p(x, y)f(y)d\mu \sim \Sigma \lambda_k^p(f, \chi_k)\psi_k(x) \quad (p = 3, 4, \dots).$$

(Follows from Ch. 12, § 15, Th. 10).

REFERENCES

[1] A. C. Zaanen, On the theory of linear integral equations III, Proc. Akad. Amsterdam 49 (1946), 292—301 (Indagationes Math. 8, 161—170).

[2] J. Ernest Wilkins, Definitely self-conjugate adjoint integral equations, Duke Math. Journal 11 (1944), 155—166.

[3] W. T. Reid, Expansion problems associated with a system of linear integral equations, Transactions Amer. Math. Soc. 33 (1931), 475—485.

[4] A. C. Zaanen, On the theory of linear integral equations VIII and VIII*a*, Proc. Akad. Amsterdam 50 (1947), 465—473 and 612—617 (Indagationes Math. 9, 271—279 and 320—325).

[5] H. J. Zimmerberg, Definite integral systems, Duke Math. Journal 15 (1948), 371—388.

CHAPTER 16

INTEGRAL EQUATION WITH MARTY KERNEL

§ 1. Introduction

We assume as before that Δ is a μ-measurable set of finite or infinite measure, and that μ is separable, and we consider now the linear integral equation

$$\int_\Delta K(x, y)f(y)d\mu - \lambda f(x) = g(x)$$

in the Lebesgue space $L_2(\Delta, \mu)$, where $K(x, y)$ is of finite double-norm (relative to $L_2(\Delta, \mu)$) and fully symmetrisable relative to the kernel $H(x, y)$ of finite double-norm and of positive type. Hence $S(x, y) = \int_\Delta H(x, z)K(z, y)d\mu$ is Hermitian, and we have $Hf \neq 0$ for any $f(x) \in L_2$ satisfying $Kf = \lambda f \neq 0$. We shall call any kernel $K(x, y)$ of this kind a *Marty kernel*, since it was MARTY [1] who introduced them in a special case.

Most of the theorems which follow here have their obvious analogues for systems with a matrixkernel $\{K_{ij}(x, y)\}$ of finite double-norm, which is fully symmetrisable relative to a matrixkernel $\{H_{ij}(x, y)\}$ of finite double-norm and of positive type.

§ 2. Marty Kernel

Considering the equation $Kf - \lambda f = g$ with Marty kernel, introduced in § 1, the results obtained in Ch. 12 (in particular §§ 3, 4, 6, 9) may be applied. Every non-real number λ is in the resolvent set of K, and every real $\lambda \neq 0$ is either a characteristic value or it belongs to the resolvent set of K. Every characteristic value $\neq 0$ has finite multiplicity (algebraic and geometric multiplicity are the same here by Ch. 12, § 2, 10°). The total number of characteristic values is finite or enumerable, and in the latter case the characteristic values tend to zero. We shall assume that $\lambda_1, \lambda_2, \ldots$ is the sequence of all characteristic values $\neq 0$ of K, each of them repeated according to its multiplicity and arranged such that $|\lambda_1| \geqslant |\lambda_2| \geqslant \ldots$, and that $\psi_1(x)$, $\psi_2(x)$, ... is a corresponding H-orthonormal sequence of characteristic functions. Hence

$$\int_{\Delta\times\Delta} H(x, y)\overline{\psi_i(x)}\psi_j(y)d(\mu \times \mu) = \begin{cases} 1 \text{ for } i = j, \\ 0 \text{ for } i \neq j. \end{cases}$$

Writing $\int_\Delta H(x, y)\psi_j(y)d\mu = \chi_j(x)$ $(j = 1, 2, \ldots)$, we have therefore

$$\int_\Delta \psi_i(x)\overline{\chi_j(x)}d\mu = \begin{cases} 1 \text{ for } i = j, \\ 0 \text{ for } i \neq j. \end{cases}$$

Theorem 1. *In order that, for $f(x) \in L_2$, the relation $Sf = 0$, or*

$$\int_{\Delta\times\Delta} H(x, z)K(z, y)f(y)\, d(\mu \times \mu) = 0,$$

should hold for almost every $x \in \Delta$, it is necessary and sufficient that $\int_\Delta f(x)\overline{\chi_k(x)}d\mu = 0$ for $k = 1, 2, \ldots$.

Proof. $HKf = 0$ if and only if $(f, \chi_k) = (Hf, \psi_k) = 0$ for $k = 1, 2, \ldots$ by Ch. 12, § 4, Th. 1.

Theorem 2. *Assume that $\lambda_1^+ \geqslant \lambda_2^+ \geqslant \ldots$ is the subsequence of all positive characteristic values, and that $\psi_1^+(x), \psi_2^+(x), \ldots$ is a corresponding H-orthonormal sequence of characteristic functions. Write $\chi_k^+ = H\psi_k^+$. Then*

$$\lambda_n^+ = \max \int_{\Delta\times\Delta} S(x, y)\overline{f(x)}f(y)\, d(\mu \times \mu) \,/\, \int_{\Delta\times\Delta} H(x, y)\overline{f(x)}f(y)\, d(\mu \times \mu)$$

for all $f(x) \in L_2$, satisfying $\int_{\Delta\times\Delta} H(x, y)\overline{f(x)}f(y)d(\mu \times \mu) \neq 0$ and $\int_\Delta f\overline{\chi_1^+}d\mu = \ldots = \int_\Delta f\overline{\chi_{n-1}^+}d\mu = 0$. For $f(x) = \psi_n^+(x)$ the maximum is attained. A similar statement holds for the negative characteristic values.

Proof. Follows from Ch. 12, § 4, Th. 3.

Theorem 3. *Let $p_1(x), \ldots, p_{n-1}(x)$ be arbitrary functions belonging to L_2, and write*

$$\mu_n = \text{upper bound} \int_{\Delta\times\Delta} S(x, y)\overline{f(x)}f(y)\, d(\mu \times \mu) / \int_{\Delta\times\Delta} H(x,y)\overline{f(x)}f(y)d(\mu\times\mu)$$

for all $f(x) \in L_2$, satisfying $\int_{\Delta\times\Delta} H(x, y)\overline{f(x)}f(y)\, d(\mu \times \mu) \neq 0$ and

$$\int_{\Delta\times\Delta} H(x, y)\overline{p_1(x)}f(y)d(\mu \times \mu) = \ldots = \int_{\Delta\times\Delta} H(x, y)\overline{p_{n-1}(x)}f(y)\, d(\mu \times \mu) = 0.$$

Then μ_n depends on $p_1(x), \ldots, p_{n-1}(x)$. Letting now these functions run through the whole space L_2, we have

$$\lambda_n^+ = \min \mu_n.$$

A similar statement holds for the negative characteristic values.

Proof. Follows from Ch. 12, § 4, Th. 4.

Theorem 4 *(Expansion theorem). If $f(x) \in L_2$, we write*

$$r_k(x) = \int_\Delta K(x, y)f(y)d\mu - \Sigma_{i=1}^k \lambda_i(f, \chi_i)\psi_i(x) \quad (k = 1, 2, \ldots).$$

Then

$$lim_{k\to\infty} \int_{\Delta\times\Delta} H(x, y)\overline{r_k(x)}r_k(y)\, d(\mu \times \mu) = 0.$$

Furthermore

$$\int_{\Delta\times\Delta} S(x, y)\overline{g(x)}f(y)\, d(\mu \times \mu) = \Sigma\, \lambda_i\, (f, \chi_i)\overline{(g, \chi_i)}$$

for any pair $f(x)$, $g(x) \in L_2$.

Proof. Follows from Ch. 12, § 4, Th. 2.

Remark. The example in Ch. 12, § 13 shows that the series $\Sigma\, \lambda_i(f, \chi_i)\psi_i(x)$ does not necessarily converge in mean on Δ, and that the same holds for $\Sigma_i\, \lambda_i^p(f, \chi_i)\psi_i(x)$ $(p = 2, 3, \ldots)$. The above expansion theorem is therefore, in a certain sense, the best obtainable result.

Theorem 5. *If $\lambda \neq 0$ is no characteristic value of K, the equation $Kf - \lambda f = g$ has a uniquely determined solution $f(x) \in L_2$ for every $g(x) \in L_2$. If $\lambda \neq 0$ is a characteristic value of K, the equation $Kf - \lambda f = g$ has a solution $f(x) \in L_2$ for those and only those $g(x) \in L_2$ which are H-orthogonal to all characteristic functions of K belonging to the characteristic value λ. This solution is determined except for a linear combination of these characteristic functions.*

More precisely, if $\int_\Delta K(x, y)f(y)d\mu - \lambda f(x) = g(x)$, and we write

$$s_k(x) = f(x) + \frac{g(x)}{\lambda} + {}'\Sigma_{i=1}^k \frac{\lambda_i}{\lambda(\lambda - \lambda_i)}\, \alpha_i\psi_i(x) \quad (k = 1, 2, \ldots),$$

where $\alpha_i = \int_\Delta g\bar{\chi}_i\, d\mu$ for $\lambda_i \neq \lambda$, and where the dash in front of the Σ-symbol means that for those values of i for which $\lambda_i = \lambda$ the coefficient of $\psi_i(x)$ has the value $-\int_\Delta f\bar{\chi}_i\, d\mu$, then

$$lim_{k\to\infty} \int_{\Delta\times\Delta} H(x, y)\overline{s_k(x)}s_k(y)\, d(\mu \times \mu) = 0.$$

For every set of arbitrarily prescribed values of the coefficients of those $\psi_i(x)$ for which $\lambda_i = \lambda$ there exists a solution $f(x)$.

Proof. Follows from Ch. 12, § 6, Th. 1 and Th. 3.

Theorem 6 (*Expansion theorem for the kernel*). *Writing*

$$R_k(x, y) = K(x, y) - \Sigma_{i=1}^{k} \lambda_i \psi_i(x)\overline{\chi_i(y)} \quad (k = 0, 1, 2, \ldots),$$

we have

$$lim_{k\to\infty} \int_{\Delta\times\Delta\times\Delta} H(x, y)\, \overline{R_k(x, z)} R_k(y, z)\, d(\mu \times \mu \times \mu) = 0.$$

Proof. The present theorem is the analogue of the expansion theorem for a self-adjoint kernel of finite double-norm (cf. Ch. 14, § 4, Th. 1), and the proof, although more complicated, is analogous as well. We consider the factorspace Z of $L_2(\Delta)$ relative to the transformation H, and also the closure $\bar{Z}$ of Z (cf. Ch. 12, § 10). The transformation K in L_2 corresponds with the compact self-adjoint transformation $[K]$ in $\bar{Z}$, having the characteristic values $\lambda_1, \lambda_2, \ldots$ with the corresponding orthonormal sequence $[\psi_1], [\psi_2], \ldots$ of characteristic elements. Furthermore, if $[g] \in \bar{Z}$ satisfies $([g], [\psi_i]) = 0$ $(i = 1, 2, \ldots)$, then $[K][g] = [0]$ (cf. Ch. 12, § 10, Th. 2,5° and Th. 3).

We recall that $K^*\chi_i = \lambda_i\chi_i$, hence

$$(1) \qquad \int_\Delta \overline{K(x, y)}\chi_i(x)\, d\mu = \lambda_i\chi_i(y) \quad (i = 1, 2, \ldots)$$

for almost every $y \in \Delta$.

Consider now $K(x, z) = K_z(x)$ as a function $f(x)$ of x. Then $f(x) \in L_2(\Delta)$ for almost every $z \in \Delta$. With $f(x) \in L_2$ corresponds the element $[f]$ of the space Z, and we have, by (1),

$$([f], [\psi_i]) = (Hf, \psi_i) = (f, H\psi_i) = (f, \chi_i) =$$
$$\int_\Delta K(x, z)\overline{\chi_i(x)}d\mu = \lambda_i\overline{\chi_i(z)}$$

for almost every $z \in \Delta$.

Considering next an element $[g] \in \bar{Z}$, orthogonal to all $[\psi_i]$, there exists a sequence of elements $[g_n] \in Z$ such that $\lim [g_n] = [g]$. Since $[K][g] = [0]$, we have $\lim [Kg_n] = \lim [K][g_n] = [0]$, or $0 = \lim \| [Kg_n] \| = \lim \| H^{1/2}Kg_n \|$, so that certainly $\lim \| Sg_n \| = \lim \| HKg_n \| = 0$. Writing $Sg_n = \int_\Delta S(z, x)g_n(x)d\mu = p_n(z)$, the relation $\lim \| Sg_n \| = 0$ is equivalent to $\lim \int_\Delta | p_n(z) |^2\, d\mu = 0$; the sequence of functions $p_n(z)$ converges therefore in mean to zero. Then there exists a subsequence $p_k(z)$ $(k = n_1, n_2, \ldots)$, converging pointwise to zero for almost every $z \in \Delta$. Consequently, since

$$([f], [g]) = \lim ([f], [g_n]) = \lim (Hf, g_n) =$$
$$\lim \int_{\Delta\times\Delta} H(x, y)K(y, z)\overline{g_n(x)}\, d(\mu \times \mu) = \lim \int_\Delta S(x, z)\overline{g_n(x)}d\mu$$
$$= \lim \int_\Delta \overline{S(z, x)g_n(x)}\, d\mu = \lim \overline{p_n(z)}$$

for almost every $z \in \Delta$, and therefore certainly

$$([f], [g]) = \lim \overline{p_k(z)} \quad (k = n_1, n_2, \ldots)$$

for these values of z, we have $([f], [g]) = 0$ for almost every $z \in \Delta$.

From the relations

$$([f], [\psi_i]) = \lambda_i \overline{\chi_i(z)} \quad (i = 1, 2, \ldots),$$

$$([f], [g]) = 0 \text{ for any } [g] \in \bar{Z} \text{ orthogonal to all } [\psi_i],$$

all of them holding for almost every $z \in \Delta$, we infer now that $[f] = \Sigma \lambda_i \overline{\chi_i(z)} [\psi_i]$ for almost every $z \in \Delta$, hence

$$\| [f] - \Sigma_{i=1}^k \lambda_i \overline{\chi_i(z)} [\psi_i] \|^2 = \Sigma_{k+1} \lambda_i^2 \mid \chi_i(z) \mid^2,$$

or

$$\int_{\Delta \times \Delta} H(x, y) \overline{R_k(x, z)} R_k(y, z) \, d(\mu \times \mu) = \Sigma_{k+1} \lambda_i^2 \mid \chi_i(z) \mid^2 \tag{2}$$

for almost every $z \in \Delta$. Taking $k = 0$, we find

$$(3) \quad \begin{cases} \Sigma_{i=1} \lambda_i^2 \mid \chi_i(z) \mid^2 = \int_{\Delta \times \Delta} H(x, y) \overline{K(x, z)} K(y, z) \, d(\mu \times \mu) = \\ \qquad \int_{\Delta \times \Delta} \overline{H(y, x) K(x, z)} K(y, z) \, d(\mu \times \mu) = \\ \qquad \int_\Delta \overline{S(y, z)} K(y, z) d\mu = \int_\Delta S(z, y) K(y, z) d\mu \leqslant \\ \qquad (\int_\Delta \mid S(z, y) \mid^2 d\mu)^{1/2} (\int_\Delta \mid K(y, z) \mid^2 d\mu)^{1/2} \end{cases}$$

for almost every $z \in \Delta$, so that

$$\Sigma_{i=1} \lambda_i^2 \int_\Delta \mid \chi_i(z) \mid^2 d\mu = \int_\Delta \Sigma_{i=1} \lambda_i^2 \mid \chi_i(z) \mid^2 d\mu < \infty.$$

This shows, upon integrating (2) over z, that

$$\int_{\Delta \times \Delta \times \Delta} H(x, y) \overline{R_k(x, z)} R_k(y, z) \, d(\mu \times \mu \times \mu) = \Sigma_{k+1} \lambda_i^2 \int_\Delta \mid \chi_i(z) \mid^2 d\mu.$$

Hence, upon making $k \to \infty$, the desired result follows.

Corollary. *The kernel* $L(x, y)$ *of* $L = HK^2 = SK$ *satisfies* $L(z, z) = \Sigma \lambda_i^2 \mid \chi_i(z) \mid^2$ *for almost every* $z \in \Delta$, *so that its trace* $\tau(L) = \int_\Delta L(z, z) d\mu$ *satisfies* $\tau(L) = \Sigma \lambda_i^2 \int_\Delta \mid \chi_i(z) \mid^2 d\mu$.

Proof. Follows from (3).

Remark. The series $\Sigma \lambda_i \psi_i(x) \overline{\chi_i(y)}$ does not necessarily converge in mean on $\Delta \times \Delta$, and the same holds even if λ_i is replaced by λ_i^p ($p = 2, 3, \ldots$). Indeed, it is easily seen that the convergence in mean on $\Delta \times \Delta$ of $\Sigma_i \lambda_i^p \psi_i(x) \overline{\chi_i(y)}$ implies the convergence in mean on Δ of $\Sigma_i \lambda_i^p (f, \chi_i) \psi_i(x)$

for every $f(x) \in L_2$. Hence, since the latter series does not necessarily converge (cf. Th. 4, Remark), the same is true for $\Sigma_i \lambda_i^p \psi_i(x)\overline{\chi_i(y)}$.

§ 3. The Iterated Kernels

The compact linear transformations K^p ($p = 2, 3, \ldots$), corresponding with the iterated kernels $K_p(x, y)$ of our kernel $K(x, y)$, are also symmetrisable relative to H (cf. Ch. 12, § 2, 4°).

Theorem 1. *If p is one of the integers 2, 3, ..., then $K_p(x, y)$ is a Marty kernel with $\lambda_1^p, \lambda_2^p, \ldots$ as the sequence of its characteristic values $\neq 0$ and $\psi_1(x), \psi_2(x), \ldots$ as a corresponding sequence of characteristic functions.*

Proof. Follows from Ch. 11, § 6, Th. 3. An alternative proof is found by considering the self-adjoint transformations $[K]$ and $[K]^p = [K^p]$ in the factorspace Z, and using the results of Ch. 14, § 5.

§ 4. Expansions for $H(x, y)$

In the present paragraph we assume that the kernel $H(x, y)$ of positive type, considered in the preceding paragraphs, has the additional property that the positive transformation $H^{1/2}$ is of finite double-norm, so that $H^{1/2}$ is an integral transformation whose kernel $H_{1/2}(x, y)$ satisfies $\int_{\Delta\times\Delta} | H_{1/2}(x, y) |^2 d(\mu \times \mu) < \infty$. If $\mu_1 \geqslant \mu_2 \geqslant \ldots > 0$ is the sequence of all characteristic values $\neq 0$ of H, this additional hypothesis is equivalent to the statement that $\Sigma \mu_i < \infty$.

Theorem 1. *If $H^{1/2}$ is of finite double-norm, then $\Sigma \chi_i(x)\overline{\chi_i(y)}$ converges in mean on $\Delta \times \Delta$ to a kernel $\tilde{H}(x, y)$ of finite double-norm. The difference $Q(x, y) = H(x, y) - \tilde{H}(x, y)$ is of positive type, and, provided $Q(x, y) \neq 0$ on a set of positive measure, we shall denote its characteristic values $\neq 0$ by $\rho_1 \geqslant \rho_2 \geqslant \ldots > 0$, and a corresponding orthonormal system of characteristic functions by $\eta_1(x), \eta_2(x), \ldots$. Then*

$$H(x, y) \sim \Sigma \chi_i(x)\overline{\chi_i(y)} + \Sigma \rho_i \eta_i(x)\overline{\eta_i(y)},$$

and

$$\int_\Delta \overline{K(y, x)}\eta_i(y) d\mu = 0 \quad (i = 1, 2, \ldots)$$

almost everywhere on Δ.

Proof. Write $\Psi_i(x) = H^{1/2}\psi_i = \int_\Delta H_{1/2}(x, y)\psi_i(y)\,d\mu$ $(i = 1, 2, \ldots)$. Then the system $\Psi_i(x)$ is orthonormal, and $\chi_i(x) = H\psi_i = H^{1/2}\Psi_i = \int_\Delta H_{1/2}(x, y)\Psi_i(y)d\mu$ for almost every $x \in \Delta$. Hence, by Bessel's inequality, $\Sigma \mid \chi_i(x) \mid^2 \leqslant \int_\Delta \mid H_{1/2}(x, y) \mid^2 d\mu$ for almost every $x \in \Delta$, so that $\Sigma \int_\Delta \mid \chi_i(x) \mid^2 d\mu = \int_\Delta \Sigma \mid \chi_i(x) \mid^2 d\mu < \infty$. Observing now that $\| \Sigma_p^q \alpha_i \Psi_i(y) \|^2 = \Sigma_p^q \mid \alpha_i \mid^2$ for arbitrary complex numbers $\alpha_1, \alpha_2, \ldots$, we have

$$\| \Sigma_p^q \alpha_i \chi_i(y) \|^2 = \| H^{1/2} \Sigma_p^q \alpha_i \Psi_i(y) \|^2 \leqslant \| H^{1/2} \|^2 \| \Sigma_p^q \alpha_i \Psi_i(y) \|^2 = \\ = \| H^{1/2} \|^2 \Sigma_p^q \mid \alpha_i \mid^2,$$

hence, for $\alpha_i = \overline{\chi_i(x)}$,

$$\int_\Delta \mid \Sigma_p^q \chi_i(x)\overline{\chi_i(y)} \mid^2 d\mu \leqslant \| H^{1/2} \|^2 \Sigma_p^q \mid \chi_i(x) \mid^2$$

for almost every $x \in \Delta$. Consequently

$$\int_{\Delta\times\Delta} \mid \Sigma_p^q \chi_i(x)\overline{\chi_i(y)} \mid^2 d(\mu \times \mu) \leqslant \| H^{1/2} \|^2 \Sigma_p^q \int_\Delta \mid \chi_i(x) \mid^2 d\mu,$$

which tends to zero as $p, q \to \infty$. This shows that $\Sigma \chi_i(x)\overline{\chi_i(y)}$ converges in mean to a function $\tilde{H}(x, y)$ satisfying $\int_{\Delta\times\Delta} \mid \tilde{H}(x, y) \mid^2 d(\mu \times \mu) < \infty$. Obviously $\tilde{H}f = \Sigma (f, \chi_i)\chi_i$ for any $f(x) \in L_2$, so that $\tilde{H}$ is identical with the transformation $\tilde{H}$ in Ch. 12, § 14, Th. 1. Writing $Q = H - \tilde{H}$, the kernel $Q(x, y) = H(x, y) - \tilde{H}(x, y)$ is of finite double-norm. By Ch. 12, § 14, Th. 1 this kernel $Q(x, y)$ is of positive type, and $\int_\Delta Q(x, z)K(z, y)d\mu$ vanishes almost everywhere on $\Delta \times \Delta$.

It is of course possible that $Q(x, y)$ itself vanishes almost everywhere on $\Delta \times \Delta$ (cf. Th. 3 and Th. 4). If however $Q(x, y) \neq 0$ on a set of positive measure, then $Q(x, y) \sim \Sigma \rho_i\eta_i(x)\overline{\eta_i(y)}$ by Ch. 14, § 4, Th. 1, so that

$$H(x, y) \sim \Sigma \chi_i(x)\overline{\chi_i(y)} + \Sigma \rho_i\eta_i(x)\overline{\eta_i(y)}.$$

Finally $K^*\eta_i = 0$ $(i = 1, 2, \ldots)$ by Ch. 12, § 14, Th. 2, in other words,

$$\int_\Delta \overline{K(y, x)}\eta_i(y)d\mu = 0 \quad (i = 1, 2, \ldots)$$

almost everywhere on Δ.

Theorem 2 (*Mercer's Theorem*, [2]). *If Δ is a bounded and closed set in Euclidean space, and $H(x, y)$ is continuous on $\Delta \times \Delta$, so that $H(x, y)$ is a Mercer kernel, then $\tilde{H}(x, y)$ and $Q(x, y)$ are Mercer kernels as well, and*

$$H(x, y) = \Sigma \chi_i(x)\overline{\chi_i(y)} + \Sigma \rho_i\eta_i(x)\overline{\eta_i(y)}$$

uniformly on $\Delta \times \Delta$.

Proof. The hypothesis that $H(x, y)$ is a Mercer kernel implies by Ch. 14, § 9, Th. 5 the essential continuity in mean of $H_{1/2}(x, y)$, that is, there exists a set $E \subset \Delta$ of measure zero such that, for x_1 and x_2 belonging to $\Delta - E$,

$$\lim_{x_2 \to x_1} \int_\Delta | H_{1/2}(x_2, y) - H_{1/2}(x_1, y) |^2 \, dy = 0.$$

More precisely, as the proof of that theorem shows, we have for $x_1, x_2 \in \Delta - E$,

$$\int_\Delta | H_{1/2}(x_2, y) - H_{1/2}(x_1, y) |^2 \, dy =$$
$$H(x_2, x_2) - H(x_2, x_1) - H(x_1, x_2) + H(x_1, x_1);$$

hence, if $\varepsilon > 0$ is given, there exists a number $\delta(\varepsilon) > 0$ such that

$$\int_\Delta | H_{1/2}(x_2, y) - H_{1/2}(x_1, y) |^2 \, dy < \varepsilon$$

as soon as $x_1, x_2 \in \Delta - E$, and the distance $\rho(x_1, x_2)$ of the points x_1 and x_2 satisfies $\rho(x_1, x_2) < \delta(\varepsilon)$. Furthermore

$$\chi_i(x_2) - \chi_i(x_1) = \int_\Delta \{H_{1/2}(x_2, y) - H_{1/2}(x_1, y)\}\Psi_i(y)dy \quad (i = 1, 2, \ldots)$$

for $x_1, x_2 \in \Delta - E'$, where E' has measure zero. Consequently, for $x_1, x_2 \in \Delta - (E + E')$, $\rho(x_1, x_2) < \delta(\varepsilon)$ and p an arbitrary positive integer, we have

$$\Sigma_{i=1}^p | \chi_i(x_2) - \chi_i(x_1) |^2 \leqslant \int_\Delta | H_{1/2}(x_2, y) - H_{1/2}(x_1, y) |^2 \, dy < \varepsilon.$$

But all $\chi_i(x) = \int_\Delta H(x, y)\psi_i(y)dy$ are continuous on the interval Δ, so that $\Sigma_1^p | \chi_i(x_2) - \chi_i(x_1) |^2$ is continuous in both variables x_1 and x_2. It follows that $\Sigma_1^p | \chi_i(x_2) - \chi_i(x_1) |^2 \leqslant \varepsilon$ for all $x_1, x_2 \in \Delta$ as soon as $\rho(x_1, x_2) < \delta(\varepsilon)$. Hence, since p is arbitrary,

$$\Sigma_i | \chi_i(x_2) - \chi_i(x_1) |^2 \leqslant \varepsilon \text{ for } \rho(x_1, x_2) < \delta(\varepsilon),$$

or $\lim_{x_2 \to x_1} \Sigma_i | \chi_i(x_2) - \chi_i(x_1) |^2 = 0$. A similar argument shows easily that $\Sigma_i | \chi_i(x) |^2 < \infty$ for all $x \in \Delta$. So, since

$$| (\Sigma_i | \chi_i(x_2) |^2)^{1/2} - (\Sigma_i | \chi_i(x_1) |^2)^{1/2} | \leqslant (\Sigma_i | \chi_i(x_2) - \chi_i(x_1) |^2)^{1/2}$$

by Minkowski's inequality, the sum of $\Sigma | \chi_i(x) |^2$ is continuous. Hence, on account of Dini's Theorem (cf. Ch. 13, § 6, Th. 8), the uniform convergence of $\Sigma | \chi_i(x) |^2$. But then, since $\Sigma | \chi_i(x)\overline{\chi_i(y)} | \leqslant (\Sigma | \chi_i(x) |^2)^{1/2} (\Sigma | \chi_i(y) |^2)^{1/2}$, the series $\Sigma \chi_i(x)\overline{\chi_i(y)}$ converges uniformly on $\Delta \times \Delta$. Its sum is the Mercer kernel $\tilde{H}(x, y)$. The difference $Q(x, y) = H(x, y) - \tilde{H}(x, y)$, which is of positive type by the preceding theorem, is therefore also a Mercer kernel. Hence $Q(x, y) = \Sigma \rho_i\eta_i(x)\overline{\eta_i(y)}$ uniformly on $\Delta \times \Delta$, so that finally we find

$$H(x, y) = \Sigma \chi_i(x)\overline{\chi_i(y)} + \Sigma \rho_i\eta_i(x)\overline{\eta_i(y)},$$

uniformly on $\Delta \times \Delta$.

We shall finally consider the problem under what conditions the transformation Q in $Hf = \tilde{H}f + Qf = \Sigma\,(f, \chi_i)\chi_i + \Sigma\,\rho_i(f, \eta_i)\eta_i$ is identical with the null transformation. Denote, as in Chapter 12, the null space of H (and of $H^{1/2}$) by $[L]$ and its orthogonal complement by $[M]$. Then $[M]$ is the closure of the range of H (and also the closure of the range of $H^{1/2}$) by Ch. 9, § 14, Th. 1, Corollary.

Theorem 3. *We have $Q = O$ if and only if the system $\Psi_i = H^{1/2}\psi_i$ $(i = 1, 2, \ldots)$ is complete in $[M]$.*

Proof. We know by Ch. 12, § 14, Th. 1 that $Q = H^{1/2}(I - P_1)H^{1/2}$, where P_1 is the orthogonal projection on the subspace determined by the system $\Psi_i = H^{1/2}\psi_i$. Hence, for every element g, $P_1 g \in [M]$, which implies $(I - P_1)H^{1/2}f = H^{1/2}f - P_1 H^{1/2}f \in [M]$ for every element f. Observing now that $Q = H^{1/2}(I - P_1)H^{1/2} = O$ if and only if $(I - P_1)H^{1/2}f \in [L]$ for every element f, we may conclude therefore that $Q = O$ is equivalent to the statement that $(I - P_1)H^{1/2}f = 0$ for every element f. In other words, $Q = O$ if and only if $(I - P_1)g = 0$, or $g = P_1 g$ for all $g \in [M]$. This shows that $Q = O$ if and only if the system Ψ_i $(i = 1, 2, \ldots)$ is complete in $[M]$.

Remark. Denoting by P the orthogonal projection on $[M]$ (cf. Ch. 12, § 2) and writing $\varphi_i = P\psi_i$ $(i = 1, 2, \ldots)$, it is evidently sufficient for $Q = O$ to hold that the system φ_i should be complete in $[M]$, since in that case the system $\Psi_i = H^{1/2}\psi_i = H^{1/2}\varphi_i$ is certainly complete in $[M]$.

Theorem 4. *In the special case that $K = AH$ (cf. Ch. 12, § 12), we have $Q = O$ if and only if $H^{1/2}AH^{1/2}f = 0$ implies $f \in [L]$. It is therefore sufficient for $Q = O$ to hold that $H^{1/2}Ag = 0$ only for $g = 0$, and it is certainly sufficient that $Hg = 0$ only for $g = 0$ and $Ah = 0$ only for $h = 0$.*

Proof. Since in the present case the system Ψ_i is an orthonormal system of characteristic elements of $H^{1/2}AH^{1/2}$, corresponding with the sequence λ_i $(i = 1, 2, \ldots)$ of all characteristic values $\neq 0$, we see that the null space of $H^{1/2}AH^{1/2}$ is the orthogonal complement of the subspace determined by the elements Ψ_i. It follows that this subspace is identical with $[M]$ if and only if the null space of $H^{1/2}AH^{1/2}$ is identical with $[L]$.

§ 5. Expansions for the Kernels $S_p(x, y)$ of $S_p = HK^p$ $(p = 1, 2, \ldots)$

We assume no longer, as in the preceding paragraph, that $H^{1/2}$ is of finite double-norm.

Theorem 1. *If* $S_p = HK^p$ $(p = 1, 2, \ldots)$ *has the kernel* $S_p(x, y)$, *then*

$$S_p(x, y) \sim \Sigma_i \lambda_i^p \chi_i(x)\overline{\chi_i(y)} \quad (p = 1, 2, \ldots).$$

Proof. Take first $p = 1$. Then, since $S_1 = S = HK$ is self-adjoint, we have $S = K^*H$, hence $\lambda_i \chi_i = \lambda_i H\psi_i = HK\psi_i = K^*H\psi_i = K^*H^{1/2}\Psi_i$. Writing $D = K^*H^{1/2}$, the transformation D is of finite double-norm, so that $\lambda_i \chi_i(x) = \int_\Delta D(x, y)\Psi_i(y)\, d\mu$ $(i = 1, 2, \ldots)$ for almost every $x \in \Delta$. It follows that $\Sigma \mid \lambda_i \chi_i(x) \mid^2 \leqslant \int_\Delta \mid D(x, y) \mid^2 d\mu$ for almost every $x \in \Delta$, hence $\Sigma \int_\Delta \mid \lambda_i \chi_i(x) \mid^2 d\mu < \infty$. The convergence in mean on $\Delta \times \Delta$ of $\Sigma\, \lambda_i \chi_i(x)\overline{\chi_i(y)}$ is now proved by a similar argument as that which was used in proving the convergence in mean of $\Sigma\, \chi_i(x)\overline{\chi_i(y)}$ in Theorem 1 of the preceding paragraph. Denoting the sumfunction of $\Sigma\, \lambda_i \chi_i(x)\overline{\chi_i(y)}$ by $\tilde{S}(x, y)$, we have therefore $\tilde{S}f = \Sigma\, \lambda_i(f, \chi_i)\chi_i$. But, $Hf = \Sigma\, (f, \chi_i)\chi_i + \Sigma\, \rho_i(f, \eta_i)\eta_i$ implying $Sf = K^*Hf = \Sigma\, (f, \chi_i)K^*\chi_i + \Sigma\, \rho_i(f, \eta_i)K^*\eta_i = \Sigma\, \lambda_i(f, \chi_i)\chi_i$ on account of $K^*\chi_i = \lambda_i \chi_i$ and $K^*\eta_i = 0$, we see that $\tilde{S} = S$, hence

$$S(x, y) \sim \Sigma\, \lambda_i \chi_i(x)\overline{\chi_i(y)}.$$

The proof for $p = 2, 3, \ldots$ is similar.

§ 6. Cases in which $K(x, y)$ has an Expansion

Under certain conditions for the kernels $H(x, y)$ and $K(x, y)$ there may exist a value of the positive integer p for which the series $\Sigma_i \lambda_i^p \psi_i(x)\overline{\chi_i(y)}$ converges in mean to a function $L_p(x, y)$ of finite double-norm. It is reasonable to make the conjecture that in this case there exists a connection between $L_p(x, y)$ and the iterated kernel $K_p(x, y)$, and in the now following theorem we shall prove that this conjecture is right.

Theorem 1. *If* $L_p(x, y) \sim \Sigma_i \lambda_i^p \psi_i(x)\overline{\chi_i(y)}$ *for a positive integer* p, *and we write* $K_p(x, y) - L_p(x, y) = M_p(x, y)$, *then*

$$\int_\Delta H(x, z)M_p(z, y)\, d\mu = 0$$

almost everywhere on $\Delta \times \Delta$.

Proof. Denoting the transformations which correspond with $L_p(x, y)$ and $M_p(x, y)$ by L_p and M_p respectively, our hypotheses imply $L_p f = \Sigma_i \lambda_i^p (f, \chi_i)\psi_i$ and $M_p = K^p - L_p$. Hence, using Theorem 1 of the preceding paragraph, we find $HL_p f = \Sigma_i \lambda_i^p (f, \chi_i)\chi_i = HK^p f$, or $HM_p f = H(K^p - L_p)f = 0$ for every $f(x) \in L_2$.

Theorem 2. *If, besides the hypotheses of the preceding theorem, $K(x, y)$ is strongly symmetrisable relative to $H(x, y)$ (hence $Kf = 0$ if $Hf = 0$), then*

$$\left.\begin{aligned} K_q(x, y) &\sim \Sigma_i \lambda_i^q \psi_i(x)\overline{\chi_i(y)} \\ \tau_q = \tau(K^q) &= \textstyle\int_\Delta K_q(x, x)d\mu = \Sigma_i \lambda_i^q \end{aligned}\right\} (q = p+1,\ p+2, \ldots).$$

Proof. By the preceding theorem we have $K_p(x, y) - M_p(x, y) \sim \Sigma_i \lambda_i^p \psi_i(x)\overline{\chi_i(y)}$, where $HM_p = O$. Hence also $KM_p = O$, so that $\int_\Delta K(x, z)M_p(z, y)d\mu = 0$ almost everywhere on $\Delta \times \Delta$. It follows that

$$K_{p+1}(x, y) \sim \Sigma_i \lambda_i^p \overline{\chi_i(y)} \int_\Delta K(x, z)\psi_i(z)d\mu = \Sigma_i \lambda_i^{p+1}\psi_i(x)\overline{\chi_i(y)}.$$

Furthermore, observing that $KM_p = O$ implies $\tau(KM_p) = 0$, we find

$$\begin{aligned} \tau_{p+1} &= \textstyle\int_{\Delta\times\Delta} K(x, z)L_p(z, x)\, d(\mu \times \mu) + \int_{\Delta\times\Delta} K(x, z)M_p(z, x)\, d(\mu \times \mu) \\ &= \Sigma_i \lambda_i^{p+1} \textstyle\int_\Delta \psi_i(x)\overline{\chi_i(x)}\, d\mu = \Sigma_i \lambda_i^{p+1}. \end{aligned}$$

The corresponding relations for $q = p + 2, p + 3, \ldots$ follow now easily by induction.

Remark. The present proof of $\tau_q = \Sigma_i \lambda_i^q$ is independent of the much more general statement in Ch. 11, § 7, Th. 3 that we have $\tau_q = \Sigma_i \lambda_i^q$ $(q = 3, 4, \ldots)$ for any linear transformation K of finite double-norm.

Theorem 3. *In the special case that $K = AH$ we have*

$$K_p(x, y) \sim \Sigma_i \lambda_i^p \psi_i(x)\overline{\chi_i(y)} \quad (p = 2, 3, \ldots),$$

$$\tau_q = \textstyle\int_\Delta K_q(x, x)d\mu = \Sigma_i \lambda_i^q \quad (q = 3, 4, \ldots).$$

Proof. By Theorem 1 of the preceding paragraph $S(x, y) \sim \Sigma\, \lambda_i \chi_i(x)\overline{\chi_i(y)}$, where $S(x, y)$ is the kernel of $S = HK$. Since $\lambda_i\psi_i = K\psi_i = AH\psi_i = A\chi_i$, we have $\| \Sigma_p^q \lambda_i\alpha_i\psi_i \|^2 = \| A\, \Sigma_p^q \alpha_i\chi_i \|^2 \leqslant \| A \|^2 . \| \Sigma_p^q \alpha_i\chi_i \|^2$; hence, for $\alpha_i = \lambda_i\overline{\chi_i(y)}$,

$$\textstyle\int_\Delta | \Sigma_p^q \lambda_i^2\psi_i(x)\overline{\chi_i(y)} |^2 d\mu \leqslant \| A \|^2 \int_\Delta | \Sigma_p^q \lambda_i\chi_i(x)\overline{\chi_i(y)} |^2 d\mu.$$

Integration over y shows that $\Sigma\, \lambda_i^2 \psi_i(x)\overline{\chi_i(y)}$ converges in mean. From $HKf = Sf = \Sigma\, \lambda_i(f, \chi_i)\chi_i$ follows $K^2f = ASf = \Sigma\, \lambda_i(f, \chi_i)A\chi_i = \Sigma\, \lambda_i(f, \chi_i)\, K\psi_i = \Sigma\, \lambda_i^2 (f, \chi_i)\psi_i$. The sum of $\Sigma\, \lambda_i^2\psi_i(x)\overline{\chi_i(y)}$ is therefore $K_2(x, y)$. The remaining statements are now easy consequences.

Theorem 4. *If $K = AH$, and $H^{1/2}$ is of finite double-norm, then*

$$K(x, y) \sim \Sigma\, \lambda_i \psi_i(x)\overline{\chi_i(y)} + \Sigma\, \rho_i \xi_i(x)\overline{\eta_i(y)},$$

where the positive numbers ρ_i and the functions $\eta_i(x)$ are the same as in § 4, Th. 1, and where the functions $\xi_i(x) = A\eta_i(x)$ $(i = 1, 2, \ldots)$ satisfy $H\xi_i = 0$. Hence, if $H(x, y)$ is a general kernel (that is, if $Hf = 0$ implies $f = 0$), all $\xi_i(x)$ vanish almost everywhere. Furthermore, whether $H(x, y)$ is general or not,

$$\tau_q = \tau(K^q) = \textstyle\int_\Delta K_q(x, x)\, d\mu = \Sigma_i\, \lambda_i^q \quad (q = 2, 3, \ldots).$$

Proof. By § 4, Th. 1 we have $H(x, y) \sim \Sigma\, \chi_i(x)\overline{\chi_i(y)} + \Sigma\, \rho_i\eta_i(x)\overline{\eta_i(y)}$ with $K^*\eta_i = 0$ $(i = 1, 2, \ldots)$. Since $\| \Sigma_p^q \lambda_i\alpha_i\psi_i \|^2 = \| A\, \Sigma_p^q \alpha_i\chi_i \|^2 \leqslant \| A \|^2 . \| \Sigma_p^q \alpha_i\chi_i \|^2$, we find for $\alpha_i = \overline{\chi_i(y)}$ that

$$\textstyle\int_\Delta | \Sigma_p^q \lambda_i\psi_i(x)\overline{\chi_i(y)} |^2\, d\mu \leqslant \| A \|^2 \int_\Delta | \Sigma_p^q \chi_i(x)\overline{\chi_i(y)} |^2\, d\mu.$$

Integration over y shows then that $\Sigma\, \lambda_i\psi_i(x)\overline{\chi_i(y)}$ converges in mean. In the same way, since $\| \Sigma_p^q \beta_i\xi_i \|^2 \leqslant \| A \|^2 . \| \Sigma_p^q \beta_i\eta_i \|^2$, the choice $\beta_i = \rho_i\overline{\eta_i(y)}$ leads to the result that $\Sigma\, \rho_i\xi_i(x)\overline{\eta_i(y)}$ converges in mean. Hence, denoting the sum of $\Sigma\, \lambda_i\psi_i(x)\overline{\chi_i(y)} + \Sigma\, \rho_i\xi_i(x)\overline{\eta_i(y)}$ by $\tilde{K}(x, y)$, we have $\tilde{K}f = \Sigma\, \lambda_i(f, \chi_i)\psi_i + \Sigma\, \rho_i(f, \eta_i)\xi_i$. On the other hand $Hf = \Sigma\, (f, \chi_i)\chi_i + \Sigma\, \rho_i(f, \eta_i)\eta_i$ implies $Kf = AHf = \Sigma\, \lambda_i(f, \chi_i)\psi_i + \Sigma\, \rho_i(f, \eta_i)\xi_i$; hence $Kf = \tilde{K}f$ for all $f(x) \in L_2$. This shows that $\tilde{K}(x, y) = K(x, y)$, which is the desired result.

The relations $H\xi_i = 0$ $(i = 1, 2, \ldots)$ follow from

$$\rho_i H\xi_i = HA(\rho_i\eta_i) = HAQ\eta_i = H^{1/2}H^{1/2}AH^{1/2}(I - P_1)H^{1/2}\eta_i =$$

$$H^{1/2}H^{1/2}A^*H^{1/2}(I - P_1)H^{1/2}\eta_i = HA^*Q\eta_i = \rho_i K^*\eta_i = 0.$$

Finally, on account of Theorem 2 with $p = 1$, we find $\tau_q = \Sigma_i\, \lambda_i^q$ $(q = 2, 3, \ldots)$.

Theorem 5. *If $K = AH$, and A is of finite double-norm, then*

$$K(x, y) \sim \Sigma\, \lambda_i\psi_i(x)\overline{\chi_i(y)} + \Sigma\, \rho_i\xi_i(x)\overline{\eta_i(y)},$$

where the positive numbers ρ_i and the functions $\eta_i(x)$ are, as in the preceding theorem, the characteristic values and characteristic functions of the transformation Q, and where the functions $\xi_i(x) = A\eta_i(x)$ $(i = 1, 2, \ldots)$ satisfy $H\xi_i = 0$. Hence, if $H(x, y)$ is a general kernel, all $\xi_i(x)$ vanish. Further-

more, whether $H(x, y)$ *is general or not,*

$$\tau_q = \tau(K^q) = \int_\Delta K_q(x, x)\, d\mu = \Sigma_i \lambda_i^q \ (q = 2, 3, \ldots).$$

Proof. Since $Hf = \Sigma (f, \chi_i)\chi_i + \Sigma \rho_i(f, \eta_i)\eta_i$ implies $Kf = AHf = \Sigma \lambda_i(f, \chi_i)\psi_i + \Sigma \rho_i(f, \eta_i)\xi_i$, it will be sufficient to prove that both $\Sigma \lambda_i\psi_i(x)\overline{\chi_i(y)}$ and $\Sigma \rho_i\xi_i(x)\overline{\eta_i(y)}$ converge in mean. By hypothesis A is an integral transformation with a kernel $A(x, y)$ such that $| A(x, y) |^2$ is integrable over $\Delta \times \Delta$; hence, taking $f(z) = \overline{A(x, z)}$, the function $f(z)$ belongs to $L_2(\Delta)$ for almost every $x \in \Delta$. This implies

$$\lambda_i\psi_i(x) = \int_\Delta K(x, y)\psi_i(y)d\mu =$$

$$\int_\Delta A(x, z)\, [\int_\Delta H(z, y)\psi_i(y)d\mu]d\mu = (H\psi_i, f)$$

for these values of x, so that

$$\Sigma \lambda_i^2 \mid \psi_i(x) \mid^2 = \Sigma \mid (H\psi_i, f) \mid^2 = \Sigma \mid (Hf, \psi_i) \mid^2 =$$

$$\Sigma \mid (H^{1/2}f, \Psi_i) \mid^2 \leqslant \| H^{1/2}f \|^2 \leqslant \| H^{1/2} \|^2 . \| f \|^2 = \| H^{1/2} \|^2 \int_\Delta \mid A\ (x, z) \mid^2 d\mu,$$

hence

$$\Sigma \lambda_i^2 \int_\Delta \mid \psi_i(x) \mid^2 d\mu < \infty. \tag{1}$$

Furthermore, since $\| \Sigma_p^q \alpha_i\chi_i(y) \|^2 = \| H^{1/2} \Sigma_p^q \alpha_i\Psi_i(y) \|^2 \leqslant \| H^{1/2} \|^2 \Sigma_p^q \mid \alpha_i \mid^2$, the choice $\alpha_i = \lambda_i\overline{\psi_i(x)}$ shows that

$$\int_{\Delta\times\Delta} \mid \Sigma_p^q \lambda_i\psi_i(x)\overline{\chi_i(y)} \mid^2 d(\mu \times \mu) \leqslant \| H^{1/2} \|^2 \Sigma_p^q \lambda_i^2 \int_\Delta \mid \psi_i(x) \mid^2 d\mu.$$

By (1) this last expression tends to zero as $p, q \to \infty$, which proves the convergence in mean of $\Sigma \lambda_i\psi_i(x)\overline{\chi_i(y)}$.

For the same function $f(z) = \overline{A(x, z)}$ we have $\xi_i(x) = \int_\Delta A(x, z)\eta_i(z)d\mu = (\eta_i, f)$; hence, the system η_i being orthonormal,

$$\Sigma \mid \xi_i(x) \mid^2 = \Sigma \mid (\eta_i, f) \mid^2 \leqslant \| f \|^2 = \int_\Delta \mid A(x, z) \mid^2 d\mu$$

for almost every $x \in \Delta$. It follows that $\Sigma \int_\Delta \mid \xi_i(x) \mid^2 d\mu < \infty$, so that certainly $\Sigma \rho_i^2 \int_\Delta \mid \xi_i(x) \mid^2 d\mu < \infty$. Furthermore, since $\| \Sigma_p^q \alpha_i\eta_i(y) \|^2 = \Sigma_p^q \mid \alpha_i \mid^2$, the choice $\alpha_i = \rho_i\overline{\xi_i(x)}$ shows that

$$\int_{\Delta\times\Delta} \mid \Sigma_p^q \rho_i\xi_i(x)\overline{\eta_i(y)} \mid^2 d(\mu \times \mu) = \Sigma_p^q \rho_i^2 \int_\Delta \mid \xi_i(x) \mid^2 d\mu.$$

The expression on the right tending to zero as $p, q \to \infty$, we may conclude that $\Sigma \rho_i\xi_i(x)\overline{\eta_i(y)}$ converges in mean.

The relations $H\xi_i = 0$ $(i = 1, 2, \ldots)$ and $\tau_q = \Sigma_i \lambda_i^q$ $(q = 2, 3, \ldots)$ are proved as in the preceding theorem.

REFERENCES

[1] J. Marty, Valeurs singulières d'une équation de Fredholm, C.R. Acad. sc. Paris 150 (1910), 1499–1502.

[2] J. Mercer, Symmetrisable functions and their expansion in terms of biorthogonal functions, Proc. Royal Soc. (A) 97 (1920), 401–413.

CHAPTER 17

INTEGRAL EQUATION WITH GARBE KERNEL OR PELL KERNEL

§ 1. Introduction

Supposing, as in the preceding chapters, that Δ is a μ-measurable set of finite or infinite measure, where μ is separable, we shall consider in this final chapter the linear integral equation

$$\int_\Delta K(x, y)f(y)\, d\mu - \lambda f(x) = g(x)$$

in the Lebesgue space $L_2(\Delta, \mu)$, where $K(x, y)$ is either a Garbe kernel $A(x)H(x, y)$ [1] or a Pell kernel $\int_\Delta A(x, z)H(z, y)d\mu$ [2]. We shall assume that the following conditions are satisfied:

1°. $H(x, y)$ is of finite double-norm (relative to $L_2(\Delta, \mu)$) and of positive type.

2°. $A(x)$ is measurable and bounded (in the case of a Garbe kernel), or $A(x, y)$ is of finite double-norm (in the case of a Pell kernel).

3°. The kernel $S(x, y) = \int_\Delta H(x, z)K(z, y)d\mu$ is Hermitian.

Hence $K = AH$ is strongly symmetrisable relative to the positive transformation H, so that $K(x, y)$ is certainly a Marty kernel. We observe that the condition 3° is automatically satisfied whenever A is self-adjoint, that is, whenever $A(x)$ is real in the Garbe case, or whenever $A(x, y)$ is Hermitian in the Pell case.

Most of the theorems for Garbe kernels have obvious analogues for systems with a matrixkernel $\{K_{ij}(x, y)\} = \{A_{ij}(x)\}.\{H_{ij}(x, y)\}$, where $\{H_{ij}(x, y)\}$ is of finite double-norm and of positive type, and where the bounded measurable functions $A_{ij}(x)$ are such that $\{S_{ij}(x, y)\} = \{\Sigma_{k=1}^n \int_\Delta H_{ik}(x, z)K_{kj}(z, y)d\mu\}$ is Hermitian. Similarly, most of the theorems for Pell kernels have analogues for systems with a matrixkernel $\{K_{ij}(x, y)\} = \{\Sigma_{k=1}^n \int_\Delta A_{ik}(x, z)H_{kj}(z, y)\, d\mu\}$, where $\{H_{ij}(x, y)\}$ is as above, $\{A_{ij}(x, y)\}$ is of finite double-norm and $\{S_{ij}(x, y)\}$, defined as above, is again Hermitian.

§ 2. Garbe Kernel

For the equation $Kf - \lambda f = g$ with Garbe kernel $K(x, y)$ the results obtained in the preceding chapter hold. We shall not repeat them all, and merely pay attention to some points.

Theorem 1 *(Expansion theorem). If $f(x) \in L_2$, then*

$$\int_\Delta K(x, y)f(y)d\mu \sim \Sigma \lambda_k(f, \chi_k)\psi_k(x) + p(x),$$

$$\int_\Delta K_p(x, y)f(y)\, d\mu \sim \Sigma_k \lambda_k^p(f, \chi_k)\psi_k(x) \quad (p = 2, 3, \ldots),$$

where $Hp = \int_\Delta H(x, y)p(y)d\mu = 0$ (almost everywhere).

Proof. Follows from Ch. 12, § 12, Th. 5.

Theorem 2 *(Expansion theorem for the kernels). We have*

$$K_p(x, y) \sim \Sigma_k \lambda_k^p \psi_k(x)\overline{\chi_k(y)} \quad (p = 2, 3, \ldots),$$

$$\tau_q = \int_\Delta K_q(x, x)\, d\mu = \Sigma_i \lambda_i^q \quad (q = 3, 4, \ldots).$$

If the positive transformation $H^{1/2}$ is of finite double-norm (that is, if $\Sigma \mu_i$ converges, where μ_i $(i = 1, 2, \ldots)$ is the sequence of characteristic values of $H(x, y)$), we have moreover

$$K(x, y) \sim \Sigma \lambda_k \psi_k(x)\overline{\chi_k(y)} + \Sigma \rho_k \xi_k(x)\overline{\eta_k(y)},$$

$$\tau_2 = \int_\Delta K_2(x, x)\, d\mu = \Sigma \lambda_i^2,$$

where the positive numbers ρ_k and the functions $\eta_k(x)$ are the characteristic values $\neq 0$ and the corresponding orthonormal characteristic functions of a certain kernel $Q(x, y)$ of positive type (cf. Ch. 12, § 14, Th. 1), and where the functions $\xi_k(x) = A(x)\eta_k(x)$ all satisfy $H\xi_k = 0$. Hence, if $H(x, y)$ is a general kernel (that is, if $Hf = 0$ implies $f = 0$), all $\xi_k(x)$ vanish almost everywhere.

Proof. Follows from Ch. 16, § 6, Th. 3 and Th. 4.

Theorem 3. *We have*

$$\int_\Delta K_p(x, y)f(y)d\mu = \Sigma_k \lambda_k^p(f, \chi_k)\psi_k(x) \quad (p = 2, 3, \ldots)$$

(pointwise convergence) almost everywhere on Δ. If $H^{1/2}$ is of finite double-norm, then

$$\int_\Delta K(x, y)f(y)d\mu = \Sigma \lambda_k(f, \chi_k)\psi_k(x) + p(x)$$

almost everywhere on Δ, where $p(x)$ is the same function as in Theorem 1.

Proof. We give the proof of the first statement for $p = 2$. Since $\lambda_k\psi_k = K\psi_k = AH\psi_k = AH^{1/2}H^{1/2}\psi_k = AH^{1/2}\Psi_k = D\Psi_k$ (where we have written $D = AH^{1/2}$), we find $\| \lambda_k\alpha_k\psi_k \| \leqslant \| D \| . | \alpha_k |$; hence $\Sigma \| \lambda_k\alpha_k\psi_k \|^2 < \infty$ whenever $\Sigma | \alpha_k |^2 < \infty$. In particular, taking $\alpha_k = \lambda_k$, we see that $\Sigma \| \lambda_k^2\psi_k \|^2 < \infty$. Hence $\Sigma \lambda_k^4 | \psi_k(x) |^2$ converges almost everywhere on Δ. Furthermore $\Sigma | (f, \chi_k) |^2 < \infty$. But then

$$\Sigma | \lambda_k^2(f, \chi_k)\psi_k(x) | \leqslant (\Sigma | (f, \chi_k) |^2)^{1/2}(\Sigma \lambda_k^4 | \psi_k(x) |^2)^{1/2}$$

shows that $\Sigma \lambda_k^2(f, \chi_k)\psi_k(x)$ converges for almost every $x \in \Delta$.

Now suppose that $H^{1/2}$ is of finite double-norm. Then $D = AH^{1/2}$ is of finite double-norm as well. Hence $\lambda_k\psi_k(x) = D\Psi_k = \int_\Delta D(x, y)\Psi_k(y)\, d\mu$, so that $\Sigma \lambda_k^2 | \psi_k(x) |^2 \leqslant \int_\Delta | D(x, y) |^2 d\mu < \infty$ for almost every x. The convergence almost everywhere of $\Sigma \lambda_k(f, \chi_k)\psi_k(x)$ follows then immediately.

Theorem 4. *We have*

$$K_p(x, y) = \Sigma_k \lambda_k^p\psi_k(x)\overline{\chi_k(y)} \quad (p = 3, 4, \ldots)$$

(pointwise convergence) almost everywhere on $\Delta \times \Delta$. *If* $H^{1/2}$ *is of finite double-norm, then*

$$K(x, y) = \Sigma \lambda_k\psi_k(x)\overline{\chi_k(y)} + \Sigma \rho_k\xi_k(x)\overline{\eta_k(y)},$$

$$K_p(x, y) = \Sigma_k \lambda_k^p\psi_k(x)\overline{\chi_k(y)} \quad (p = 2, 3, \ldots)$$

almost everywhere on $\Delta \times \Delta$.

Proof. The series $\Sigma \lambda_k^4 | \psi_k(x) |^2$ converges by the preceding theorem almost everywhere on Δ. Furthermore, since $\| \chi_k \| = \| H^{1/2}\Psi_k \| \leqslant \| H^{1/2} \|$ and $\Sigma | \lambda_k |^p < \infty$ $(p \geqslant 2)$, the series $\Sigma_k | \lambda_k |^p . \| \chi_k \|^2$ converges, so that $\Sigma | \lambda_k |^p . | \chi_k(y) |^2$ $(p = 2, 3, \ldots)$ converges for almost every $y \in \Delta$. The inequality

$$\Sigma | \lambda_k^p\psi_k(x)\overline{\chi_k(y)} | \leqslant (\Sigma \lambda_k^4 | \psi_k(x) |^2)^{1/2} (\Sigma \lambda_k^{2p-4} | \chi_k(y) |^2)^{1/2}$$

shows then that, for $p \geqslant 3$, the series $\Sigma_k \lambda_k^p\psi_k(x)\overline{\chi_k(y)}$ converges almost everywhere on $\Delta \times \Delta$.

Now suppose that $H^{1/2}$ is of finite double-norm. Then, by the preceding theorem, $\Sigma \lambda_k^2 | \psi_k(x) |^2$ converges for almost every $x \in \Delta$. Furthermore, since $\chi_k(x) = H^{1/2}\Psi_k = \int_\Delta H_{1/2}(x, y)\Psi_k(y)\, d\mu$, we have $\Sigma | \chi_k(x) |^2 \leqslant \int_\Delta | H_{1/2}(x, y) |^2 d\mu < \infty$ for almost every $x \in \Delta$. The inequality

$$\Sigma | \lambda_k^p\psi_k(x)\overline{\chi_k(y)} | \leqslant (\Sigma \lambda_k^2 | \psi_k(x) |^2)^{1/2} (\Sigma \lambda_k^{2p-2} | \chi_k(y) |^2)^{1/2}$$

shows now that, for $p \geqslant 1$, the series $\Sigma\, \lambda_k^p \psi_k(x)\overline{\chi_k(y)}$ converges almost everywhere on $\Delta \times \Delta$. Since $\Sigma\, \rho_k \eta_k(x)\overline{\eta_k(y)}$ is the expansion of the self-adjoint transformation $Q = H^{1/2}(I - P_1)H^{1/2}$ (cf. the proof of Ch. 12, § 14, Th. 1), and since Q may be considered as the product of two transformations of finite double-norm, $\Sigma\, \rho_k \eta_k(x)\overline{\eta_k(y)}$ converges almost everywhere on $\Delta \times \Delta$ (cf. Ch. 14, § 4, Th. 4). But then, since $\xi_k(x) = A(x)\eta_k(x)$, the same is true of $\Sigma\, \rho_k \xi_k(x)\overline{\eta_k(y)}$.

§ 3. Garbe Kernel in the Case that $H(x, y)$ is a Mercer Kernel

We now assume that Δ is a bounded and closed set in Euclidean space, and that the kernel $H(x, y)$ of positive type in $K(x, y) = A(x)H(x, y)$ is continuous on $\Delta \times \Delta$; in other words, we assume that $H(x, y)$ is a Mercer kernel. Hence, by Ch. 16, § 4, Th. 2,

$$H(x, y) = \Sigma\, \chi_k(x)\overline{\chi_k(y)} + \Sigma\, \rho_k \eta_k(x)\overline{\eta_k(y)} \tag{1}$$

uniformly on $\Delta \times \Delta$.

Theorem 1. *If $H(x, y)$ is a Mercer kernel, we have*

$$K(x, y) = \Sigma\, \lambda_k \psi_k(x)\overline{\chi_k(y)} + \Sigma\, \rho_k \xi_k(x)\overline{\eta_k(y)}, \tag{2}$$

$$K_p(x, y) = \Sigma_k\, \lambda_k^p \psi_k(x)\overline{\chi_k(y)} \quad (p = 2, 3, \ldots) \tag{3}$$

uniformly on $\Delta \times \Delta$, where

$$\textstyle\int_\Delta H(x, y)\xi_k(y)\, dy = 0 \quad (k = 1, 2, \ldots)$$

for all $x \in \Delta$. Furthermore, if $f(x) \in L_2$, then

$$\textstyle\int_\Delta K(x, y)f(y)dy = \Sigma\, \lambda_k(f, \chi_k)\psi_k(x) + \Sigma\, \rho_k(f, \eta_k)\xi_k(x), \tag{4}$$

$$\textstyle\int_\Delta K_p(x, y)f(y)dy = \Sigma\, \lambda_k^p(f, \chi_k)\psi_k(x) \quad (p = 2, 3, \ldots) \tag{5}$$

uniformly on Δ.

Proof. Since $K(x, y) = A(x)H(x, y)$, and $A(x)$ is bounded, the formula (2) is an immediate consequence of (1). We know already that $H\xi_k = 0$, hence

$$\zeta_k(x) = \textstyle\int_\Delta H(x, y)\xi_k(y)dy = 0 \quad (k = 1, 2, \ldots)$$

for almost every $x \in \Delta$. But $\zeta_k(x)$ is continuous, hence $\zeta_k(x) = 0$ for all $x \in \Delta$. The relation (3) follows now by observing that

$$\textstyle\int_\Delta K(x, y)\xi_k(y)dy = A(x) \int_\Delta H(x, y)\xi_k(y)dy = 0$$

for all k and all $x \in \Delta$.

The relations (4) and (5) are immediate consequences of (2) and (3).

Definition. *Let $f(x)$ be a Lebesgue measurable function on the bounded closed set Δ; let E_1 be the subset of Δ where $f(x) = 0$ and $E_2 = \Delta - E_1$ the set where $f(x) \neq 0$. We shall say that $f(x)$ possesses the property (G) whenever every measurable set $E_3 \subset E_2$, for which the measure $m(E_2 - E_3) = 0$, is lying dense in E_2; in other words, when E_2 is contained in the closure $\bar{E}_3$ of E_3.*

Lemma α. *If $f(x) \neq 0$ almost everywhere on Δ, then $f(x)$ possesses the property (G).*
Proof. Supposing that $f(x) \neq 0$ almost everywhere on Δ, we have $m(E_2) = m(\Delta)$. Hence, if $E_3 \subset E_2$ and $m(E_2 - E_3) = 0$, then also $m(E_3) = m(\Delta)$. This implies $\bar{E}_3 = \Delta$, so that $E_2 \subset \bar{E}_3$.

Lemma β. *If $f(x)$ is continuous on Δ, then $f(x)$ possesses the property (G).*
Proof. Let $f(x)$ be continuous on Δ. Then the set E_1 is closed, so that E_2 is open (relative to Δ). In other words, E_2 contains only internal points. Given now the set $E_3 \subset E_2$ such that $m(E_2 - E_3) = 0$, every neighbourhood of a point $x \in E_2$ contains points of E_3; hence $E_2 \subset \bar{E}_3$.

Theorem 2. *If the Mercer kernel $H(x, y)$ is general, and if $A(x)$ has the property (G), then*

$$K(x, y) = \Sigma\, \lambda_k \psi_k(x)\overline{\chi_k(y)}$$

uniformly on $\Delta \times \Delta$;

$$\int_\Delta K(x, y)f(y)dy = \Sigma\, \lambda_k(f, \chi_k)\psi_k(x)$$

uniformly on Δ for every $f(x) \in L_2$, and

$$\int_\Delta K(x, x)dx = \Sigma\, \lambda_k.$$

Proof. On account of (2) we have only to prove that $\xi_k(x) = A(x)\eta_k(x) = 0$ $(k = 1, 2, \ldots)$ for all $x \in \Delta$. Denoting by E_1 the subset of Δ where $A(x) = 0$ and by E_2 the complementary subset where $A(x) \neq 0$, we have $\xi_k(x) = 0$ for all $x \in E_1$. Furthermore, since $H\xi_k = 0$ $(k = 1, 2, \ldots)$ and $H(x, y)$ is general, we know already that $\xi_k(x) = 0$ almost everywhere on Δ. Hence $\eta_k(x) = \xi_k(x)/A(x) = 0$ for almost every $x \in E_2$, that is, $\eta_k(x) = 0$ for $x \in E_3$, where the measure $m(E_2 - E_3) = 0$. But then also $\eta_k(x) = 0$

for $x \in \bar{E}_3$ on account of the continuity of $\eta_k(x)$. Since however $A(x)$ has the property (G), we have $E_2 \subset \bar{E}_3$, and this implies $\eta_k(x) = 0$ for $x \in E_2$, and so $\xi_k(x) = 0$ for $x \in E_2$. The relations $\xi_k(x) = 0$ for $x \in E_1$ and for $x \in E_2$ now imply $\xi_k(x) = 0$ for all $x \in \Delta$.

Theorem 3 (*Garbe's Theorem,* [1]). *If the Mercer kernel $H(x, y)$ is general, and if moreover $A(x) \neq 0$ for almost every $x \in \Delta$, then*

$$H(x, y) = \Sigma\, \chi_k(x)\overline{\chi_k(y)}$$

uniformly on $\Delta \times \Delta$.

Proof. Follows from (1) by observing that on account of our hypotheses on H and A the relations $\eta_k(x) = 0$ $(k = 1, 2, \ldots)$ for almost every $x \in \Delta$ (and therefore for all $x \in \Delta$) are a consequence of $HA\eta_k = H\xi_k = 0$.

Remark. In the case of a matrixkernel there seems to be no hypothesis for $\{A_{ij}(x)\}$ which is wholly analogous to the hypothesis for $A(x)$ to possess the property (G). However, it is easily seen that if $\{H_{ij}(x, y)\}$ is of Mercer type and general, and if either all $A_{ij}(x)$ are continuous or the determinant $\| A_{ij}(x) \|$ is $\neq 0$ for almost every $x \in \Delta$, then the analogue of Theorem 2 holds, while in the case that det $\| A_{ij}(x) \| \neq 0$ the analogue of Theorem 3 holds as well.

It may be asked whether, in the case that the Mercer kernel $H(x, y)$ is general, but $A(x) = 0$ on a set of positive measure, the relation $H(x, y) = \Sigma\, \chi_k(x)\overline{\chi_k(y)}$ remains true. We shall show that this is not necessarily so. On account of Ch. 16, § 4, Th. 4 we shall then have to prove the existence of a function $\Psi(x) \in L_2(\Delta)$ for which $H^{1/2}AH^{1/2}\Psi = 0$ and $H^{1/2}\Psi \neq 0$. This may be done as follows:

Let Δ be the linear interval $0 \leqslant x \leqslant 2\pi$, and $t_i(x)$ $(i = 1, 2, \ldots)$ the orthonormal trigonometrical system, hence

$$t_1(x) = (2\pi)^{-1/2}, \quad \left.\begin{aligned} t_{2n}(x) &= \pi^{-1/2} \cos nx \\ t_{2n+1}(x) &= \pi^{-1/2} \sin nx \end{aligned}\right\} (n = 1, 2, \ldots).$$

Then the system $\{t_i(x)\}$ is complete in $L_2(\Delta)$.

Let now the general Mercer kernel $H(x, y)$ be defined by

$$H(x, y) = \Sigma_i\, i^{-4} t_i(x) t_i(y);$$

it has the characteristic values i^{-4} $(i = 1, 2, \ldots)$ with the corresponding characteristic functions $t_i(x)$. The transformation $H^{1/2}$ corresponds with the general Mercer kernel

$$H_{1/2}(x, y) = \Sigma_i \, i^{-2} t_i(x) t_i(y),$$

having the characteristic values i^{-2} with the characteristic functions $t_i(x)$. Furthermore we define the bounded self-adjoint transformation A by $Af = A(x)f(x)$, where

$$A(x) = \begin{cases} 0 \text{ on } 0 \leqslant x \leqslant \pi, \\ 1 \text{ on } \pi < x \leqslant 2\pi. \end{cases}$$

Let us consider now the function $f(x)$ of period 2π, defined by

$$f(x) = \begin{cases} x^5(\pi - x)^5 \text{ on } 0 \leqslant x \leqslant \pi, \\ 0 \quad\quad \text{ on } \pi \leqslant x \leqslant 2\pi. \end{cases}$$

The fourth derivative of $f(x)$ is continuous and has the period 2π; hence, if the Fourier series of $f(x)$ is $\Sigma\,(f, t_i)t_i(x)$, we find by partial integration that there exists a constant M such that $|\,(f, t_i)\,| \leqslant Mi^{-4}$ $(i = 1, 2, \ldots)$. It follows that $f(x) = \Sigma\,(f, t_i)t_i(x)$ uniformly on Δ. Writing now $\alpha_i = i^2(f, t_i)$ $(i = 1, 2, \ldots)$, we have $|\,\alpha_i\,| \leqslant Mi^{-2}$, which shows that $\Sigma\,\alpha_i t_i(x)$ also converges uniformly on Δ. Putting $\Psi(x) = \Sigma\,\alpha_i t_i(x)$, we find

$$H^{1/2}\Psi = \Sigma\,\alpha_i H^{1/2} t_i = \Sigma\,\alpha_i i^{-2} t_i = \Sigma(f, t_i)t_i = f \neq 0,$$

while from the definitions of $A(x)$ and $f(x)$ we derive immediately $A(x)f(x) = 0$; hence

$$H^{1/2}AH^{1/2}\Psi = H^{1/2}Af = 0.$$

The function $\Psi(x)$ has therefore the desired properties.

We might end the proof here, and refer to Ch. 16, § 4, Th. 4. It is, however, easy to complete the proof without doing so. The relation $H^{1/2}AH^{1/2}\Psi = 0$ shows that $\Psi(x)$ is orthogonal to all characteristic functions $\Psi_i(x)$ $(i = 1, 2, \ldots)$ of $H^{1/2}AH^{1/2}$. Hence, writing $\Psi^*(x) = \Psi(x)/\|\,\Psi\,\|$, the system $\{\Psi^*(x), \Psi_i(x)\}$ is orthonormal, so that, on account of

$$\chi_i(x) = H^{1/2}\Psi_i = \int_\Delta H_{1/2}(x, y)\Psi_i(y)dy,$$

$$f(x)/\|\,\Psi\,\| = H^{1/2}\Psi^* = \int_\Delta H_{1/2}(x, y)\Psi^*(y)dy$$

for every $x \in \Delta$, we find

$$\Sigma\,|\,\chi_i(x)\,|^2 + |\,f(x)\,|^2/\|\,\Psi\,\|^2 \leqslant \int_\Delta |\,H_{1/2}(x, y)\,|^2\,dy = H(x, x).$$

This shows, since $f(x) \neq 0$ for $0 < x < \pi$, that

$$\Sigma\, \chi_i(x)\overline{\chi_i(x)} < H(x, x)$$

for $0 < x < \pi$. Consequently, the functions $H(x, y)$ and $\Sigma\, \chi_i(x)\overline{\chi_i(y)}$ being continuous on $\Delta \times \Delta$, there exists for every point $(x_0, x_0) \in \Delta \times \Delta$, subject to $0 < x_0 < \pi$, a twodimensional neighbourhood $E(x_0) \subset \Delta \times \Delta$ such that

$$H(x, y) > \Sigma\, \chi_i(x)\overline{\chi_i(y)}$$

for $(x, y) \in E(x_0)$.

§ 4. An Example

We shall illustrate the theorems, proved in the preceding paragraph, by an example showing that the second sums in the expansions $K(x, y) = \Sigma\, \lambda_k\psi_k(x)\overline{\chi_k(y)} + \Sigma\, \rho_k\xi_k(x)\overline{\eta_k(y)}$ and $\int_\Delta K(x, y)f(y)dy = \Sigma\, \lambda_k(f, \chi_k)\psi_k(x) + \Sigma\, \rho_k(f, \eta_k)\xi_k(x)$ (cf. § 3, Th. 1, (2) and (4)) need not vanish identically. The construction of the example is based upon the same principle as that used in Ch. 12, § 12, Th. 6 and Ch. 15, § 6.

Let Δ be the linear interval $[0, 2\pi]$ and Δ_1, Δ_2, Δ_3 the subintervals $[0, \pi/2]$, $(\pi/2, \pi)$, $[\pi, 2\pi]$. The orthonormal system $\varphi_1(x)$, $\varphi_2(x)$, $\varphi_3(x)$ is defined by

$$\varphi_1(x) = \begin{cases} (2/\pi)^{1/2}\, |\sin 2x| & \text{for } x \in \Delta_1 + \Delta_2, \\ 0 & \text{for } x \in \Delta_3, \end{cases}$$

$$\varphi_2(x) = \begin{cases} -(2/\pi)^{1/2} \sin 2x & \text{for } x \in \Delta_1 + \Delta_2, \\ 0 & \text{for } x \in \Delta_3, \end{cases}$$

$$\varphi_3(x) = \begin{cases} 0 & \text{for } x \in \Delta_1 + \Delta_2, \\ -(2/\pi)^{1/2} \sin x & \text{for } x \in \Delta_3. \end{cases}$$

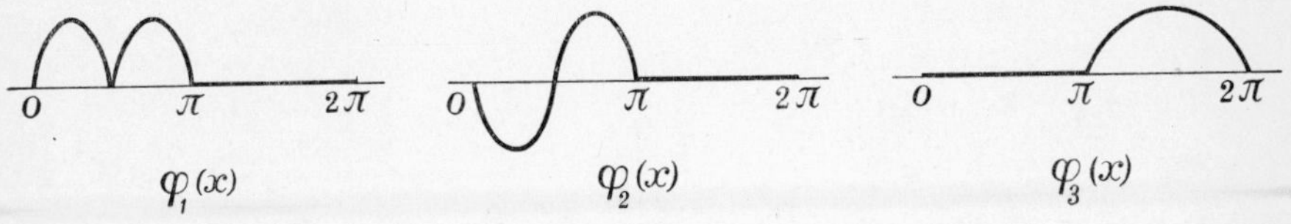

The self-adjoint transformation H in $L_2(\Delta)$ is now defined by

$$Hf = \int_\Delta H(x, y)f(y)dy,$$

where

$$H(x, y) = \varphi_1(x)\varphi_1(y) + \varphi_3(x)\varphi_3(y).$$

The kernel $H(x, y)$ is continuous, and $H\varphi_1 = \varphi_1$, $H\varphi_2 = 0$, $H\varphi_3 = \varphi_3$, while $Hf = 0$ for any f which is orthogonal to φ_1, φ_2 and φ_3. Hence H is positive. It follows that $H(x, y)$ is a Mercer kernel.

Let furthermore the bounded self-adjoint transformation A be given by $Af = A(x)f(x)$, where

$$A(x) = \begin{cases} -1 & \text{for} \quad x \in \Delta_1, \\ 1 & \text{for} \quad x \in \Delta_2 + \Delta_3. \end{cases}$$

Then $A\varphi_1 = \varphi_2$, $A\varphi_2 = \varphi_1$, $A\varphi_3 = \varphi_3$, so that the transformation $K = AH$ has the Garbe kernel

$$K(x, y) = A(x)H(x, y) = \varphi_2(x)\varphi_1(y) + \varphi_3(x)\varphi_3(y).$$

Finally, since evidently $H^{1/2} = H$, the self-adjoint transformation $\tilde{K} = H^{1/2}AH^{1/2}$ has the kernel

$$\tilde{K}(x, y) = \int_\Delta H(x, z)K(z, y)dz = \varphi_3(x)\varphi_3(y).$$

0	$\dfrac{2}{\pi} \sin x \sin y$
$\dfrac{2}{\pi} \| \sin 2x \sin 2y \|$	0

$H(x, y)$

0		$\dfrac{2}{\pi} \sin x \sin y$
$-\dfrac{2}{\pi} \| \sin 2x \sin 2y \|$	$\dfrac{2}{\pi} \| \sin 2x \sin 2y \|$	0

$K(x, y)$

0	$\dfrac{2}{\pi} \sin x \sin y$
0	0

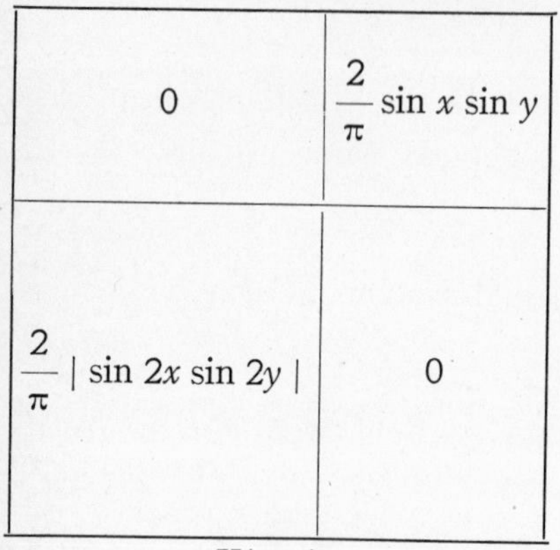

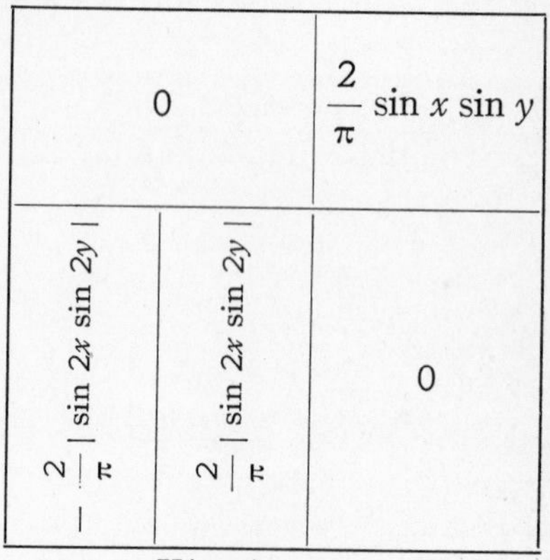

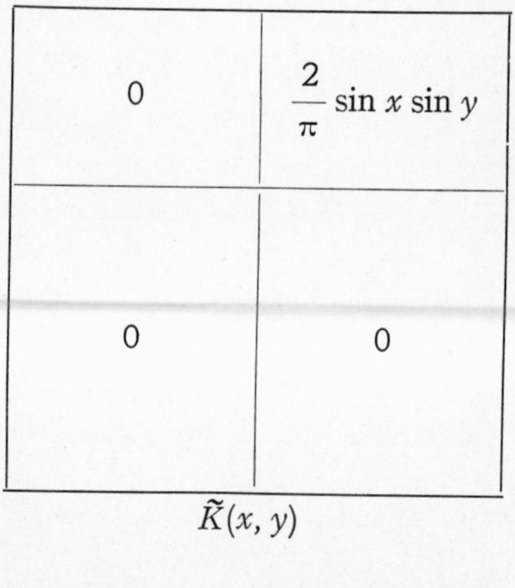

$\tilde{K}(x, y)$

As we know, $K(x, y)$ and $\tilde{K}(x, y)$ have the same characteristic values $\neq 0$; hence, since $\tilde{K}(x, y)$ has evidently only the characteristic value $\lambda = 1$, different from zero, with the characteristic function $\varphi_3(x)$, the kernel $K(x, y)$ has also $\lambda_1 = 1$ as the only characteristic value $\neq 0$ with the H-normal characteristic function $\psi_1(x) = \varphi_3(x)$. Observing that $\overline{\chi_1} = \overline{H\psi_1} = \overline{H\varphi_3} = \overline{\varphi_3} = \varphi_3$, so that $\lambda_1\psi_1(x)\overline{\chi_1(y)} = \varphi_3(x)\varphi_3(y)$, we find therefore

$$K(x, y) - \lambda_1\psi_1(x)\overline{\chi_1(y)} = K(x, y) - \varphi_3(x)\varphi_3(y) = \varphi_2(x)\varphi_1(y),$$

hence

$$K(x, y) = \lambda_1\psi_1(x)\overline{\chi_1(y)} + \varphi_2(x)\varphi_1(y),$$

where $\varphi_2(x)\varphi_1(y) \neq 0$ for x and y in the interior of Δ_1 or Δ_2.

Furthermore

$$\int_\Delta K(x, y)f(y)dy = \lambda_1(f, \chi_1)\psi_1(x) + (f, \varphi_1)\varphi_2(x).$$

Taking $f(x) = \varphi_1(x)$, we have $(f, \varphi_1) = 1$, hence $(f, \varphi_1)\varphi_2(x) = \varphi_2(x) \neq 0$ in the interior of Δ_1 and Δ_2. Evidently $H\varphi_2 = 0$, as required (cf. § 3, Th. 1).

§ 5. Pell Kernel

We now assume that the kernel in the equation $Kf - \lambda f = g$ is a Pell kernel $K(x, y) = \int_\Delta A(x, z)H(z, y)d\mu$ (cf. § 1). All results obtained in the preceding chapter for Marty kernels hold in the present case, and we shall not repeat them all, but, as in the case of a Garbe kernel, pay attention to some points only.

Theorem 1 (*Expansion theorem*). *We have*

$$K(x, y) \sim \Sigma\, \lambda_k\psi_k(x)\overline{\chi_k(y)} + \Sigma\, \rho_k\xi_k(x)\overline{\eta_k(y)},$$

$$K_p(x, y) \sim \Sigma_k\, \lambda_k^p\psi_k(x)\overline{\chi_k(y)} \quad (p = 2, 3, \ldots),$$

$$\tau_p = \int_\Delta K_p(x, x)d\mu = \Sigma_i\, \lambda_i^p \quad (p = 2, 3, \ldots),$$

where the positive numbers ρ_k and the functions $\eta_k(x)$ are the characteristic values $\neq 0$ and the corresponding orthonormal characteristic functions of a certain kernel $Q(x, y)$ of positive type (cf. Ch. 12, § 14, Th. 1), and where the functions $\xi_k(x) = \int_\Delta A(x, y)\eta_k(y)d\mu$ all satisfy $H\xi_k = 0$. Hence, if $H(x, y)$ is a general kernel, all $\xi_k(x)$ vanish almost everywhere.

Furthermore, if $f(x) \in L_2(\Delta)$, *then*

$$\int_\Delta K(x, y)f(y)d\mu \sim \Sigma \lambda_k(f, \chi_k)\psi_k(x) + \Sigma \rho_k(f, \eta_k)\xi_k(x),$$

$$\int_\Delta K_p(x, y)f(y)d\mu \sim \Sigma \lambda_k^p(f, \chi_k)\psi_k(x) \quad (p = 2, 3, \ldots).$$

Proof. Follows from Ch. 16, § 6, Th. 5 (and Th. 3).

§ 6. Pell Kernel in the Case that $A(x, y)$ is Continuous in Mean

If the kernel $A(x, y)$, corresponding with the transformation A in $K = AH$, is continuous in mean, we may prove somewhat more. We observe first that the set Δ in Euclidean space is bounded now by the definition of mean continuity. Furthermore, since $h(x) = Af$ is now continuous for any $f \in L_2$, the same is true of $g(x) = Kf = AHf$ for any $f \in L_2$. In particular, all characteristic functions $\psi_k(x) = \lambda_k^{-1}K\psi_k$ are continuous on Δ.

Theorem 1. *If* $A(x, y)$ *is continuous in mean, then both* $\Sigma \lambda_k^2 \mid \psi_k(x) \mid^2$ *and* $\Sigma \mid \xi_k(x) \mid^2$ *converge uniformly on* Δ.

Proof. Take $f(z) = \overline{A(x_2, z)} - \overline{A(x_1, z)}$, where x_1 and x_2 are in Δ. Then

$$\lambda_k\{\psi_k(x_2) - \psi_k(x_1)\} = \int_\Delta \{K(x_2, y) - K(x_1, y)\}\psi_k(y)dy =$$

$$\int_\Delta \{A(x_2, z) - A(x_1, z)\}[\int_\Delta H(z, y)\psi_k(y)dy]dz = (H\psi_k, f),$$

so that

$$\Sigma \lambda_k^2 \mid \psi_k(x_2) - \psi_k(x_1) \mid^2 = \Sigma \mid (H\psi_k, f) \mid^2 = \Sigma \mid (Hf, \psi_k) \mid^2 =$$

$$\Sigma \mid (H^{1/2}f, \Psi_k)\mid^2 \leqslant \| H^{1/2}f \|^2 \leqslant \| H^{1/2} \|^2 \int_\Delta \mid A(x_2, z) - A(x_1, z) \mid^2 dz,$$

hence

$$\lim_{x_2 \to x_1} \Sigma \lambda_k^2 \mid \psi_k(x_2) - \psi_k(x_1) \mid^2 = 0.$$

By the same argument it is immediately seen that $\Sigma \lambda_k^2 \mid \psi_k(x) \mid^2 < \infty$ for every $x \in \Delta$.

But

$$\mid (\Sigma \lambda_k^2 \mid \psi_k(x_2) \mid^2)^{1/2} - (\Sigma \lambda_k^2 \mid \psi_k(x_1) \mid^2)^{1/2} \mid \leqslant (\Sigma \lambda_k^2 \mid \psi_k(x_2) - \psi_k(x_1) \mid^2)^{1/2};$$

the sum of $\Sigma \lambda_k^2 \mid \psi_k(x) \mid^2$ is therefore continuous. Hence, in virtue of Dini's Theorem, the series $\Sigma \lambda_k^2 \mid \psi_k(x) \mid^2$ converges uniformly on Δ.

In the same way, since

$$\xi_k(x_2) - \xi_k(x_1) = \int_\Delta \{A(x_2, z) - A(x_1, z)\}\eta_k(z)dz$$

and the system $\{\eta_k(z)\}$ is orthonormal, we find that $\Sigma \mid \xi_k(x) \mid^2$ converges uniformly on Δ.

Theorem 2 (*Expansion theorem*). *If $A(x, y)$ is continuous in mean, then*

(1) $$\int_\Delta K(x, y)f(y)dy = \Sigma \lambda_k(f, \chi_k)\psi_k(x) + \Sigma \rho_k(f, \eta_k)\xi_k(x),$$

(2) $$\int_\Delta K_p(x, y)f(y)dy = \Sigma \lambda_k^p(f, \chi_k)\psi_k(x) \quad (p = 2, 3, \ldots)$$

uniformly on Δ for any $f \in L_2$.

Proof. Since $\Sigma \lambda_k^2 \mid \psi_k(x) \mid^2$ and $\Sigma \mid \xi_k(x) \mid^2$ converge uniformly on Δ by the preceding theorem, and since $\Sigma \mid (f, \chi_k) \mid^2 < \infty$ and $\Sigma \mid (f, \eta_k) \mid^2 < \infty$, the uniform convergence follows immediately by an application of Schwarz's inequality. Equality almost everywhere on Δ between the expressions on the left and the right of (1) and (2) is now a consequence of § 5, Th. 1. Since however all these expressions are continuous functions, we have equality for every $x \in \Delta$.

Theorem 3. *Let $A(x, y)$ be continuous in mean, and let $H(x, y)$ be general. Let furthermore $\lambda \neq 0$, and $g(x) \in L_2$ be H-orthogonal to all characteristic functions of $K(x, y)$ belonging to the characteristic value λ (if λ is no characteristic value, $g(x)$ may be any function belonging to L_2). Then the solution $f(x)$ of the integral equation $Kf - \lambda f = g$ is given by*

$$f(x) = -\frac{g(x)}{\lambda} - {}'\Sigma \frac{\lambda_k}{\lambda(\lambda - \lambda_k)} \alpha_k\psi_k(x),$$

where $\alpha_k = (g, \chi_k)$ for $\lambda_k \neq \lambda$, the dash in front of Σ denotes that for those values of k for which $\lambda_k = \lambda$ the coefficient of $\psi_k(x)$ is arbitrary, and where the series ${}'\Sigma$ converges uniformly on Δ.

Proof. By the preceding theorem we have

$$g(x) + \lambda f(x) = \int_\Delta K(x, y)f(y)dy = \Sigma \lambda_k(f, \chi_k)\psi_k(x)$$

uniformly on Δ (all $\xi_k(x)$ vanish, since $H(x, y)$ is general). Since

$$\lambda_k(f, \chi_k) = \lambda_k(f, H\psi_k) = (f, HK\psi_k) = (HKf, \psi_k) =$$

$$(Kf, H\psi_k) = (g + \lambda f, \chi_k) = (g, \chi_k) + \lambda(f, \chi_k),$$

we find $(f, \chi_k) = -(g, \chi_k)/(\lambda - \lambda_k)$ for $\lambda_k \neq \lambda$. Furthermore, the solution $f(x)$ being determined except for a characteristic function of $K(x, y)$, belonging to the characteristic value λ, the coefficients α_k may be taken arbitrarily for those values of k for which $\lambda_k = \lambda$. Hence the desired result follows.

§ 7. Pell Kernel in the Case that $A(x, y)$ and $H(x, y)$ are Continuous in Mean

Theorem 1. *If $H(x, y)$ (but not necessarily $A(x, y)$) is continuous in mean, then $\Sigma \lambda_k^2 \mid \chi_k(x) \mid^2$ converges uniformly on Δ.*

Proof. We observe first that the functions $\chi_k(x) = H\psi_k$ are continuous on Δ on account of the mean continuity of $H(x, y)$. Furthermore, if $f(y) \in L_2$, we have $(f, A\chi_k) = (Af, H^{1/2}\Psi_k) = (H^{1/2}Af, \Psi_k)$, hence

$$(1) \qquad \Sigma \mid (A\chi_k, f) \mid^2 = \Sigma \mid (f, A\chi_k) \mid^2 \leqslant \| H^{1/2}Af \|^2 \leqslant \| H^{1/2} \|^2 . \| A \|^2 . \| f \|^2.$$

Taking now $f(y) = \overline{H(x, y)}$, there exists a constant M such that $\| f \|^2 = \int_\Delta \mid H(x, y) \mid^2 dy \leqslant M$ for every $x \in \Delta$. Moreover

$$(A\chi_k, f) = (AH\psi_k, f) = (K\psi_k, f) = \lambda_k(\psi_k, f) = \lambda_k \int_\Delta H(x, y)\psi_k(y)dy = \lambda_k\chi_k(x).$$

Hence, by (1),

$$\Sigma \lambda_k^2 \mid \chi_k(x) \mid^2 \leqslant \| H^{1/2} \|^2 . \| A \|^2 . M < \infty$$

for every $x \in \Delta$.

Substituting now $f(y) = \overline{H(x_2, y)} - \overline{H(x_1, y)}$ in (1), we find in the same way

$$\Sigma \lambda_k^2 \mid \chi_k(x_2) - \chi_k(x_1) \mid^2 \leqslant \| H^{1/2} \|^2 . \| A \|^2 \int_\Delta \mid H(x_2, y) - H(x_1, y) \mid^2 dy,$$

hence

$$\lim_{x_2 \to x_1} \Sigma \lambda_k^2 \mid \chi_k(x_2) - \chi_k(x_1) \mid^2 = 0.$$

But then, in virtue of Minkowski's inequality, the sum of $\Sigma \lambda_k^2 \mid \chi_k(x) \mid^2$ is continuous on Δ, so that, on account of Dini's Theorem, the series $\Sigma \lambda_k^2 \mid \chi_k(x) \mid^2$ converges uniformly on Δ.

Theorem 2 (*Expansion theorem for the iterated kernels*). *If both $A(x, y)$ and $H(x, y)$ are continuous in mean, then*

$$K_p(x, y) = \Sigma_k \lambda_k^p \psi_k(x)\overline{\chi_k(y)} \quad (p = 2, 3, \ldots)$$

uniformly on $\Delta \times \Delta$.

Proof. Since under the stated hypotheses $K(x, y)$ is continuous in mean, all iterated kernels $K_p(x, y)$ $(p = 2, 3, \ldots)$ are continuous on $\Delta \times \Delta$. Furthermore, since both $\Sigma\, \lambda_k^2 \mid \psi_k(x) \mid^2$ and $\Sigma\, \lambda_k^2 \mid \chi_k(x) \mid^2$ are converging uniformly on Δ (cf. § 6, Th. 1 and the preceding theorem), the inequality

$$\Sigma_k \mid \lambda_k^p \psi_k(x) \overline{\chi_k(y)} \mid \leqslant (\Sigma\, \lambda_k^2 \mid \psi_k(x) \mid^2)^{1/2} (\Sigma\, \lambda_k^{2p-2} \mid \chi_k(y) \mid^2)^{1/2}$$

shows that, for $p \geqslant 2$, the series $\Sigma_k\, \lambda_k^p \psi_k(x) \overline{\chi_k(y)}$ converges uniformly on $\Delta \times \Delta$. By § 5, Th. 1 the sum is equal to $K_p(x, y)$ almost everywhere on $\Delta \times \Delta$. But, both $K_p(x, y)$ and this sum being continuous on $\Delta \times \Delta$, equality holds for every point $(x, y) \in \Delta \times \Delta$.

§ 8. Pell Kernel in the Case that *H*(*x*, *y*) is a Mercer Kernel

Let us assume now that $H(x, y)$ is a Mercer kernel. Then, by Ch. 16, § 4, Th. 2,

$$H(x, y) = \Sigma\, \chi_k(x) \overline{\chi_k(y)} + \Sigma\, \rho_k \eta_k(x) \overline{\eta_k(y)}$$

uniformly on $\Delta \times \Delta$, where the sums of both series separately are Mercer kernels, and where the functions $\eta_k(x)$ satisfy $HA\eta_k = 0$ $(k = 1, 2, \ldots)$ (cf. Ch. 16, § 6, Th. 4). Hence, if both $H(x, y)$ and $A(x, y)$ are general,

$$H(x, y) = \Sigma\, \chi_k(x) \overline{\chi_k(y)}$$

uniformly on $\Delta \times \Delta$. This is the analogue of Garbe's Theorem for Garbe kernels (cf. § 3, Th. 3).

Theorem 1 (*Expansion theorem for the kernel*). *If $H(x, y)$ is a Mercer kernel, and $A(x, y)$ is continuous in mean, then*

$$K(x, y) = \Sigma\, \lambda_k \psi_k(x) \overline{\chi_k(y)} + \Sigma\, \rho_k \xi_k(x) \overline{\eta_k(y)}$$

uniformly on $\Delta \times \Delta$, where $\zeta_k(x) = H\xi_k = 0$ $(k = 1, 2, \ldots)$ for every $x \in \Delta$. Hence, if $H(x, y)$ is general, the second sum in the expansion vanishes.

Proof. Multiplying

$$H(z, y) = \Sigma\, \chi_k(z) \overline{\chi_k(y)} + \Sigma\, \rho_k \eta_k(z) \overline{\eta_k(y)}$$

by $A(x, z)$, and integrating term by term, which is permitted on account of the uniform convergence, we obtain the desired result.

It is not difficult to show by an example that the second sum in the expansion above for $K(x, y)$ need not vanish. For this purpose we may use Ch. 12, § 12, Th. 6.

Let Δ be the linear interval $[0, 2\pi]$, and let $\{t_k(x)\}$ be the (real) orthonormal trigonometrical system in Δ. Take the sequences $\mu_3, \mu_4, \ldots$ and $\nu_3, \nu_4, \ldots$ of positive numbers such that $\lim \mu_k = \lim \nu_k = 0$, $\mu_3 > \mu_4 > \ldots$ and $\nu_3 > \nu_4 > \ldots$, $\Sigma_3^\infty \mu_k < \infty$ and $\Sigma_3^\infty \nu_k < \infty$. The Hermitian kernel $A(x, y)$ and the Mercer kernel $H(x, y)$ are now defined by

$$A(x, y) = \tfrac{1}{2}\{t_1(x) + t_2(x)\}\{t_1(y) + t_2(y)\}$$
$$- \tfrac{1}{2}\{t_1(x) - t_2(x)\}\{t_1(y) - t_2(y)\} + \Sigma_3^\infty \nu_k t_k(x) t_k(y),$$
$$H(x, y) = t_1(x)t_1(y) + \Sigma_3^\infty \mu_k t_k(x) t_k(y).$$

Hence, if K is defined by $K = AH$, its kernel $K(x, y)$ is

$$K(x, y) = \int_\Delta A(x, z)H(z, y)dz = t_2(x)t_1(y) + \Sigma_3^\infty \nu_k \mu_k t_k(x) t_k(y).$$

We observe that

$$Ht_1 = t_1,\ Ht_2 = 0,\ Ht_k = \mu_k t_k \quad (k = 3, 4, \ldots),$$
$$At_1 = t_2,\ At_2 = t_1,\ At_k = \nu_k t_k \quad (k = 3, 4, \ldots),$$

so that

$$Kt_1 = t_2,\ Kt_2 = 0,\ Kt_k = \nu_k \mu_k t_k \quad (k = 3, 4, \ldots).$$

It follows easily that K has the numbers $\lambda_k = \nu_{k+2}\mu_{k+2}$ $(k = 1, 2, \ldots)$ as its characteristic values $\neq 0$ with the functions $\psi_k(x) = \mu_{k+2}^{-1/2} t_{k+2}(x)$ as corresponding H-orthonormal characteristic functions. Hence $\chi_k(x) = H\psi_k = \mu_{k+2}^{1/2} t_{k+2}(x)$, so that

$$\Sigma\, \lambda_k \psi_k(x)\overline{\chi_k(y)} = \Sigma_3^\infty \nu_k \mu_k t_k(x) t_k(y) = K(x, y) - t_2(x)t_1(y)$$

or

$$K(x, y) = \Sigma\, \lambda_k \psi_k(x)\overline{\chi_k(y)} + t_2(x)\, t_1(y).$$

EXAMPLES

1) If $K(x, y)$ is a Pell kernel, satisfying only the hypotheses of § 5, Th. 1, and if $f(x) \in L_2$, then

$$\int_\Delta K(x, y)f(y)d\mu = \Sigma\, \lambda_k (f, \chi_k)\psi_k(x) + \Sigma\, \rho_k (f, \eta_k)\xi_k(x),$$
$$\int_\Delta K_p(x, y)f(y)d\mu = \Sigma_k \lambda_k^p (f, \chi_k)\psi_k(x) \qquad (p = 2, 3, \ldots)$$

(pointwise convergence) almost everywhere on Δ.

(It will be sufficient, in virtue of § 5, Th. 1, to prove the convergence almost everywhere of the series in question. For every $g \in L_2$ we have $\Sigma \mid (g, \chi_k) \mid^2 = \Sigma \mid (H^{1/2}g, \Psi_k) \mid^2 \leqslant \| H^{1/2}g \|^2 \leqslant \| H^{1/2} \|^2 . \| g \|^2$. Furthermore, for $g(z) = \overline{A(x, z)}$, we find

$$\lambda_k \psi_k(x) = \int_\Delta K(x, y)\psi_k(y)d\mu =$$
$$\int_{\Delta\times\Delta} A(x, z)H(z, y)\psi_k(y)d(\mu \times \mu) = (H\psi_k, g) = (\chi_k, g).$$

Hence

$$\Sigma \lambda_k^2 \mid \psi_k(x) \mid^2 \leqslant \| H^{1/2} \|^2 \int_\Delta \mid A(x, z) \mid^2 d\mu < \infty$$

for almost every $x \in \Delta$ (compare the proof of § 6, Th. 1). Since $\Sigma \mid (f, \chi_k) \mid^2 < \infty$, it follows easily that $\Sigma \lambda_k(f, \chi_k)\psi_k(x)$ and $\Sigma_k \lambda_k^p(f, \chi_k)\psi_k(x)$ ($p = 2, 3, \ldots$) converge almost everywhere on Δ. In the same way, since $\xi_k(x) = \int_\Delta A(x, z)\eta_k(z)d\mu$ and the system $\{\eta_k(z)\}$ is orthonormal, we find that $\Sigma \mid \xi_k(x) \mid^2 < \infty$ almost everywhere on Δ, and this implies the convergence of $\Sigma \rho_k(f, \eta_k)\xi_k(x)$ for almost every $x \in \Delta$).

2) Under the same hypotheses as in the preceding example we have

$$K_p(x, y) = \Sigma_k \lambda_k^p \psi_k(x)\overline{\chi_k(y)} \quad (p = 2, 3, \ldots)$$

(pointwise convergence) almost everywhere on $\Delta \times \Delta$.

(It will be sufficient to prove the convergence almost everywhere of $\Sigma \lambda_k^2 \psi_k(x)\overline{\chi_k(y)}$. Since $\| \chi_k \| = \| H^{1/2}\Psi_k \| \leqslant \| H^{1/2} \|$ and $\Sigma \lambda_k^2 < \infty$, we have $\Sigma \lambda_k^2 \| \chi_k \|^2 < \infty$, so that the series $\Sigma \lambda_k^2 \mid \chi_k(y) \mid^2$ converges for almost every $y \in \Delta$. By the preceding example $\Sigma \lambda_k^2 \mid \psi_k(x) \mid^2$ converges for almost every $x \in \Delta$. An application of Schwarz's inequality yields now the desired result).

REFERENCES

[1] E. Garbe, Zur Theorie der Integralgleichung dritter Art, Math. Annalen 76 (1915), 409—416.

[2] A. J. Pell, Applications of biorthogonal systems of functions to the theory of integral equations, Transactions Amer. Math. Soc. 12 (1911), 165—180.

INDEX

TABLE OF CONTENTS

PART I. MEASURE AND INTEGRAL, THE LEBESGUE FUNCTIONSPACES L_p AND THE ORLICZ FUNCTIONSPACES L_Φ

PART II. BOUNDED TRANSFORMATIONS AND COMPACT TRANSFORMATIONS IN BANACH SPACE AND HILBERT SPACE

PART III. NON-SINGULAR LINEAR INTEGRAL EQUATIONS